Handbook of Secondary Fungal Metabolites

VOLUME I

Handbook of Secondary Fungal Metabolites

VOLUME I

RICHARD J. COLE
Albany, Georgia

MILBRA A. SCHWEIKERT
National Peanut Research Laboratory
Dawson, Georgia

ACADEMIC PRESS
An imprint of Elsevier Science
Amsterdam Boston London New York Oxford Paris
San Diego San Francisco Singapore Sydney Tokyo

Cover images: Photography by Dr. Bruce Horn and design by Brian E. Cole. The cover is a collage of various fungi, some presented in pure culture and others in their natural forms, i.e. mushrooms, which are the easily recognizable fruiting structures of some fungi, superimposed on these fungi are the chemical structures of some representative secondary fungal metabolites.

Academic Press Rapid Manuscript Reproduction

This book is printed on acid-free paper. ∞

Academic Press
An imprint of Elsevier Science
525 B Street, Suite 1900, San Diego, California 92101-4495, USA
http://www.academicpress.com

Academic Press
84 Theobald's Road, London WC1X 8RR, UK
http://www.academicpress.com

Library of Congress Catalog Card Number: 2003103019

International Standard Book Number: 0-12-179460-1 (Set)
International Standard Book Number: 0-12-179461-X (Volume 1)
International Standard Book Number: 0-12-179462-8 (Volume 2)
International Standard Book Number: 0-12-179463-6 (Volume 3)

PRINTED IN THE UNITED STATES OF AMERICA
03 04 05 06 07 8 7 6 5 4 3 2 1

Contents

Preface

The "Handbook of Secondary Fungal Metabolites" is presented in three volumes and is comprehensive to the extent that all major groups of secondary fungal metabolites are included. The format is similar to that presented in the "Handbook of Toxic Fungal Metabolites" with the major exception that actual spectra are not included; however, spectral data are included where available. Also included in these volumes are the methods used by the authors to isolate and purify metabolites. Another major difference is that the appropriate references are presented with each metabolite, negating the need to turn to the end of each group to find the appropriate references. Each volume contains four indexes: secondary metabolite index, molecular formula index, molecular weight index, and fungal/plant source index. In a few instances, plant sources are included when the metabolites are closely related to fungal metabolites or the source of precursors may be fungal; i.e., the baccharins, which are found in extracts from *Baccharis megapotamica*. These metabolites are closely related to the macrocyclic trichothecenes found in extracts of fungi such as *Myrothecium* spp. and *Stachybotrys* spp. Also, metabolites from the fungal symbiont of lichens are sometimes presented. To aid in the interpretation of NMR data, the numbering system presented in the literature is included for the major representative fungal metabolite and, at times, for several related metabolites. Fungal sources are given as reported in the original references. It is recognized that the taxonomy in several cases has been revised, perhaps more than once. It is beyond the scope of these volumes to deal with what is "currently accepted taxonomy" because this is a dynamic science that, in many cases, is as yet undefined.

The "Handbook" has been divided into sections, and the placement of metabolites is based on chemical relationships. One section of each volume contains a miscellaneous section to accommodate metabolites difficult to place into one of the sections. The miscellaneous section of Volume III contains some metabolites related to those that appear in Volumes I and II. This occurred when related metabolites were discovered after Volumes I and II were completed.

It is hoped that this compilation of data on secondary fungal metabolites will aid investigators in the identification of known or related fungal metabolites. Because fungal metabolites represent a wide diversity of chemical species, these volumes will be useful to scientists interested in correlations of structural features with various spectral and biological characteristics. The known biological activity of metabolites is presented, which may aid in future studies related to the identification of new uses for fungal metabolites.

Richard J. Cole
Milbra A. Schweikert

Acknowledgments

The authors thank the following investigators for their assistance in producing the "Handbook of Secondary Fungal Metabolites." Their contributions made this compilation of data on fungal metabolites possible.

Wayne L. Bryden
University of Queensland
Gotton, Queensland 4343
Australia

Brian E. Cole
Images, Inc.
Snellville, Georgia

Horace G. Cutler
Department of Pharmacology
Mercer University
Atlanta, Georgia

Jens C. Frisvad
Department of Biotechnology
Technical University of Denmark
DK-2800 Lyngby
Denmark

Bruce Horn
USDA-ARS
National Panut Research Laboratory
Dawson, Georgia

William Norred
Toxicology and Mycotoxin Research Unit
USDA-ARS
Athens, Georgia

James K. Porter
Toxicology and Mycotoxin Research Unit
USDA-ARS
Athens, Georgia

Ronald T. Riley
Toxicology and Mycotoxin Research Unit
USDA-ARS
Athens, Georgia

Victor S. Sobolev
USDA-ARS
National Peanut Research Laboratory
Dawson, Georgia

Bruce B. Jarvis
Department of Chemistry and Biochemistry
University of Maryland
College Park, Maryland

1

Indole Alkaloids

3-(3-Indolyl)propane-1,2,3-triol
3-(3,3-Diindolyl)propane-1,2-diol
4-(3-Indolyl)butane-1,2,3-triol
N-Methyl-4-dimethylallyltryptophan
Lysergic Acid
Ergine; Lysergic acid amide
8-Hydroxyergine
Erginine; Isolysergic acid amide
8-Hydroxyerginine
Lysergol
Lysergene
Lysergine
Ergonovine; Ergometrine; Ergobasine
Ergonovinine; Ergometrinine; Ergobasinine
Agroclavine
6,7-*seco*-Agroclavine
Dihydroagroclavine
Festuclavine
Elymoclavine
Elymoclavine-*O*-ß-fructofuranoside
Elymoclavine-*O*-ß-fructofuranosyl-(2-1)-*O*-ß-D-fructofuranoside
Chanoclavine-I; Chanoclavine
Isochanoclavine-I
Chanoclavine-II
N-Demethylchanoclavine-II; Norchanoclavine II
Setoclavine
Isosetoclavine
Costaclavine
Pyroclavine
Molliclavine
Penniclavine
Cycloclavine
Ergotamine
Ergotaminine
8-Hydroxyergotamine
Ergosine
Ergosinine
Ergostine
Ergostinine
Ergonine
Ergovaline
Ergoptine
Ergocornine

Ergocorninine
O-12'-Methylergocornine
Ergocristine
Ergocristinine
Ergosecaline
Ergosecalinine
Ergobalansine
Ergobalansinine
α-Ergocryptine
O-12'-Methyl-α-ergocryptine
β-Ergocryptine
5'-epimer of ß-Ergocryptine
β-Ergocryptam
β,β-Ergoannam
Ergobutine
Ergobutyrine
Rugulovasine A
8-Chlororugulovasine A
Rugulovasine B
8-Chlororugulovasine B
Fumigaclavine A; 9β-Acetoxy-6,8α-dimethylergoline
Roquefortine A; Isofumigaclavine A; 9-Acetoxy-6,8-dimethylergoline
Fumigaclavine B; 9-Hydroxy-6,8-dimethylergoline
Roquefortine B; Isofumigaclavine B; 9-Hydroxy-6,8-dimethylergoline
Fumigaclavine C; 2-Dimethylallyl-9-acetoxy-6,8-dimethylergoline

Common/Systematic Name

3-(3-Indolyl)propane-1,2,3-triol

Molecular Formula/Molecular Weight

$C_{11}H_{13}NO_3$; MW = 207.08954

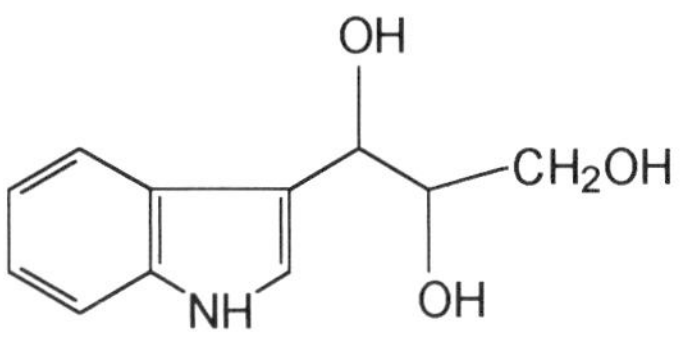

General Characteristics

Red-violet color reaction with *p*-dimethylaminocinnamaldehyde.

Fungal Source

Balansia epichloë.

Isolation/Purification

Purification was achieved by column chromatography on Porapak Q and preparative TLC on silica gel GF_{254} [TLC developing systems were chloroform-methanol (80:20, v/v) and benzene-dimethylformamide (86.5:13.5)].

Biological Activity

Toxic to fertile Leghorn chicken eggs: 23µg/egg = 80%; 68µg/egg = 100% mortality.

Spectral Data

UV:

λ_{max}^{MeOH} 220(log ϵ=4.95), 273(4.00), 280(4.02), and 289nm (3.95).

IR:

(KBr) 1550, 1420, 1410, 1335, 1065, 1050, 740, and 780cm^{-1}.

Mass Spectrum:

207.08, 189.07, 188.06, 186.05, 172.07, 171.06, 170.05, 160.07, 159.06, 146.05, 145.05, 144.08, 144.04, 142.06, 130.06, 118.06, 117.05, 116.05, 103.05, 91.05, 90.04, and 89.03*m/e*.

Reference

J. K. Porter, C. W. Bacon, J. D. Robbins, D. S. Himmelsbach, and H. C. Higman; Indole Alkaloids from *Balansia epichloë* (Weese); J. Agric. Chem., Vol. 25, pp. 88-93 (1977).

Common/Systematic Name

3-(3,3-Diindolyl)propane-1,2-diol

Molecular Formula/Molecular Weight

$C_{19}H_{18}N_2O_2$; MW = 306.13683

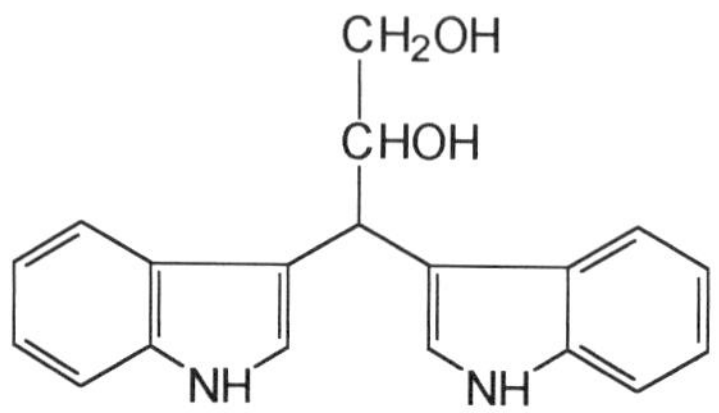

General Characteristics

Red-violet color reaction with *p*-dimethylaminocinnamaldehyde.

Fungal Source

Balansia epichloë.

Isolation/Purification

Purification was achieved by column chromatography on Porapak Q and preparative TLC on silica gel GF_{254} [TLC developing systems were chloroform-methanol (80:20, v/v) and benzene-dimethylformamide (86.5:13.5, v/v)].

Biological Activity

Toxic to fertile Leghorn chicken eggs: 20μg/egg = 20%; 60μg/egg = 55% mortality; 99μg/egg = 100% mortality.

Spectral Data

UV:

λ_{max}^{MeOH} 221(log ε=4.88), 275(3.97), 282(4.01), and 291nm (3.96).

IR:

(KBr) 1550, 1410, 1335, 1080, 1050, and 780cm^{-1}.

Mass Spectrum:

306.1368(M^+), 272.1326, 270.1145, 258.1132, 257.1049, 256.0993, 245.1069, 218.0958, 217.0887, 188.0671, 171.0675, 170.06, 160.07, 159.06, 144.04, 142.06, 130.06, 118.06, 117.05, 116.05, 103.05, 91.05, 90.04, and 89.03*m/e*.

Reference

J. K. Porter, C. W. Bacon, J. D. Robbins, D. S. Himmelsbach, and H. C. Higman; Indole Alkaloids from *Balansia epichloë* (Weese); J. Agric. Chem., Vol. 25, pp. 88-93(1977).

Common/Systematic Name

4-(3-Indolyl)butane-1,2,3-triol

Molecular Formula/Molecular Weight

$C_{12}H_{15}NO_3$; MW = 221.10519

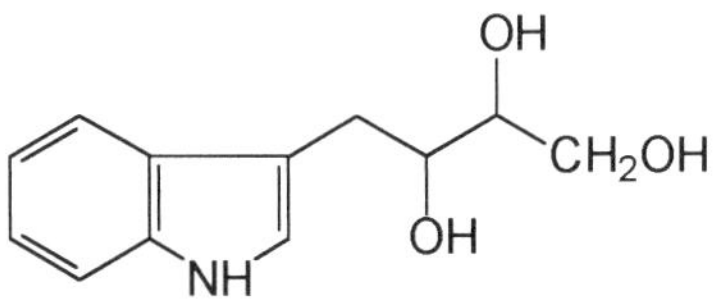

General Characteristics

Red-violet color reaction with *p*-dimethylaminocinnamaldehyde.

Fungal Source

Balansia epichloë

Isolation/Purification

Purification was achieved by column chromatography on Porapak Q and preparative TLC on silica gel GF_{254} [TLC developing systems were chloroform-methanol (80:20, v/v) and benzene-dimethylformamide (86.5:13.5, v/v)].

Biological Activity

Toxic to fertile Leghorn chicken eggs: 57µg/egg = 53% mortality; 113µg/egg = 100% mortality.

Spectral Data

UV:

λ_{max}^{MeOH} 221(log ϵ=4.65), 272(3.78), 279(3.8), and 288nm (3.73).

IR:

(KBr) 1550, 1410, 1340 1080, 1030, and 780cm^{-1}.

Mass Spectrum:

221.10(M^+), 203.09, 201.08, 189.07, 188.07, 186.05, 172.07, 171.06, 170.06, 160.07, 159.06, 146.05, 145.05, 144.08, 144.04, 142.06, 130.06, 118.06, 117.05, 116.05, 103.05, 91.04, 91.05, 90.04, and 89.08*m/e*.

Reference

J. K. Porter, C. W. Bacon, J. D. Robbins, D. S. Himmelsbach, and H. C. Higman; Indole Alkaloids from *Balansia epichloë* (Weese); J. Agric. Chem., Vol. 25, pp. 88-93(1977).

Common/Systematic Name

N-Methyl-4-dimethylallyltryptophan

Molecular Formula/Molecular Weight

$C_{17}H_{22}N_2O_2$; MW = 286.16813

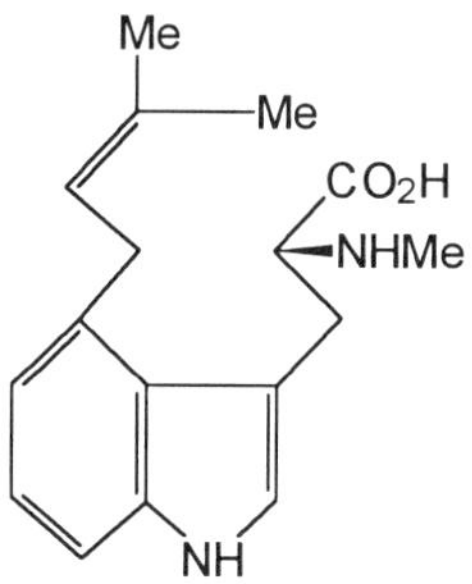

General Characteristics

N-Methyl-4-dimethylallyltryptophan crystallized from methanol as needles; mp., 232°C.

Fungal Source

Claviceps fusiformis.

Isolation/Purification

Claviceps fusiformis was grown aerobically in submerged cultures in both shaken flasks and stirred fermenters. When alkaloid production began, anaerobic conditions were imposed and the cultures stood for three days. Clavine alkaloids were extracted with chloroform at alkaline pH and then the amphoteric metabolites extracted with *n*-butanol at neutral pH. The butanol extract, which contained considerable quantities of chanoclavines and other oxygenated clavine alkaloids, was chromatographed on silica gel with chloroform/methanol/ammonia as the eluant.

Biological Activity

All natural ergot alkaloids possess to a greater or lesser degree, biological effects that can be classified as direct peripheral effects on smooth muscle (uterine contraction and vasoconstriction), indirect peripheral effects (humoral, serotonin antagonism, and adrenergic blockage), and central nervous system effects (bulbomedullary and mesodiencephalic components).

Spectral Data

UV:

λ_{max}^{MeOH} 274, 280, and 295nm.

IR:

(KBr) 3580, 3250(broad) 1640, 1400, and 770cm^{-1}.

^{1}H NMR:

(CD_3COOD) *inter alia* 8.64(s, 6H), 7.64(s, 3H), 5.06(t, 1H, *J*=7.0Hz), and 6.3-7.0ppm (complex, 4H).

Mass Spectrum:

286, 198, 156, 155, and 154*m/e*. The fragmentation under electron-impact was very similar to bis-seco-dehydrocyclopiazonic acid with allylic cleavage of the amino acid side chain giving the ion of *m/e* 198, followed by cyclization to a series of tricyclic ions *m/e* 156, 155, and 154 with elimination of a C-3 unit. Cyclization of this type is only possible if the two side chains are located in the *peri*-position of the indole nucleus, *i.e.* at positions 3 and 4.

TLC Purification

Silica gel plates developed with methylene chloride-isopropyl alcohol (92:8, v/v) three times which results in the separation of alkaloids into the isolysergic acid group, the ergotoxine group, the ergoxine group and a mixture of the ergotamine and clavine groups. Extraction of the alkaloids from the silica using methanol-chloroform (1:4 or 1:1, v/v) followed by rechromatography in chloroform-methanol (9:1 or 4:1, v/v) separates ergovaline from the clavine alkaloids (agroclavine and chanoclavines).

TLC Solvent systems for silica gel chromatography (v/v):

a) Methylene chloride-isopropyl alcohol (92:8; 90:10; 75:25).
b) Chloroform-methanol (90:10; 80:20; 90:10 in saturated NH_3 atmosphere).
c) Chloroform-methanol-NH_3 (94:5:1).
d) Chloroform-ethylamine (90:10).
e) Benzene-dimethylformamide (86.5:13.5).

References

K. D. Barrow and F. R. Quigley; Ergot Alkaloids III : The Isolation of *N*-Methyl-4-dimethylallyltryptophan from *Claviceps fusiformis;* Tetrahedron Letters, pp. 4269-4270 (1975).

B. Berde and H. O. Scheld (eds.); Ergot Alkaloids and Related Compounds; In Handbook of Experimental Pharmacology; Springer-Verlag, New York (1978).

J. K. Porter; Analysis of Endophyte Toxins: Fescue and Other Grasses Toxic to Livestock; J. Animal Science, Vol. 73, pp. 871-880(1994).

Common/Systematic Name

Lysergic acid

Molecular Formula/Molecular Weight

$C_{16}H_{16}N_2O_2$; MW = 268.12118

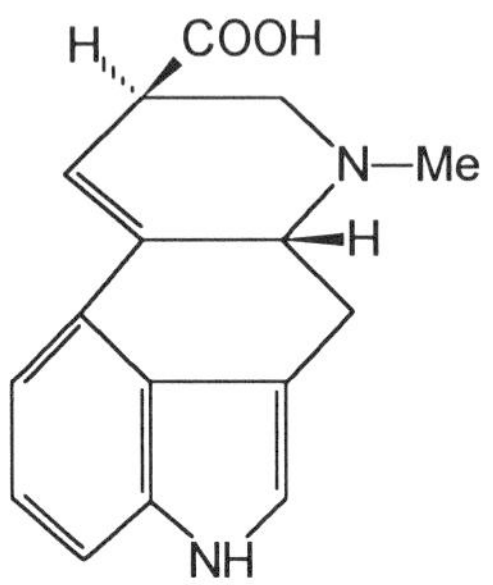

General Characteristics

Hexagonal scales, plates from water (associated with one or two moles water); mp., 240°C (dec.); $[\alpha]_D^{20}$ +40° (*c*=0.5, in pyridine); pK_a=3.44/pK_b=7.68. Moderately soluble in pyridine; sparingly soluble in water and neutral organic solvents; soluble in NaOH, NH_4OH, Na_2CO_3, and HCl solutions; and slightly soluble in dilute H_2SO_4. Methyl ester derivative, thin leaflets from benzene; mp., 168°C.

Fungal Source

Sclerotia and saprophytic culture of *Claviceps purpurea*.

Biological Activity

All natural ergot alkaloids possess to a greater or lesser degree, biological effects that can be classified as direct peripheral effects on smooth muscle (uterine contraction and vasoconstriction), indirect peripheral effects (humoral, serotonin antagonism, and adrenergic blockage), and central nervous system effects (bulbomedullary and mesodiencephalic components).

Spectral Data

IR:

See A. Hofmann, 1964.

^{13}C NMR:

($CDCl_3$) (methyl lysergate) C-2, 118.2; C-3, 110.2; C-4, 26.9; C-5, 62.6; C-7, 54.6; C-8, 41.8; C-9, 117.6; C-10, 136.0; C-11, 127.6; C-12, 112.0; C-13, 122.9; C-14, 109.4; C-15, 133.7; C-16, 125.9; C-17, 172.4; Me, 51.9; and NMe, 43.4ppm.

Mass Spectrum:
LREIMS: 268(M^+, 100%), 224, 221, 207, 192, 180, 167, and 154*m/e*.

References

N. J. Bach, H. E. Boaz, E. C. Kornfeld, C-J Chang, H. G. Floss, E. W. Hagaman, and E. Wenkert; Nuclear Magnetic Resonance Spectral Analysis of the Ergot Alkaloids; J. Org. Chem., Vol. 39, pp. 1272-1276(1974).

B. Berde and H. O. Scheld (eds.); Ergot Alkaloids and Related Compounds; In Handbook of Experimental Pharmacology; Springer-Verlag, New York (1978) .

A. Hofmann; Die Mutterkorn Alkaloide; Enke Verlag, Stuttgart, 218 pp., 1964.

Common/Systematic Name

Ergine; Lysergic acid amide

Molecular Formula/Molecular Weight

$C_{16}H_{17}N_3O$; MW = 267.13716

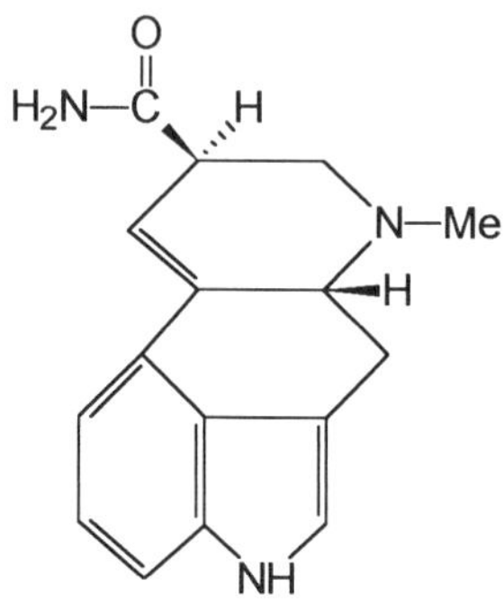

General Characteristics

Crystallized from acetone as massive colorless prisms; m.p. 196°C; $[\alpha]_D^{20}$ + 414°, $[\alpha]_{5461}^{20}$ + 520° (c=1.0, in $CHCl_3$); pK= 6.2 (in 80% methylcellosolve); blue color with Keller's reagent.

Fungal Source

Ergot of *Claviceps purpurea* and *Paspalum distichum L.* (also isolated from seeds of *Rivea corymbosa* (L.) and *Ipomoea tricolor*; Convolvulaceae).

Biological Activity

The ergopeptine alkaloids produce a wide range of biological activities and some are used routinely in medical practice. All natural ergot alkaloids possess to a greater or lesser degree, biological effects that can be classified as direct peripheral effects on smooth muscle (uterine contraction and vasoconstriction), indirect peripheral effects (humoral, serotonin antagonism, and adrenergic blockage), and central nervous system effects (bulbomedullary and mesodiencephalic components). Some ergopeptine alkaloids are used routinely in medical practice. Central American Indians used seeds of *Rivea corymbosa* and *Ipomoea tricolor* as a magic drug called "Ololiuqui".

Spectral Data

IR:

See A. Hofmann, 1964.

UV:

UV spectrum identical to that of lysergic acid or isolysergic acid.

Mass Spectrum:
LREIMS: 267(M^+, 100%), 249, 224, 221, 207, 192, 180, 167, and 154*m/e*.

TLC Purification

Silica gel plates developed with methylene chloride-isopropyl alcohol (92:8, v/v) three times which results in the separation of alkaloids into the isolysergic acid group, the ergotoxine group, the ergoxine group and a mixture of the ergotamine and clavine groups. Extraction of the alkaloids from the silica using methanol-chloroform (1:4 or 1:1, v/v) followed by rechromatography in chloroform-methanol (9:1 or 4:1, v/v) separates ergovaline from the clavine alkaloids (agroclavine and chanoclavines).

TLC Solvent systems for silica gel chromatography (v/v):

a) Methylene chloride-isopropyl alcohol (92:8; 90:10; 75:25).
b) Chloroform-methanol (90:10; 80:20; 90:10 in saturated NH_3 atmosphere).
c) Chloroform-methanol-NH_3 (94:5:1).
d) Chloroform-ethylamine (90:10).
e) Benzene-dimethylformamide (86.5:13.5).

HPLC Data

Extract with alkaline methanol, filter, followed by direct HPLC analysis with fluorescence detection; mobile phase, either 60% or 70% alkaline methanol. This technique works well for ergopeptide alkaloids.

References

B. Berde and H. O. Scheld (eds.); Ergot Alkaloids and Related Compounds; In Handbook of Experimental Pharmacology; Springer-Verlag, New York (1978).

A. Hofmann; Die Mutterkorn Alkaloide; Enke Verlag, Stuttgart, 218 pp., 1964.

Common/Systematic Name

8-Hydroxyergine

Molecular Formula/Molecular Weight

$C_{16}H_{17}N_3O_2$; MW = 283.13208

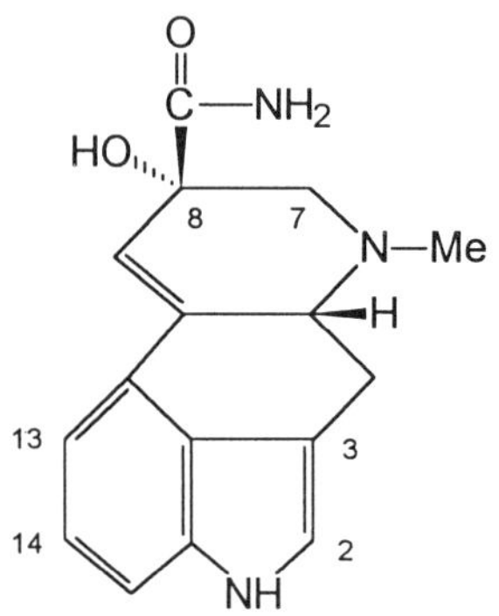

Fungal Source

Claviceps paspali (strain MG-6).

Isolation/Purification

The strain *C. paspali* MG-6 was isolated from the grass *Paspalum dilatatum* in the vicinity of Rome. Alkaloids were separated by adsorption on bentonite (Flieger *et al.*, 1989b). A crude alkaloid mixture was chromatographed on Kieselgel 60 F_{254}, Merck preparative TLC plates and eluted with chloroform-isopropyl alcohol-ammonia (90:10:0.036, v/v/v); R_f values of 8-hydroxyergine and 8-hydroxyerginine were 0.50 and 0.91, respectively. Prepurified alkaloids were chromatographed on a Separon SGX C_{18} column (Tessek, Czechoslovakia) particle size 7μm. The mobile phase consisted of (A) MeOH-H_2O-NH_3 (90:10:0.036, v/v/v) and (B) MeOH-H_2O-NH_3 (20:80:0.036, v/v/v). The column was equilibrated with 4% A in B and subsequently eluted with a linear gradient up to 54% A in B.

Biological Activity

The ergopeptine alkaloids produce a wide range of biological activities and some are used routinely in medical practice. All natural ergot alkaloids possess to a greater or lesser degree, biological effects that can be classified as direct peripheral effects on smooth muscle (uterine contraction and vasoconstriction), indirect peripheral effects (humoral, serotonin antagonism, and adrenergic blockage), and central nervous system effects (bulbomedullary and mesodiencephalic components). The ergopeptine alkaloids produce a wide range of biological activities and some are used routinely in medicine.

Spectral Data

^{1}H NMR:

(CD$_3$OD) H-2, 6.984($J_{2,4a}$=1.8Hz); H-4a, 2.749; H-4b, 3.569($J_{2,4b}$=>0, $J_{4a,4b}$=-14.5Hz); H-5, 3.265($J_{4a,5}$=11.8Hz, $J_{4b,5}$=5.9Hz); H-7a, 2.936($J_{7a,7b}$=-11.7Hz, $J_{7a,9}$=1.0Hz); H-7b, 2.965; H-9, 6.358($J_{4b,9}$=>0, $J_{5,9}$=2.1Hz); H-12, 7.193($J_{12,13}$=7.4Hz, $J_{12,14}$=0.7Hz); H-13, 7.107($J_{13,14}$=7.9Hz); H14, 7.231; and N-Me, 2.590ppm.

^{13}C NMR:

(CD$_3$OD) C-2, 120.66; C-3, 110.52; C-4, 27.15; C-5, 64.20; C-6, 62.7 1; C-7, 73.84; C-8, 121.00; C-9, 139.91; C-10, 128.13; C-11, 113.43; C-12, 123.93; C-13, 111.95; C-14, 136.02; C-15, 128.13; C-16, 177.92; and N-Me, 43.75ppm.

Mass Spectrum:

EIMS: 283(M$^+$, $C_{16}H_{17}N_3O_2$, 61%), 266($C_{16}H_{16}N_3O$, 27), 265($C_{16}H_{15}N_3O$, 37), 248($C_{16}H_{12}N_2O$, 59), 240($C_{14}H_{12}N_2O_2$, 86), 223($C_{14}H_{12}N_2O_2$, 86), 221($C_{15}H_{13}N_2$, 42), 206($C_{14}H_{10}N_2$, 19), 195($C_{13}H_9NO$, 36), 194($C_{13}H_8NO$, 32), 181($C_{13}H_{11}N$, 26), 180($C_{13}H_{10}N$, 26), 167($C_{12}H_9N$, 83), and 154($C_{11}H_8N$, 100).

TLC Purification

Silica gel plates developed with methylene chloride-isopropyl alcohol (92:8, v/v) three times which results in the separation of alkaloids into the isolysergic acid group, the ergotoxine group, the ergoxine group and a mixture of the ergotamine and clavine groups. Extraction of the alkaloids from the silica using methanol-chloroform (1:4 or 1:1, v/v) followed by rechromatography in chloroform-methanol (9:1 or 4:1, v/v) separates ergovaline from the clavine alkaloids (agroclavine and chanoclavines).

TLC Solvent systems for silica gel chromatography (v/v):

a) Methylene chloride-isopropyl alcohol (92:8; 90:10; 75:25).
b) Chloroform-methanol (90:10; 80:20; 90:10 in saturated NH_3 atmosphere).
c) Chloroform-methanol-NH_3 (94:5:1).
d) Chloroform-ethylamine (90:10).
e) Benzene-dimethylformamide (86.5:13.5).

References

M. Flieger, R. Linhartova, P. Sedmera, J. Zima, P. Sajdl, J. Stuchlik, and L. Cvak; New Alkaloids of *Claviceps paspali*; J. Nat. Prod., Vol. 52, pp. 1003-1007 (1989a).

J. K. Porter; Analysis of Endophyte Toxins: Fescue and Other Grasses Toxic to Livestock; J. Animal Science, Vol. 73, pp. 871-880(1994).

Common/Systematic Name

Erginine; Isolysergic acid amide

Molecular Formula/Molecular Weight

$C_{16}H_{17}N_3O$; MW = 267.13716

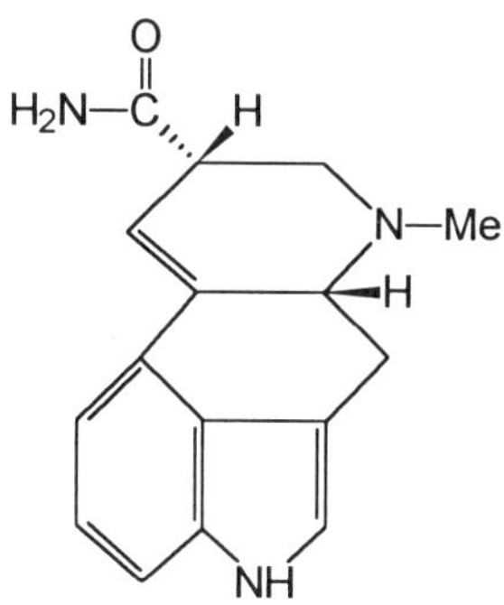

General Characteristics

Crystallized from methanol as solvated prisms; mp., 132-134°C; $[\alpha]_D^{20}$ + 480°, $[\alpha]_{5461}^{20}$ + 608° (*c*=0.5, in pyridine); pK=6.1 (in 80% methylcellosolve).

Fungal Source

Ergot and saprophytic culture of *Claviceps purpurea*. Epimers are not considered as naturally occurring, but as products formed during extraction and purification; epimerization at C-8 occurs in either acid or base.

Biological Activity

The ergopeptine alkaloids produce a wide range of biological activities and some are used routinely in medical practice. All natural ergot alkaloids possess to a greater or lesser degree, biological effects that can be classified as direct peripheral effects on smooth muscle (uterine contraction and vasoconstriction), indirect peripheral effects (humoral, serotonin antagonism, and adrenergic blockage), and central nervous system effects (bulbomedullary and mesodiencephalic components). Some ergopeptine alkaloids are used routinely in medical practice. Central American Indians used seeds of *Rivea corymbosa* and *Ipomoea tricolor* as a magic drug called "Ololiuqui".

Spectral Data

IR:

See A. Hofmann, 1964.

TLC Purification

Silica gel plates developed with methylene chloride-isopropyl alcohol (92:8, v/v) three times which results in the separation of alkaloids into the isolysergic acid group, the ergotoxine group, the ergoxine group and a mixture of the ergotamine and clavine groups. Extraction of the alkaloids from the silica using methanol-chloroform (1:4 or 1:1, v/v) followed by rechromatography in chloroform-methanol (9:1 or 4:1, v/v) separates ergovaline from the clavine alkaloids (agroclavine and chanoclavines).

TLC Solvent systems for silica gel chromatography (v/v):

a) Methylene chloride-isopropyl alcohol (92:8; 90:10; 75:25).
b) Chloroform-methanol (90:10; 80:20; 90:10 in saturated NH_3 atmosphere).
c) Chloroform-methanol-NH_3 (94:5:1).
d) Chloroform-ethylamine (90:10).
e) Benzene-dimethylformamide (86.5:13.5).

HPLC Data

Extract with alkaline methanol, filter, followed by direct HPLC analysis with fluorescence detection; mobile phase, either 60% or 70% alkaline methanol. This technique works well for ergopeptide alkaloids.

References

B. Berde and H. O. Scheld (eds.); Ergot Alkaloids and Related Compounds; In Handbook of Experimental Pharmacology; Springer-Verlag, New York (1978).

A. Hofmann; Die Mutterkorn Alkaloide; Enke Verlag, Stuttgart, 218 pp., 1964.

J. K. Porter; Analysis of Endophyte Toxins: Fescue and Other Grasses Toxic to Livestock; J. Animal Science, Vol. 73, pp. 871-880(1994).

Common/Systematic Name

8-Hydroxyerginine

Molecular Formula/Molecular Weight

$C_{16}H_{17}N_3O_2$; MW = 283.13208

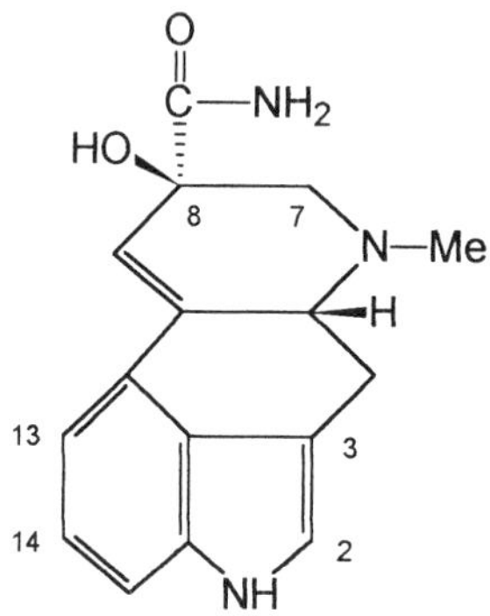

Fungal Source

Claviceps paspali MG-6.

Epimers are not considered as naturally occurring but as products formed during extraction and purification; epimerization at C-8 occurs in either acid or base.

Isolation/Purification

The strain *C. paspali* MG-6 was isolated from the grass *Paspalum dilatatum* in the vicinity of Rome. Alkaloids were separated by adsorption on bentonite (Flieger *et al.*, 1989b). A crude alkaloid mixture was chromatographed on Kieselgel 60 F_{254}, Merck preparative TLC plates, and eluted with chloroform-isopropyl alcohol-ammonia (90:10:0.036, v/v/v); R_f values of 8-hydroxyergine and 8-hydroxyerginine were 0.50 and 0.91, respectively. Prepurified alkaloids were chromatographed on a Separon SGX C_{18} column (Tessek, Czechoslovakia) of particle size 7μ. The mobile phase consisted of (A) MeOH-H_2O-NH_3 (90:10:0.036, v/v/v) and (B) MeOH-H_2O-NH_3 (20:80:0.036, v/v/v). The column was equilibrated with 4% A in B and subsequently eluted with a linear gradient up to 54% A in B.

Spectral Data

^1H NMR:

(CD_3OD) H-2, 6.974($J_{2,4a}$=1.6Hz); H-4a, 2.649; H-4b, 3.606($J_{2,4b}$=>0, $J_{4a,4b}$=-14.6Hz); H-5, 3.150($J_{4a,5}$=11.5Hz, $J_{4b,5}$=5.9Hz); H-7a, 3.080($J_{7a,7b}$=-11.3Hz, $J_{7a,9}$=1.5Hz); H-7b, 2.626; H-9, 6.268($J_{4b,9}$=0.8Hz, $J_{5,9}$=2.2Hz); H-12, 7.118($J_{12,13}$=7.0Hz, $J_{12,14}$=1.7Hz); H-13, 7.090($J_{13,14}$=7.2Hz); H-14, 7.219ppm; and N-Me, 2.614ppm.

^{13}C NMR:

(CD$_3$OD) C-2, 120.53; C-3, 110.55; C-4, 28.27; C-5, 64.11; C-6, 63.06; C-7, 71.87; C-8, 124.30; C-9, 139.13; C-10, 128.04; C-11, 113.15; C-12, 123.96; C-13, 111.72; C-14, 135.95; C-15, 127.99; C-16, 179.59; and N-Me, 43.39ppm.

Mass Spectrum:

EIMS: 283(M$^+$, $C_{16}H_{17}N_3O_2$, 100), 266($C_{16}H_{16}N_3O$, 14), 265($C_{16}H_{15}N_3O$, 29), 248($C_{16}H_{12}N_2O$, 35), 240($C_{14}H_{12}N_2O_2$, 93), 223($C_{14}H_{12}N_2O_2$, 31), 221($C_{15}H_{13}N_2$, 42), 206($C_{14}H_{10}N_2$, 12), 195($C_{13}H_9N$, 60), 194($C_{13}H_8N$, 61), 181($C_{13}H_{11}N$, 50), 180($C_{13}H_{10}N$, 20), 167($C_{12}H_9N$, 94), and 154($C_{11}H_8N$, 96%).

Reference

M. Flieger, R. Linhartova, P. Sedmera, J. Zima, P. Sajdl, J. Stuchlík, and L. Cvak; New Alkaloids of *Claviceps paspali*; J. Nat. Prod.; Vol. 52, pp. 1003-1007(1989a).

Common/Systematic Name

Lysergol

Molecular Formula/Molecular Weight

$C_{16}H_{18}N_2O$; MW = 254.14191

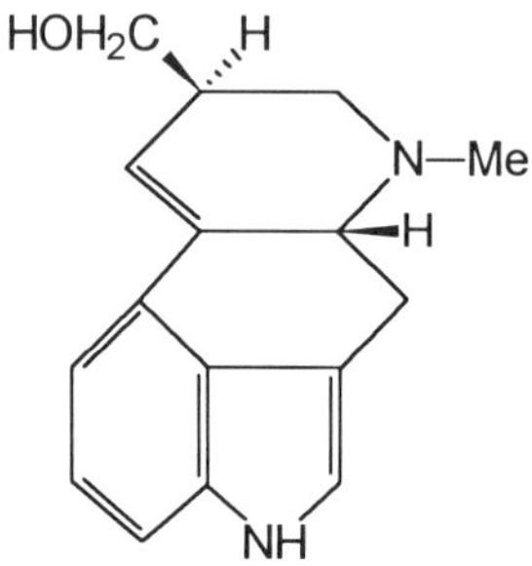

General Characteristics

Colorless prisms from ethanol; mp., 245°C (uncorr. decomp.); as plates and prisms; mp., 253-255°C (dec.); $[\alpha]_D^{18}$ +49° (*c*=0.2, in pyridine); $[\alpha]_D^{20}$ +54°, $[\alpha]_{5461}^{20}$ +87° (*c*=0.3, in pyridine). Gave a light purple and purplish blue colors with van Urk's and Allport-Cocking's reagents, respectively. Sublimes at high vacuum at 180°C; pK=6.6 (in 80% aqueous methylcellosolve). Soluble in 350 parts of boiling methanol or 100 parts boiling ethanol, sparingly soluble in chloroform or water.

Fungal Source

Saprophytic cultures of *Elymus*-type ergot fungus.

Isolation/Purification

Purified either by countercurrent distribution or by column chromatography using Hyflo Super Cell treated with a buffer solution (McIlvaine).

Biological Activity

All natural ergot alkaloids possess to a greater or lesser degree, biological effects that can be classified as direct peripheral effects on smooth muscle (uterine contraction and vasoconstriction), indirect peripheral effects (humoral, serotonin antagonism, and adrenergic blockage), and central nervous system effects (bulbomedullary and mesodiencephalic components).

Spectral Data

UV:

λ_{max}^{MeOH} 225, 242, and 312nm.

IR:
See A. Hofmann, 1964.

Mass Spectrum:
LREIMS: 254(M^+, 100%), 235, 223, 221, 207, 205, 193, 192, 180, 167, and 154*m/e*.

References

M. Abe, S. Yamatodani, T. Yamano, and M. Kusumoto; Isolation of Lysergol, Lysergene and Lysergine from the Saprophytic Cultures of Ergot Fungi; Agric. Biol. Chem. [Tokyo], Vol. 25, pp. 594-595(1961).

B. Berde and H. O. Scheld (eds.); Ergot Alkaloids and Related Compounds; In Handbook of Experimental Pharmacology; Springer-Verlag, New York (1978).

A. Hofmann; Die Mutterkorn Alkaloide; Enke Verlag, Stuttgart, 218 pp., 1964.

Common/Systematic Name

Lysergene

Molecular Formula/Molecular Weight

$C_{16}H_{16}N_2$; MW = 236.13135

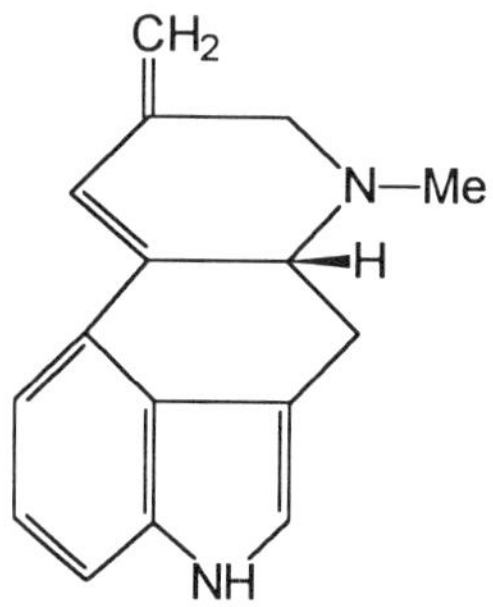

General Characteristics

Colorless needles or prisms from ethyl acetate; mp., 244°C (uncorr. decomp.); colorless needles or prisms from methanol, 247-249°C (dec.); $[\alpha]_D^{18}$ +461 (*c*=0.2, in pyridine); $[\alpha]_D^{20}$ +504° (*c*=0.4, in pyridine). Sparingly soluble in most organic solvents, moderately soluble in chloroform or pyridine. Gave a yellowish-green color with both van Urk's and Allport-Cocking's reagents, respectively.

Fungal Source

Saprophytic cultures of *Elymus*-type ergot fungus.

Isolation/Purification

Purified either by countercurrent distribution or by column chromatography using Hyflo Super Cell treated with a buffer solution (McIlvaine).

Biological Activity

All natural ergot alkaloids possess to a greater or lesser degree, biological effects that can be classified as direct peripheral effects on smooth muscle (uterine contraction and vasoconstriction), indirect peripheral effects (humoral, serotonin antagonism, and adrenergic blockage), and central nervous system effects (bulbomedullary and mesodiencephalic components).

Spectral Data

UV:

λ_{max}^{MeOH} 243, 263, and 335nm.

IR:

See A. Hofmann, 1964.

References

M. Abe, S. Yamatodani, T. Yamano, and M. Kusumoto; Isolation of Lysergol, Lysergene and Lysergine from the Saprophytic Cultures of Ergot Fungi; Agric. Biol. Chem. Vol., pp. 594-595(1961).

B. Berde and H. O. Scheld (eds.); Ergot Alkaloids and Related Compounds; In Handbook of Experimental Pharmacology; Springer-Verlag, New York (1978).

A. Hofmann; Die Mutterkorn Alkaloide; Enke Verlag, Stuttgart, 218 pp., 1964.

Common/Systematic Name

Lysergine

Molecular Formula/Molecular Weight

$C_{16}H_{18}N_2$; MW = 238.14700

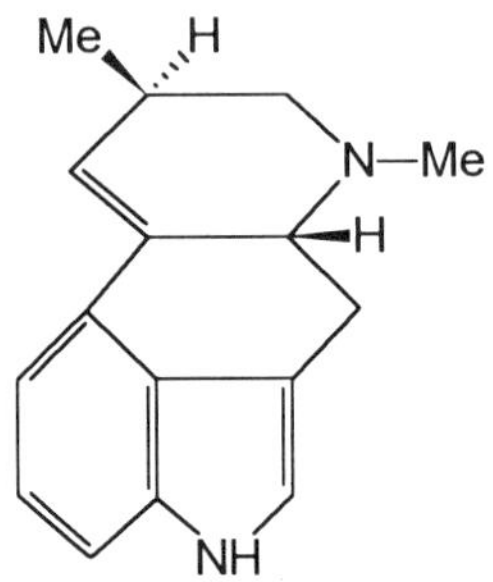

General Characteristics

Colorless prisms from ethyl acetate; mp., 275°C (uncorr. decomp.); prisms from methanol, ethanol, or ethyl acetate, 286-289°C (dec.); $[\alpha]_D^{18}$ = +70° (*c*=0.2, in pyridine), $[\alpha]_D^{20}$ +65° (*c*=0.5, in pyridine); sparingly soluble in methanol, ethanol, and ethyl acetate.

Fungal Source

Ergot or saprophytic cultures of *Agropyrum* sp.

Biological Activity

All natural ergot alkaloids possess to a greater or lesser degree, biological effects that can be classified as direct peripheral effects on smooth muscle (uterine contraction and vasoconstriction), indirect peripheral effects (humoral, serotonin antagonism, and adrenergic blockage), and central nervous system effects (bulbomedullary and mesodiencephalic components).

Spectral Data

UV:

Very similar to lysergic acid.

IR:

See A. Hofmann, 1964.

References

Abe, S. Yamatodani, T. Yamano, and M. Kusumoto; Isolation of Lysergol, Lysergene and Lysergine from the Saprophytic Cultures of Ergot Fungi; Agric. Biol. Chem. [Tokyo], Vol. 25, pp. 594-595(1961).

B. Berde and H. O. Scheld (eds.); Ergot Alkaloids and Related Compounds; In Handbook of Experimental Pharmacology; Springer-Verlag, New York (1978)

A. Hofmann; Die Mutterkorn Alkaloide, Enke Verlag, Stuttgart, 218 pp., 1964.

Common/Systematic Name
Ergonovine; Ergometrine; Ergobasine

Molecular Formula/Molecular Weight
$C_{19}H_{23}N_3O_2$; MW = 325.17903

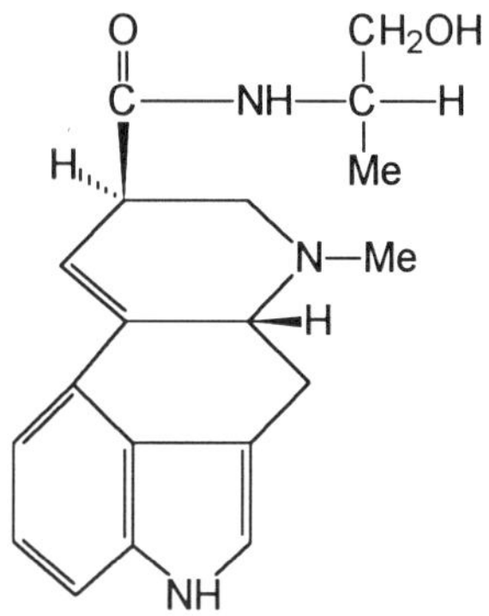

General Characteristics
Tetrahedra from ethyl acetate; fine needles from benzene; tendency to form solvated crystals; mp., 162°C (nonsolvated, mp., 212°C, dec.); $[\alpha]_D^{20}$ + 90°(*c*=0.23, in water); -16° (*c*=1.0, in pyridine); $[\alpha]_D^{20}$ + 41°, $[\alpha]_{5461}^{20}$ + 60° (*c*=1.0, in alcohol); pK = 6.8. Freely soluble in lower alcohols, ethyl acetate, and acetone; more soluble in water than other principal alkaloids of ergot; slightly soluble in chloroform.

Fungal Source
Claviceps purpurea, *Balansia epichloë*, *B. henningsiana*, and *B. claviceps.*

Isolation/Purification/Analysis
Extract with either aqueous tartaric or lactic acid solution, partition chromatography with chloroform or methylene chloride at appropriate pH, column clean-up procedures using either silica, alumina or ion exchange resin, and identification and analysis using a combination of co-chromatography using TLC and/or HPLC with UV or fluorescence detection. Mass spectrometry is quite useful for identification, analysis and quantitation.

Biological Activity
All natural ergot alkaloids possess to a greater or lesser degree, biological effects that can be classified as direct peripheral effects on smooth muscle (uterine contraction and vasoconstriction), indirect peripheral effects (humoral, serotonin antagonism, and adrenergic blockage), and central nervous system effects (bulbomedullary and mesodiencephalic components). MLD (IV) in rabbits was 7.5mg/kg.

Spectral Data

IR:

See A. Hofmann, 1964.

UV:

Identical to that of lysergic acid or isolysergic acid.

^{13}C NMR:

(DMSO-d_6) C-2, 119.1; C-3, 108.9; C-4, 26.8; C-5, 62.6; C-7, 55.5; C-8, 42.8; C-9, 120.1; C-10, 135.0; C-11, 127.4; C-12, 111.0; C-13, 122.4; C-14, 109.0; C-15, 133.7; C-16, 125.8; C-17, 171.2; Me, 17.4; NCH, 46.4; OCH_2, 64.4; and N-Me, 43.4ppm.

TLC Purification

Silica gel plates developed with methylene chloride-isopropyl alcohol (92:8, v/v) three times which results in the separation of alkaloids into the isolysergic acid group, the ergotoxine group, the ergoxine group and a mixture of the ergotamine and clavine groups. Extraction of the alkaloids from the silica using methanol-chloroform (1:4 or 1:1) followed by rechromatography in chloroform-methanol (9:1 or 4:1) separates ergovaline from the clavine alkaloids (agroclavine and chanoclavines).

TLC Solvent systems for silica gel chromatography:

a) Methylene chloride-isopropyl alcohol (92:8; 90:10; 75:25).
b) Chloroform-methanol (90:10; 80:20; 90:10 in saturated NH_3 atmosphere).
c) Chloroform-methanol-NH_3 (94:5:1).
d) Chloroform-ethylamine (90:10).
e) Benzene-dimethylformamide (86.5:13.5).

HPLC Data

Extract with alkaline methanol, filter, followed by direct HPLC analysis with fluorescence detection; mobile phase, either 60% or 70% alkaline methanol. This technique works well for ergopeptide alkaloids.

References

N. J. Bach, H. E. Boaz, E. C. Kornfeld, C-J Chang, H. G. Floss, E. W. Hagaman, and E. Wenkert; Nuclear Magnetic Resonance Spectral Analysis of the Ergot Alkaloids; J. Org. chem., Vol. 39, pp. 1272-1276(1974).

C. W. Bacon, J. K. Porter, and J. D. Robbins; Lysergic Acid Amide Derivatives from *Balansia epichloë* and *Balansia claviceps* (Clavicipitaceae); J. Nat. Prod., 42: 309-314 (1979).

C. W. Bacon, J. K. Porter, and J. D. Robbins; Laboratory Production of Ergot Alkaloids by Species of *Balansia*; J. Gen. Microbiol., 113: 119-126(1979).

C. W. Bacon, J. K. Porter, and J. D. Robbins; Ergot Alkaloids Biosynthesis by Isolates of *Balansia epichloë* and *Balansia henningsiana*; Can. J. Bot., 59: 2534-2538(1981).

C. W. Bacon, J. K. Porter, J. D. Robbins, and D. Betowski; Ergot Alkaloids Identification in Clavicipitaceae Systemic Fungi of Pasture Grass; J. Agric. Food Chem., 29: 653-657 (1981).

B. Berde and H. O. Scheld (eds.); Ergot Alkaloids and Related Compounds; In Handbook of Experimental Pharmacology; Springer-Verlag, New York (1978).

A. Hofmann; Die Mutterkorn Alkaloide; Enke Verlag, Stuttgart, 218 pp., 1964.

W. A. Jacobs and L. C. Craig; On an Alkaloid from Ergot; Science, Vol. 82, pp. 16-17 (1935).

J. K. Porter; Analysis of Endophyte Toxins: Fescue and Other Grasses Toxic to Livestock; J. Animal Science, Vol. 73, pp. 871-880(1994).

Common/Systematic Name

Ergonovinine; Ergometrinine; Ergobasinine

Molecular Formula/Molecular Weight

$C_{19}H_{23}N_3O_2$; MW = 325.17903

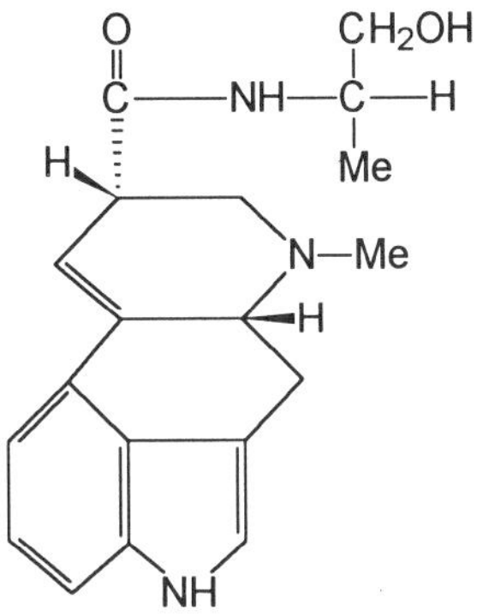

General Characteristics

Forms large colorless prisms from acetone; mp., 196°C (dec.); $[\alpha]_D^{20}$ + 414°, $[\alpha]_{5461}^{20}$ + 520° (c=1.0, in $CHCl_3$); pK=6.2 (in 80% methylcellosolve); blue color with Keller's reagent.

Fungal Source

Claviceps purpurea.

Epimers are not considered as naturally occurring, but as products formed during extraction and purification; epimerization at C-8 occurs in either acid or base.

Isolation/Purification/Analysis

Extract with either aqueous tartaric or lactic acid solution, partition chromatography with chloroform or methylene chloride at appropriate pH, column clean-up procedures using either silica, alumina or ion exchange resin, and identification and analysis using a combination of co-chromatography using TLC and/or HPLC with UV or fluorescence detection. Mass spectrometry is quite useful for identification, analysis and quantitation.

Biological Activity

All natural ergot alkaloids possess to a greater or lesser degree, biological effects that can be classified as direct peripheral effects on smooth muscle (uterine contraction and vasoconstriction), indirect peripheral effects (humoral, serotonin antagonism and adrenergic blockage) and central nervous system effects (bulbomedullary and mesodiencephalic components). MLD (IV) in rabbits was 7.5mg/kg.

Spectral Data

IR:

See A. Hofmann, 1964.

UV:

Identical to that of lysergic acid or isolysergic acid.

^{13}C NMR:

(DMSO-d_6) C-2, 119.0; C-3, 108.9; C-4, 26.9; C-5, 62.0; C-7, 54.0; C-8, ca. 42.2; C-9, 119.0; C-10, 136.1; C-11, 127.6; C-12, 111.0; C-13, 122.1; C-14, 109.8; C-15, 133.7; C-16, 125.7; C-17, 172.1; Me, 17.2; NCH, 46.2; OCH_2, 64.3; and N-Me, 43.6ppm.

TLC Purification

Silica gel plates developed with methylene chloride-isopropyl alcohol (92:8, v/v) three times which results in the separation of alkaloids into the isolysergic acid group, the ergotoxine group, the ergoxine group and a mixture of the ergotamine and clavine groups. Extraction of the alkaloids from the silica using methanol-chloroform (1:4 or 1:1, v/v) followed by rechromatography in chloroform-methanol (9:1 or 4:1, v/v) separates ergovaline from the clavine alkaloids (agroclavine and chanoclavines).

TLC Solvent systems for silica gel chromatography (v/v):

a) Methylene chloride-isopropyl alcohol (92:8; 90:10; 75:25).
b) Chloroform-methanol (90:10; 80:20; 90:10 in saturated NH_3 atmosphere).
c) Chloroform-methanol-NH_3 (94:5:1).
d) Chloroform-ethylamine (90:10).
e) Benzene-dimethylformamide (86.5:13.5).

HPLC Data

Extract with alkaline methanol, filter, followed by direct HPLC analysis with fluorescence detection; mobile phase, either 60% or 70% alkaline methanol. This technique works well for ergopeptide alkaloids.

References

N. J. Bach, H. E. Boaz, E. C. Kornfeld, C-J Chang, H. G. Floss, E. W. Hagaman, and E. Wenkert; Nuclear Magnetic Resonance Spectral Analysis of the Ergot Alkaloids; J. Org. chem., Vol. 39, pp. 1272-1276(1974).

C. W. Bacon, J. K. Porter, and J. D. Robbins; Lysergic Acid Amide Derivatives from *Balansia epichloë* and *Balansia claviceps* (Clavicipitaceae); J. Nat. Prod., 42: 309-314 (1979).

C. W. Bacon, J. K. Porter, and J. D. Robbins; Laboratory Production of Ergot Alkaloids by Species of *Balansia*; J. Gen. Microbiol., 113: 119-126(1979).

C. W. Bacon, J. K. Porter, and J. D. Robbins; Ergot Alkaloids Biosynthesis by Isolates of *Balansia epichloë* and *Balansia henningsiana*; Can. J. Bot., 59: 2534-2538(1981).

C. W. Bacon, J. K. Porter, J. D. Robbins, and D. Betowski; Ergot Alkaloids Identification in Clavicipitaceae Systemic Fungi of Pasture Grass; J. Agric. Food Chem., 29: 653-657 (1981).

B. Berde and H. O. Scheld (eds.); Ergot Alkaloids and Related Compounds; In Handbook of Experimental Pharmacology; Springer-Verlag, New York (1978).

A. Hofmann; Die Mutterkorn Alkaloide; Enke Verlag, Stuttgart, 218 pp., 1964.

W. A. Jacobs and L. C. Craig; On an Alkaloid from Ergot; Science, Vol. 82, pp. 16-17 (1935).

J. K. Porter; Analysis of Endophyte Toxins: Fescue and Other Grasses Toxic to Livestock; J. Animal Science, Vol. 73, pp. 871-880(1994).

Common/Systematic Name

Agroclavine

Molecular Formula/Molecular Weight

$C_{16}H_{18}N_2$; MW = 238.14700

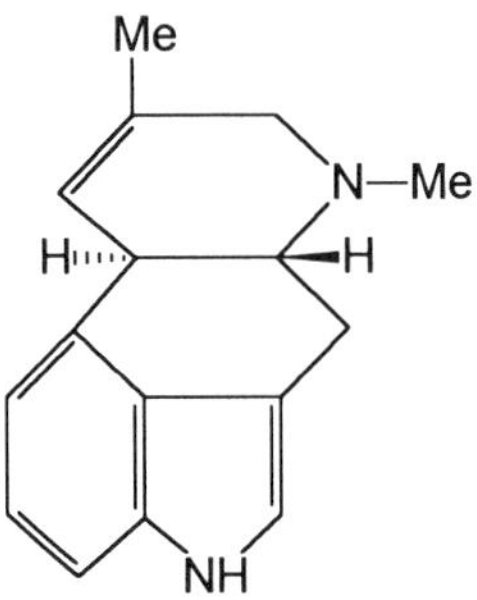

General Characteristics

Colorless needles from acetone; mp., 205-206°C; sublimed under high vacuum between 110-130°C; $[\alpha]_D^{20}$ -155° (*c*=0.9 in $CHCl_3$); $[\alpha]_D^{20}$ -182° (*c*=0.5 in pyridine); pK=6.8 (in 80% aqueous methylcellosolve). Violet/blue color with Keller's reagent.

Fungal Source

First found from sclerotia and cultures of *Agropyrum semicostatum* Nees and *A. ciliare* Fr. Also found in *Pennisetum typhoideum*.

Biological Activity

All natural ergot alkaloids possess to a greater or lesser degree, biological effects that can be classified as direct peripheral effects on smooth muscle (uterine contraction and vasoconstriction), indirect peripheral effects (humoral, serotonin antagonism, and adrenergic blockage), and central nervous system effects (bulbomedullary and mesodiencephalic components).

Spectral Data

UV:

λ_{max}^{MeOH} 225, 284 and 293nm (log ϵ=4.47, 3.88 and 3.81, respectively).

IR:

See A. Hofmann, 1964.

^{1}H NMR:

(pyridine- d_5) H-6, 2.38(3H, s); H-7, 2.73(1H, d); H-4, 2.90(1H, ddd); H-7', 3.18(1H, d); H-4', 2.51(1H, ddd); H-5, 3.36(1H, dd); H-10, 3.89(1H, m); 7-CH_3 , 1.68(3H, s);

H-9, 6.30(1H, m); aromatic-H, 7.1-7.4(4H, m); and H-1, 11.43ppm (1H, s). (Note: Possible incorrect assignment of the 4α, 4β, and 5 hydrogens).

($CDCl_3$) H-4α, 2.78(dd, *J*=15, 12Hz); H-4β, 3.31(dd, *J*=15, 4Hz); H-5, 2.52(ddd, *J*=12, 9.5 and 4Hz); H-7α, 3.24(d, *J*=17Hz); H-7β, 2.93(dd, broad signal, *J*=17, 4Hz); H-9α and β, 6.18(s, broad signal); H-10, 3.74(dd, broad signal, *J*=9.5, 4Hz); H-17, 1.77(s); and N-Me, 2.49ppm (s).

^{13}C NMR:

(pyridine- d_5) C-2, 118.3; C-3, 111.2; C-4, 26.4; C-5, 63.6; C-7, 60.2; C-8, 131.9; C-9, 119.4; C-10, 40.8; C-11, 131.9; C-12, 112.0; C-13, 122.0; C-14, 108.4; C-15, 134.0; C-16, 126.6; C-17, 19.9; and N-Me, 40.2ppm.

Mass Spectrum:

LREIMS: 238(M^+, 52%), 237(100), 167(17), and 154*m/e* (16).

References

M. Abe, T. Yamano, Y. Kozu, and M. Kusumoto; Isolation of Further Two Water-soluble Ergot Alkaloids; J. Age. Chem. Soc., Vol. 28, pp. 501-510(1954).

N. J. Bach, H. E. Boaz, E. C. Cornfield, C-J Chang, H. G. Floss, E. W. Hegemon, and E. Wenkert; Nuclear Magnetic Resonance Spectral Analysis of the Ergot Alkaloids; J. Org. Chem., Vol. 39, pp. 1272-1276(1974).

B. Berde and H. O. Scheld (eds.); Ergot Alkaloids and Related Compounds; In Handbook of Experimental Pharmacology, Springer-Verlag, New York (1978).

A. Hofmann; Die Mutterkorn Alkaloide; Enke Verlag, Stuttgart, 218 pp., 1964.

R. G. Mrtek, H. L. Crespi, G. Norman, M. I. Blake, and J. J. Katz; Biosynthesis of Clavine Alkaloids: Proton Magnetic Resonance Studies; Phytochemistry, Vol. 7, pp. 1535-1541(1968).

A. Stoll, A. Brack, H. Kobel, A. Hofmann, and R. Brunner; Die Alkaloide eines Mutterkornpilzes von *Pennisetum typhoideum* rich. und deren Bildung in Saprophytischer Kultur; Helvetica Chimica Acta, Vol. 37, pp. 1815-1825(1954).

Common/Systematic Name

6,7-*seco*-Agroclavine

Molecular Formula/Molecular Weight

$C_{16}H_{20}N_2$; MW = 240.16265

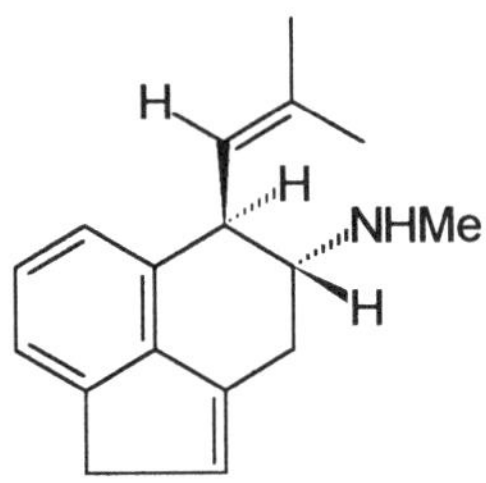

General Characteristics

Crystals; mp., 126-129°C subl.; gives a blue color with Allport and Cocking's reagent.

Fungal Source

Claviceps purpurea, strain AA-218, *Balansia epichloë, B. strangulans,* and *Epichloë typhina.*

Isolation/Purification

Purified by HPLC followed by PLC using 1% conc. ammonia, 5% MeOH, and 94% chloroform. TLC using silica gel with same solvent system.

Spectral Data

UV:

λ_{max}^{EtOH} 225, 283, and 293nm.

IR:

($CHCl_3$): 3480(indole NH), 3320(aliphatic NH), 1605, and 1445cm^{-1} (C=C).

^{1}H NMR:

($CDCl_3$): 1.85(s, 6H); 2.53(s, with hyperfine splitting, 3H); 2.4(br s, 1H); 2.6-3.5(m, 4H); 3.75-4.15(m, 1H); 5.0-5.3(d, 1H (C-10-H)); 6.6-7.3(m, 4H); and 8.1-8.5ppm (br s, 1H(indole)).

Mass Spectrum:

EIMS: 240, 225, 208, 197, 184, 168, and 155*m/e*.

References

C. Horwell and J. P. Verge; Isolation and Identification of 6,7-*seco*-Agroclavine from *Claviceps purpurea*; Phytochemistry, Vol. 18, p. 519 (1979).

J. K. Porter, C. W. Bacon, J. D. Robbins, and D. Betowski; Ergot Alkaloid Identification in Clavicipitaceae Systemic Fungi of Pasture Grasses; J. Agric. Food Chem., 29: 653-657 (1981).

Common/Systematic Name

Dihydroagroclavine

Molecular Formula/Molecular Weight

$C_{16}H_{20}N_2$; MW = 240.16265

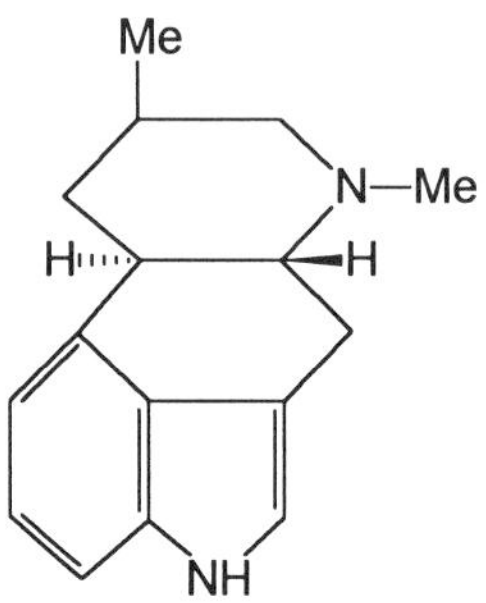

General Characteristics

Crystals as long needles from toluene, benzene, ether, chloroform, ethyl acetate, acetone, methanol, ethanol or pyridine; mp., 242°C (dec.); $[\alpha]_D^{20}$ - 69°, $[\alpha]_{5461}^{20}$ - 83° (*c*=0.5, in $CHCl_3$); $[\alpha]_D^{0}$ - 111°, $[\alpha]_{5461}^{20}$ - 129° (*c*=0.5, in pyridine). Insoluble in toluene, benzene and ether; readily soluble in chloroform, ethyl acetate, acetone, methanol, ethanol and pyridine. Succinate derivative, $C_{16}H_{20}N_2$. 0.5 $C_4H_6O_4$, crystals as prisms from water; mp., 213°C (dec.); $[\alpha]_D^{17}$ - 87° (*c*=0.13, in pyridine).

Fungal Source

Ergot and saprophytic culture of *Phalaris* and *Agropyrum* sp.

Spectral Data

Mass Data:

Found: C 79.94, H 8.34, N 11.64 (calcd. for $C_{16}H_{20}N_2$: C 79.95, H 8.39, N 11.66).

Reference

M. Abe and S. Yamatodani; Isolation of Further Two Water Soluble Ergot Alkaloids; J. Agr. Chem. Soc., Vol. 28, p. 501 (1954).

Common/Systematic Name

Festuclavine

Molecular Formula/Molecular Weight

$C_{16}H_{20}N_2$; MW = 240.16265

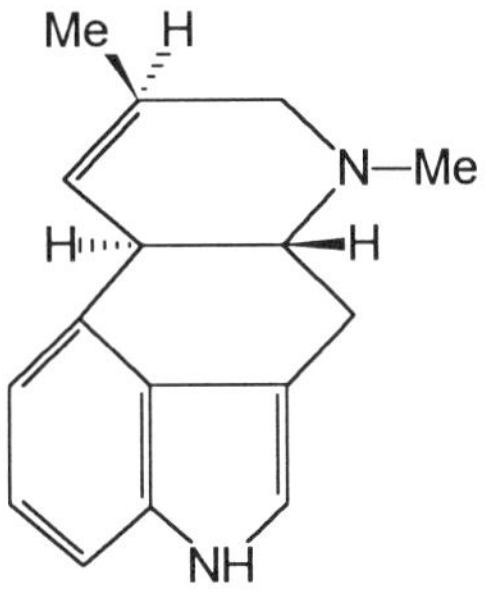

General Characteristics

Crystals (long needles) from methanol; mp., 238-239°C (dec.); 242-244°C (dec.); $[\alpha]_D^{15}$ -98° (*c*=0.3, pyridine); $[\alpha]_D^{20}$ -70°, $[\alpha]_{5461}^{20}$ -83° (*c*=0.5, in $CHCl_3$); $[\alpha]_D^{20}$ -110°, $[\alpha]_{5461}^{20}$ -128°; pK=7.4 (in 80% aqueous methylcellosolve); positive for van Urk's reaction; insoluble in petroleum ether, sparingly soluble in ethyl acetate, moderately soluble in benzene and chloroform and readily soluble in acetone, methanol, ethanol, and pyridine.

Fungal Source

Penicillium chermesinum (PC 106-I), *Agropyrum* type ergot fungus parasitic on *Agropyrum semicostatum*, *Trisetum bifidum* Ohwi, *Festuca rubra* L., etc. growing in Japan.

Biological Activity

All natural ergot alkaloids possess to a greater or lesser degree, biological effects that can be classified as direct peripheral effects on smooth muscle (uterine contraction and vasoconstriction), indirect peripheral effects (humoral, serotonin antagonism, and adrenergic blockage), and central nervous system effects (bulbomedullary and mesodiencephalic components).

Spectral Data

UV:

λ_{max}^{MeOH} 224(log ε=4.54), 275(3.81), and 281nm (3.84).

IR:

See A. Hofmann, 1964.

^{1}H NMR:

(CDCl$_3$) H-4α, 2.68(dd, *J*=15.0, 11.5Hz); H-4β, 3.39(dd, *J*=15.0, 4.5Hz); H-5, 2.10(ddd, *J*=11.5, 9.5, 4.5Hz); H-7α, 2.95(d[broad], *J*=11.0Hz); H-7β, 1.87(t, *J*=11.0Hz); H-8, 2.01(ddd, *J*=12, 11, 6.5Hz); H-9α, 2.63(dd, *J*=12.0, 3.5Hz); H-9β, 1.08(q, *J*=12.0Hz); H-10, 2.97(ddd, *J*=12.0, 9.5, 3.5Hz); H-17, 0.99(d, *J*=6.5Hz); and N-Me, 2.45ppm (s).

^{13}C NMR:

(CDCl$_3$) C-2, 117.7; C-3, 110.5; C-4, 26.6; C-5, 66.7; C-7, 65.0; C-8, 30.2; C-9, 36.2; C-10, 40.4; C-11, 132.7*; C-12, 112.0; C-13, 122.0; C-14, 108.3; C-15, 133.1; C-16, 125.9; C-17, 19.3; and N-Me, 42.7ppm.

* Assignment may be reversed.

Mass Spectrum:

LREIMS: 240(M$^+$, 100%), 197, 182, 167, 154, and 144*m/e*.

References

N. J. Bach, H. E. Boaz, E. C. Kornfeld, C-J Chang, H. G. Floss, E. W. Hagaman, and E. Wenkert; Nuclear Magnetic Resonance Spectral Analysis of the Ergot Alkaloids; J. Org. Chem., Vol. 39, pp. 1272-1276(1974).

B. Berde and H. O. Scheld (eds.); Ergot Alkaloids and Related Compounds; In Handbook of Experimental Pharmacology; Springer-Verlag, New York (1978).

A. Hofmann; Die Mutterkorn Alkaloide, Enke Verlag, Stuttgart, 218 pp., 1964.

S. Ohmomo, T. Sato, T. Utagawa, and M. Abe; Isolation of Festuclavine and Three New Indole Alkaloids, Roquefortine A, B and C from the Cultures of *Penicillium roqueforti*; Agr. Biol. Chem., Vol. 39, pp. 1333-1334(1975).

Common/Systematic Name
Elymoclavine

Molecular Formula/Molecular Weight
$C_{16}H_{18}N_2O$; MW = 254.14191

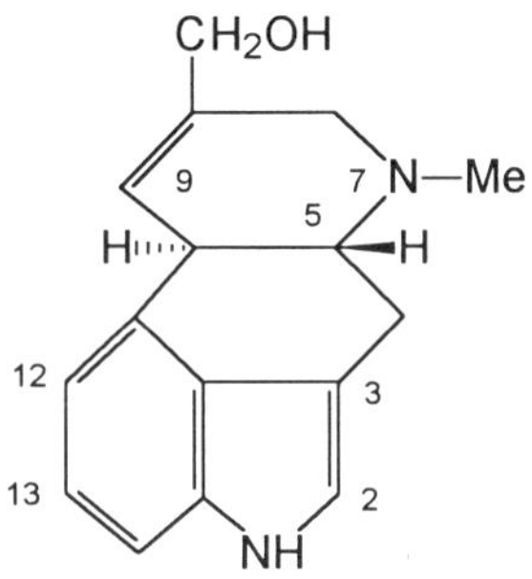

General Characteristics
Crystallized as prisms from methanol; mp., 245-249°C; $[\alpha]_D^{20}$ -152° (*c*=0.9, in pyridine), $[\alpha]_D^{20}$ -111° (*c*=0.1, in EtOH); pK=6.7 (in 80% aqueous methylcellosolve); violet-blue color with Keller's reagent.

Fungal Source
Saprophytic culture of ergot fungus *Claviceps* sp. SD 58 (ATCC 26019), *Pennisetum typhoideum* sclerotia and saprophytic cultures, and *Elymus mollis*.

Biological Activity
All natural ergot alkaloids possess to a greater or lesser degree, biological effects that can be classified as direct peripheral effects on smooth muscle (uterine contraction and vasoconstriction), indirect peripheral effects (humoral, serotonin antagonism, and adrenergic blockage), and central nervous system effects (bulbomedullary and mesodiencephalic components).

Spectral Data

UV:
λ_{max}^{MeOH} 227, 283, and 293nm (log ϵ=4.31, 3.84, and 3.76, respectively).

IR:
See A. Hofmann, 1964.

^{1}H NMR:
(pyridine-d_5) H-6, 2.41(3H, s); H-7, 3.05(1H, d); H-4, 2.92(1H, ddd); H-7', 3.61(1H, d); H-4', 2.59(1H, ddd); H-5, 3.35(1H, dd); H-10, 3.94(1H, m); H-17, 4.36(2H); 17-

OH, 4.75(1H, s); H-9, 6.71(1H, m); aromatic-H, 7.1-7.4(4H, m); and H-1, 11.40ppm(1H, s). (CD_3OD) H-2, 6.922; H-4α, 2.798; H-4β, 3.357; H-5, 2.622; H-7α, 3.026; H-7β, 3.444; H-9, 6.464; H-10, 3.798; H-12, 6.967; H-13, 7.121; H-14, 7.191; H-17upfield, 4.106; H-17downfield, 4.141; and N-Me, 2.523ppm.

^{13}C NMR:
(CD_3OD) C-2, 119.09; C-3, 111.45; C-4, 27.17; C-5, 64.76; N(6)-Me, 41.15; C-7, 57.20; C-8, 134.37; C-9, 121.55; C-10, 40.98; C-11, 131.74; C-12, 112.83; C-13, 123.12; C-14, 109.60; C-15, 136.12; C-16, 126.88; and C-17, 65.06ppm.

Mass Spectrum:
LREIMS: 254(M^+, 52%), 253(100), 237(23), 167(36), and 154*m/e* (30).

References

N. J. Bach, H. E. Boaz, E. C. Kornfeld, C-J Chang, H. G. Floss, E. W. Hagaman, and E. Wenkert; Nuclear Magnetic Resonance Spectral Analysis of the Ergot Alkaloids; J. Org. Chem., Vol. 39, pp. 1272-1276(1974).

B. Berde and H. O. Scheld (eds.); Ergot Alkaloids and Related Compounds; In Handbook of Experimental Pharmacology; Springer-Verlag, New York (1978).

M. Flieger, N. F. Zelenkova, P. Sedmera, V. Kren, J. Novak, V. Rylko, P. Sajdl, and Z. Řeháček, Ergot Alkaloid Glycosides from Saprophytic Cultures of *Claviceps*, I. Elymoclavine Fructosides; J. Natural Products, Vol. 52, pp. 506-510(1989).

A. Hofmann; Die Mutterkorn Alkaloide; Enke Verlag, Stuttgart, 218 pp., 1964.

R. G. Mrtek, H. L. Crespi, G. Norman, M. I. Blake, and J. J. Katz; Biosynthesis of Clavine Alkaloids: Proton Magnetic Resonance Studies; Phytochemistry, Vol. 7, pp. 1535-1541(1968).

A. Stoll, A. Brack, H. Kobel, A. Hofmann, and R. Brunner; Die Alkaloide eines Mutterkornpilzes von *Pennisetum typhoideum* rich. und deren Bildung in Saprophytischer Kultur; Helvetica Chimica Acta, Vol. 37, pp. 1815-1825(1954).

Common/Systematic Name

Elymoclavine-*O*-β-fructofuranoside

Molecular Formula/Molecular Weight

$C_{22}H_{28}N_2O_6$; MW = 416.19474

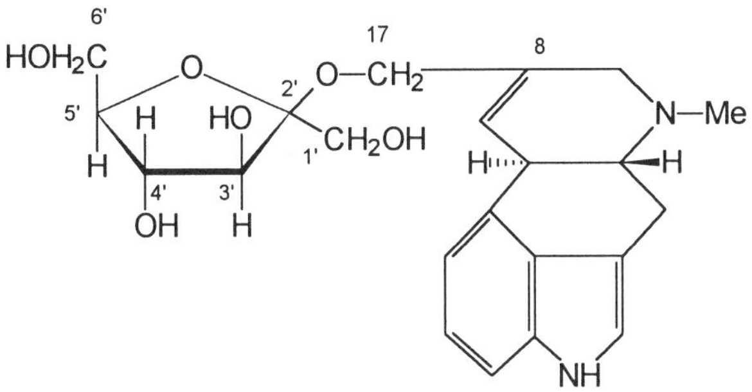

Fungal Source

Saprophytic culture of ergot fungus *Claviceps* sp. SD 58 (ATCC 26019) and 88 EP; evidence suggested that this alkaloid formed from elymoclavine and the sucrose in the medium by the action of invertase present in the fungal mycelium.

Isolation/Purification

Alkaloids were separated from the culture broth (pH adjusted to 7.5 with concentrated NH_3) by adsorption on bentonite (Lachema, Brno, Czechoslovakia) and desorbed with MeOH and the crude alkaloid solution was concentrated to a final volume of 10ml under low pressure conditions. The MeOH solution was loaded on a Separon SGX C_{18} column and eluted with MeOH-H_2O-concentrated NH_3 (30:70:0.34, v/v/v). The column effluent was monitored by UV (288nm). The first alkaloid fraction contained a mixture of all elymoclavine fructosides. The mixture of elymoclavine fructosides was repeatedly loaded on Separon SGX C_{18} column and eluted with the above-mentioned mixture. A base line separation of all fructosides was reached. The Separon SGX C_{18} column with the same mobile phase was also used for checking purity. Column effluent was monitored by UV at 224nm.

Spectral Data

^{1}H NMR:

(CD_3OD) 6.937, H-2; 2.797, H-4α; 3.379, H-4β; 2.691, H-5; 3.174, H-7α; 3.631, H-7β; 6.553, H-9; 3.854, H-10; 6.950, H-12; 7.163, H-13; 7.143, H-14; 4.112, H-17u; 4.327, H-17d; 2.588, N-Me; 3.590, H-1'u; 3.717, H-1'd; 4.154, H-3'; 4.008, H-4'; 3.779, H-5'; 3.628, H-6'u; and 3.734ppm, H-6'd.

^{13}C NMR:
(CD_3OD) C-2, 119.98; C-3, 111.58; C-4, 27.56; C-5, 65.87; N(6)-Me, 41.02; C-7, 58.13; C-8, 134.63; C-9, 123.34; C-10, 41.65; C-11, 131.91; C-12, 113.51; C-13, 123.74; C-14, 110.35; C-15, 135.61; C-16, 127.74; C-17, 65.01; C-1', 62.41; C-2', 105.79; C-3', 78.85; C-4', 77.26; C-5', 83.82; and C-6', 64.88ppm.

Mass Spectrum:
CIMS: (NH_3) 417(33%), 416(22), 254(23), 253(30), 237(100), 236(85), 223(9), 207(6), 167(9), 154(6), and 127*m/e* (1).

References

M. Flieger, N. F. Zelenkova, P. Sedmera, V. Kren, J. Novak, V. Rylko, P. Sajdl, and Z. Řeháček; Ergot Alkaloid Glycosides from Saprophytic Cultures of *Claviceps*, I. Elymoclavine Fructosides; J. Natural Products, Vol. 52, pp. 506-510(1989).

H. G. Floss, H. Gunter, U. Mothes, and I. Becker. Z.; Isolierung von Elymocalvin-*O*-β-fruktosid aus Kulturen des Mutterkornpilzes; Naturforsch,. Vol. 22b, pp. 399-402(1967).

Common/Systematic Name

Elymoclavine-*O*-β-fructofuranosyl-(2→1)-*O*-β-D-fructofuranoside

Molecular Formula/Molecular Weight

$C_{28}H_{38}N_2O_{11}$; MW = 578.24756

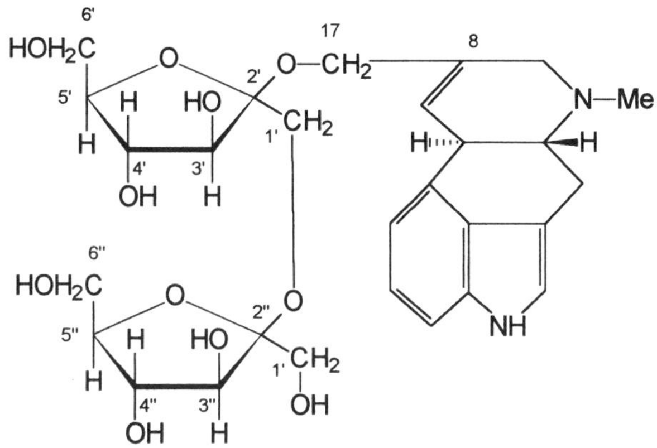

Fungal Source

Saprophytic culture of ergot fungus *Claviceps* sp. SD 58 (ATCC 26019) and 88 EP.

Isolation/Purification

Alkaloids were separated from the culture broth (pH adjusted to 7.5 with concentrated NH_3) by adsorption on bentonite (Lachema, Brno, Czechoslovakia) and desorbed with MeOH and the crude alkaloid solution concentrated to a final volume of 10ml under low pressure conditions. The MeOH solution was loaded on a Separon SGX C_{18} column and eluted with MeOH-H_2O-concentrated NH_3 (30:70:0.34, v/v/v). The column effluent was monitored by UV (288nm). The first alkaloid fraction contained a mixture of all elymoclavine fructosides. The mixture of elymoclavine fructosides was repeatedly loaded on Separon SGX C_{18} column and eluted with the above-mentioned mixture. A base line separation of all fructosides was reached. The Separon SGX C_{18} column with the same mobile phase was also used for checking purity. Column effluent was monitored by UV at 224nm.

Spectral Data

^{1}H NMR:

(CD_3OD) 6.949, H-2; 2.841, H-4α; 3.404, H-4β; 2.797, H-5; 3.230, H-7α; 3.676, H-7β; 6.557, H-9; 3.851, H-10; 6.966, H-12; 7.073, H-13; 7.151, H-14; 4.131, H-17u; 4.328, H-17d; 2.648, N-Me; 3.577, H-1'u; 3.649, H-1'd; 4.165, H-3'; 4.012, H-4'; N. D., H-5'; 3.627, H-6'u; and N. D., H-6'd.

^{13}C NMR:
(CD_3OD) C-2, 120.07; C-3, 111.30; C-4, 27.38; C-5, 65.82; N(6)-Me, 40.81; C-7, 58.02; C-8, 134.13; C-9, 123.62; C-10, 41.43; C-11, 131.58; C-12, 113.58; C-13, 123.76; C-14, 110.44; C-15, 135.60; C-16, 127.67; C-17, 64.81; C-1', 62.54; C-2', 105.52; C-3', 79.21; C-4', 77.06; C-5', 83.80; C-6', 64.77; C-1", 62.85; C-2", 105.00; C-3", 80.01; C-4", 76.50; C-5", 83.67; and C-6", 63.91ppm.

Mass Spectrum:
CIMS: (NH_3) 579(25%), 578(8), 416(25), 254(60), 253(45), 237(100), 236(93), 223(7), 207(3), 167(9), 154(10), and 127*m/e* (24).

Reference

M. Flieger, N. F. Zelenkova, P. Sedmera, V. Křen, J. Novák, V. Rylko, P. Sajdl, and Z. Řeháček; Ergot Alkaloid Glycosides From Saprophytic Cultures of *Claviceps*, I. Elymoclavine Fructosides; J. Natural Products, Vol. 52, pp. 506-510(1989).

Common/Systematic Name
Chanoclavine-I; Chanoclavine

Molecular Formula/Molecular Weight
$C_{16}H_{20}N_2O$; MW = 256.15756

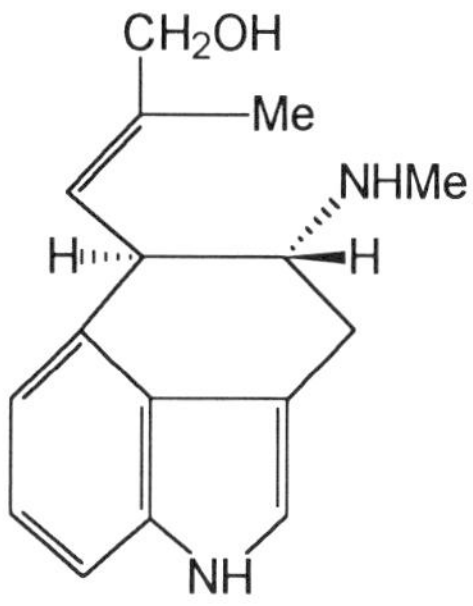

General Characteristics
Prisms and polyhedral crystals from acetone/methanol; mp., 220-222°C (dec.), $[\alpha]_D^{20}$ - 240°; $[\alpha]_{5461}^{20}$ - 294° (*c*=1.0, in pyridine); $[\alpha]_D^{20}$ - 205° (*c*=0.75, in alcohol); pK_b=5.80; pK=8.2 (in aqueous methylcellosolve); violet-blue color with Keller's or van Urk's reagents. *N*-acetyl derivative crystallized as massive prisms; mp., 226-227° C (dec.); $[\alpha]_D^{20}$ - 180° (*c*=0.5, in pyridine).

Fungal Source
Saprophytic culture of ergot fungus isolated from a tropical millet (*Pennisetum typhoideum*). Ergots of *Elymus* sp., *Phragmites* sp., *Phalaris* sp., *Agropyrum* sp., *Balansia epichloë*, *B. strangulans*, *B. claviceps*, *B. henningsiana*, and *Acremonium coenophialum*.

Biological Activity
All natural ergot alkaloids possess to a greater or lesser degree, biological effects that can be classified as direct peripheral effects on smooth muscle (uterine contraction and vasoconstriction), indirect peripheral effects (humoral, serotonin antagonism, and adrenergic blockage), and central nervous system effects (bulbomedullary and mesodiencephalic components).

Spectral Data

UV:
λ_{max}^{MeOH} 225, 284, and 293nm (log ε=4,44, 3.82, and 3.76, respectively).

IR:
1600-1650cm^{-1} (characteristic of indole); see A. Hofmann, 1964.

Mass Spectrum:
256(M^+), 237, 183(100%), 182, 167, 168, 154, and 155*m/e*.

References

W. Achlin, T. Fehr, and D. Arigoni; The Stereochemistry of Chanoclavine-I and Isochanoiclavine-I; Chemical Communications, pp. 799-800(1966).

C. W. Bacon, J. K. Porter, and J. D. Robbins; Lysergic Acid Amide Derivatives from *Balansia epichloë* and *Balansia claviceps* (Clavicipitaceae); J. Nat. Prod., 42: 309-314 (1979).

C. W. Bacon, J. K. Porter, and J. D. Robbins; Laboratory Production of Ergot Alkaloids by Species of *Balansia*; J. Gen. Microbiol., 113: 119-126(1979).

C. W. Bacon, J. K. Porter, and J. D. Robbins; Ergot Alkaloids Biosynthesis by Isolates of *Balansia epichloë* and *Balansia henningsiana*; Can. J. Bot., 59: 2534-2538(1981).

C. W. Bacon, J. K. Porter, J. D. Robbins, and D. Betowski; Ergot Alkaloids Identification in Clavicipitaceae Systemic Fungi of Pasture Grass; J. Agric. Food Chem., 29: 653-657 (1981).

B. Berde and H. O. Scheld (eds.); Ergot Alkaloids and Related Compounds; In Handbook of Experimental Pharmacology; Springer-Verlag, New York (1978).

A. Hofmann; Die Mutterkorn Alkaloide; Enke Verlag, Stuttgart 218 pp., 1964.

A. Hofmann, R. Brunner, H. Kobel, and A. Brack; Neue Alkaloide aus der saprophytischen Kultur des Mutterkornpilzes von *Pennisetum typhoideum* Rich.; Helvetica Chimica Acta, Vol. XI, pp. 1358-1373(1957)

P. C. Lyons, R. D. Plattner, and C. W. Bacon; Occurance of Peptide and Clavine Ergot Alkaloids in Tall Fescue Grass; Science, 232: 487-489(1986).

D. Stauffacher and H. Tscherter; Isomere des Chanoclavins aus *Claviceps purpurea* (Fr.) Tul.; Helvetica Chimica Acta, Vol. 47, pp. 2186-2194(1964).

Common/Systematic Name
Isochanoclavine-I

Molecular Formula/Molecular Weight
$C_{16}H_{20}N_2O$; MW = 272.15248

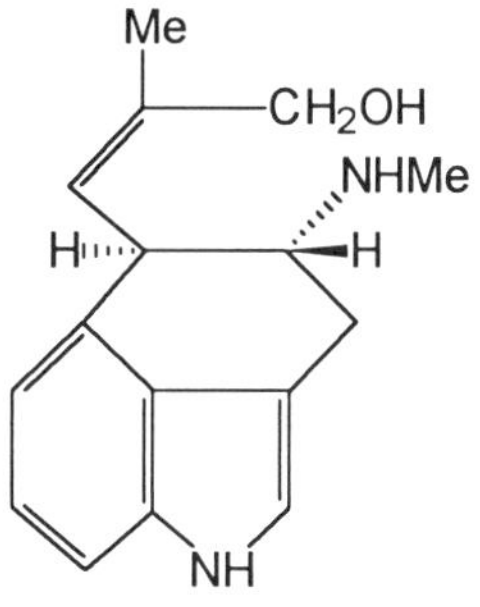

General Characteristics
Crystals; mp., 190°C, $[\alpha]_D$ -208° (in pyridine); rods from isopropanol; mp., 181°C,; $[\alpha]_D^{20}$ -216° (*c*=0.5, in pyridine); blue color with van Urk's reagent; violet-blue with Keller's reagent.

Fungal Source
Saprophytic culture of ergot fungus, *Claviceps purpurea* (Fr.).

Isolation/Purification
The alkaloid was purified by aluminum oxide column chromatography (Act. III) eluted with chloroform/0.75% MeOH. The crude alkaloid fraction was crystallized from acetone followed by isopropanol to give rods, mp., 181°C; sublimed under high vacuum at 170°C.

Spectral Data

UV:
λ_{max}^{MeOH} 222, 281, 275(sh), and 291nm (log ϵ=4.5, 3.89, 3.86, and 3.82, respectively).

IR:
See Stauffacher and Tscherter, 1964.

^1H NMR:
See Stauffacher and Tscherter, 1964.

References
W. Achlin, T. Fehr, and D. Arigoni; The Stereochemistry of Chanoclavine-I and Isochanoclavine-I; Chemical Communications, pp. 799-800(1966).

D. Stauffacher and H. Tscherter; Isomere des chanoclavins aus *Claviceps purpurea* (Fr.) Tul.; Helvetica Chimica Acta, Vol. 47, pp. 2186-2194(1964).

Common/Systematic Name

Chanoclavine-II

Molecular Formula/Molecular Weight

$C_{16}H_{20}N_2O$; MW = 256.15756

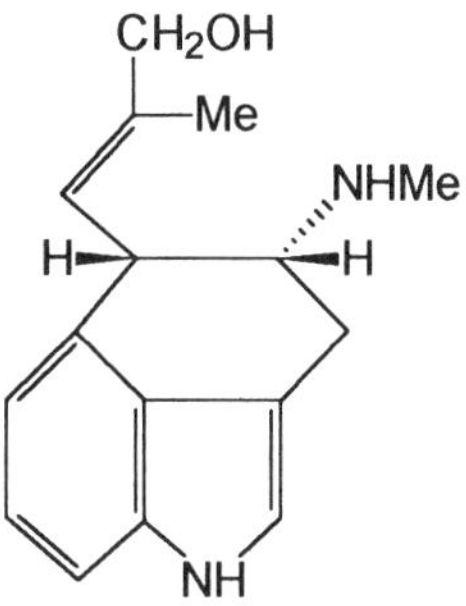

General Characteristics

Prisms from acetone; mp., 174°C; $[\alpha]_D^{20}$ -332° (*c*=0.5, in pyridine); violet-blue color with Keller's and blue with van Urk's reagents. HCl•salt crystals from alcohol; mp., 247°C, $[\alpha]_D^{20}$ -271° (*c*=0.5, in 50% alcohol). *N*-Acetyl derivative, large crystalline prisms from methanol; mp., 203°C; $[\alpha]_D^{20}$ -455° (*c*=0.54, in pyridine).

Fungal Source

Saprophytic culture of ergot fungus, *Claviceps purpurea* (FR.).

Spectral Data

UV:

λ_{max}^{MeOH} 222, 281, and 291nm (log ε=4,50, 3.89, and 3.82, respectively); shoulders at λ_{max} 275(log ε=3.86), 245, and 289nm.

IR:

(Nujol) *N*-acetyl derivative: 1610cm^{-1}, (N-C)CH_3.

^{1}H NMR:

N-acetyl derivative: 4.82(1H, dd, *J*=10 and 4Hz, H-10); 5.53(1H, octet, *J*=4, 5, and 11Hz, H-5); and 2.67-3.61ppm (2H, AB part of an ABX system, J_{AB}=14Hz, J_{AX}=11Hz, J_{BX}=5Hz, H-4). *N*-acetyl derivative, 4.28ppm (2H, s, allyl-CH_2-O group).

Reference

D. Stauffacher and H. Tscherter; Isomere des Chanoclavins aus *Claviceps purpurea* (Fr.) Tul.; Helvetica Chimica Acta, Vol. 47, pp. 2186-2194(1964).

Common/Systematic Name

N-Demethylchanoclavine-II; Norchanoclavine II

Molecular Formula/Molecular Weight

$C_{15}H_{18}N_2O$; MW = 242.14191

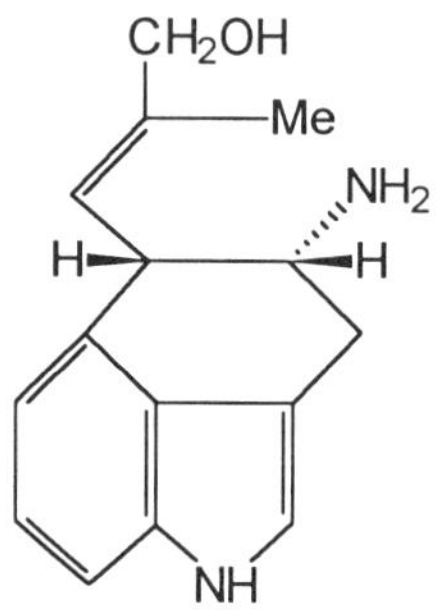

General Characteristics

Gray color, turning blue with Ehrlich's reagent.

Fungal Source

Claviceps sp. (strain SD 58).

Isolation/Purification

Culture filtrates were made alkaline to pH 11 with ammonia and extracted several times with chloroform or chloroform-isopropanol (3:1, v/v). The extracts were combined and evaporated to dryness in a vacuum. The residue was dissolved in 2% aqueous succinic acid, the solution washed 3 times with methylene chloride, made alkaline with ammonia to pH 11 and extracted with methylene chloride. This alkaloid extract was dried over anhydrous sodium sulfate, concentrated in a vacuum and left in the refrigerator overnight. The solution was filtered through a fine sintered glass funnel to remove the crystallized elymoclavine, which was washed with 3ml cold methylene chloride. The filtrate and washings were then passed through an alumina column (Brockmann activity II-III) suspended in methylene chloride. The column was eluted with methylene chloride containing 2% methanol until no more isochanoclavine-I could be detected in the eluate. These fractions contained agroclavine, elymoclavine and isochanoclavine-I, chanoclavine-II and chanoclavine-I. The elution was continued with methylene chloride containing 10% methanol to give two more fractions. The first contained the chanoclavine-I, some chanoclavine-II and *N*-demethylchanoclavine -II and the following fraction contained mainly *N*-demethylchanoclavine-II. These two fractions were evaporated and streaked, respectively, on silica gel G plates. The plates were developed twice in acetone-ethyl acetate-*N,N*-dimethylformamide (5:5:1, v/v/v) system. The band containing *N*-demethylchanoclavine-II was scraped off and the alkaloid was eluted from the gel. This material was rechromatographed in chloroform-methanol (9:1, v/v) in an ammonia atmosphere to yield a chromatographically homogeneous material.

Biological Activity

The ergopeptine alkaloids produce a wide range of biological activities and some are used routinely in medical practice.

Spectral Data

UV:

λ_{max}^{MeOH} 223, 274, 283, and 294nm.

Mass Spectrum:

HREIMS: 242.1430 (calcd for $C_{15}H_{18}N_2O$, 242.1419). The mass spectrum also showed strong peaks at 154, 156, 167, 169, 182, 194, 209, and 223*m/e*. The M^+ ion peak (242*m/e*) was the base peak (100%).

Reference

J. M. Cassady, C. I. Abou-chaar, and H. G. Floss; Ergot Alkaloids. Isolation of *N*-Demethylchanoclavine-II from *Claviceps* Strain SD 58 and the Role of Demethylchanoclavines in Ergoline Biosynthesis; Lloydia, Vol. 36, pp. 390-396(1973).

Common/Systematic Name

Setoclavine

Molecular Formula/Molecular Weight

$C_{16}H_{18}N_2O$; MW = 254.14191

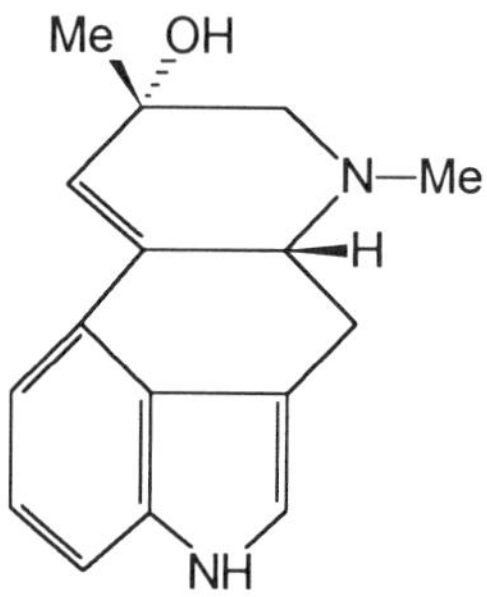

General Characteristics

Prisms from methanol-acetone; m.p. 229-234°C (dec.); $[\alpha]_D^{20}$ + 174°; $[\alpha]_{5461}^{20}$ + 232° (*c*=1.1, in pyridine); $[\alpha]_D^{20}$ + 165° (*c*=0.3, in alcohol); pK=6.4 (in 80% aqueous methylcellosolve).

Fungal Source

Saprophytic culture of ergot fungus isolated from a tropical millet (*Pennisetum typhoideum*); *Elymus mollis, Agropyrum semicostatum, Trisetum bifidum,* and *Festuca rubra.*

Biological Activity

All natural ergot alkaloids possess to a greater or lesser degree, biological effects that can be classified as direct peripheral effects on smooth muscle (uterine contraction and vasoconstriction), indirect peripheral effects (humoral, serotonin antagonism and adrenergic blockage), and central nervous system effects (bulbomedullary and mesodiencephalic components).

Spectral Data

UV:

λ_{max}^{MeOH} 243 and 313nm (log ϵ=4.38 and 4.04).

IR:

See A. Hofmann, 1964.

Mass Spectrum:

254(M^+), 236, 235, 234, 219, 211, 196, 181, 168, and 154*m/e* (100%).

References

B. Berde and H. O. Scheld (eds.); Ergot Alkaloids and Related Compounds; In Handbook of Experimental Pharmacology; Springer-Verlag, New York (1978).

A. Hofmann; Die Mutterkorn Alkaloide; Enke Verlag, Stuttgart, 218 pp., 1964.

A. Hofmann, R. Brunner, H. Kobel, and A. Brack; Neue Alkaloide aus der saprophytischen Kultur des Mutterkornpilzes von *Pennisetum typhoideum* Rich.; Helvetica Chimica Acta, Vol. XI, pp. 1358-1373(1957).

Common/Systematic Name

Isosetoclavine

Molecular Formula/Molecular Weight

$C_{16}H_{18}N_2O$; MW = 254.14191

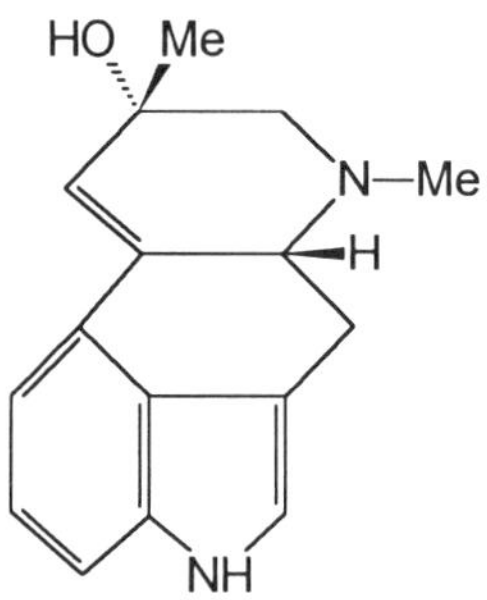

General Characteristics

Large polyhedral crystals from methanol; m.p. 234-237°C; $[\alpha]_D^{20}$ + 107°; $[\alpha]_{5461}^{20}$ + 147° (*c*=0.5, in pyridine); $[\alpha]_D^{20}$ + 129° (*c*=0.4, in alcohol); pK=5.9 (in 80% aqueous methylcellosolve). Soluble in 70 parts boiling methanol, 60 parts boiling acetone or 160 parts boiling chloroform. Responses to various color reactions were similar to setoclavine. Hydrochloride crystallized as rosettes from methanol diluted with acetone, did not melt at temperatures up to 300°C.

Fungal Source

Saprophytic culture of ergot fungus isolated from a tropical millet (*Pennisetum typhoideum*).

Biological Activity

All natural ergot alkaloids possess to a greater or lesser degree, biological effects that can be classified as direct peripheral effects on smooth muscle (uterine contraction and vasoconstriction), indirect peripheral effects (humoral, serotonin antagonism, and adrenergic blockage), and central nervous system effects (bulbomedullary and mesodiencephalic components).

Spectral Data

UV:

λ_{max}^{MeOH} 242 and 317nm (log ϵ=4.42 and 4.10).

IR:

See A. Hofmann, 1964.

References

B. Berde and H. O. Scheld (eds.); Ergot Alkaloids and Related Compounds; In Handbook of Experimental Pharmacology; Springer-Verlag, New York (1978).

A. Hofmann; Die Mutterkorn Alkaloide; Enke Verlag, Stuttgart, 218 pp., 1964.

A. Hofmann, R. Brunner, H. Kobel, and A. Brack; Neue Alkaloide aus der saprophytischen Kultur des Mutterkornpilzes von *Pennisetum typhoideum* Rich.; Helvetica Chimica Acta, Vol. XI, pp. 1358-1373(1957).

Common/Systematic Name

Costaclavine

Molecular Formula/Molecular Weight

$C_{16}H_{20}N_2$, MW = 240.16265

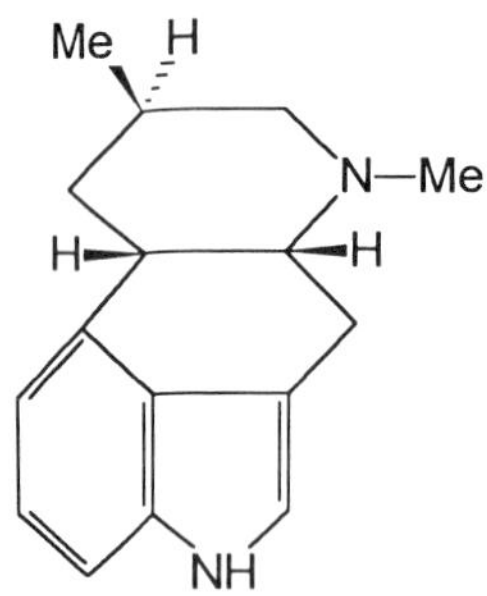

General Characteristics

Crystals (prisms) from ether-acetone, acetone, methanol or ethanol; mp., 182-184°C (dec.); $[\alpha]_D^{20}$ + 44°, $[\alpha]_{5461}^{20}$ + 59° (*c*=0.2 in pyridine); positive for van Urk's reaction; insoluble in petroleum ether, sparingly soluble in ethyl acetate, moderately soluble in benzene and chloroform and readily soluble in acetone, methanol, ethanol, and pyridine.

Fungal Source

Penicillium chermesinum (PC 106-I), *Agropyrum* type ergot fungus parasitic on *Agropyrum semicostatum* Nees., *Trisetum bifidum* Ohwi, and *Festuca rubra* L., etc. growing in Japan.

Biological Activity

All natural ergot alkaloids possess to a greater or lesser degree, biological effects that can be classified as direct peripheral effects on smooth muscle (uterine contraction and vasoconstriction), indirect peripheral effects (humoral, serotonin antagonism, and adrenergic blockage), and central nervous system effects (bulbomedullary and mesodiencephalic components).

Spectral Data

UV:

λ_{max}^{MeOH} 225, 275, 282, and 292nm.

IR:

See A. Hofmann, 1964.

References

M. Abe, S. Yamatodani, T. Yamono, and M. Kusumoto; Bull. Agr. Chem. Soc. (Japan), Vol. 20, pp. 59-60(1956).

S. L. Agurell; Costaclavine from *Penicillium chermesinum*; Experientia, Vol. 20, pp. 25-26(1964).

B. Berde and H. O. Scheld (eds.); Ergot Alkaloids and Related Compounds; In Handbook of Experimental Pharmacology; Springer-Verlag, New York (1978).

A. Hofmann; Die Mutterkorn Alkaloide; Enke Verlag, Stuttgart, 218 pp., 1964.

Common/Systematic Name

Pyroclavine

Molecular Formula/Molecular Weight

$C_{16}H_{20}N_2$; MW = 240.16265

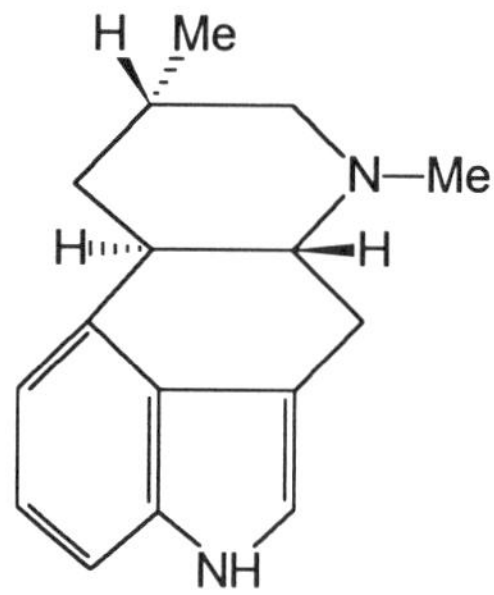

General Characteristics

Crystals (needles) from ethyl acetate, methanol or benzene, mp., 204°C (uncorr.); $[\alpha]_D^{20}$ - 90°, $[\alpha]_{5461}^{20}$ - 105° (*c*=0.2 in pyridine); gave a deep blue color with Allport and Cockings's reagent and concd. sulfuric acid; insoluble in petroleum ether; moderately soluble in ethyl acetate and benzene; readily soluble in chloroform, acetone, methanol, ethanol and pyridine. Color reactions were identical to festuclavine.

Fungal Source

Agropyrum-type ergot fungus parasitic on *Agropyrum semicostatum*, *Trisetum bifidum*, *Festuca rubra* L., etc. growing in Japan.

Biological Activity

All natural ergot alkaloids possess to a greater or lesser degree, biological effects that can be classified as direct peripheral effects on smooth muscle (uterine contraction and vasoconstriction), indirect peripheral effects (humoral, serotonin antagonism, and adrenergic blockage), and central nervous system effects (bulbomedullary and mesodiencephalic components).

Spectral Data

UV:

λ_{max}^{MeOH} 225, 275, 282, and 292nm.

IR:

See A. Hofmann, 1964.

References

M. Abe, S. Yamatodani, T. Yamono, and M. Kusumoto; Bull. Agr. Chem. Soc. (Japan), Vol. 20, pp 59-60(1956).

B. Berde and H. O. Scheld (eds.); Ergot Alkaloids and Related Compounds; In Handbook of Experimental Pharmacology; Springer-Verlag, New York (1978).

A. Hofmann; Die Mutterkorn Alkaloide; Enke Verlag, Stuttgart, 218 pp., 1964.

Common/Systematic Name

Molliclavine

Molecular Formula/Molecular Weight

$C_{16}H_{18}N_2O_2$; MW = 270.13683

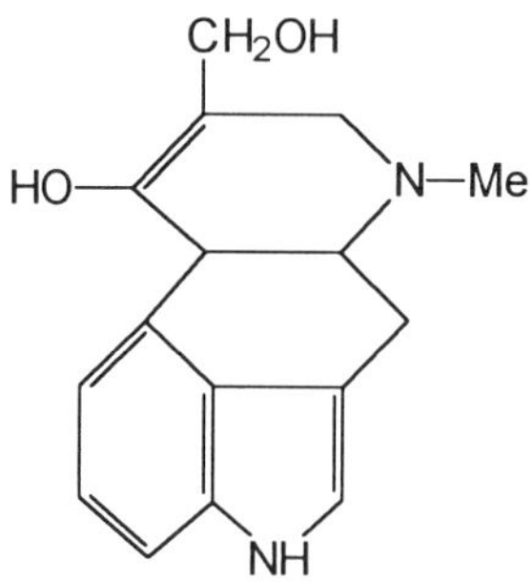

General Characteristics

Crystallized as prisms from methanol or acetone; mp., 253°C (dec.); $[\alpha]_D^{17}$ + 30°; $[\alpha]_{5461}^{17}$ + 42° (*c*=0.2, in pyridine); green color with Keller's and van Urk's reagent. Soluble in methanol and acetone; sparingly soluble in benzene and chloroform; and very soluble in water.

Fungal Source

Sclerotia and saprophytic cultures of *Elymus mollis*.

Biological Activity

All natural ergot alkaloids possess to a greater or lesser degree, biological effects that can be classified as direct peripheral effects on smooth muscle (uterine contraction and vasoconstriction), indirect peripheral effects (humoral, serotonin antagonism, and adrenergic blockage), and central nervous system effects (bulbomedullary and mesodiencephalic components).

Spectral Data

UV:

λ_{max}^{MeOH} 226, 287, and 294nm.

IR:

See A. Hofmann, 1964.

References

Abe and S. Yamatodani; Isolation of Further Two Water Soluble Ergot Alkaloids; J. Agric. Chem. Soc. Japan, Vol. 28, p. 501 (1954).

A. Hofmann; Die Mutterkorn Alkaloide; Enke Verlag, Stuttgart, 218 pp., 1964.

B. Berde and H. O. Scheld (eds.); Ergot Alkaloids and Related Compounds; In Handbook of Experimental Pharmacology, Springer-Verlag, New York (1978).

Common/Systematic Name

Penniclavine

Molecular Formula/Molecular Weight

$C_{16}H_{18}N_2O_2$; MW = 270.13683

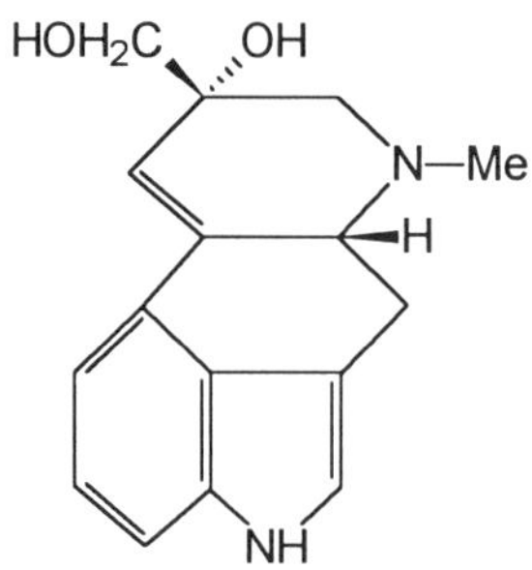

General Characteristics

Crystals from methanol or acetone; mp., 222-225°C; $[\alpha]_D^{20}$ +151°; $[\alpha]_{5461}^{20}$ +201° (*c*=0.5, in pyridine); pK=6.4 (in 80% aqueous methylcellosolve).

Fungal Source

Sclerotia and cultures of *Pennisetum typhoideum*.

Biological Activity

All natural ergot alkaloids possess to a greater or lesser degree, biological effects that can be classified as direct peripheral effects on smooth muscle (uterine contraction and vasoconstriction), indirect peripheral effects (humoral, serotonin antagonism, and adrenergic blockage), and central nervous system effects (bulbomedullary and mesodiencephalic components).

Spectral Data

UV:

λ_{max}^{MeOH} 240 and 315nm (log ϵ=4.29 and 3.93, respectively).

IR:

See A. Hofmann, 1964.

^1H NMR:

(pyridine-d_5) H-6, 2.46(3H, s); H-7, 2.79(1H, d); H-4, 2.73(1H, ddd); H-7', 3.17(1H, dd); H-4', 3.20(1H, ddd); H-5, 3.53(·1H, dd); 17-CH_2, 4.00(2H, s); 17-OH, 5.2-6.2(2H); H-9, 6.85(1H, m); aromatic-H, 7.1-7.4(4H, m); and H-1, 11.43ppm (1H, s).

Mass Spectrum:
LREIMS: 270(M^+, 93%), 243(23), 234(72), 219(98), 208(60), 196(57), 192(43), 181(57), 167(32), and 154*m/e* (100).

References
B. Berde and H. O. Scheld (eds.); Ergot Alkaloids and Related Compounds; In Handbook of Experimental Pharmacology; Springer-Verlag, New York (1978).

A. Hofmann; Die Mutterkorn Alkaloide; Enke Verlag, Stuttgart, 218 pp., 1964.

R. G. Mrtek, H. L. Crespi, G. Norman, M. I. Blake, and J. J. Katz; Biosynthesis of Clavine Alkaloids: Proton Magnetic Resonance Studies; Phytochemistry, Vol. 7, pp. 1535-1541(1968).

A. Stoll, A. Brack, H. Kobel, A. Hofmann, and R. Brunner; Die Alkaloide eines Mutterkornpilzes von *Pennisetum typhoideum* rich. und deren Bildung in Saprophytischer Kultur; Helvetica Chimica Acta, Vol. 37, pp. 1815-1825(1954).

Common/Systematic Name
Cycloclavine

Molecular Formula/Molecular Weight
$C_{16}H_{18}N_2$; MW = 238.14700

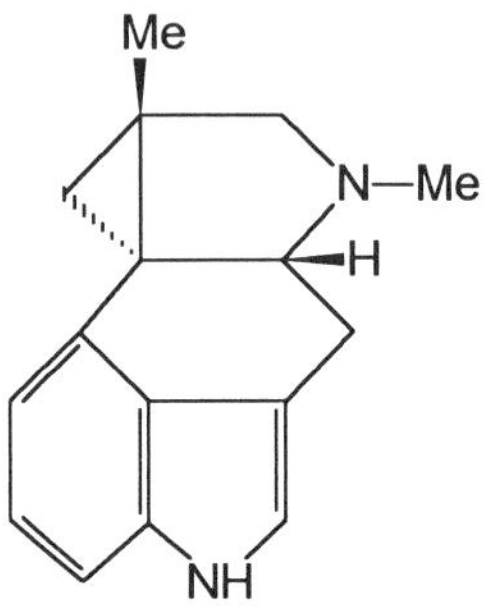

General Characteristics
Colorless needles from methanol; mp 164-165° C; $[\alpha]_D^{22}$ + 40° (*c*=0.175, in pyridine); $[\alpha]_{546}^{22}$ + 58°(*c*=0.175, in pyridine); gave a reddish purple color, turning to bluish-purple, with Allport-Cocking's reagent; an orange color with Dragendorff reagent. Sparingly soluble in benzene; moderately soluble in acetone, methanol, ethanol, chloroform, and ethyl and butyl acetate; readily soluble in pyridine; almost insoluble in cold water; readily soluble in dilute acids. It yielded no isomer on treatment with acid or alkali.

Fungal Source
Aspergillus japonicus.

Isolation/Purification
Mycelia extracted with 0.1N H_2SO_4, combined with the culture filtrate, pH adjusted to 10 and the mixture repeatedly extracted with ethyl acetate. The alkaloid residue purified with silica gel column chromatography eluting with chloroform-methanol (95:5, v/v).

Biological Activity
All natural ergot alkaloids possess to a greater or lesser degree, biological effects that can be classified as direct peripheral effects on smooth muscle (uterine contraction and vasoconstriction), indirect peripheral effects (humoral, serotonin antagonism, and adrenergic blockage), and central nervous system effects (bulbomedullary and mesodiencephalic components).

Spectral Data

UV:
λ_{max}^{EtOH} 227(log ϵ=19.6), 276(3.66), 282(3.84), and 293nm (2.66).

IR:
(KBr) 3400(indole NH) and $3150cm^{-1}$.

^1H NMR:
($CDCl_3$) 0.45 and 1.62ppm (2H, AB system, cyclopropyl-CH_2); 1.69ppm (3H, s, C-CH_3); 2.35ppm (3H, s, N-CH_3); 2.4-3.3ppm (5H, m, -CH-N- or -CH-C=C-); 6.7-7.3ppm (4H, m, indole protons); and 8.2ppm (1H, s, indole NH).

Mass Data:
238(M^+), 237(base peak), 167, and 154*m/e*; anal. found; C, 80.24; H, 7.72; N, 11.77; calcd. for $C_{16}H_{18}N_2$: C, 80.63; H, 7.61; N, 11.75%.

TLC Purification

Silica gel plates developed with methylene chloride-isopropyl alcohol (92:8, v/v) three times which results in the separation of alkaloids into the isolysergic acid group, the ergotoxine group, the ergoxine group and a mixture of the ergotamine and clavine groups. Extraction of the alkaloids from the silica using methanol-chloroform (1:4 or 1:1, v/v) followed by rechromatography in chloroform-methanol (9:1 or 4:1, v/v) separates ergovaline from the clavine alkaloids (agroclavine and chanoclavines).

TLC Solvent systems for silica gel chromatography (v/v):

a) Methylene chloride-isopropyl alcohol (92:8; 90:10; 75:25).
b) Chloroform-methanol (90:10; 80:20; 90:10 in saturated NH_3 atmosphere).
c) Chloroform-methanol-NH_3 (94:5:1).
d) Chloroform-ethylamine (90:10).
e) Benzene-dimethylformamide (86.5:13.5).

References

B. Berde and H. O. Scheld (eds.); Ergot Alkaloids and Related Compounds; In Handbook of Experimental Pharmacology; Springer-Verlag, New York (1978).

J. K. Porter; Analysis of Endophyte Toxins: Fescue and Other Grasses Toxic to Livestock; J. Animal Science, Vol. 73, pp. 871-880(1994).

S. Ohmomo, T. Sato, T. Utagawa, and M. Abe; Isolation of Festuclavine and Three New Indole Alkaloids, Roquefortine A, B and C from the Cultures of *Pellicillium roqueforti*; Agr. Biol. Chem., Vol. 39, pp. 1333-1334(1975).

Common/Systematic Name

Ergotamine

Molecular Formula/Molecular Weight

$C_{33}H_{35}N_5O_5$; MW = 581.26382

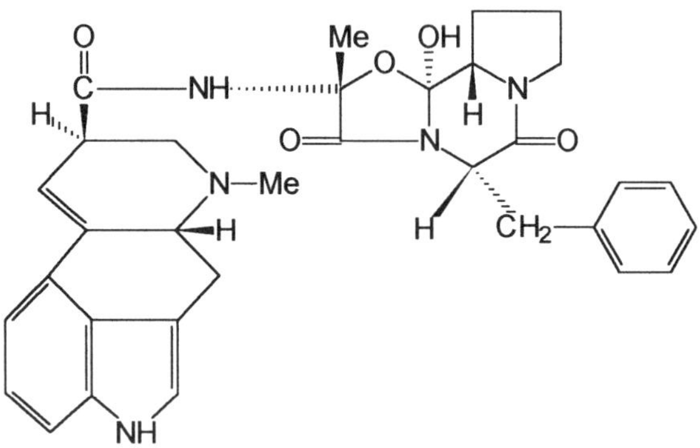

General Characteristics

Elongated prisms from benzene; mp., 212-214°C (dec.); $[\alpha]_D^{20}$ -160°, $[\alpha]_{5461}^{20}$ -192° (*c*=0.5, in $CHCl_3$); $[\alpha]_D^{20}$ -12.7°, $[\alpha]_{5461}^{20}$ -8.6° (*c*=0.5, in pyridine). Becomes solvent-free only after prolonged heating at high vacuum; darkens and decomposes on exposure to air, heat, and light. Very hygroscopic; pK = 5.6 (in 80% aqueous methylcellosolve); blue color with Keller's reagent. Soluble in 70 parts methanol, 150 parts acetone, 300 parts ethanol; freely soluble in chloroform, pyridine, and glacial acetic acid; slightly soluble in benzene; almost insoluble in water and petroleum ether.

Fungal Source

Claviceps purpurea.

Isolation/Purification/Analysis

Extract with either aqueous tartaric or lactic acid solution, partition chromatography with chloroform or methylene chloride at appropriate pH, column clean-up procedures using either silica, alumina or ion exchange resin, and identification and analysis using a combination of co-chromatography using TLC and/or HPLC with UV or fluorescence detection. Mass spectrometry is quite useful for identification, analysis, and quantitation.

Biological Activity

All natural ergot alkaloids possess to a greater or lesser degree, biological effects that can be classified as direct peripheral effects on smooth muscle (uterine contraction and vasoconstriction), indirect peripheral effects (humoral, serotonin antagonism, and adrenergic blockage), and central nervous system effects (bulbomedullary and mesodiencephalic components). LD_{50} in rats 62mg/kg (IV).

Spectral Data

IR:

(See A. Hofmann, 1964).

^{1}H NMR:

($CDCl_3$) H-1, 8.14(s); H-2, 6.91(m); H-4a, 2.79(m, *J*=14.2, 11.9Hz); H-4b, 3.32(*J*=14.2, 5.0Hz); H-5, 3.73(m, *J*=11.9, 5.0Hz); 6-N-Me, 2.61(s); H-7a, 2.96(*J*=11.9, 3.9Hz); H-7b, 2.78(dd, *J*=11.9, 3.4Hz); H-8b, 3.18(*J*=5.5, 3.9, 3.4Hz); H-9, 6.34(*J*=5.5Hz); 8-NH, 9.04(s); H-12-14, 7.0-7.5(m); H-2'Me, 1.51(s); H-5', 4.69; OH, 6.97(s); and 7'-NH, not obs.

^{13}C NMR:

(DMSO-d_6) C-2, 119.4; C-3, 108.8; C-4, 26.6; C-5, 62.4; C-7, 55.1; C-8, 42.5; C-9, 118.3; C-10, 136.0; C-11, 127.1; C-12, 111.0; C-13, 122.2; C-14, 110.2; C-15, 133.8; C-16, 125.9; C-17, 174.3; and N-Me, 43.4ppm.

TLC Data

Silica gel plates developed with methylene chloride-isopropyl alcohol (92:8, v/v) three times which results in the separation of alkaloids into the isolysergic acid group, the ergotoxine group, the ergoxine group and a mixture of the ergotamine and clavine groups. Extraction of the alkaloids from the silica using methanol-chloroform (1:4 or 1:1, v/v) followed by rechromatography in chloroform-methanol (9:1 or 4:1, v/v) separates ergovaline from the clavine alkaloids (agroclavine and chanoclavines).

HPLC Data

Extract with alkaline methanol, filter, followed by direct HPLC analysis with fluorescence detection; mobile phase, either 60% or 70% alkaline methanol. This technique works well for ergopeptide alkaloids.

References

N. J. Bach, H. E. Boaz, E. C. Kornfeld, C-J Chang, H. G. Floss, E. W. Hagaman, and E. Wenkert; Nuclear Magnetic Resonance Spectral Analysis of the Ergot Alkaloids; J. Org. Chem., Vol. 39, pp. 1272-1276(1974).

B. Berde and H. O. Scheld (eds.); Ergot Alkaloids and Related Compounds; In Handbook of Experimental Pharmacology; Springer-Verlag, New York (1978).

A. Hofmann; Die Mutterkorn Alkaloide; Enke Verlag, Stuttgart, 218 pp., 1964.

R. G. Mrtek, H. L. Crespi, G. Norman, M. I. Blake, and J. J. Katz; Biosynthesis of Clavine Alkaloids: Proton Magnetic Resonance Studies; Phytochemistry, Vol. 7, pp. 1535-1541(1968).

J. K. Porter; Analysis of Endophyte Toxins: Fescue and Other Grasses Toxic to Livestock; J. Animal Science, Vol. 73, pp. 871-880(1994).

J. K. Porter and D. Betowski; Chemical-ionization Mass Spectrometry of Ergot Cyclol Alkaloids; J. Agric. Food Chem., Vol. 29, pp. 651-653(1981).

R. G. Powell, R. D. Plattner, S. G. Yates, K. Clay, and A. Leuchtmann; Ergobalansine, A New Ergot-Type Peptide Alkaloid Isolated from *Cenchrus echinatus* (Sandbur Grass) Infected with *Balansia obtecta*, and Produced in Liquid Cultures of *B. obtecta* and *B. cyperi;* Journal of Natural Products, Vol. 53, pp. 1272-1279(1990).

Common/Systematic Name

Ergotaminine

Molecular Formula/Molecular Weight

$C_{33}H_{35}N_5O_5$; MW = 579.24817

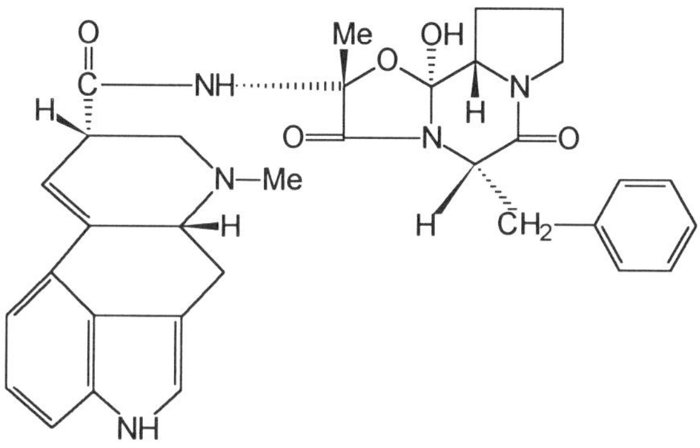

General Characteristics

Crystallizes solvent-free as thin rhombic plates from methanol; m.p. 241-243°C (dec.); $[\alpha]_D^{20}$ + 369° (*c*=0.5, in $CHCl_3$); $[\alpha]_D^{20}$ + 397° (*c*=0.5, in pyridine). Soluble in about 1000 parts boiling ethanol, 1500 parts boiling methanol; fairly soluble in chloroform, pyridine, and glacial acetic acid; pK = 5.6 (in 80% aqueous methylcellosolve); blue color with Keller's reagent; does not form salts.

Fungal Source

Claviceps purpurea.

Epimers are not considered as naturally occurring, but as products formed during extraction and purification; epimerization at C-8 occurs in either acid or base.

Isolation/Purification/Analysis

Extract with either aqueous tartaric or lactic acid solution, partition chromatography with chloroform or methylene chloride at appropriate pH, column clean-up procedures using either silica, alumina or ion exchange resin, and identification and analysis using a combination of co-chromatography using TLC and/or HPLC with UV or fluorescence detection. Mass spectrometry is quite useful for identification, analysis, and quantitation.

Biological Activity

All natural ergot alkaloids possess to a greater or lesser degree, biological effects that can be classified as direct peripheral effects on smooth muscle (uterine contraction and vasoconstriction), indirect peripheral effects (humoral, serotonin antagonism, and adrenergic blockage), and central nervous system effects (bulbomedullary and mesodiencephalic components).

Spectral Data

IR:
(See A. Hofmann, 1964.)

^{1}H NMR:
($CDCl_3$) H-1, 8.00(s); H-2, 6.91(m); H-4a, 3.59(m, J=15.3, 4.9Hz); H-4b, 2.62(J=15.3, 10.4Hz); H-5, 3.23(m, J=10.4, 4.9Hz); 6-N-Me, 2.61(s); H-7a, 3.13(J=11.7, 1.7Hz); H-7b, 2.76(dd, J=11.7, 3.8Hz); H-8b, 3.07(J=6.3Hz); H-9, 6.25(J=6.3Hz); 8-NH, 9.83(s); H-2'Me, 1.49(s); H-5', 4.61; OH, 6.94(s); and 7'-NH, not obs.

^{13}C NMR:
(DMSO-d_6) C-2, 119.7; C-3, 109.0; C-4, 26.9; C-5, 61.7;
C-7, 53.0; C-8, 41.8; C-9, 118.1; C-10, 137.1; C-11, 127.9; C-12, 111.4; C-13, 122.4; C-14, 110.3; C-15, 133.8; C-16, 126.1; C-17, 175.3; and N-Me, 42.5ppm.

References

N. J. Bach, H. E. Boaz, E. C. Kornfeld, C-J Chang, H. G. Floss, E. W. Hagaman, and E. Wenkert; Nuclear Magnetic Resonance Spectral Analysis of the Ergot Alkaloids; J. Org. Chem., Vol. 39, pp. 1272-1276(1974).

B. Berde and H. O. Scheld (eds.); Ergot Alkaloids and Related Compounds; In Handbook of Experimental Pharmacology; Springer-Verlag, New York (1978).

A. Hofmann; Die Mutterkorn Alkaloide; Enke Verlag, Stuttgart, 218 pp., 1964.

R. G. Mrtek, H. L. Crespi, G. Norman, M. I. Blake, and J. J. Katz; Biosynthesis of Clavine Alkaloids: Proton Magnetic Resonance Studies; Phytochemistry, Vol. 7, pp. 1535-1541(1968).

J. K. Porter; Analysis of Endophyte Toxins: Fescue and Other Grasses Toxic to Livestock; J. Animal Science, Vol. 73, pp. 871-880(1994).

R. G. Powell, R. D. Plattner, S. G. Yates, K. Clay, and A. Leuchtmann; Ergobalansine, A New Ergot-Type Peptide Alkaloid Isolated from *Cenchrus echinatus* (Sandbur Grass) Infected with *Balansia obtecta*, and Produced in Liquid Cultures of *B. obtecta* and *B. cyperi;* Journal of Natural Products, Vol. 53, pp. 1272-1279(1990).

Common/Systematic Name

8-Hydroxyergotamine

Molecular Formula/Molecular Weight

$C_{33}H_{35}N_5O_6$; MW = 597.25873

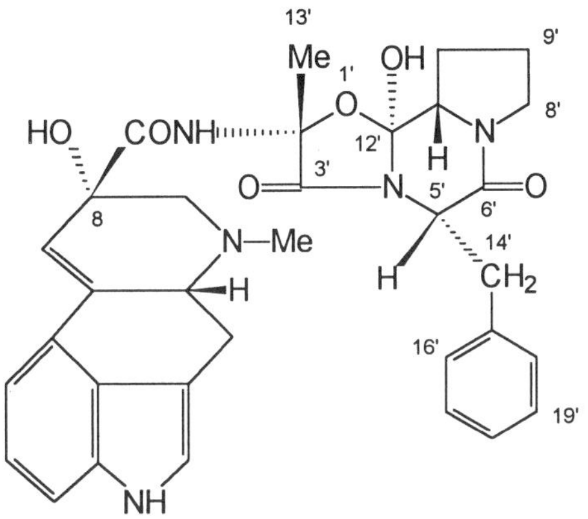

General Characteristics

Crystals from hot ethyl acetate and chloroform were obtained; mp., 197°C; $[\alpha]_D^{20°}$ +14° (*c*=1%, in pyridine); $[\alpha]_{2546.1}^{20}$ +32.9 (*c*=1%, in pyridine). The compound has good solubility in dioxane, pyridine, and dimethyl sulfoxide;is less soluble in methanol and chloroform. It gave positive van Urk's and Keller's tests.

Fungal Source

Natural ergot (*Claviceps purpurea*).

Isolation/Purification

Ground ergot from the field culture containing mainly ergotamine was extracted with a mixture of ether and ethanol (1:1, v/v) at room temperature. The extracted alkaloids were treated with 1% tartaric acid. After neutralization by aqueous ammonia to pH 7.5, crude alkaloid mixture was obtained. The peptide alkaloids were then transformed to their levorotatory forms by reaction with 1N sulfuric acid in absolute ethanol and acetic acid. The bases were prepared from the mixture of crude crystalline sulfates by aqueous sodium hydrocarbonate and extracted with ether. Ergotamine was removed by crystallization. Mother liquors were concentrated *in vacuo* at 40°C giving the bases. Ergotamine, ergocristine and ergostine were transformed into their poorly soluble dextrorotatory forms by boiling eight hours in twenty-fold excess of methanol and their crystals were filtered off after cooling. The residue in the mother liquors was subjected again to the same operation. It was further separated by chromatography on silica gel using chloroform-ethanol, 99:1, v/v. The new alkaloid was rechromatographed on silica gel using chloroform-benzene, 4:1, v/v. The product was crystallized from hot ethyl acetate and then from hot chloroform.

Biological Activity

The ergopeptine alkaloids produce a wide range of biological activities and some are used routinely in medical practice. All natural ergot alkaloids possess to a greater or lesser degree, biological effects that can be classified as direct peripheral effects on smooth muscle (uterine contraction and vasoconstriction), indirect peripheral effects (humoral, serotonin antagonism, and adrenergic blockage), and central nervous system effects (bulbomedullary and mesodiencephalic components).

Spectral Data

UV:

λ_{max}^{EtOH} 261(log ϵ=3.95) and 381nm (3.57).

^{13}C NMR:

(DMSO-*d6*) Peptide part- C-2', 86.8 s; C-3', 166.9 s; C-5', 57.2 d; C-6', 165.3 s; C-8', 46.8 t; C-9', 22.6 t; C-10', 26.8 t; C-11', 64.8 d; C-12', 103.7 s; C-13', 24.8 q; C-14', 39.4 d; C-15', 139.7 s; C-16', C-20', 130.7 d; C-17', C-19', 128.6 d; and C-18', 128.5ppm d. Ergoline part- C-2, 120.6 d; C-3, 109.5 s; C-4, 26.8 t; C-5, 62.4 d; C-7, 62.9 t; C-8, 72.7 s; C-9, 121.5 d; C-10, 139.0 s; C-11, 127.1 s; C-12, 112.3 d; C-13, 123.2 d; C-14, 111.5 d; C-15, 134.8 s; C-16, 127.1 s; C-17, 176.6 s; and N-CH_3, 43.8ppm q.

Mass Data:

314(30%, $C_{17}H_{18}N_2O_4$), 283(13, $C_{16}H_{17}N_3O_2$), 265($C_{16}H_{15}N_3O$), 244($C_{14}H_{16}N_2O_2$), 240(21, $C_{14}H_{12}N_2O_2$), 196(10, $C_{13}H_{12}N_2$), 167(22, $C_{12}H_9N$), 154(36, $C_{11}H_8N$), 153(78, $C_7H_9N_2O_2$), 125(53, $C_6H_9N_2O$), 120(7, $C_8H_{10}N$), 91(50, C_7H_7), 70(100, C_4H_8N), and 43*m/e* (535, C_2H_3O); elemental analyses found: 66.88% C, 6.0% H, 11.7% N; for $C_{33}H_{35}N_5O_6$ calcd 66.32% C, 5.90% H, 11.72% N.

References

B. Berde and H. O. Scheld (eds.); Ergot Alkaloids and Related Compounds, In Handbook of Experimental Pharmacology; Springer-Verlag, New York (1978).

A. Krajícek, B. Trtík, J. Spáčil, P. Sedmera, J. Vokoun, and Z. Rehâček; 8-Hydroxyergotamine, a New Ergot Alkaloid; Czechoslov. Chem. Commun. Vol. 44, pp. 2255-2260(1979).

Common/Systematic Name
Ergosine

Molecular Formula/Molecular Weight
$C_{30}H_{37}N_5O_5$; MW = 547.27947

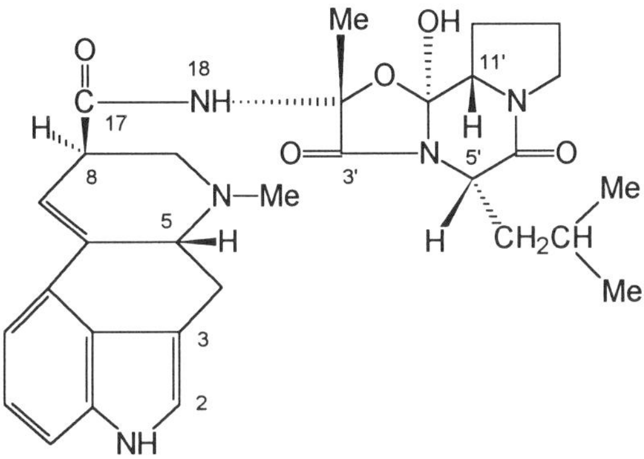

General Characteristics
Prisms from ethyl acetate; mp., 228°C (dec.); $[\alpha]_D^{20}$ - 161° (*c*=1.0, in $CHCl_3$), $[\alpha]_D^{20}$ -8° (*c*=1.0, in pyridine). Soluble in chloroform; fairly soluble in methanol and acetone; sparingly soluble in ethyl acetate and benzene; pK = 5.5 (in 80% aqueous methylcellosolve); blue color with Keller's reagent; does not form salts.

Fungal Source
Claviceps purpurea.

Isolation/Purification/Analysis
Extract with either aqueous tartaric or lactic acid solution, partition chromatography with chloroform or methylene chloride at appropriate pH, column clean-up procedures using either silica, alumina or ion exchange resin, and identification and analysis using a combination of co-chromatography using TLC and/or HPLC with UV or fluorescence detection. Mass spectrometry is quite useful for identification, analysis, and quantitation.

Biological Activity
All natural ergot alkaloids possess to a greater or lesser degree, biological effects that can be classified as direct peripheral effects on smooth muscle (uterine contraction and vasoconstriction), indirect peripheral effects (humoral, serotonin antagonism, and adrenergic blockage), and central nervous system effects (bulbomedullary and mesodiencephalic components).

Spectral Data

IR:
(See A. Hofmann, 1964.)

Mass Spectrum:
CIMS: (isobutane) 268, 281, and 211*m/e*; LREIMS: 267,196, 154, 125, 86, 70 (100%), 44, and 43*m/e*.

TLC Data

Silica gel plates developed with methylene chloride-isopropyl alcohol (92:8, v/v) three times which results in the separation of alkaloids into the isolysergic acid group, the ergotoxine group, the ergoxine group and a mixture of the ergotamine and clavine groups. Extraction of the alkaloids from the silica using methanol-chloroform (1:4 or 1:1, v/v) followed by rechromatography in chloroform-methanol (9:1 or 4:1, v/v) separates ergovaline from the clavine alkaloids (agroclavine and chanoclavines).

HPLC Data

Extract with alkaline methanol, filter, followed by direct HPLC analysis with fluorescence detection; mobile phase, either 60% or 70% alkaline methanol. This technique works well for ergopeptide alkaloids.

References

B. Berde and H. O. Scheld (eds.); Ergot Alkaloids and Related Compounds; In Handbook of Experimental Pharmacology; Springer-Verlag, New York (1978).

A. Hofmann; Die Mutterkorn Alkaloide; Enke Verlag, Stuttgart, 218 pp., 1964.

J. K. Porter; Analysis of Endophyte Toxins: Fescue and Other Grasses Toxic to Livestock; J. Animal Science, Vol. 73, pp. 871-880(1994).

R. G. Powell, R. D. Plattner, S. G. Yates, K. Clay, and A. Leuchtmann; Ergobalansine, A New Ergot-Type Peptide Alkaloid Isolated from *Cenchrus echinatus* (Sandbur Grass) Infected with *Balansia obtecta*, and Produced in Liquid Cultures of *B. obtecta* and *B. cyperi*; Journal of Natural Products, Vol. 53, pp. 1272-1279(1990).

Common/Systematic Name

Ergosinine

Molecular Formula/Molecular Weight

$C_{30}H_{37}N_5O_5$; MW = 547.27947

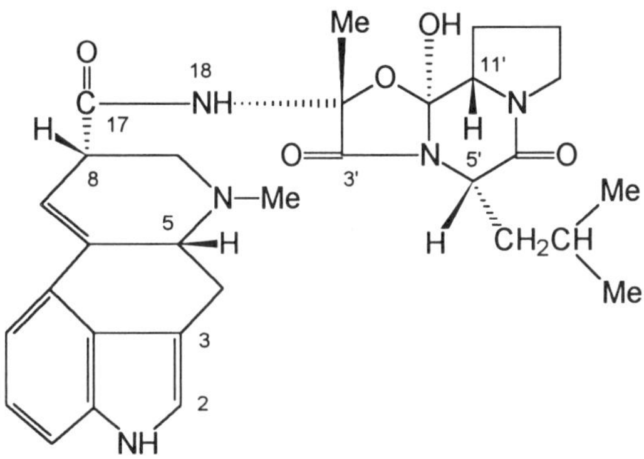

General Characteristics

Prisms from ethyl acetate, 90% alcohol, aqueous acetone or benzene; mp., 228°C (dec.); $[\alpha]_D^{20}$ + 420° (*c*=1.0, in $CHCl_3$), $[\alpha]_{5461}^{20}$ + 522° (*c*=1.0, in $CHCl_3$), $[\alpha]_D^{20}$ +380° (*c*=1.0, in acetone). Very readily soluble in chloroform; readily soluble in acetone; less soluble in ethyl acetate; very sparingly soluble in methanol; almost insoluble in water; pK = 5.5 (in 80% aqueous methylcellosolve); blue color with Keller's reagent; some amorphous salts have been prepared, but only with difficulty.

Fungal Source

Claviceps purpurea.

Epimers are not considered as naturally occurring, but as products formed during extraction and purification; epimerization at C-8 occurs in either acid or base.

Isolation/Purification/Analysis

Extract with either aqueous tartaric or lactic acid solution, partition chromatography with chloroform or methylene chloride at appropriate pH, column clean-up procedures using either silica, alumina or ion exchange resin, identification and analysis using a combination of co-chromatography using TLC and/or HPLC with UV or fluorescence detection. Mass spectrometry is quite useful for identification, analysis and quantitation.

Biological Activity

All natural ergot alkaloids possess to a greater or lesser degree, biological effects that can be classified as direct peripheral effects on smooth muscle (uterine contraction and vasoconstriction), indirect peripheral effects (humoral, serotonin antagonism, and adrenergic blockage), and central nervous system effects (bulbomedullary and mesodiencephalic components).

Spectral Data

IR:
(See A. Hofmann, 1964.)

TLC Data

Silica gel plates developed with methylene chloride-isopropyl alcohol (92:8, v/v) three times which results in the separation of alkaloids into the isolysergic acid group, the ergotoxine group, the ergoxine group, and a mixture of the ergotamine and clavine groups. Extraction of the alkaloids from the silica using methanol-chloroform (1:4 or 1:1, v/v) followed by rechromatography in chloroform-methanol (9:1 or 4:1, v/v) separates ergovaline from the clavine alkaloids (agroclavine and chanoclavines).

HPLC Data

Extract with alkaline methanol, filter, followed by direct HPLC analysis with fluorescence detection; mobile phase, either 60% or 70% alkaline methanol. This technique works well for ergopeptide alkaloids.

References

B. Berde and H. O. Scheld (eds.); Ergot Alkaloids and Related Compounds; In Handbook of Experimental Pharmacology; Springer-Verlag, New York (1978).

A. Hofmann; Die Mutterkorn Alkaloide; Enke Verlag, Stuttgart, 218 pp., 1964.

J. K. Porter; Analysis of Endophyte Toxins: Fescue and Other Grasses Toxic to Livestock; J. Animal Science, Vol. 73, pp. 871-880(1994).

Common/Systematic Name
Ergostine

Molecular Formula/Molecular Weight
$C_{34}H_{37}N_5O_5$; MW = 595.27947

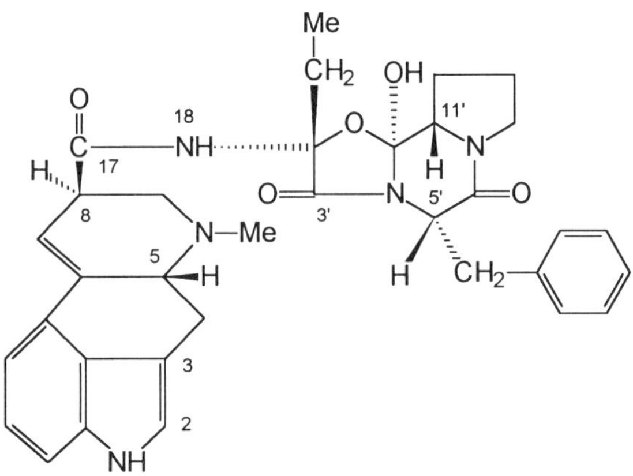

General Characteristics
Prisms from acetone or ethyl acetate; mp., 211-212°C (dec.); $[\alpha]_D^{20}$ - 169°, $[\alpha]_{5461}^{20}$ - 203°(*c*=1.0, in $CHCl_3$); $[\alpha]_D^{20}$ - 38°, $[\alpha]_{5461}^{20}$ - 39°(*c*=1.0, in pyridine). Moderately soluble in acetone; slightly soluble in chloroform and ethanol; sparingly soluble in benzene and ethyl acetate. Blue color with Keller's reagent changing to blue-green in approximately 15 seconds.

Fungal Source
Claviceps purpurea strain D-3-18.

Biological Activity
All natural ergot alkaloids possess to a greater or lesser degree, biological effects that can be classified as direct peripheral effects on smooth muscle (uterine contraction and vasoconstriction), indirect peripheral effects (humoral, serotonin antagonism, and adrenergic blockage), and central nervous system effects (bulbomedullary and mesodiencephalic components). Some are used routinely in medicine.

Spectral Data

IR:
(See Hofmann, 1964.)

Mass Spectrum:

328, 267, 244, 154, 153, 125, 91, 70(100%), and 57*m/e*. CIMS: (isobutane) 268(74%), 329(100), and 245*m/e* (47).

TLC Purification

Silica gel plates developed with methylene chloride-isopropyl alcohol (92:8, v/v) three times which results in the separation of alkaloids into the isolysergic acid group, the ergotoxine group, the ergoxine group and a mixture of the ergotamine and clavine groups. Extraction of the alkaloids from the silica using methanol-chloroform (1:4 or 1:1, v/v) followed by rechromatography in chloroform-methanol (9:1 or 4:1, v/v) separates ergovaline from the clavine alkaloids (agroclavine and chanoclavines).

TLC Solvent systems for silica gel chromatography (v/v):

a) Methylene chloride-isopropyl alcohol (92:8; 90:10; 75:25).
b) Chloroform-methanol (90:10; 80:20; 90:10 in saturated NH_3 atmosphere).
c) Chloroform-methanol-NH_3 (94:5:1).
d) Chloroform-ethylamine (90:10).
e) Benzene-dimethylformamide (86.5:13.5).

References

B. Berde and H. O. Scheld (eds.); Ergot Alkaloids and Related Compounds; In Handbook of Experimental Pharmacology; Springer-Verlag, New York (1978).

M. Flieger, P. Sedmera, J. Vokoun, Z. Řeháček, J. Stuchlik, Z. Malinka, L. Cvak, and P. Harazim; New Alkaloids from a Saprophytic Culture of *Claviceps purpurea;* J. Natural Products, Vol. 47, pp. 970-976(1984).

J. K. Porter; Analysis of Endophyte Toxins: Fescue and Other Grasses Toxic to Livestock; J. Animal Science, Vol. 73, pp. 871-880(1994).

J. K. Porter and D. Betowski; Chemical-Ionization Mass Spectrometry of Ergot Cyclol Alkaloids; J. Agric. Food Chem., Vol. 29, pp. 651-653(1981).

Common/Systematic Name

Ergostinine

Molecular Formula/Molecular Weight

$C_{34}H_{37}N_5O_5$; MW = 595.27947

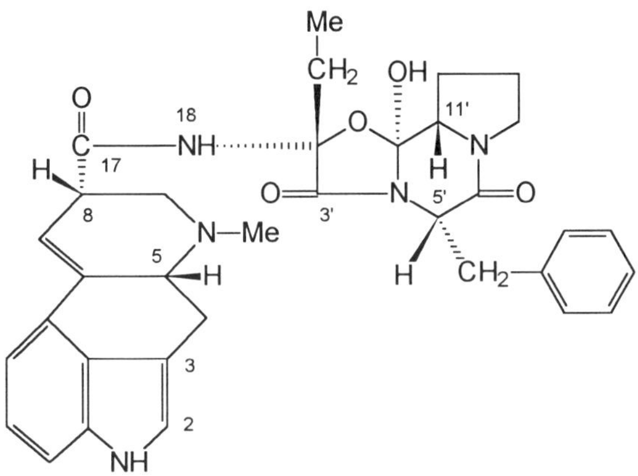

General Characteristics

Prisms from methanol; mp., 215-216°C (dec.); $[\alpha]_D^{20}$ +357°, $[\alpha]_{5461}^{20}$ + 446°(*c*=1.0, in $CHCl_3$); $[\alpha]_D^{20}$ +429°, $[\alpha]_{5461}^{20}$ + 538°(*c*=1.0, in pyridine). Slightly soluble in chloroform and sparingly soluble in benzene. Blue color with Keller's reagent changing to blue-green in 2-3 minutes.

Fungal Source

Claviceps purpurea strain D-3-18.

Epimers are not considered as naturally occurring, but as products formed during extraction and purification; epimerization at C-8 occurs in either acid or base.

Biological Activity

All natural ergot alkaloids possess to a greater or lesser degree, biological effects that can be classified as direct peripheral effects on smooth muscle (uterine contraction and vasoconstriction), indirect peripheral effects (humoral, serotonin antagonism, and adrenergic blockage), and central nervous system effects (bulbomedullary and mesodiencephalic components). Some are used routinely in medicine.

Spectral Data

IR:

(See Hofmann, 1964.)

TLC Purification

Silica gel plates developed with methylene chloride-isopropyl alcohol (92:8, v/v) three times which results in the separation of alkaloids into the isolysergic acid group, the ergotoxine group, the ergoxine group and a mixture of the ergotamine and clavine groups. Extraction of the alkaloids from the silica using methanol-chloroform (1:4 or 1:1, v/v) followed by rechromatography in chloroform-methanol (9:1 or 4:1, v/v) separates ergovaline from the clavine alkaloids (agroclavine and chanoclavines).

TLC Solvent systems for silica gel chromatography (v/v):

a) Methylene chloride-isopropyl alcohol (92:8; 90:10; 75:25).
b) Chloroform-methanol (90:10; 80:20; 90:10 in saturated NH_3 atmosphere).
c) Chloroform-methanol-NH_3 (94:5:1).
d) Chloroform-ethylamine (90:10).
e) Benzene-dimethylformamide (86.5:13.5).

References

B. Berde and H. O. Scheld (eds.); Ergot Alkaloids and Related Compounds; In Handbook of Experimental Pharmacology; Springer-Verlag, New York (1978).

A. Hofmann; Die Mutterkorn Alkaloide, Enke Verlag, Stuttgart, 218 pp., 1964.

J. K. Porter; Analysis of Endophyte Toxins: Fescue and Other Grasses Toxic to Livestock; J. Animal Science, Vol. 73, pp. 871-880(1994).

Common/Systematic Name

Ergonine

Molecular Formula/Molecular Weight

$C_{30}H_{37}N_5O_5$; MW = 547.27947

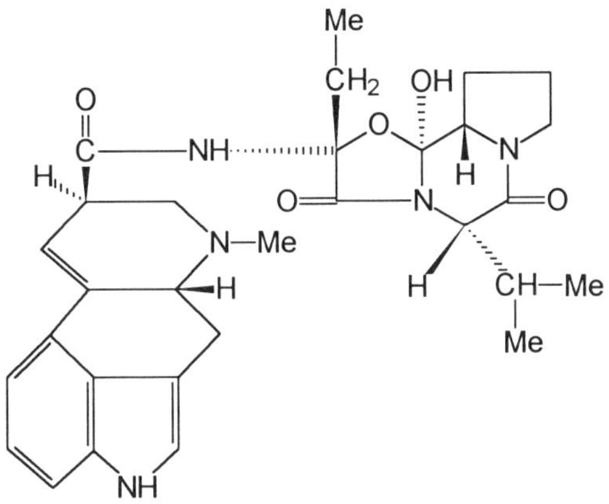

General Characteristics

Crystals from EtOH/diisopropylether; mp., 206-207°C (synthetic ergonine; mp., 207-208°C).

Fungal Source

Claviceps purpurea.

Isolation/Purification

The mother liquor of the ergokryptine-ergocornine producing strain of *Claviceps purpurea* consisting of ergosine (90%) and ergonine (10%) was chromatographed on alumina (activity II) after removing the ergosine as the di-*p*-toluyl-L-tartaric acid salt (twice). Elution with dichloromethane/0.3% methanol followed by crystallization from ethanol/diisopropylether yielded purified ergonine.

Biological Activity

All natural ergot alkaloids possess to a greater or lesser degree, biological effects that can be classified as direct peripheral effects on smooth muscle (uterine contraction and vasoconstriction), indirect peripheral effects (humoral, serotonin antagonism, and adrenergic blockage), and central nervous system effects (bulbomedullary and mesodiencephalic components).

Spectral Data

UV:

$\lambda_{max}^{Dichloromethane}$ 238(log ϵ=4.31) and 307.5nm (3.95).

IR:

(dichloromethane) 3460, 1728, 1668(sh), and 1649cm^{-1}.

^{1}H NMR:

($CDCl_3$) 9.05(1H, s, N1-H); 8.20(1H, s, CONH); 7.0-7.3(3 + 1H, m, aromatic H, OH); 6.90(1H, s, C2-H); 6.20-6.5(1H, m, C9-H); 4.40(1H, d, *J*=5Hz, C5'-H); 1.5-4(~16H, m), 2.6(3H, s, N6-CH_3); 1.15(3 + 3H, d, *J*=7Hz, CH(CH_3)2; and 0.91(3H, t, *J*=7Hz, CH_2-CH_3).

Mass Spectrum:

(Field desorption) Found 547*m/e*; calcd for $C_{30}H_{37}N_5O_5$ 547*m/e*.

References

B. Berde and H. O. Scheld (eds.); Ergot Alkaloids and Related Compounds; In Handbook of Experimental Pharmacology; Springer-Verlag, New York (1978).

R. Brunner, P. L. Stutz, H. Tschekter, and P. A. Stadler; Isolation of ergovaline, ergoptine, and ergonine, new alkaloids of the peptide type, from ergot sclerotia ; Can. J. Chem., Vol. 57, pp. 1638-1641(1979).

Common/Systematic Name
Ergovaline

Molecular Formula/Molecular Weight
$C_{29}H_{35}N_5O_5$; MW = 533.26382

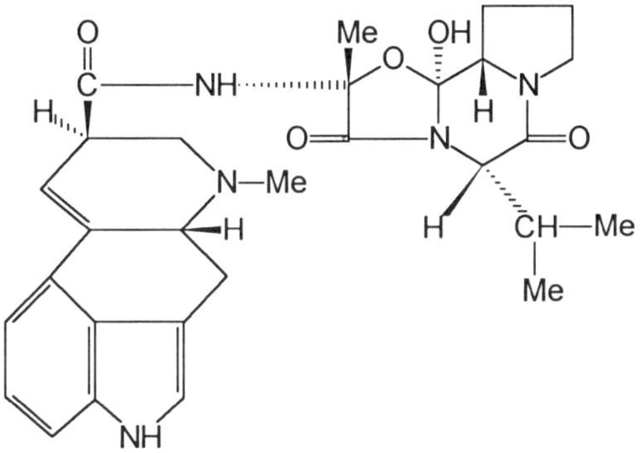

General Characteristics
Crystallized from ethyl acetate; mp., 207-208°C (synthetic ergovaline; mp., 207-208°C; $[\alpha]_D^{20}$ - 172° (*c*=0.5, in $CHCl_3$).

Fungal Source
Claviceps purpurea (strain No. 235), *Epichloë typhina* and *Acremonium coenophialum* infected fescue (*Festuca arundinacea* Schreb.).

Isolation/Purification
Sclerotia of *Claviceps purpurea* were ground and defatted by extraction with petroleum ether. The dark violet residue was extracted with a mixture of 70% acetone and 30% water containing 5% tartaric acid. The extracts were concentrated *in vacuo* at 50°C. The acidic solution was rendered alkaline by addition of Na_2CO_3, extracted with ethyl acetate, washed with water, dried (Na_2SO_4), and evaporated at 50°C *in vacuo*. Chromatography of the crude extract on alumina, activity II followed by chromatography on DS-O Camag, activity I and crystallization from ethyl acetate gave purified ergovaline.

Biological Activity
The ergopeptine alkaloids produce a wide range of biological activities and some are used routinely in medical practice. All natural ergot alkaloids possess to a greater or lesser degree, biological effects that can be classified as direct peripheral effects on smooth muscle (uterine contraction and vasoconstriction), indirect peripheral effects (humoral, serotonin antagonism, and adrenergic blockage), and central nervous system effects (bulbomedullary and mesodiencephalic components).

Spectral Data

UV:

$\lambda_{max}^{Dichloromethane}$ 238(log ϵ=4.3) and 307nm (3.95).

IR:

(dichloromethane) 3466, 1727, 1665(sh), and 1650cm^{-1}.

^{1}H NMR:

(DMSO) 10.8(1H, s, N1-H); 9.37(1H, s, CONH); 7.0-7.3(4H, m, aromatic H); 6.75(1H, d, *J*=2Hz, OH); 6.33(1H, s, C9-H); 4.31(1H, d, *J*=5Hz, C5'-H); 2.61(3H, s, N6-CH_3); 1.7-3.9(~14H, m); 1.58(3H, s, C2'-CH_3); and 1.08ppm (6H, d, *J*=7Hz, $CH(CH_3)_2$).

Mass Spectrum:

HRIMS: found 533.2602*m/e*; calcd for $C_{29}H_{35}N_5O_5$ 533.2638; CIMS (isobutane): 534(M^+ + 1, 8), 268(100), 267(74), and 197*m/e* (12%).

References

B. Berde and H. O. Scheld (eds.); Ergot Alkaloids and Related Compounds; In Handbook of Experimental Pharmacology, Springer-Verlag, New York (1978).

R. Brunner, P. L. Stutz, H. Tschekter, and P. A. Stadler; Isolation of Ergovaline, Ergoptine, and Ergonine, New Alkaloids of the Peptide Type, from Ergot Sclerotia; Can. J. Chem., Vol. 57, pp. 1638-1641(1979).

A. Hofmann; Die Mutterkorn Alkaloide; Elke Verlag, Stuttgart, 218 pp., 1964.

J. K. Porter, C. W. Bacon, J. D. Robbins, and D. Betowski; Ergot Alkaloid Identification in Clavicipitaceae Systemic Fungi of Pasture Grass; J. Agric. Food Chem., Vol. 29, pp. 653-657(1981).

J. K. Porter and D. Betowski; Chemical Ionization Mass Spectrometry of Ergot Cyclol Alkaloids; J. Agric. Food Chem., Vol. 29, pp. 651-653(1981).

M. R. Siegel, G. C. M. Latch, L. B. Bush, F. F. Fannin, D. D. Rowan, B. A. Tapper, C. W. Bacon, and M. C. Johnson; Fungal Endophyte-infected Grasses: Alkaloid Accumulation and Aphid Response; J. Chem. Ecol., 16: 3301-3315(1990).

Common/Systematic Name

Ergoptine

Molecular Formula/Molecular Weight

$C_{31}H_{39}N_5O_5$; MW = 561.29512

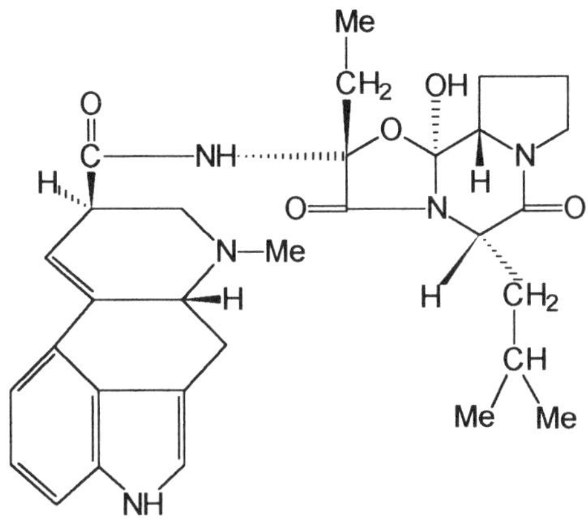

General Characteristics

Crystals from acetone/water (7:3); mp., 198-199°C (synthetic ergoptine; mp., 199-200°C); $[\alpha]_D^{20}$ -188° (*c*=0.8, in $CHCl_3$).

Fungal Source

Claviceps purpurea.

Isolation/Purification

The mother liquor from ergokryptine-ergocornine production with a total alkaloid content of about 80% (determined colorimetrically with van Urk's reagent) was chromatographed on alumina (activity II). Elution with chloroform/0.3% methanol led to a first fraction, which consisted primarily of ergokryptine and ergocornine. A second fraction was obtained by elution with chloroform/0.6% methanol which contained about 25% ergoptine. This fraction was further enriched by chromatography on alumina (activity II). The first fraction obtained on elution with chloroform/0.3% methanol contained kryptine and ergocornine. Elution with chloroform/0.6% methanol gave ergoptine (80% purity). Ergoptine was further purified by conversion into a salt with di-*p*-toluyl-L-tartaric acid. The product was crystallized and cleaved by partition between chloroform Na_2CO_3 giving an amorphous resin which was again converted into the salt with di-*p*-toluyl-L-tartaric acid. The salt obtained, mp 177-178°C, was cleaved by partition in chloroform/2 N Na_2CO_3 and afforded ergoptine with a 95% purity. Further purification of the base by silica gel column chromatography followed by crystallization from acetone/water (7:3, v/v) yielded homogeneous ergoptine.

Biological Activity

All natural ergot alkaloids possess to a greater or lesser degree, biological effects that can be classified as direct peripheral effects on smooth muscle (uterine contraction and vasoconstriction), indirect peripheral effects (humoral, serotonin antagonism, and adrenergic blockage), and central nervous system effects (bulbomedullary and mesodiencephalic components).

Spectral Data

UV:

$\lambda_{max}^{Dichloromethane}$ 238(log ϵ=4.34) and 308nm (3.98).

IR:

(dichloromethane) 3470, 3150-3300, 1732, 1671(sh), and 1653cm^{-1}.

^{1}H NMR:

($CDCl_3$) 9.58(1H, s, N1-H); 8.17(1H, s, CONH); 7.1-7.3(3 + 1H, m, aromatic H, OH); 6.99(1H, s, C2-H); 6.34-6.5(1H, m, C9-H); 4.58(1H, t, *J*=6Hz, C5'-H); 2.8-4(~9H, m, C4-H, C5-H, C7-H, C8-H, C8'-H, and C11'-H); 2.68(3H,s C6-CH3); 1.7-2.4(~9H, m, C2'-CH_2, C5'-CH_2, C9'-CH_2, C10'-CH_2 and side chain CH); and 1.9-2.2ppm (9H, side chain CH_3).

Mass Spectrum:

HRIMS: Found 561.2875*m/e*; calcd for $C_{31}H_{39}N_5O_5$, 561.2951.

TLC Purification

Silica gel plates developed with methylene chloride-isopropyl alcohol (92:8, v/v) three times which results in the separation of alkaloids into the isolysergic acid group, the ergotoxine group, the ergoxine group and a mixture of the ergotamine and clavine groups. Extraction of the alkaloids from the silica using methanol-chloroform (1:4 or 1:1, v/v) followed by rechromatography in chloroform-methanol (9:1 or 4:1, v/v) separates ergovaline from the clavine alkaloids (agroclavine and chanoclavines).

TLC Solvent systems for silica gel chromatography (v/v):

a) Methylene chloride-isopropyl alcohol (92:8; 90:10; 75:25).
b) Chloroform-methanol (90:10; 80:20; 90:10 in saturated NH_3 atmosphere).
c) Chloroform-methanol-NH_3 (94:5:1).
d) Chloroform-ethylamine (90:10).
e) Benzene-dimethylformamide (86.5:13.5).

References

B. Berde and H. O. Scheld (eds.); Ergot Alkaloids and Related Compounds; In Handbook of Experimental Pharmacology, Springer-Verlag, New York (1978).

R. Brunner, P. L. Stutz, H. Tschekter, and P. A. Stadler; Isolation of ergovaline, ergoptine, and ergonine, new alkaloids of the peptide type, from ergot sclerotia , Can. J. Chem., Vol. 57, pp. 1638-1641(1979).

J. K. Porter; Analysis of Endophyte Toxins: Fescue and Other Grasses Toxic to Livestock; J. Animal Science, Vol. 73, pp. 871-880(1994).

Common/Systematic Name

Ergocornine

Molecular Formula/Molecular Weight

$C_{31}H_{39}N_5O_5$; MW = 561.29512

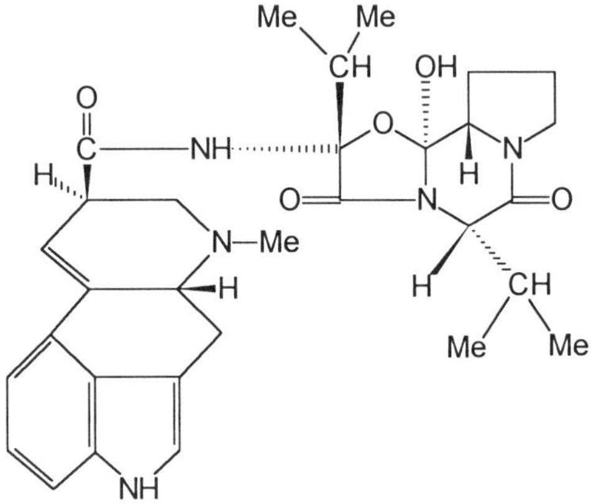

General Characteristics

Solvated polyhedra from methanol; mp., 182-184°C (dec.); $[\alpha]_D^{20}$ -188°, $[\alpha]_{5461}^{20}$ -224°(c=1.0, in $CHCl_3$); $[\alpha]_D^{20}$ -111°, $[\alpha]_{5461}^{20}$ -129° (c=1.0, in pyridine); pK = 5.5 (in 80% methylcellosolve); blue color changing to green with Keller's reagent. Soluble in acetone, chloroform, and ethyl acetate; slightly soluble in ethyl and methyl alcohol; nearly insoluble in water.

Fungal Source

Sclerotia of *Claviceps purpurea.*

Isolation/Purification/Analysis

Extract with either aqueous tartaric or lactic acid solution, partition chromatography with chloroform or methylene chloride at appropriate pH, column clean-up procedures using either silica, alumina or ion exchange resin, and identification and analysis using a combination of co-chromatography using TLC and/or HPLC with UV or fluorescence detection. Mass spectrometry is quite useful for identification, analysis, and quantitation.

Biological Activity

The ergopeptine alkaloids produce a wide range of biological activities and some are used routinely in medical practice. All natural ergot alkaloids possess to a greater or lesser degree, biological effects that can be classified as direct peripheral effects on smooth muscle (uterine contraction and vasoconstriction), indirect peripheral effects (humoral, serotonin antagonism, and adrenergic blockage), and central nervous system effects (bulbomedullary and mesodiencephalic components). LD_{50} IV in rabbits 1.17mg/kg.

Spectral Data

IR:
(See A. Hofmann, 1964.)

Mass Spectrum:
CIMS: (isobutane) 562(M^+ + 1, 14%), 268(100), 297(72), and 197*m/e* (11).

TLC Purification

Silica gel plates developed with methylene chloride-isopropyl alcohol (92:8, v/v) three times which results in the separation of alkaloids into the isolysergic acid group, the ergotoxine group, the ergoxine group and a mixture of the ergotamine and clavine groups. Extraction of the alkaloids from the silica using methanol-chloroform (1:4 or 1:1, v/v) followed by rechromatography in chloroform-methanol (9:1 or 4:1, v/v) separates ergovaline from the clavine alkaloids (agroclavine and chanoclavines).

TLC Solvent systems for silica gel chromatography (v/v):

a) Methylene chloride-isopropyl alcohol (92:8; 90:10; 75:25).
b) Chloroform-methanol (90:10; 80:20; 90:10 in saturated NH_3 atmosphere).
c) Chloroform-methanol-NH_3 (94:5:1).
d) Chloroform-ethylamine (90:10).
e) Benzene-dimethylformamide (86.5:13.5).

HPLC Data

Extract with alkaline methanol, filter, followed by direct HPLC analysis with fluorescence detection; mobile phase, either 60% or 70% alkaline methanol. This technique works well for ergopeptide alkaloids.

References

B. Berde and H. O. Scheld (eds.); Ergot Alkaloids and Related Compounds; In Handbook of Experimental Pharmacology; Springer-Verlag, New York (1978).

A. Hofmann; Die Mutterkorn Alkaloide; Enke Verlag, Stuttgart, 218 pp., 1964.

R. D. Plattner, S. H. Yates, and J. K. Porter; Quadrupole Mass Spectrometry/Mass Spectrometry of Ergot Cyclol Alkaloids; J. Agric. Food Chem., Vol. 31, pp. 785-789 (1983).

J. K. Porter and D. Betowski; Chemical Ionization Mass Spectrometry of Ergot Cyclol Alkaloids; J. Agric. Food Chem., Vol. 29, pp. 651-653(1981).

Common/Systematic Name
Ergocorninine

Molecular Formula/Molecular Weight
$C_{31}H_{39}N_5O_5$; MW = 561.29512

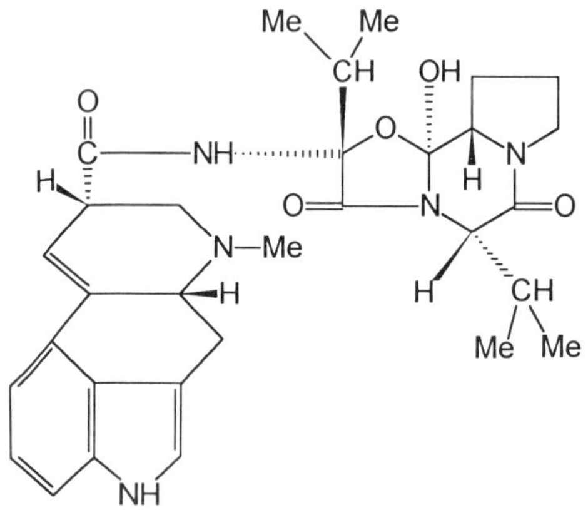

General Characteristics
Crystallizes solvent-free, prisms from alcohol; mp., 228 °C (dec.); $[\alpha]_D^{20}$ + 404 °, $[\alpha]_{5461}^{20}$ + 504° (c=1.0, in $CHCl_3$); $[\alpha]_D^{20}$ + 488 °, $[\alpha]_{5461}^{20}$ + 624° (c=1.0, in pyridine); pK = 4.8 (in 80% methylcellosolve); blue color changing to green with Keller's reagent. Soluble in 15 parts boiling ethanol, 25 parts boiling methanol, 30 parts boiling benzene, 30 parts boiling ethyl acetate; freely soluble in acetone and chloroform; nearly insoluble in water. Does not seem to form salts.

Fungal Source
Sclerotia of *Claviceps purpurea*.
Epimers are not considered as naturally occurring, but as products formed during extraction and purification; epimerization at C-8 occurs in either acid or base.

Isolation/Purification/Analysis
Extract with either aqueous tartaric or lactic acid solution, partition chromatography with chloroform or methylene chloride at appropriate pH, column clean-up procedures using either silica, alumina or ion exchange resin, and identification, and analysis using a combination of co-chromatography using TLC and/or HPLC with UV or fluorescence detection. Mass spectrometry is quite useful for identification, analysis, and quantitation.

Biological Activity
The ergopeptine alkaloids produce a wide range of biological activities and some are used routinely in medical practice. All natural ergot alkaloids possess to a greater or lesser

degree, biological effects that can be classified as direct peripheral effects on smooth muscle (uterine contraction and vasoconstriction), indirect peripheral effects (humoral, serotonin antagonism, and adrenergic blockage), and central nervous system effects (bulbomedullary and mesodiencephalic components). Some ergopeptine alkaloids are used routinely in medicine. LD_{50} IV in rabbits 1.17mg/kg.

Spectral Data

IR:
See A. Hofmann, 1964.

TLC Purification

Silica gel plates developed with methylene chloride-isopropyl alcohol (92:8, v/v) three times which results in the separation of alkaloids into the isolysergic acid group, the ergotoxine group, the ergoxine group and a mixture of the ergotamine and clavine groups. Extraction of the alkaloids from the silica using methanol-chloroform (1:4 or 1:1, v/v) followed by rechromatography in chloroform-methanol (9:1 or 4:1, v/v) separates ergovaline from the clavine alkaloids (agroclavine and chanoclavines).

TLC Solvent systems for silica gel chromatography (v/v):

a) Methylene chloride-isopropyl alcohol (92:8; 90:10; 75:25).
b) Chloroform-methanol (90:10; 80:20; 90:10 in saturated NH_3 atmosphere).
c) Chloroform-methanol-NH_3 (94:5:1).
d) Chloroform-ethylamine (90:10).
e) Benzene-dimethylformamide (86.5:13.5).

HPLC Data

Extract with alkaline methanol, filter, followed by direct HPLC analysis with fluorescence detection; mobile phase, either 60% or 70% alkaline methanol. This technique works well for ergopeptide alkaloids.

References

B. Berde and H. O. Scheld (eds.); Ergot Alkaloids and Related Compounds; In Handbook of Experimental Pharmacology; Springer-Verlag, New York (1978).

A. Hofmann; Die Mutterkorn Alkaloide, Enke Verlag, Stuttgart, 218 pp., 1964.

R. D. Plattner, S. H. Yates, and J. K. Porter; Quadrupole Mass Spectrometry/Mass Spectrometry of Ergot Cyclol Alkaloids; J. Agric. Food Chem., Vol. 31, pp. 785-789 (1983).

J. K. Porter and D. Betowski; Chemical Ionization Mass Spectrometry of Ergot Cyclol Alkaloids; J. Agric. Food Chem., Vol. 29, pp. 651-653(1981).

Common/Systematic Name

O-12'-Methylergocornine

Molecular Formula/Molecular Weight

$C_{32}H_{41}N_5O_5$; MW = 575.31077

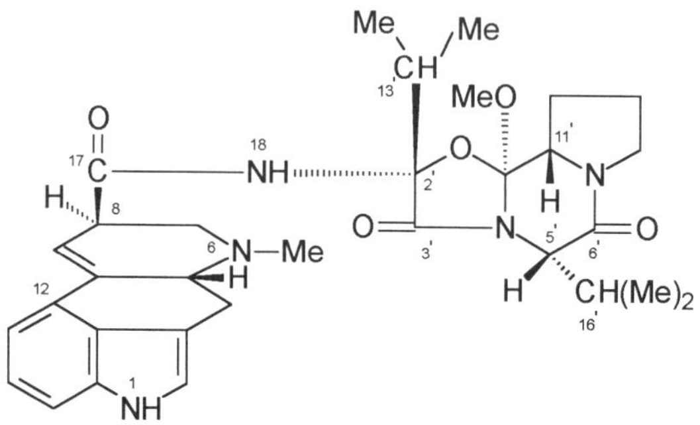

Fungal Source

Claviceps purpurea Strain 231 FI.

Isolation/Purification

Crude alkaloids were obtained by extraction of fungal cultures with CH_2Cl_2-MeOH (80:20, v/v) followed by precipitation with petroleum ether; the crude alkaloid extract was chromatographed Extrelut (Merck) column chromatography eluted with CH_2Cl_2. The crude alkaloids thus obtained chromatographed on a Silica gel 60 (Merck) column eluted with CH_2Cl_2-MeOH (98:2, v/v); the was monitored by UV and TLC. Final purification was by preparative TLC in a cold room in the TLC was performed on Silica gel F_{254}, plates (Merck) using the following solvent systems: CH_2Cl_2-isopropyl alcohol (92:8, v/v) or CH_2Cl_2-MeOH (90:10, v/v). The alkaloids were detecte examination under UV light at 254 and 366 nm while some were sprayed with N,N-*p*-dimethylaminobenzaldehyde. The various bands were scraped off and eluted with CH_2Cl_2 (1:1, v/v).

Biological Activity

The ergopeptine alkaloids produce a wide range of biological activities and some are used routin medical practice. All natural ergot alkaloids possess to a greater of lesser degree, biological effec can be classified as direct peripheral effects on smooth muscle (uterine contraction and vasoconstriction), indirect peripheral effects (humoral, serotonin antagonism, and adrenergic bloc and central nervous system effects (bulbomedullary and mesodiencephalic components).

Spectral Data

^{1}H NMR:

($CDCl_3$) 8.07(1H, s, NH-1); 2.66 (3H, s, N-CH_3); 6.40(1H, dd, *J*=2.0, 5.9Hz, H-9); 9.17 (1H, CONH); 3.31 (3H, s, OCH_3); and 4.51ppm (1H, d, *J*=4.1Hz, H-5').

^{13}C NMR

(CDCl_3) C-2, 119.0*; C-3, 110.8; C-4, 26.6; C-5, 59.4; N(6)-CH_3, 44.1; C-7, 49.2; C-8, 41.3; C-9, (119.2); C-10, 138.8; C-11, 129.8; C-12, 112.0; C-13, 123.4; C-14, 110.0; C-15, 133.8; C-16, 126.2; 8-CONH, 173.9; C-2', 89.2; C-3', 164.7**, C-5', 60.7; C-6', 168.7**; C-8', 45.8; C-9', 22 .1***; C-10', 22.2***; C-11', 61.4; C-12' , 106.8; 12'-OCH_3, 49.2; (2')-C, 35.7; (2')-CH-$(CH_3)_2$, 16.0, 16.7; (5')-C, 32.2; and (5')-C-C-$(CH_3)_2$, 19.5, 19.2ppm.

*, **, and *** assignments may be reversed.

Mass Spectrum:

EIMS: 575(M^+), 543, 446, 418, 347, 319, 304, 221, 196, 154, and 70*m/e* (100%).

ence

N. Crespi-Perellino, M. Ballabio, B. Gioia, and A. Minghetti; Two Unusual Ergopeptines Produced by a Saprophytic Culture of *Claviceps purpurea*; J. Natural Products, Vol. 50, pp. 1065-1074(1987).

Common/Systematic Name

Ergocristine

Molecular Formula/Molecular Weight

$C_{35}H_{39}N_5O_5$; MW = 609.29512

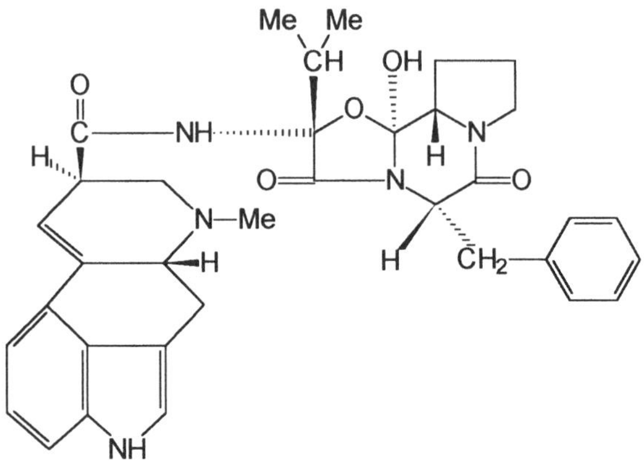

General Characteristics

Orthorhombic crystals from benzene with 2 molecules benzene of crystallization; the solvent-free base melts at 155-157°C (dec.); $[\alpha]_D^{20}$ -183°, $[\alpha]_{5461}^{20}$ -217° (*c*=1.0, in $CHCl_3$); $[\alpha]_D^{20}$ -108°, $[\alpha]_{5461}^{20}$ -125° (*c*=1.0, in pyridine); pK = 5.5 (in 80% methylcellosolve); blue color slowly changing to olive-green with Keller's reagent. Very soluble in ethyl and methyl alcohol, acetone, chloroform, and ethyl acetate; slightly soluble in ether; practically insoluble in water and petroleum ether.

Fungal Source

Claviceps purpurea.

Isolation/Purification/Analysis

Extract with either aqueous tartaric or lactic acid solution, partition chromatography with chloroform or methylene chloride at appropriate pH, column clean-up procedures using either silica, alumina or ion exchange resin, and identification, and analysis using a combination of co-chromatography using TLC and/or HPLC with UV or fluorescence detection. Mass spectrometry is quite useful for identification, analysis, and quantitation.

Biological Activity

All natural ergot alkaloids possess to a greater or lesser degree, biological effects that can be classified as direct peripheral effects on smooth muscle (uterine contraction and vasoconstriction), indirect peripheral effects (humoral, serotonin antagonism, and adrenergic blockage), and central nervous system effects (bulbomedullary and mesodiencephalic components).

Spectral Data

IR:
See A. Hofmann, 1964.

^{13}C NMR:
($CDCl_3$) C-2, 119.2; C-3, 110.6; C-4, 30.9; C-5, 59.3; 6-NMe, 40.9; C-7, 48.2; C-8, 44.3; C-9, 118.8; C-10, 138.9; C-11, 129.6; C-12, 111.9; C-13, 123.3; C-14, 110.2; C-15, 133.8; C-16, 125.9; 17-CONH, 176.2; C-2', 89.9; C-3', 165.7*; C-5', 56.8; C-6', 165.4*; C-8', 46.1; C-9' 21.7; C-10', 22.4; C-11', 64.3; and C-12', 103.7ppm.

* Assignment may be reversed.

Mass Spectrum:
LREIMS: 342(10%), 267(11), 244(29), 154(19), 153(73), 125(81), 91(64), and 70*m/e* (100); CIMS: (isobutane) 268(100%), 343(55), and 245*m/e* (47).

TLC Purification

Silica gel plates developed with methylene chloride-isopropyl alcohol (92:8, v/v) three times which results in the separation of alkaloids into the isolysergic acid group, the ergotoxine group, the ergoxine group and a mixture of the ergotamine and clavine groups. Extraction of the alkaloids from the silica using methanol-chloroform (1:4 or 1:1, v/v) followed by rechromatography in chloroform-methanol (9:1 or 4:1, v/v) separates ergovaline from the clavine alkaloids (agroclavine and chanoclavines).

TLC Solvent systems for silica gel chromatography (v/v):

a) Methylene chloride-isopropyl alcohol (92:8; 90:10; 75:25).
b) Chloroform-methanol (90:10; 80:20; 90:10 in saturated NH_3 atmosphere).
c) Chloroform-methanol-NH_3 (94:5:1).
d) Chloroform-ethylamine (90:10).
e) Benzene-dimethylformamide (86.5:13.5).

HPLC Data

Extract with alkaline methanol, filter, followed by direct HPLC analysis with fluorescence detection; mobile phase, either 60% or 70% alkaline methanol. This technique works well for ergopeptide alkaloids.

References

B. Berde and H. O. Scheld (eds.); Ergot Alkaloids and Related Compounds; In Handbook of Experimental Pharmacology; Springer-Verlag, New York (1978).

A. Hofmann; Die Mutterkorn Alkaloide; Enke Verlag, Stuttgart, 218 pp., 1964.

R. D. Plattner, S. H. Yates, and J. K. Porter; Quadrupole Mass Spectrometry/Mass Spectrometry of Ergot Cyclol Alkaloids; J. Agric. Food Chem., Vol. 31, pp. 785-

789(1983).

J. K. Porter; Analysis of Endophyte Toxins: Fescue and Other Grasses Toxic to Livestock; J. Animal Science, Vol. 73, pp. 871-880(1994).

J. K. Porter and D. Betowski; Chemical Ionization Mass Spectrometry of Ergot Cyclol Alkaloids; J. Agric. Food Chem., Vol. 29, pp. 651-653(1981).

R. G. Powell, R. D. Plattner, S. G. Yates, K. Clay, and A. Leuchtmann; Ergobalansine, A New Ergot-Type Peptide Alkaloid Isolated From *Cenchrus echinatus* (Sandbur Grass) Infected With *Balansia obtecta*, and Produced in Liquid Cultures of *B. obtecta* and *B. cyperi;* Journal of Natural Products, Vol. 53, pp. 1272-1279(1990).

Common/Systematic Name

Ergocristinine

Molecular Formula/Molecular Weight

$C_{35}H_{39}N_5O_5$; MW = 609.29512

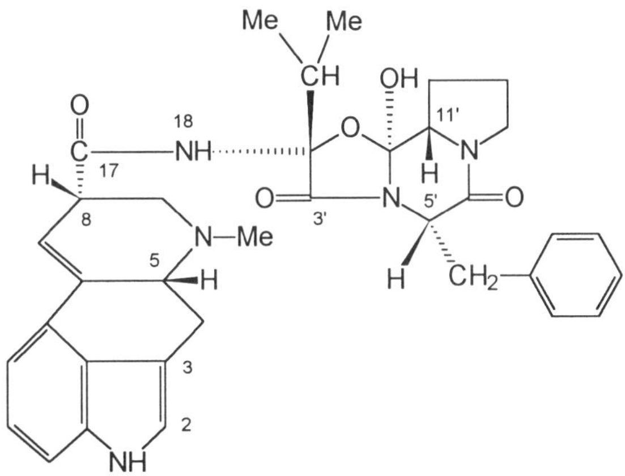

General Characteristics

Crystallizes solvent-free as long prisms from absolute alcohol solution; mp., 226°C (dec.); $[\alpha]_D^{20}$ + 366°, $[\alpha]_{5461}^{20}$ + 460° (c=0.7, in $CHCl_3$); $[\alpha]_D^{20}$ + 462°, $[\alpha]_{5461}^{20}$ + 582° (c=1.0, in pyridine); pK = 5.0 (in 80% methylcellosolve); blue color slowly changing to olive-green with Keller's reagent. Much less soluble than ergocristine; apparently does not form salts.

Fungal Source

Claviceps purpurea strain D-3-18. Epimers are not considered as naturally occurring, but as products formed during extraction and purification; epimerization at C-8 occurs in either acid or base.

Isolation/Purification via TLC

Silica gel plates developed with methylene chloride-isopropyl alcohol (92:8, v/v) three times which results in the separation of alkaloids into the isolysergic acid group, the ergotoxine group, the ergoxine group and a mixture of the ergotamine and clavine groups. Extraction of the alkaloids from the silica using methanol-chloroform (1:4 or 1:1, v/v) followed by rechromatography in chloroform-methanol (9:1 or 4:1, v/v) separates ergovaline from the clavine alkaloids (agroclavine and chanoclavines).

TLC Solvent systems for silica gel chromatography (v/v):

a) Methylene chloride-isopropyl alcohol (92:8; 90:10; 75:25)

b) Chloroform-methanol (90:10; 80:20; 90:10 in saturated NH_3 atmosphere).
c) Chloroform-methanol-NH_3 (94:5:1).
d) Chloroform-ethylamine (90:10).
e) Benzene-dimethylformamide (86.5:13.5).

Biological Activity

The ergopeptine alkaloids produce a wide range of biological activities and some are used routinely in medical practice. All natural ergot alkaloids possess to a greater or lesser degree, biological effects that can be classified as direct peripheral effects on smooth muscle (uterine contraction and vasoconstriction), indirect peripheral effects (humoral, serotonin antagonism, and adrenergic blockage), and central nervous system effects (bulbomedullary and mesodiencephalic components).

Spectral Data

IR:

See A. Hofmann, 1964.

References

B. Berde and H. O. Scheld (eds.); Ergot Alkaloids and Related Compounds; In Handbook of Experimental Pharmacology; Springer-Verlag, New York (1978).

A. Hofmann; Die Mutterkorn Alkaloide; Enke Verlag, Stuttgart, 218 pp., 1964.

J. K. Porter; Analysis of Endophyte Toxins: Fescue and Other Grasses Toxic to Livestock; J. Animal Science, Vol. 73, pp. 871-880(1994).

Common/Systematic Name

Ergosecaline

Molecular Formula/Molecular Weight

$C_{24}H_{28}N_4O_4$; MW = 436.21106

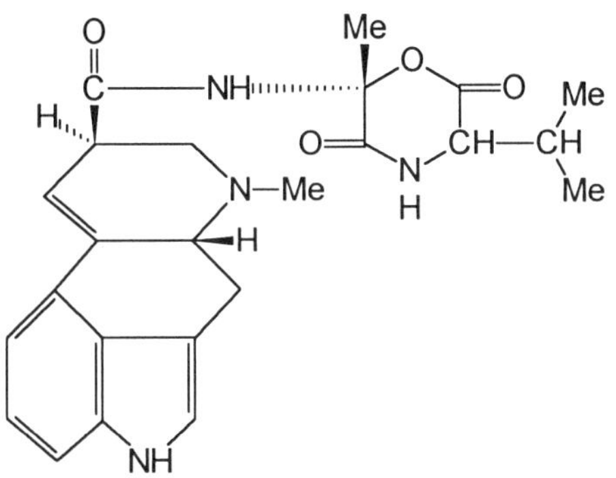

Fungal Source

Claviceps purpurea strain D-3-18.

Biological Activity

All natural ergot alkaloids possess to a greater or lesser degree, biological effects that can be classified as direct peripheral effects on smooth muscle (uterine contraction and vasoconstriction), indirect peripheral effects (humoral, serotonin antagonism, and adrenergic blockage), and central nervous system effects (bulbomedullary and mesodiencephalic components). Some are used routinely in medical practice.

Spectral Data

IR:

See Hofmann, 1964.

TLC Purification

Silica gel plates developed with methylene chloride-isopropyl alcohol (92:8, v/v) three times which results in the separation of alkaloids into the isolysergic acid group, the ergotoxine group, the ergoxine group and a mixture of the ergotamine and clavine groups. Extraction of the alkaloids from the silica using methanol-chloroform (1:4 or 1:1, v/v) followed by rechromatography in chloroform-methanol (9:1 or 4:1, v/v) separates ergovaline from the clavine alkaloids (agroclavine and chanoclavines).

TLC Solvent systems for silica gel chromatography (v/v):

a) Methylene chloride-isopropyl alcohol (92:8; 90:10; 75:25).

b) Chloroform-methanol (90:10; 80:20; 90:10 in saturated NH_3 atmosphere).
c) Chloroform-methanol-NH_3 (94:5:1).
d) Chloroform-ethylamine (90:10).
e) Benzene-dimethylformamide (86.5:13.5).

References

B. Berde and H. O. Scheld (eds.); Ergot Alkaloids and Related Compounds; In Handbook of Experimental Pharmacology; Springer-Verlag, New York (1978).

A. Hofmann; Die Mutterkorn Alkaloide; Enke Verlag, Stuttgart, 218 pp., 1964.

J. K. Porter; Analysis of Endophyte Toxins: Fescue and Other Grasses Toxic to Livestock; J. Animal Science, Vol. 73, pp. 871-880(1994).

Common/Systematic Name
Ergosecalinine

Molecular Formula/Molecular Weight
$C_{24}H_{28}N_4O_4$; MW = 436.21106

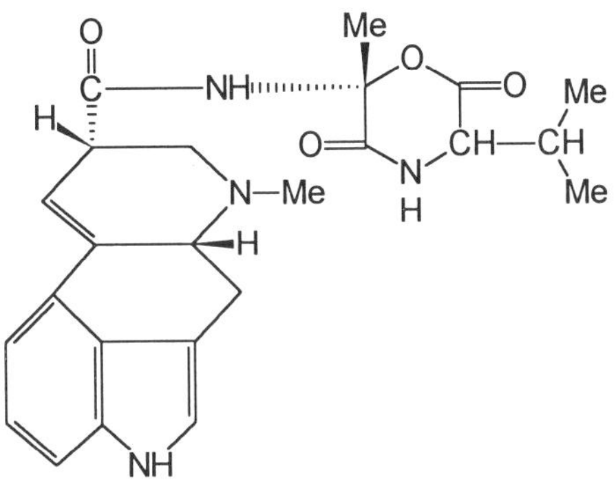

General Characteristics
Prisms from ethyl acetate; mp., 217°C (dec.); $[\alpha]_D^{18}$ + 298°, $[\alpha]_{5461}^{18}$ + 375° (*c*=1.0, in $CHCl_3$); $[\alpha]_D^{18}$ + 417°, $[\alpha]_{5461}^{18}$ + 512° (*c*=1.0, in pyridine); blue color with Allport-Cocking's reagent. Readily soluble in acetone and methanol; moderately soluble in ethyl acetate; sparingly soluble in benzene and chloroform.

Fungal Source
Sclerotia and saprophytic culture of *Claviceps purpurea*. Epimers are not considered as naturally occurring, but as products formed during extraction and purification; epimerization at C-8 occurs in either acid or base.

Biological Activity
All natural ergot alkaloids possess to a greater or lesser degree, biological effects that can be classified as direct peripheral effects on smooth muscle (uterine contraction and vasoconstriction), indirect peripheral effects (humoral, serotonin antagonism, and adrenergic blockage), and central nervous system effects (bulbomedullary and mesodiencephalic components). Some are used routinely in medicine.

Spectral Data

IR:
See Hofmann, 1964.

TLC Purification

Silica gel plates developed with methylene chloride-isopropyl alcohol (92:8, v/v) three times which results in the separation of alkaloids into the isolysergic acid group, the ergotoxine group, the ergoxine group and a mixture of the ergotamine and clavine groups. Extraction of the alkaloids from the silica using methanol-chloroform (1:4 or 1:1, v/v) followed by rechromatography in chloroform-methanol (9:1 or 4:1, v/v) separates ergovaline from the clavine alkaloids (agroclavine and chanoclavines).

TLC Solvent systems for silica gel chromatography (v/v):

a) Methylene chloride-isopropyl alcohol (92:8; 90:10; 75:25).
b) Chloroform-methanol (90:10; 80:20; 90:10 in saturated NH_3 atmosphere).
c) Chloroform-methanol-NH_3 (94:5:1).
d) Chloroform-ethylamine (90:10).
e) Benzene-dimethylformamide (86.5:13.5).

References

B. Berde and H. O. Scheld (eds.); Ergot Alkaloids and Related Compounds; In Handbook of Experimental Pharmacology; Springer-Verlag, New York (1978).

A. Hofmann; Die Mutterkorn Alkaloide; Enke Verlag, Stuttgart, 218 pp., 1964.

J. K. Porter; Analysis of Endophyte Toxins: Fescue and Other Grasses Toxic to Livestock; J. Animal Science, Vol. 73, pp. 871-880(1994).

Common/Systematic Name
Ergobalansine

Molecular Formula/Molecular Weight
$C_{28}H_{35}N_5O_5$; MW = 521.26382

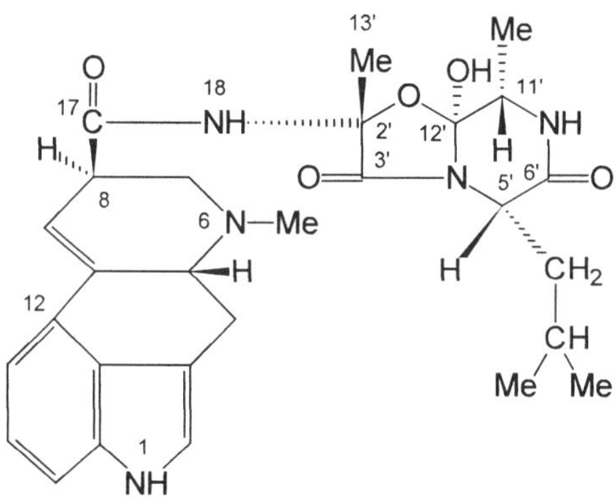

General Characteristics
Ergobalansine was obtained as a white solid.

Fungal Source
Cenchrus echinatus infected with *Balansia obtecta* and *Cyperus virens* infected with *B. cyperi*.

Isolation/Purification
Aerial parts of *C. echinatus* infected with *B. obtecta* were ground in a Wiley mill fitted with a 1/4 inch screen and extracted with 95% EtOH for 24 h. The extraction process was repeated three additional times and combined EtOH extracts were evaporated to a volume of 6 liters on a rotary evaporator below 42°C. An aliquot was evaporated to dryness and a portion of the concentrate was coated onto silica gel. The material was added to the top of a silica gel column packed in methylene chloride and the column was eluted with CH_2Cl_2, 5%, 10%, and 25% MeOH in CH_2Cl_2. Fractions were analyzed by TLC and recombined into fractions on the basis of similarity of TLC patterns. The remaining extract was processed by dividing into 6 portions and repeating the chromatographic procedure 6 additional times. Like materials were combined and all 8 fractions were examined for the presence of ergot-peptide alkaloids. An alkaloid-enriched fraction was prepared by solvent partitioning the entire sample in EtOAc and aqueous 2% tartaric acid. The aqueous layer was partitioned a second time with EtOAc. The aqueous layer was adjusted to pH 9 by slow addition of concentrated NH_4OH. The resulting basic solution was extracted with EtOAc, and the EtOAc extract yielded an alkaloidal material. Analysis of the alkaloid-enriched fractions by reversed-phase HPLC revealed two highly fluorescent

compounds. Final purification of ergobalansine and ergobalansinine was achieved by preparative TLC. Purified ergobalansine and ergobalansinine readily epimerized to an approximate 1:1 equilibrium mixture on standing in solutions containing MeOH, particularly at elevated temperatures.

Biological Activity

All natural ergot alkaloids possess to a greater or lesser degree, biological effects that can be classified as direct peripheral effects on smooth muscle (uterine contraction and vasoconstriction), indirect peripheral effects (humoral, serotonin antagonism, and adrenergic blockage), and central nervous system effects (bulbomedullary and mesodiencephalic components). Some are used routinely in medicine.

Spectral Data

^{1}H NMR:

($CDCl_3$) H-1, 7.99(s); H-2, 6.93(m); H-4a, 2.82(m, *J*=14.3, 12.2Hz); H-4b, 3.32(m, *J*=14.3, 5.0Hz); H-5, 3.79(m, *J*=12.2, 5.0Hz); 6-NMe, 2.64(s); H-7a, 2.98(dd, *J*=12.0, 3.7Hz); H-7b, 2.88(dd, *J*=12.0, 2.8Hz); H-8a, 3.18(m, *J*=5.6, 3.7, 2.8Hz); H-9, 6.35(dd, *J*=5.6Hz); 8-NH, 9.26(s); H-12-14, 7.18(m); H-2'Me, 1.52(s); H-5', 4.52(dd); 5'-CH_2, 1.94(m); 5'-CH_2CH, 1.94(m); 5'-$CH_2CH(CH_3)_2$, 1.05(d), 1.00(d); H-11', 3.56(m); 11'-CH_3, 1.34(d); OH, 5.84(s); and 7'-NH, 6.78ppm(bs).

^{13}C NMR:

($CDCl_3$) C-2, 119.0; C-3, 110.8; C-4, 22.1; C-5, 59.6; 6-NMe, 41.1; C-7, 48.9; C-8, 44.1; C-9, 118.4; C-10, 139.2; C-11, 129.5; C-12, 112.0; C-13, 123.4; C-14, 110.0; C-15, 133.8; C-16, 126.2; 17-CONH, 175.7; C-2', 85.4; C-3', 166.3*; C-5', 53.2; C-6', 169.1*; C-8', not obs.; C-9' not obs.; C-10', not obs.; C-11', 57.O; C-12', 102.7; 2'-Me, 24.6; 5'-CH_2, 43.5; 5'-CH_2CH, 24.7; 5'-$(Me)_2$, 21.9, 22.8; and 11'-CH_3, 14.7ppm.

* Assignment may be reversed.

Mass Data:

EIMS: $[M]^+$ 521(3%), 337(6), 267(100), 224(30), 221(52), 207(49), 196(21), 184(38), 180(29), 167(19), 154(22), 141(17), 128(54), 113(21), 44(48), and 43(59); CIMS: (isobutane) MH^+ 522(6%), 504(2), 268(93), 255(100), and 185(12); negative ion CIMS: (isobutane) $[M]^-$ 521(36), and 254(100). The MS-MS daughter spectrum of 254*m/e* (negative ion CIMS) was: 254(27), 211(7), 183(100), 126(2), 113(2), and 86(4). Found for $[AH]^+$ 268.1422 ($C_{16}H_{18}N_3O$ requires 268.1450); $[BH]^+$ 255.1362($C_{12}H_{19}N_2O$; requires 255.1345).

TLC Data

Analytical and preparative TLC were carried out on Silica gel 60-F_{254} plates (E. Merck) developed with chloroform-methanol (9:1, v/v).

HPLC Data

Preparative HPLC utilized a Rainin Dynamax-60Å silica column with isocratic elution using methylene chloride-methanol (93:7, v/v).

References

B. Berde and H. O. Scheld (eds.); Ergot Alkaloids and Related Compounds; In Handbook of Experimental Pharmacology; Springer-Verlag, New York (1978).

R. G. Powell, R. D. Plattner, S. G. Yates, K. Clay, and A. Leuchtmann; Ergobalansine, A New Ergot-Type Peptide Alkaloid Isolated From *Cenchrus echinatus* (Sandbur Grass) Infected with *Balansia obtecta*, and Produced in Liquid Cultures of *B. obtecta* and *B. cyperi;* Journal of Natural Products, Vol. 53, pp. 1272-1279(1990).

Common/Systematic Name

Ergobalansinine

Molecular Formula/Molecular Weight

$C_{28}H_{35}N_5O_5$; MW = 521.26382

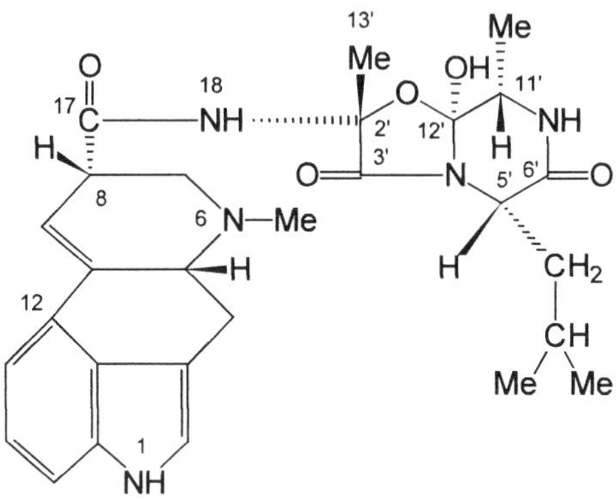

General Characteristics

Ergobalansinine was obtained as a white solid; ergobalansine and ergobalansinine readily epimerized to an approximate 1:1 equilibrium mixture on standing in solutions containing MeOH.

Fungal Source

Cenchrus echinatus infected with *Balansia obtecta* and *Cyperus virens* infected with *B. cyperi*. Epimers are not considered as naturally occurring, but as products formed during extraction and purification; epimerization at C-8 occurs in either acid or base.

Isolation/Purification

Aerial parts of *C. echinatus* infected with *B. obtecta* were ground in a Wiley mill fitted with a ¼ inch screen and extracted with 95% EtOH 24 h. The extraction process was repeated three additional times and combined EtOH extracts were evaporated to a volume of 6 liters, below 42 °C on a rotary evaporator. An aliquot was evaporated to dryness and a portion of the concentrate was coated onto silica gel. The material was added to the top of a silica gel column packed in methylene chloride and the column was eluted with CH_2Cl_2, 5%, 10%, and 25% MeOH in CH_2Cl_2. Fractions were analyzed by TLC and recombined into fractions on the basis of similarity of TLC patterns. The remaining extract was processed by dividing into 6 portions and repeating the chromatographic procedure 6 additional times. Like materials were combined and all 8 fractions were examined for the presence of ergot-peptide alkaloids. An alkaloid-enriched fraction was prepared by solvent partitioning the entire sample in EtOAc and aqueous 2% tartaric acid. The aqueous layer was partitioned a second time with EtOAc. The aqueous layer was partitioned a second time with EtOAc. The aqueous layer was adjusted to pH 9 by slow addition of concentrated NH_4OH. The resulting basic solution was extracted with EtOAc, and the EtOAc extract yielded an alkaloidal material. Analysis of the alkaloid-enriched fractions by reversed-phase HPLC revealed two highly fluorescent compounds. Final purification of ergobalansine and ergobalansinine was achieved by preparative TLC. Purified ergobalansine and ergobalansinine readily epimerized to an approximate 1:1 equilibrium mixture on standing in solutions containing MeOH, particularly at elevated temperatures.

Spectral Data

^{1}H NMR:

($CDCl_3$) H-1, 8.05(s); H-2, 6.90(m); H-4a, 3.59(m, *J*=14.4, 5.3Hz); H-4b, 2.64(m, *J*=14.4, 12.0Hz); H-5, 3.20(m, *J*=12.0, 5.3Hz); 6-NMe, 2.61(s); H-7a, 3.12(*J*=11.9Hz); H-7b, 2.75(dd, *J*=11.9, 3.5Hz); H-8b, 3.06(m, *J*=6.3Hz); H-9, 6.49(dd, *J*=6.3Hz); 8-NH, 9.85(s); H-12-14, 7.15(m); H-2'Me, 1.50(s); H-5', 4.42(dd); 5'-CH_2, 1.90(m); 5'-CH_2CH, 1.90(m); 5'-$CH_2CH(CH_3)_2$, 0.96(d), 0.95(d); H-11', 3.51(m); 11'-CH_3, 1.32(d); OH, 6.01(s); and 7'-NH, 6.77ppm (brs).

^{13}C NMR:

($CDCl_3$) C-2, 118.4; C-3, 110.1; C-4, 27.7; C-5, 62.6; 6-NMe, 43.6; C-7, 54.5; C-8, 43.0; C-9, 117.6; C-10, 137.5; C-11, 127.5; C-12, 112.8; C-13, 123.3; C-14, 110.2; C-15, 133.9; C-16, 126.2; 17-CONH, 176.0; C-2', 85.4; C-3', 165.7*; C-5', 53.0; C-6', 169.1*; C-8', not obs.; C-9' not obs.; C-10', not obs.; C-11', 56.9; C-12', 102.5; 2'-Me, 24.5; 5'-CH_2, 43.4; 5'-CH_2CH, 24.6; 5'-$(Me)_2$, 22.0, 22.7; and 11'-CH_3, 14.7ppm.

* Assignments may be reversed.

Mass Data:

EIMS: $[M]^+$ 521(3%), 337(4), 267(64), 221(43), 207(47), 196(25), 184(36), 180(34), 167(22), 154(33), 141(25), 128(96), 113(33), 44(89), and 43(100); CIMS: (isobutane) MH^+ 522(8%), 504(2), 268(97), 255(100), and 185(13); negative ion CIMS (isobutane) ($[M]^-$ 42), and 254(100). Found for $[AH]^+$ 268.1412 ($C_{16}H_{18}N_3O$ requires 268.1450); $[BH]^+$ 255.1362 ($C_{12}H_{19}N_2O$; requires 255.1345).

TLC Data

Analytical and preparative TLC were carried out on silica gel 60-F_{254} plates (E. Merck) developed with chloroform-methanol (9:1).

HPLC Data

Preparative HPLC utilized a Rainin Dynamax-60Å silica column with isocratic elution using methylene chloride-methanol (93:7, v/v).

References

R. G. Powell, R. D. Plattner, S. G. Yates, K. Clay, and A. Leuchtmann; Ergobalansine, A New Ergot-Type Peptide Alkaloid Isolated From *Cenchrus echinatus* (Sandbur Grass) Infected With *Balansia obtecta*, and Produced in Liquid Cultures of *B. obtecta* and *B. cyperi;* Journal of Natural Products, Vol. 53, pp. 1272-1279(1990).

B. Berde and H. O. Scheld (eds.); Ergot Alkaloids and Related Compounds; In Handbook of Experimental Pharmacology; Springer-Verlag, New York (1978).

J. K. Porter; Analysis of Endophyte Toxins: Fescue and Other Grasses Toxic to Livestock; J. Animal Science, Vol. 73, pp. 871-880(1994).

Common/Systematic Name

α-Ergocryptine

Molecular Formula/Molecular Weight

$C_{32}H_{41}N_5O_5$; MW = 575.31077

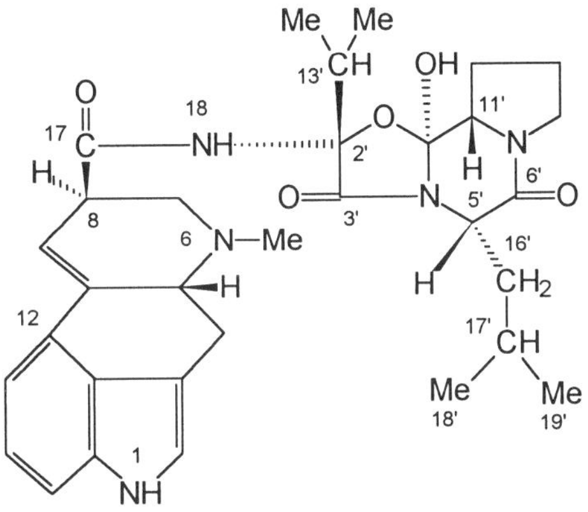

Fungal Source

Claviceps purpurea strain D-3-18.

Isolation/Purification

The fungal mycelium was wetted and extracted with Et_2O-EtOH (9:1, v/v). Alkaloids were extracted into a 1% tartaric acid solution and precipitated by adjusting the pH to 7.5. They were collected by filtration and dried. The crude alkaloid mixture was defatted with petroleum ether; the resulting alkaloid mixture was chromatographed on a silica gel column eluted with $CHCl_3$. The alkaloids were further purified by HPLC on a semi-preparative column: MicroPak NH_2, particle size 10μM; mobile phase, Et_2O-EtOH (22:3, v/v); flow rate, 220ml/h; UV detection at 240nm. Purity was monitored on an analytical HPLC column: Perkin-Elmer NH_2; particle size 10μM; mobile phase, hexane-Et_2O-EtOH (41:41:8, v/v/v); flow rate 0.6ml/min; detection with UV at 240nm.

Biological Activity

The ergopeptine alkaloids produce a wide range of biological activities and some are used routinely in medical practice. All natural ergot alkaloids possess to a greater or lesser degree, biological effects that can be classified as direct peripheral effects on smooth muscle (uterine contraction and vasoconstriction), indirect peripheral effects (humoral, serotonin antagonism, and adrenergic blockage), and central nervous system effects (bulbomedullary and mesodiencephalic components).

Spectral Data

IR:

See A. Hofmann, 1964.

^{1}H NMR:

($CDCl_3$) NH(1), 8.37(s); H-2, 6.94(s); H-9, 6.37(dd, *J*=6.4, 1.5Hz); N-CH_3(6), 2.63(s); N-H(18), 9.86(s); H-5', 4.52(t, *J*=6.4Hz); C-2' side chain methyls, 1.03(d, 6.1Hz), 0.91(d, 6.1Hz); and C-5' side chain methyls, 1.02ppm (d, *J*=7.3Hz).

^{13}C NMR:

($CDCl_3$) C-2, 119.2; C-3, 110.6; C-4, 26.5; C-5, 64.5; C-7, 48.1; C-8, 40.9; C-9, 118.8; C-10, 139.2; C-11, 129.6; C-12, 111.9; C-13, 123.3; C-14, 110.1; C-15, 133.9; C-16, 126.3; C-17, 176.3; N-Me, 44.3; C-2', 89.7; C-3', 165.8; C-5', 53.3; C-6', 166.2; C-8', 46.0; C-9' 21.6; C-10', 22.2; C-11', 59.3; C-12', 103.4; C-13', 34.3; C-14', 15.3*; C-15', 16.9*; C-16', 43.5; C-17', 25.1; C-18', 22.1**; and C-19', 22.6**ppm.

*, ** Assignments may be reversed.

Mass Spectrum:

No M^+ observed in the mass spectrum; 308($C_{16}H_{24}N_2O_4$, 3%), 267($C_{16}H_{17}N_3O$, 22); 210($C_{11}H_{18}N_2O_2$, 14), 209($C_{11}H_{17}N_2O_2$, 33), 154($C_7H_{10}N_2O_2$, 53), 125($C_6H_9N_2O$, 8), 86($C_5H_{12}N$, 6), 71(C_4H_7O, 61), and 70*m/e* (C_4H_8N, 100).

CIMS: (isobutane) Results suggested that major fragments for the cyclol alkaloids are due to cleavage of the bond joining the tricyclic peptide moiety with the lysergic acid amide portion of the molecule. $(M^+ + 1)^+$ was not observed in the CI spectrum; however, daughter ions 268(100%), 309 (30), and 211(3) were observed.

Quadrupole MS/MS: (CI with isobutane) 576[$(M^+H)^+$, 35%], 268(AH^+, 100), 309(BH^+, 64), and 211(CH^+, 7); Negative CIMS, 575(M^-, 65%), 266[$(A\text{-}H)^-$, 0.1], 308(B^-, 100), and 209[$(C\text{-}H)^-$, 0.1].

TLC Purification

Silica gel plates developed with methylene chloride-isopropyl alcohol (92:8, v/v) three times which results in the separation of alkaloids into the isolysergic acid group, the ergotoxine group, the ergoxine group and a mixture of the ergotamine and clavine groups. Extraction of the alkaloids from the silica using methanol-chloroform (1:4 or 1:1, v/v) followed by rechromatography in chloroform-methanol (9:1 or 4:1, v/v) separates ergovaline from the clavine alkaloids (agroclavine and chanoclavines).

TLC Solvent systems for silica gel chromatography (v/v):

a) Methylene chloride-isopropyl alcohol (92:8; 90:10; 75:25).
b) Chloroform-methanol (90:10; 80:20; 90:10 in saturated NH_3 atmosphere).

c) Chloroform-methanol-NH_3 (94:5:1).
d) Chloroform-ethylamine (90:10).
e) Benzene-dimethylformamide (86.5:13.5).

References

M. Flieger, P. Sedmera, J. Vokoun, Z. Řeháček, J. Stuchlik, Z. Malinka, L. Cvak, and P. Harazim; New Alkaloids from a Saprophytic Culture of *Claviceps purpurea*; J. Natural Products, Vol. 47, pp. 970-976(1984).

A. Hofmann; Die Mutterkorn Alkaloide; Enke Verlag, Stuttgart, 218 pp., 1964.

R. D. Plattner, S. G. Yates, and J. K. Porter; Quadrupole Mass Spectrometry/Mass Spectrometry of Ergot Cyclol Alkaloids; J. Agric. Food Chem., Vol. 31, pp. 785-789(1983).

J. K. Porter and D. Betowski; Chemical Ionization Mass Spectrometry of Ergot Cyclol Alkaloids; J. Agric. Food Chem., Vol. 29, pp. 650-653(1981).

R. G. Powell, R. D. Plattner, S. G. Yates, K. Clay, and A. Leuchtmann; Ergobalansine, A New Ergot-Type Peptide Alkaloid Isolated from *Cenchrus echinatus* (Sandbur Grass) Infected With *Balansia obtecta*, and Produced in Liquid Cultures of *B. obtecta* and *B. cyperi;* Journal of Natural Products, Vol. 53, pp. 1272-1279(1990).

Common/Systematic Name

O-12'-Methyl-α-ergokryptine

Molecular Formula/Molecular Weight

$C_{33}H_{43}N_5O_5$; MW = 589.32642

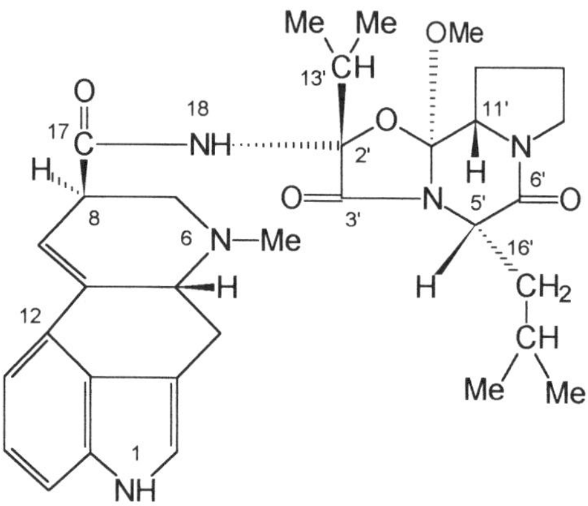

Fungal Source

Claviceps purpurea strain 231 FI.

Isolation/Purification

Crude alkaloids were obtained by extraction of fungal cultures with CH_2Cl_2-MeOH (80:20) followed by precipitation with petroleum ether; the crude alkaloid extract was chromatographed by Extrelut (Merck) column chromatography eluted with CH_2Cl_2. The crude alkaloids thus obtained were chromatographed on a Silica gel 60 (Merck) column eluted with CH_2Cl_2-MeOH (98:2, v/v); the column was monitored by UV and TLC. Final purification was by preparative TLC in a cold room in the dark. TLC was performed on Silica gel F_{254} plates (Merck) using the following solvent systems: CH_2Cl_2-isopropyl alcohol (92:8, v/v) or CH_2Cl_2-MeOH (90:10, v/v). The alkaloids were detected by examination under UV light at 254 and 366nm while some were sprayed with *N,N-p*-dimethylaminobenzaldehyde. The various bands were scraped off and eluted with CH_2Cl_2-MeOH (1:1, v/v).

Biological Activity

The ergopeptine alkaloids produce a wide range of biological activities and some are used routinely in medical practice. All natural ergot alkaloids possess to a greater or lesser degree, biological effects that can be classified as direct peripheral effects on smooth muscle (uterine contraction and vasoconstriction), indirect peripheral effects (humoral, serotonin antagonism, and adrenergic blockage), and central nervous system effects (bulbomedullary and mesodiencephalic components).

Spectral Data

^{1}H NMR:
(CDCl$_3$) NH(1), 8.09(s); N(6)-CH$_3$, 2.66; H-9, 6.41(*J*=1.8, 5.5Hz); (8)-CONH, 9.16; OCH$_3$-12', 3.24; and H-5', 4.62ppm (*J*=3.8, 10.8Hz).

^{13}C NMR:
(CDCl$_3$) C-2, 119.0*; C-3, 110.3; C-4, 26.4; C-5, 59.5; N(6)-CH$_3$, 44.6; C-7, 48.4; C-8, 41.3; C-9, 119.2*; C-10, 138.8; C-11, 129.8; C-12, 112.1; C-13, 123.5; C-14, 110.0; C-15, 133.8; C-16, 126.2; 8-CONH, 174.0; C-2', 89.2; C-3', 165.7**; C-5', 53.1; C-6', 167.4**; C-8', 46.1; C-9', 21.9***; C-10', 22.0***; C-11', 61.9; C-12', 106.4; 12'-OCH$_3$, 48.8; (2')-C, 35.9; (2')-CH-(CH$_3$)$_2$, 16.0, 16.8; (5')-C, 42.2; (5')-C-C, 25.0; and (5')-C-C-(CH$_3$)$_2$, 22.1, 21.4ppm.

*, **, and *** Assignments may be reversed.

Mass Spectrum:
EIMS: 589(M$^+$), 557, 432, 347, 319, 304, 221, 196, 154, and 70*m/e* (100%).

Reference

N. Crespi-Perellino, M. Ballabio, B. Gioia, and A. Minghetti; Two Unusual Ergopeptines Produced by a Saprophytic Culture of *Claviceps purpurea*; J. Natural Products, Vol. 50, pp. 1065-1074(1987).

Common/Systematic Name

β-Ergocryptine

Molecular Formula/Molecular Weight

$C_{32}H_{41}N_5O_5$; MW = 575.31077

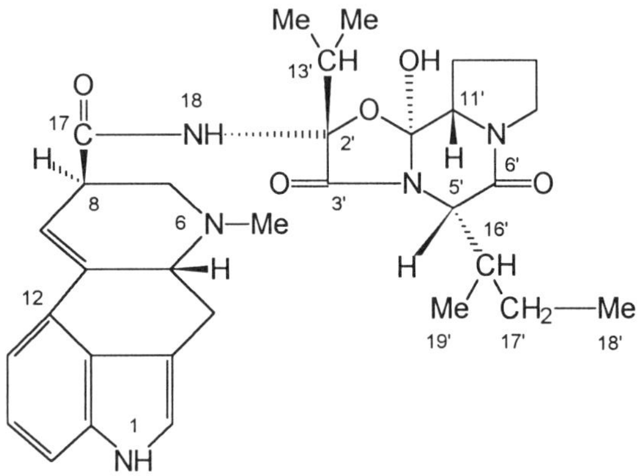

General Characteristics

Prisms from methanol solution (solvated with MeOH); mp., 210-212°C (dec.); $[\alpha]_D^{20}$ -191°, $[\alpha]_{5461}^{20}$ - 228° (c=1.0, in $CHCl_3$); $[\alpha]_D^{20}$ - 117°, $[\alpha]_{5461}^{20}$ - 138° (c=1.0, in pyridine); pK = 5.5 (in 80% methylcellosolve); blue color slowly changing to olive-green with Keller's reagent.

Fungal Source

Claviceps purpurea strain D-3-18.

Isolation/Purification

The fungal mycelium was wetted and extracted with Et_2O-EtOH (9:1, v/v). Alkaloids were extracted into a 1% tartaric acid solution and precipitated by adjusting the pH to 7.5. They were collected by filtration and dried. The crude alkaloid mixture was defatted with petroleum ether; the resulting alkaloid mixture was chromatographed on a silica gel column eluted with $CHCl_3$. The alkaloids were further purified by HPLC on a semi-preparative column: MicroPak NH_2, particle size 10μm; mobile phase, Et_2O-EtOH (22:3, v/v); flow rate, 220ml/h; UV detection at 240nm. Purity was monitored on an analytical HPLC column: Perkin-Elmer NH_2; particle size 10μm; mobile phase, hexane-Et_2O-EtOH (41:41:8, v/v/v); flow rate 0.6ml/min; detection with UV at 240nm.

Biological Activity

The ergopeptine alkaloids produce a wide range of biological activities and some are used routinely in medical practice. All natural ergot alkaloids possess to a greater or lesser degree, biological effects that can be classified as direct peripheral effects on smooth muscle (uterine contraction and vasoconstriction), indirect peripheral effects (humoral, serotonin antagonism, and adrenergic blockage), and central nervous system effects (bulbomedullary and mesodiencephalic components). LD_{50} IV in rabbits, 1.05mg/kg.

Spectral Data

IR:

See A. Hofmann, 1964.

^{1}H NMR:

($CDCl_3$) NH(1), 8.21(s); H-2, 6.92(s); H-9, 6.35(dd, *J*=6.1, 1.4Hz); N-CH_3(6), 2.63(s); N-H(18), 9.88(s); H-5', 4.49(d, *J*=2.5Hz); C-2' side chain methyls, 1.113(d, 6.1Hz), 0.87(d, 6.1Hz); and C-5' side chain methyls, 1.04(d, *J*=6.8Hz, and 0.94ppm (t, *J*=7.3Hz).

^{13}C NMR:

($CDCl_3$) C-2, 119.1; C-3, 110.7; C-4, 26.6; C-5, 64.0; C-7, 48.0; C-8, 40.9; C-9, 119.2; C-10, 139.2; C-11, 129.7; C-12, 112.0; C-13, 123.3; C-14, 110.1; C-15, 133.8; C-16, 126.3; 17-CONH, 176.3; N-Me, 44.3; C-2', 89.5; C-3', 164.6; C-5', 59.7; C-6', 166.6; C-8', 45.9; C-9' 21.3; C-10', 22.2; C-11', 59.2; C-12', 106.3; C-13', 34.3; C-14', 15.3*; C-15', 17.0*; C-16', 39.4; C-17', 27.9; C-18', 12.6; and C-19', 16.6ppm.

* Assignments may be reversed.

Mass Spectrum:

No M^+ observed in the mass spectrum; 308($C_{16}H_{24}N_2O_4$, 2%), 267($C_{16}H_{17}N_3O$, 47); 210($C_{11}H_{18}N_2O_2$, 8), 209($C_{11}H_{17}N_2O_2$, 22), 154($C_7H_{10}N_2O_2$, 90), 125($C_6H_9N_2O$, 17), 86($C_5H_{12}N$, 10%), 71(C_4H_7O, 44), and 70*m/e* (C_4H_8N, 100).

CIMS (isobutane) Results suggested that major fragments for the cyclol alkaloids are due to cleavage of the bond joining the tricyclic peptide moiety with the lysergic acid amide portion of the molecule. $(M^+ + 1)^+$ was not observed in the CI spectrum; however, daughter ions 268(100%), 309(53), and 211(4) were observed.

Quadrupole MS/MS: (CI with isobutane) 576[$(M+H)^+$, 52%], 268(AH^+, 100), 309(BH^+, 67), and 211(CH^+, 8); Negative CIMS 575(M^-, 37%), 266[$(A-H)^-$, 0.1], 308(B^-, 100), and 209[$(CH)^-$, 0.2].

TLC Purification

Silica gel plates developed with methylene chloride-isopropyl alcohol (92:8, v/v) three times which results in the separation of alkaloids into the isolysergic acid group, the ergotoxine group, the ergoxine group and a mixture of the ergotamine and clavine groups. Extraction of the alkaloids from the silica using methanol-chloroform (1:4 or 1:1, v/v) followed by rechromatography in chloroform-methanol (9:1 or 4:1, v/v) separates ergovaline from the clavine alkaloids (agroclavine and chanoclavines).

TLC Solvent systems for silica gel chromatography (v/v):

a) Methylene chloride-isopropyl alcohol (92:8; 90:10; 75:25).
b) Chloroform-methanol (90:10; 80:20; 90:10 in saturated NH_3 atmosphere).
c) Chloroform-methanol-NH_3 (94:5:1).
d) Chloroform-ethylamine (90:10).
e) Benzene-dimethylformamide (86.5:13.5).

References

B. Berde and H. O. Scheld (eds.); Ergot Alkaloids and Related Compounds; In Handbook of Experimental Pharmacology; Springer-Verlag, New York (1978).

M. Fllieger, P. Sedmera, J. Vokoun, Z. Řeháček, J. Stuchlik, Z. Malinka, L. Cvak, and P. Harazim; New Alkaloids from a Saprophytic Culture of *Claviceps purpurea*; J. Natural Products, Vol. 47, pp. 970-976(1984).

A. Hofmann; Die Mutterkorn Alkaloide; Enke Verlag, Stuttgart, 218 pp., 1964.

R. D. Plattner, S. G. Yates, and J. K. Porter; Quadrupole Mass Spectrometry/Mass Spectrometry of Ergot Cyclol Alkaloids; J. Agric. Food Chem., Vol. 31, pp. 785-789(1983).

J. K. Porter and D. Betowski; Chemical Ionization Mass Spectrometry of Ergot Cyclol Alkaloids; J. Agric. Food Chem., Vol. 29, pp. 650-653(1981).

R. G. Powell, R. D. Plattner, S. G. Yates, K. Clay, and A. Leuchtmann; Ergobalansine, A New Ergot-Type Peptide Alkaloid Isolated From *Cenchrus echinatus* (Sandbur Grass) Infected With *Balansia obtecta*, and Produced in Liquid Cultures of *B. obtecta* and *B. cyperi;* Journal of Natural Products, Vol. 53, pp. 1272-1279(1990).

Common/Systematic Name

5'-epimer of β-Ergocryptine

Molecular Formula/Molecular Weight

$C_{32}H_{41}N_5O_5$; MW = 575.31077

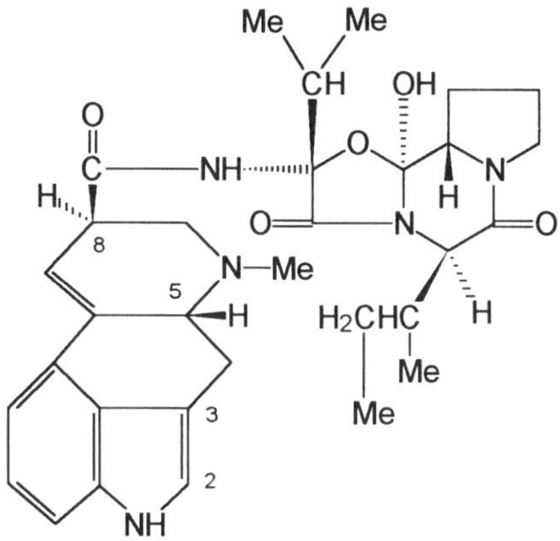

Fungal Source

Claviceps purpurea strain D-3-18.

Isolation/Purification

The fungal mycelium was wetted and extracted with Et_2O-EtOH (9:1, v/v). Alkaloids were extracted into a 1% tartaric acid solution and precipitated by adjusting the pH to 7.5. They were collected by filtration and dried. The crude alkaloid mixture was defatted with petroleum ether; the resulting alkaloid mixture was chromatographed on a silica gel column that was eluted with $CHCl_3$. The alkaloids were further purified by HPLC on a semi-preparative column: MicroPak NH_2, particle size 10μm; mobile phase, Et_2O-EtOH (22:3, v/v); flow rate, 220ml/h; UV detection at 240nm. Purity was monitored on an analytical HPLC column: Perkin-Elmer NH_2; particle size 10μm; mobile phase, hexane-Et_2O-EtOH (41:41:8, v/v/v); flow rate 0.6ml/min; detection with UV at 240nm.

Biological Activity

All natural ergot alkaloids possess to a greater or lesser degree, biological effects that can be classified as direct peripheral effects on smooth muscle (uterine contraction and vasoconstriction), indirect peripheral effects (humoral, serotonin antagonism, and adrenergic blockage), and central nervous system effects (bulbomedullary and mesodiencephalic components). Some are used routinely in medicine.

Spectral Data

^1H NMR:

(CDCl$_3$) NH(1), 8.47(s); H-2, 6.94(s); H-9, 6.36(dd, J=5.5, 1.3Hz); N-CH$_3$(6), 2.65(s); N-H(18), 9.84(s); H-5', 4.53(d, J=3.1Hz); C-2' side chain methyls, 1.03(d, 6.1Hz), 0.89(d, 6.1Hz); and C-5' side chain methyls, 1.14(d, J=6.8Hz), 0.96ppm (t, J=7.3Hz).

^{13}C NMR:

(CDCl$_3$) C-2, 119.2; C-3, 110.5; C-4, 26.7; C-5, 64.1; C-7, 48.2; C-8, 40.9; C-9, 118.9; C-10, 139.0; C-11, 129.6; C-12, 111.9; C-13, 123.2; C-14, 110.2; C-15, 133.9; C-16, 126.3; C-17, 176.1; N-Me, 44.3; C-2', 89.5; C-3', 165.0; C-5', 60.4; C-6', 167.1; C-8', 46.0; C-9' 21.7; C-10', 22.1; C-11', 59.3; C-12', 103.7; C-13', 34.3; C-14', 15.3*; C-15', 16.9*; C-16', 39.8; C-17', 26.3; C-18', 12.5; and C-19', 16.6ppm.

* Assignment may be reversed.

Mass Spectrum:

No M$^+$ observed in the mass spectrum; 308($C_{16}H_{24}N_2O_4$, 1%), 267($C_{16}H_{17}N_3O$, 15); 210($C_{11}H_{18}N_2O_2$, 8), 209($C_{11}H_{17}N_2O_2$, 22), 154($C_7H_{10}N_2O_2$, 67), 125($C_6H_9N_2O$, 12), 86($C_5H_{12}N$, 8), 71 (C_4H_7O, 47), and 70*m/e* (C_4H_8N, 100).

TLC Purification

Silica gel plates developed with methylene chloride-isopropyl alcohol (92:8, v/v) three times which results in the separation of alkaloids into the isolysergic acid group, the ergotoxine group, the ergoxine group and a mixture of the ergotamine and clavine groups. Extraction of the alkaloids from the silica using methanol-chloroform (1:4 or 1:1, v/v) followed by rechromatography in chloroform-methanol (9:1 or 4:1, v/v) separates ergovaline from the clavine alkaloids (agroclavine and chanoclavines).

TLC Solvent systems for silica gel chromatography (v/v):

a) Methylene chloride-isopropyl alcohol (92:8; 90:10; 75:25).
b) Chloroform-methanol (90:10; 80:20; 90:10 in saturated NH_3 atmosphere).
c) Chloroform-methanol-NH_3 (94:5:1).
d) Chloroform-ethylamine (90:10).
e) Benzene-dimethylformamide (86.5:13.5).

References

B. Berde and H. O. Scheld (eds.); Ergot Alkaloids and Related Compounds, In Handbook of Experimental Pharmacology; Springer-Verlag, New York (1978).

M. Flieger, P. Sedmera, J. Vokoun, Z. Řeháček, J. Stuchlik, Z. Malinka, L. Cvak, and P. Harazim; New Alkaloids from a Saprophytic Culture of *Claviceps purpurea*; J. Natural Products, Vol. 47, pp. 970-976(1984).

J. K. Porter; Analysis of Endophyte Toxins: Fescue and Other Grasses Toxic to Livestock; J. Animal Science, Vol. 73, pp. 871-881(1994).

Common/Systematic Name

β-Ergocryptam

Molecular Formula/Molecular Weight

$C_{32}H_{41}N_5O_4$; MW = 559.15855

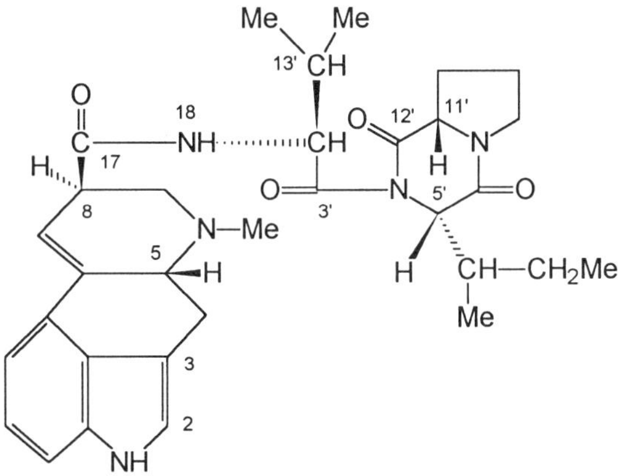

Fungal Source

Claviceps purpurea strain D-3-18.

Isolation/Purification

The fungal mycelium was wetted and extracted with Et_2O-EtOH (9:1, v/v). Alkaloids were extracted, into a 1% tartaric acid solution and precipitated by adjusting the pH to 7.5. They were collected by filtration and dried. The crude alkaloid mixture was defatted with petroleum ether; the resulting alkaloid mixture was chromatographed on a silica gel column eluted with $CHCl_3$. The alkaloids were further purified by HPLC on a semi-preparative column: MicroPak NH_2, particle size 10μm; mobile phase, Et_2O-EtOH (22:3, v/v); flow rate, 220ml/h; UV detection at 240nm. Purity was monitored on an analytical HPLC column: Perkin-Elmer NH_2; particle size 10μm; mobile phase, hexane-Et_2O-EtOH (41:41:8, v/v/v); flow rate 0.6ml/min; detection with UV at 240nm.

Biological Activity

All natural ergot alkaloids possess to a greater or lesser degree, biological effects that can be classified as direct peripheral effects on smooth muscle (uterine contraction and vasoconstriction), indirect peripheral effects (humoral, serotonin antagonism, and adrenergic blockage), and central nervous system effects (bulbomedullary and mesodiencephalic components). Some are used routinely in medicine.

Spectral Data

^{1}H NMR:

(CDCl$_3$) NH(1), 8.30(s); H-2, 6.92(s); H-9, 6.46(dd, *J*=4.3, 1.2Hz); N-CH$_3$(6), 2.67(s); N-H(18), 8.22(d, *J*=9.2Hz); H-2', 5.83(dd, *J*=9.2, 3.1Hz); H-5', 4.96(d, *J*=9.2Hz); H-11', 4.36(t, *J*=7.8Hz); C-2' side chain methyls, 0.75(d, 6.7Hz), 0.94(d, 6.7Hz); and C-5' side chain methyls, 0.98(d, *J*=6.7Hz), and 0.93ppm (t, *J*=7.3Hz).

^{13}C NMR:

(CDCl$_3$) C-2, 118.9; C-3, 110.9; C-4, 29.6; C-5, 63.2; C-7, 50.6; C-8, 41.7; C-9, 119.2; C-10, 137.8; C-11, 129.4; C-12, 111.8; C-13, 123.2; C-14, 109.9; C-15, 133.9; C-16, 126.3; C-17, 174.4; N-Me, 44.3; C-2', 58.1; C-3', 173.6; C-5', 60.0; C-6', 165.6; C-8', 45.5; C-9' 22.9; C-10', 23.3; C-11', 60.4; C-12', 170.0; C-13', 30.3; C-14', 16.1*; C-15', 20.1*; C-16', 37.2; C-17', 25.7; C-18', 10.9; and C-19', 15.5ppm.

* Assignments may be reversed.

Mass Spectrum:

M$^+$ observed in the mass spectrum, 559(1%), 349($C_{21}H_{23}N_3O_2$, 2), 321($C_{20}H_{23}N_3O$, 4), 221($C_{15}H_{13}N_2$, 9), 154($C_7H_{10}N_2O_2$, 100), 125($C_6H_9N_2O$, 26), 86($C_5H_{12}N$, 13), and 70*m/e* (C_4H_8N, 87).

TLC Purification

Silica gel plates developed with methylene chloride-isopropyl alcohol (92:8, v/v) three times which results in the separation of alkaloids into the isolysergic acid group, the ergotoxine group, the ergoxine group and a mixture of the ergotamine and clavine groups. Extraction of the alkaloids from the silica using methanol-chloroform (1:4 or 1:1, v/v) followed by rechromatography in chloroform-methanol (9:1 or 4:1, v/v) separates ergovaline from the clavine alkaloids (agroclavine and chanoclavines).

TLC Solvent systems for silica gel chromatography (v/v):

a) Methylene chloride-isopropyl alcohol (92:8; 90:10; 75:25).
b) Chloroform-methanol (90:10; 80:20; 90:10 in saturated NH_3 atmosphere).
c) Chloroform-methanol-NH_3 (94:5:1).
d) Chloroform-ethylamine (90:10).
e) Benzene-dimethylformamide (86.5:13.5).

References

B. Berde and H. O. Scheld (eds.); Ergot Alkaloids and Related Compounds; In Handbook of Experimental Pharmacology; Springer-Verlag, New York (1978).

M. Flieger, P. Sedmera, J. Vokoun, Z. Řeháček, J. Stuchlik, Z. Malinka, L. Cvak, and P. Harazim; New Alkaloids from a Saprophytic Culture of *Claviceps purpurea;* J. Natural Products, Vol. 47, pp. 970-976(1984).

J. K. Porter; Analysis of Endophyte Toxins: Fescue and Other Grasses Toxic to Livestock; J. Animal Science, Vol. 73, pp. 871-880(1994).

Common/Systematic Name

β,β-Ergoannam

Molecular Formula/Molecular Weight

$C_{33}H_{43}N_5O_4$; MW = 573.33151

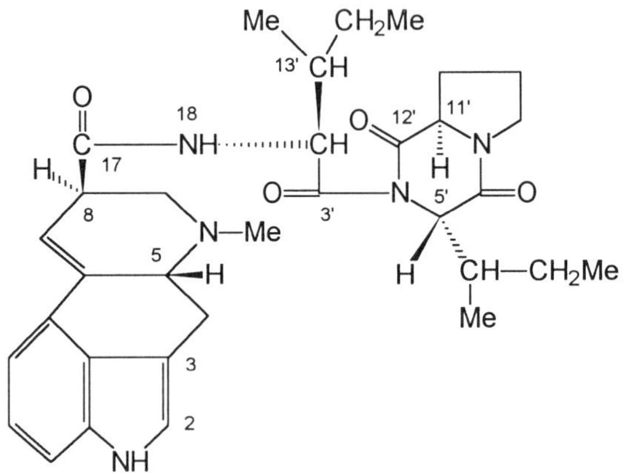

Fungal Source

Claviceps purpurea strain D-3-18.

Isolation/Purification

The fungal mycelium was wetted and extracted with Et_2O-EtOH (9:1, v/v). Alkaloids were extracted into a 1% tartaric acid solution and precipitated by adjusting the pH to 7.5. They were collected by filtration and dried. The crude alkaloid mixture was defatted with petroleum ether; the resulting alkaloid mixture was chromatographed on a silica gel column eluted with $CHCl_3$. The alkaloids were further purified by HPLC on a semi-preparative column: MicroPak NH_2, particle size 10μm; mobile phase, Et_2O-EtOH (22:3, v/v); flow rate, 220ml/h; UV detection at 240nm. Purity was monitored on an analytical HPLC column: Perkin-Elmer NH_2; particle size 10μm; mobile phase, hexane-Et_2O-EtOH (41:41:8, v/v/v); flow rate 0.6ml/min; detection with UV at 240nm.

Biological Activity

All natural ergot alkaloids possess to a greater or lesser degree, biological effects that can be classified as direct peripheral effects on smooth muscle (uterine contraction and vasoconstriction), indirect peripheral effects (humoral, serotonin antagonism, and adrenergic blockage), and central nervous system effects (bulbomedullary and mesodiencephalic components). Some are used routinely in medicine.

Spectral Data

^{1}H NMR:

($CDCl_3$) NH(1), 8.00(s); H-2, 6.92(s); H-9, 6.46(dd, *J*=4.4, 1.5Hz); N-CH_3(6), 2.67(s); N-H(18), 8.26(d, *J*=9.8Hz); H-2', 5.94(dd, *J*=9.8, 2.4Hz); H-5', 4.94(d, *J*=9.3Hz); H-11', 4.36(t, *J*=7.6Hz); C-2' side chain methyls, 0.70(d, 6.8Hz), 0.90(d, 7.3Hz); and C-5' side chain methyls, 1.06(d, *J*=6.8Hz); 0.92ppm (t, *J*=7.3Hz).

^{13}C NMR:

($CDCl_3$) C-2, 118.8; C-3, 111.1; C-4, 29.8; C-5, 63.3; C-7, 50.4; C-8, 41.7; C-9, 119.8; C-10, 137.9; C-11, 129.7; C-12, 111.8; C-13, 123.3; C-14, 109.8 C-15, 133.9; C-16, 126.3; C-17, 174.7; N-Me, 44.4; C-2', 56.5; C-3', 173.6; C-5', 60.0; C-6', 165.6; C-8', 45.5; C-9' 22.9; C-10', 23.1; C-11', 60.3; C-12', 170.0; C-13', 36.8; C-14', 27.4; C-15', 11.7; C-16', 13.6; C-17', 37.3; C-18', 25.7; C-19', 10.9, and C-20', 15.5ppm.

Mass Spectrum:

M^+ observed in the mass spectrum, 573(4%), 363($C_{22}H_{25}N_3O_2$, 7), 335($C_{21}H_{25}N_3O$, 12), 221($C_{15}H_{13}N_2$, 21), 154($C_7H_{10}N_2O_2$, 91), 125($C_6H_9N_2O$, 22), 86($C_5H_{12}N$, 12), and 70*m/e* (C_4H_8N, 100).

TLC Purification

Silica gel plates developed with methylene chloride-isopropyl alcohol (92:8, v/v) three times which results in the separation of alkaloids into the isolysergic acid group, the ergotoxine group, the ergoxine group and a mixture of the ergotamine and clavine groups. Extraction of the alkaloids from the silica using methanol-chloroform (1:4 or 1:1, v/v) followed by rechromatography in chloroform-methanol (9:1 or 4:1, v/v) separates ergovaline from the clavine alkaloids (agroclavine and chanoclavines).

TLC Solvent systems for silica gel chromatography (v/v):

a) Methylene chloride-isopropyl alcohol (92:8; 90:10; 75:25).
b) Chloroform-methanol (90:10; 80:20; 90:10 in saturated NH_3 atmosphere).
c) Chloroform-methanol-NH_3 (94:5:1).
d) Chloroform-ethylamine (90:10).
e) Benzene-dimethylformamide (86.5:13.5).

References

B. Berde and H. O. Scheld (eds.); Ergot Alkaloids and Related Compounds; In Handbook of Experimental Pharmacology; Springer-Verlag, New York (1978).

M. Flieger, P. Sedmera, J. Vokoun, Z. Řeháček, J. Stuchlik, Z. Malinka, L. Cvak, and P. Harazim; New Alkaloids from a Saprophytic Culture of *Claviceps purpurea;* J. Natural Products, Vol. 47, pp. 970-976(1984).

J. K. Porter; Analysis of Endophyte Toxins: Fescue and Other Grasses Toxic to Livestock; J. Animal Science, Vol. 73, pp. 871-880(1994).

Common/Systematic Name

Ergobutine

Molecular Formula/Molecular Weight

$C_{29}H_{35}N_5O_5$; MW = 533.26382

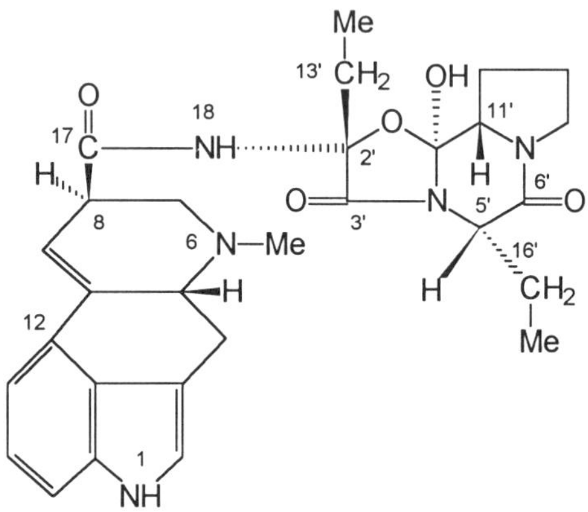

Fungal Source

Claviceps purpurea strain 231 FI.

Isolation/Purification

The whole broth culture was acidified to pH 2.5 with solid tartaric acid, homogenized, and centrifuged. The sediment was extracted twice with an aqueous solution of tartaric acid. The pooled supernatants were adjusted to pH 9-10 with 5N NaOH and extracted three times with chloroform-methanol (1:1, v/v). The combined extracts were dried over anhydrous Na_2SO_4 and concentrated *in vacuo*. The alkaloids were precipitated with petroleum ether, washed with the same solvent and dried *in vacuo*. The solid material was subjected to partial purification by dissolving it into 15ml of methanol and 15ml of an aqueous solution of 5% tartaric acid (w/v). The solution was brought to 600ml with water, and aliquots of 20ml were adsorbed onto 30 Extrelut (Merck) columns. Each column was percolated with chloroform, and the combined eluates were concentrated; the alkaloids were precipitated with petroleum ether, and the recovered material was washed and dried as above. Thin-layer chromatography was performed with silica gel 60 F_{254} (Merck). The crude extract was applied after being dissolved in chloroform-methanol (1:1, v/v). Solvent systems were: chloroform-isopropanol (92:8, v/v); chloroform-methanol (90:10, v/v); and chloroform-methanol-conc. ammonia (90:10:1, v/v/v). The alkaloids were detected under UV light at 254 and 366nm and/or detected by spraying with *N,N-p*-dimethylaminobenzaldehyde. The alkaloids were scraped and eluted from the silica gel with chloroform-methanol (1:1 v/v).

Biological Activity

The ergopeptine alkaloids produce a wide range of biological activities and some are used routinely in medical practice. All natural ergot alkaloids possess to a greater or lesser degree, biological effects that can be classified as direct peripheral effects on smooth muscle (uterine contraction and vasoconstriction), indirect peripheral effects (humoral, serotonin antagonism and adrenergic blockage), and central nervous system effects (bulbomedullary and mesodiencephalic components).

Spectral Data

UV:

λ_{max}^{MeOH} 310nm typical for lysergic acid derivatives.

Mass Spectrum:

Field desorption mass spectrum 533(M^+) and 267*m/e* (fragment ion for lysergamide); EIMS: 533(M^+), 351, 267, 181, 154, and 70*m/e* (100%).

Reference

M. L. Bianchi, N. C. Perellino, B. Gioia, and A. Minghetti; Production by *Claviceps purpurea* of Two New Peptide Ergot Alkaloids Belonging to a New Series Containing α-Aminobutyric Acid; J. Natural Products, Vol. 45, pp. 191-196(1982).

Common/Systematic Name

Ergobutyrine

Molecular Formula/Molecular Weight

$C_{30}H_{37}N_5O_5$; MW = 547.27947

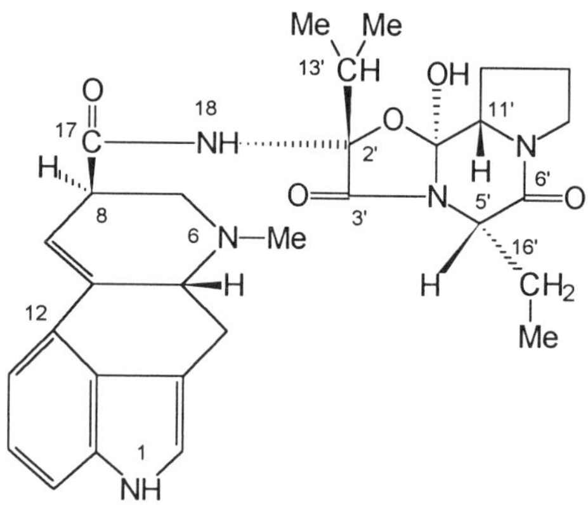

Fungal Source

Claviceps purpurea strain 231 FI.

Isolation/Purification

The whole broth culture was acidified to pH 2.5 with solid tartaric acid, homogenized, and centrifuged. The sediment was extracted twice with an aqueous solution of tartaric acid. The pooled supernatants were adjusted to pH 9-10 with 5 N NaOH and extracted three times with chloroform-methanol (1:1, v/v). The combined extracts were dried over anhydrous Na_2SO_4 and concentrated *in vacuo*. The alkaloids were precipitated with petroleum ether, washed with the same solvent and dried *in vacuo*. The solid material was subjected to partial purification by dissolving it into 15 ml of methanol and 15 ml of an aqueous solution of 5% tartaric acid (w/v). The solution was brought to 600ml with water, and aliquots of 20ml were adsorbed onto 30 Extrelut (Merck) columns. Each column was percolated with chloroform, and the combined eluates were concentrated; the alkaloids were precipitated with petroleum ether, and the recovered material was washed and dried as above. Thin-layer chromatography was performed with silica gel 60 F_{254} (Merck). The crude extract was applied after being dissolved in chloroform-methanol (1:1, v/v). Solvent systems were: chloroform-isopropanol (92:8, v/v); chloroform-methanol (90:10, v/v); and chloroform-methanol-conc. ammonia (90:10:1, v/v/v). The alkaloids were detected under UV light at 254 and 366nm and/or detected by spraying with *N,N-p*-dimethylaminobenzaldehyde. The alkaloids were scraped and eluted from the silica gel with chloroform-methanol (1:1, v/v).

Biological Activity

The ergopeptine alkaloids produce a wide range of biological activities and some are used routinely in medical practice. All natural ergot alkaloids possess to a greater or lesser degree, biological effects that can be classified as direct peripheral effects on smooth muscle (uterine contraction and vasoconstriction), indirect peripheral effects (humoral, serotonin antagonism, and adrenergic blockage), and central nervous system effects (bulbomedullary and mesodiencephalic components).

Spectral Data

UV:

λ_{max}^{MeOH} 310nm typical for lysergic acid derivatives.

Mass Spectrum:

Field desorption mass spectrum 547(M^+) and 267*m/e* (fragment ion for lysergamide); EIMS: 547(M^+), 365, 280, 267, 181, 154, and 70*m/e* (100%).

Reference

M. L. Bianchi, N. C. Perellino, B. Gioia, and A. Minghetti; Production by *Claviceps purpurea* of Two New Peptide Ergot Alkaloids Belonging to a New Series Containing α-Aminobutyric Acid; J. Natural Products, Vol. 45, pp. 191-196(1982).

Common/Systematic Name

Rugulovasine A

Molecular Formula/Molecular Weight

$C_{16}H_{16}N_2O_2$; MW = 268.12118

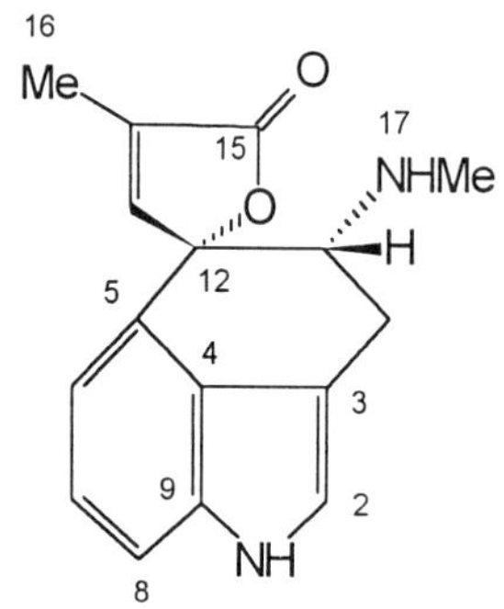

General Characteristics

Crystallizes as large, clear cubes from chloroform; mp., 138°C (dec.); $[\alpha]_{436}^{22}$ -3.0° (c=1.0, in pyridine); $[\alpha]_D^{22}$ 0.0. Rugulovasine A can be interconverted with its diastereomer, rugulovasine B upon warming in polar solvents.

Fungal Source

Penicillium islandicum, *P. concavo-rugulosum*, *P. verruculosum*, *P. rubrum*, and *P. biforme.*

Isolation/Purification

See 8-chlororugulovasine A.

Biological Activity

Rugulovasine A exhibited hypotensive action on chloralose-urethanized cats; the minimum effective dose was 0.2-0.5mg/kg.

Spectral Data

UV:

λ_{max}^{EtOH} 224(ϵ=23,400), 277(5,000), 288(6,000), and 295nm (6,000).

^{13}C NMR:

C-2, 119.6 d; C-3, 109.8 s; C-4, 126.4 s*; C-5, 128.2 s*; C-6, 114.8 d; C-7, 122.8 d; C-8. 111.4 d; C-9, 133.9 s; C-10, 25.4 t; C-11, 63.7 d; C-12, 88.5 s; C-13, 150.6 d; C-14, 129.2 s; C-15, 174.3 s; C-16, 10.8 q; and C-17, 35.1ppm q.

* Assignments could be reversed.

TLC Data

Silica gel PF_{254}; Solvent: chloroform-acetone-methanol, 93:7:5, v/v/v; R_f: 0.22. Detection: rose-colored spot after spraying with 50% ethanolic H_2SO_4 followed immediately by spraying with ninhydrin and heating at 100°C for 5-10 min.

References

R. J. Cole and R. H. Cox; Handbook of Toxic Fungal Metabolites; Academic Press, New York, p. 537 (1981).

R. J. Cole, J. W. Kirksey, J. Clardy, N. Eichman, S. M. Weinreb, P. Singh, and D. Kim; Structures of rugulovasine-A and rugulovasine-B and 8-chlororugulovasine-A and B; Tet. Lett., pp. 3849-3852(1976).

R. J. Cole, J. W. Kirksey, H. G. Cutler, D. M. Wilson, and G. Morgan-Jones; Two toxic indole alkaloids from *Penicillium islandicum*; Can. J. Microbiol., Vol. 22, pp. 741-744 (1976).

Common/Systematic Name

8-Chlororugulovasine A

Molecular Formula/Molecular Weight

$C_{16}H_{15}N_2O_2Cl$; MW = 302.08221

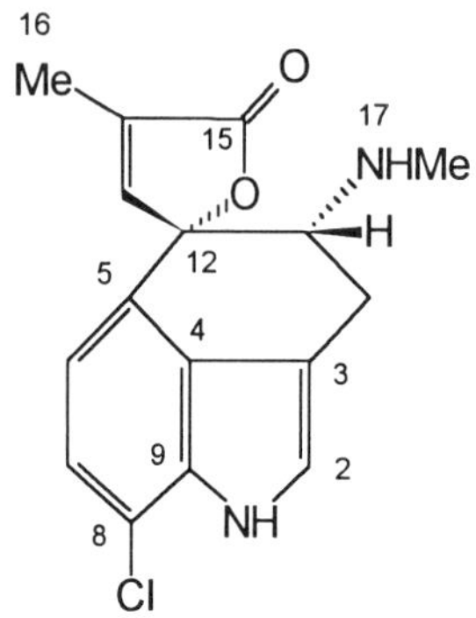

Fungal Source

Penicillium islandicum.

Isolation/Purification

Rugulovasines A & B and chlororugulovasines A & B were extracted from fungal cultures with ethyl acetate in a Waring Blender after the pH was adjusted to 10.5 with aqueous sodium carbonate. The ethyl acetate fraction was separated from the aqueous fraction and dried over anhydrous sodium sulfate. After filtering, the crude extract was evaporated to dryness under vacuum and chromatographed on a silica gel column (70-230 mesh). The column was packed as a slurry in ethyl acetate and the extract was applied to the column in ethyl acetate solution. Toxins were eluted from the column by a linear gradient of ethyl acetate to acetone. 8-Chlororugulovasine A can be interconverted with its diastereomer, chlororugulovasine B upon warming in polar solvents.

Biological Activity

LD_{50} in day old cockerels dosed orally, 75-125mg/kg.

Spectral Data

UV:

λ_{max}^{EtOH} 225(ϵ=21,400), 280(sh)(4,600), 292(5,200), and 298nm (5,400).

^{1}H NMR:

H-1, 8.60; H-2, 7.00; H-6, 6.77(*J*=7.6); H-7, 7.11(*J*=7.6); H-10, 3.30; H-11, 3.30; NH-1, 1.43; H-13, 7.35(*J*=1.5); H-16, 2.02(*J*=1.5); and H-17, 2.43ppm.

^{13}C NMR:

C-2, 120.6 d; C-3, 109.9 s; C-4, 124.8 s; C-5, 127.4 s; C-6, 116.0 d; C-7, 122.3 d; C-8, 116.5 s; C-9, 131.1 s*; C-10, 24.3 t; C-11, 63.6 d; C-12, 87.4 s; C-13, 150.2 d; C-14, 129.8 s*; C-15, 173.5 s; C-16, 10.8 q; and C-17, 34.8ppm q.

* Assignments could be reversed.

Mass Spectrum:

HREIMS mass spectrum showed 302.0800*m/e* (M^+). The presence of a chlorine atom was supported by the expected isotope ratios (relative intensity) 302.0800 = 86.5 ; 304.0778 = 25. Base peak was at 259.0641*m/e*.

TLC Data

Silica gel PF_{254}, chloroform-acetone-methanol, 93:7:5, v/v/v; R_f: 0.27. Detection: rose-colored spot after spraying with 50% ethanolic H_2SO_4 followed immediately by spraying with ninhydrin and heating at 100°C for 5-10 min.

References

R. J. Cole, J. W. Kirksey, H. G. Cutler, D. M. Wilson, and G. Morgan-Jones; Two Toxic Indole Alkaloids from *Penicillium islandicum*; Can. J. Microbiol., Vol. 22, pp. 741-744(1976).

R. J. Cole, J. W. Kirksey, J. Clardy, N. Eichman, S. M. Weinreb, P. Singh, and D. Kim; Structures of Rugulovasine-A and Rugulovasine-B and 8-Chlororugulovasine-A and B; Tet. Lett., pp. 3849-3852(1976).

R. J. Cole and R. H. Cox; Handbook of Toxic Fungal Metabolites; Academic Press, New York, p. 528 (1981).

Common/Systematic Name

Rugulovasine B

Molecular Formula/Molecular Weight

$C_{16}H_{16}N_2O_2$; MW = 268.12118

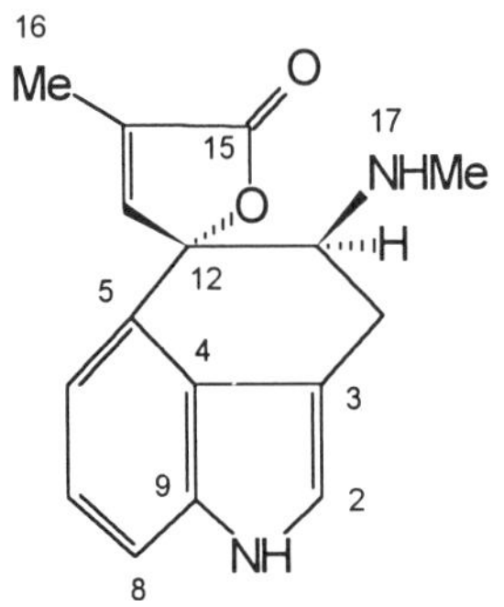

General Characteristics

Colorless resinous oil; $[\alpha]_{436}^{22}$ +1.4° (*c*=1.0, in pyridine); $[\alpha]_D^{22}$ 0.0.

Fungal Source

Penicillium islandicum, P. concavo-rugulosum, P. rubrum, and *P. biforme.*

Isolation/Purification

See 8-chlororugulovasine A.

Biological Activity

Rugulovasine B exhibited hypotensive action in experimental animals; in chloralose-urethanized cats, the minimum effective dose was 0.025-0.05mg/kg.

Spectral Data

UV:

λ_{max}^{EtOH} 224(ϵ=14,500), 277(4,800), 288(5,400), and 295nm (5,200).

^{1}H NMR:

H-1, 8.68; H-2, 7.00; H-6, 6.83; H-7, 7.2: H-8, 7.2; H-10, 3.25; H-11, 3.25; NH-1, 1.70; H-13, 6.98; H-16, 2.02; and H-17, 2.43ppm.

^{13}C NMR:

C-2, 120.0 d; C-3, 108.4 s; C-4, 125.8 s*;C-5, 126.1 s*; C-6, 114.4 d; C-7, 122.7 d; C-8, 111.2 d; C-9, 133.9 s; C-10, 24.3 t; C-11, 63.6 d; C-12, 88.2 s; C-13, 150.9 d; C-14, 129.2 s; C-15, 174.0 s; C-16, 10.7 q; and C-17, 34.7ppm q.

* Assignments could be reversed.

TLC Data

Silica gel PF_{254}; solvent chloroform-acetone-methanol, 93:7:5, v/v/v; R_f: 0.34. Detection: rose-colored spot after spraying with 50% ethanolic H_2SO_4 followed immediately by spraying with ninhydrin and heating at 100°C for 5-10 min.

References

R. J. Cole and R. H. Cox; Handbook of Toxic Fungal Metabolites; Academic Press, New York, p. 540 (1981).

R. J. Cole, J. W. Kirksey, J. Clardy, N. Eichman, S. M. Weinreb, P. Singh, and D. Kim; Structures of Rugulovasine-A and Rugulovasine-B and 8-Chlororugulovasine-A and B; Tet. Lett., pp. 3849-3852(1976).

R. J. Cole, J. W. Kirksey, H. G. Cutler, D. M. Wilson, and G. Morgan-Jones; Two Toxic Indole Alkaloids from *Penicillium islandicum*; Can. J. Microbiol., Vol. 22, pp. 741-744 (1976).

Common/Systematic Name

8-Chlororugulovasine B

Molecular Formula/Molecular Weight

$C_{16}H_{15}N_2O_2Cl$; MW = 302.08221

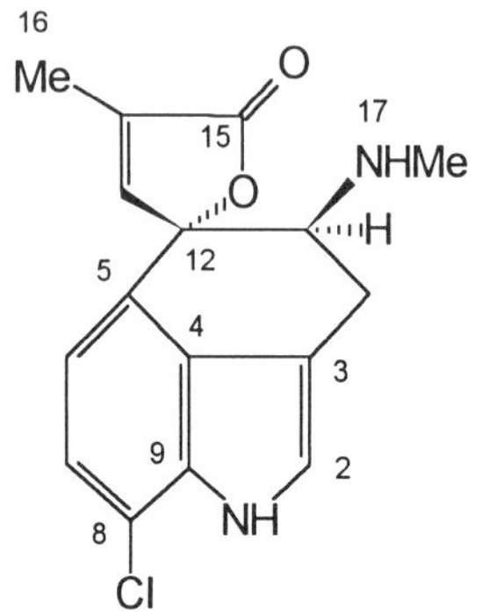

Fungal Source

Penicillium islandicum.

Isolation/Purification

See 8-chlororugulovasine A

Biological Activity

LD_{50} of chlororugulovasine B in preliminary studies showed it to be as toxic as chlororugulovasine A in day-old cockerels dosed orally (75-125mg/kg).

Spectral Data

UV:

λ_{max}^{EtOH} 224(ϵ=22,400), 278(4,700), 288(5,100), and 295nm (5,400).

^{1}H NMR:

H-1, 8.89; H-2, 7.09; H-6, 6.73(*J*=7.6); H-7, 7.05(*J*=7.6); H-10, 3.07; H-11, 3.07; NH-1, 1.61; H-13, 6.78(*J*=1.5); H-16, 2.01(*J*=1.5); and H-17, 2.44ppm.

^{13}C NMR:

C-2, 120.1 d; C-3, 110.6 s; C-4, 124.9 s; C-5, 127.5 s; C-6, 115.8 d; C-7, 122.0 d; C-8, 116.5 s; C-9, 130.9 s*; C-10, 25.1 t; C-11, 63.0 d; C-12, 87.8 s; C-13, 149.9 d; C-14, 129.3 s*; C-15, 173.8 s;.C-16, 10.7 q; and C-17, 34.9ppm q.

* Assignments could be reversed.

TLC Data

Silica gel PF_{254}; solvent: chloroform-acetone-methanol, 73:7:5, v/v/v; R_f 0.44. Detection: rose-colored spot after spraying with 50% ethanolic H_2SO_4 followed immediately with ninhydrin spraying and heating at 100°C for 5-10 min.

References

R. J. Cole, J. W. Kirksey, J. Clardy, N. Eichman, S. M. Weinreb, P. Singh, and D. Kim; Structures of Rugulovasine-A and Rugulovasine-B and 8-Chlororugulovasine-A and B; Tet. Lett., pp. 3849-3852(1976).

R. J. Cole, J. W. Kirksey, H. G. Cutler, D. M. Wilson, and G. Morgan-Jones; Two Toxic Indole Alkaloids from *Penicillium islandicum*; Can. J. Microbiol., Vol. 22, pp. 741-744 (1976).

R. J. Cole and R. H. Cox; Handbook of Toxic Fungal Metabolites; Academic Press, New York, p. 532 (1981).

Common/Systematic Name

Fumigaclavine A

9-Acetoxy-6,8-dimethylergoline

Molecular Formula/Molecular Weight

$C_{18}H_{22}N_2O_2$; MW = 298.16813

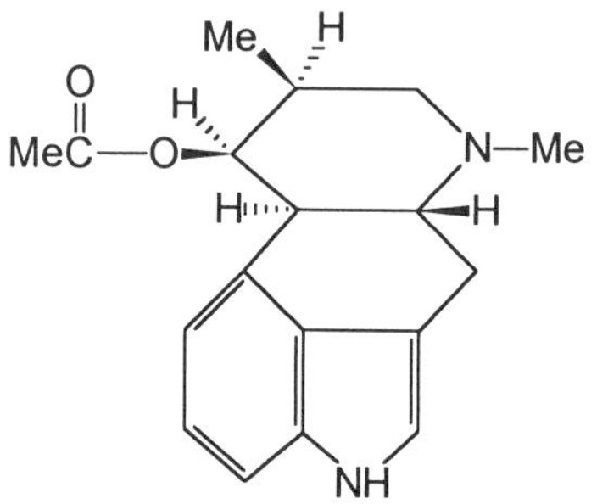

General Characteristics

Colorless needles; mp., 84-°85°C (crystals from aqueous MeOH); $[\alpha]_{5461}$ -56.7° (pyridine); intense blue color with Allport and Cocking's reagent. Hydrochloride: prisms from EtOH; mp., 304°-305° (dec.), $[\alpha]_{5246}^{22}$, -56.7° (*c*=1.5, in MeOH)

Fungal Source

Aspergillus fumigatus.

Isolation/Purification

Extracted with chloroform, filtered, and dried over anhydrous sodium sulfate. The crude chloroform extract was concentrated under vacuum, redissolved in ethyl acetate, and partitioned three times between an aqueous solution adjusted to pH 2.0 with HCl. The acidic phases were combined, made basic (pH 10.0) with sodium carbonate, and partitioned three times with chloroform. The chloroform fractions were pooled and washed three times with distilled water. The extract was dried over anhydrous sodium sulfate, filtered, and concentrated under vacuum. The resulting concentrate was chromatographed on a column containing neutral alumina that was deactivated to activity grade IV. The column was packed as a slurry in benzene, the sample was applied in benzene solution, and the column was eluted with benzene. This yielded fumagaclavines A and C in pure form after crystallization from methanol solution.

Biological Activity

All natural ergot alkaloids possess to a greater or lesser degree, biological effects that can be classified as direct peripheral effects on smooth muscle (uterine contraction and vasoconstriction), indirect peripheral effects (humoral, serotonin antagonism, and adrenergic blockage), and central nervous system effects (bulbomedullary and mesodiencephalic components).

Spectral Data

UV:
λ_{max}^{MeOH} 225, 275, 282, and 293nm (ε max not reported).

IR:
See Hofmann, 1964

^{1}H NMR:
1-NH, 7.94; H-2, 6.86; H-9, 5.70; H-12, 7.12; H-13, 6.76; H-14, 7.16; H-17, 2.47; H-18, 1.35(*J*=7.0); and H-20, 1.90ppm.

^{13}C NMR:
C-2, 117.7 d; C-3, 111.6 s; C-4, 26.8 t; C-5, 61.9 d; C-7, 57.9 t; C-8 33.2 d; C-9, 71.6 d; C-10, 39.8 d; C-11, 129.9 s; C-12, 112.9 d; C-13, 123.2 d; C-14, 108.3 d; C-15, 133.6 s; C-16, 126.8 s; C-17, 43.6 q; C-18, 16.8 q; C-19, 170.8 s; and C-20, 21.2ppm q.

TLC Data

Silica gel G-HR; toluene-ethyl acetate-formic acid, 5:4:1 v/v/v; R_f: 0.05. Detection: purple spot after spraying with 50% ethanolic H_2SO_4 and heating at 100°C for 5-10 min.

References

B. Berde and H. O. Scheld (eds.); Ergot Alkaloids and Related Compounds; In Handbook of Experimental Pharmacology; Springer-Verlag, New York (1978).

R. J. Cole, J. W. Kirksey, J. W. Dorner, D. M. Wilson, J. C. Johnson, Jr., A. N. Johnson, D. M. Bedel, J. P. Springer, K. K. Chexal, J. C. Clardy, and R. H. Cox; Mycotoxins Produced by *Aspergillus fumigatus* Species Isolated From Molded Silage; Agric. Food Chem., Vol. 25, pp. 826-830(1977).

A. Hofmann; Die Mutterkorn Alkaloide; Enke Verlag, Stuttgart, 218 pp., 1964.

J. F. Spilsbury and S. Wilkinson; J. Chem. Soc. p. 2085 (1961).

Common/Systematic Name

Roquefortine A; Isofumigaclavine A

9-Acetoxy-6,8-dimethylergoline

Molecular Formula/Molecular Weight

$C_{18}H_{22}N_2O_2$; MW = 298.16831

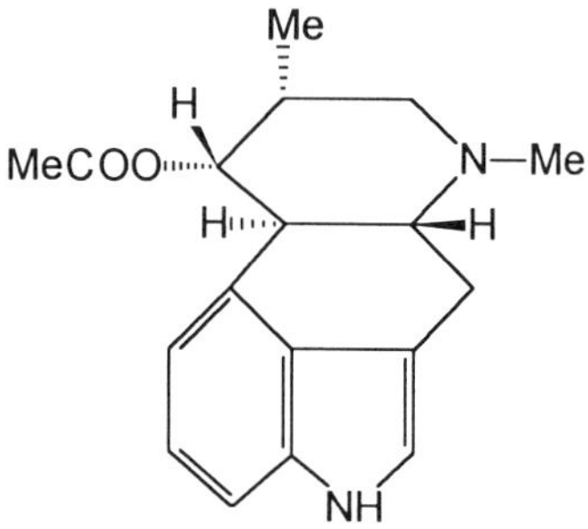

General Characteristics

Crystals from benzene; mp., 190°-193°C; $[\alpha]_D^{22}$ -54.1° (*c*=0.67, in $CHCl_3$).

Fungal Source

Penicillium roqueforti.

Biological Activity

Roquefortine A exhibited a variety of weak pharmacological actions, such as muscle relaxant, antidepressant, local anesthetic, etc., in experimental animals. Its LD_{50} in mice dosed IP was 340mg/kg.

Spectral Data

UV:

λ_{max}^{MeOH} 226(ε=46,300), 277(sh)(6,000), 283(6,500), and 293nm (5,600).

^{1}H NMR:

1-NH, 10.76; H-2, 7.07; H-9, 5.06; H-12, 6.70(*J*=6.7); H-13, 7.07; H-14, 7.25(*J*=8.5); H-17, 2.40; H-18, 0.95(*J*=4.0); and H-20, 2.28ppm.

^{13}C NMR:

C-2, 119.1 d; C-3, 110.7 s; C-4,28.4 t; C-5, 62.3 d; C-7, 55.4 t; C-8, 37.5 d; C-9, 79.6 d; C-10, 38.5 d; C-11, 131.5 s; C-12, 113.9 d; C-13, 122.8 d; C-14, 110.0 d; C-15, 134.2 s; C-16, 113.9 s; C-17, 45.9 q; C-18, 16.4 q; C-19, 171.5 s; and C-20, 22.2ppm q.

TLC Data

Silica gel F 1500/LS 254 (Schleicher and Schuell); solvent: chloroform-methanol-28% ammonium hydroxide, 85:15:1 v/v/v; R_f 0.62. Detection: a mauve spot after spraying with 50% H_2SO_4 and heating at about 100°C for 10 min.

References

R. J. Cole and R. H. Cox; Handbook of Toxic Fungal Metabolites; Academic Press, New York, p. 549 (1981).

P. M. Scott, J. Polonsky, and M. A. Merrien; Configuration of the 3,12- Double Bond of Roquefortine; J. Agric. Food Chem. Vol. 27, p. 201 (1979).

Common/Systematic Name

Fumigaclavine B

9-Hydroxy-6,8-dimethylergoline

Molecular Formula/Molecular Weight

$C_{16}H_{20}N_2O$; MW = 256.15756

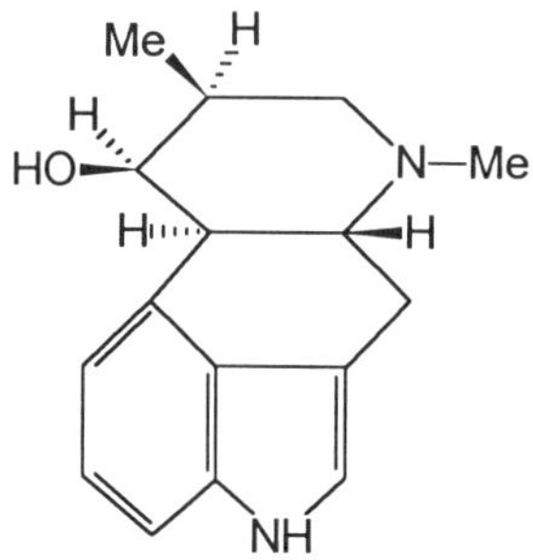

General Characteristics

Needles from aqueous methanol; 244-245°C (at 260°C, the melt solidified and remelted at 265-267°C); $[\alpha]_{5461}^{22}$ -6.3° (*c*=1.2, in MeOH); -113° (*c*=0.6, in pyridine).

Fungal Source

Aspergillus fumigatus and *Rhizopus arrhizus*.

Spectral Data

UV:

λ_{max}^{MeOH} 225(ϵ=30,900), 275(6,200), 282(6,600), and 293nm (5,200).

IR:

(See A. Hofmann, 1964).

^{1}H NMR:

1-NH, 8.04; H-2, 6.96; H-9, 4.54; H-11, 6.87; H-12, 7.18; H-13, 7.21; H-17, 2.43; and H-18, 1.30ppm.

^{13}C NMR:

C-2, 117.6 d; C-3, 111.6 s; C-4, 26.2 t; C-5, 60.9 d; C-7, 57.4 t; C-8, 34.0 d; C-9, 69.0 d; C-10, 41.6 d; C-11, 129.5 s; C-12, 112.2 d; C-13, 123.0 d; C-14, 108.7 d; C-15, 133.5 s; C-16, 126.9 s; C-17, 43.4 q; and C-18, 16.9ppm q.

TLC Data

Silica gel G-HR; toluene-ethyl acetate-formic acid, 5:4:1 v/v/v; R_f origin. Detection: purple spot after spraying with 50% ethanolic H_2SO_4 and heating at 100°C for 5-10 min.

References

B. Berde and H. O. Scheld (eds.); Ergot Alkaloids and Related Compounds; In Handbook of Experimental Pharmacology; Springer-Verlag, New York (1978).

R. J. Cole and R. H. Cox; Handbook of Toxic Fungal Metabolites; Academic Press, New York, p. 553 (1981).

R. J. Cole, J. W. Kirksey, J. W. Dorner, D. M. Wilson, J. C. Johnson, Jr., A. N. Johnson, D. M. Bedel, J. P. Springer, K. K. Chexal, J. C. Clardy, and R. H. Cox; Mycotoxins Produced by *Aspergillus fumigatus* Species Isolated from Molded Silage; Agric. Food Chem., Vol. 25, pp. 826-830(1977).

A. Hofmann; Die Mutterkorn Alkaloide, Enke Verlag, Stuttgart, 218 pp., 1964.

J. F. Spilsbury and S. Wilkinson; J. Chem. Soc., p. 2085 (1961).

Common/Systematic Name

Roquefortine B; Isofumigaclavine B
9-Hydroxy-6,8-dimethylergoline

Molecular Formula/Molecular Weight

$C_{16}H_{20}N_2O$; MW = 256.15756

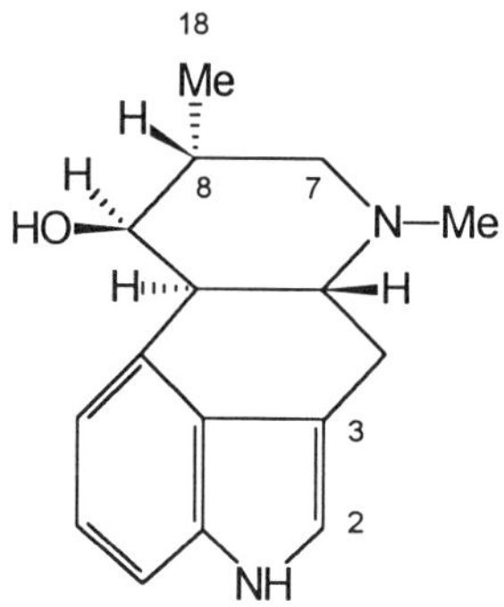

General Characteristics

Melting point, 278°-282°C (dec.); colorless needles from methanol; mp., 222°-225°C (760mm Hg); $[\alpha]_D^{15}$ -147°(*c*=0.5, in pyridine).

Fungal Source

Penicillium roqueforti.

Biological Activity

The LD_{50} of roquefortine B dosed IP to mice was 1000mg/kg.

Spectral Data

UV:

λ_{max}^{MeOH} 224(ϵ=44,700), 275(6,200), 282(7,000), and 294nm(6,000); λ_{max} 225(ϵ=25,100), 277(sh)(4,300), 283(4,600), and 293nm(3,800).

TLC Data

Silica gel F 1500/LS254 thin-layer sheets; chloroform-methanol-28% ammonium hydroxide, 85:15:1 v/v/v; R_f: 0.31. Detection: a mauve spot after spraying with 50% H_2SO_4 and heating at about 100°C for 10 min.

References

R. J. Cole and R. H. Cox; Handbook of Toxic Fungal Metabolites; Academic Press, New York, p. 557 (1981).

P. M. Scott, J. Polonsky, and M. A. Merrien; Configuration of the 3,12-Double Bond of Roquefortine; J. Agric. Food Chem. Vol. 27, p. 201 (1979).

Common/Systematic Name

Fumigaclavine C

2-Dimethylallyl-9-acetoxy-6,8-dimethylergoline

Molecular Formula/Molecular Weight

$C_{23}H_{30}N_2O_2$; MW = 366.23073

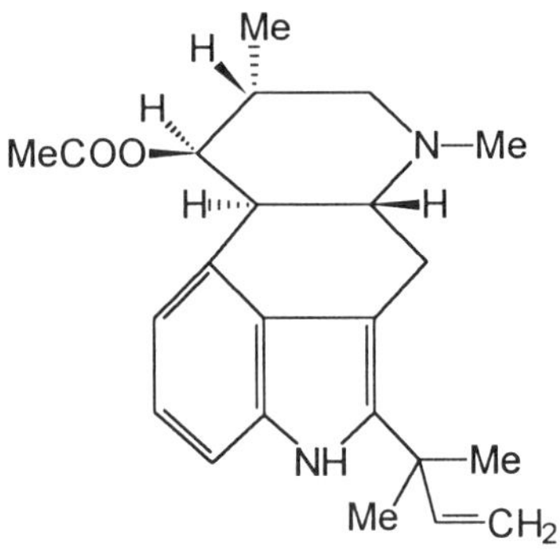

General Characteristics

Crystals from ethanol, acetone, or ethyl acetate (prisms), mp 191-193°C. Needles from methanol; mp., 198°C; $[\alpha]_D^{22}$ -90; $[\alpha]_{5461}^{22}$ -119° (*c*=1.0, in $CHCl_3$); $[\alpha]_D^{22}$ -132°; $[\alpha]_{5461}^{22}$ -160° (*c*=1.0, in pyridine).

Fungal Source

Aspergillus fumigatus.

Isolation/Purification

See fumigaclavine A.

Biological Activity

The LD_{50} of fumigaclavine C dosed orally to day-old cockerels was 150mg/kg. Histopathology of surviving cockerels showed vacuolation of the hepatic parenchymal cells that may have been directly related to the toxic action of the toxin or due to anorexia.

Spectral Data

UV:

λ_{max}^{MeOH} 229, 284, and 292nm (ϵ max not reported); λ_{max}^{MeOH} 225(ϵ=34,700), 227(10,200), 283(11,000), and 292nm(9,500).

^{1}H NMR:

1-NH, 7.76; H-9, 5.67; H-12, 7.04; H-13, 6.72; H-14, 7.08; H-17, 2.46; H-18, 1.35; H-20, 1.90; H-22, 1.56; H-23, 1.56; H-24, 6.10; H-25a, 5.05; and H-25b, 5.20ppm.

^{13}C NMR:

C-2, 131.1 s; C-3, 106.2 s; C-4, 28.1 t; C-5, 61.6 d; C-7, 57.8 t; C-8, 33.1 d; C-9, 71.4 d; C-10, 39.4 d; C-11, 129.1 s; C-12, 112.8 d; C-13, 122.2 d; C-14, 107.6 d; C-15, 136.6 s; C-16, 128.0 s; C-17, 43.5 q; C-18, 16.7 q; C-19, 170.8 s; C-20, 21.2 q; C-21, 39.1 s; C-22, 27.3 q; C-23, 27.4 q; C-24, 145.7 d; and C-25, 111.8ppm t.

TLC Data

Silica gel G-HR; toluene-ethyl acetate-formic acid, 5:4:1 v/v/v; R_f: 0.14. Detection: blue spot after spraying with 50% ethanolic H_2SO_4 and heating at 100°C for 5-10 min.

References

R. J. Cole and R. H. Cox; Handbook of Toxic Fungal Metabolites; Academic Press, New York, pp. 560-561(1981).

R. J. Cole, J. W. Kirksey, J. W. Dorner, D. M. Wilson, J. C. Johnson, Jr., A. N. Johnson, D. M. Bedel, J. P. Springer, K. K. Chexal, J. C. Clardy, and R. H. Cox; Mycotoxins Produced by *Aspergillus fumigatus* Species Isolated from Molded Silage; Agric. Food Chem., Vol. 25, pp. 826-830(1977).

2

Diketopiperazines

Roquefortine; Roquefortine C
Aurantiamine
Viridamine
Okaramine A
Okaramine B
cyclo-L-Phenylalanyl-L-alanine
cyclo-L-Prolylglycine
L-Propyldiketopiperazine B; L-Homoleucyl-D-proline-lactam
L-Propyl-L-tyrosine
Isoleucylisoleucyl anhydride
Phomamide
D-Valyl-L-tryptophan anhydride
L-Alanyl-L-tryptophan anhydride
cyclo-(L-Isoleucyl-L-valine)
cyclo-(L-Alanyl-L-proline)
Neoxaline
Oxaline
Aszonalenin
LL-S490β; Acetylaszonalenin
Bipolaramide
Austamide
12,13-Dihydroaustamide
12,13-Dihydro-12-hydroxyaustamide
Cycloechinulin
12,13-Dehydroprolyl-2-(1',1'-dimethylallyltryptophyl)diketopiperazine
Alanyl-2-(1,1-dimethyl-2-propenyl)dehydrotryptophan anhydride
10,20-Dehydro[12,13-dehydroprolyl]-2-(1',1'-dimethylallyltryptophyl)diketopiperazine
Deoxybrevianamide E
Brevianamide C
Brevianamide D
Brevianamide F
Echinulin
Preechinulin
Neoechinulin
Neoechinulin A
Neoechinulin B; Cryptoechinulin C; E10
Neoechinulin C; Cryptoechinulin A; E8
Neoechinulin D
Neoechinulin E
Isoechinulin A
Isoechinulin B
Isoechinulin C
E-7
Cryptoechinulin G

Cryptoechinulin B; Aurechinulin; E6
Cryptoechinulin D
Fumitremorgin A
Fumitremorgin B; Lanosulin
Fumitremorgin C; SM-Q
Verruculogen
15-Acetoxyverruculogen
TR-2
Epiamauromine
N-Methylepiamauromine
Ditryptophenaline
Exserohilone
9,10-Dihydroexserohilone
Epoxyexserohilone

Common/Systematic Name

Roquefortine; Roquefortine C

10β-(Dimethyl-2-propenyl)-3-(imidazol-4-ylmethylene)-5α,10β,11,11α-tetrahydro-2*H*-pyrazino[1',2':1,5]pyrrolo[2,3-*b*]indole-1,4-(3*H*,6*H*)-dione

Molecular Formula/Molecular Weight

$C_{22}H_{23}N_5O_2$; MW = 389.18518

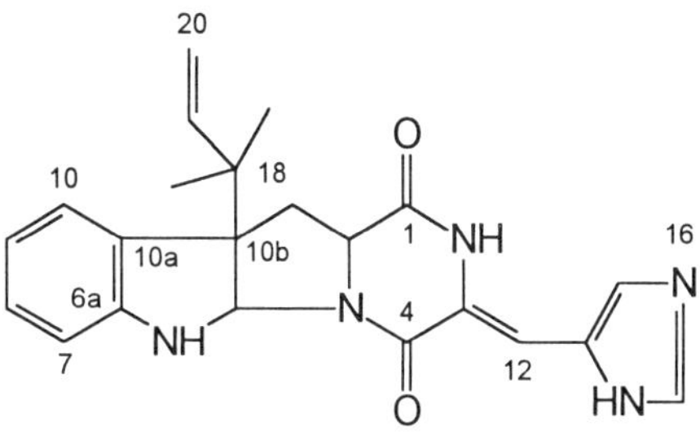

General Characteristics

Colorless needles of the solvate from methanol-water; mp., 195-200°C (dec.); $[\alpha]_D^{22}$ -703° (*c*=1.0, in $CHCl_3$).

Fungal Source

Penicillium roqueforti, P. notatum, P. oxalicum, P. commune, P. corymbiferum, P. expansum, and *P. urticae.*

Isolation/Purification

Fungal cultures were filtered and the mycelium macerated with acetone in a Waring blender. The acetone solution was evaporated and the aqueous residue partitioned between dichloromethane and water. The residue from the dichloromethane solution was partitioned between *n*-hexane and 90% methanol. The 90% methanol solution was evaporated and the aqueous residue once again partitioned between dichloromethane and water. The crude extract obtained from the dichloromethane solution was percolated through a short silica-gel column with benzene-acetone (4:1, v/v). Residual material on the column was eluted with benzene-acetone (1:4, v/v) to give the fraction containing crude roquefortine. This material was purified by percolation through an aluminum oxide (activity II-III) column with chloroform-methanol (9:1, v/v) to yield, after crystallization from aqueous methanol, crystalline roquefortine.

Biological Activity

The LD_{50} (IP, male mice) was 15-20mg/kg. Doses of 50-100mg/kg caused prostration and an atonic posture. The prostration was interrupted for a few seconds by opisthotonoid seizures which could be brought about by noise or a tap on the cage. Death followed within a few hours. At doses of 10mg/kg, convulsions were replaced by simple contractions and the state of prostration by equilibrium disorders during movement.

Spectral Data

UV:
λ_{max}^{EtOH} 209(ϵ= 29,500), 240(16,200), and 328nm (27,000).

IR:
($CHCl_3$) 3430, 3380, 3190, 1685, 1665, and 1608cm^{-1}.

^{1}H NMR:
($CDCl_3$) H-5a, 5.71; H-7-10, 6.58-7.30; H-11, 2.56; H-11a, 4.00; H-12, 6.48; H-15, 7.73; H-17, 7.20; H-19, 6.12; H-20, 5.10; H-21, 1.06; and H-22, 1.17pm.

^{13}C NMR:
($CDCl_3$) C-1, 166.2 s; C-3, 123.7 s; C-4, 159.8 s; C-5a, 78.9 d; C-6a, 151.9 s; C-7, 110.3 d; C-8, 129.8 d; C-9, 118.9 d; C-10, 125.6 d; C-10a, 129.4 s; C-10b, 62.1 d; C-11,38.0 t; C-11a, 59.4 d; C-12, 109.6 d; C-13, 125.6 d; C-15, 137.3 d; C-17, 134.5 d; C-18, 41.7 s; C-19, 144.9 d; C-20, 114.2 t; C-21, 23.0 q; and C-22, 23.3ppm q.

Mass Spectrum:
LREIMS: 389(M$^+$), 320(base peak), 198, 192, 157, 130, and 108*m/e*.

TLC Data
TLC: silica gel F 1500/LS_{254}; chloroform-methanol-28% ammonium hydroxide, 90:10:1 v/v/v; R_f: 0.46. Detection: a blue spot after spraying with 50% H_2SO_4 and heating at 110°C for 10 min.

References
R. J. Cole and R. H. Cox; Handbook of Toxic Fungal Metabolites; Academic Press, New York, pp.564 (1981).

A. E. de Jesus, P. S. Steyn, F. R. van Heerden, R. Vleggaar, P. L. Wessels, and W. E. Hull; Tremorgenic Mycotoxins from *Penicillium crustosum:* Isolation of Penitrems A-F and the Structure Elucidation and Absolute Configuration of Penitrem A; J. Chem. Soc. Perkin Trans. I, pp. 1847-1856(1983).

P. M. Scott; Roquefortine, In Mycotoxins-Production, Isolation, Separation, and Purification; V. Betina (ed.) Elsevier Science Publishers B.V., Amsterdam (1984).

P. M. Scott, M. A. Merrien, and J. Polonsky; Roquefortine and Isofumigaclavine A, Metabolites from *Penicillium roqueforti*; Experientia, Vol. 32, pp. 140-141(1976).

P. M. Scott, M. A. Merrien, and J. Polonsky; Roquefortine and Isofumigaclavine A, Metabolites from *Penicillium roqueforti;* Annales De La Nutrition et De L'Alimentation, Vol. 31, pp. 693-698(1977).

P. M. Scott, J. Polonsky, and M. A. Merrien; Configuration of the 3, 12 Double Bond of Roquefortine; J. Agric, Food Chem. Vol. 27, p. 201 (1979).

Common/Systematic Name

Aurantiamine (Isomeric with viridamine)

Molecular Formula/Molecular Weight

$C_{16}H_{22}N_4O_2$; MW = 302.17428

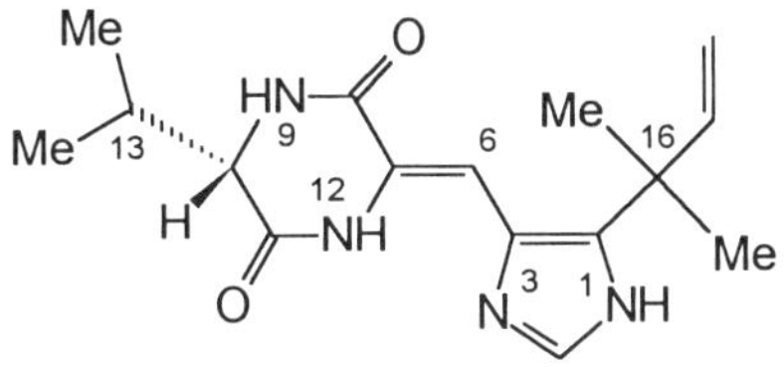

General Characteristics

Crystals from ethyl acetate; mp., 238-239°C; $[\alpha]_D^{23}$ -116° (*c*=0.5, in MeOH).

Fungal Source

Aurantiamine was produced by the majority of strains of *Penicillium aurantiogriseum* var. *aurantiogriseum* and var. *neoechinulatum*. *P. aurantiogriseum* Diercks var. *aurantiogriseum* is the most common of all fungi in cereals and it is considered highly toxigenic.

Isolation/Purification

The fungal mat was extracted with $CHCl_3$-MeOH (2:1, v/v). The extract was taken to dryness and the residue chromatographed on a silica gel column eluted with toluene-EtOAc (1:1 to 1:4, v/v). The fractions containing aurantiamine by TLC were pooled and taken to dryness, dissolved in hot EtOAc and filtered through activated charcoal. Crystals were formed on cooling and partial evaporation of the solvent. This procedure was repeated to give pure aurantiamine.

Spectral Data

UV:

λ_{max} (H_2O/MeCN with CF_3CO_2H) 230(40) and 320nm (100%).

^1H NMR:

($CDCl_3$) 12.16(exch., brs, H-12); 10.0(exch., brs, H-1); 7.57(brs, H-2); 6.96(s, H-6); 6.81(exch., brd, *J*=2Hz, H-9); 6.04[dd, *J*=10.8 and 17.1Hz (X part of ABX pattern) H-17]; 5.15(2H, AB part of ABX pattern, CH_2-18); 4.08(dd, *J*=2 and 3Hz, H-10); 2.47(dhept, *J*=3 and 7Hz, H-13); 1.49(6H, s, Me-19 and Me-20); and 10.9 and 0.95ppm (each 3H, d, *J*=7.0Hz, Me-14 and Me-15).

^{13}C NMR:

($CDCl_3$) C-2, 132.6 Dd; C-4, 132.1 Sdd; C-5, 136.7 Sm; C-6, 105.3 D; C-7, 123.5 Sd;

C-8, 160.8 Sm; C-10, 61.1 Dm; C-11, 165.1 Stm; C-13, 33.0 Dm; C-14, 18.6 Qm; C-15, 15.8 Qm; C-16, 37.5 Sm; C-17, 144.6 Dm; C-18, 113.1 DDs; and C-19/20, 27.9 Qm. (CD_3OD) C-2,133.0 Ds ; C-4,130.5 Sdd ; C-5, 137.0 Sm; C-6, 105.3 D; C-7, 122.5 S; C-8, 160.6 Sdd; C-10, 60.0 Dm; C-11, 165.5 Sddd; C-13, 33.1 Dm; C-14, 16.8 Qm; C-15, 14.8 Qm; C-16, 36.8 Sm; C-17, 144.4 Dm; C-18, 110.9 DDs; and C-19/20, 26.5 Qm.

* Capital letters refer to directly bonded protons and small letters to long-range couplings.

Mass Spectrum:
EIMS: 302(M^+, 50%), 287(15), 260(28), 231(35), 203(100), and 188*m/e*.

Reference

T. O. Larsen, J. C. Frisvad, and S. R. Jensen; Aurantiamine, a Diketopiperazine from Two Varieties of *Penicillium aurantiogriseum*; Phytochemistry, Vol. 31, pp. 1613-1615 (1992).

Common/Systematic Name

Viridamine

2-(3',3'-Dimethylallyl)-6,7-didehydrocyclo-L-prolylhistdyl

Molecular Formula/Molecular Weight

$C_{16}H_{22}N_4O_2$; MW = 302.17428

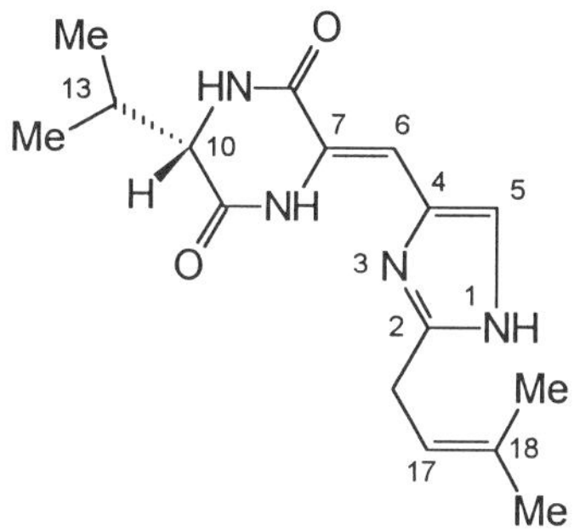

General Characteristics

A colorless glass; $[\alpha]_D^{20}$ - 95,0° (c=1.0, in $CHCl_3$).

Fungal Source

Penicillium viridicatum (strain no. CSIR 354).

Isolation/Purification

Viridamine was extracted from the dried moldy maize meal with 1:1 chloroform-methanol. An equal volume of water was added to the extract and the chloroform phase was collected. The aqueous phase was re-extracted with chloroform, the chloroform extracts were combined and the solvent was removed under reduced pressure. The residue was dissolved in a minimum of chloroform and diethyl ether was added. Precipitated material was removed by filtration and the diethyl ether-chloroform solution was repeatedly extracted with ice cold 2N hydrochloric acid. The hydrochloric acid extract was neutralized with sodium carbonate and extracted with chloroform. The chloroform was washed with 5N ammonia solution and water. The chloroform solution was dried over anhydrous Na_2SO_4 and evaporated under reduced pressure to yield a basic fraction which was chromatographed over alumina. The column was developed in chloroform-benzene (3:1, v/v) and chloroform. Elution with chloroform-methanol (95:5, v/v) gave viridamine as a colorless glass which could not be induced to crystallize.

Spectral Data

UV:

λ_{max}^{MeOH} 315(ϵ=33,795), shifting to 300(28,280), and 338nm (39,610) on the addition of HCl and NaOH, resp.

IR:

($CHCl_3$) 3460, 3420, 3140-3340, 1680, and 1645 cm^{-1}.

^1H NMR:

(CDl_3) 11.88(s, 12-H); 10.1(s, 1-H); 7.22(d, *J*=2.0Hz, 9-H); 7.05(s, 5-H); 6.63(s, 6-H); 5.32(t, *J*=7Hz, 17-H); 4.04(t, *J*=2 and 4Hz, 10-H); 3.43(d, *J*=7Hz, 16-H_2); 2.35(m, $J_{13,14}$ and $J_{13,15}$=7Hz, $J_{13,10}$=4Hz); 1.71 and 1.65(2xs, 19- and 20-H_3); 1.05 and 0.94ppm (2xd, $J_{14,13}$ and $J_{15,13}$=7Hz; 14- and 15-H_3).

(DMSO-d_6) 12.14(s, 12-H); 11.56(s, 1-H); 8.21(d, *J*=2Hz, 9-H); 7.31(s, 5-H); 6.45(s, 6-H); 5.33(t, *J*=7Hz, 17-H); 3.91(q, *J*=4 and 2Hz, 10-H); 3.41(d, *J*=7Hz, 16-H_2); 2.14(m, $J_{13,14}$ and $J_{15,13}$=7Hz, $J_{13,10}$=4Hz, 13-H); 1.68(s, 19-and 20-H_3); 0.93 and 0.83ppm (2xd, $J_{14,13}$ and $J_{15,13}$=7Hz, 14- and 15-H_3).

Mass Spectrum:

LREIMS: 302(49%), 287(4), 274(3), 259(3), 258(4), 231(11), 203(12), 176(13), 175(100), 174(5), 120(13), 119(24), 79(5), and 69*m/e* (5); HREIMS: found: M^+, 302.1701; calc. for $C_{16}H_{22}N_4O_2$, 302.1743.

Reference

C. W. Holzapfel and J. J. Marsh; Isolation and Structure of Viridamine, A New Nitrogenous Metabolite of *Penicillium viridicatum*; S. Afr. J. Chem., Vol. XXX, pp. 197-204(1977).

Common/Systematic Name
Okaramine A

Molecular Formula/Molecular Weight
$C_{32}H_{32}N_4O_3$; MW = 520.24744

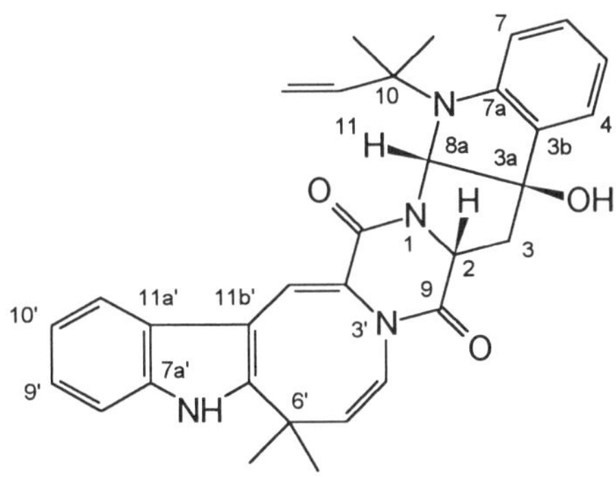

General Characteristics
Pale green needles from toluene; mp., 210-212°C; $[\alpha]_D^{30}$ +101 (*c*=0.09, in MeOH).

Fungal Source
Penicillium simplicissimum (AK-40) → *P. brasilianum.*

Isolation/Purification
The acetone extract of okara (the insoluble residue of whole soybean) fermented with this fungal strain was concentrated and partitioned against ethyl acetate. Column chromatography of the ethyl acetate extract resulted in the isolation of okaramine A.

Biological Activity
Okaramine A caused about 90% of the test insects to die within 24hr at a dose of 30ppm in the diet when applied to the third instar larvae of *Bombyx mori*.

Spectral Data

UV:
λ_{max}^{MeOH} 229(ε=29,900), 255(21,100). 284(17,400), and 371nm (19,400).

IR:
(KBr) 3460. 3300, 1610, 1480, 1375, and 742cm^{-1}.

^{1}H NMR:
Spectrum indicated the presence of the following partial structures: four tertiary methyls [1.52(3H, s), 1.65(3H, s), 1.69(3H s), 1.70(3H, s)]; -CH_2CH-[2.55(1H, dd,

J=13.5, 9.6Hz); 3.11(1H, dd, *J*=13.5, 5.9); 4.54(1H, dd, *J*=9.6, 5.9)]; a vinyl [5.04(1H, dd, *J*=11.0, 1.1); 5.17(1H, dd, *J*=17.8, 1.1); 6.11(1H, dd, *J*=17.8, 11.0)]; an isolated methine [5.52(1H, s)], a *cis* substituted ene [5.60(1H, d, J=7.9), 5.87(1H, d, J=7.9)]; a 2,3-disubstituted indole [7.08-7.20(2H, m); 7.38(1H, dd, *J*=7.2, 1.0); 7.2 1H, dd, *J*=6.5, 2.6); 10.64(1H, br, s)]; a 1,2-disubstituted benzene ring [6.75(1H, td, *J*=7.2, 1.0); 6.90(1H, dd, *J*=8.4, 1.0); 7.05(1H, ddd, *J*=8.4, 7.2, 1.5); 7.72(1H, dd, *J*=7.2, 1.5)]; an olefinic methine [7.68(1H, s)], and a hydroxyl [4.71(1H, s)].

Mass Spectrum:

The molecular formula of okaramine A was established to be $C_{32}H_{32}N_4O_3$, by high-resolution mass spectral data (found, 520.2477; calcd., 520.2457).

Reference

S. Murao, H. Ayashi, K. Takiuchi, and M. Arai; Okaramine A, a Novel Indole Alkaloid with Insecticidal Activity, from *Penicillium simplicissimum* AK-40; Agric. Biol. Chem.,Vol. 52, pp. 885-886(1988).

Common/Systematic Name
Okaramine B

Molecular Formula/Molecular Weight
$C_{33}H_{34}N_4O_5$; MW = 566.25292

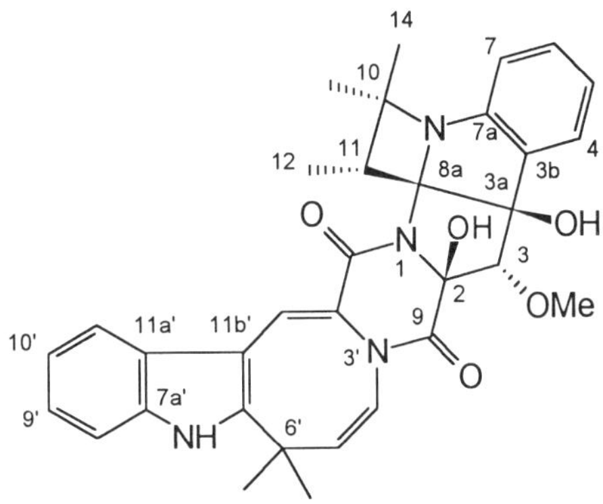

General Characteristics
Crystallized from methanol to afford okaramine B as pale yellow needles; mp., 295-298°C (dec.); $[\alpha]_D^{20}$ +570° (*c*=0.24, pyridine).

Fungal Source
Penicillium simplicissimum (AK-40) → *P. brasilianum.*

Isolation/Purification
The cultures were extracted with acetone, partitioned with ethyl acetate and chromatographed on a column containing Wakogel C-200 eluted with various concentrations of hexane in acetone. The active fractions eluted with 40 and 60% acetone-hexane. The active fractions were concentrated and chromatographed on alumina eluted with various concentrations of ethyl acetate-hexane. The 60% and 80% ethyl acetate fractions contained okaramine B which was crystallized from methanol as pale yellow needles.

Biological Activity
Insecticidal activity against third instar larvae of silkworm at 0.3ppm, 100% of the larvae were killed within 24hr.

Spectral Data

UV:
λ_{max}^{MeOH} 233(ϵ=27,000), 288 (12,900), and 375nm (17,900).

IR:

(KBr) 3400, 3320, 1670, 1610, 1465, 1360, and 750cm-1.

^{1}H NMR:

(DMSO-d_6) H-3, 4.19 s; H-4, 7.38 d (*J*=7.8); H-5, 7.01 t (*J*=7.8);H-6, 7.20 t (*J*=7.8); H-7, 6.72 d (*J*=7.8); H-11, 3.10 q (*J*=7.3); H-12, 1.23 d (*J*=7.3); H-13, 1.65 s; H-14, 0.86 s; H-1', 7.39 s; H-4', 5.90 d (*J*=8.3); H-5', 5.67 d (*J*=8.3); H-7', 11.42 br s; H-8', 7.41 d (*J*=4.4); H-9', 7.14 m; H-10' 7.13 m; H-11', 7.59 dd (*J*=5.4, 2.8); H-13', 1.58 s; H-14', 1.66 s; 2-OH, 6.42 s; 3-OMe, 3.73 s; and 3a-OH, 5.26ppm s.

^{13}C NMR:

(DMSO-d_6) C-2, 86.0; C-3, 82.7; C-3a, C-3b, 126.4; C-4, 125.2; C-5, 123.0; C-6, 129.4; C-7, 117.8; C-7a, 140.1; C-8a, 93.6; C-9, 164.1; C-10, 62.3; C-11, 40.9; C-12, 11.1; C-13, 25.2; C-14, 26.3; C-1', 112.1; C-2', 150.3; C-4', 139.5; C-5', 122.3; C-6', 36.2; 6a', 148.1; C-7a', 134.2; C-8', 113.8; C-9', 121.9; C-10', 120.8; C-11', 116.7, C-11a', 129.8; C-11b', 104.6; C-12', 162.4; C-13', 28.1; C-14' 27.3; and 3-OMe, 60.1ppm.

Reference

H. Hayashi, K. Takiuchi, S. Murao, and M. Arai; Okaramine B and Insecticidal Indole Alkaloid, Produced by *Penicillium simplicissimum* AK-40; Agric. Biol. Chem., Vol. 52, pp. 2131-2133(1988).

Common/Systematic Name

cyclo-L-Phenylalanyl-L-alanine

Molecular Formula/Molecular Weight

$C_{12}H_{14}N_2O_2$; MW = 218.10553

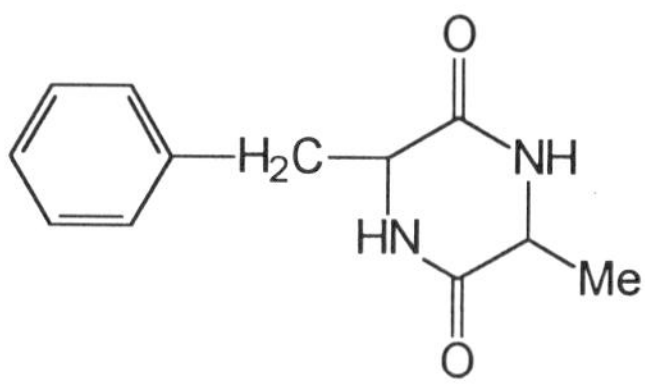

General Characteristics

Crystals from methanol; mp., 272-274°C; 285°C (sealed tube); sublimed at 240°C; $[\alpha]_D^{19}$ + 63°(*c*=0.95, in acetic acid).

Fungal Source

Entoloma haastii (fruiting bodies).

Spectral Data

UV:

λ_{max}^{MeOH} 204 and 285nm (weak).

IR:

(KBr) 3340, 3200, 1660, 1600, 1500, 750, 700, 1340, 1245, 1212, 1192, 1160, 970, 923, and 780cm^{-1}.

Mass Data:

HREIMS: 318.1060*m/e;* found: C, 65.9, 66.1; H, 6.8, 6.9; N, 11.1, 12.1; calcd for $C_{12}H_{14}N_2O_2$: C, 66.0; H, 6.4; N, 12.9%.

Reference

E. P. White; 2,5-Dioxopiperazines from the Fungal Genera *Entoloma* and *Fusarium;* New Zealand J. of Science, Vol. 15, pp. 178-181(1972).

Common/Systematic Name

cyclo-L-Prolylglycine

Molecular Formula/Molecular Weight

$C_7H_{10}N_2O_2$; MW = 154.07423

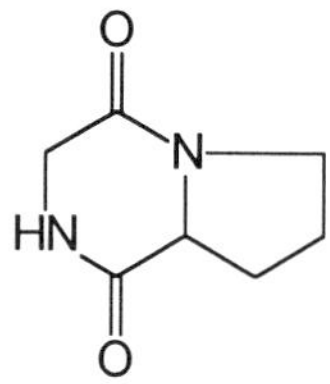

General Characteristics

Crystals from ethanol-ethyl acetate; mp., 202-204°C; $[\alpha]_D^{20}$ - 88°(*c*=1.07, in water).

Fungal Source

Fusarium equiseti, and *F. scirpi* (CMI 112503).

Isolation/Purification

Cultures were extracted with chloroform, reduced to dryness, and material soluble in hot ether concentrated to yield heavy crystals. These were washed with acetone and recrystallized from ethanol-ethyl acetate.

Spectral Data

UV:

λ_{max}^{MeOH} 202nm

IR:

(Nujol) 3150, 3160, 3200, 1675, 1640, 1295, 1270, 1110, 1005, 900, 890, 790, and 775cm^{-1}.

Mass Analysis:

LREIMS: 154*m/e;* found: C, 54.3; H, 6.7; N, 18.2; calcd for $C_7H_{10}N_2O_2$, C, 54.5; H, 6.5; N, 18.1%.

Reference

E. P. White; 2,5-Dioxopiperazines from the Fungal Genera *Entoloma* and *Fusarium;* New Zealand J. of Science, Vol. 15, pp. 178-181(1972).

Common/Systematic Name

Prolyldiketopiperazine B; L-Homoleucyl-D-proline lactam

Molecular Formula/Molecular Weight

$C_{12}H_{20}N_2O_2$; MW = 224.15248

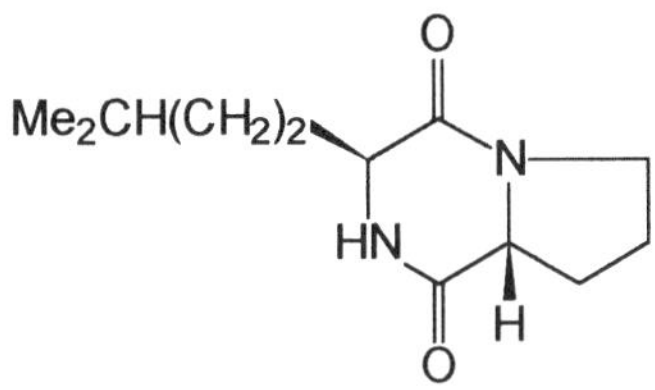

Fungal Source

Sclerotia and saprophytic cultures of *Claviceps* sp.

Spectral Data

Mass Spectrum:

LREIMS: 224(M^+), 223, 195, 180, 153(100%), 99, 69, 43, and 28*m/e*.

Reference

S. Ohmomo and M. Abe; On a New Prolyldiketopiperazine Produced by Ergot Fungi; Nippon Nogei Kagaku Kaishi, Vol. 50, pp. 37-40(1976).

Common/Systematic Name

L-Propyl-L-tyrosine

Molecular Formula/Molecular Weight

$C_{14}H_{16}N_2O_3$; MW = 260.11609

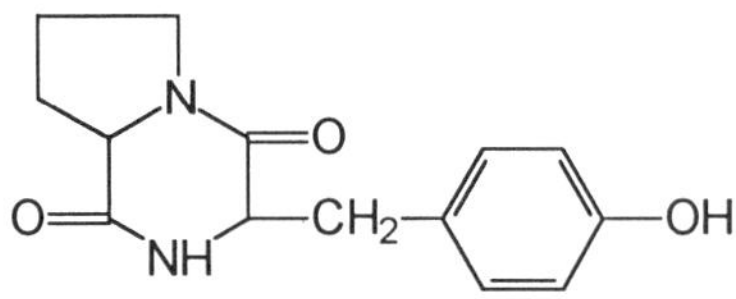

General Characteristics

Crystals from benzene (contained benzene of crystallization); mp., 127°C; after drying over P_2O_5 for 24hrs. at 70°C, mp., 154°C; $[\alpha]_D^{25}$ - 58.6°(*c*=0.5, in MeOH).

Fungal Source

Fusarium nivale Fn-2-B.

Isolation/Purification

The metabolite was adsorbed onto activated carbon directly from the culture broth. The metabolite was eluted from the carbon with methanol, precipitated with the addition of chloroform, and purified with silica gel column chromatography by elution with chloroform-methanol (10:1, v/v) followed by crystallization from benzene solution.

Spectral Data

UV:

λ_{max}^{MeOH} 205(ε=9,620), 228(5,850), and 280nm (1,040).

IR:

(KBr) 3300, 3200, 3005, 2945, 2855, 1660, 1635, 1602, 1590, 1510, 1450, 1440, 1340, 1320, 1210, 1180, 1010, 870, and 805cm^{-1}.

^{1}H NMR:

($CDCl_3$) 1.60; 2.30(2H, dd, *J*=72 and 11Hz); 2.02(2H, quintet); 3.32(2H, dd, *J*=43 and 15Hz); 3.70(2H); 4.32(1H); 4.68(1H, t); and 7.05ppm (4H, aromatic, dd, *J*=39 and 9Hz).

Mass Data:

Found: C, 71.27; H, 7.55; N, 8.27; calcd for $C_{14}H_{16}N_2O_3 \bullet C_6H_6$: C, 70.92; H, 6.39; N, 8.31; found: C, 65.68; H, 6.29; N, 9.37; calcd for $C_{14}H_{16}N_2O_3$: C, 64.74; H, 6.14; N, 10.75%.

Reference

T. Tatsuno, M. Sato, Y. Kubota, and H. Tsunoda; Recherches Toxicologiques des substances Metaboliques du *Fusarium nivale*. VIII. La Quatrieme Substance Metabolique de *F. nivale*; Chem. Pharm. Bull., Vol. 19, pp. 1498-1500(9171).

Common/Systematic Name

Isoleucylisoleucyl anhydride

Molecular Formula/Molecular Weight

$C_{12}H_{22}N_2O_2$; MW = 226.16813

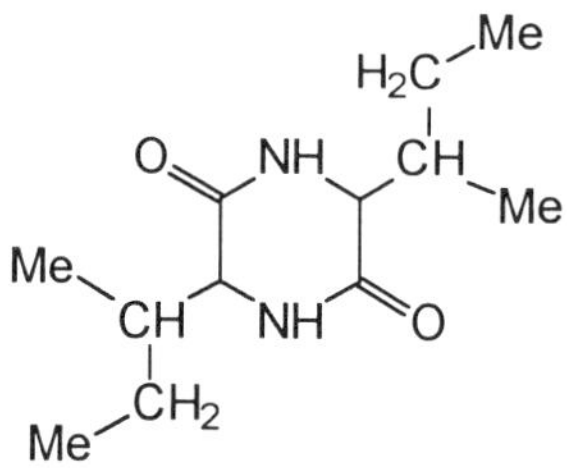

Fungal Source

Ustilago cynodontis, a plant pathogenic microorganism isolated from Bermuda grass, and *Beauveria bassiana.*

Isolation/Purification

Fungal cultures were extracted with dichloromethane after the removal of the mycelium by centrifugation. After evaporation of the dichloromethane, a small amount of ether was added to afford the white crystals of isoleucylisoleucyl anhydride. The metabolite sublimed at 253°C.

Spectral Data

IR:

(Nujol) 3200 and 1660cm^{-1} for N-H and amide carbonyl groups.

Mass Data:

226(M^+), 170(M^+ - C_4H_8), 113(M^+ - C_8H_{17}), 86, 69, and 57*m/e*; found: C, 63.29; H, 10.25; N, 12.32; calcd. for $C_{12}H_{22}N_2O_2$: C, 63.68; H, 9.80; N, 12.38%.

References

J. F. Grove and M. Pople; Nitrogen-Containing Minor Metabolic Products of *Beauveria bassiana*; Phytochem., Vol. 20, pp. 815-816(1981).

Y. Yamada, S. Sawada, and H. Okada; Production of Isoleucylisoleucyl Anhydride by *Ustilago cynodontis*; J. Ferment. Technol., Vol. 52, pp. 143-145(1974).

Common/Systematic Name
Phomamide

Molecular Formula/Molecular Weight
$C_{17}H_{22}N_2O_4$; MW = 318.15796

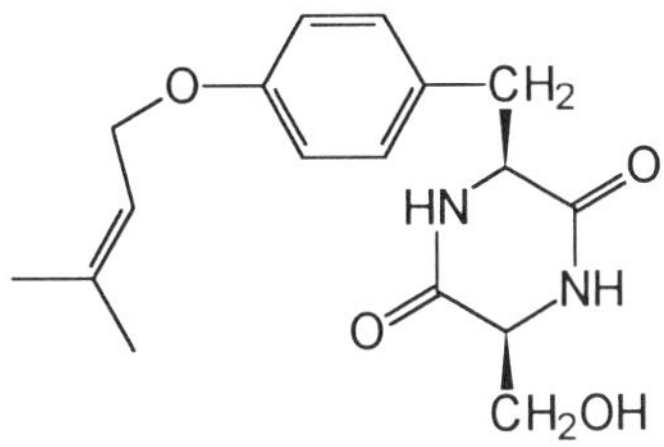

General Characteristics
White prisms from ethyl acetate; mp., 213-215°C; $[\alpha]_D^{20}$ -76° (MeOH).

Fungal Source
Phoma lingam.

Isolation/Purification
The fungal cultures were extracted with ethyl acetate and submitted to silica gel column chromatography using a gradient of methanol in ethyl acetate as eluant; the more polar fraction was combined and a second chromatography eluting with chloroform-ethyl acetate-methanol (12:4:1, v/v) afforded a crude product (amorphous). The final purification was achieved on a Sephadex LH 20 column using methanol for elution while monitoring by TLC (R_f 0.50; ethyl acetate-methanol, 4:1, v/v; Schleicher-Schüll F_{254} SiO_2 films). The pure phomamide was obtained after crystallization from ethyl acetate as white prisms.

Biological Activity
Biological activity not reported, but the metabolite is related to the sirodesmin group of antibiotics.

Spectral Data

UV:
λ_{max}^{MeOH} 209(ϵ=12,400), 229(13,500), and 277nm (1,450).

IR:
(KBr) 3500, 3320, 3200, 1680, 1650, 1620, 1585, 1515, and 825cm^{-1}.

CD:
(MeOH) 217(-10.4), 227(-0.2), and 275nm (+1).

^{1}H NMR:

[$(CD_3)_2SO$] 1.69(3H, s, 17-H_3); 1.73(3H, s, 16-H); 2.91(1H, m, A part of $A_1B_1X_1$ system, J=4.5 and 14Hz, 8-Ha); 2.91(1H, m, A part of $A_2B_2X_2$ system, J=6 and 11Hz, 7-Ha); 3.01(1 H, dd, B part of $A_1B_1X_1$ system, J=6.1 and 14Hz, 8-Hb); 3.35(1H, m, B part of $A_2B_2X_2$ system, J=3 and 11Hz, 7-Hb); 3.67 (1 H, m, X part of $A_2B_2X_2$ system, J=6 and 3Hz, 6-H); 3.99(1H, m, X part of $A_1B_1X_1$ system, J=4.5 and 6.1Hz, 3-H); 4.48(2H, d, J=6.8Hz, 13-H_2); 4.89(1H, t, exchangeable with D_2O, 7-OH); 5.41(1H, m, 14-H); 6.95(4H, m, aromatic); and 7.90 and 7.92ppm (2H, m, exchangeable with D_2O, 1- and 4-NH).

13C NMR:

$(CD_3)_2SO$ 17.9(q, C-17); 25.3(q, C-16); 38.9(t, C-8); 55.6(d, C-3 or -6); 57.1(d, C-3 or -6); 63.1(t, C-7); 64.2(t, C-13); 114.3(d, C-11 and-11'); 120.1(d, C-1 and C-10'); 128.3(s, C-9); 130.9(d, C-14); 136.7(s, C-15); 157.2(s, C-12); 165.8(s, C-2 or -5); and 166.7ppm (s, C-2 or C-5, C-carbonyl atoms).

Mass Data:

318(M^+, 2%), 250(30), 144(95), 107(97), and 69*m/e* (100); found: C, 64.3; H, 7; N, 8.5; O, 20.2; calcd. for $C_{17}H_{22}N_2O_4$: C, 64.1; H, 7; N, 8.8; O, 20.1%.

<u>Reference</u>

J-P Ferezou, A. Quesneau-Thierry, M. Barbier, A. Kollmann, and J-F Bousquet; Structure and Synthesis of Phomamide, A New Piperazine-2,5-dione Related to the Sirodesmins, Isolated from the Culture Medium of *Phoma lingam* Tode; J. C. S. Perkin I, pp. 113-115(1980).

Common/Systematic Name

D-Valyl-L-tryptophan anhydride

Molecular Formula/Molecular Weight

$C_{16}H_{19}N_3O_2$; MW = 285.14773

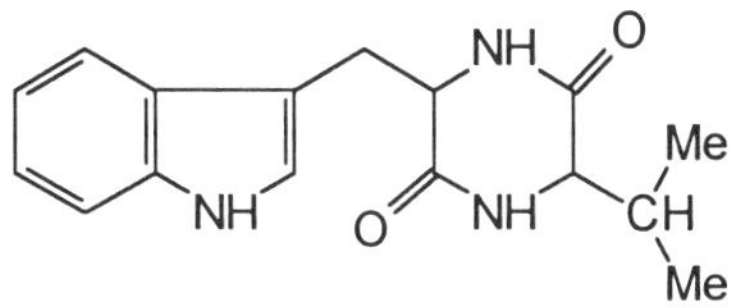

General Characteristics

Rhombic crystals changed to long needles upon heating between 235-255°C; melted between 277-279°C; $[\alpha]_D$ +78° (*c*=0.16, in acetic acid).

Fungal Source

Aspergillus chevalieri = *Eurotium chevalieri*.

Isolation/Purification

Isolated by silica gel column chromatography eluted with 1.5% methanol in chloroform. Partially purified fractions were combined and rechromatographed as above; D-valyl-L-tryptophan anhydride containing fractions crystallized as rhombic crystals.

Spectral Data

UV:

λ_{max}^{EtOH} 290(ϵ=5,800), 281(6,900), 274.5(6,500), and 220nm (43,400).

IR:

(KBr) 1660cm^{-1} indicated amide functionality.

^{1}H NMR:

Spectrum revealed a six proton doublet of doublets at 0.85 and 0.88ppm (derived from proline) that was coupled to a single proton centered at 2.23ppm (m). A one proton doublet appeared at 3.23ppm.

Mass Spectrum:

LREIMS: 285 and 130*m/e*(100%). HREIMS indicated that 285 was $C_{16}H_{19}N_3O_2$ (M^+), and 130*m/e* was C_9H_8N.

Reference

R. D. Stipanovic, H.W. Schroeder, and H. Hein, Jr.; Identification of D-Valyl-L-tryptophan Anhydride from *Aspergillus chevalieri*; Lloydia, Vol. 39, pp. 158-159(1976).

Common/Systematic Name

L-Alanyl-L-tryptophan anhydride

Molecular Formula/Molecular Weight

$C_{14}H_{15}N_3O_2$; MW = 257.11643

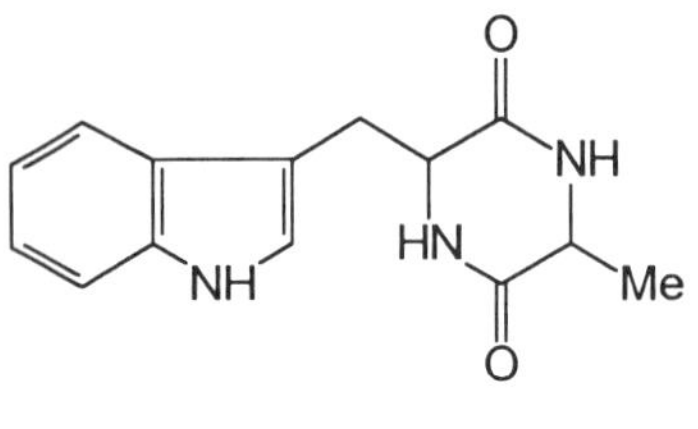

General Characteristics

Colorless needles; mp., 290-292°C (decomp.); $[\alpha]_D^{25}$ + 36° (*c*=0.5, in EtOH); positive to Ehrlich's reagent, negative to ninhydrin reagent. Treatment with 6N HCl afforded L-alanine and L-tryptophan.

Fungal Source

Aspergillus chevalieri, IFO 4090.

Isolation/Purification

The fungus was grown as a surface culture for 3 weeks at 24°C on potato extract medium. The culture filtrates were stirred with activated charcoal and the adsorbed metabolites were eluted with acetone. The acetone extracts were chromatographed on a column of silicic acid and eluted with benzene-acetone (4:1, v/v) which gave L-alanyl-2-(1,1-dimethylallyl)-L-tryptophan anhydride. Elution with benzene-acetone (2:1, v/v) gave L-alanyl-L-tryptophan anhydride.

Spectral Data

UV:

λ_{max} 220(ϵ=38,000), 273(6,100), 280(6,300), and 290nm (5,800).

IR:

3420(NH), 1675(C=O, amide), and 1665cm^{-1} (C=O, amide).

^{1}H NMR:

The spectrum revealed: a doublet at 0.48ppm (3H, doublet, *J*=7Hz) due to the alanyl methyl protons which showed coupling with a proton at 3.63ppm (1H, quartet of doublets, *J*=7 and 2Hz); two doublets of doublets at 3.05ppm (1H, doublet of doublets, *J*=15 and 5Hz) and 3.22ppm (1H, doublet of doublets, *J*=15 and 3Hz) assigned to the allylic methylene protons which showed coupling with a proton at 4.12ppm (1H, multiplet); a signal at 10.86ppm (1H, broad) assigned to the -NH group proton in the indole ring system. This proton coupled with a proton at 7.09ppm (1H, doublet, *J*=3Hz) because of a proton at position 2 in the indole ring system. Protons at 7.90ppm (1H, broad) and 7.95ppm (1H, broad) assigned to -NH groups in the dioxopiperazine ring system showed coupling with protons at 3.63 and 4.12ppm, respectively. These three protons at 7.90, 7.95, and 10.86ppm disappeared on treatment with deuterium oxide. Signals of the four aromatic protons were observed at 6.8-7.8ppm (4H, multiplet).

Mass Data:

LREIMS: 257(M^+); found: C, 65.00; H, 5.79; N, 16.18; calcd. for $C_{14}H_{15}N_3O_2$: C, 65.35; H, 5.88; N, 16.33%

Reference

T. Hamasaki, K. Nagayama, and Y. Hatsuda; A New Metabolite, L-Alanyl-L-tryptophan Anhydride from *Aspergillus chevalieri*; Agr. Biol. Chem., Vol. 40, p. 2487(1976).

Common/Systematic Name

cyclo-(L-Isoleucyl-L-valine)

Molecular Formula/Molecular Weight

$C_{11}H_{20}N_2O_2$; MW = 212.15248

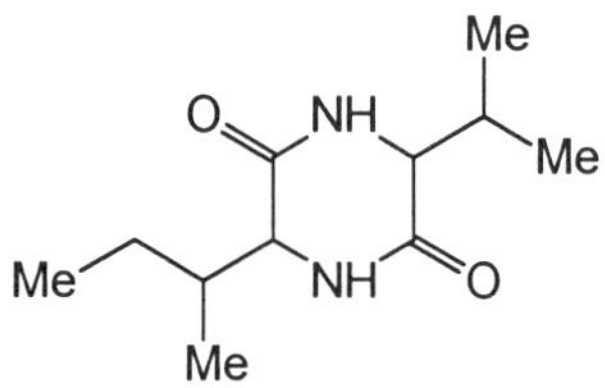

General Characteristics

Sublimed without melting at 250°C; $[\alpha]_D^{22}$ - 40°(*c*=0.908, in EtOH)

Fungal Source

Beauveria bassiana.

Isolation/Purification

The metabolite was purified with silica gel column chromatography by elution with benzene-ethyl acetate (9:1, v/v) followed by sublimation at 250°C.

Spectral Data

IR:

(Nujol) 3195, 3050, and 1642 cm^{-1} for N-H and amide carbonyl groups.

Mass Spectrum:

LREIMS: 212(M^+), 197(-CH_3), 183(-C_2H_5), 170, 156(100%), 141, 127, 114, 113(100), 86, 85, 72, 69, and 57*m/e*.

References

S. Eriksen and I. S. Fagerson; Mass Spectra of Some Cyclic Dipeptides (2,5-Diketopiperazines); J. Agric. Food Chem., Vol. 24, pp. 1242-1243(1976).

J. F. Grove and M. Pople; Nitrogen-Containing Minor Metabolic Products of *Beauveria bassiana*; Phytochem., Vol. 20, pp. 815-816(1981).

Common/Systematic Name

cyclo-(L-Alanyl-L-proline)

Molecular Formula/Molecular Weight

$C_8H_{12}N_2O_2$; MW = 168.08988

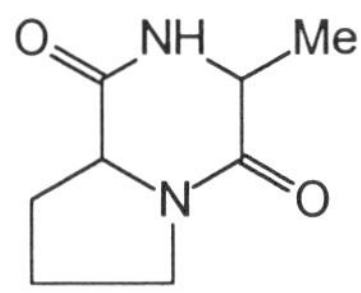

General Characteristics

Crystals from methanol; mp., 162-166°C; $[\alpha]_D^{22}$ - 85°(*c*=0.17, in EtOH)

Fungal Source

Beauveria bassiana.

Isolation/Purification

The metabolite was purified with silica gel column chromatography by elution with benzene-ethyl acetate (9:1, v/v) followed by crystallization from methanol.

Spectral Data

IR:

(Nujol) 3280, and 1657cm^{-1} for N-H and amide carbonyl groups.

Mass Spectrum:

HREIMS: 168.0904*m/e* (M^+); $C_8H_{12}N_2O_2$ requires 168.0898.

Reference

J. F. Grove and M. Pople; Nitrogen-Containing Minor Metabolic Products of *Beauveria bassiana*; Phytochem., Vol. 20, pp. 815-816(1981).

Common/Systematic Name

Neoxaline

Molecular Formula/Molecular Weight

$C_{23}H_{25}N_5O_4$; MW = 435.19065

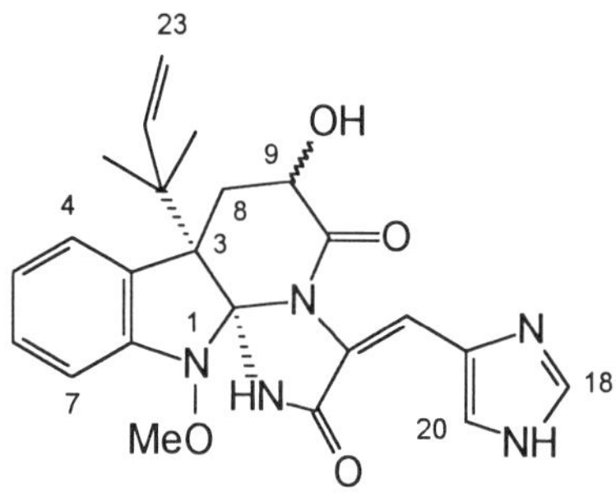

General Characteristics

Colorless needles from benzene; mp., 202°C (dec.); $[\alpha]_D^{24}$ -16.3° (*c*=1.0, in $CHCl_3$).

Fungal Source

Penicillium sp. Fg-234 and *Aspergillus japonicus* Fg-551.

Spectral Data

UV:

λ_{max}^{MeOH} 330(є=29,560) and 237nm (17,620).

IR:

3500(OH), 3425(CONH), 3200(NH, imidazole), 1710, and 1685cm^{-1} (NC=O).

CD:

(c=0.0009, in EtOH) - 430(372nm) (negative maximum), + 1,200(339nm) (positive maximum), + 800(335.5nm) (negative maximum), + 1,200(328nm) (positive maximum), + 800(311nm) (negative maximum), + 4,800(290nm) (positive maximum), + 4,750(285nm) (negative maximum), + 8,970(267nm) (positive maximum), - 11,200(245.5nm) (negative maximum), and + 5,600(223nm) (positive maximum).

^{1}H NMR:

(acetone-d_6) H-4, 7.58(dd, *J*=8.0, 2.0Hz); H-5, 7.02(dt, *J*=2.0, 8.0Hz); H-6, 7.27(dt, *J*=2.0, 8.0Hz); H-7, 6.91(dd, *J*=2.0, 8.0Hz); H-8, 2.44(t, *J*=12.0Hz), 2.23(dd, *J*=12.0, 6.0Hz); H-9, 4.60(dd, *J*=12.0, 6.0Hz); H-15, 8.29(s); H-18, 7.79(s); H-20, 7.31(s); H-22, 6.12(dd, *J*=18.0, 10.0Hz); H-23, 5.11(d, *J*=18Hz), ca. 4.97; 1-OMe, 3.73(s); 21-OMe$_2$, 1.31(s), 1.31(s); NH, 8.98(br s), 2.32(s); and OH, ca. 1.31ppm.

^{13}C NMR:

C-2, 100.6(s); C-3, 53.3(s); C-3a, 128.2(s); C-4, 124.8(d); C-5, 123.6(d); C-6, 128.9(d); C-7, 111.5(d); C-7a, 145.7(s); C-8, 40.8(t); C-9, 66.4(d); C-10, 171.65(s); C-12, 122.3(s); C-13, 165.6(s); C-15, 110.3(d); C-16, 125.8(s); C-18, 136.8(d); C-20, 134.4(d); C-21, 43.5(s); C-22, 144.5(d); C-23, 114.1(t); 1-OMe, 65.2(q); and 21-Me_2, 24.7(q), 24.5ppm (q).

Mass Data:

HREIMS: 435.191*m/e* (M^+) (calcd. 435.190); anal calcd. for $C_{23}H_{25}N_5O_4$: C, 63.43%; H, 5.79; N, 16.08; found: 63.23; H, 5.70; N, 15.90.

Reference

Y. Konda, M. Onda, A. Hirano, and S. Omura; Oxaline and Neoxaline; Chem. Pharm. Bull., Vol. 28, pp. 2987-2993(1980).

Common/Systematic Name

Oxaline

Molecular Formula/Molecular Weight

$C_{24}H_{25}N_5O_4$; MW = 447.19065

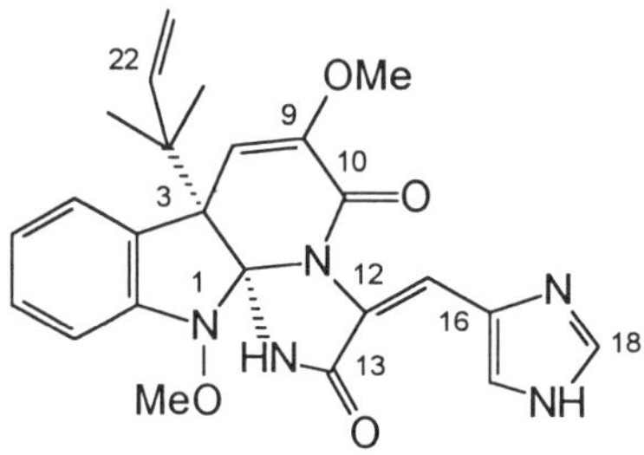

General Characteristics

Colorless prisms from acetone; mp., 230-232°C; $[\alpha]_D^{22}$ -45° (*c*=0.3, in MeOH).

Fungal Source

Penicillium sp. Fg-234, *P. oxalicum* M-555, and *Aspergillus japonicus* Fg-551.

Isolation/Purification

The culture broth including mycelium was adjusted to pH 10.0 with aqueous ammonia and extracted with butyl acetate. The extract was concentrated *in vacuo* and the precipitate removed by filtration. The filtrate,which was dried over Na_2SO_4 and concentrated *in vacuo*, yielded pale brownish crystals which were recrystallized from acetone to yield colorless prisms.

Biological Activity

Biologically inactive.

Spectral Data

UV:

λ_{max}^{MeOH} 345(ε=25,200) and 228nm (21,300).

IR:

($CHCl_3$) 3420(CONH), 3180(NH), 1710, and 1680cm^{-1} (NC=O).

CD:

(*c*=0.001, in MeOH) - 24,400(344nm) (negative maximum), + 38,200(273nm) (positive maximum), + 34,300(260nm) (negative maximum), + 42,00(247nm) (positive maximum), and - 98,300 (223nm) (negative maximum).

^{1}H NMR:
(CDCl$_3$) H-4, 7.57(d, J=8.0Hz); H-5, 7.06(t, J=8.0Hz); H-6, 7.27(t, J=8.0Hz); H-7, 6.95(d, J=8.0Hz); H-8, 5.12(s); H-15, 8.32(s); H-18, 7.42(s); H-20, 7.02(s); H-22, 6.09(dd, J=18.0, 10.0Hz); H-23, 5.06(d, J=18Hz), 5.02(d, J=10.0Hz); 1-OMe, 3.70(s); 9-OMe, 3.62(s); 21-Me$_2$, 1.29(s), 1.25(s); NH, 12.76(s); and 9.59ppm (s).

^{13}C NMR:
C-2, 101.7(s); C-3, 52.5(s); C-3a, 126.1(s); C-4, 124.7(d); C-5, 123.2(d); C-6, 128.5(d); C-7, 112.0(d); C-7a, 146.8(s); C-8, 106.9(d); C-9, 146.4(s); C-10, 157.5(s); C-12, 123.2(s); C-13, 166.3(s); C-15, 109.6(d); C-16, 126.1(s); C-18, 136.4(d); C-20, 133.8(d); C-21, 42.5(s); C-22, 142.8(d); C-23, 113.9(t); 1-OMe, 65.2(q); 9-OMe, 55.7(q); and 21-Me$_2$, 24.1(q), 23.7ppm (q).

Reference

Y. Konda, M. Onda, A. Hirano, and S. Omura; Oxaline and Neoxaline; Chem. Pharm. Bull., Vol. 28, pp. 2987-2993(1980).

Common/Systematic Name
Aszonalenin

Molecular Formula/Molecular Weight
$C_{23}H_{23}N_3O_2$; MW = 373.17903

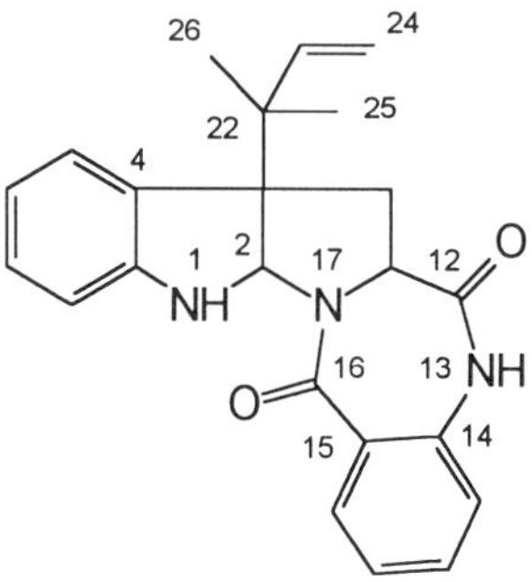

General Characteristics
Colorless needles from chloroform-methanol; mp., 244-247°C; $[\alpha]_D^{20}$ + 53° (c=1.31, in $CHCl_3$); positive to Ehrlich's reagent.

Fungal Source
Aspergillus zonatus IFO 8817.

Isolation/Purification
The fungus was stationarily cultured at 24°C for 21 days in malt extract medium. The acetone extract from the dry mycelial mats was chromatographed on a silica gel column eluted with benzene-acetone (19:1, v/v). After elution of LL-S490β, aszonalenin was obtained as a crude substance, which was rechromatographed over silica gel eluted with benzene-ethyl acetate (19:1, v/v) to give colorless crystals of aszonalenin.

Biological Activity
Application of aszonalenin at a concentration of 50μg/ml apparently induced the abnormal cleavage of sea urchin embryos.

Spectral Data

UV:
λ_{max}^{EtOH} 210(ε=44,700), 233(sh, 25,100), and 290nm (5,050).

IR:
(KBr) 3400(NH), 1700(C=O, amide), 1640(C=O, amide), 1620(C=C), and 1578cm^{-1} (aromatic).

^{1}H NMR:

(CDCl$_3$) ^{1}H NMR spectrum was very similar to that of LL-S490β. A signal at 2.59ppm due to methyl protons of an acetyl group in the spectrum of LL-S490β was not observed in the NMR spectrum of aszonalenin; an additional signal at ca. 7.0ppm assignable to -NH- was present in the spectrum of aszonalenin. Signals from a 1,1-dimethyl-2-propenyl group were observed at 1.08, 1.16, 5.04, 5.07, and 6.10ppm; a signal at 8.77ppm was assigned to an amide proton; and signals between 6.55-7.92ppm were assigned to eight aromatic protons.

^{13}C NMR:

(CDCl$_3$) Signals at 24.2(q) and 171.7(s) due to an acetyl group in spectrum of LL-S490β were not observed in this case. Signals from a 1,1-dimethyl-2-propenyl group were observed at 22.6, 22.9, 41.7, 114.3, and 144.1ppm; C-10, 33.6; C-11, 57.5; C-12, 170.2; C-16, 168.0; twelve signals between 119.3-141.8, aromatic carbons; 82.0, C-2; and 61.1ppm, C-3.

Mass Spectrum:

LREIMS: 373(M$^+$), 304(M$^+$ - 69, base peak), and 130*m/e* (due to indoline-3-methylene ion).

Reference

Y. Kimura, T. Hamasaki, and H. Nakajima; Structure of Aszonalenin, a New Metabolite of *Aspergillus zonatus*; Tetrahedron Letters, Vol. 23, pp. 225-228(1982).

Common/Systematic Name

LL-S490β; Acetylaszonalenin

Molecular Formula/Molecular Weight

$C_{25}H_{25}N_3O_3$; MW = 415.18959

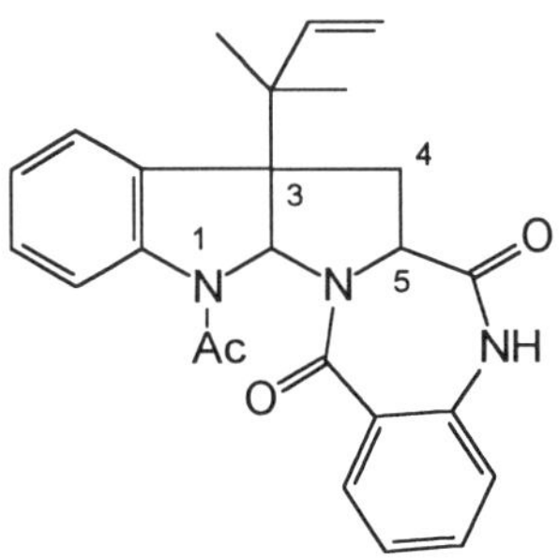

General Characteristics

Crystals from ethyl acetate-benzene; mp., 238-240°C; $[\alpha]_D^{20}$ + 425° (*c*=0.20, in MeOH).

Fungal Source

Aspergillus sp.

Isolation/Purification

The whole mash from a fermentation was extracted with an equal volume of ethyl acetate at pH 5.0. The extract was concentrated to dryness and the residue was partitioned between methanol and heptane to remove fatty material. Evaporation to dryness of the methanol portion gave a crude residue. This residue was chromatographed over a silica gel column (acid washed) packed in methylene chloride. A gradient elution between 0.5% methanol-methylene chloride and 3% methanol-methylene chloride provided cladosporin after evaporation of the solvent and crystallization from ethyl acetate-benzene. Further elution, removal of the solvent, and crystallization from ethyl acetate gave LL-S490β.

Spectral Data

UV:

λ_{max}^{MeOH} 210(ϵ=61,000), 245(22,000), and 284nm (sh, 3,940).

IR:

(KBr) 3300(NH), 1689(C=O, amide), and 1647cm^{-1} (C=O, amide).

^{1}H NMR:

($CDCl_3$) 1.02 and 1.21(3H, s); 2.60(3H, s); 2.46(q, J_{AB}=14, J_{AX}= 8.0Hz); 3.42(q, J_{AB}=14, J_{BX}=8.5Hz); 3.90(t, J=8 Hz); 5.16(m, AB of vinylidene); 5.92 (q, J_{trans}=18, J_{cis}=9.5Hz, X of vinylidene); 6.00(1H, s); 6.83-8.17(8H, m); and 8.45ppm (1H, S).

Mass Data:
HREIMS: 415.18919 (calcd.for $C_{25}H_{25}N_3O_3$, 415.18959).

Reference

G. A. Ellestad, P. Mirando, and M. P. Kunstmann; Structure of the Metabolite LL-S490β from an Unidentified *Aspergillus* species; J. Org. Chem., Vol. 38, pp. 4204-4205(1973).

Common/Systematic Name
Bipolaramide

Molecular Formula/Molecular Weight
$C_{18}H_{14}N_2O_4$; MW = 322.09536

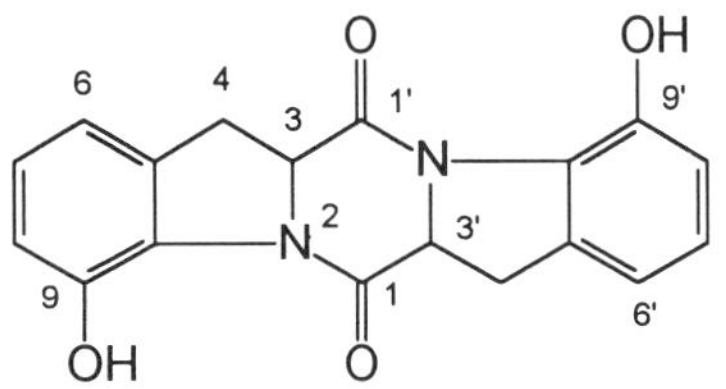

General Characteristics
Crystallized from acetone as colorless needle-shaped crystals; mp., 296-297°C; $[\alpha]_D$ -210° (*c*=1.0, in acetone).

Fungal Source
Bipolaris sorokiniana (IMI 115076); a toxigenic strain isolated in the Karroo from an indigenous weed *Tribulis terrestris.*

Spectral Data

UV:
λ_{max}^{MeOH} 218, 260, and 294nm (log ϵ=4.65, 4.17, and 3.88, respectively).

IR:
(KBr) 1645(amide CO) and 1610cm^{-1}.

^{1}H NMR:
(acetone-d_6) 7.15(1H, t, *J*=7.5Hz); 6.87(1H, dd, *J*=7.5, 2.8Hz); 6.80(1H, dd, *J*=7.5, 2.8Hz); 5.53(1H, t, *J*=9.8Hz); 3.78(1H, dd, *J*=17.3, 9.8Hz); 3.51(1H, dd, *J*=17.3, 9.8Hz); and 11.40ppm (D_2O-exchangeable hydroxy group).

^{13}C NMR:
[$(CD_3)_2CO$] 164.5(s); 145.1(s); 132.4(d); 127.5(d); 126.3(d); 116.4(d); 115.4(d); 61.4(d); and 30.3ppm (t). These data indicated the presence of three contiguous aromatic protons and of an ABX aliphatic system. The vicinal coupling constants (*J*=9.8Hz) observed for the ABX system are in accordance with the dihedral angular relationship obtained from X-ray crystallography: 149.8 and 31.6° for H(3)-C(3)-C(4)-H(4A) and H(3)-C(3)-C(4)-H(4B), respectively.

Mass Spectrum:
322(M$^+$) and 161*m/e*.

Reference

C. M. Maes, P. S. Steyn, P. H. van Rooyen, and C. J. Rabieb; The Structure of Bipolaramide, a Novel Dioxopiperazine from *Bipolaris sorokiniana*; J. Chem. Soc. Chem. Commun., pp. 350-351(1982).

Common/Systematic Name

Austamide

Molecular Formula/Molecular Weight

$C_{21}H_{21}N_3O_3$; MW = 363.15829

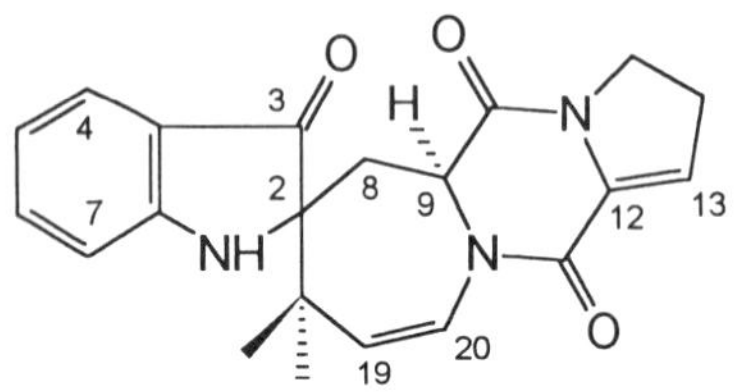

General Characteristics

A yellow amorphous compound or homogeneous powder; $[\alpha]_D^{20}$ +152° (*c*=1, in EtOH).

Fungal Source

Aspergillus ustus (C.S.I.R. 1128; NRRL 5856).

Isolation/Purification

The dried *Aspergillus ustus* cultures were extracted with $CHCl_3$-MeOH and the solvent removed under reduced pressure which yielded homogenous crystalline material. This represented the main toxic component of the fungal culture. The latter in $CHCl_3$ was extracted twice with water. Evaporation of the $CHCl_3$ yielded material which was partitioned between 90% MeOH and hexane, yielding toxic material in the MeOH layer. This toxic material was further purified by chromatography on formamide-impregnated cellulose powder. The cellulose column was developed with a mixture of hexane and benzene. The toxic material was further separated on Al_2O_3 (activity III). Elution with mixtures of benzene and $CHCl_3$ gave pure austamide and a mixture of austamide and 12,13-dehydroaustamide.

Biological Activity

Austamide was one of the active components in extracts of *A. ustus* (cultured on maize) causing acute toxicosis in day old ducklings.

Spectral Data

UV:

λ_{max}^{EtOH} 234(ϵ=26,302), 256(117), 268 sh (1,096), 282(8,709), and 392nm (2,691) (unchanged upon addition of acid or base).

IR:

($CHCl_3$) 3420, 1700, 1680, and 1650cm^{-1}.

CD:
(in MeOH) 390(+2.0), 285(+1.8), and 234nm (20-25).

^{13}C NMR:
23.6, 26.1, 28.0, 41.9, 42.0, 45.5, 62.5, 70.7, 111.9, 118.7, 120.3, 120.4, 124.4, 125.4, 128.3, 132.2, 137.3, 154.7, 160.1, 161.1, and 200.8ppm.

TLC Data
Silica gel; chloroform-methanol, 97:3 v/v; R_f not reported. Detection: not reported.

References
R. J. Cole and R. H. Cox; Handbook of Toxic Fungal Metabolites; Academic Press, New York, pp.484 (1981).

P. S. Steyn; The Structures of Five Diketopiperazines from *Aspergillus ustus;* Tetrahedron, Vol. 29, pp. 107-120(1973).

Common/Systematic Name

12,13-Dihydroaustamide

Molecular Formula/Molecular Weight

$C_{21}H_{23}N_3O_3$; MW = 365.17394

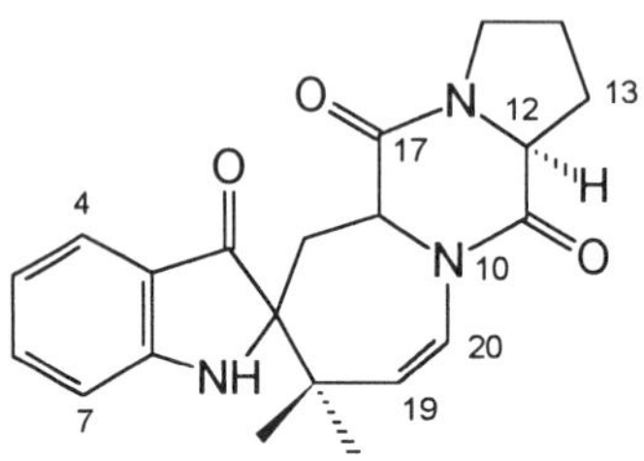

General Characteristics

Crystallized from acetone; mp., 235-238°C; $[\alpha]_D^{22}$ +55° (*c*=1.1, in $CHCl_3$).

Fungal Source

Aspergillus ustus (C.S.I.R. 1128; NRRL 5856) and *Penicillium italicum*.

Isolation/Purification

The dried moldy maize culture was extracted with $CHCl_3$-MeOH and the solvent removed under reduced pressure which yielded homogenous crystalline material which represented the main toxic components of the fungal culture. The latter in $CHCl_3$ was twice extracted with water. Evaporation of the $CHCl_3$ yielded material which was partitioned between 90% MeOH and hexane, yielding toxic material in the MeOH layer. This toxic material was further purified by chromatography on formamide-impregnated cellulose powder. The cellulose column was developed with a mixture of hexane and benzene. The toxic material was further separated on Al_2O_3 (activity III). Elution with mixtures of benzene and $CHCl_3$ gave a mixture of austamide and 12,13-dehydroaustamide. The latter metabolites were separated by repeated preparatory silica gel TLC developed in $CHCl_3$-MeOH (97:3, v/v) yielding pure 12,13-dehydroaustamide.

Biological Activity

Toxic to ducklings.

Spectral Data

UV:

λ_{max}^{EtOH} 238(log ϵ=4.49), 256(sh)(4.13), and 390nm (3.52).

IR:

($CHCl_3$) 3420, 3335, 3,000, 1670, and 1620cm^{-1}.

^{1}H NMR:

The NMR spectrum of 12,13-dihydroaustamide when compared with that of austamide showed the absence of the olefinic triplet at 3.74τ and the newly formed proton at C12 at 5.82τ. Concurrently the peaks comprising the proline part became more complex.

Mass Spectrum:

HREIMS: 365.1750(M^+, $C_{21}H_{23}N_3O_3$ requires 365.1739), 192.1268 ($C_{11}H_{16}N_2O$ requires 192.1262), and 70.0656*m/e* (C_4H_8N requires 70.0656).

Reference

P. S. Steyn; The Structures of Five Diketopiperazines from *Aspergillus ustus*; Tetrahedron, Vol. 29, pp. 107-120(1973).

Common/Systematic Name

12,13-Dihydro-12-hydroxyaustamide

2*S*,9*S*,12*R*-12,13-Dihydro-12-hydroxyaustamide

Molecular Formula/Molecular Weight

$C_{21}H_{23}N_3O_4$; MW = 381.16886

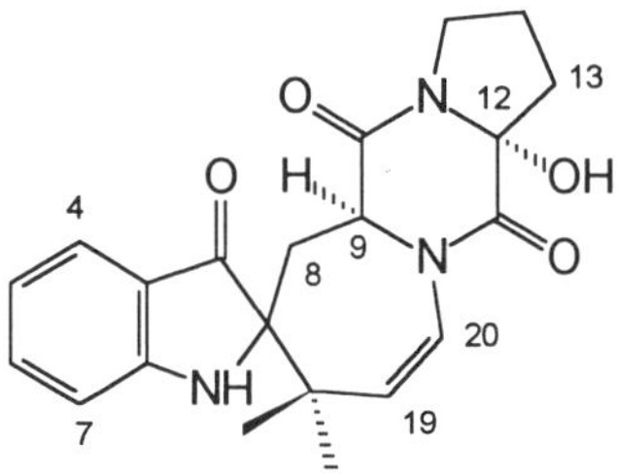

General Characteristics

Crystals from MeOH; mp., 164-165°C.

Fungal Source

Aspergillus ustus.

Isolation/Purification

Isolated from *A. ustus* fermented corn and separated by chromatography on formamide-impregnated cellulose powder; further purified by extensive column chromatography and TLC on silica gel and aluminum oxide; crystallized from methanol.

Biological Activity

Toxic to ducklings.

Spectral Data

UV:

λ_{max}^{MeOH} 231, 255, and 390nm (log ϵ= 4.48, 4.04, and 3.47, respectively).

CD:

λ_{max}^{MeOH} 420(0), 374(-2.0), 355(0), 341(+2.35), 3140, 305(-0.34), and 290 (0).

IR:

($CHCl_3$) 3430-3350, 1670, and 1618cm^{-1}.

^{1}H NMR:

($CDCl_3$) Spectrum showed 2 singlets at 8.48(3H) and 9.16τ (3H) which were assigned to the two geminal methyl groups; the *cis*-olefinic protons appeared as an AB-pattern at 3.29 and 4.98τ(J_{AB}=10Hz); protons at C-8 and C-9 appeared as an ABX system, HA being H_{8eq}, 7.13τ(q, J_{AB}=15Hz, J_{BX}=12Hz); a complex pattern centered around 6.36τ was assigned to the methylene protons adjacent to the proline N-atom; the remaining 4 methylene protons which comprised the proline ring appeared as an unresolved multiplet between 7.6 and 8.1τ; the proton at C-12 resonated between 5.80-5.90τ; and the splitting pattern of the aromatic region was identical to that of dihydroaustamide.

Mass Spectrum:
HREIMS: 381.1685(M^+, $C_{21}H_{23}N_3O_4$ requires 381.1688) and 363*m/e* for $C_{12}H_{14}N_2O_2$.

Reference

P. S. Steyn and R. Vleggaar; 12,13-Dihydro-12-hydroxyaustamide, A New Dioxopiperazine from *Aspergillus ustus*; Phytochemistry, Vol. 15, pp. 355-356(1976).

Common/Systematic Name

Cycloechinulin

Molecular Formula/Molecular Weight

$C_{20}H_{21}N_3O_3$; MW = 352.15829

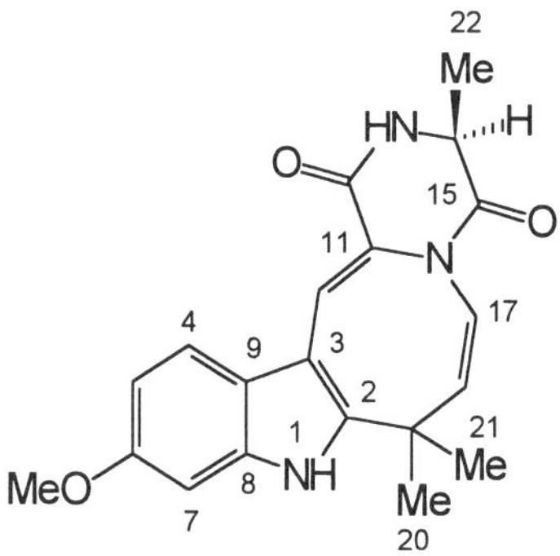

General Characteristics

Cycloechinulin was isolated as a yellow solid; $[\alpha]_D$ -23.3° (*c*=0.06g/dl, in $CHCl_3$).

Fungal Source

Sclerotia of *Aspergillus ochraceus* (NRRL 3519).

Isolation/Purification

Intact sclerotia of *A. ochraceus* were extracted at room temperature with hexane, then $CHCl_3$. After removal of the solvent *in vacuo*, the hexane extract was subjected to reversed-phase HPLC [MeOH-H_2O (9:1, v/v), 2ml/min} to give *N*-methylepiamauromine. The $CHCl_3$ extract, after removal of the solvent *in vacuo*, was fractionated through a column of Sephadex LH-20 (25-100μ) using CH_2Cl_2-hexane (1:1, v/v), then CH_2Cl_2-MeOH (1:1, v/v) as eluents. The fractions obtained with CH_2Cl_2-hexane (1:1, v/v) were combined, concentrated, and purified by HPLC as above to give epiamauromine and *N*-methylepiamauromine. The fractions eluted with CH_2Cl_2-MeOH (1:1, v/v) were likewise combined, concentrated, rechromatographed on Sephadex LH-20 using $CHCl_3$-MeOH (2:1, v/v), and purified by reversed-phase HPLC to yield cycloechinulin.

Biological Activity

Caused moderate reduction in weight gain in assays against the lepidopteran crop pest *Helicoverpa zea*.

Spectral Data

UV:

λ_{max}^{MeOH} 214(log ϵ=4.3), 228(4.2), 267(4.0), 300(4.1), and 377nm (3.9).

^{1}H NMR:

(CDCl$_3$) H-1,8.39, br s; H-4, 7.63, d(J=8.7); H-5, 6.84, dd(J=2.2, 8.7); H-7, 6.81, d(J=2.1); H-10, 7.57, s; H- 13, 6.37, br s; H-14, 4.13, dq(J=2.3, 6.9); H-17, 5.82, d(J=8.2); H-18, 5.94, d(J=8.2); H-20, 1.68, s; H-21, 1.67, s; H-22, 1.51, d(J=6.9); and H-23, 3.81ppm, s.

^{13}C NMR:

(CDCl$_3$) C-2, 145.8; C-3, 105.7; C-4, 118.7; C-5, 110.9; C-6, 157.2; C-7, 94.8; C-8, 134.0; C-9, 124.4; C-10, 115.4; C-11, 125.0; C-12, 165.6; C-14, 51.1; C-15, 167.2; C-17, 122.4; C-18, 139.7; C-19, 36.0; C-20, 27.2; C-21, 27.0; C-22, 18.4; and C-23, 55.8ppm.

Mass Spectrum:

EIMS: $[M]^+$ 351(77), 336(100), 308(20), 296(26), 293(37), 280(93), 265(34), 252(46), 251(47), 237(94), 225(82), 222(31), and 197*m/e* (64); HRFABMS found 352.1671; calcd for $C_{20}H_{21}N_3O_3$ +H 352.1661.

HPLC Data

Beckman Ultrasphere 5µm (10mm x 25cm) C_{18} reversed-phase column was used on all HPLC separations; HPLC retention time for cycloechinulin was 7.5 min.

Reference

F. S. de Guzman, J. B. Gloer, D. T. Wicklow, and P. F. Dowd; New Diketopiperazine Metabolites from the Sclerotia of *Aspergillus ochraceus*; Journal of Natural Products, Vol. 55, pp. 931-939(1992).

Common/Systematic Name

12,13-Dehydroprolyl-2-(1',1'-dimethylallyltryptophyl) diketopiperazine

Molecular Formula/Molecular Weight

$C_{21}H_{23}N_3O_2$; MW = 349.17903

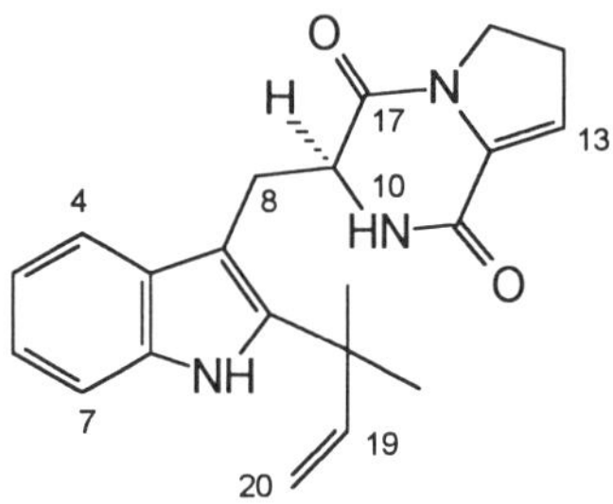

General Characteristics

Homogenous powder; $[\alpha]_D^{22}$ -38° (*c*=1.3, in $CHCl_3$).

Fungal Source

Aspergillus ustus (C.S.I.R. 1128; NRRL 5856) and *Penicillium italicum*.

Isolation/Purification

The dried moldy corn was extracted with $CHCl_3$-MeOH and the solvent removed under reduced pressure which yielded homogenous crystalline material which represented the main toxic components of the fungal culture. The latter in $CHCl_3$ was twice extracted with water. Evaporation of the $CHCl_3$ yielded material which was partitioned between 90% MeOH and hexane, yielding toxic material in the MeOH layer. This toxic material was further purified by chromatography on formamide-impregnated cellulose powder. The cellulose column was developed with a mixture of hexane and benzene. The toxic material was further separated on Al_2O_3 (activity III). Elution with benzene gave a mixture of compounds. The latter material was separated by silica gel TLC developed in $CHCl_3$-MeOH (98:2, v/v) yielding pure 10,20-dehydro[12,13-dehydropropyl]-2-(1',1'-dimethyl-allyltryptophyl)diketopiperazine. Elution of the foregoing Al_2O_3 column with $CHCl_3$-benzene (6:4, v/v) gave pure 12,13-dehydroprolyl-2-(1',1'- dimethylallyltryptophyl)-diketopiperazine as a homogenous powder.

Biological Activity

Toxic to ducklings.

Spectral Data

UV:

λ_{max}^{EtOH} 223(log ϵ=4.54), 268(sh)(4.03), 283(4.00), and 292nm (3.89).

IR:
(CHCl$_3$) 3482, 3460, 3380, 1670, and 1650cm^{-1}.

^{1}H NMR:
The NMR spectra of deoxybrevianamide E and 12,13-dehydroprolyl-2-(1',1'-dimethyl allyltryptophyl)diketopiperazine had many features in common, the most striking difference being due to protons of the proline ring. These protons appeared as an A_2M_2X pattern, represented by a triplet at 6.0τ (2H, *J*=9Hz, C-15 CH$_2$), a sextet at 7.31τ (2H, *J*=3, 9, 9Hz, C-14 CH$_2$), and a triplet at 3.94τ (1H, *J*=3Hz, C-13 CH).

Mass Spectrum:
HREIMS: 349.1720(M$^+$, $C_{21}H_{23}N_3O_2$ requires 349.1708).

References

R. J. Cole and R. H. Cox; Handbook of Toxic Fungal Metabolites; Academic Press, New York, p. 453 (1981).

P. S. Steyn; The Structures of Five Diketopiperazines from *Aspergillus ustus*; Tetrahedron, Vol. 29, pp. 107-120(1973).

Common/Systematic Name

Alanyl-2-(1,1-dimethyl-2-propenyl)dehydrotryptophan anhydride

Molecular Formula/Molecular Weight

$C_{19}H_{21}N_3O_2$; MW = 323.16338

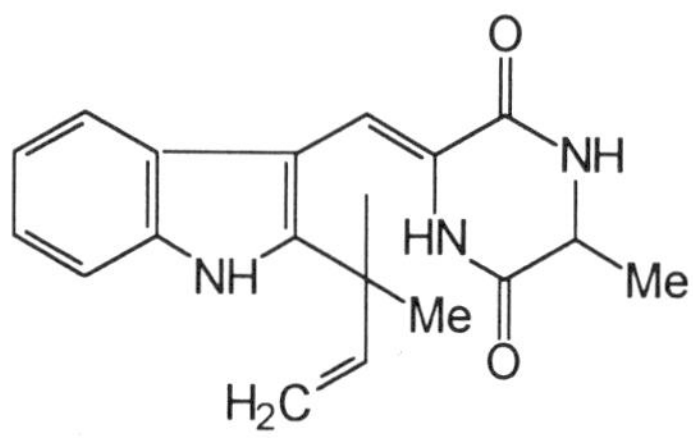

General Characteristics

Crystals; mp., 262-264°C.

Fungal Source

Aspergillus ruber → *Eurotium rubrum* isolated from beet pulp.

Isolation/Purification

Mycelia was extracted with ethyl acetate. The ethyl acetate-soluble/neutral fraction was chromatographed on a silica gel column using benzene-ethyl acetate. The benzene-40% ethyl acetate eluant gave two indole metabolites which were separated with preparative thin-layer chromatography developed with benzene-ethyl acetate (1:1, v/v).

Biological Activity

Growth retardant for silkworm larvae (*Bombyx mori* L.).

Spectral Data

UV:

λ_{max}^{MeOH} 224(ϵ=31,600), 283 (8,300), 290(8,050), and 338nm (9,340).

IR:

(Nujol) 1675 and 1633cm^{-1}.

^{1}H NMR:

(DMSO-d_6) 11.03(lH, s, -NH-, indole nucleus), 8.57(1H, s, -NH-CO-), 8.31(1H, s,-NH-CO-), 7.44-7.00(4H, m), 6.92(1H, s), 6.10(1H, dd, J=9.9Hz and 17.8Hz -CH=CH_2), 5.02(1H, dd, J=9.9Hz and 1.1Hz; 1H, dd, J=17.8Hz and 1.1Hz, -CH=CH_2), 4.17(1H, q, J=7.0Hz, =CH-CH_3), 1.48(6H, s, $(CH_3)_2C$=), and 1.38ppm (3H, d, J=7.0Hz, =CH-CH_3).

Mass Spectrum:
323.1601*m/e* (M^+) and 254(M^+ - C_5H_9); calcd for $C_{19}H_{21}N_3O_2$, 323.1631.

Reference

H. Nagasawa, A. Isogal, K. Ikeda, S. Sato, S. Murakoshi, A. Suzuki, and S. Tamura; Isolation and Structure Elucidation of a New Indole Metabolite from *Aspergillus ruber*; Agr. Biol. Chem., Vol. 39, pp. 1901-1902(1975).

Common/Systematic Name

10,20-Dehydro[12,13-dehydroprolyl]-2-(1',1'-dimethylallyltryptophyl)diketopiperazine

Molecular Formula/Molecular Weight

$C_{21}H_{21}N_3O_2$; MW = 349.16338

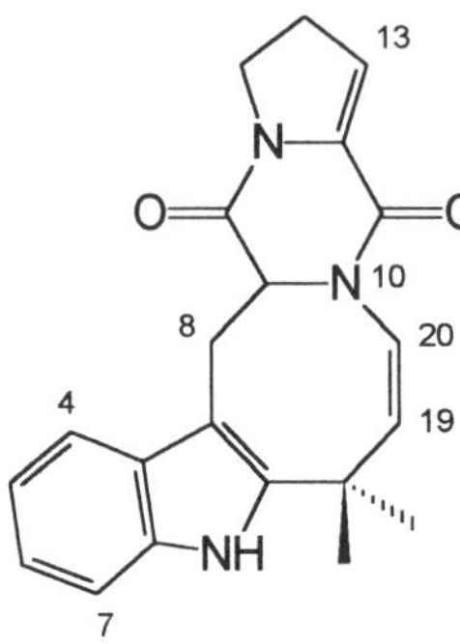

Fungal Source

Aspergillus ustus (C.S.I.R. 1128; NRRL 5856) and *Penicillium italicum*.

Isolation/Purification

Dried moldy maize was extracted with $CHCl_3$-MeOH and the solvent removed under reduced pressure which yielded homogenous crystalline material which represented the main toxic components of the fungal culture. The latter in $CHCl_3$ was twice extracted with water. Evaporation of the $CHCl_3$ yielded material which was partitioned between 90% MeOH and hexane, yielding toxic material in the MeOH layer. This toxic material was further purified by chromatography on formamide-impregnated cellulose powder. The cellulose column was developed with a mixture of hexane and benzene. The toxic material was further separated on Al_2O_3 (activity III). Elution with benzene gave a mixture of compounds. The latter material was separated by silica gel TLC developed in $CHCl_3$-MeOH (98:2, v/v) yielding pure 10,20-dehydro[12,13-dehydropropyl]-2-(1',1'-dimethyl-allyltryptophyl)diketopiperazine. Elution of the foregoing Al_2O_3 column with $CHCl_3$-benzene (6:4, v/v) gave pure 12,13-dehydroprolyl-2-(1',1'-dimethylallyltryptophyl)-diketopiperazine as a homogenous powder.

Biological Activity

Toxic to ducklings.

Spectral Data

UV:

λ_{max}^{EtOH} 224(log ϵ=4.44), 272(sh)(3.93), 284(3.84), and 292nm (3.71).

IR:
(CHCl$_3$) 3485(sharp peak), 3350(weak broad band), 3,000, 1675, and 1650cm^{-1}.

^{1}H NMR:
The NMR spectrum showed the presence of an indole NH-proton 1.70τ (s) and four contiguous aromatic protons 2.4-3.1τ (m). The two 3-proton singlets at 8.39 and 8.66τ were assigned to the *gem*-dimethyl group and the 2-proton singlet at 4.26τ to the olefinic protons at positions 19 and 20. The three protons at C-8 and C-9 appeared as an ABX pattern as quartets: H_x at 5.75τ (*J*=l, 6Hz, C9-H), H_A at 6.40(*J*=1, 15Hz, C8-H, q), and H_B at 6.54τ (*J*=6, 15Hz, C8 $H_{ax.}$). The small coupling constant (1Hz) between C9-H and C8-H_{eq} is consonant with a dihedral angle of close to 90°, while JBX 6Hz is consistent with a dihedral angle of close to 135°; the dihedral values are in agreement with those obtained from an inspection of a Dreiding model of 10,20-dehydro[12,13-dehydroprolyl]-2-(1',1'-dimethylallyltryptophyl)diketopiperazine. A two-proton triplet at 6.42τ was assigned to the protons at C_{15}, a 2-proton sextet at 8.17τ (*J*=3, 10, 10Hz) was assigned to the methylene protons at C_{14}, while the olefinic proton at C_{13} resonated as a triplet at 4.58τ (*J*=3Hz). Irradiation at the center of this latter triplet led to the collapse of the sextet to a triplet at 8.17τ (*J*=10Hz).

Mass Spectrum:
HREIMS: 347.161(M^+, $C_{21}H_{21}N_3O_2$ requires 347.162).

Reference

P. S. Steyn; The Structures of Five Diketopiperazines from *Aspergillus ustus*; Tetrahedron, Vol. 29, pp. 107-120(1973).

Common/Systematic Name

Deoxybrevianamide E

L-Prolyl-2-(1',1'-dimethylallyl)-L-tryptophyldiketopiperazine

Molecular Formula/Molecular Weight

$C_{21}H_{25}N_3O_2$; MW = 351.19468

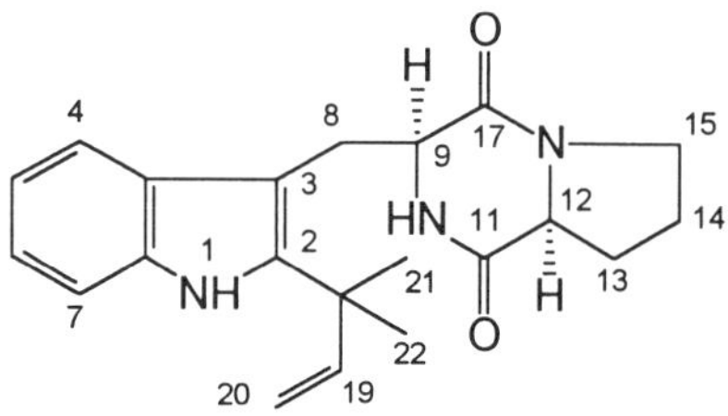

General Characteristics

Homogeneous powder from benzene; $[\alpha]_D^{22}$ -59° (*c*=1.2, in $CHCl_3$).

Fungal Source

Aspergillus ustus (C.S.I.R. 1128; NRRL 5856) and *Penicillium italicum*.

Biological Activity

Toxic to ducklings.

Spectral Data

UV:

λ_{max}^{EtOH} 225(ϵ=32,300), 275(sh)(7,000), 283(8,100), and 291nm (7,000).

IR:

($CHCl_3$) 3481, 3458, 3366, 1670, and 1665cm^{-1}.

^{1}H NMR:

Two exchangeable singlets at 1.25 and 4.28ppm were assigned to NH protons. A multiplet at 2.48-3.05ppm was attributed to the four neighboring aromatic protons. A 6-proton singlet at 8.50 was due to the *gem*-dimethyl group while the three exocyclic olefinic protons appeared as an AA'X system at 3.90(1H, X part, J_{ax} 18.2, $J_{A'X}$9Hz, C19-H) and 4.92(2H, AA' part of AA'X system, J_{ax} 18.2, $J_{A'X}$ 9Hz,-C=CH_2). The protons at C-8 and C-9 appeared as an ABX system at 5.56(1H, X part of ABX system, J_{AX} 4.0, J_{BX} 11.0Hz, C9-H, 6.25 and 6.83(2H, AB part of an ABX system, HA(6.25) J_{AB} 15.5, J_{AX} 4.0Hz, and HB(6.83) J_{AB} 15.5, J_{BX} 11.0Hz, 8 CH_2). The triplet at 5.95ppm (J=7.0Hz) was assigned to the methine proton at position 12. The protons adjacent to the proline nitrogen resonated as an ill-defined triplet at 6.34ppm; the other four protons comprising the proline ring appeared as an unstructured multiplet between 7.6-8.2ppm.

Mass Spectrum:
Only one prominent fragment ion at 198*m/e* ($C_{14}H_{16}N$) from cleavage of the 8,9-bond.

TLC Data
Silica gel, chloroform-acetone, 9:1 v/v, R_f: 0.75. Detection: blue spot after spraying with 65% H_2SO_4 and heating at ca. 120°C for 10 min.

References
R. J. Cole and R. H. Cox; Handbook of Toxic Fungal Metabolites; Academic Press, New York, p. 453 (1981).

P. S. Steyn; The Structures of Five Diketopiperazines from *Aspergillus ustus*; Tetrahedron, Vol. 29, pp. 107-120(1973).

Common/Systematic Name

Brevianamide C

Molecular Formula/Molecular Weight

$C_{21}H_{23}N_3O_3$; MW = 365.17394

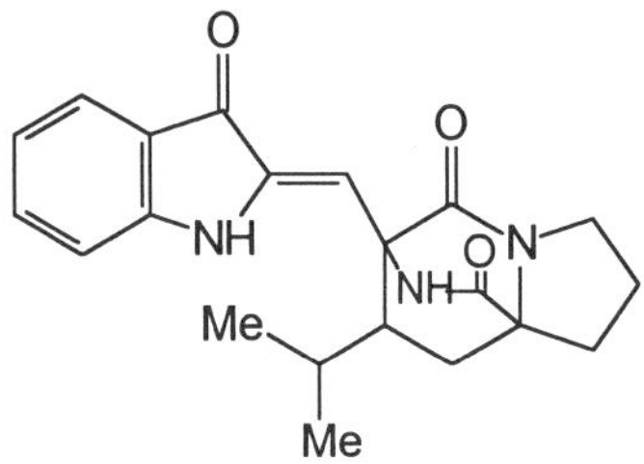

General Characteristics

Brevianamide C was obtained as an orange glass that could not be induced to crystallize.

Fungal Source

Penicillium brevi-compactum.

Isolation/Purification

The fungus was cultured on Czapek-Dox broth at 25 °C. Brevianamide C was isolated from the crude pigment mixture remaining after the crystallization of brevianamide A by repetitive preparative TLC using 5% methanol in chloroform or 1% ethanol in ether. The various metabolites in descending R_f, brevianamide C, D, A, B, and F were scraped from the plates and eluted with methanol.

Spectral Data

UV:

λ_{max}^{EtOH} 234, 259, 277(inf), 300(inf), and 450nm.

IR:

($CHCl_3$) 3410, 3350, 1710, 1680, and 1615cm^{-1}.

^{1}H NMR:

Refer to Birch and Russell (1972) for copy of spectrum.

Mass Spectrum:

HREIMS: 365.1741*m/e*, M^+, $C_{21}H_{23}N_3O_3$ requires 365.1739; LREIMS: 365(13%), 322(15), 295(100), 177(5), 171(4), and 146*m/e* (3).

Reference

A. J. Birch, and R. A. Russell; Studies in Relation to Biosynthesis-XLIV Structural Elucidations of Brevianamides-B, -C, -D and -F; Tetrahedron, Vol. 28, pp. 2999-3008 (1972).

Common/Systematic Name

Brevianamide D

Molecular Formula/Molecular Weight

$C_{21}H_{23}N_3O_3$; MW = 365.17394

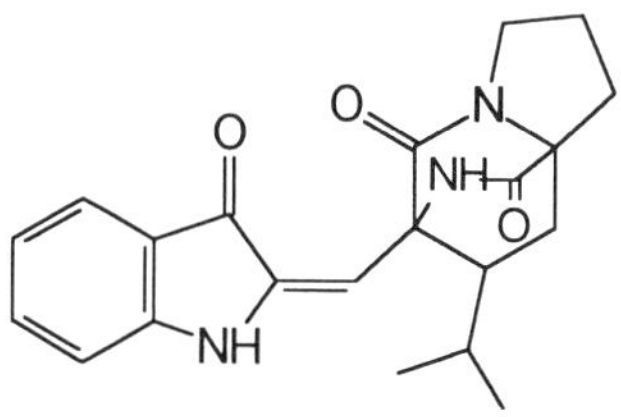

General Characteristics

Brevianamide D was obtained as a red glass that could not be induced to crystallize.

Fungal Source

Penicillium brevi-compactum.

Isolation/Purification

The fungus was cultured on Czapek-Dox broth at 25°C. Brevianamide C was isolated from the crude pigment mixture remaining after the crystallization of brevianamide A by repetitive preparative TLC using 5% methanol in chloroform or 1% ethanol in ether. The various metabolites in descending R_f, brevianamide C, D, A, B, and F were scraped from the plates and eluted with methanol.

Spectral Data

UV:

λ_{max} 235, 264, 306, and 470nm.

IR:

3440, 3200, 1710(sh), 1680, 1630, and 1615cm^{-1}.

^{1}H NMR:

Refer to Birch and Russell (1972) for copy of spectrum.

Mass Spectrum:

HREIMS: 365.1738*m/e*, M^+, $C_{21}H_{23}N_3O_3$ requires 365.1739; LREIMS: 365(25%), 322(14), 295(100), 177(14), 171(6), 146(3), and 133*m/e* (7).

Reference

A. J. Birch, and R. A. Russell; Studies in Relation to Biosynthesis-XLIV Structural Elucidations of Brevianamides-B, -C, -D and -F; Tetrahedron, Vol. 28, pp. 2999-3008 (1972).

Common/Systematic Name

Brevianamide F; L-Tryptophanyl-L-prolyl anhydride

Molecular Formula/Molecular Weight

$C_{16}H_{17}N_3O_2$; MW = 283.13208

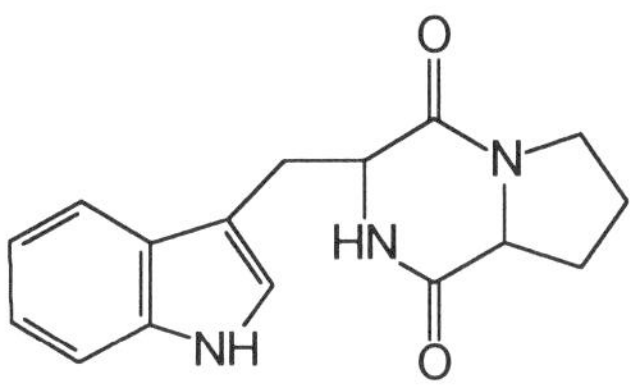

General Characteristics

Brevianamide F was obtained as white needles from ethanol; mp., 173-175°C; blue color with Ehrlich's reagent.

Fungal Source

Penicillium brevi-compactum.

Isolation/Purification

The fungus was cultured on Czapek-Dox broth at 25°C. Brevianamide C was isolated from the crude pigment mixture remaining after the crystallization of brevianamide A by repetitive preparative TLC using 5% methanol in chloroform or 1% ethanol in ether. The various metabolites in descending R_f, brevianamide C, D, A, B, and F were scraped from the plates and eluted with methanol.

Spectral Data

UV:

λ_{max} 277(inf), 283, and 292nm.

IR:

3280, 1670, 1650(weak), and 1640 cm^{-1} (weak).

^1H NMR:

(DMSO-d_6) 1.2-2.1(4H, methylene multiplet); 2.9-3.5(4H, $=CCH_AH_B$, N-CH_2CH_2); 4.05(1H, broad triplet, NHCHCO, J=7.0Hz); 4.30(1H, triplet, NCHCO, J=6Hz); 6.9-7.6(4H, m, aromatic H); 7.98(1H, d, indole NHCH=C, $J_{NH/CH}$=2Hz); 7.66(1H, s, NH); and 10.8ppm (1H, b.s., indole NH).

Mass Data:

LREIMS: 282(9%), 154(8), 130(100), and 83*m/e* (9); found: C, 67.8; H, 6.1; N, 14.8 $C_{16}H_{17}N_3O_2$ requires C, 67.7; H, 5.9; N, 14.7%.

Reference

A. J. Birch and R. A. Russell; Studies in Relation to Biosynthesis-XLIV Structural Elucidations of Brevianamides-B, -C, -D and -F; Tetrahedron, Vol. 28, pp. 2999-3008 (1972).

Common/Systematic Name

Echinulin

3{[2-(1,1-Dimethylallyl)-5,7-bis(3-methyl-2-butenyl)indol-3-yl]methyl}-6-methyl-2,5-piperazinedione

Molecular Formula/Molecular Weight

$C_{29}H_{39}N_3O_2$; MW = 461.30423

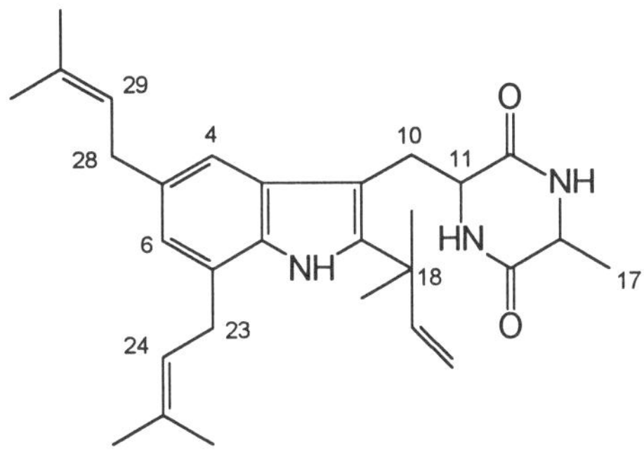

General Characteristics

Needles from butanol; mp., 242-243 °C. Soluble in glacial acetic acid, chloroform, pyridine, dioxane; slightly soluble in warm alcohol, butanol, benzene, ethyl ether, acetone, and carbon tetrachloride.

Fungal Source

Aspergillus amstelodami = *Eurotium amstelodami*, *A. chevalieri* = *E. chevalieri*, and *A. echinulatus* = *E. echinulatum*.

Spectral Data

UV:

λ_{max}^{EtOH} 230(39,810), 279(9,549), and 286nm (9,120).

^{13}C NMR:

C-2, 141.1 s; C-3, 104.5 s; C-4, 121.5 d; C-5, 130.4 s; C-6, 114.5 d; C-7, 124.4 s; C-8, 131.8 s; C-9, 130.4 s; C-10, 29.9 t; C-11, 55.2 d; C-12, 167.4 s; C-14, 50.4 d; C-15, 167.8 s; C-17, 20.2 q; C-18, 38.9 s; C-19, 27.9 q; C-20, 27.9 q; C-21, 145.9 d; C-22, 111.2 t; C-23, 30.4 t; C-24, 122.3 d; C-25, 130.4 s; C-26, 25.6 q; C-27, 17.7 q; C-28, 34.3 t; C-29, 123.2 d; C-30, 131.9 s; C-31, 25.6 q; and C-32, 17.7ppm q.

TLC Data

Silica gel HF_{254}; A: ethyl acetate-hexane, 2:1 v/v; B: benzene-ethyl acetate, 1:1 v/v; C: benzene-ethyl acetate, 2:1 v/v. Detection: not reported.

Reference

R. J. Cole and R. H. Cox; Handbook of Toxic Fungal Metabolites; Academic Press, New York, p. 480 (1981).

Common/Systematic Name

Preechinulin
(+)-L-Alanyl(1,1-dimethylallyl)tryptophan anhydride

Molecular Formula/Molecular Weight

$C_{19}H_{23}N_3O_2$; MW = 325.17903

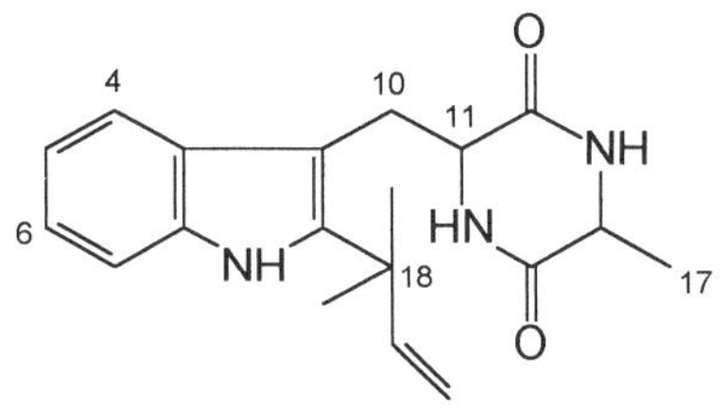

General Characteristics

Fine white needles from methylene chloride-benzene; mp., 294°-297°C; $[\alpha]_D^{24}$ +50° (c=0.38, in acetic acid); $[\alpha]_D^{20}$ +22.3° (in acetic acid).

Fungal Source

Aspergillus amstelodami = *Eurotium amstelodami*, *A. chevalieri* = *E. chevalieri*, and *A. repens* = *E. repens*.

Spectral Data

UV:

λ_{max}^{EtOH} 225(ϵ=32,500), 283(7,750), and 291nm (7,000).

IR:

(KCl) 3380, 3210, 1670, 1460, 993, and 910cm^{-1}.

References

R. J. Cole and R. H. Cox; Handbook of Toxic Fungal Metabolites; Academic Press, New York, p. 459 (1981).

W. B. Turner and D. C. Aldridge; Fungal Metabolites II; Academic Press, New York, New York, 631 pp. (1983).

Common/Systematic Name
Neoechinulin

Molecular Formula/Molecular Weight
$C_{23}H_{25}N_3O_3$; MW = 391.18959

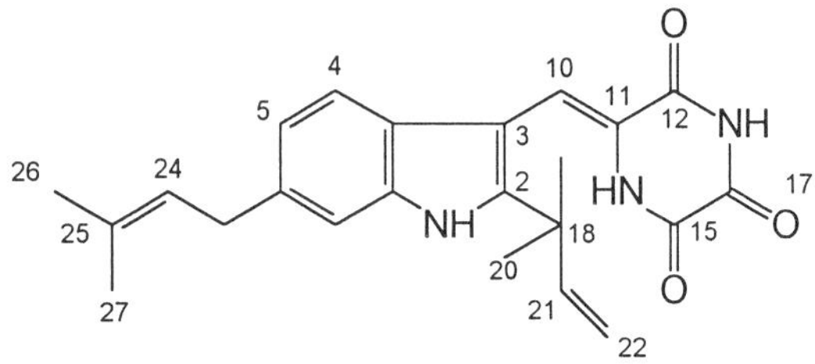

Fungal Source
Aspergillus amstelodami = *Eurotium amstelodami*.

Spectral Data

UV:
λ_{max}^{EtOH} 231(ϵ=32,300), 287(13,100), and 420nm (9,700).

^{1}H NMR:
H-4,7.11; H-5,6.83; H-7,7.51; H-19,1.57; H-20,1.57; H-21, 6.10; H-22, 5.12; 5.11; H-23, 3.42; H-24, 5.38; H-26, 1.75; H-27, 1.75; and NH, 9.59; 11.06; 12.07ppm.

^{13}C NMR:
C-2, 131.1; C-3, 103.4; C-4, 116.3; C-5, 119.2; C-6, 124.0; C-7, 110.8; C-8, 134.6; C-9, 123.1; C-10, 120.9; C-11, 145.7; C-12, 152.0; C-14, 157.0; C-15, 160.2; C-18, 38.9; C-19, 27.7; C-20, 27.7; C-21, 145.1; C-22, 111.9; C-23, 33.9; C-24, 124.0; C-25, 135.7; C-26, 25.4; and C-27, 17.6ppm.

TLC Data
Silica gel HF_{254}. Solvent: A, ethyl acetate-hexane, 2:1 v/v; B, benzene-ethyl acetate, 1:1 v/v; C, benzene-ethyl acetate, 2:1 v/v. R_f: A, 0.75; B, 0.50; C, 0.30. Detection: not reported.

References

R. J. Cole and R. H. Cox; Handbook of Toxic Fungal Metabolites; Academic Press, New York, pp. 463 (1981).

W. B. Turner and D. C. Aldridge; Fungal Metabolites II; Academic Press, New York, New York, 631 pp. (1983).

Common/Systematic Name

Neoechinulin A

Molecular Formula/Molecular Weight

$C_{19}H_{21}N_3O_2$; MW = 323.16338

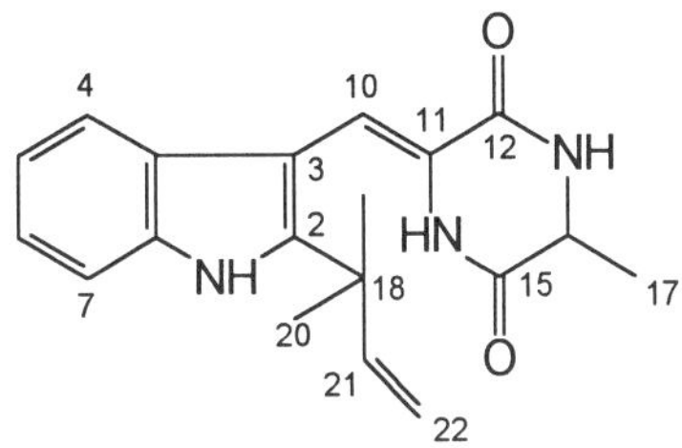

General Characteristics

Ivory crystals from methanol; mp., 264-265°C.

Fungal Source

Aspergillus ruber = *Eurotium rubrum* and *A. amstelodami* = *E. amstelodami.*

Spectral Data

UV:

λ_{max}^{EtOH} 229(ε=23,300), 286(11,700), 292(10,400), and 338nm (9,500).

IR:

(KBr) 3360, 2980, 1670, and 1630cm^{-1}.

^{1}H NMR:

H-1, 8.30; H-4, 7.00-7.50; H-5, 7.00-7.50; H-6, 7.00-7.50; H-7, 7.00-7.50; H-10, 6.93; H-13, 8.30; H-14, 4.15; H-16, 10.96; H-17, 1.42; H-19, 1.50; H-20, 1.50; H-21, 6.12; H-23, 5.04; and H-24, 5.06ppm.

^{13}C NMR:

C-2, 144.1; C-3, 103.3; C-4, 118.7; C-5, 120.8; C-6, 119.5; C-7, 110.2; C-8, 135.2; C-9, 126.0; C-10, 111.6; C-11, 124.8; C-12, 159.7; C-14, 50.5; C-15, 166.3; C-17, 17.9; C-18, 40.2; C-19, 27.5; C-20, 27.5; C-21, 145.2; and C-22, 111.6ppm.

TLC Data

Silica gel HF_{254}; A: ethyl acetate-hexane, 2:1 v/v; B: benzene-ethyl acetate, 1:1 v/v; C: benzene-ethyl acetate, 2:1 v/v. R_f: A, 0.24, B, 0.17, C, 0.09. Detection: not reported.

References

R. J. Cole and R. H. Cox; Handbook of Toxic Fungal Metabolites; Academic Press, New

York, pp. 469 (1981).

W. B. Turner and D. C. Aldridge; Fungal Metabolites II; Academic Press, New York, New York, 631 pp. (1983).

Common/Systematic Name

Neoechinulin B; Cryptoechinulin C; E10

Molecular Formula/Molecular Weight

$C_{19}H_{19}N_3O_2$; MW = 321.14773

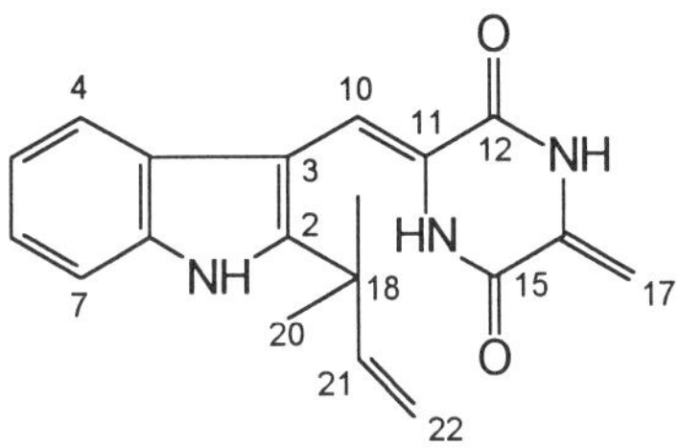

General Characteristics

Yellow crystals from methanol; mp., 234-236°C.

Fungal Source

Aspergillus amstelodami = *Eurotium amstelodami.*

Spectral Data

UV:

λ_{max}^{EtOH} 228(ϵ=28,100), 273(19,000), 284(18,100), and 374nm (10,400).

IR:

(KBr) 3360, 2980, 2925, 1680, and 1645cm^{-1}.

^{1}H NMR:

H-1, 8.36; H-4-7, 6.70-7.50; H-10, 6.85; H-13, 10.61; H-16, 10.86; H-17, 5.08, 5.34; H-19, 1.50; H-20, 1.50; H-21, 6.07; H-23, 5.07; and H-24, 5.09ppm.

TLC Data

Silica gel HF_{254}; A: ethyl acetate-hexane, 2:1 v/v; B: benzene-ethyl acetate, 1:1 v/v; C: benzene-ethyl acetate, 2:1 v/v. R_f: A, 0.77; B, 0.46; C, 0.26. Detection: not reported.

References

R. J. Cole and R. H. Cox; Handbook of Toxic Fungal Metabolites; Academic Press, New York, pp. 471 (1981).

W. B. Turner and D. C. Aldridge; Fungal Metabolites II; Academic Press, New York, New York, 631 pp. (1983).

Common/Systematic Name

Neoechinulin C; E8; Cryptoechinulin A

Molecular Formula/Molecular Weight

$C_{24}H_{27}N_3O_2$; MW = 389.21033

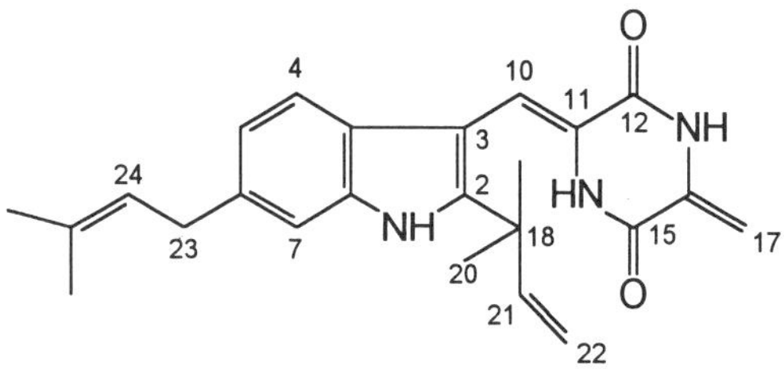

General Characteristics

Optically inactive; yellow crystals from light petroleum-benzene, 1:1 v/v; mp., 205-207°C.

Fungal Source

Aspergillus amstelodami = *Eurotium amstelodami.*

Spectral Data

UV:

λ_{max}^{EtOH} 231(ϵ=34,600), 275(22,300), 290(18,600), and 380nm (12,000).

IR:

(KBr) 3350, 2970, 2925, 1680, and $1640cm^{-1}$.

^1H NMR:

H-1, 8.66; H-4,5,7, 6.80-7.40; H-10, 7.01; H-13, 10.79; H-16, 10.96; H-17, 4.96, 5.27; H-19, 1.48; H-20, 1.48; H-21, 6.07; H-23, 5.06; H-24, 5.08; H-25, 3.40; H-26, 5.35; H-28, 1.76; and H-29, 1.76ppm.

^{13}C NMR:

C-2, 131.1; C-3, 102.8; C-4, 112.0; C-5, 118.5; C-6,124.0; C-7, 110.9; C-8, 134.4; C-9, 124.0; C-10, 120.9; C-11, 142.2; C-12, 155.7; C-14, 134.8; C-15, 157.1; C-17, 100.0; C-18, 38.6; C-19, 27.5; C-20, 27.5; C-21, 144.1; C-22, 111.7; C-23, 33.9; C-24, 124.0; C-25, 135.6; C-26, 25.4; and C-27, 17.6ppm.

TLC Data

Silica gel HF_{254}; A, ethyl acetate-hexane, 2:1 v/v; B, benzene-ethyl acetate, 1:1 v/v; C, benzene-ethyl acetate, 2:1 v/v. R_f: A, 0.80; B, 0.53; C, 0.39. Detection: not reported.

References

R. J. Cole and R. H. Cox; Handbook of Toxic Fungal Metabolites; Academic Press, New York, p. 473 (1981).

A. Dossena, R. Marchelli, and A. Pochini; Neoechinulin D, a New Isoprenylated Dehydrotryptophyl Metabolite from *Aspergillus amstelodami*; Experientia, Vol. 31, p. 1249 (1975).

W. B. Turner and D. C. Aldridge; Fungal Metabolites II; Academic Press, New York, New York, p. 407 (1983).

Common/Systematic Name

Neoechinulin D

Alanyl-2-(1,1-dimethyl-2-propenyl-6-isopentyl)-dehydrotryptophan anhydride

Molecular Formula/Molecular Weight

$C_{24}H_{29}N_3O_2$; MW = 391.22598

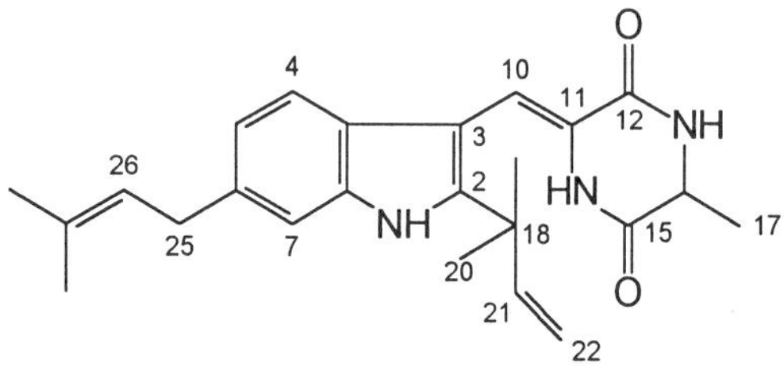

General Characteristics

Ivory crystals from methanol; mp., 223-225°C.

Fungal Source

Aspergillus amstelodami = *Eurotium amstelodami* and *A. rubrum* = *E. ruber* (Isolated from beet pulp).

Isolation/Purification

Neoechinulin D was isolated from the crude ethereal extract of the mycelium by silica gel 60 column chromatography eluted with hexane-ethyl acetate (1:1, v/v). Neoechinulin D rich fractions were combined, concentrated, and further purified by preparatory TLC followed by crystallization from petroleum ether-benzene as ivory crystals; recrystallized from methanol.

Biological Activity

Growth retardant for silkworm larvae (*Bombyx mori* L.).

Spectral Data

UV:

λ_{max}^{EtOH} 231(ϵ=34,600), 265(11,400), 296(10,400), and 345nm (10,900).

IR:

(KBr) 3340, 2940, 1670, and 1630.

^{1}H NMR:

H-1, 8.32; H-4,5,7, 6.95-7.40; H-10, 7.01; H-13, 10.38; H-14, 4.25; H-16, 10.62; H-17, 1.53; H-19, 1.48; H-20, 1.48; H-21, 6.11; H-23, 5.06; H-24, 5.08; H-25, 3.40; H-26, 5.33; H-28, 1.72; and H-29, 1.72ppm.

Mass Spectrum:
391.2262*m/e* (M^+); calcd for $C_{24}H_{29}N_3O_2$, 391.2258.

TLC Data

Silica gel HF_{254}; A: ethyl acetate-hexane, 2:1 v/v; B: benzene-ethyl acetate, 1:1 v/v; C: benzene-ethyl acetate, 2:1 v/v. R_f: A, 0.37; B, 0.23; C, 0.12. Detection not reported.

References

R. J. Cole and R. H. Cox; Handbook of Toxic Fungal Metabolites; Academic Press, New York, pp. 466 (1981).

A. Dossena, R. Marchelli, and A. Pochini; Neoechinulin D, a New Isoprenylated Dehydrotryptophanyl Metabolite from *Aspergillus amstelodami*; Experientia, Vol. 31, p. 1249 (1975).

W. B. Turner and D. C. Aldridge; Fungal Metabolites II; Academic Press, New York, New York, 631 pp. (1983).

H. Nagasawa, A. Isogal, K. Ikeda, S. Sato, S. Murakoshi, A. Suzuki, and S. Tamura; Isolation and Structure Elucidation of a New Indole Metabolite from *Aspergillus ruber*; Agr. Biol. Chem., Vol. 39, pp. 1901-1902(1975).

Common/Systematic Name
Neoechinulin E

Molecular Formula/Molecular Weight
$C_{18}H_{17}N_3O_3$; MW = 323.12670

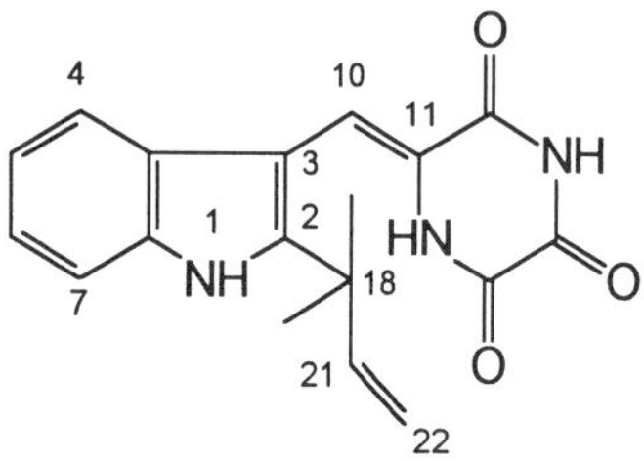

General Characteristics
Orange-red crystals from methanol; mp., 275°C.

Fungal Source
Aspergillus amstelodami = *Eurotium amstelodami*.

Spectral Data

UV:
λ_{max}^{EtOH} 228(ϵ=37,100), 281(9,100), and 410nm (8,100).

IR:
(KBr) 3330, 3150, 3020, 2840, 1740, 1690, and 1600cm^{-1}.

^{1}H NMR:
H-1, 8.64, H-4-7, 6.90-7.55, H-10, 7.40; H-13, 10.58; H-16, 10.58; H-19, 1.54; H-20, 1.54; H-21, 6.06; H-23, 5.06; and H-24, 5.20ppm.

TLC Data
Silica gel HF_{254}; A: ethyl acetate-hexane, 2:1 v/v; B: benzene-ethyl acetate, 1:1 v/v; C: benzene-ethyl acetate, 2:1 v/v. R_f: A: 0.51; B: 0.36; C: 0.17. Detection: visible light.

References
R. J. Cole and R. H. Cox; Handbook of Toxic Fungal Metabolites; Academic Press, New York, p. 464 (1981).

A. Dossena, R. Marchelli, and A. Pochini; Neoechinulin D, a New Isoprenylated Dehydrotryptophyl Metabolite from *Aspergillus amstelodami*; Experientia, Vol. 31, p. 1249 (1975).

W. B. Turner and D. C. Aldridge; Fungal Metabolites II; Academic Press, New York, New York, 631 pp. (1983).

Common/Systematic Name
Isoechinulin A

Molecular Formula/Molecular Weight
$C_{24}H_{29}N_3O_2$; MW = 391.22598

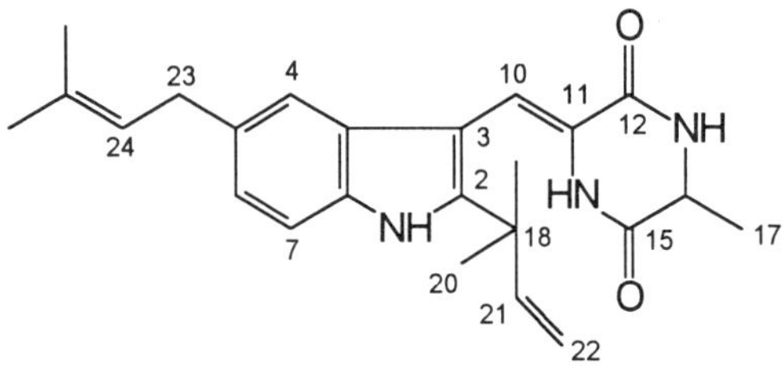

Fungal Source
Aspergillus ruber = Eurotium rubrum.

Biological Activity
Isoechinulin A inhibited growth of silkworm larvae.

Spectral Data

UV:
λ_{max}^{EtOH} 227(ε=31,500), 289(8,900), and 341nm (9,400).

IR:
(KBr) 3260, 1675, and 1633cm^{-1}.

^{1}H NMR:
H-1, 10.21; H-4, 7.10; H-6, 6.99; H-7, 7.34; H-10, 7.15; H-13, 7.92; H-14, 4.28; H-16, 7.53; H-17, 1.55; H-19, 1.55; H-20, 1.55; H-21, 6.16; H-23, 5.13; H-24, 5.13; H-25, 3.40; H-26, 5.38; H-28, 1.71; and H-29, 1.71ppm.

^{13}C NMR:
C-2, 143.9; C-3, 102.8; C-4, 123.2*; C-5, 132.9**; C-6, 117.9; C-7, 111.1***; C-8, 134.6; C-9, 126.4; C-10, 112.1***; C-11, 124.3; C-12, 160.3; C-14, 51.6; C-15,165.8; C-17, 20.9; C-18, 39.3; C-19, 27.4; C-20, 27.4; C-21, 144.1; C-22, 113.1; C-23, 34.6; C-24, 124.0*; C-25, 132.0**; C-26, 25.8; and C-27, 17.9.

*, **, *** Assignments may be reversed.

References
R. J. Cole and R. H. Cox; Handbook of Toxic Fungal Metabolites; Academic Press, New York, pp. 475 (1981).

W. B. Turner and D. C. Aldridge; Fungal Metabolites II; Academic Press, New York, New York, p. 407 (1983).

Common/Systematic Name

Isoechinulin B

Molecular Formula/Molecular Weight

$C_{24}H_{27}N_3O_2$; MW = 389.21033

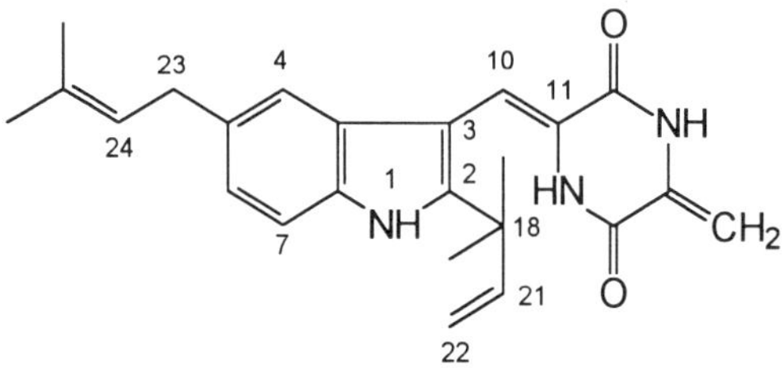

Fungal Source

Aspergillus ruber = Eurotium rubrum.

Spectral Data

UV:

λ_{max}^{MeOH} 228(ϵ=27,900), 272(18,700), 285(sh) (16,600), and 370nm (10,400).

IR:

(KBr) 3310, 1678, and 1643cm^{-1}.

^1H NMR:

($CDCl_3$) H-1, 10.23; H-4, 7.00-7.20; H-6, 6.96; H-7, 7.30; H-10, 7.00-7.20; H-13, 9.80; H-16, 8.08; H-17, 5.00-5.40; H-19, 1.54; H-20, 1.54; H-21, 6.13; H-23, 5.00-5.40; H-24, 5.00-5.40; H-25, 3.38; H-26, 5.00-5.40; H-28, 1.68; and H-29, 1.68ppm.

^{13}C NMR:

C-2, 144.6; C-3, 102.7; C-4, 123.2*; C-5, 133.0**; C-6, 118.0; C-7, 111.3***; C-8, 134.7; C-9, 126.0; C-10, 113.5***; C-11, 124.0; C-12, 158.5; C-14, 133.6; C-15, 156.1; C-17, 103.0; C-18, 39.2; C-19, 27.4; C-20, 27.4; C-21, 144.2; C-23, 34.5; C-24, 124.0*; C-25, 132.0**; C-26, 25.7; and C-27, 17.8ppm.

*, **, *** Assignments may be interchanged.

References

R. J. Cole and R. H. Cox; Handbook of Toxic Fungal Metabolites; Academic Press, New York, p. 476 (1981).

W. B. Turner and D. C. Aldridge; Fungal Metabolites II; Academic Press, New York, New York, 631 pp. (1983).

Common/Systematic Name
Isoechinulin C

Molecular Formula/Molecular Weight
$C_{24}H_{27}N_3O_3$; MW = 405.20524

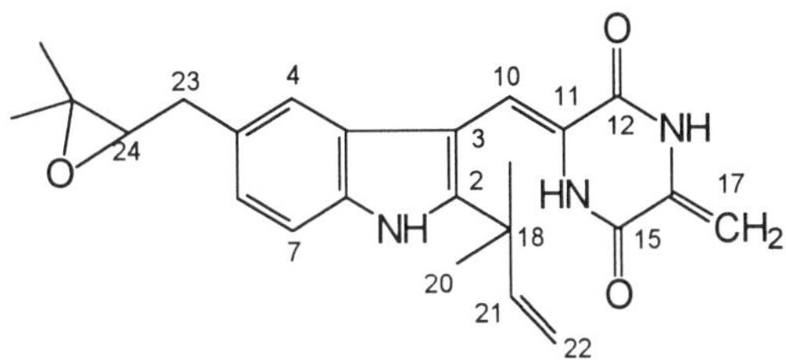

Fungal Source
Aspergillus ruber = *Eurotium rubrum.*

Spectral Data

UV:
λ_{max}^{MeOH} 229(ϵ=26,700), 272(18,000),286 sh (15,800), and 371nm (9,700).

IR:
(KBr) 3250, 1676, and 1644cm^{-1}.

^{1}H NMR:
H-1, 10.21; H-4, 7.02; H-6, 7.02; H-7, 7.31; H-10, 7.07; H-13, 9.73; H-16, 8.12; H-17, 5.00; 5.34; H-19, 1.56; H-20, 1.56; H-21, 6.11; H-23, 5.08; H-24, 5.05; H-25, 2.70-3.10; H-26, 2.70-3.10; H-28, 1.22; and H-29, 1.33ppm.

^{13}C NMR:
C-2, 140.2; C-3, 104.5; C-4, 124.5; C-5, 131.2; C-6, 119.9; C-7, 112.8*; C-8, 136.4; C-9, 127.8; C-10, 112.9*; C-11, 126.4; C-12, 158.3; C-14, 135.5; C-15, 157.0; C-17, 100.6; C-18, 40.6; C-19, 28.4; C-20, 28.4; C-21, 146.2; C-22, 112.9*; C-23, 36.7; C-24, 65.9; C-25, 59.4; C-26, 25.5; and C-27, 19.6ppm.

* Assignments may be interchanged.

References
R. J. Cole and R. H. Cox; Handbook of Toxic Fungal Metabolites; Academic Press, New York, p.477 (1981).

W. B. Turner and D. C. Aldridge; Fungal Metabolites II; Academic Press, New York, New York, p. 407 (1983).

Common/Systematic Name

E7

Molecular Formula/Molecular Weight

$C_{29}H_{35}N_3O_2$; MW = 457.27293

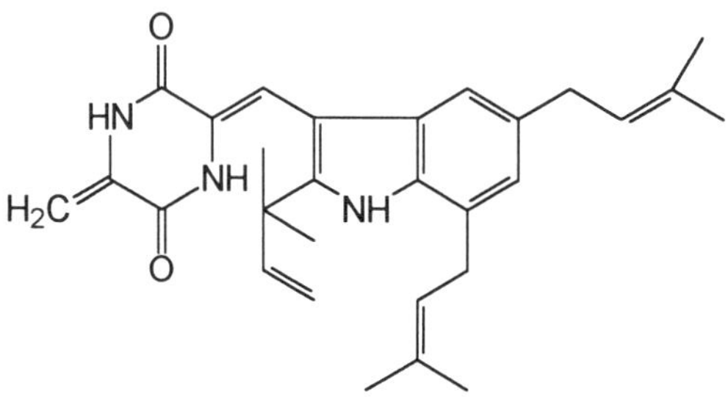

General Characteristics

Crystals from ether; mp., 146-148°C.

Fungal Source

Aspergillus amstelodami IFO 6667 = *Eurotium amstelodami*.

Spectral Data

IR:

(KBr) 1680, and 1640cm^{-1}.

Mass Spectrum:

HREIMS: 457.2697(M^+), 402, 388, 332, 294, and 69*m/e*.

Reference

S. Inoue, J. Murata, N. Takamatsu, H. Nagano, and Y. Kishi; Synthetic Studies on Echinulin and Related Natural Products. V. Isolation, Structure and Synthesis of Echinulin-Neoechinulin Type Alkaloids Isolated from *Aspergillus amstelodami*; Yakugaku Zasshi, Vol. 97, pp. 576-581(1977).

Common/Systematic Name
Cryptoechinulin G

Molecular Formula/Molecular Weight
$C_{29}H_{35}N_3O_2$; MW = 457.27293

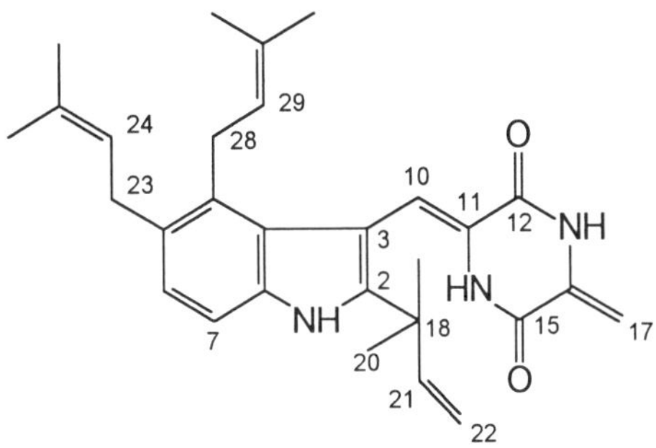

General Characteristics
Amorphous solid, optically inactive.

Fungal Source
Aspergillus ruber = *Eurotium rubrum.*

Spectral Data

^{13}C NMR*:
C-2, 126.6; C-3, 101.3; C-4, 128.9; C-5, 130.3; C-6, 123.0; C-7, 109.5; C-8, 134.5; C-9, 130.2; C-10, 114.6; C-11, 142.2; C-12, 156.6; C-14, 134.6; C-15, 156.1; C-17, 100.4; C-21, 145.4; C-22, 111.1; C-24, 124.9; C-25, 130.2; C-29, 124.7; and C-30, 130.2.

* Data for saturated carbons not reported.

References
R. J. Cole and R. H. Cox; Handbook of Toxic Fungal Metabolites; Academic Press, New York, pp. 468 (1981).

G. Gatti; Molecular Structure of Cryptoechinulin G, an Isoprenylated Dehydrotryptophan Metabolite Isolated from *Aspergillus ruber*; Tetrahedron Lett., p. 2605-2606(1978).

W. B. Turner and D. C. Aldridge; Fungal Metabolites II; Academic Press, New York, New York, 631 pp. (1983).

Common/Systematic Name

Cryptoechinulin B; Aurechinulin; E6

Molecular Formula/Molecular Weight

$C_{43}H_{49}N_3O_5$; MW = 687.36722

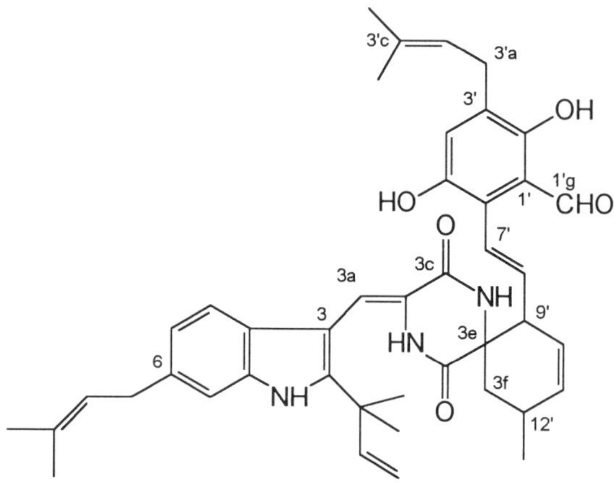

General Characteristics

Crystals; mp., 188 °C.

Fungal Source

Aspergillus amstelodami → *Eurotium amstelodami*.

Spectral Data

^{1}H NMR:

[$(CD_3)_2SO$] Similar to that of cryptoechinulin D except for the addition of two methyl resonances at 1.7ppm and a -CH_2CH= pattern at 3.3 and 5.3ppm.

Mass Spectrum:

LREIMS: 687, 618, 481, 412, 344, 320, 298, 265, 243, 206, and 69*m/e*.

References

R. Cardillo, C. Fuganti, D. Ghiringhelli, and P. Grasselli; New Minor Metabolites of *Aspergillus amstelodami*; La Chimica E L'Industria, Vol. 57, pp. 678-679(1975).

G. Gatti, R. Cardillo, C. Fuganti, and D. Ghiringhelli; Structure Determination of Two Extractives from *Aspergillus amstelodami* by NMR Spectroscopy; J. C. S. Chem. Comm., pp. 435-436(1976).

Common/Systematic Name
Cryptoechinulin D

Molecular Formula/Molecular Weight
$C_{38}H_{41}N_3O_5$; MW = 619.30462

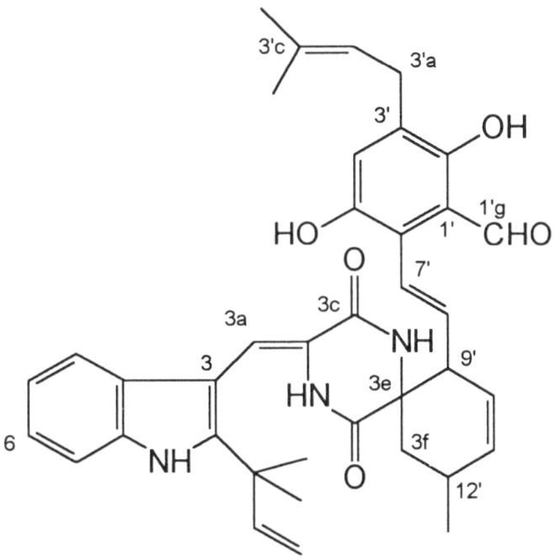

General Characteristics
Crystals; mp., 198°C.

Fungal Source
Aspergillus amstelodami → *Eurotium amstelodami*.

Spectral Data

^{1}H NMR:
[$(CD_3)_2SO$] Five protons that were exchangeable with D_2O (11.8; 10.9; 9.2; 8.8, CONH; and 7.8ppm, CONH); 10.9(NH); 6.9-7.5ppm (4 aromatic protons); 1.4(3H); 6.97(3a-H); 6.7(7'H); 3.2 and 5.2ppm (-CH_2CH=); 1.6ppm (3H); and 10.2ppm (CHO).

^{13}C NMR:
[$(CD_3)_2SO$] 161.5 and 167.8ppm (two CONH groups); 36.8 (suggests the α,α-dimethylallyl chain in position 2 of tryptophan); 144.4(C-3b) and 111.7ppm (C-3a); 17.7 and 25.6ppm (methyl resonances); 197.3ppm (CHO).

References
R. Cardillo, C. Fuganti, D. Ghiringhelli, and P. Grasselli; New Minor Metabolites of *Aspergillus amstelodami*, La Chimica E L'Industria, Vol. 57, pp. 678-679(1975).

G. Gatti, R. Cardillo, C. Fuganti, and D. Ghiringhelli; Structure Determination of Two Extractives from *Aspergillus amstelodami* by NMR Spectroscopy; J. C. S. Chem. Comm., pp. 435-436(1976).

Common/Systematic Name
Fumitremorgin A

Molecular Formula/Molecular Weight
$C_{32}H_{41}N_3O_7$; MW = 579.29445

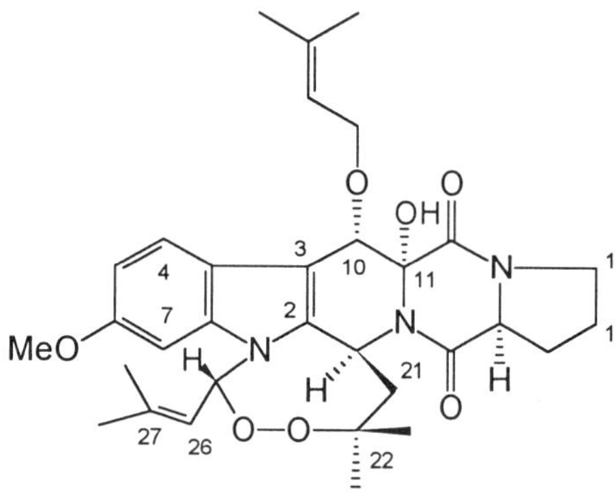

General Characteristics
Colorless prisms from methanol; mp., 206-209°C; $[\alpha]_D^{10}$ +61° (acetone). Soluble in chloroform and ethyl acetate; slightly soluble in methanol and ethanol; unstable to prolonged exposure to light.

Fungal Source
Aspergillus fumigatus and *A. caespitosus.*

Biological Activity
Tremorgenic: 1mg dosed IP to mice caused perceptible tremors; 5mg dosed IP to mice caused sustained tremors and 70% mortality.

Spectral Data

UV:
λ_{max}^{EtOH} 226(ϵ=31,700), 277(5,300), and 296nm (4,900).

^{1}H NMR:
H-4, 6.59; H-5, 6.82; H-7, 7.68; H-10, 5.50; 11 OH, 4.48; H-14, 3.63; H-15, 1.60-2.20; H-16, 1.60-2.20; H-17, 6.13; H-20, 5.06; H-21, 2.40; H-23, 0.99; H-24, 2.00; H-25, 6.62; H-26, 5.02; H-28, 1.71; H-29, 1.71; H-30, 3.84; H-31, 4.71; H-32, 5.60; H-34, 1.81; and H-35, 1.81ppm.

TLC Data
Silica gel G-HR; A: chloroform-acetone, 93:7, v/v; B: toluene-ethyl acetate-formic acid,

5:4:1, v/v/v; R_f: A, 0.30, B, 0.65. Detection: slate gray-blue spot in visible light or mustard-colored spot under UV light; develops immediately after spraying with 50% ethanolic H_2SO_4.

NOTE: The color response and R_f's of verruculogen are identical to those of fumitremorgin A in the above conditions.

References

R. J. Cole and R. H. Cox; Handbook of Toxic Fungal Metabolites; Academic Press, New York, pp. 357-359(1981).

M. Yamazaki, H. Fujimoto, and T. Kawasaki; Tremorgenic Toxins from *Aspergillus fumigatus*; Tetrahedron Lett., p. 1241 (1975).

Common/Systematic Name

Fumitremorgin B; Lanosulin

Molecular Formula/Molecular Weight

$C_{27}H_{33}N_3O_5$; MW = 479.24202

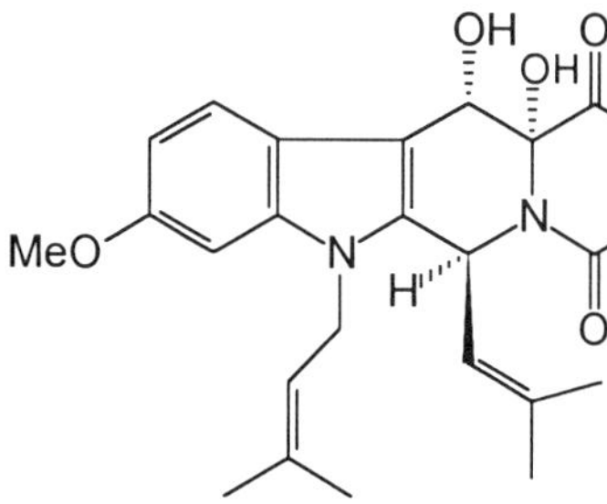

General Characteristics

Colorless needles from methanol; mp., 211-212°C.

Fungal Source

Aspergillus fumigatus, A. caespitosus (NRRL 1929), *Penicillium lanosum,* and *P. piscarium.*

Isolation/Purification

Cultures were comminuted in 70% aqueous acetone, filtered and extracted with chloroform, adsorbed on a silica gel column and eluted in sequence with benzene and 3% methanol/benzene. The tremorgenic fractions were further purified on a second silica gel column eluted with 1.5% acetone in chloroform. Verruculogen and fumitremorgen B were crystallized from benzene-ethanol solution and finally from methanol solution.

Biological Activity

Tremorgenic: Fumitremorgin B dosed at 1mg/mouse (IP) caused perceptible tremors; at 5mg/mouse (IP), it caused sustained tremors and 70% mortality.

Spectral Data

UV:

λ_{max}^{MeOH} 228(ϵ=36,400), 278(7,500), and 297nm (8,400).

IR:

(KBr) 3460, 3420, and 1665cm^{-1}.

^{1}H NMR:

($CDCl_3$) H-4, 7.80(*J*=9.0); H-5, 6.73(*J*=9.0, 2.0); H-7, 6.64(*J*=2.0); H-10, 5.72;

H-14, 3.80; H-15, 2.00; H-16, 2.00; H-17, 4.50; H-20, 5.95; H-21, 4.70; H-23, 1.67; H-24, 1.97; H-25, 4.50; H-26, 4.50; H-28, 1.60; H-29, 1.81; and H-30, 3.82ppm.

^{13}C NMR:

($CDCl_3$) C-2, 130.8 s; C-3, 104.2 s; C-4, 121.1 d; C-5, 104.0 d; C-6, 155.8 s; C-7, 93.7 d; C-8, 137.6 s; C-9, 120.3 s; C-10, 68.8 d; C-11, 82.8 d; C-12, 170.0 s; C-14, 48.9 t; C-15, 22.5 t; C-16, 28.9 t; C-17, 58.6 d; C-18, 165.8 s; C-20, 58.2 d; C-21, 122.7 d; C-22, 134.8 s; C-23, 25.5 q; C-24, 18.3 q; C-25, 45.1 t; C-26, 120.0 d; C-27, 134.4 s; C-28, 25.5 q; C-29, 18.3 q; and C-30, 55.6ppm q.

References

R. J. Cole and R. H. Cox; Handbook of Toxic Fungal Metabolites; Academic Press, New York, pp. 360-363(1981).

H. W. Schroeder, R. J. Cole, H. Hein, Jr., and J. W. Kirksey; Tremorgenic Mycotoxins from *Aspergillus caespitosus*; Applied Microbiology, pp. 857-858(1975).

W. B. Turner and D. C. Aldridge; Fungal Metabolites II; Academic Press, New York, New York, p. 435 (1983).

M. Yamazaki, K. Sasago, and K. Mikyaki; Tremorgenic Toxins from *Aspergillus fumigatus* Fres.; J. Chem. Soc., Chem. Commun., p. 408 (1974).

Common/Systematic Name

Fumitremorgin C (SM-Q)

Molecular Formula/Molecular Weight

$C_{22}H_{25}N_3O_3$; MW = 379.18959

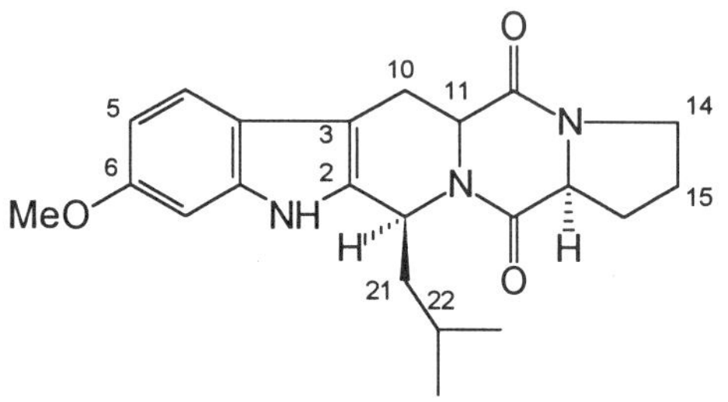

General Characteristics

Crystals from ethyl acetate; mp., 125-130°C.

Fungal Source

Aspergillus fumigatus isolated from moldy silage suspected of causing disease in beef cattle.

Biological Activity

Tremorgenic to day-old cockerels at levels down to 25mg/kg (oral).

Spectral Data

UV:

λ_{max}^{MeOH} 224, 272, and 294nm.

^{1}H NMR:

($CDCl_3$) 1-NH, 8.32; H-4, 7.48(*J*=9.0); H-5, 6.86(*J*=9.0, 2.0); H-7, 6.92(*J*=2.0); H-17, 4.16; H-20, 4.98(*J*=9.0); H-21, (6.06) (*J*=9.0); H-23, 2.07; H-24, 1.72; and H-25, 3.91ppm.

^{13}C NMR:

($CDCl_3$) C-2, 132.1 s; C-3, 106.2 s; C-4, 118.8 d; C-5, 109.4 d; C-6, 156.4 s; C-7, 95.2; C-8, 136.9 s; C-9, 120.7 s; C-10, 45.4 t; C-11, 51.0 d; C-12, 169.4 s; C-14, 45.4 t; C-15, 23.0 t; C-16, 28.6 t; C-17, 59.2 d; C-18, 165.6 s; C-20, 56.8 d; C-21, 124.1 d; C-22, 133.9 s; C-23, 18.1 q; C-24, 25.7 q; and C-25, 55.7ppm, q

TLC Data

Silica gel G-HR; toluene-ethyl acetate-formic acid, 5:4:1, v/v/v; R_f: 0.55. Detection: bright orange spot develops immediately after spraying with 50% ethanolic H_2SO_4 and minimal heating.

References

R. J. Cole and R. H. Cox; Handbook of Toxic Fungal Metabolites; Academic Press, New York, pp. 364-367(1981).

R. J. Cole, J. W. Kirksey, J. W. Dorner, D. M. Wilson, J. Johnson, Jr., D. Bedell, J. P. Springer, K. K. Chexal, and J. Clardy; Ann. Nutr. Alim., Vol. 31, pp. 685-692 (1977).

Common/Systematic Name
Verruculogen

Molecular Formula/Molecular Weight
$C_{27}H_{33}N_3O_7$; MW = 511.23185

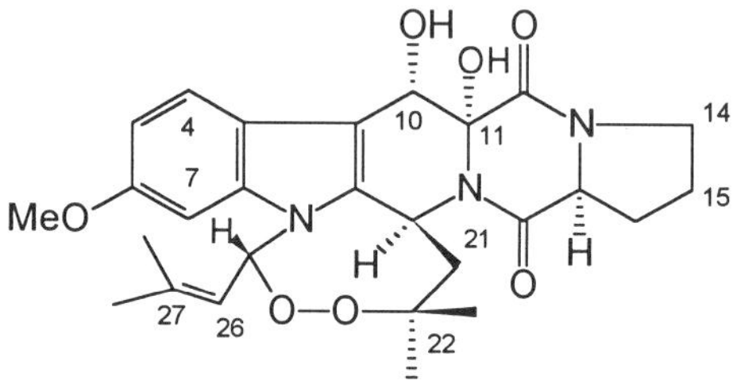

General Characteristics
Colorless plates from benzene-ethanol, 1:1, v/v; mp., 233-235°C (dec.); $[\alpha]_D$ -27.7° (in $CHCl_3$). Soluble in benzene, ethyl acetate, and acetone; slightly soluble in ethanol; and very soluble in $CHCl_3$. Verruculogen is unstable to prolonged exposure to light.

Fungal Source
Penicillium verruculosum (ATCC 24640; NRRL 5881) → *P. brasilianum, P. paraherquei* → *P. brasilianum, P. piscarium* → *P. brasilianum, P. janthinellum, P. paxilli* → *P. graminicola, P. estinogenum* → *P. brasilianum, Aspergillus caespitosus* (NRRL 1929), and *A. fumigatus.*

Isolation/Purification
Cultures were extracted in hot chloroform. Chloroform extracts were filtered, dried, evaporated to dryness *in vacuo*. The crude extract was chromatographed on a silica gel (Merck 70-325 mesh) column packed in *n*-hexane and eluted with *n*-hexane to remove non-polar triglycerides; the toxin was eluted with ethyl ether. The toxin was purified further on a silica gel column packed in toluene and eluted with toluene followed with a linear gradient from toluene to ethyl acetate. The tremorgen was further purified using a column packed with Florisil and eluted with 5% ethyl acetate in hexane. Active fractions were combined, concentrated *in vacuo*, and crystallized from benzene-ethanol solution (1:1, v/v).

Biological Activity
The ED_{50} for tremor response in mice was 0.39mg/kg (IP); in day-old cockerels it was 0.33mg/kg (IP). Tremors are sustained at higher levels, intermittent at lower levels, and enhanced by enforced movement. Verruculogen administration produced a decrease in γ-aminobutyric acid levels in mouse central nervous system; verruculogen-induced tremor is mediated by a loss of inhibitory GABA function. The LD_{50} of verruculogen to mice was 2.4mg/kg (IP) and 126.7mg/kg (oral); to day-old cockerels, 15.2mg/kg (IP) and 265.5mg/kg (oral).

Spectral Data

UV:

λ_{max}^{EtOH} 226(ϵ=47,500), 277(11,000), and 295nm (9,750).

CD:

$\Delta\epsilon$ (in EtOH solution): 290(+0.16) and 265nm (+0.56).

^{1}H NMR:

H-4, 7.90(*J*=9.0); H-5, 6.80(*J*=9.0, 2.0); H-7, 6.60(*J*=2.0); H-10, 5.65; 10-OH, 4.80; H-14, 3.65; H-15, 2.00; H-16, 2.00; H-17, 4.50; H-20, 6.05; H-21, 2.00; H-23, 1.02; H-24, 1.80; H-25, 6.70(*J*=8.0); H-26, 5.05; H-28, 1.80; H-29, 2.00; and H-30, 3.86ppm.

^{13}C NMR:

C-2, 131.6 s; C-3, 105.7 s; C-4, 121.7 d; C-5, 109.3 d; C-6, 156.4 s; C-7, 93.9 d; C-8, 136.3 s; C-9, 121.1 s; C-10, 68.7 d; C-11, 82.6 s; C-12, 170.7 s; C-14, 51.3 t; C-15, 22.7 t; C-16, 29.1 t; C-17, 58.7 d; C-18, 166.2 s; C-20, 48.9 d; C-21, 45.3 t; C-22, 82.1 s; C-23, 27.1 q; C-24, 25.6 q; C-25, 85.8 q; C-26, 118.7 d; C-27, 142.9 s; C-28, 18.8 q; C-29, 24.2 q; and C-30, 55.7ppm q.

TLC Data

Silica gel G-HR; A: chloroform-acetone, 93:7, v/v; B: toluene-ethyl acetate-formic acid, 5:4:1, v/v/v. R_f: A = 0.30, B = 0.65. Detection: slate gray-blue spot in visible light or mustard-colored spot under UV light; develops immediately after spraying with 50% ethanolic H_2SO_4.

References

R. J. Cole and R. H. Cox; Handbook of Toxic Fungal Metabolites; Academic Press, New York, pp. 368-373(1981).

R. J. Cole, J. W. Kirksey, J. H. Moore , B. R. Blankenship, U. L. Diener, and N. D. Davis; Tremorgenic Toxin from *Penicillium verruculosum*; Applied Microbiology, pp. 248-256 (1972).

Common/Systematic Name

15-Acetoxyverruculogen

Molecular Formula/Molecular Weight

$C_{29}H_{35}N_3O_9$; MW = 569.23733

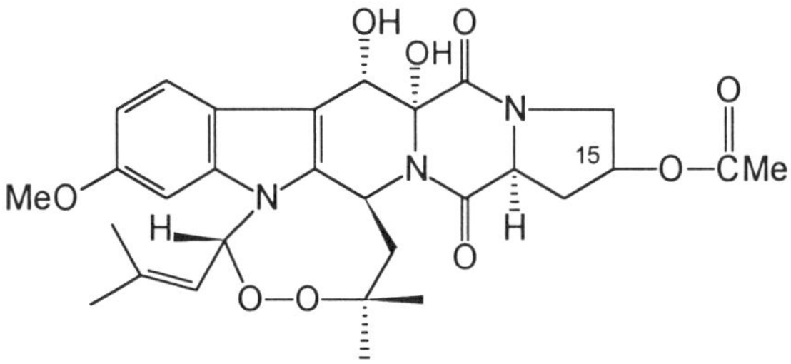

General Characteristics

Melting point, 217-218°C (dec.)

Fungal Source

Penicillium verruculosum → *P. brasilianum.*

Biological Activity

Tremorgenic but activity less than that observed for comparable amount of verruculogen.

Spectral Data

UV:

λ_{max}^{MeOH} 227 and 295nm (ϵ max not reported).

TLC Data

Silica gel G-HR, toluene-ethyl acetate-formic acid, 5:4:1, v/v/v. R_f: 0.66. Detection: slate-gray spot develops immediately after spraying with 50% ethanolic H_2SO_4.

Reference

R. J. Cole and R. H. Cox; Handbook of Toxic Fungal Metabolites; Academic Press, New York, pp. 374-376(1981).

Common/Systematic Name

TR-2

Molecular Formula/Molecular Weight

$C_{22}H_{27}N_3O_6$; MW = 429.18999

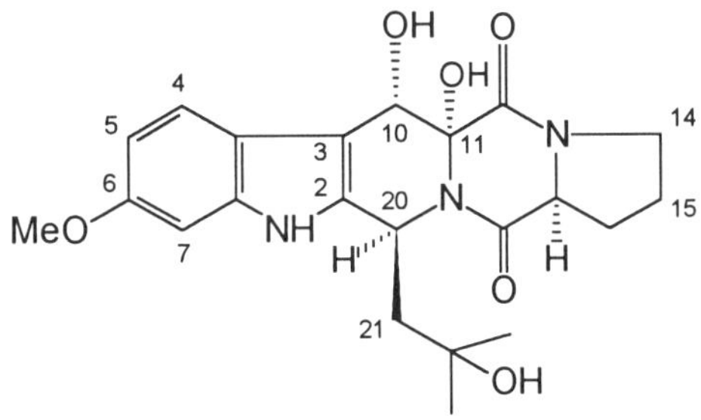

General Characteristics

Crystals from benzene-ethyl acetate, 95:5, v/v; mp., 150-152°C.

Fungal Source

Penicillium verruculosum → *P. brasilianum*, and *Aspergillus fumigatus* Fres. Also, obtained as one of two products from reductive cleavage of verruculogen.

Biological Activity

Perceptible tremors in day-old cockerels dosed orally at levels down to 12.5mg/kg.

Spectral Data

UV:

λ_{max}^{EtOH} 224(ϵ= 37,400), 268(6,830), and 294nm (7,540).

^{1}H NMR:

($CDCl_3$) H-4, 7.60(*J*=9.0); H-5, 6.60(*J*=9.0, 3.0); H-7, 6.87; H-10, 5.52; 10-OH, 5.00; 11-OH, 4.20; H-14,3.54; H-15, 1.85; H-16, 1.85; H-17, 4.33; H-20, 5.37; H-21, 1.85; H-23, 1.05; H-24, 1.30; 22-OH, 5.94; and H-25, 3.71ppm.

^{13}C NMR:

($CDCl_3$) C-2, 131.8 s; C-3, 105.1 s; C-4, 121.2 d; C-5, 109.8 d; C-6, 156.6 s; C-7, 95.2; C-8, 137.2 s; C-9, 120.8 s; C-10, 68.8 d; C-11, 83.4 d; C-12, 171.4 s; C-14, 49.9 t; C-15, 22.7 t; C-16, 29.6 t; C-17, 58.9 d; C-18, 166.2 s; C-20, 57.4 d; C-21, 45.3 t; C-22, 71.2 s; C-23, 31.9 q; C-24, 29.7 q; and C-25, 55.7ppm q.

Mass Spectrum:

429 M^+ with prominent losses of -15(CH_3), 18(OH), and 84*m/e* (C_5H_8O).

TLC Data

Silica gel G-HR, toluene-ethyl acetate-formic acid, 5:4:1, v/v/v. R_f: 0.46. Detection: light brown fluorescent spot after spraying with 50% ethanolic H_2SO_4 and heating at 100°C for 5 min.

References

R. J. Cole and R. H. Cox; Handbook of Toxic Fungal Metabolites; Academic Press, New York, pp. 377-381(1981).

R. J. Cole and J. W. Kirksey; The Mycotoxin Verruculogen: a 6-*O*-Methylindole; Agric. Food Chem., Vol. 21, pp. 927-929(1973).

Common/Systematic Name

Epiamauromine

Molecular Formula/Molecular Weight

$C_{32}H_{36}N_4O_2$; MW = 508.28383

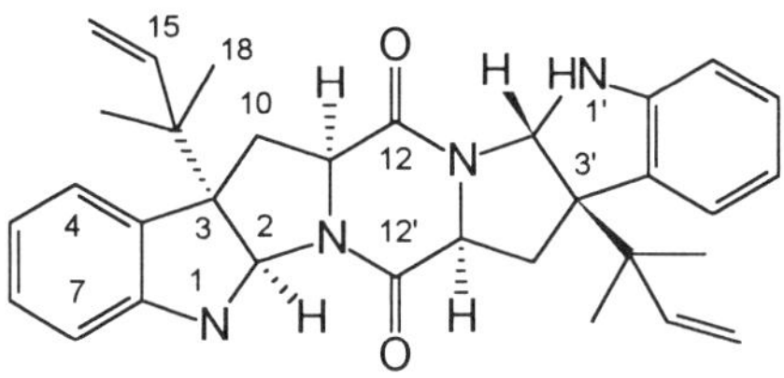

General Characteristics

Epiamauromine was isolated as a white solid; mp., 134°C; $[\alpha]_D$ -50.0° (*c*=0.18g/dl, in $CHCl_3$) and $[\alpha]_D$ -29.1° (*c*=0.46g/dl, $CHCl_3$).

Fungal Source

Sclerotia of *Aspergillus ochraceus* (NRRL 3519).

Isolation/Purification

Intact sclerotia of *A. ochraceus* were extracted at room temperature with hexane, then $CHCl_3$. After removal of the solvent *in vacuo*, the hexane extract was subjected to reversed-phase HPLC [MeOH-H_2O (9:1, v/v), 2ml/min] to give *N*-methylepiamauromine. The $CHCl_3$ extract, after removal of the solvent *in vacuo*, was fractionated through a column of Sephadex LH-20 (25-100μm) using CH_2Cl_2-hexane (1:1, v/v), then CH_2Cl_2-MeOH (1:1, v/v) as eluents. The fractions obtained with CH_2Cl_2-hexane (1:1, v/v) were combined, concentrated, and purified by HPLC as above to give epiamauromine and *N*-methylepiamauromine. The fractions eluted with CH_2Cl_2-MeOH (1:1, v/v) were likewise combined, concentrated, rechromatographed on Sephadex LH-20 using $CHCl_3$-MeOH (2:1, v/v), and purified by reversed-phase HPLC to yield cycloechinulin.

Biological Activity

Caused moderate reduction in weight gain in assays against the lepidopteran crop pest *Helieoverpa zea*.

Spectral Data

UV:

λ_{max}^{MeOH} 215(log ϵ=5.0), 243(5.0), and 300nm (4.6).

^1H NMR:

($CDCl_3$) H-1,5.36, br s; H-2, 5.30, s; H-4, 7.16(dd, *J*=1.2, 7.8); H-5, 6.74(ddd, *J*=1.2,

4.2, 7.2); H-6, 7.08(dt, J=1.2, 7.8); H-7, 6.56(ddd, J=0.6, 1.2, 7.8); H-10, 2.45(dd, J=9.6, 13.8); 2.75(dd, J=9.0, 13.3); H-11, 4.04(dt, J=1.8, 9.0); H-15, 5.86(dd, J=10.8, 17.4); H-16, 5.06(dd, J=1.2, 17.4); 5.09(dd, J=0.6, 10.8); H-17, 1.10, s; H-18, 0.93, s; H-1', 4.91, br s; H-2', 5.30, s; H-4', 7.12(dd, J=1.2, 7.2); H-5', 6.72(dd, J=1.2, 4.2, 7.2); H-6', 7.06(dt, J=1.2, 7.8); H-7', 6.52(dm, J=0.6, 1.2, 7.8); H-10', 2.50(dd, J=6.0, 12.6); 2.35(dd, J=10.8, 12.6); H-11', 3.90(ddd, J=1.8, 6.0, 11.4); H-15', 5.90(dd, J=10.8, 17.4); H-16', 5.01(dd, J=1.2, 17.4); 5.07(dd, J=0.6, 10.8); H-17',1.05 s; and H-18', 0.95ppm s.

^{13}C NMR:

(CDCl$_3$) C-2, 79.3; C-3, 62.1; C-4, 125.7; C-5, 118.6; C-6, 128.3; C-7, 108.8; C-8, 148.4; C-9, 131.4; C-10, 36.0; C-11, 60.7; C-12, 166.0; C-14, 41.7; C-15, 143.3; C-16, 14.7; C-17, 22.9; C-18, 22.5; C-2', 77.6; C-3', 61.8; C-4', 125.0; C-5', 118.9; C-6', 128.8; C-7', 109.3; C-8', 150.0; C-9', 129.0; C-10', 35.2; C-11',62.0; C-12', 168.0; C-14', 40.8; C-15', 143.4; C-16', 114.4; C-17', 22.9; and C-18', 22.5ppm.

Mass Spectrum:

EIMS: $[M]^+$ 508(0.03), 199(61), 158(20), 150(7), and 131*m/e* (100); HREIMS: found 508.2846; calcd for $C_{32}H_{36}N_4O_2$, 508.2838.

HPLC Data

Beckman Ultrasphere 5µ (10mm x 25cm) C_{18} reversed-phase column was used on all HPLC separations; HPLC retention time for epiamauromine was 12.7 min.

Reference

F. S. de Guzman, J. B. Gloer, D. T. Wicklow, and P. F. Dowd; New Diketopiperazine Metabolites from the Sclerotia of *Aspergillus ochraceus*; Journal of Natural Products, Vol. 55, pp. 931-939(1992).

Common/Systematic Name
N-Methylepiamauromine

Molecular Formula/Molecular Weight
$C_{33}H_{38}N_4O_2$; MW = 522.29948

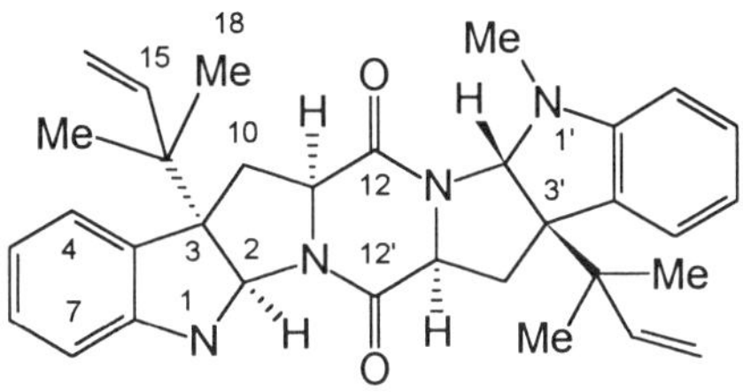

General Characteristics
N-Methylepiamauromine was isolated as a white solid; $[\alpha]_D$ -29.1° (*c*=0.46g/dl, in $CHCl_3$).

Fungal Source
Sclerotia of *Aspergillus ochraceus* (NRRL 3519).

Isolation/Purification
Intact sclerotia of *A. ochraceus* were extracted at room temperature with hexane, then $CHCl_3$. After removal of the solvent *in vacuo*, the hexane extract was subjected to reversed-phase HPLC [MeOH-H_2O (9:1, v/v), 2ml/min] to give *N*-methylepiamauromine. The $CHCl_3$ extract, after removal of the solvent *in vacuo*, was fractionated through a column of Sephadex LH-20 (25-100μm) using CH_2Cl_2-hexane (1:1, v/v), then CH_2Cl_2-MeOH (1:1, v/v) as eluents. The fractions obtained with CH_2Cl_2-hexane (1:1, v/v) were combined, concentrated, and purified by HPLC as above to give epiamauromine and *N*-methylepiamauromine. The fractions eluted with CH_2Cl_2-MeOH (1:1, v/v) were likewise combined, concentrated, rechromatographed on Sephadex LH-20 using $CHCl_3$-MeOH (2:1, v/v), and purified by reversed-phase HPLC to yield cycloechinulin.

Biological Activity
Caused moderate reduction in weight gain in assays against the lepidopteran crop pest *Helieoverpa zea*.

Spectral Data

UV:
λ_{max}^{MeOH} 214(log ϵ=4.4), 244(4.1), and 303nm (3.8).

IR:
(film on NaCl plate) 3380, 1665, and 1605cm^{-1}.

^{1}H NMR:

(CDCl$_3$) H-1, 5.37, s; H-2, 5.32, S; H-4, 7.16(d, *J*=7.5); H-5, 6.73(dt, *J*=0.9, 7.5); H-6, 7.07, dd (*J*=<1, 7.2); H-7, 6.56, d, (*J*=7.5); H-10, 2.45(dd, *J*=9.3, 13.8); 2.75(dd, *J*=8.5, 13.8); H-11, 4.12(dt, *J*=1.8, 9.3); H-15, 5.88(dd, *J*=10.8, 17.2); H-16, 5.07(dd, *J*=<1, 17.1); 5.10(dd, *J*=0.9, 10.8); H-17, 1.11, s; H-18, 0.95, s; H-2', 5.41, s; H-4', 7.06(dt, *J*=0.9, 7.5); H-5', 6.65(dt, *J*=0.9, 7.2); H-6', 7.10(dt, *J*=0.9, 7.5); H-7', 6.31(d, *J*=7.8); H-10', 2.48(dd, *J*=6.3, 12.3); 2.25(dd, *J*=11.1, 12.3); H-11', 3.96(ddd, *J*=1.8, 6.2, 11.1); H-15', 5.80(dd, *J*=10.8, 17.4); H-16', 4.98(dd, *J*=0.9, 17.4); 5.03(dd, *J*=0.9, 9.6); H-17',1.00 s; H-18', 0.89 s; and H-19', 2.98ppm, s.

^{13}C NMR:

(CDCl$_3$) C-2, 79.3; C-3, 61.8; C-4, 125.6; C-5, 118.5; C-6, 128.1; C-7, 108.7; C-8, 148.3; C-9, 131.3; C-10, 36.0; C-11, 58.6; C-12, 165.3; C-14, 41.5; C-15, 143.4; C-16, 114.6; C-17, 22.3; C-18, 22.3; C-2', 82.2; C-3', 60.7; C-4', 128.9; C-5', 117.2; C-6', 124.6; C-7', 105.7; C-8', 151.2; C-9', 129.3; C-10', 37.0; C-11',60.6; C-12', 168.3; C-14', 40.7; C-15', 143.4; C-16', 114.3; C-17', 22.2; C-18', 22.9; and C-19', 33.0ppm.

Mass Spectrum:

EIMS: $[M]^+$ 522(29), 453(59), 384(14), 255 (17), 184(14), 171(58), 157(17), and 144*m/e* (100); HREIMS: found 522.3010; calcd. for $C_{33}H_{38}N_4O_2$, 522.2994.

HPLC Data

Beckman Ultrasphere 5μ (10mm x 25cm) C_{18} reversed-phase column was used on all HPLC separations; HPLC retention time for *N*-methylepiamauromine was 17.9 min.

Reference

F. S. de Guzman, J. B. Gloer, D. T. Wicklow, and P. F. Dowd; New Diketopiperazine Metabolites from the Sclerotia of *Aspergillus ochraceus*; Journal of Natural Products, Vol. 55, pp. 931-939(1992).

Common/Systematic Name
Ditryptophenaline

Molecular Formula/Molecular Weight
$C_{42}H_{40}N_6O_4$; MW = 692.31110

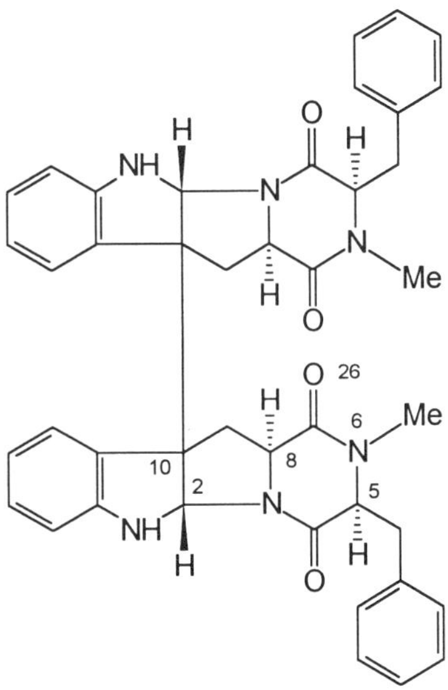

General Characteristics
Clear octahedral crystals from methylene chloride-methanol; mp., 204-205°C; $[\alpha]_D^{23.5}$ -330° (c=0.52, in CH_2Cl_2).

Fungal Source
Aspergillus flavus (strains MIT-M25, 26 and 27).

Isolation/Purification
Extracted with methylene chloride, precipitated with petroleum ether, and purified by column and preparative thin-layer chromatography. The R_f of ditryptophenaline measured on 0.25mm silica gel plates developed with $CHCl_3$:MeOH (20:1, v/v) was 0.80, and a dark green color was produced with van Urk's reagent.

Biological Activity
Possesses neither significant toxic nor antibiotic properties.

Spectral Data

UV:

λ_{max}^{EtOH} 244(ϵ=15,250) and 303nm (6,200).

IR:

($CHCl_3$) 3415, 2995, 2930, 1662 br, 1611, 1498, 1480, 1470, 1455, 1401, 1355, 1323, 1270, 1162, 1151, 1135, 1078, 1052, 1027, 1020, 994, 974, 948, 906, 870, and 700cm^{-1}.

^{1}H NMR*:

($CDCl_3$) 1.59(t, 1-H, *J*=12Hz), 2.05(d of d, 1-H, *J*=12 and 5Hz), 3.03(s, 3-H), 3.21(d of d, 1-H, *J*=14 and 5Hz), 3.55(d of d, 1-H, *J*=14 and 4Hz), 3.65 (d of d, 1-H, *J*=12 and 5Hz), 1.25(br mult, 1-H), 4.79(s, 1-H, exchanges), 4.89(s, 1-1-H), 6.5-6.9(m, 2-H), 6.5 - 7.3(m, 4-H), and 7.4-7.7ppm (m, 3-H).

* Indicated a dimer.

Mass Spectrum:

The high resolution electron-impact mass spectrum gave a parent ion at 692.3095*m/e* (calcd for $C_{42}H_{40}N_6O_4$, 692.3111).

Reference

J. P. Springer, G. Büchi, B. Kobbe, and A. L. Demain; The Structure of Ditrypto-phenaline-: A New Metabolite of *Aspergillus flavus*; Tet. Lett., pp. 2403-2406(1977).

Common/Systematic Name

Exserohilone

Molecular Formula/Molecular Weight

$C_{20}H_{22}N_2O_6S_2$; MW = 450.09193

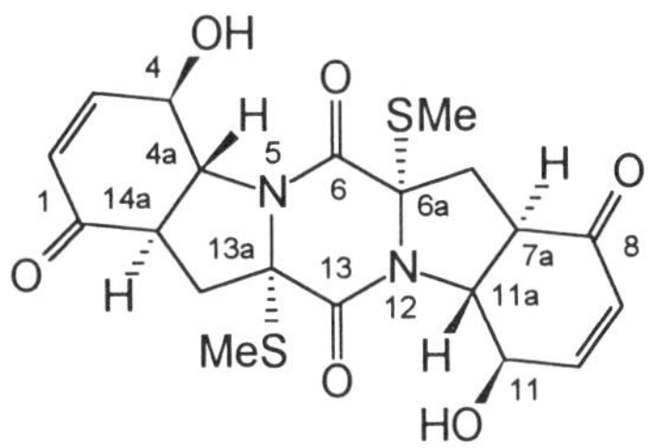

General Characteristics

Colorless glass; $[\alpha]_D^{21}$ -247° (*c*=0.32, in $CHCl_3$).

Fungal Source

Exserohilum holmii, a pathogenic fungus of the weedy plant *Dactyloctenium aegyptium* (crowfoot grass), which is a serious weed in all major tropical and semitropical agricultural areas of the world.

Isolation/Purification

The mycelium of *E. holmii* was cultured on M-1-D culture broth shaken at 200 rpm for 2-3 weeks at 26°C under luminescence. Both the culture filtrate and the fluid obtained after centrifugation of the homogenized mycelium were extracted with EtOAc, and the extract evaporated to dryness under reduced pressure and subjected to flash chromatography using (a) toluene-EtOAc (2:1, v/v) and (b) $CHCl_3$-MeOH (70:1, v/v). Both exserohilone and 9,10-dihydroexserohilone were isolated by reversed phase HPLC (Merck, RP_{18}) with CH_3CN-H_2O (63:35, v/v) as the eluting solvent (1ml/min). The retention time of both exserohilone and 9,10-dihydroexserohilone was 3.5 min in this HPLC system.

Spectral Data

IR:

(KBr) 3320, 2910, 1680, 1640, 1395, and 1260cm^{-1}.

^{1}H NMR:

($CHCl_3$) 2.26(6H, s, SMe); 2.23(2H, overlapping, d, d, *J*=12.6, 13.6Hz, H_a-7, H_a-14); 2.67(2H, d, d, *J*=4.7, 13.6Hz, H_e-7, H_e-14); 3.49(2H, d, d, *J*=4.7, 12.6Hz, H-7_a, H-14_a); 3.89(2H, d, d, *J*=8.7, 12.6Hz, (H-4_a, H-11_a); 4.70(2H, d, d, d, *J*=1.9, 1.9, 8.7Hz, H-4, H-11); 6.10(2H, s, OH); 6.11(2H, d, d, *J*=1.9, 9.1Hz, H-3, H-10); and 6.93ppm (2H, d, d, *J*=1.9, 9.1Hz, H-2, H-9).

^{13}C NMR:

(CDCl$_3$) 15.1(q, SMe); 32.1(t, C-7, C-14); 46.3(d, C-7$_a$, C-14$_a$); 69.0(d, C-4$_a$, C-11$_a$); 72.4(s, C-6$_a$, C-13$_a$); 72.9(d, C-4, C-11); 128.6(d, C-2, C-9); 151.1(d C-3, C-10); 168.0(s, C-6, C-13); and 195.2ppm (s, C-1, C-8).

Mass Data:

LREIMS: 450(2%), 405(24), 403(100), 375(27), 356(27), 355(28), 329(9), 328(18), 160(6), 133(8), 132(8), 110(5), and 95*m/e* (7); HREIMS: (M^+; obsd 450.0919*m/e*; calcd for $C_{20}H_{22}N_2O_6S_2$, 450.0920) and $C_{19}H_{19}N_2O_6S_1$ (M^+ - SMe; obsd 403.0963*m/e*; calcd 403.0964).

TLC Data

R_f values on silica gel using $CHCl_3$-MeOH (50:1, v/v) were 0.19 for exserohilone and 0.15 for 9,10-dihydroexserohilone.

Reference

K. Sugawara, F. Sugawara, G. A. Strobel, Y. Fu, H. Cun-Heng, and J. Clardy; Exserohilone: a Novel Phytotoxin Produced by *Exserohilum holmii*; J. Org. Chem., Vol. 50, pp. 5631-5633(1985).

Common/Systematic Name
9,10-Dihydroexserohilone

Molecular Formula/Molecular Weight
$C_{20}H_{24}N_2O_6S_2$; MW = 450.09193

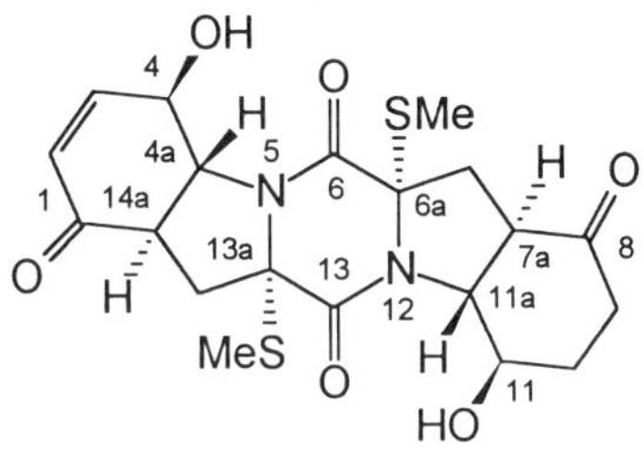

General Characteristics
$[\alpha]_D^{21}$ -110° (c=0.33, in $CHCl_3$).

Fungal Source
Exserohilum holmii, a pathogenic fungus of the weedy plant *Dactyloctenium aegyptium* (crowfoot grass), which is a serious weed in all major tropical and semitropical agricultural areas of the world.

Isolation/Purification
The mycelium of *E. holmii* was cultured on M-1-D culture broth shaken at 200 rpm for 2-3 weeks at 26°C under luminescence. Both the culture filtrate and the fluid obtained after centrifugation of the homogenized mycelium were extracted with EtOAc, and the extract evaporated to dryness under reduced pressure and subjected to flash chromatography using (a) toluene-EtOAc (2:1, v/v) and (b) $CHCl_3$-MeOH (70:1, v/v). Both exserohilone and 9,10-dihydroexserohilone were isolated by reversed phase HPLC (Merck, RP_{18}) with CH_3CN-H_2O (63:35, v/v) as the eluting solvent (1ml/min). The retention time of both exserohilone and 9,10-dihydroexserohilone was 3.5 min in this HPLC system.

Spectral Data

^{1}H NMR:
($CHCl_3$) 1.6(2H, m, H-10); 1.96(1H, m, H-7); 2.238(3H, s, SMe); 2.242(3H, s, SMe); 2.27(1H, d, d, J=12.0, 13.7Hz, H_a-14); 2.51(3H, overlapping, m, H-7', H-9); 2.64(1H, d, d, J=4.7, 13.7Hz, H_e-14); 3.49(2H, m, H-7a, H-14a); 3.77(1H, d, d, J=8.6, 13.9Hz, H-11_a); 3.86(1H, d, d, J=8.6, 13.9Hz, H-4_a); 4.27(1H, d, d, J=ca. 6.0, 8.6Hz, H-11); 4.69(1H, d, d, d, J=ca. 1.6, 2.0, 8.6Hz, H-4); 5.66(1H, s, OH); 6.09(1H, d, d, J=2.0, 10.1Hz, H-3); 6.12(1H, s, OH); and 6.92ppm (1H, d, d, J=1.6, 10.1Hz, H-2).

Mass Data:

LREIMS: 452(1.8%, M^+), 406(8), 405(33), M^+ - SMe, 359(9), 358(33, M^+ - 2 SMe), 357(100), 341(5), 339(7), 323(96), and 273*m/e* (13); HREIMS: (M^+, obsd 452.1075*m/e*; calcd for $C_{20}H_{24}N_2O_6S_2$ 452.1077) and $C_{19}H_{21}N_2O_6S_1$ (M^+ - SMe; obsd 405.1120*m/e*; calcd 405.1121).

TLC Data

R_f values on silica gel using $CHCl_3$-MeOH (50:1, v/v) were 0.19 for exserohilone and 0.15 for 9,10-dihydroexserohilone.

Reference

K. Sugawara, F. Sugawara, G. A. Strobel, Y. Fu, H. Cun-Heng, and J. Clardy; Exserohilone: a Novel Phytotoxin Produced by *Exserohilum holmii*; J. Org. Chem., Vol. 50, pp. 5631-5633(1985).

Common/Systematic Name

Epoxyexserohilone

Molecular Formula/Molecular Weight

$C_{20}H_{22}N_2O_6S_2$; MW = 450.09193

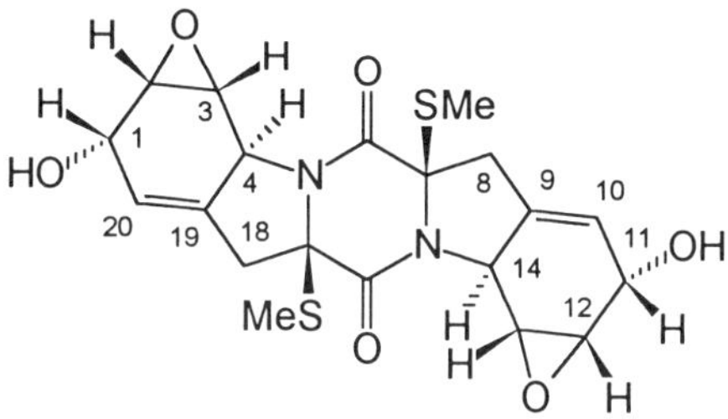

General Characteristics

Crystals from benzene-acetone; mp., 190-192°C.

Fungal Source

Nigrospora sphaerica.

Isolation/Purification

Cultures were extracted with acetone, reduced in volume and reextracted with ethyl acetate. The crude extract was chromatographed on a silica gel column eluted with a polarity series: benzene, *t*-butylmethyl ether, ethyl acetate, acetone, and acetonitrile. The epoxyexserohilone-rich fractions (*t*-butylmethyl ether, ethyl acetate, and acetone) were combined, reduced in volume, and chromatographed on a silica gel column eluted with a linear gradient from benzene to acetone. Epoxyexserohilone crystallized from enriched fractions upon sitting for 72hr at room temperature.

Spectral Data

UV:

λ_{max}^{EtOH} End absorption.

IR:

(KBr) 1384, 1068, 1022, 971, 892, 878, 852, 834, 792, 725, 672, 659, and 645cm^{-1}.

1H NMR:

(acetone-d_6) H-10, 5.90; H-11, 4.57(m, J=8.8, 5.7, 4.5, ca. 1.5Hz); H-12, 3.45(ddd, J=4.5, 3.4, 1.0Hz); H-13, 3.75(dt, 3.5, 0.4Hz); H-14, 4.31(sextet, 1.4Hz); OH, 3.71(d, 8.8Hz); H-8_{ax}, 3.00(ddt, 14.1, 2.2, 1.5Hz); H-8_{eq}, 2.91(dm, 14.1Hz); and CH_3S, 2.15ppm (s).

Mass Spectrum:
450(M^+), 403.0964(100%) (M^+ - SCH_3), 356, 337, and 160*m/e*.

TLC Data

Silica gel G, F_{254} thin-layer plates developed in toluene-ethyl acetate-formic acid, 5:4:1, v/v/v; R_f 0.10-0.16; detected as a lemon yellow-colored spot by spraying with anisaldehyde and heating to 100°C.

Reference

H. G. Cutler, K. Hoogsteen, R. H. Littrell, and B. H. Arison; Epoxyexserohilone, a Novel Metabolite from *Nigrospora sphaerica*; Agric. Biol. Chem., Vol. 55, pp. 2037-2042 (1991).

Chaetoglobosins/Cytochalasins

3

Chaetoglobsin A
Chaetoglobosin B
Chaetoglobosin C
Chaetoglobosin D
Chaetoglobosin E
Chaetoglobosin F
Chaetoglobosin G
Chaetoglobosin J
19-*O*-Acetylchaetoglobosin A
19-*O*-Acetylchaetoglobosin B
19-*O*-Acetylchaetoglobosin D
Chaetoglobosin K
Chaetoglobosin L
Chaetoglobosin M
Cytochalasin A; Dehydrophomin
Cytochalasin B; Phomin
Cytochalasin C
Cytochalasin D; Zygosporin A
Cytochalasin F
Cytochalasin L
Cytochalasin M
Zygosporin D
Zygosporin E
Zygosporin F; Cytochalasin D monoacetate
Zygosporin G
Cytochalasin H; Kodocytochalasin-1; Paspalin-P
Cytochalasin U
Deacetylcytochalasin H; Cytochalasin J; Kodocytochalasin-2; Paspalin-P2
Epoxycytochalasin H
Deacetylepoxycytochalasin H; Epoxydeacetylcytochalasin H; Epoxycytochalasin J
Engleromycin
Pyrichalasin H
Cytochalasin N_{pho}
Cytochalasin O_{pho}
Cytochalasin P_{pho}
Cytochalasin Q_{pho}
Cytochalasin R_{pho}
Cytochalasin S
Cytochalasin N_{hyp}
Cytochalasin O_{hyp}
Cytochalasin P_{hyp}
Cytochalasin Q_{hyp}
19,20-Epoxycytochalasin Q

19,20-Epoxydeacetylcytochalasin Q
Cytochalasin R_{HYP}
Cytochalasin G
Aspochalasin A
Aspochalasin B
Aspochalasin C
Aspochalasin D
Cytochalasin E
Rosellichalasin
Cytochalasin K_{ASP}
Deoxaphomin
Proxiphomin
Protophomin
Ascochalasin
Cytochalasin K_{CHA}

Common/Systematic Name

Chaetoglobosin A

(6*R*,7*S*,16*S*,19*R*)-6,7-Epoxy-10-(indol-3-yl)-19-hydroxy-16,18-dimethyl[13]cytochalasa-13(*E*),17(*E*),21(*E*)-triene-1,20,23-trione

Molecular Formula/Molecular Weight

$C_{32}H_{36}N_2O_5$; MW = 528.26242

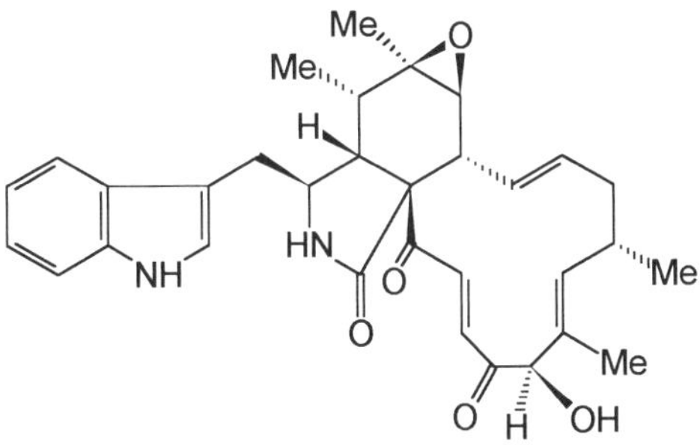

General Characteristics

Crystals from dichloromethane; mp, 168-170°C; $[\alpha]_D$ -270° (in MeOH).

Fungal Source

Chaetomium globosum, C. cochlioides, C. mollipilium, C. rectum, and *C. subaffine*.

Isolation/Purification

The culture filtrates of *Chaetomium globosum* were extracted with methylene chloride and the major metabolites, chaetoglobosin A and 19-*O*-acetylchaetoglobosin A separated by crystallization.

Biological Activity

Cytotoxicity to HeLa cells, ED_{50} between 3.2 and 10μg/ml. Caused inhibition of cytoplasmic cleavage resulting in polynucleate cells. LD_{50} in male mice dosed subcutaneously, 6.5mg/kg; in female mice, 17.8mg/kg.

Spectral Data

UV:

λ_{max}^{MeOH} 223(ε=40,700), 274(6,600), 282(6,600), and 291nm (5,300);

λ_{max}^{EtOH} 196(log ε=4.63), 220(4.62), 271(3.82), 280(3.82), and 290nm (3.72).

IR:

(KBr) 3600-3200, 1665, 1610, 1450, 1420, 1380, 1290, 1240, 1040, and 965cm^{-1}.

^{1}H NMR:

H-2, 5.85; H-3, 3.81(*J*=3.0, 4.3, 7.5); H-4, 3.03(*J*=3.0, 5.0); H-5, 1.85(*J*=5.0, 7.0); H-7, 2.78(*J*=5.0), H-8, 2.14(*J*=5.0, 9.5); H-10, 2.63(*J*=1.5, 7.5, 15); H-11, 1.24(*J*=7.0); H-12, 1.29; H-13, 6.05(*J*=9.5, 15); H-14, 5.20(*J*=4.0, 10.0, 15); H-15, 1.8-2.4; H-16, 2.42(*J*=6.5, 9.0); H-17, 5.57(*J*=9.0); H-19, 5.01; H-21, 7.72(*J*=16.5); H-22, 6.50(*J*=16.5); H-24, 1.00(*J*=6.5); H-25, 1.31; 19-OH, 3.84; H-1', 8.21; and H-2', 6.94; H-4', 7', 7.0-7.5. (400 MHZ, $CDCl_3$): 0.99(d *J*=6.5, 3H); 1.25(d *J*=7.5 3H); 1.30(s, 3H); 1.32(d *J*=1, 3H); 1.85(m, 1H); 2.0-2.1(m, 1H); 2.13(dxd *J*=5 and 10, 1H); 2.2-2.3(m, 1H); 2.4-2.6(m, 1H); 2.64(dxd *J*=15, *J*=8, 1H); 2.79(d *J*=5, 1H); 2.96(dxd *J*=15, *J*=4, 1H); 3.03(dxd *J*=3 and 5, 1H); 3.81(m, 1H); 3.87(d *J*=4, 1H; exchangeable with D_2O); 5.03(d *J*=4, 1H); 5.22(m, 1H); 5.59(dxd *J*=1, 1H); 5.94(s, 1H; exchangeable with D_2O); 6.06(dxd *J*=15 and 10, 1H); 6.48(d *J*=17, 1H); 6.9-7.5(m, 5H); 7.73(d *J*=17, 1H); and 8.25ppm (br. s, 1H; exchangeable with D_2O).

^{13}C NMR:

($CDCl_3$) C-1, 173.2; C-3, 52.8; C-4, 46.8; C-5, 36.3; C-6, 58.0; C-7, 62.4; C-8, 48.8; C-9, 63.4; C-10, 33.7; C-11, 13.2; C-12, 19.7; C-13, 128.3; C-14, 133.1; C-15, 41.7; C-16, 32.0; C-17, 139.9; C-18, 132.3; C-19, 81.7; C-20, 201.4; C-21, 131.6; C-22, 136.1; C-23, 197.1; C-16CH_3, 20.9; C-18CH_3, 10.5; C-2', 121.7; C-3', 109.4; C-3a', 127.4; C-4', 118.4; C-5', 124.0; C-6', 119.3; C-7', 111.7; and C-7a',136.6ppm.

Mass Spectrum:

528(M^+), 398, and 130*m/e*.

TLC Data

Silica gel G-HR, Solvent A: chloroform-acetone, 93:7, v/v; Solvent B: toluene-ethyl acetate-formic acid, 5:4:1, v/v/v. R_f values of A: 0.05; B: 0.65. Detection: a light olive-gray fluorescent spot under UV light after spraying with 50% ethanolic H_2SO_4 and heating.

References

R. J. Cole and R. H. Cox; Handbook of Toxic Fungal Metabolites; Academic Press, New York, p. 304 (1981).

A. Probst and C. Tamm; 19-*O*-Acetylchaetoglobosin B and 19-*O*-Acetylchaetoglobosin D, Two New Metabolites of *Chaetomium globosum*; Helvetica Chimica Acta, Vol. 64, pp. 2056-2064(1981).

S. Nator and I. Yahara; In Mycotoxins and Phytoalexins, R. P. Sharma, and D. K. Salunkhe (eds.), CRC Press, pp. 291-338(1991).

S. Sekita, K. Yoshihira, S. Natoriand, and H. Kuwano; Structures of Chaetoglobosins A and B, Cytotoxic Metabolites of *Chaetomium globosum*; Tetrahedron Lett., p. 2109 (1973).

Common/Systematic Name

Chaetoglobosin B

(7*S*,16*S*,19*R*)-10-(Indol-3-yl)-7,19-dihydroxy-16,18-dimethyl[13]cytochalasa-5(6),13(*E*),17(*E*),21(*E*)-tetraene-1,20,23-trione

Molecular Formula/Molecular Weight

$C_{32}H_{36}N_2O_5$; MW = 528.26242

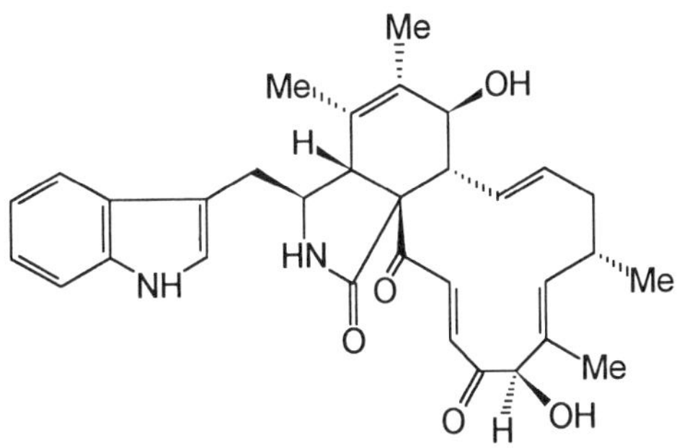

General Characteristics

Crystals from benzene; mp., 186-187°C; $[\alpha]_D$ -176° (in MeOH).

Fungal Source

Chaetomium globosum, C. cochlioides, C. mollipilium, C. rectum, and *C. subaffine.*

Biological Activity

Cytotoxicity to HeLa cells, ED_{50} between 3.2 and 10μg/ml; caused inhibition of cytoplasmic cleavage, resulting in polynucleate cells.

Spectral Data

UV:

λ_{max}^{EtOH} 222(ε=43,600), 274(7,900), 281(7,900), and 290nm (6,700).

^{1}H NMR:

H-4, 3.40; H-7, 3.53; H-8, 2.06; H-11 ,1.64; and H-12, 1.73ppm. The remainder of the protons are the same as in chaetoglobosin A.

TLC Data

Silica gel G-HR, Solvent: A: chloroform-acetone, 93:7 v/v; B: toluene-ethyl acetate-formic acid, 5:4:1, v/v/v. R_f values for A: 0.05; B: 0.61. Detection: a dark olive-gray fluorescent spot under UV light after spraying with 50% ethanolic H_2SO_4 and heating.

References

R. J. Cole and R. H. Cox; Handbook of Toxic Fungal Metabolites; Academic Press, New York, p. 308 (1981).

S. Natori and I. Yahara; In Mycotoxins and Phytoalexins, R. P. Sharma, and D. K. Salunkhe (eds.), CRC Press, pp. 291-338(1991).

S. Sekita, K. Yoshihira, S. Natori, and H. Kuwano; Structures of Chaetoglobosins A and B, Cytotoxic Metabolites of *Chaetomium globosum*; Tetrahedron Lett., p. 2109 (1973).

Common/Systematic Name

Chaetoglobosin C

(6*R*,7*S*,16*S*)-6,7-Epoxy-10-(indol-3-yl)-16,18-dimethyl[13]cytochalasa-13(*E*),17(*E*)-diene-1,19,20,23-tetraone

Molecular Formula/Molecular Weight

$C_{32}H_{36}N_2O_5$; MW = 528.26242

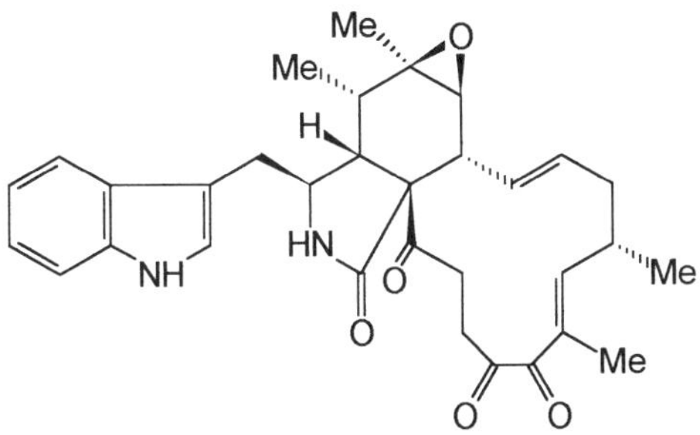

General Characteristics

Colorless leaflets from acetone; mp, 260-263 °C; $[\alpha]_D$ -30° (in MeOH); acetone gave colorless crystals; mp, 259-261 °C.

Fungal Source

Chaetomium globosum (strain Lederle H-124), *C. cochlioides*, *C. mollipilium*, *C. rectum*, *C. subaffine*, and *Penicillium aurantiovirens*.

Isolation/Purification

To extract the culture broth, an equal volume of ethanol was added, the mixture kept overnight at 4 °C, and the mycelium separated by filtration. The ethanol was then evaporated and the aqueous layer extracted with CH_2Cl_2. The organic layer was dried (Na_2SO_4) and evaporated to dryness. The brown residue was dissolved in benzene and kept 3 days at room temperature. The crystallized mixture of chaetoglobosin A and 19-*O*-acetylchaetoglobosin A was separated by filtration and chromatographed on silica gel using increasing amounts of methanol in CH_2Cl_2. The benzene solution was evaporated and the residue chromatographed on silica gel in the same manner to yield 19-*O*-acetyl-chaetoglobosin A, chaetoglobosin A, chaetoglobosin C, 19-*O*-acetylchaetoglobosin D, and 19-*O*-acetylchaetoglobosin B.

Biological Activity

Cytotoxicity to HeLa cells, ED_{50} between 10 and 32µg/ml. Oral LD_{50} determination using day-old chicks was not successful due to insolubility of purified toxin; crude extracts were highly toxic.

Spectral Data

UV:

λ_{max}^{EtOH} 222(ϵ=36,300), 273(6,700), 281(6,700), and 291nm (5,700).

^{13}C NMR:

C-1, 173.8 s; C-3, 52.3 d; C-4, 48.4 d; C-5, 36.1 d; C-6, 56.6 s; C-7, 60.3 d; C-8, 48.4 d; C-9, 62.2 s; C-10, 39.5 t; C-11, 9.9 q; C-12, 19.3 q; C-13, 127.0 d; C-14, 133.1 d; C-15, 32.6 t; C-16, 37.0 d; C-17, 155.8 d; C-18, 130.9 s; C-19, 196.1 s; C-20, 205.2 s; C-21, 31.9 t; C-22, 31.9 t; C-23, 208.1 s; C-24, 12.3 q; C-25, 19.1 q; C-2', 120.9 d; C-3', 108.0 s; C-4', 118.6 d; C-5', 125.1 d; C-6', 118.3 d; C-7', 111.3 d; C-8', 135.8 s; and C-9', 127.6ppm s.

TLC Data

Silica gel G-HR, Solvent A: chloroform-acetone, 93:7, v/v; B: toluene-ethyl acetate-formic acid, 5:4:1, v/v/v. R_f value of A: 0.13; B: 0.71. Detection: a slate gray fluorescent spot under UV light after spraying with 50% ethanolic H_2SO_4 and heating.

References

R. J. Cole and R. H. Cox; Handbook of Toxic Fungal Metabolites; Academic Press, New York, p. 313 (1981).

S. Natori and I. Yahara; In Mycotoxins and Phytoalexins, R. P. Sharma, and D. K. Salunkhe (eds.), CRC Press, pp. 291-338(1991).

A. Probst and C. Tamm; 19-*O*-Acetylchaetoglobosin B and 19-*O*-Acetylchaetoglobosin D, Two New Metabolites of *Chaetomium globosum*; Helvetica Chimica Acta, Vol. 64, pp. 2056-2064(1981).

J. P. Springer, J. Clardy, J. M. Wells, R. J. Cole, J. W. Kirksey, R. D. MacFarlane, and D. F. Torgerson; Tetrahedron Lett., p. 1355 (1976).

Common/Systematic Name

Chaetoglobosin D

(7*S*,16*S*,19*R*)-7,19-Dihydroxy-10-(indol-3-yl)-16,18-dimethyl[13]cytochalasa-6(12),13(*E*),17(*E*),21(*E*)-tetraene-1,20,23-trione

Molecular Formula/Molecular Weight

$C_{32}H_{36}N_2O_5$; MW = 528.26242

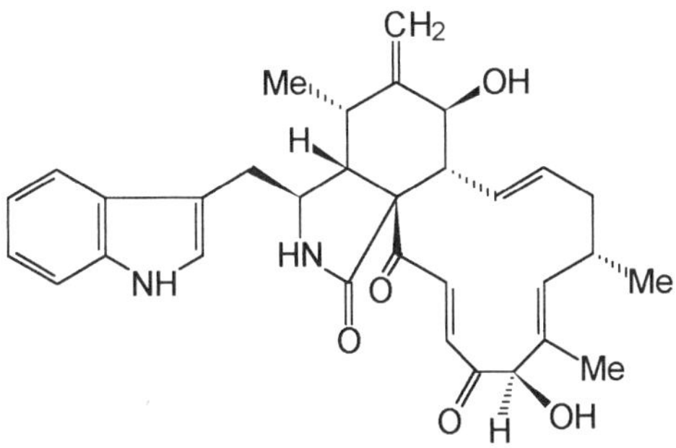

General Characteristics

Pale yellow prisms from chloroform solution; mp, 216°C; $[\alpha]_D$ -269° (in MeOH).

Fungal Source

Chaetomium globosum, C. cochlioides, C. mollipilium, C. rectum, and *C. subaffine.*

Biological Activity

Cytotoxicity to HeLa cells, ED_{50} between 3.2 and 10μg/ml.

Spectral Data

UV:

λ_{max}^{EtOH} 221(ε=43,600), 273(9,100), 281(9,100), and 290nm (7,500).

IR:

(KBr) 3421, 3280, 1686, 1606, 972, 908, and 750cm^{-1}.

^{1}H NMR:

H-4, 3.30; H-5, 3.14; H-7, 4.59; H-8, 2.92; H-11, 1.23; H-12, 5.21, 5.66; H-13, 6.53; and H-14, 5.44. The remainder of the protons are the same as in chaetoglobosin A.

Mass Spectrum:

Molecular ion (M^+) 528.261*m/e*; base peak 130.037*m/e* (C_9H_8N).

References

R. J. Cole and R. H. Cox; Handbook of Toxic Fungal Metabolites; Academic Press, New York, p. 319 (1981).

S. Natori and I. Yahara; In Mycotoxins and Phytoalexins, R. P. Sharma, and D. K. Salunkhe (eds.), CRC Press, pp. 291-338 (1991).

S. Sekita, K. Yoshihira, S. Natori, and H. Kuwano; Structures of Chaetoglobosins A and B, Cytotoxic Metabolites of *Chaetomium globosum*; Tetrahedron Lett. p. 2109 (1973).

Common/Systematic Name

Chaetoglobosin E

(7*S*,16*S*,20*S*)-7,20-Dihydroxy-10-(indol-3-yl)-16,18-dimethyl[13]cytochalasa-5(6),13(*E*),17(*E*)-triene-1,19,23-trione

Molecular Formula/Molecular Weight

$C_{32}H_{38}N_2O_5$; MW = 530.27807

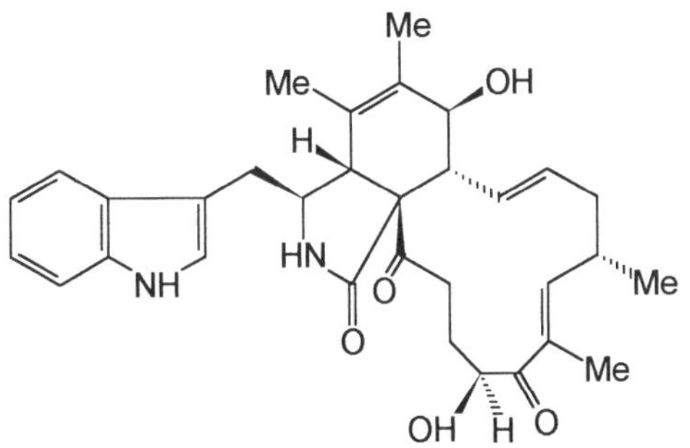

General Characteristics

Colorless needles from methanol; mp., 279-280°C; $[\alpha]_D$ +158° (in MeOH).

Fungal Source

Chaetomium globosum, C. cochlioides, C. mollipilium, C. rectum, and *C. subaffine*.

Biological Activity

Cytotoxicity to HeLa cells, ED_{50} between 3.2 and 10μg/ml.

Spectral Data

UV:

λ_{max}^{EtOH} 221(ϵ=56,200), 275(7,000), 281(7,000), and 291nm (6,300).

IR:

(KBr) 3410, 1704, 1676, 1048, and 746cm^{-1}.

^{1}H NMR:

H-7, 4.56; 7-OH, 5.97; H-11, 1.49; H-12, 1.90; H-17, 6.34; H-20, 5.29; 20-OH, 6.10; H-21, 2.41; and H-22, 3.41ppm. The remainder of the protons are the same as in chaetoglobosin A.

Mass Spectrum:

530.275*m/e* (M^+); base peak 130.131*m/e* (C_9H_8N).

References

R. J. Cole and R. H. Cox; Handbook of Toxic Fungal Metabolites; Academic Press, New York, p. 322 (1981).

S. Natori and I. Yahara; In Mycotoxins and Phytoalexins, R. P. Sharma, and D. K. Salunkhe (eds.), CRC Press, pp. 291-338(1991).

S. Sekita, K. Yoshihira, S. Natori, and H. Kuwano; Structures of Chaetoglobosins A and B, Cytotoxic Metabolites of *Chaetomium globosum*; Tetrahedron Lett., p. 2109 (1973).

S. Sekita, K. Yoshihira, S. Natori, and H. Kuwano; Structures of Chaetoglobosins C, D, E, and F, Cytotoxic indol-3-yl[13]cytochalasins from *Chaetomium globosum*; Tetrahedron Lett., p. 1351 (1976).

Common/Systematic Name

Chaetoglobosin F

(6*R*,7*S*,16*S*,20*S*)-6,7-Epoxy-20-hydroxy-10-(indol-3-yl)-16,18-dimethyl[13]-cytochalasa-13(*E*),17(*E*)-diene-1,19,23-trione

Molecular Formula/Molecular Weight

$C_{32}H_{38}N_2O_5$; MW = 530.27807

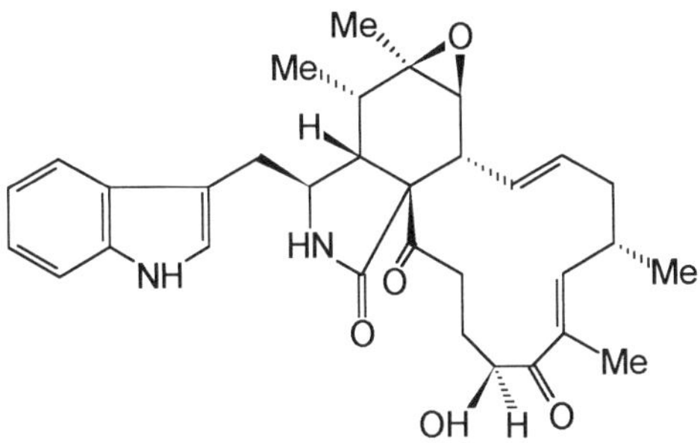

General Characteristics

Colorless leaflets from benzene; mp., 177-178°C; $[\alpha]_D$ -69° (in $CHCl_3$).

Fungal Source

Chaetomium globosum.

Biological Activity

Cytotoxicity to HeLa cells, ED_{50} 10µg/ml.

Spectral Data

UV:

λ_{max}^{EtOH} 222(ε=47,800), 276(6,900), 283(6,700), and 292nm (6,000).

IR:

(KBr) 3346, 1676, 1618, 979, 879, and 740cm^{-1}.

^{1}H NMR:

H-5, 2.01; H-7, 3.12; H-11, 0.97; H-12, 1.25; H-17, 6.26; H-20, 5.14; H-21, 2.27; H-22, 2.95; and H-25, 1.93ppm. The remainder of the protons are the same as in chaetoglobosin A.

Mass Spectrum:

530.275*m/e* (M^+); base peak 130.107*m/e* (C_9H_8N).

References

R. J. Cole and R. H. Cox; Handbook of Toxic Fungal Metabolites, Academic Press, New York, p. 325 (1981).

S. Natori and I. Yahara; In Mycotoxins and Phytoalexins, R. P. Sharma, and D. K. Salunkhe (eds.), CRC Press, pp. 291-338(1991).

S. Sekita, K. Yoshihira, S. Natori, and H. Kuwano; Structures of Chaetoglobosins C, D, E, and F, Cytotoxic Indol-3-yl[13]cytochalasins from *Chaetomium globosum*; Tetrahedron Lett., p. 1351 (1976).

Common/Systematic Name

Chaetoglobosin G

(7*S*,16*S*)-7-Hydroxy-10-(indol-3-yl)-16,18-dimethyl[13]cytochalasa-5(6),13(*E*),17(*E*)-triene-1,19,20,23-tetraone

Molecular Formula/Molecular Weight

$C_{32}H_{36}N_2O_5$; MW = 528.26242

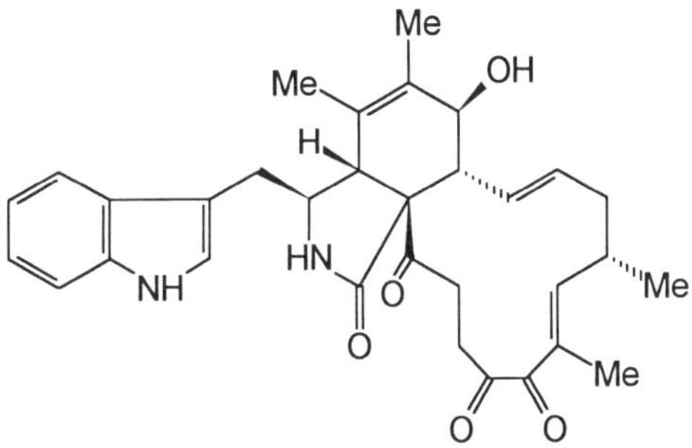

General Characteristics

Colorless leaflets from methanol; mp, 251-253°C; $[\alpha]_D$ + 89°.

Fungal Source

Chaetomium globosum.

Biological Activity

Cytotoxicity to cultured HeLa cells at ca. 3μg/ml, forms multinucleated cells.

Spectral Data

UV:

λ_{max}^{EtOH} 222(ϵ=32,300), 275(6,000), 282(6,000), and 291nm (5,300).

IR:

(KBr) 3455, 3300, 1713, 1693, 1646, 1623, 987, 948, and 741cm^{-1}.

^{1}H NMR:

Perhydroisoindolone protons same as in chaetoglobosin B and E. Thirteen-membered ring protons are the same as in chaetoglobosin C.

References

R. J. Cole and R. H. Cox; Handbook of Toxic Fungal Metabolites, Academic Press, New York, p. 328 (1981).

S. Natori and I. Yahara; In Mycotoxins and Phytoalexins, R. P. Sharma, and D. K. Salunkhe (eds.), CRC Press, pp. 291-338(1991).

S. Sekita, K. Yoshihira, S. Natori, and H. Kuwano; Chaetoglobosins G and J, Cytotoxic Indol-3-yl-[13]-Cytochalasins from *Chaetomium globosum*; Tetrahedron Lett., Vol. 32, p. 2771 (1977).

Common/Systematic Name

Chaetoglobosin J

(16*S*,19*R*)-19-Hydroxy-10-(indol-3-yl)-16,18-dimethyl[13]cytochalasa-6(7),13(*E*),17(*E*),21(*E*)-tetraene-1,20,23-trione

Molecular Formula/Molecular Weight

$C_{32}H_{36}N_2O_4$; MW = 512.26751

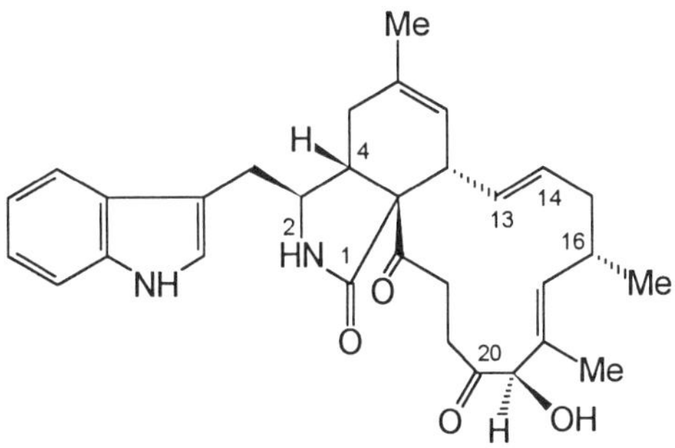

General Characteristics

Pale yellow prisms from benzene; mp, 149-151°C.

Fungal Source

Chaetomium globosum.

Biological Activity

Cytotoxicity to cultured HeLa cells at ca. 3μg/ml. Unlike other members of the group, chaetoglobosin J does not form multinucleated cells.

Spectral Data

UV:

λ_{max}^{EtOH} 224(ε=47,800), 270(7,000), 280(7,000), and 290nm (6,000).

IR:

(KBr) 3412, 3273, 1683, 1639, 1612, 980, 975, 925, and 750cm^{-1}.

^{1}H NMR:

H-4, 3.12; H-5, 2.46; H-7, 5.30; H-8, 2.56; H-11, 1.42; and H-12, 1.80ppm. The remainder of the protons are the same as in chaetoglobosin A.

References

R. J. Cole and R. H. Cox; Handbook of Toxic Fungal Metabolites, Academic Press, New York, p. 329 (1981).

S. Natori and I. Yahara; In Mycotoxins and Phytoalexins, R. P. Sharma, and D. K. Salunkhe (eds.), CRC Press, pp. 291-338(1991).

S. Sekita, K. Yoshihira, S. Natori, and H. Kuwano; Chaetoglobosins G and J, Cytotoxic Indol-3-yl-[13]-Cytochalasins from *Chaetomium globosum*; Tetrahedron Lett., Vol. 32, p. 2771 (1977).

Common/Systematic Name

19-*O*-Acetylchaetoglobosin A

(6*R*,7*S*,16*S*,19*R*)-19-Acetoxy-10-(indol-3-yl)-16,18-dimethyl[13]cytochalasa-13(*E*),17(*E*),21(*E*)-triene-1,20,23-trione

Molecular Formula/Molecular Weight

$C_{34}H_{38}N_2O_6$; MW = 570.27299

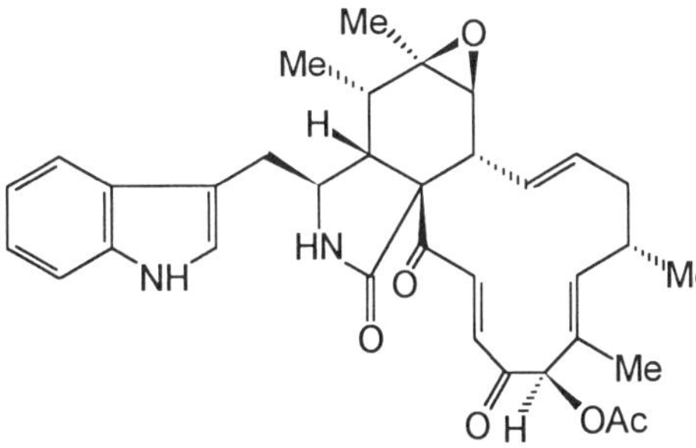

General Characteristics

19-*O*-Acetylchaetoglobosin A was crystallized from benzene to give a yellow powder; mp, 223-225°; $[\alpha]_D^{20}$ -304° (*c*=0.5, in $CHCl_3$).

Fungal Source

Chaetomium globosum (strain Lederle H-124).

Isolation/Purification

The culture filtrates of *Chaetomium globosum* were extracted with methylene chloride and the major metabolites chaetoglobosin A and 19-*O*-acetylchaetoglobosin A separated by crystallization.

Biological Activity

Biological activity not reported but probably typical activity of other related metabolites.

Spectral Data

UV:

λ_{max}^{EtOH} 196(log ϵ=4.65), 220(4.64), 271(3.83), 280(3.83), and 289nm (3.74).

IR:

(KBr): 3380, 1675, 1620, 1450, 1425, 1365, 1240, 1220, 1180, 1030, 970, and 960cm^{-1}.

^{1}H NMR:

2N-H, 6.05, br s; H-3, 3.80, m; H-4, 2.93, dxd, *J*=3 and 5; H-5, 1.84, m; H-7, 2.80, d,

J=5; H-8, 2.14, dxd, *J*=5 and 10; H-10, 2.91, dxd, *J*=15, and 4 ; H-10, 2.67, dxd, *J*=15 and 7.5; H-11, 1.22, d, *J*=7; H-12, 1.28, s; H-13, 6.08, dxd, *J*=15 and 10; H-14, 5.18, m; H-15, 2.3-2.3, m; 1.9-2.0, m; H-16, 2.4-2.6, m; H-17, 5.66, dxd, *J*=9.0 and 1; H-19, 5.90, s; H-21, 7.55, d, *J*=17; H-22, 6.61, d, *J*=17; 16-CH_3, 0.99, d, *J*=6.5; 18-CH_3, 1.45, d, *J*=1; 19-*O*-acetyl, 2.17, s; 1'-NH, 8.31, br, s; and 5H-indolyl, 7.0-7.5ppm.

^{13}C NMR:

[$(CD_3)_2SO$] C-1, 173.6; C-3, 52.8; C-4, 47.3; C-5, 36.4; C-6, 58.0; C-7, 62.3; C-8, 48.3; C-9, 63.4; C-10, 34.0; C-11, 13.3; C-12, 19.7; C-13, 128.3; C-14, 133.4; C-15, 41.3; C-16, 32.2; C-17, 142.5; C-18, 127.6; C-19, 83.4; C-20, 194.8; C-21, 133.4; C-22, 134.8; C-23, 196.9; C-16CH_3, 20.7; C-18CH_3, 11.5; acetyl-CH_3, 20.7; Acetyl-CO, 170.1; C-2', 122.3; C-3', 110.1; C-3a', 127.3; C-4', 118.3; C-5', 123.7; C-6', 119.9; C-7', 111.7; and C-7a', 136.5ppm.

Mass Spectrum:

570(M^+) and 527*m/e*.

References

A. Probst and C. Tamm; 19-*O*-Acetylchaetoglobosin B and 19-*O*-Acetylchaetoglobosin D, Two New Metabolites of *Chaetomium globosum*; Helvetica Chimica Acta, Vol. 64, pp. 2056-2064(1981).

S. Natori and I. Yahara; In Mycotoxins and Phytoalexins, R. P. Sharma, and D. K. Salunkhe (eds.), CRC Press, pp. 291-338(1991).

Common/Systematic Name

19-*O*-Acetylchaetoglobosin B

(7*S*,16*S*,19*R*)-19-Acetoxy-10-(indol-3-yl)-7-hydroxy-16,18-dimethyl[13]cytochalasa-5(6),13(*E*),17(*E*),21(*E*)-tetraene-1,20,23-trione

Molecular Formula/Molecular Weight

$C_{34}H_{38}N_2O_6$; MW = 570.27299

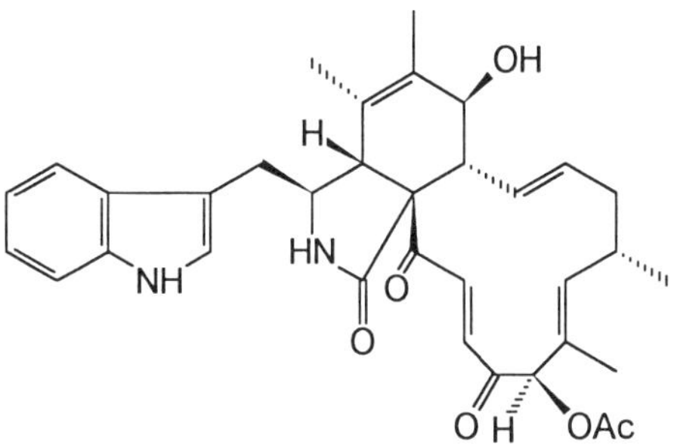

General Characteristics

Gave yellow needles from benzene; mp., 154-157°C; $[\alpha]_D^{20}$ -148° (*c*=0.5, in $CHCl_3$).

Fungal Source

Chaetomium globosum (strain Lederle H-124).

Isolation/Purification

The culture filtrates of *Chaetomium globosum* were extracted with methylene chloride and the major metabolites chaetoglobosin A and 19-*O*-acetylchaetoglobosin A separated by crystallization. The remaining extract was purified by column chromatography on silica gel. Chaetoglobosin C, 19-*O*-acetylchaetoglobosin B and D were enriched. Crystallization of chaetoglobosin C led to a mixture of 19-*O*-acetylchaetoglobosin B and 19-*O*-acetylchaetoglobosin D which were separated and obtained pure by chromatography on silica gel 60 GF_{254} using the chromatotron.

Spectral Data

UV:

λ_{max}^{EtOH} 221(log ε=4.64), 272(3.83), 279(3.83), and 289nm (3.74).

IR:

(KBr) 3600, 3200, 1730, 1710, 1620, 1455, 1430, 1375, 1290, 1250, 1230, 1035, and 970cm^{-1}.

^{1}H NMR:

2N-H, 5.84, br s; H-3, 3.55, m; H-4, 3.24, br s, *J*=<1; H-7, 3.92, br d, *J*=10; H-8, 2.09, t, *J*=10 and 10; H-10, 2.86, dxd, *J*=14, 6; H-10, 2.71, dxd, *J*=14,8; H-11, 1.63, br s; H-12, 1.72, br, s; H-13, 6.18, dxd, *J*=16, 10; H-14, 5.28, m; H-15, 2.3-2.4, m 2.0-2.1, m; H-16, 2.4-2.6, m; H-17, 5.64, dxd, *J*=10,1; H-19, 5.87, s; H-21, 7.54, d, *J*=17; H-22, 6.73, d, *J*=17; 16-CH_3, 1.02, d, *J*=6.5; 18-CH_3, 1.51, d, *J*=1; 19-*O*-acetyl, 2.17, s; 1'-NH, 8.20, br, s; 5H-indoyl, 7.0-7.5; and 7-OH, 1.88ppm, br, s.

^{13}C NMR:
C-1, 172.4; C-3, 57.8; C-4, 46.9; C-5, 125.2; C-6, 133.7; C-7, 67.7; C-8, 50.1; C-9, 60.8; C-10, 31.7; C-11, 14.4; C-12, 16.9; C-13, 127.2; C-14, 133.7; C-16, 32.0; C-17, 141.7; C-18, 127.2; C-19, 83.1; C-20, 194.0; C-21, 134.1; C-22, 135.2; C-23, 199.8; C-16CH_3, 20.3; C-18CH_3, 11.1; Acetyl-CH_3, 20.6; Acetyl-CO, 169.2; C-2', 121.0; C-3', 109.9; C-3a' 126.1; C-4', 118.1; C-5', 123.5; C-6', 118.4; C-7', 111.4; and C-7a', 136.2ppm.

Mass Spectrum:
570(M^+), 528, 185, 173, 130, 103, and 60*m/e*.

References

A. Probst and C. Tamm; 19-*O*-Acetylchaetoglobosin B and 19-*O*-Acetylchaetoglobosin D, Two New Metabolites of *Chaetomium globosum*; Helvetica Chimica Acta, Vol. 64, pp. 2056-2064(1981).

S. Natori and I. Yahara; In Mycotoxins and Phytoalexins, R. P. Sharma, and D. K. Salunkhe (eds.), CRC Press, pp. 291-338(1991).

Common/Systematic Name

19-*O*-Acetylchaetoglobosin D

(7*S*,16*S*,19*R*)-19-Acetoxy-7-hydroxy-10-(indol-3-yl)-16,18-dimethyl[13]cytochalasa-6(12),13(*E*),17(*E*),21(*E*)-tetraene-1,20,23-trione

Molecular Formula/Molecular Weight

$C_{34}H_{38}N_2O_6$; MW = 570.27299

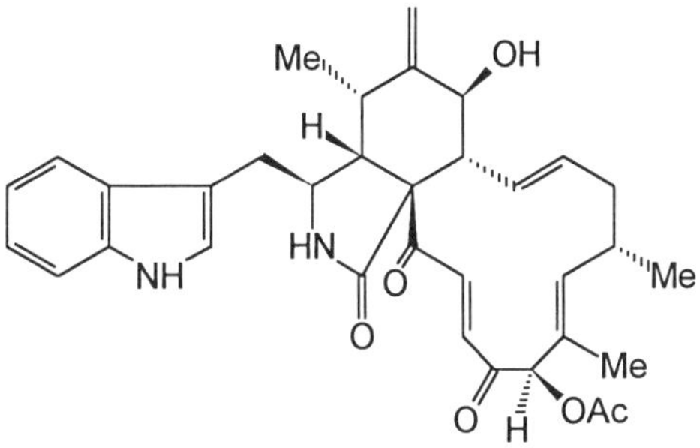

General Characteristics

Gave yellow prisms from $CHCl_3$; mp., 239-241°C ; $[\alpha]_D^{20}$ -176°.

Fungal Source

Chaetomium globosum (strain Lederle H-124).

Isolation/Purification

The culture filtrates of *Chaetomium globosum* were extracted with methylene chloride and the major metabolites chaetoglobosin A and 19-*O*-acetylchaetoglobosin A separated by crystallization. The remaining extract was purified by column chromatography on silica gel. Chaetoglobosin C, 19-*O*-acetylchaetoglobosin B and D were enriched. Crystallization of chaetoglobosin C led to a mixture of 19-*O*-acetylchaetoglobosin B and 19-*O*-acetylchaetoglobosin D which were separated and obtained pure by chromatography on silica gel 60 GF_{254} using the chromatotron.

Spectral Data

UV:

λ_{max}^{EtOH} 221(log ϵ=4.64), 272(3.83), 279(3.83), and 289nm (3.74).

IR:

(KBr) 3600-3200, 1730, 1700-1680, 1610, 1450, 1425, 1370, 1250, 1230, 1030, 970, and 900cm^{-1}.

^{1}H NMR:

2N-H, 5.88, br s; H-3, 3.48, m; H-4, 2.96, br s, *J*=5 and 5; H-5, 2.84, m; H-7, 3.95, br d, *J*=10; H-8, 2.33, t, *J*=10 and 10; H-10, 3.04, dxd, *J*=14, 3.56; H-10, 2.62, dxd, *J*=14, 9; H-11, 1.31, d, *J*=7; H-12, 5.41, br, s; H-13, 5.92, dxd, *J*=15, 10; H-14, 5.31, m; H-15, 2.3-2.4, m 2.0-2.1, m; H-16, 2.4-2.6, m; H-17, 5.70, dxd, *J*=9.5, 1; H-19, 5.98, s; H-21, 7.88, d, *J*=17; H-22, 6.55, d, *J*=17; 16-CH_3, 0.99, d, *J*=7.5; 18-CH_3, 1.48, d, *J*=1; 19-*O*-acetyl, 2.16, s; 1'-NH, 8.30, br, s; 5H-indolyl, 7.0-7.5; and 7-OH, 1.88ppm, br, s.

^{13}C NMR:

[$(CD_3)_2SO$] C-1, 171.9; C-3, 52.0; C-4, 44.8; C-5, 31.3; C- 6, 151.0; C-7, 70.1; C-8, 47.9; C-9, 61.3; C-10, 31.8; C-11, 13.4; C-12, 111.4; C-13, 128.3; C-14, 133.1; C-16, 32.3; C-17, 141.9; C-18, 127.4; C-19, 82.8; C-20, 194.2; C-21, 133.3; C-22, 136.0; C-23, 198.9; C-16CH_3, 20.3; C-18CH_3, 11.1; acetyl-CH_3, 20.6; acetyl-CO, 169.3; C-2', 120.8; C-3', 109.4; C-3a' 126.4; C-4', 118.0; C-5', 124.0; C-6', 118.4; C-7', 111.4; and C-7a', 136.2ppm.

Mass Spectrum:

570(M^+), 528, 185, 173, 130, 103, 60, and 43*m/e*.

References

A. Probst and C. Tamm; 19-*O*-Acetylchaetoglobosin B and 19-*O*-Acetylchaetoglobosin D, Two New Metabolites of *Chaetomium globosum*; Helvetica Chimica Acta, Vol. 64, pp. 2056-2064(1981).

S. Natori and I. Yahara; In Mycotoxins and Phytoalexins, R. P. Sharma, and D. K. Salunkhe (eds.), CRC Press, pp. 291-338(1991).

Common/Systematic Name

Chaetoglobosin K

(6*R*,7*S*,16*S*,19*R*)-6,7-Epoxy-5-ethyl-19-hydroxy-10-(indol-3-yl)-10,16,18-trimethyl-11-nor[13]cytochalasa-13(*E*),17(*E*),21(*E*)-triene-1,20,23-trione

Molecular Formula/Molecular Weight

$C_{34}H_{40}N_2O_5$; MW = 556.29372

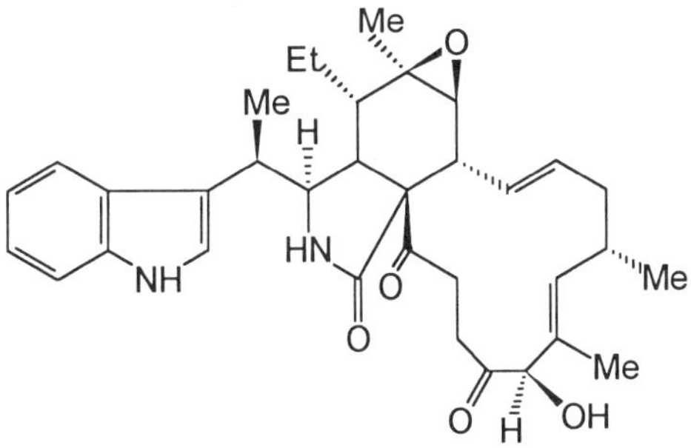

General Characteristics

Rectangular trapezoids from acetone; mp., 264-266°C. The uncorrected melting point was 264-266°C, though the crystals turned white at 60°C and most probably indicated the loss of acetone of crystallization.

Fungal Source

Diplodia macrospora (ATCC accession No. 36896).

Isolation/Purification

Extracted with ethyl acetate, dried over anhydrous sodium sulfate, reduced to a small volume under vacuum, then placed on a silica gel (70-230 mesh) column that had been slurry packed in benzene; followed by a stepwise elution with 1.0L each of benzene, ethyl ether, ethyl acetate, acetone, and methanol. The acetone fraction was biologically active and was further fractionated on a silica gel (70-230 mesh) column packed in benzene and eluted with a linear gradient of benzene to acetone. The biologically active fractions were combined, reduced in volume and crystallized from acetone solution.

Biological Activity

Significant growth inhibitor of wheat coleoptiles; activity down to 10^{-7} M. Studies indicated that chaetoglobosin K is biologically active as a plant growth regulator and is also toxic to day-old chicks (LD_{50} between 25 and 62.5mg/kg body weight).

Spectral Data

UV:

λ_{max}^{EtOH} 219nm (ϵ=44,600); also absorptions at 274, 282, and 290nm in concentrated solutions.

IR:

(KBr) 3340, 2970, 2930, 2880, 1725, 1685, 1655, 1615, 1455, 1427, 1375, 1250, 1156, 1105, 1048, 972, 875 and 742cm^{-1}.

^{1}H NMR:

H-2, 6.23; H-3, 3.89(*J*=4.4); H-4, 3.14; H-5, 1.90; H-7, 2.74(*J*=5.3); H-8, 2.16; H-10, 3.14; H-10', 1.16(*J*=7.3); H-11, 1.51; H-11', 1.01(*J*=7.0); H-12, 1.29; H-13, 6.09(*J*=10.2, 15.6); H-14, 5.01; H-15, 2.16; H-16, 2.35; H-16', 1.12(*J*=7.1); H-17, 5.56(*J*=8.4); H-18', 1.29; H-19, 4.99(*J*=4.5); H-21, 7.65(*J*=16.5); H-22, 6.49; H-1', 8.53; H-2', 6.90; H-4-7, 7.0-7.5ppm.

^{13}C NMR:

C-1, 173.2 s; C-3, 56.7 d; C-4, 49.2 d; C-5, 36.3 d; C-6, 57.2 s; C-7, 61.6 d; C-8, 44.0 d; C-9, 63.9 s; C-10, 44.0 d; C-10', 10.6 q; C-11, 21.7 t; C-11', 13.8 q; C-12, 19.6 q; C-13, 133.2 d; C-14, 128.2 d; C-15, 41.9 t; C-16, 31.9 d; C-16', 12.6 q; C-17, 140.1 d; C-18, 125.8 s; C-18', 20.9 q; C-19, 81.6 d; C-20, 190.0 s; C-21, 130.9 d; C-22, 136.4 d; C-23, 193.9 s; C-2', 122.3 d; C-3', 116.5 s; C-19', 132.2 s; C-4', 118.4 d; C-5', 119.7 d; C-6, 121.7 d; C-7', 111.5 d; and C-8', 136.4ppm s.

TLC Data

The R_f of chaetoglobosin K was 0.53-0.56 on silica gel 60 thin-layer plates developed with toluene/ethyl acetate/formic acid (5:4:1, v/v/v). It was observed as a dark spot under shortwave light.

References

R. J. Cole and R. H. Cox; Handbook of Toxic Fungal Metabolites; Academic Press, New York, p. 330 (1981).

H. G. Cutler, F. G. Crumley, R. H. Cox, R. J. Cole, J. W. Dorner, J. P. Springer, F. M. Latterell, J. E. Thean and A. E. Rossi; Chaetoglobosin K: A New Plant Growth Inhibitor and Toxin from *Diplodia macrospora*; J. Agric. Food Chem., Vol. 28, pp. 139-142 (1980).

S. Natori and I. Yahara; In Mycotoxins and Phytoalexins, R. P. Sharma, and D. K. Salunkhe (eds.), CRC Press, pp. 291-338(1991).

Common/Systematic Name

Chaetoglobosin L

(7*S*,16*S*,19*R*)-5-Ethyl-7,9-dihydroxy-10-(indol-3-yl)ethyl-10,16,18-trimethyl-11-nor[13]cytochalasa-6(12),13(*E*),17(*E*),-21(*E*)-tetraene-1,20,23-tetraone

Molecular Formula/Molecular Weight

$C_{34}H_{40}N_2O_5$; MW = 556.29372

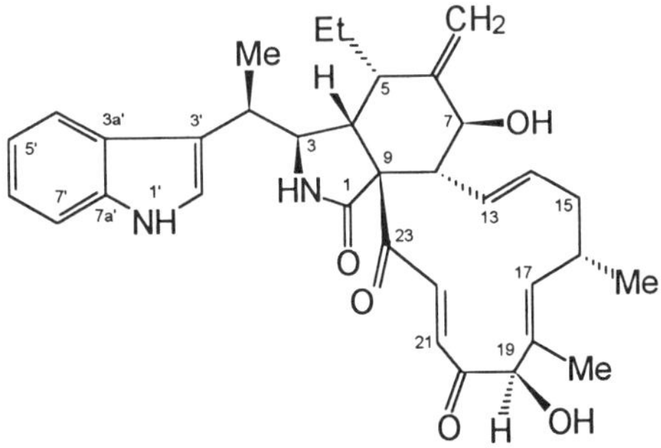

General Characteristics

Yellow gum.

Fungal Source

Diplodia macrospora (strain ATTC No. 36,896).

Isolation/Purification

The microorganism was grown in standing culture on a medium containing 400g of shredded wheat, 150g of sucrose, 50g of mycological broth (Difco) and 20g of yeast extract (Difco) per 1000ml of H_2O. After incubation for 27 days at 27°C, the cultures were refluxed with $CHCl_3$. The mixture was filtered and the extraction repeated 4 times. The combined extracts were dried (Na_2SO_4) and evaporated. The residue was washed with petroleum ether. The crude extract was purified on a silica gel column (increasing amounts of MeOH in CH_2Cl_2) yielding chaetoglobosin K and chaetoglobosin L.

Spectral Data

IR:

(film) 3400, 2930, 1720, 1640s, 1360, 1220, 970, 900, and 740cm^{-1}.

^{1}H NMR:

($CDCl_3$) H-3, 3.55(m); H-4, 2.55(m); H-7, 3.90(d, *J*=10Hz); H-8, 2.39(m); H-10, 3.10(m); H-11, 1.57(m), 1.88(m); H-12, 5.29(s), 5.33(s); H-13, 5.99(dd); H-14, 5.37(m); H-15, 2.03(m), 2.28(m); H-16, 2.47(m); H-17, 6.61(d, *J*=9.0Hz); H-21, 6.63(d, *J*=18Hz); H-22, 7.94(d, *J*=18Hz); H-2', 6.90(d, *J*=1Hz); H-4', 7.50(d, *J*=7Hz);

H-5', 7.10-7.22(m); H-6', 7.10-7.22(m); H-7', 7.37(d, *J*=7Hz); H-10' 1.10-1.15; H-11', 1.10-1.15; H-16', 1.00(d, *J*=7Hz); H-18', 1.32(s); OH-7, 2.00; OH-19, 3.90; NH-1, 5.61; and NH-1', 8.35ppm (s).

^{13}C NMR:
(CDCl$_3$) C-1, 172.6; C-3, 56.1; C-4*, 39.8; C-5*, 41.0; C-6, 146.8; C-7, 71.1; C-8, 50.6; C-9, 62.2; C-10, 35.0; C-11, 21.4; C-12, 114.3; C-13, 128.5; C-14, 136.0; C-15, 42.0; C-16, 32.1; C-17, 140.3; C-18, 137.7; C-19, 81.7; C-20, 201.6; C-21**, 131.5; C-22**, 137.0; C-23, 197.7; C-2', 121.4; C-3', 117.7; C-4', 118.7; C-5', 122.5; C-6', 119.8; C-7', 111.6; C-10'***, 12.9; C-11***, 12.1; C-16', 21.1; C-18', 10.7; C-3'a, 126.0; and C-7'a, 136.6ppm.

*, ** and, *** Assignments may be reversed.

Mass Spectrum:
556(M$^+$), 423, 412, 157, 144(100), 130, and 117*m/e*.

References

C. Spondlin and C. Tamm; Chaetoglobosin L, a New Metabolite of *Diplodia macrospora*; Helvetica Chimica Acta, Vol. 65, pp. 1543-1546(1982).

C. Spondlin and C. Tamm; Chaetoglobosin M, a New Metabolite of a Mutant of *Diplodia macrospora*, Belonging to the Family of (1*H*-Indol-3-yl)-Substituted 10,11-Diethyl-10,11-dinorcytochalasins; Helvetica Chimica Acta, Vol. 71, pp. 1881-1884(1988).

Common/Systematic Name

Chaetoglobosin M

6,7-Epoxy-5-ethyl-3-[1-(1*H*-indol-3-yl)ethyl]-16,18-dimethyl-10,11-dinor[13]-cytochalasa-13,17-diene-1,19,21,23-tetraone

Molecular Formula/Molecular Weight

$C_{34}H_{40}N_2O_5$; MW = 556.29372

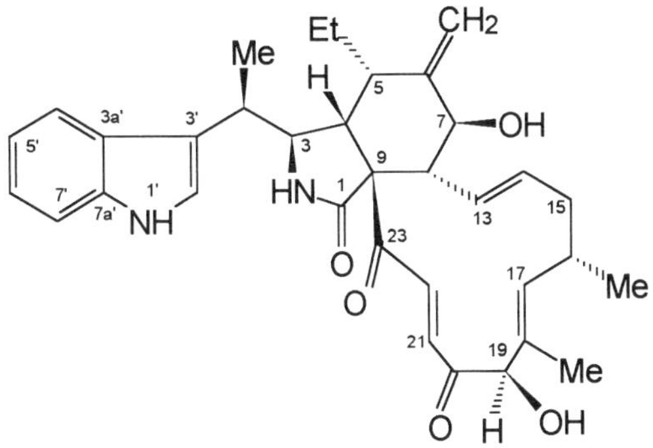

General Characteristics

A slightly yellow gum; $[\alpha]_D^{22}$ -18.3° (c=0.92, in CH_2Cl_2).

Fungal Source

Diplodia macrospora (strain DM 7).

Isolation/Purification

The microorganism was grown in standing culture on a medium containing 400g of shredded wheat, 150g of sucrose, 50g of mycological broth (Difco) and 20g of yeast extract (Difco) per 1000ml of H_2O. After incubation for 27 days at 27°C, the cultures were refluxed with $CHCl_3$. The mixture was filtered and the extraction repeated 4 times. The combined extracts were dried (Na_2SO_4) and evaporated. The residue was washed with petroleum ether. The crude extract was purified on a silica gel column (increasing amounts of MeOH in CH_2Cl_2) yielding chaetoglobosin K and chaetoglobosin L. The chaetoglobosin M containing fractions were further purified on a silica-gel column a second time with the same solvent system.

Spectral Data

UV:

$\lambda_{max}^{\text{Methylene chloride}}$ 230(log ϵ=4.09) and 290nm (3.60).

IR:

(film) 3350, 3030, 2970, 2930, 2880, and 1695cm^{-1}.

^{1}H NMR:

($CDCl_3$) H-3, 3.78(m); H-4, 1.5- 1.7; H-7, 2.65(d, *J*=7Hz); H-8, 2.28(m); H-10, 3.12(m); H-11, 1.5-1.7(m), 1.7-1.8(m); H-12, 1.22(s); H-13, 6.14(dd); H-14, 5.10(m); H-15, 1.88(m), 2.35(m); H-16, 2.14-2.4 or 2.6-2.8; H-17, 6.04(d, *J*=9.0Hz); H-21, 2.1-2.4; H-22, 2.6-2.8; H-2', 6.90(d, *J*=2Hz); H-4', 7.55(d, *J*=7Hz); H-5', 7.13-7.25; H-6', 7.137.25; H-7', 7.35(d, *J*=7Hz); H-10', 1.30(d, *J*=7.0Hz); H-11', 0.97(d, *J*=7Hz); H-16', 1.05(d, *J*=7Hz); H-18', 1.82(d, *J*=1Hz); NH-1, 7.05(s); and NH-1', 8.55ppm (s).

^{13}C NMR:

($CDCl_3$) C-1, 175.5; C-3, 57.8; C-4*, 46.6; C-5*, 44.4; C-6, 56.7; C-7, 60.6; C-8, 49.6; C-9, 63.5; C-10, 36.3; C-11, 21.5; C-12, 19.4; C-13, 126.7; C-14, 134.5; C-15, 40.2; C-16, 33.4; C-17, 156.5; C-18, 132.3; C-19, 196.8; C-20, 205.6; C-21**, 32.6; C-22**, 38.3; C-23, 208.3; C-2', 122.5; C-3', 115.9; C-4', 118.5; C-5',122.5; C-6', 120.0; C-7', 111.6; C-10'***, 16.2; C-11***, 12.6; C-16', 19.4; C18', 10.3; C-3'a, 126.7; and C-7'a, 136.1ppm.

*, ** and *** Assignments may be reversed.

Mass Spectrum:

556(M^+) 538, 413, 412, 394, 214, 179, 144(100%), 130, and 117*m/e*.

Reference

C. Spondlin and C. Tamm; Chaetoglobosin M, a New Metabolite of a Mutant of *Diplodia macrospora*, Belonging to the Family of (1*H*-Indol-3-yl)-Substituted 10,11-Diethyl-10,11-dinor-cytochalasins; Helvetica Chimica Acta, Vol. 71, pp. 1881-1884(1988).

Common/Systematic Name

Cytochalasin A; Dehydrophomin

(7*S*,16*R*)-7-Hydroxy-16-methyl-10-phenyl-24-oxa[14]cytochalasa-6(12),13(*E*),21(*E*)-triene-1,20,23-trione

Molecular Formula/Molecular Weight

$C_{29}H_{35}NO_5$; MW = 477.25152

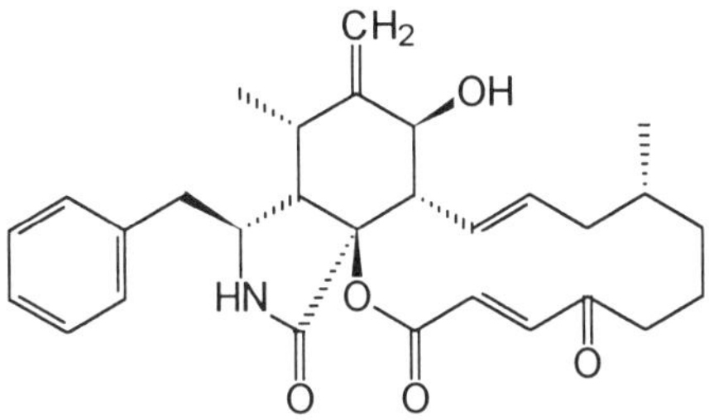

General Characteristics

Crystals; mp., 193-195°C; $[\alpha]_D^{21}$ +83.7° (*c*=1.0, in MeOH).

Fungal Source

Helminthosporium dematioideum, *Phoma exigua* var. *exigua*, and *Ascochyta heteromorpha*.

Biological Activity

Cytotoxic to HeLa cells with an ED_{50} of 3.2μg/ml. Inhibits movement (reversible) and cytoplasmic cleavage in cultured cells leading to multinucleated giant cells; at higher levels nuclear extrusion occurred. Acts selectively as a respiratory inhibitor in bacteria and fungi. Inhibited spore germination and hyphal tip growth in *Gilbertella persicaria.* Cytochalasin A interfered with normal growth patterns and also affected the intracellular organization of *Mucor mucedo*. The presence of an α,β-unsaturated carbonyl group in the macrolide moiety of cytochalasin A with appropriate bioisoteric placement were the requisite molecular features for its microbiological activity.

Spectral Data

^{13}C NMR:

($CDCl_3$) C-1, 169.9 s; C-3, 52.8 d; C-4, 46.7 d; C-5, 30.9 d; C-6, 150.8 s; C-7, 68.1 d; C-8, 49.2 d; C-9, 83.5 s; C-10, 42.3 t; C-11, 13.5 q; C-12, 112.2 t; C-13, 128.1 d; C-14, 133.5 d; C-15, 32.4 t; C-16, 30.9 d; C-17, 30.6 t; C-18, 21.3 t; C-19, 40.8 t; C-20, 201.6 s; C-21, 140.5 d; C-22, 127.9 d; C-23, 163.5 s; C-24, 20.2 q; C-1', 137.4 s; C-2', 6', 129.5 d; C-3', 5', 128.1 d; and C-4', 126.2ppm d.

TLC Data

Adsorbent; silica gel G-HR; solvent A: chloroform-acetone, 93:7 (v/v); B: toluene-ethyl acetate-formic acid, 5:4:1 (v/v/v); R_f value for A: 0.29, B: 0.68; detection: a blue fluorescent spot under UV light after spraying with 50% ethanolic H_2SO_4 and heating.

References

R. J. Cole and R. H. Cox; Handbook of Toxic Fungal Metabolites; Academic Press, New York, p. 276 (1981).

E. K. Manavathu and D. D. S. Thomas; FEMS, Microbiol. Lett., Vol. 7, pp. 199-202 (1980).

S. Natori and I. Yahara; Cytochalasins; In Mycotoxins and Phytoalexins; R. P. Sharma, and D. K. Salunkhe (eds.); CRC Press, pp. 291-338(1991).

W. Rothweiler and C. Tamm; Isolation and Structure of Phomin; Experientia, Vol. 22, p. 750 (1966).

Common/Systematic Name

Cytochalasin B; Phomin

(7*S*,16*R*,20*R*)-7,20-Dihydroxy-16-methyl-10-phenyl-24-oxa[14]cytochalasa-6(12),13(*E*),21(*E*)-triene-1,23-dione

Molecular Formula/Molecular Weight

$C_{29}H_{37}NO_5$; MW = 479.26717

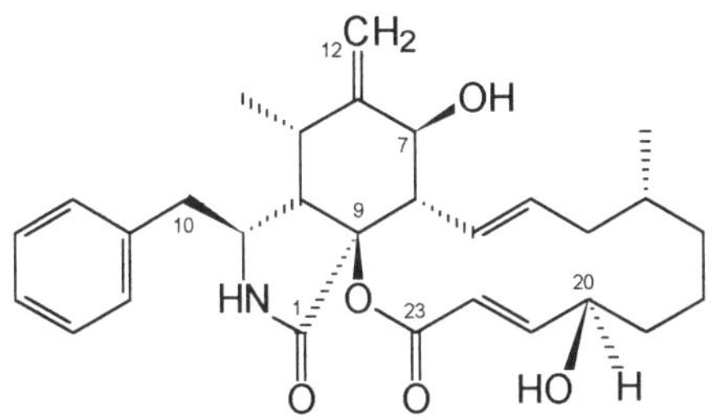

General Characteristics

Crystals; mp., 221-223°C; $[\alpha]_D^{25}$ +86.7° (*c*=0.9, in MeOH); crystals from chloroform solution; mp., 218°C; $[\alpha]_D^{25}$ +84° (*c*=1.0, in EtOH).

Fungal Source

Helminthosporium dematioideum, Hormiscium spp., *Phoma exigua* var. *exigua, Curvularia lunata, Drechslera biseptata, Gnomonia erythrostoma, Hypomyces odoratus,* and *Ascochyta heteromorpha.*

Isolation/Purification

Purified by methanol extraction, followed by reverse-phase C_{18} silica gel chromatography and elution with hexane-tetrahydrofuran (1:1, v/v). Final purification was by crystallization, followed by preparative TLC and recrystallization.

Biological Activity

Cytochalasin B inhibited cellular motility of moving L cells. Cytoplasmic cleavage was inhibited without interference with nuclear division, resulting in binucleate and multinucleate cells. The effect was reversible. Mammalian cells can be enucleated by treatment with cytochalasin B (10μg/ml) followed by centrifugation. Cytochalasin B has been reported to inhibit the following cellular functions: release of growth hormone; thyroid secretion; phagocytosis; platelet aggregation and clot retraction; and hexase transport. Cytotoxicity to HeLa cells, ED_{50} between 1 and 2.5μg/ml. It was reported to inhibit certain gliding mycoplasmas and internalization of *Herpes simplex* virus type 1 (HSV)KOS strain by HEp-2 cells was reversibly inhibited by pretreatment with cytochalasins B and D.

Spectral Data

UV:

λ_{max}^{EtOH} 220(ϵ=44,668), 257(sh), 265(sh), and 269 (sh).

^{13}C NMR:

C-1, 170.6 s; C-3, 52.3 d; C-4, 46.5 d; C-5, 30.4 d; C-6, 150.9 s; C-7, 69.4 d; C-8, 47.5 d; C-9, 83.3 s; C-10, 42.9 t; C-11, 13.2 q; C-12, 112.2 t; C-13, 128.4 d; C-14, 133.0 d; C-15, 34.8 t; C-16, 30.9 d; C-17, 34.2 t; C-18, 20.1 t; C-19, 41.6 t; C-20, 68.6 d; C-21, 153.2 d; C-22, 118.1 d; C-23, 164.0 s; C-24, 20.2 q; C-1', 136.9 s; C-2', 6', 129.6 d; C-3', 5', 128.1 d; and C-4', 126.3ppm d.

TLC Data

Silica gel G-HR; solvent: A: chloroform-acetone, 93:7, v/v; B: toluene-ethyl acetate-formic acid, 5:4:1, v/v/v; R_f value of A: 0.11; B: 0.60; detection: a blue fluorescent spot under UV light after spraying with 50% ethanolic H_2SO_4 and heating.

HPLC Data

Lichrosorb Si_{60} silica gel column, mobile phase was hexane-tetrahydrofuran and UV detection at 230nm.

References

R. J. Cole and R. H. Cox; Handbook of Toxic Fungal Metabolites; Academic Press, New York, p. 281 (1981).

M. A. Kolber, K. O. Broschat, and B. Landa-Gonzalez; Cytochalasin B induces cellular DNA fragmentation, FASEB J., Vol 4, pp. 3021-3027(1990).

K. M. Lipski, J. D. McQuiggan, K. H. Loucy, and T. P. Fondy; Cytochalasin B: Preparation, analysis in tissue extracts and pharmacokinetics after intraperitoneal bolus administration in mice; Anal. Biochem., Vol. 161, pp. 332-340(1987).

J. Maniloff and U. Chaudhuri; Gliding mycoplasms are inhibited by cytochalasin B and contain a polymerizable protein fraction; J. Supramol. Struct., Vol. 12, pp. 299-304 (1979).

S. Natori and I. Yahara; Cytochalasins; In Mycotoxins and Phytoalexins, R. P. Sharma, and D. K. Salunkhe (eds.); CRC Press, pp. 291-338(1991).

A. Pribela, J. Tomko, and L. Dolejs; Chem. Zvesti Vol. 28, p. 710 (1974).

K. Rosenthal, R. Perez, and C. Hodnichak; Inhibition of *Herpes simplex* type 1 virus penetration by cytochalasins B and D; J. Gen. Virol., Vol 66, pp. 1601-1605(1985).

W. Rothweiler and C. Tamm; Isolation and Structure of Phomin; Experientia, Vol. 22, p. 750 (1966).

Common/Systematic Name

Cytochalasin C

(7*S*,16*S*,18*R*,21*R*)-21-Acetoxy-7,18-dihydroxy-16,18-dimethyl-10-phenyl-[11]cytochalasa-5(6),13*E*,19(*E*)-triene-1,17-dione

Molecular Formula/Molecular Weight

$C_{30}H_{37}NO_6$; MW = 507.26209

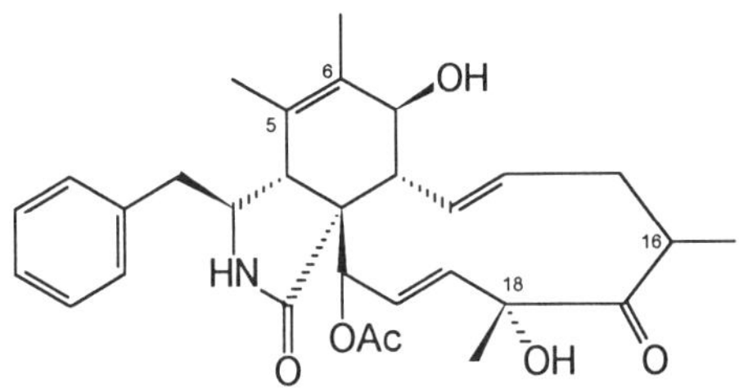

General Characteristics

Crystals; mp, 260°C (dec.); $[\alpha]_D^{28}$ -14.7° (*c*=0.82, in dioxane).

Fungal Source

Metarrhizium anisopliae and *Hypoxylon terricola*.

Biological Activity

Cytochalasin C showed essentially the same biological activity as cytochalasin B except it is about 10 times more potent in mammalian cell culture (inhibited movement and cytoplasmic cleavage); at higher doses caused nuclear extrusion which may lead to total enucleation.

Spectral Data

UV:

End absorption.

^{13}C NMR:

C-l, 173.9 s; C-3, 48.9 d; C-4, 59.6 d; C-5, 125.4 s; C-6, 133.0 s; C-7, 67.8 d; C-8, 48.5 d; C-9, 52.5 s; C-10, 43.6 t; C-11, 14.1 q; C-12, 16.4 q; C-13, 131.0 d; C-14, 131.5 d; C-15, 37.1 t; C-16, 40.4 d; C-17, 209.8 s; C-18, 77.5 s; C-19, 127.5 d; C-20, 131.7 d; C-21, 74.9 d; C-22, 19.2 q; C-23, 24.6 q; C-1', 137.6 s; C-2', 6', 129.2 d; C-3', 5', 128.4 d; C-4', 126.4 d; $CH_3\underline{C}{=}O$, 170.1 s; and $\underline{C}H_3C{=}O$, 20.5ppm q.

TLC Data

TLC: silica gel G-HR; solvent A: chloroform-acetone, 93:7, v/v; B: toluene-ethyl acetate-formic acid, 5:4:1, v/v/v. R_f A: 0.09; B: 0.55; detection: a dull yellow fluorescent spot under UV light after spraying with 50% ethanolic H_2SO_4 and heating.

References

D. C. Aldridge, J. J. Armstrong, R. N. Speake, and W. B. Turner; The Structures of Cytochalasins A and B; Chem. Commun. p. 1667 (1967).

D. C. Aldridge and W. B. Turner; Structures of Cytochalasins C and D; J. Chem. Soc., p. 923 (1969).

R. J. Cole and R. H. Cox; Handbook of Toxic Fungal Metabolites; Academic Press, New York, p. 294 (1981).

R. L. Edwards, D. J. Maitland, and A. J. S. Whalley; Metabolites of the Higher Fungi. Part 24. Cytochalasin N, O, P, Q, and R, New Cytochalasins from the Fungus *Hypoxylon terricola* Mill.; J. Chem. Soc. Perkin Trans. I, pp. 57-65(1989).

S. Natori and I. Yahara; Cytochalasins; In Mycotoxins and Phytoalexins, R. P. Sharma, and D. K. Salunkhe (eds.); CRC Press, pp. 291-338(1991).

Common/Systematic Name
Cytochalasin D; Zygosporin A
(7*S*,16*S*,18*R*,21*R*)-21-Acetoxy-7,18-dihydroxy-16,18-dimethyl-10-phenyl-[11]cytochalasa-6(12),13*E*,19(*E*)-triene-1,17-dione

Molecular Formula/Molecular Weight
$C_{30}H_{37}NO_6$; MW = 507.26209

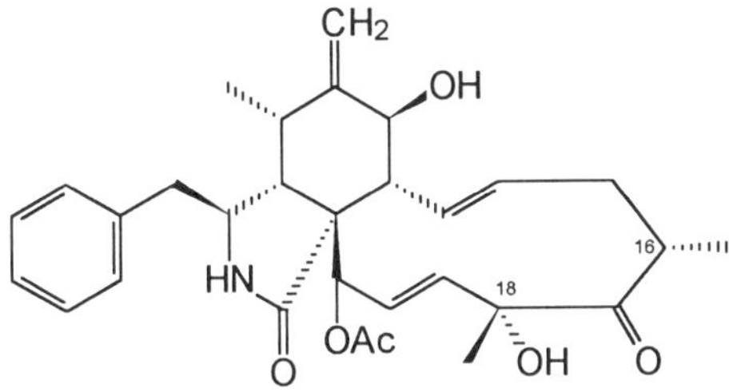

General Characteristics
Needles from acetone-petroleum ether; mp, 267-271°C; $[\alpha]_D^{25}$ -7.5° (*c*=0.55, in dioxane).

Fungal Source
Metarrhizium anisopliae, Zygosporium masonii, Coriolus vernicipes, Hypoxylon terricola, and *Engleromyces goetzii.*

Isolation/Purification
The culture filtrate was extracted with ethyl acetate, washed with sodium carbonate and water and evaporated to dryness *in vacuo.* The residue gave cytochalasin D (zygosporin A) as colorless needles from acetone.

Biological Activity
Cytochalasin D showed similar activity to cytochalasin B, except it was about 10 times more potent in mammalian cells (inhibited movement and cytoplasmic cleavage); at higher doses causes nuclear extrusion which may lead to total enucleation. It was embryolethal with a tendency toward teratogenicity in chick embryos. It inhibited the growth of *Bipolaris sorokiniana* and *Rhizoctonia solani* and induced profuse hyphal branching; at high concentrations it induced swellings in the hyphal tips. It was reported to reversely inhibit internalization of *Herpes simplex* virus type 1 (HSV) KOS strain by HEp-2 cells.

Spectral Data

UV:
λ_{max}^{MeOH} 286nm (ϵ=330)

IR:
(KBr) 3404, 3240, 1742, 1703. 1693, 1233, 1049, 1009, 962, 907, 751, and 706 cm^{-1}.

^1H NMR:
($CDCl_3$) 9.07(d, *J*=6.8, Me), 8.82(d, *J*=6.3, Me), 8.51(s, MeC-OH), 7.76(OAc), 6.23(dm, *J*=10.4, OH), 4.95-3.76(8H), and 2.77ppm (5H, Ph).

^{13}C NMR:
C-l, 173.4 s; C-3, 52.4 d; C-4, 47.6 d; C-5, 31.5 d; C-6, 150.6 s; C-7, 70.0 d; C-8,46.0 d; C-9, 53.1 s; C-10,43.6 t; C-ll, 12.7 q; C-12, 111.3 t; C-13, 130.7 d; C-14, 131.6 d; C-15, 36.8 t; C-16, 40.2 d; C-17, 209.8 s; C-18, 77.4 s; C-19, 126.9 d; C-20, 132.0 d; C-21, 76.3 d; C-22, 19.1 q; C-23, 24.5 q; C-l', 136.9 s; C-2',6', 129.5 d; C-3',5', 128.1 d; C-4', 126.4 d; $CH_3\underline{C}$=O, 169.8 s; $\underline{C}H_3C$=O, 20.4ppm q.

Mass Data:
M^+ 507*m/e* (found: C, 71.1; H, 7.35, N, 2.5; $C_{30}H_{37}NO_6$ requires C, 71.0; H, 7.35; N, 2.75%).

TLC Data

Silica gel G-HR; solvent: A: chloroform-acetone, 93:7 (v/v); B: toluene-ethyl acetate-formic acid, 5:4:1 (v/v/v); R_f: A: 0.06, B: 0.51; detection: a bright yellow fluorescent spot under UV light after spraying with 50% ethanolic H_2SO_4 and heating.

References

D. C. Aldridge, J. J. Armstrong, R. N. Speake, and W. B. Turner; The Structures of Cytochalasins A and B; Chem. Commun., p. 1667 (1967).

D. C. Aldridge and W. B. Turner; Structures of Cytochalasins C and D; J. Chem. Soc., p. 923 (1969).

R. J. Cole and R. H. Cox; Handbook of Toxic Fungal Metabolites; Academic Press, New York, p. 299 (1981).

R. L. Edwards, D. J. Maitland, and A. J. S. Whalley; Metabolites of the Higher Fungi. Part 24. Cytochalasin N, O, P, Q, and R, New Cytochalasins from the Fungus *Hypoxylon terricola* Mill.; J. Chem. Soc. Perkin Trans. I, pp. 57-65(1989).

S. H. Gilani and C. Kreshal; Teratogenicity of cytochalasin D in chick embryos; J. Environ. Pathol. Toxicol. Oncol., Vol.6, pp 67-72(1986).

H. Minato and M. Matsumoto; Studies on the Metabolites of *Zygosporium masonii*. Part I. Structure of Zygosporin A; J. Chem. Soc. (C), pp. 38-45(1970).

S. Natori and I. Yahara; In Mycotoxins and Phytoalexins, R. P. Sharma, and D. K. Salunkhe (eds.), CRC Press, pp. 291-338(1991).

K. Rosenthal, R. Perez, and C. Hodnichak; Inhibition of *Herpes simplex* type 1 penetration by cytochalasins B and D; J. Gen. Virol., Vol 66, pp. 1601-1605(1985).

Common/Systematic Name

Cytochalasin F

(6*R*,7*S*,16*R*,20*R*)-6,7-Epoxy-20-hydroxy-16-methyl-10-phenyl-24-oxa[14]cytochalas-13(*E*),21(*E*)-diene-1,23-dione

Molecular Formula/Molecular Weight

$C_{29}H_{37}NO_5$; MW = 479.26717

NOTE: There is some confusion in the literature as to the correct structure of cytochalasin F. The structure proposed here is based on X-ray analysis of cytochalasin E (Büchi *et al.*, 1973).

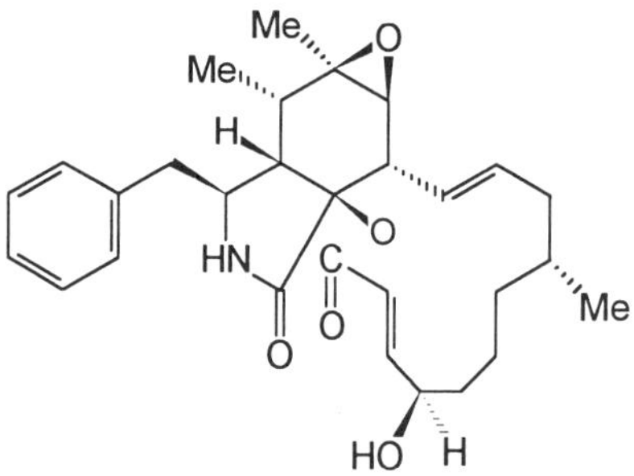

Fungal Source

Helminthosporium dematioideum.

References

D. C. Aldridge, B. F. Burrows, and W. B. Turner; The Structures of the Fungal Metabolites Cytochalasin E and F; J. C. S. Chem. Comm., pp. 148-149(1972).

G. Büchi, Y. Kitaura, S. Yuan, H. E. Wright, J. Clardy, A. L. Demain, T. Glinsukon, N. Hunt, and G. N. Wogan; Structure of Cytochalasin , a Toxic Metabolite of *Aspergillus clavatus*; J. Am. Chem. Soc., Vol. 95, p. 5423-5425(1973).

R. J. Cole and R. H. Cox; Handbook of Toxic Fungal Metabolites; Academic Press, New York, p. 286 (1981).

S. Natori and I. Yahara; Cytochalasins; In Mycotoxins and Phytoalexins, R. P. Sharma, and D. K. Salunkhe (eds.); CRC Press, pp. 291-338(1991).

Common/Systematic Name

Cytochalasin L

(6*R*,7*S*,16*S*,19*R*)-19-Acetoxy-6,7-epoxy-16,18-dimethyl-10-phenyl-24-oxa[14] cytochalasa-13(*E*),17(*E*),21(*E*)-triene-1,20,23-trione

Molecular Formula/Molecular Weight

$C_{32}H_{37}NO_7$; MW = 547.25700

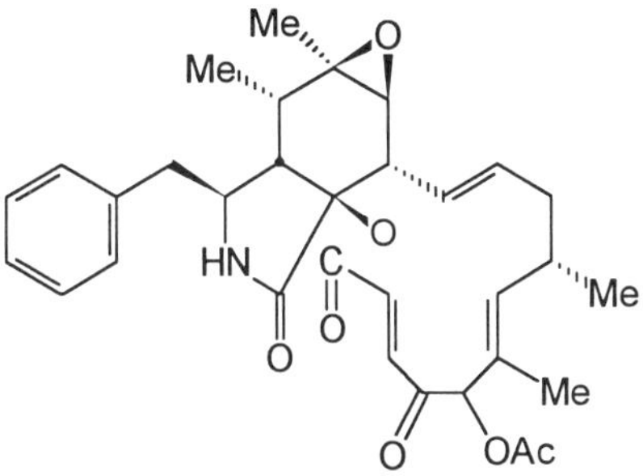

General Characteristics

Cytochalasin L was amorphous; $[\alpha]_D^{25}$ -165° (in EtOH).

Fungal Source

Chalara microspora.

Isolation/Purification

Extracted with EtOAc and isolated using reversed-phase chromatography.

Spectral Data

UV:

No characteristic absorption observed.

IR:

(KBr) 3400(OH) and 1720cm^{-1} (broad, C=O).

^{1}H NMR:

($CDCl_3$) NH, 6.00; H-3, 3.71($J_{3\text{-}10a}$=8.8, $J_{3\text{-}10b}$=4.8, $J_{3\text{-}4}$=3.3Hz); H-4, 2.80($J_{4\text{-}5}$=4.5); H-5, 2.24($J_{5\text{-}11}$=7.5); H-7, 2.67; H-8, 2.68($J_{8\text{-}13}$=10.0); H-10a, 3.02($J_{10a\text{-}10b}$=13.3); H-10b, 2.89; 3H-11, 1.03; 3H-12, 1.29; H-13, 6.17($J_{13\text{-}14}$=14.5); H-14, 5.40($J_{14\text{-}15a}$=10.0, $J_{14\text{-}15b}$=3.0); H-15a, 2.23($J_{15a\text{-}15b}$=13.0); H-15b, 2.35; H-16, 2.6($J_{16\text{-}16Me}$=7.0, $J_{16\text{-}17}$=7.5); H-17, 5.72; H-19, 5.70; H-21, 7.49($J_{21\text{-}22}$=16.0); H-22, 6.52; 16-CH_3, 1.10; 18-CH_3, 1.56; -$OOCCH_3$, 2.19; and H-2', H-3', H-4', 7.1-7.4Hz.

^{13}C NMR:

($CDCl_3$) C-1, 171.1; C-3, 54.4; C-4, 49.3a; C-5, 33.0b; C-6, 57.5; C-7, 60.4; C-8, 48.5a; C-9, 84.1; C-10, 44.0; C-11, 13.5c; C-12, 20.0d; C-13, 130.0e; C-14, 134.7f; C-15, 41.2; C-16, 35.7b; C-17, 136.8f; C-18, 127.1e; C-19, 84.9; C-20, 193.59; C-21, 142.7; C-22, 126.5f; C-23, 164.0; 16-CH_3, 11.5c; 18-CH_3, 21.6d; -$OOCCH_3$, 169.5; -$OOCCH_3$ 20.6d; C-1', 136.8; C-2', 129.2; C-3', 128.9; and C-4', 127.1ppm e.

(a-f may be interchanged).

Mass Spectrum:

HRMS: 547.2535*m/e*, $C_{32}H_{37}NO_7$; calcd 547.2570.

References

T. Fex; Structures of Cytochalasin K, L and M, Isolated From *Chalara microspora*; Tet. Lett., Vol. 22, pp. 2703-2706(1981).

S. Natori and I. Yahara; Cytochalasins; In Mycotoxins and Phytoalexins, R. P. Sharma, and D. K. Salunkhe (eds.); CRC Press, pp. 291-338(1991).

Common/Systematic Name

Cytochalasin M

(6*R*,7*S*,16*S*,20*S*)-6,7-Epoxy-20-hydroxy-10-phenyl-24-oxa[14]cytochalasa-13(*E*),17(*E*)-diene-1,19,23-trione

Molecular Formula/Molecular Weight

$C_{30}H_{37}NO_6$; MW = 507.26209

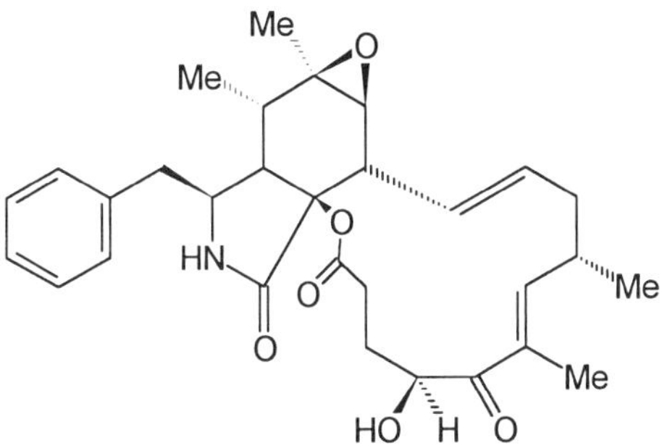

General Characteristics

Cytochalasin M crystallized from methanol-water; mp., 161-162°C; $[\alpha]_D^{25}$ +18° (EtOH).

Fungal Source

Chalara microspora.

Isolation/Purification

Extracted with EtOAc and isolated using reversed-phase chromatography.

Spectral Data

UV:

$\lambda_{max}^{Abs. EtOH}$ 235nm (ϵ=11,300).

IR:

(KBr) 3380(OH), 1750, 1705(broad, C=O), and 1670cm^{-1} (C=C).

^{1}H NMR:

($CDCl_3$) NH, 5.63; H-3, 3.63 ($J_{3\text{-}10a}$=10.0, $J_{3\text{-}10b}$=4.0, $J_{3\text{-}4}$=4.0Hz); H-4, 2.53($J_{4\text{-}5}$=4.0); H-5, 2.07($J_{5\text{-}11}$=7.0); H-7, 2.70($J_{7\text{-}8}$=5.5); H-8, 2.49($J_{8\text{-}13}$=9.5); H-10a, 3.17($J_{10a\text{-}10b}$=13.5); H-10b, 2.88; 3H-11, 1.08; 3H-12, 1.32; H-13, 5.89,($J_{13\text{-}14}$=15.0), $J_{13\text{-}15}$=1.5; H-14, 5.46($J_{14\text{-}15}$=10.0 and 3.5); 2H-15, 2.2-2.5; H-16, 2.85 ($J_{16\text{-}16Me}$=7.0, $J_{16\text{-}17}$=9.5); H-17, 6.55($J_{17\text{-}18Me}$=1.3); H_2O, 4.98($J_{20\text{-}21}$=4.0 and 6.0, $J_{20\text{-}OH}$=5.8); 2H-21, 1.95; 2H-22, 2.45; 16-CH_3, 1.13; 18-CH_3, 1.88; 20-OH, 3.67; and H-2', H-3', H-4', 7.2-7.45Hz.

^{13}C NMR:
($CDCl_3$) C-1, 171.3; C-3, 54.5; C-4, 49.2a; C-5, 33.6c; C-6, 57.5; C-7, 59.7; C-8, 50.8b; C-9, 82.7; C-10, 43.0; C-11, 13.8d; C-12, 20.3e; C-13, 127.6f; C-14, 132.5f; C-15, 39.8; C-16, 35.9c; C-17, 150.2; C-18, 132.5; C-19, 203.2; C-20, 70.9; C-21, 30.5g; C-22, 33.1gf; C-23, 171.9a; 16-CH_3, 12.0d; 18-CH_3, 19.6e; and C-1', 137.8; C-2', 128.9; C-3', 128.9; and C-4', 126.9f ppm.

(a-g: may be interchanged).

Mass Spectrum:
HRMS: 507.2708*m/e*, $C_{30}H_{37}NO_6$; calcd 507.2631.

References

T. Fex; Structures of Cytochalasin K, L and M, Isolated from *Chalara microspora*; Tet. Lett., Vol. 22, pp. 2703-2706(1981).

S. Natori and I. Yahara; Cytochalasins: In Mycotoxins and Phytoalexins, R. P. Sharma, and D. K. Salunkhe (eds.); CRC Press, pp. 291-338(1991).

Common/Systematic Name

Zygosporin D

(7*S*,16*S*,18*R*,21*R*)-7,18,21-Trihydroxy-16,18-dimethyl-10-phenyl[11]cytochalasa-6(12),13(*E*),19(*E*)-triene-1,17-dione

Molecular Formula/Molecular Weight

$C_{28}H_{37}NO_4$; MW = 451.27226

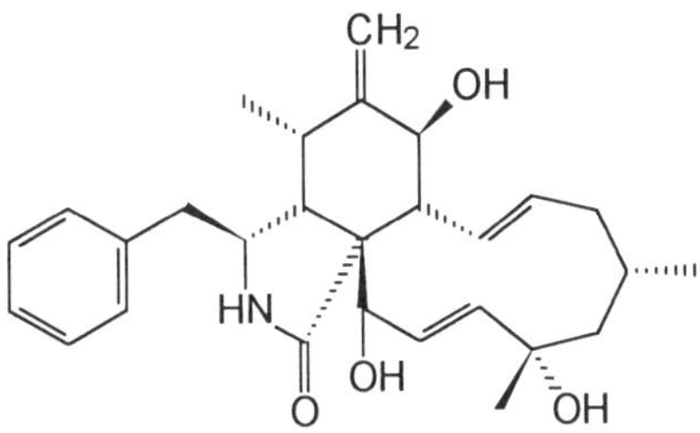

General Characteristics

Colorless plates from methanol; mp 180-190°C; $[\alpha]_D^{23}$ -14.9° (c=0.759, in dioxane).

Fungal Source

Zygosporium masonii.

Biological Activity

Cytotoxicity to HeLa cells.

Spectral Data

IR:

(KBr) 3400, 1700, 1127, 1107, 1075, 1005, 968, and 910cm^{-1}.

TLC Data

Silica gel; Solvent: chloroform-methanol, 10:1, v/v; R_f=0.50. Detection: not reported

References

H. Minato and M. Matsumoto; Studies on the Metabolites of *Zygosporium masonii*. Part I. Structure of Zygosporin A; J. Chem. Soc., p. 38 (1970).

S. Natori and I. Yahara; Cytochalasin; In Mycotoxins and Phytoalexins, R. P. Sharma, and D. K. Salunkhe (eds.); CRC Press, pp. 291-338(1991).

Common/Systematic Name

Zygosporin E

(7*S*,16*R*,18*R*)-21-Acetoxy-7-hydroxy-16,18-dimethyl-10-phenyl[11]cytochalasa-6(12),13(*E*),19(*E*)-triene-1,17-dione

Molecular Formula/Molecular Weight

$C_{30}H_{37}NO_5$; MW = 491.26717

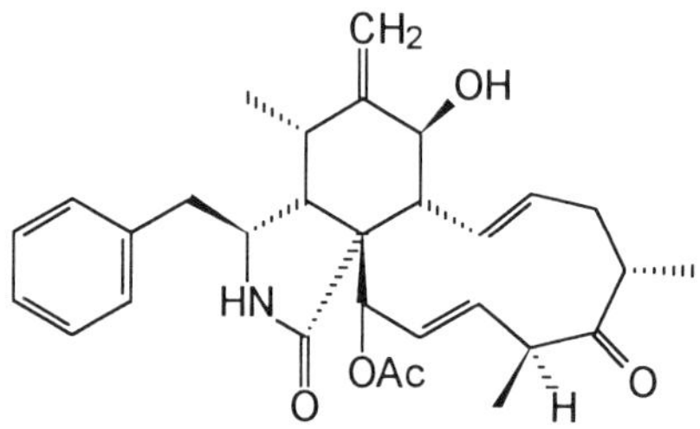

General Characteristics

Colorless needles from acetone-*n*-hexane; mp 218-223.5°C; $[\alpha]_D^{24}$ +6.2°(*c*=0.971 in dioxane).

Fungal Source

Zygosporium masonii.

Biological Activity

Cytotoxic to HeLa cells.

Spectral Data

IR:

(KBr) 3524, 3420, 1743, 1703, 1113, 1010, 973, and 912cm^{-1}.

TLC Data

Silica gel; solvent: ethyl acetate; R_f=0.48. Detection: not reported.

References

H. Minato and M. Matsumoto; Studies on the Metabolites of *Zygosporium masonii*. Part I. Structure of Zygosporin A; J. Chem. Soc., p. 38 (1970).

S. Natori and I. Yahara; Cytochalasin; In Mycotoxins and Phytoalexins, R. P. Sharma, and D. K. Salunkhe (eds.); CRC Press, pp. 291-338(1991).

Common/Systematic Name

Zygosporin F; Cytochalasin D monoacetate
(7*S*,16*S*,18*R*,21*R*)-7,21-Diacetoxy-18-hydroxy-16,18-dimethyl-10-phenyl-[11]cytochalasa-6(12),13(*E*),19(*E*)-triene-1,17-dione

Molecular Formula/Molecular Weight

$C_{32}H_{39}NO_7$; MW = 549.27265

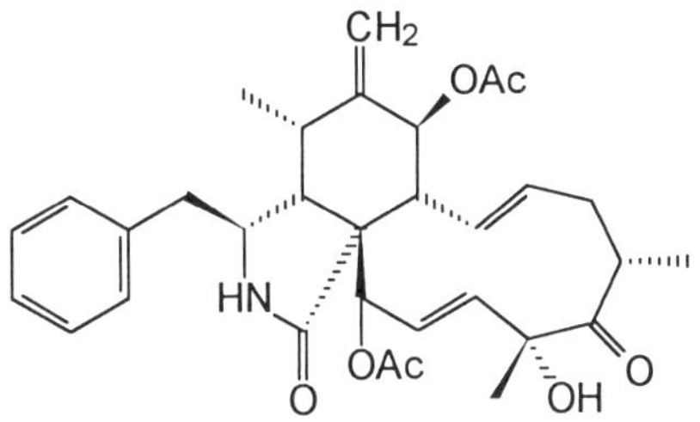

General Characteristics

Colorless prisms from diisopropyl ether; mp, 126-129°C; $[\alpha]_D$ -12.0° (*c*=0.775, in dioxane).

Fungal Source

Zygosporium masonii.

Biological Activity

Cytotoxic to HeLa cells.

Spectral Data

IR:
(KBr) 3420, 1740, 1704, 1113, 1043, 1009, 965, and 910cm^{-1}.

TLC Data

Silica gel; solvent: toluene-methanol, 10:1, v/v; R_f=0.28; detection: not reported.

References

H. Minato and M. Matsumoto; Studies on the Metabolites of *Zygosporium masonii*. Part I. Structure of Zygosporin A; J. Chem. Soc., p. 38 (1970).

S. Natori and I. Yahara; Cytochalasins; In Mycotoxins and Phytoalexins; R. P. Sharma, and D. K. Salunkhe (eds.), CRC Press, pp. 291-338(1991).

Common/Systematic Name

Zygosporin G

(16*S*,18*R*,21*R*)-21-Acetoxy-18-hydroxy-16,18-dimethyl-10-phenyl[11]cytochalasa-6(7),13(*E*),19(*E*)-triene-1,17-dione

Molecular Weight/Molecular Formula

$C_{30}H_{37}NO_5$; MW = 491.26717

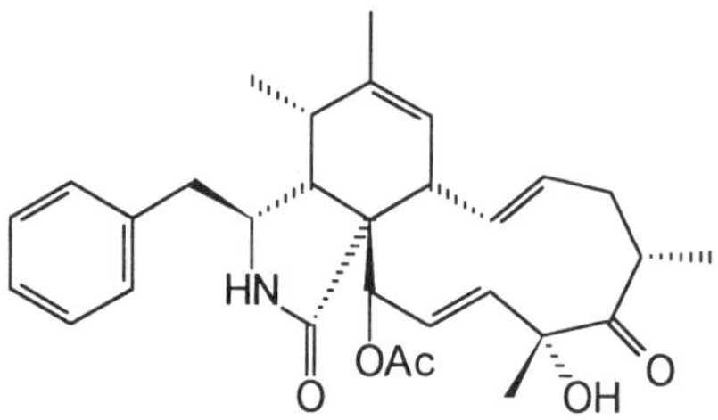

General Characteristics

Colorless prisms from diisopropyl ether; mp, 115-125°C; $[\alpha]_D^{24}$ -82.0° (*c*=0.870, in dioxane).

Fungal Source

Zygosporium masonii.

Biological Activity

Cytotoxic to HeLa cells.

Spectral Data

IR:

(KBr) 3410, 1743, 1701, 1122, 1045, 1008, and 965cm^{-1}; (Nujol) 3430, 3285, 1742, 1693, 1228, 1121, 1044, 1007, 965, 745, and 703cm^{-1}.

TLC Data

Silica gel; solvent: toluene-methanol, 10:1, v/v; R_f=0.35; detection: not reported.

References

H. Minato and M. Matsumoto; Studies on the Metabolites of *Zygosporium masonii*. Part I. Structure of Zygosporin A; J. Chem. Soc., p. 38 (1970).

S. Natori and I. Yahara; Cytochalasins; In Mycotoxins and Phytoalexins; R. P. Sharma, and D. K. Salunkhe (eds.); CRC Press, pp. 291-338(1991).

Common/Systematic Name

Cytochalasin H; Kodocytochalasin-1; Paspalin-P
(7*S*,16*S*,18*R*,21*R*)-21-Acetoxy-7,18-dihydroxy-16,18-dimethyl-10-phenyl-[11]cytochalasa-6(12),13(*E*),19(*E*)-trien-1-one

Molecular Formula/Molecular Weight

$C_{30}H_{39}NO_5$; MW = 493.28282

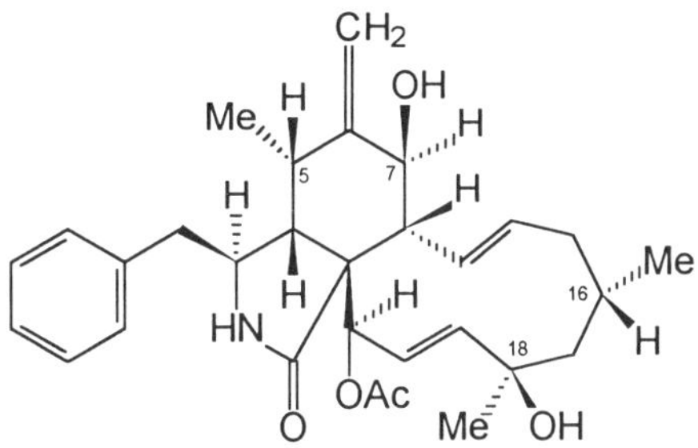

General Characteristics

Crystals from ethyl ether; mp, 255-257°C; colorless needles from methanol; mp, 268-269°C; $[\alpha]_D^{25}$ +63° (*c*=0.103, in MeOH). White needles from chloroform-ethyl ether; mp, 258-263°C; $[\alpha]_D$ -9.0° (in $CHCl_3$); +91.2° (in MeOH).

Isolation/Purification

Cultures were extracted with chloroform-methanol, 2:1 (v/v) and chromatographed on silica gel 60 eluted with a linear gradient from hexane to ethyl ether. Cytochalasin H was crystallized from ethyl ether solution.

Fungal Source

Phomopsis spp. and *Phomopsis paspalli.*

Biological Activity

LD_{50} 12.5mg/kg dosed orally to day-old cockerels. A plant growth inhibitor; inhibited floral development in tobacco.

Spectral Data

UV:

End absorption and weak π-π* transition due to the aromatic ring.

^{13}C NMR:

C-1, 174.4 s; C-3, 57.8 d; C-4, 50.3 d; C-5, 32.9 d; C-6, 148.2 s; C-7, 69.8 d; C-8, 47.3 d; C-9, 51.9 s; C-10, 45.6 t; C-11, 14.0 q; C-12, 113.8 t; C-13, 127.2 d; C-14, 138.3 d; C-15, 42.9 t; C-16, 31.2 d; C-17, 57.8 t; C-18, 74.2 s; C-19, 127.0 d; C-20,

138.5 d; C-21, 77.5 d; C-22, 26.5 q; C-23, 28.5 q; C-1', 137.4 s; C-2',6', 129.1 d; C-3',5', 128.9 d; C-4', 125.9 d; $CH_3\underline{C}$=0, 170.0 s; and $\underline{C}H_3C$=0, 20.8ppm q.

TLC Data

Silica gel G-HR. Solvent: A: toluene-ethyl acetate-formic acid, 5:4:1, v/v/v. B: chloroform-acetone, 93:7, v/v. R_f value for A: 0.62, B: 0.13. Detection: 50% ethanolic H_2SO_4 sprayed alone or in combination with 3% ethanolic phosphomolybdic acid followed by heating for 5 min at 100°C.

References

R. J. Cole and R. H. Cox; Handbook of Toxic Fungal Metabolites; Academic Press, New York, p. 289 (1981).

R. J. Cole, J. M. Wells, R. H. Cox, and H. G. Cutler; Isolation and Biological Properties of Deacetylcytochalasin H from *Phomopsis* sp.; J. Agric. Food Chem., Vol. 29, pp. 205-206(1981).

S. Natori and I. Yahara; In Mycotoxins and Phytoalexins, R. P. Sharma, and D. K. Salunkhe (eds.), CRC Press, pp. 291-338(1991).

S. A. Patwardhan, R. C. Pandey, S. Dev, and G. S. Pendse; Toxic Cytochalasins of *Phomopsis paspalli*, a Pathogen of Kodo Millet; Phytochemistry., Vol. 13, p. 1985 (1974).

Common/Systematic Name

Cytochalasin U

Molecular Formula/Molecular Weight

$C_{30}H_{39}NO_5$; MW = 493.28282

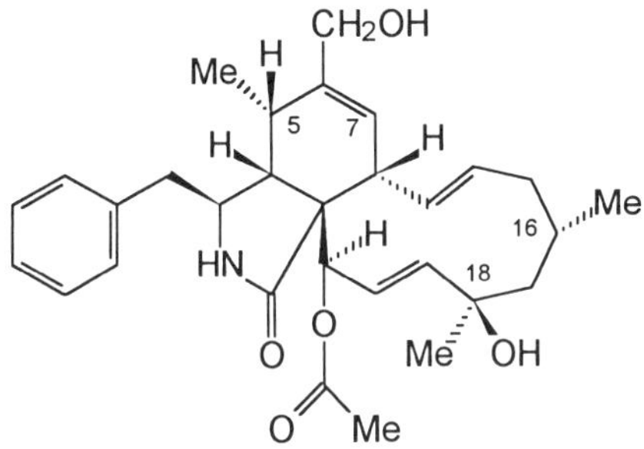

Fungal Source

Isolated from the fermentation broth of *Pestalotia* sp. (AB 1942R-114). The fungus was isolated from a partridge pea plant (*Cassia fasciculata*) collected in Missouri, USA.

Isolation/Purification

The whole broth was centrifuged and the supernatant adsorbed in batch onto SP-207 (Mitsubishi Kasei Corp.). The resin was washed in a fritted glass filter with water, 50% methanol-water and methanol, successively. The active methanol eluate was concentrated to dryness under reduced pressure and the residue was triturated with ethyl acetate. The soluble material was purified on a C_{18} column using a methanol-water gradient. Final purification was achieved by HPLC using 5% isopropylhexane over silica (Waters μBondapak).

Biological Activity

In vitro immunosuppressant activity as measured by the ability to inhibit [^{3}H]thymidine uptake in mixed BALB/c and C57BL 6 spleen cell suspensions. MLR IC_{50} was 5.2μg/ml for cytochalasin U compared with 0.2μg/ml for cytochalasin H.

Spectral Data

^{1}H NMR and ^{13}C NMR:

Both spectra were similar to that of cytochalasin H except at positions 6, 7 and 12. The 13 vinyl signal at 130.14ppm was that of a methine; its proton coupling partners (8 and 12) were indicative of its position on 7. The coupling patterns in the heteronuclear and homonuclear correlation experiments of the methylene signal at 63.16ppm in ^{13}C and 4.03ppm in the ^{1}H were indicative of its position at 12. Chemical shifts were well suited for a methylene disubstituted-with an olefin and hydroxyl.

Mass Spectrum:

DCI-NH_3 showed a $(M + H)^+$ peak at 494*m/e* and a high resolution peak match was determined to be 494.2924 which corresponded to a formula of $C_{30}H_{40}NO_5$ (calcd 494.2906).

Reference

N. S. Burres, U. Premachandran, P.E. Humphrey, M. Jackson, and R. H. Chen; a New Immunosuppressive Cytochalasin Isolated from a *Pestalotia* sp.; J. Antibiotics, Vol. 45, pp. 1367-1369(1992).

Common/Systematic Name

Cytochalasin J; Deacetylcytochalasin H; Kodocytochalasin-2; Paspalin-P2
(7*S*,16*S*,18*R*,21*R*)-7,18,21-Trihydroxy-16,18-dimethyl-10-phenyl[11]cytochalasa-6(12),13(*E*),19(*E*)-trien-1-one

Molecular Formula/Molecular Weight

$C_{28}H_{37}NO_4$; MW = 451.27226

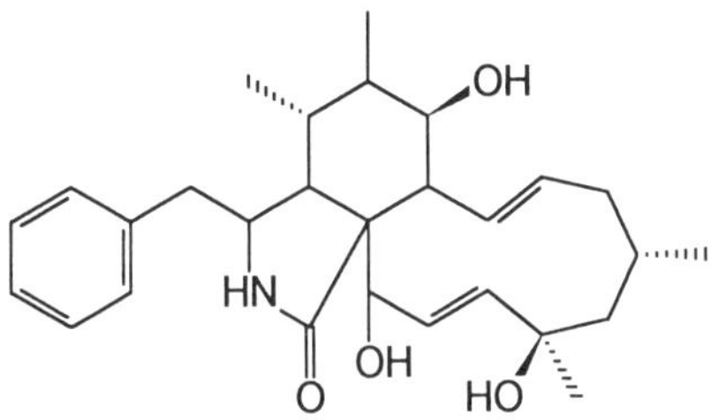

General Characteristics

Purified deacetylcytochalasin H formed large crystals from ethyl ether; mp, 274-276°C (partial decomposition); $[\alpha]_D^{27}$ +47.8° (*c*=0.43, in MeOH).

Fungal Source

Phomopsis sp.

Isolation/Purification

Extraction was identical to that of cytochalasin H. They eluted together from silica gel 60 columns eluted with ethyl ether. A second silica gel 60 column eluted with a linear gradient from *n*-hexane to ethyl ether effected separation of cytochalasin H from the more polar deacetylcytochalasin H.

Biological Activity

Biological data presented an LD_{50} in day-old chickens of a single oral dose at 37.5mg/kg and plant growth inhibitory activity down to 10^{-5} M in wheat coleoptiles.

Spectral Data

UV:

Showed strong end absorption and a series of weak bands in the region of 240-280nm due to the π-π* transition of the monosubstituted aromatic ring.

IR:

Conspicuous in the IR spectrum of deacetylcytochalasin H was the absence of ester carbonyl absorption (1735cm^{-1}), which was present in the IR spectrum of cytochalasin H.

^{13}C NMR:

C-1, 175.84 s; C-2(6.64); C-3, 53.14 d(3.20); C-4, 49.23 d(2.97); C-5, 32.69 d(2.70); C-6, 149.72 s; C-7, 70.05 d(3.94); C-8, 45.54 d(3.20); C-9, 53.24 s; C-10, 42.91 t(2.70,2.83); C-11, 13.72 q(0.87); C-12, 112.19 t(4.97,5.21); C-13, 128.02 d(5.76); C-14, 137.24 d(5.31); C-15, 45.00 t(1.80); C-16, 32.69 d(1.75); C-17, 53.77 t(1.75); C-18, 73.42 s; C-19, 136.37 d(5.83); C-20, 130.65 d(5.90); C-21, 75.71 d(4.52); C-22, 26.39 q(1.01); C-23, 28.19 q(1.28); C-1', 137.53 d; C-2', 6', 129.24 d(7.23); C-3',C-5', 128.24(7.23); and C-4', 126.38ppm d(7.23).

Mass Spectrum:

The HRP spectrum of deacetylcytochalasin H gave a molecular ion peak at 451.2676 (calcd for $C_{28}H_{37}NO_4$, 451.2722). In addition to the molecular ion peak, the LRP mass spectrum showed major peaks at *m/e* 415, 361, 342, 324, 270, 120, and 91(base peak).

TLC Data

It was visualized on TLC as a rose-colored spot at R_f=0.44 compared to 0.53 for cytochalasin H.

References

R. J. Cole, J. M. Wells, R. H. Cox, and H. G. Cutler; Isolation and Biological Properties of Deacetylcytochalasin H from *Phomopsis* sp.; J. Agric. Food Chem., pp. 205-206 (1981).

S. Natori and I. Yahara; In Mycotoxins and Phytoalexins, R. P. Sharma, and D. K. Salunkhe (eds.), CRC Press, pp. 291-338(1991).

S. A. Patwardhan, R. C. Pandey, S. Dev, and S. E. Pendse; Toxic Cytochalasins of *Phomopsis paspalli*, a Pathogen of Kodo Millet; Phytochem., Vol. 13, p. 1985 (1974).

Common/Systematic Name

Epoxycytochalasin H

(6*R*,7*S*,16*S*,18*R*,21*R*)-21-Acetoxy-6,7-epoxy-18-hydroxy-16,18-dimethyl-10-phenyl-[11]cytochalasa-6(12),13(*E*),19(*E*)-trien-1-one

Molecular Formula/Molecular Weight

$C_{30}H_{39}NO_4$; MW = 493.28282

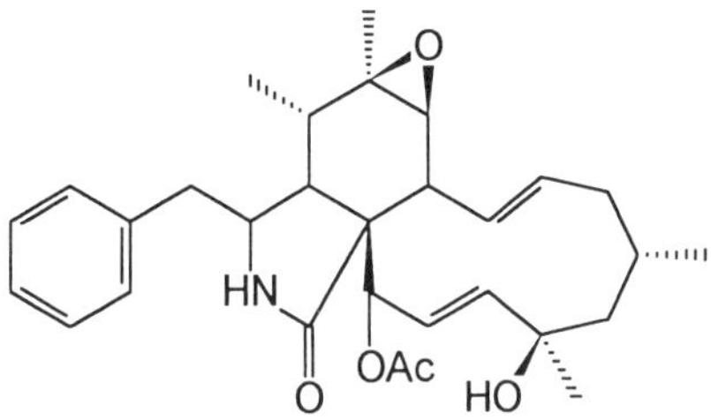

General Characteristics

Purified epoxycytochalasin H formed crystals from ethyl ether; mp., 128-130°C, $[\alpha]_D^{30}$ -84.68° (*c*=0.33, in $CHCl_3$).

Fungal Source

Phomopsis sojae.

Isolation/Purification

The crude chloroform extract was fractionated on a silica gel 60 column packed as a slurry in benzene and eluted with 3 column volumes each of benzene, ethyl ether, ethyl acetate, acetone, and methanol. The ethyl ether and ethyl acetate fractions were highly toxic, and TLC analyses suggested the same toxins were involved. These two fractions were combined, concentrated under vacuum at 60°C, and added to a second silica gel 60 column packed in ethyl ether. The column was eluted with a linear gradient from ethyl ether to ethyl acetate. The fractions associated with acute toxicity to day-old chickens were combined and reduced to dryness under vacuum at 60°C. The combined fractions were applied to a C_{18} reverse phase column packed in acetonitrile and reequilibrated with 10% acetonitrile-water. The column was eluted with a linear gradient from 10% acetonitrile-water to 100% acetonitrile. Toxicity was associated with two distinct compounds: one combined fraction yielded epoxycytochalasin H and the other yielded epoxydeacetylcytochalasin H.

Biological Activity

Acutely toxic to day-old chicks and showed plant growth inhibition in wheat coleoptile assay.

Spectral Data

UV:

Showed strong end absorption and a series of weak bands in the region of 240-280nm.

IR:

1735cm^{-1} (carbonyl ester).

^{13}C NMR:

C-1, 175.3 s; C-2 (6.14); C-3, 54.2 d; C-4, 50.7 d; C-5, 36.7 d; C-6, 57.1 s; C-7, 62.9 d; C-8, 45.2 d; C-9, 53.6 s; C-10, 42.9 t; C-11, 12.6 q(0.83, *J*=7.0); C-12, 19.7 q(1.33); C-13, 127.1 d(5.86, *J*=9.6, 16.2); C-14, 138.2 d(5.28, *J*=5.5, 16.2); C-15, 45.9 t; C-16, 30.7 t; C-17, 53.7 t; C-18, 74.2 s; C-19, 127.7 d(5.48, *J*=2.2, 16.6); C-20, 135.2 d(5.77, *J*=2.2, 16.6); C-21, 76.1 d(5.67, *J*=2.2); C-22, 26.4 q(1.04); C-23, 28.2 q(1.19); C-1', 136.9 s; C-2', C-6', 129.2 d(7.17, m); C-3',5',128.9 d(7.26, m); C-4', 125.4 d(7.26, m); $CH_3\underline{C}O$, 170.2 s, and $\underline{C}H_3CO$, 20.8ppm q(2.20).

Mass Spectrum:

The LRP electron-impact mass spectra of epoxycytochalasin H gave ions at nominal mass *m/e* 493(M^+), 475(M^+ -H_2O), 433(M^+ -H_2O - C_2H_2O), 415(M^+ -2H_2O - C_2H_2O), 402, 343, 324, 270, 240, 120, and 91(base). The HRP electron-impact mass spectrum gave a molecular ion peak at 493.2748 (calcd for $C_{30}H_{39}NO_5$, 493.2828).

References

R. J. Cole, D. M. Wilson, J. L. Harper, R. H. Cox, T. W. Cochran, H. G. Cutler, and D. K. Bell; Isolation and Identification of Two New [11]Cytochalasins from *Phomopsis sojae*; J. Agric. Food Chem., Vol. 30, pp. 301-304(1982).

S. Natori and I. Yahara; Cytochalasins; In Mycotoxins and Phytoalexins; R. P. Sharma, and D. K. Salunkhe (eds.); CRC Press, pp. 291-338(1991).

Common/Systematic Name

Epoxydeacetylcytochalasin H; Deacetylepoxycytochalasin H; Epoxycytochalasin J
(6*R*,7*S*,16*S*,18*R*,21*R*)-6,7-Epoxy-18,21-dihydroxy-16,18-dimethyl-10-phenyl-[11]cytochalasa-6(12),13(*E*),19(*E*)-trien-1-one

Molecular Formula/Molecular Weight

$C_{28}H_{37}NO_4$; MW = 451.27226

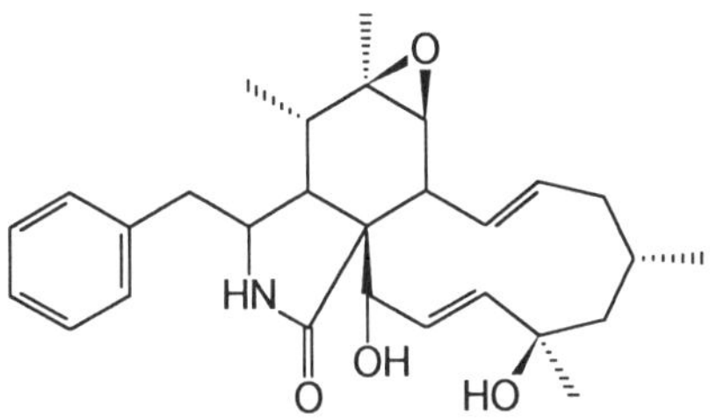

Fungal Source

Phomopsis sojae.

Isolation/Purification

The crude chloroform extract was fractionated on a silica gel 60 column packed as a slurry in benzene and eluted with 3 column volumes each of benzene, ethyl ether, ethyl acetate, acetone, and methanol. The ethyl ether and ethyl acetate fractions were highly toxic, and TLC analyses suggested the same toxins were involved. These two fractions were combined, concentrated under vacuum at 60°C, and added to a second silica gel 60 column packed in ethyl ether. The column was eluted with a linear gradient from ethyl ether to ethyl acetate. The fractions associated with acute toxicity to day-old chickens were combined and reduced to dryness under vacuum at 60°C. The combined fractions were applied to a C_{18} reversed-phase column packed in acetonitrile and reequilibrated with 10% acetonitrile-water. The column was eluted with a linear gradient from 10% acetonitrile-water to 100% acetonitrile. Toxicity was associated with two distinct compounds: one combined fraction yielded epoxycytochalasin H and the other yielded epoxydeacetylcytochalasin H.

Biological Activity

Acutely toxic to day-old chicks and showed plant growth inhibition in wheat coleoptile assay.

Spectral Data

UV:

Showed strong end absorption and a series of weak bands in the region of 240-280nm.

IR:

The distinguishing feature in the IR spectrum of epoxydeacetylcytochalasin H was the absence of carbonyl ester absorption (1735cm^{-1}) which was present in the IR spectrum of epoxycytochalasin H.

^{13}C NMR:

C-1, 176.4; C-2 (5.88); C-3, 54.3 d; C-4, 51.1 d; C-5, 36.6 d; C-6, 57.2 s; C-7, 63.2 d; C-8, 43.9 d; C-9, 54.7 s; C-10, 42.8 t; C-11, 12.8 q(1.05, *J*=7.0); C-12, 19.9 q(1.35); C-13, 128.1 d(5.85, *J*=10.1, 16.2); C-14, 136.8 d(5.22, *J*=6.1, 16.2); C-15, 46.2 t; C-16, 30.7 t; C-17, 53.7 t; C-18, 74.5 s; C-19, 134.8 d(5.72, *J*=2.2, 16.9); C-20, 130.4 d(5.95, *J*=2.2, 16.9); C-21, 75.3 d(4.23, *J*=2.2); C-22, 26.4 q(1.03, *J*=5.4); C-23, 28.2 q(1.22); C-1', 137.1 s; C-2',6', 129.0 d(7.17 m); C-3', 5', 128.7 d(7.25, m); and C-4', 126.9ppm d(7.25, m).

Mass Spectrum:

The LRP spectrum of epoxydeacetylcytochalasin H gave a molecular ion at 451 with additional peaks at 433(M^+ - H_2O), 415(M^+ - $2H_2O$), 342, 210, 240, 120, and 91(base peak). The HRP spectrum gave a molecular ion at 451.2682 (calcd for $C_{28}H_{37}NO_4$ = 451.2722).

References

R. J. Cole, D. M. Wilson, J. L. Harper, R. H. Cox, T. W. Cochran, H. G. Cutler, and D. K. Bell; Isolation and Identification of Two New [11]Cytochalasins from *Phomopsis sojae*; J. Agric. Food Chem., Vol. 30, pp. 302-304(1982).

S. Natori and I. Yahara; Cytochalasins; In Mycotoxins and Phytoalexins; R. P. Sharma, and D. K. Salunkhe (eds.); CRC Press, pp. 291-338(1991).

Common/Systematic Name

Engleromycin

(7*S*,16*S*,18*S*,21*S*)-7,18,21-Trihydroxy-19*R*,20*S*-epoxy-16,18-dimethyl-10-phenyl-[11]cytochalasa-6(12),13(*E*)-diene-1,17-dione

Molecular Formula/Molecular Weight

$C_{28}H_{35}NO_6$; MW = 481.24644

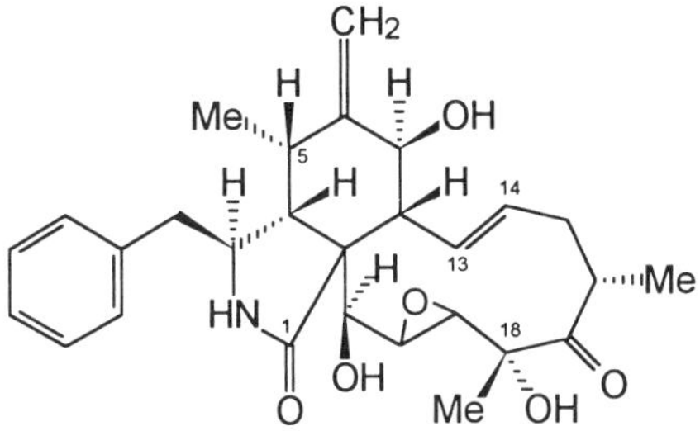

General Characteristics

Colorless needles from ethanol-water; mp, 226-228°C; $[\alpha]_D^{25}$ +64° (in EtOH).

Fungal Source

Engleromyces goetzei.

Spectral Data

^{1}H NMR:

(deuteropyridine) N-2, 8.66; H-3, 3.6; H-4, 2.7-2.9; H-5, 3.2; H-7, 4.42(*J*=10.7); H-8, 3.5(*J*=10.8); H-10, 2.7-2.9; H-11, 0.93(*J*=6.7); H-12, 5.27 or 5.08(*J*=1.4); H-13, 6.59(*J*=15.5); H-14, 5.96(J=9.9, 5.6); H-15, 2.7-2.9 or 2.02(*J*=12.6, 2.5); H-16, 3.2(*J*=2.5); H-19, 3.99(*J*=2.1); H-20, 4.27(*J*=2.1, 0.8); H-21, 4.29(*J*=0.8,4.2); C-16Me, 1.07(*J*=6.8); C-18Me, 1.67; C-21OH, 7.14; C-7OH, 5.2; and C-18OH, 5.6ppm.

^{13}C NMR:

(deuteropyridine) C-1, 177; C-3, 54.24; C-4, 52.07; C-5, 33.61; C-6, 152.33; C-7, 71.61; C-8, 46.58; C-9, 54.80; C-10, 45.59; C-11, 13.86; C-12, 111.78; C-13, 131.79; C-14, 133.10; C-15, 38.47; C-16, 42.67; C-17, 217; C-18, 77.72; C-19, 60.90; C-20, 56.38; C-21, 74.93; C-1', 138.69; C-2', C-6',130.08; C-3', C-5', 128.83; C-4', 126.89; C-16Me, 19.17; and C-18Me, 23.08ppm.

References

E. J. Pedersen, P. Larsen, and P. M. Boll; Engleromycin, a new cytochalasin from *Engleromyces goetzei* Hennings; Tet. Lett., Vol. 21, pp. 5079-5082(1980).

S. Natori and I. Yahara; Cytochalasins; In Mycotoxins and Phytoalexins; R. P. Sharma, and D. K. Salunkhe (eds.); CRC Press, pp. 291-338(1991).

Common/Systematic Name

Pyrichalasin H

(7*S*,16*S*,18*R*,21*R*)-21-Acetoxy-7,18-dihydroxy-16,18-dimethyl-10-*p*-methoxyphenyl-[11]cytochalasa-6(12),13(*E*),19(*E*)-trien-1-one

Molecular Formula/Molecular Weight

$C_{31}H_{41}NO_6$; MW = 523.29339

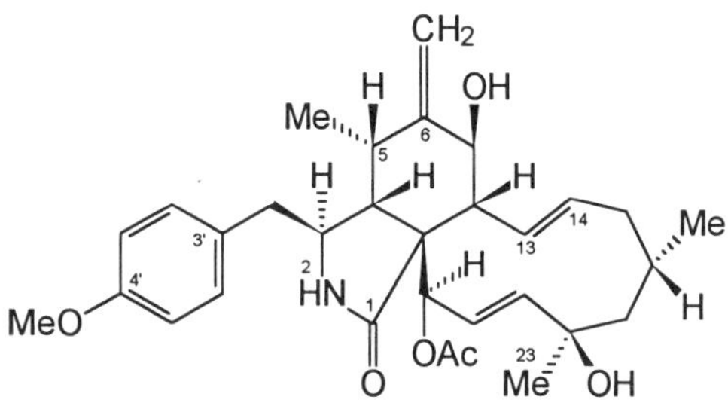

General Characteristics

Crystallized from ethyl acetate to afford colorless plates; mp 207-209°C; $[\alpha]_D^{23}$ -18.4° (*c*=1.05, in $CHCl_3$).

Fungal Source

Pyricularia grisea.

Isolation/Purification

The filtered culture broth was passed through a column of XAD-2, the column was washed with methanol. The methanol washings were combined and concentrated to an aqueous suspension which was extracted with ethyl acetate. The ethyl acetate extract was chromatographed on a silica gel column with ethyl acetate-hexane. The fractions containing pyrichalasin H as indicated by TLC (silica gel 60 F_{254}), aluminum sheet (Merck), chloroform-methanol, 10:1 (v:v); R_f=0.47 were combined, crystallized from ethyl acetate and recrystallized to give colorless plates.

Biological Activity

Phytotoxic.

Spectral Data

UV:

λ_{max}^{EtOH} Exhibited intense absorption maxima at 203(ϵ=22,000) and 224nm(17,000), with inflections at 276(2,000) and 283nm (1,640).

IR:

($CHCl_3$) bands at 3590, 3540, and 3410cm^{-1} (OH and NH); 1735(ester C=O); 1690(amide C=O); 1610, 1580, and 1512(benzene ring); and 965cm^{-1} (trans double bond).

^{1}H NMR:

H-2, 5.56 s; H-3, 3.21 m; H-4, 2.11(dd, *J*=4, 5); H-5, 2.77 m; H-7, 3.83(d, *J*=10); H-8, 2.94(dd, *J*=10, 10); H-10, 2.59(dd, *J*=14, 10); 2.80(dd, *J*=14, 5); H-11, 0.99(d, *J*=7); H-12, 5.11 br s; 5.35, br s: H-13, 5.74(dd, *J*=15, 10); H-14, 5.40 m; H-15, 2.04 m; 1.80 m; H-16, 1.79 m; H-17, 1.88(dd, *J*=14,3); 1.57(*J*=14, 2); H-19, 5.87(dd, *J*=15, 2); H-20, (dd, *J*=15, 2); H-21, 5.51(d, *J*=2); H-22, 1.05(d, *J*=7); H-23, 1.35 s; H-2',H-6', 7.06(d, *J*=8); H-3', H-5', 6.85(d, *J*=8); Ac, 2.24 s; OMe, 3.79ppm s.

^{13}C NMR:

C-1, 174.18; C-3, 53.85; C-4, 50.31; C-5, 32.84; C-6, 148.01; C-7, 69.73; C-8, 47.19; C-9, 51.77; C-10, 44.70; C-11, 14.08; C-12, 113.99; C-13, 127.15; C-14, 138.64; C-15, 42.74; C-16, 28.43; C-17, 53.69; C-18, 74.28; C-19, 125.98; C-20, 138.08; C-21, 77.47; C-22, 26.42; C-23, 31.14; C-1', 129.37; C-2', C-6', 129.99; C- 3',C-5', 114.32; C-4', 158.68; $CH_3\underline{C}OO$, 170.06; $CH_3\underline{C}OO$, 20.82; and OMe, 55.29ppm.

Mass Data:

EIMS: spectrum of pyrichalasin H showed the following prominent ions: 523(2, M^+), 506(2, M^+ -17, OH), 505(2, M^+ -18, H_2O), 464(4, -59, OAc), 463(3, -60, AcOH), 446(9, -77 (AcOH + OH or AcO + H_2O)), 445(11, -78 (AcOH + H_2O)), 402(12, -121($MeOC_6H_4CH_2$), 385(1, -138 ($MeOC_6H_4$-CH_2 + OH)), 384(5, -139($MeOC_6H_4CH_2$ + H_2O)), 343(3, -180 ($MeOC_6H_4CH_2$ + OAc)), 342(12, -181 ($MeOC_6H_4CH_2$ + AcOH)), 325(9, -198($MeOC_6H_4CH_2$ + AcOH + OH)), 324(33, -199 ($MeOC_6H_4CH_2$ + AcOH + H_2O)), 306(8, -217($MeOC_6H_4CH_2$ + $2H_2O$ + OAc)), and 121*m/e* (100, $MeOC_6H_4CH_2$+ ion); found: C 70.86; H 7.95: N 2.47; calcd for $C_{31}H_{41}NO_6$, C. 71.10; H. 7 89; N 2.67.

References

M. Nukina; Pyrichalasin H, a New Phytotoxic Metabolite Belonging to the Cytochalasins from *Pyricularia grisea* (Cooke) Saccardo; Agric. Biol. Chem., Vol. 51, pp. 2625-2628(1987).

S. Natori and I. Yahara; Cytochalasins; In Mycotoxins and Phytoalexins; R. P. Sharma, and D. K. Salunkhe (eds.); CRC Press, pp. 291-338(1991).

Common/Systematic Name

Cytochalasin N_{PHO}

(7*S*,16*S*,18*R*,21*R*)-21-Acetoxy-7,18-dihydroxy-16,18-dimethyl-10-phenyl-[11]cytochalasa-5,13(*E*),19(*E*)-trien-1-one

Molecular Formula/Molecular Weight

$C_{30}H_{39}NO_5$; MW = 493.28282

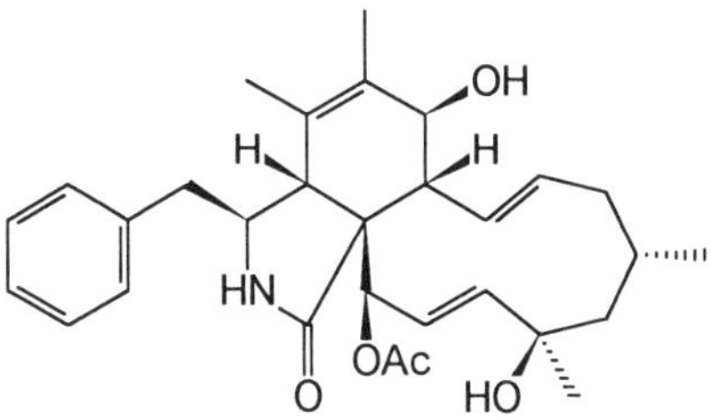

General Characteristics

Colorless powder; mp., 253-254°C; $[\alpha]_D$ +85.4° (in MeOH).

Fungal Source

Phomopsis sp.

Isolation/Purification

Extracted with dichloromethane and chromatographed on silica gel with hexane-acetone as elution solvent. Final purification by HPLC using Nucleosil 50-5 with hexane-acetone as mobile phase.

Biological Activity

Cytotoxic (binds specifically to actin).

Spectral Data

UV:

λ_{max}^{MeOH} 208nm (ϵ=19,800).

IR:

(KBr) 3400, 2725, 1690, 1470, 1235, 1150, 960, and 700cm^{-1}.

^{1}H NMR:

(DMSO-d_6) H-2, 8.15(s); H-3, 3.17(ddd, *J*=4.3, 10.5); H-4, 2.27(m); H-7, 3.60(m); H-8, 2.36(dd, *J*=10, 10); H-10, 2.96(dd, 12.8, 4.3); 2.72(dd, 12.8, 10.5); H-11, 1.51(s); H-12, 0.87(s); H-21, 5.66(dd, 1.8, 2.0); and 21-Ac, 2.25ppm (s).

^{13}C NMR:
(DMSO-d_6) C-1, 174.5(s); C-3, 49.1(d); C-4, 60.0(d); C-5, 125.5(s); C-6, 133.2(s); C-7, 68.3(d); C-8, 48.5(d); C-9, 51.4(s); C-10, 43.3(t); C-11, 14.4(q); C-12, 16.5(q); C-21, 75.1(d); and 21Ac, 20.4(q), 170.4ppm (s).

References

S. Natori and I. Yahara; Cytochalasins; In Mycotoxins and Phytoalexins; R. P. Sharma, and D. K. Salunkhe (eds.); CRC Press, pp. 291-338(1991).

T. Tomioka, Y. Izawa, K. Koyama, and S. Natori; Three New 10-Phenyl[11] cytochalasins, Cytochalasins N, O, and P from *Phomopsis* sp.; Chem. Pharm. Bull., Vol. 35, pp. 902-905(1987).

Common/Systematic Name

Cytochalasin O_{PHO}

(7*S*,16*S*,18*R*,21*R*)-7,18,21-Trihydroxy-16,18-dimethyl-10-phenyl[11]cytochalasa-5,13(*E*),19(*E*)-trien-1-one

Molecular Formula/Molecular Weight

$C_{28}H_{37}NO_4$; MW = 451.27226

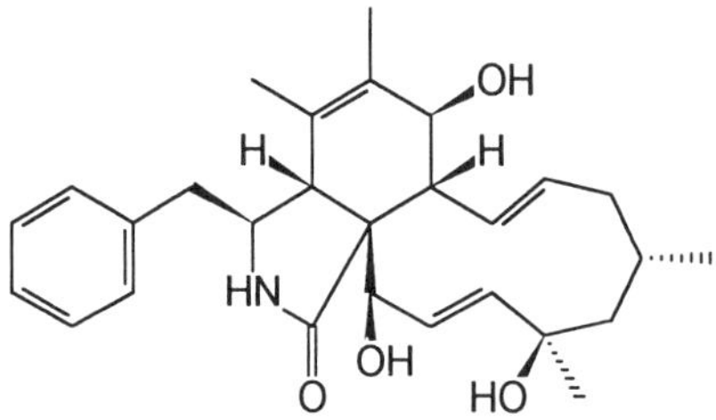

General Characteristics

Colorless needles; mp., 187-188°C; $[\alpha]_D$ +59.6° (in MeOH).

Fungal Source

Phomopsis sp.

Isolation/Purification

Extracted with dichloromethane and chromatographed on silica gel with hexane-acetone as elution solvent. Final purification by HPLC using Nucleosil 50-5 with hexane-acetone as mobile phase.

Biological Activity

Cytotoxic (binds specifically to actin).

Spectral Data

UV:

λ_{max}^{MeOH} 206nm (ϵ=20,800)

IR:

(KBr) 3425, 1670, 1250, 1140, 960, and 700cm^{-1}.

^{1}H NMR:

(DMSO-d_6) H-2, 7.83(s); H-3, 3.12(ddd, *J*=5.0, 9.8); H-4, 2.85(m); H-7, 3.57(m); H-8, 2.36(dd, *J*=10.1, 10.1); H-10, 2.92(dd, 12.9, 5.0); 2.70(dd, 12.9, 9.8); H-11, 1.51(s); H-12, 0.95(s); and H-21, 5.27ppm (s).

^{13}C NMR:
(DMSO-d_6) C-1, 176.6(s); C-3, 48.5(d); C-4, 59.8(d); C-5, 126.4(s); C-6, 132.4(s); C-7, 68.6(d); C-8, 48.0(d); C-9, 53.1(s); C-10, 43.4(t); C-11, 14.3(q); C-12, 16.6(q); and 73.4ppm (d).

References

S. Natori and I. Yahara; Cytochalasins; In Mycotoxins and Phytoalexins; R. P. Sharma, and D. K. Salunkhe (eds.); CRC Press, pp. 291-338(1991).

T. Tomioka, Y. Izawa, K. Koyama, and S. Natori; Three New 10-Phenyl[11] cytochalasins, Cytochalasins N, O, and P from *Phomopsis* sp.; Chem. Pharm. Bull., Vol. 35, pp. 902-905(1987).

Common/Systematic Name

Cytochalasin P_{PHO}
(6*S*,7*S*,16*S*,18*R*,21*R*)-21-Acetoxy-6,7,18-trihydroxy-16,18-dimethyl-10-phenyl-[11]cytochalasa-13(*E*),19(*E*)-dien-1-one

Molecular Formula/Molecular Weight

$C_{30}H_{41}NO_6$; MW = 511.29339

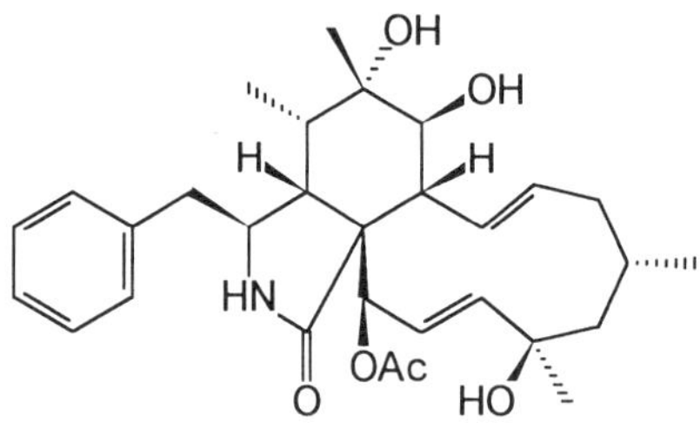

General Characteristics

Crystals from chloroform; mp., 117-118°C; [α] -116° (in MeOH).

Fungal Source

Phomopsis sp.

Isolation/Purification

Extracted with dichloromethane and chromatographed on silica gel with hexane-acetone as elution solvent. Final purification by HPLC using Nucleosil 50-5 with hexane-acetone as mobile phase.

Biological Activity

Cytotoxic (binds specifically to actin).

Spectral Data

UV:
λ_{max}^{MeOH} 208nm (ϵ=15,200).

IR:
(KBr) 3425, 2920, 1680, 1370, 1230, 960, and 700cm^{-1}.

^{1}H NMR:
(DMSO-d_6) H-2, 7.92(s); H-3, 4.02(ddd, *J*=4.6, 5.4, 5.0); H-4, 1.75(dd, 5.0, 5.1); H-5, 1.63(dq, 5.1, 7.0); H-7, 3.27(dd, 5.9, 11.4); H-8, 2.46(dd, *J*=11.4, 10.2); H-10, 2.57(dd, 13.8, 5.4); 2.78(dd, 13.8, 4.6); H-11, 0.81(d, 7.0); H-12, 0.98(s); H-21, 4.77(dd, 2.4, 2.1); and H-21Ac, 2.01(s).

^{13}C NMR:

(DMSO-d_6) C-1, 174.3(s); C-3, 52.6(d); C-4, 48.8(d); C-5, 37.8(d); C-6, 75.0(d); C-7, 75.5(d); C-8, 45.4(d); C-9, 52.9(s); C-10, 42.9(t); C-11, 12.8(q); C-12, 22.4(q); C-21, 77.6; and C-21Ac, 20.5(q), 169.2(s).

References

T. Tomioka, Y. Izawa, K. Koyama, and S. Natori; Three New 10-Phenyl[11] cytochalasins, Cytochalasins N, O, and P from *Phomopsis* sp.; Chem. Pharm. Bull., Vol. 35, pp. 902-905(1987).

S. Natori and I. Yahara; Cytochalasins; In Mycotoxins and Phytoalexins; R. P. Sharma, and D. K. Salunkhe (eds.); CRC Press, pp. 291-338(1991).

Common/Systematic Name

Cytochalasin Q_{PHO}

(6*S*,7*S*,16*S*,18*R*,21*R*)-6,7,18,21-Tetrahydroxy-16,18-dimethyl-10-phenyl[11]cytochalasa-13(*E*),19(*E*)-dien-1-one

Molecular Formula/Molecular Weight

$C_{28}H_{39}NO_5$; MW = 469.28282

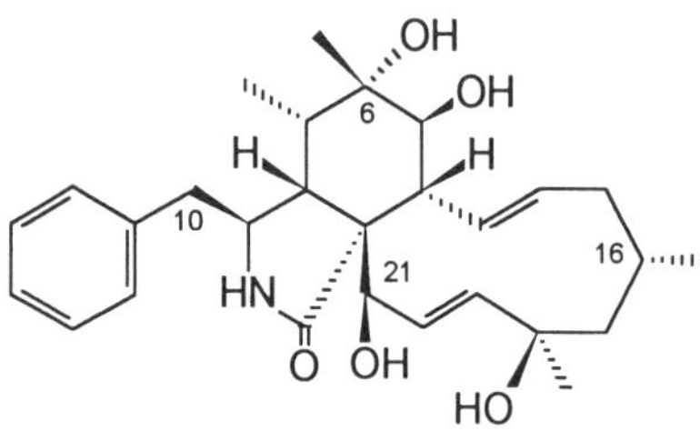

General Characteristics

Colorless powder; mp, 158-159°C (hexane-acetone); $[\alpha]_D^{23}$ -47.8°.

Fungal Source

Phomopsis sp.

Isolation/Purification

The mold was incubated in stationary culture on sterilized wheat at 26°C for 20 days. The moldy wheat was extracted three times with methylene chloride for 24 hrs at room temperature. The extract was chromatographed over silica gel using a gradient system of hexane-acetone as the developing solvents to afford several fractions (1, hexane-acetone, 5:1; 2, 3:1; 3, 2:1; 4, 1:1; and 5, 1:2, v/v). Fraction 5 was chromatographed on columns containing silica gel and eluted with chloroform-methanol (15:1, v/v) followed by hexane-acetone (5:3, v/v) and subjected to HPLC on a Nucleosil 50-5 column with hexane-acetone (5:4, v/v) as the first mobile phase followed by hexane-acetone (5:3, v/v) to give cytochalasins R, S, and Q respectively.

Biological Activity

Biological activity typically that of other cytochalasins which is based on an interaction with the protein actin.

Spectral Data

UV:

λ_{max}^{MeOH} 209nm (ε=48,750).

IR:

(KBr) 3400, 2910, 1680, 1455, 1370, and 962cm^{-1}.

^{1}H NMR:

(DMSO-d_6) H-2, 7.651(s); H-3, 4.039(ddd, $J_{3,4}$=5Hz, $J_{3,10a}$=3.8Hz, $J_{3,10bb}$=5.7Hz); H-4, 2.068(dd, $J_{4,5}$=5.0Hz); H-5, 1.785(dq, $J_{5,11}$=7.1Hz); H-7, 3.285(dd, $J_{7,8}$=12.0Hz); H-8, ca. 2.50($J_{8,13}$=10.1Hz); H-10a, 2.528(dd); H-10b, 2.853(dd); H-11, 0.932(d); H-12a, 0.969(s); H-13, 5.323(dd, $J_{13,14}$=15.0Hz); H-14, 4.881(ddd, $J_{14,15a}$=4.2Hz, $J_{14,15b}$=11.0Hz); H-15a, 1.536(ddd); H-15b, 1.850(ddd); H-16, ca. 1.68; H-17a, 1.325(dd); H-17b, 1.625(dd); H-19, 5.511(dd, $J_{19,20}$=16.8Hz, $J_{19,21}$=2.3Hz); H-20, 5.883(dd, $J_{20,21}$=2.2Hz); H-21, 3.313(ddd); 16-CH_3, 0.929(d); 18-CH_3, 1.100(s); H-2', H-6', 7.176(d); H-3', H-5', 7.276(dd); H-4', 7.184(dd); 21-OH, 4.751(d, $J_{21,21OH}$=6.6Hz); 6-OH, 4.151(s); 7-OH, 3.746(d, $J_{7,7OH}$=4.7Hz); and 18-OH, 4.142ppm (s).

^{13}C NMR:

(DMSO-d_6) C-1, 175.5(s); C-3, 52.4(d); C-4, 48.7(d); C-5, 37.9(d); C-6, 75.2(s); C-7, 75.4(d); C-8, 43.4(d); C-9, 54.3(s); C-10, 43.0(t); C-11, 12.6(q); C-12, 22.2(q); C-13, 127.6(d); C-14, 135.5(d); C-15, 42.9(t); C-16, 28.1(d); C-17, 53.2(t); C-18, 72.4(s); C-19, 135.5(d); C-20, 131.8(d); C-21, 75.5(d); C-22, 26.2(q); C-23, 32.4(q); C-1', 137.4(s); C-2', C-6', 130.1(d); C-3', C-5', 127.8(d); and C-4', 126.0ppm (d).

Mass Spectrum:

469.2808(M^+, calcd for $C_{28}H_{39}NO_5$, 469.2826), 451, 433, 417, 360, 324, 120, and 91*m/e*.

References

Y. Izawa, T. Hirose, T. Shimizu (nee Tomioka), K. Koyama, and S. Natori; Six New 10-Phenyl[11]Cytochalasins, Cytochalasins N-S from *Phomopsis* sp.; Tetrahedron, Vol. 45, pp. 2323-2335(1989).

S. Natori and I. Yahara; Cytochalasins; In Mycotoxins and Phytoalexins; R. P. Sharma, and D. K. Salunkhe (eds.); CRC Press, pp. 291-338(1991).

Common/Systematic Name

Cytochalasin R_{PHO}

(6*R*,7*S*,16*S*,18*R*,21*R*)-6,7,18,21-Tetrahydroxy-16,18-dimethyl-10-phenyl[11]cytochalasa-13(*E*),19(*E*)-dien-1-one

Molecular Formula/Molecular Weight

$C_{28}H_{39}NO_5$; MW = 469.28282

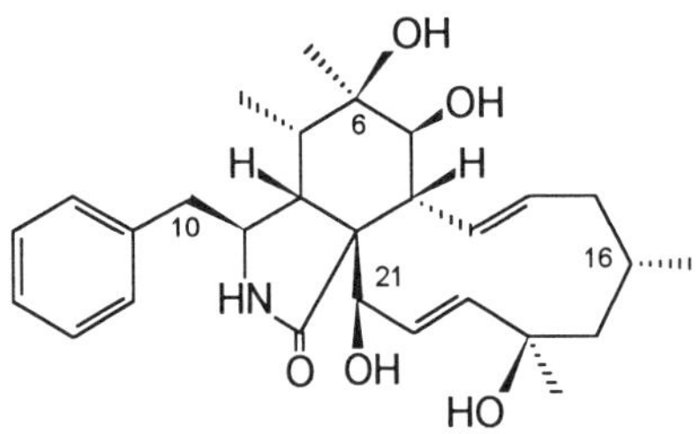

General Characteristics

Colorless powder; mp, 106-107°C (hexane-acetone); $[\alpha]_D^{23}$ -46.0°.

Fungal Source

Phomopsis sp.

Isolation/Purification

The mold was incubated in stationary culture on sterilized wheat at 26°C for 20 days. The moldy wheat was extracted three times with methylene chloride for 24 hrs at room temperature. The extract was chromatographed over silica gel using a gradient system of hexane-acetone as the developing solvents to afford several fractions: (1, hexane-acetone, 5:1; 2, 3:1; 3, 2:1; 4, 1:1; and 5, 1:2, v/v). Fraction 5 was chromatographed on columns containing silica gel and eluted with chloroform-methanol (15:1, v/v) followed by hexane-acetone (5:3, v/v) and subjected to HPLC on a Nucleosil 50-5 column with hexane-acetone (5:4, v/v) as the first mobile phase followed by hexane-acetone (5:3, v/v) to give cytochalasins R, S, and Q respectively.

Biological Activity

Biological activity typically that of other cytochalasins which is based on an interaction with the protein actin.

Spectral Data

UV:

λ_{max}^{MeOH} 206nm (ϵ=23,200).

IR:

(KBr) 3400, 2910, 1680, 1455, 1370, and 962cm^{-1}.

^{1}H NMR:

(DMSO-d_6) H-2, 7.814(s); H-3, 3.425(m, $J_{3,4}$=5.0Hz); H-4, 2.245(dd, $J_{4,5}$=5.0Hz); H-5, 1.985(dq, $J_{5,11}$=7.2Hz); H-7, 2.905(d, $J_{7,8}$=11.8Hz); H-8, 2.735($J_{8,13}$=9.9Hz); H-10a, ca. 2.66; H-11, O.681(d); 12a, 1.007(s); H-13, 5.372(dd, $J_{13,14}$=15.1Hz); H-14, 4.922(ddd, $J_{14,15a}$=4.1Hz, $J_{14,15b}$=11.0Hz); H-15a, 1.536(ddd); H-15b, 1.848(ddd); H-16, ca. 1.68; H-17a, 1.340(dd); H-17b, 1.617(dd); H-19, 5.585(dd, $J_{19,20}$=16.5Hz, $J_{19,21}$=2.2Hz); H-20, 5.825(dd, $J_{20,21}$=1.9Hz); H-21, 3.480(dd); 16-CH_3, 0.930(d); 18-CH_3, 1.120(s); H-2', H-6', ca. 7.21 ; H-3', H-5', 7.290(dd); and H-4', ca. 7.21ppm.

^{13}C NMR:

(DMSO-d_6) C-1, 176.0(s); C-3, 52.4(d); C-4, 47.3(d); C-5, 38.2(d); C-6, 71.5(s); C-7, 72.5(d); C-8, 41.5(d); C-9, 54.2(s); C-10, 44.2(t); C-11, 12.7(q); C-12, 24.5(q); C-13, 127.9(d); C-14, 134.2(d); C-15, 43.0(t); C-16, 27.9(d); C-17, 53.4(t); C-18, 72.4(s); C-19, 136.0(d); C-20, 131.3(d); C-21, 75.2(d); C-22, 26.2(q); C-23, 31.9(q); C-1', 137.1(s); C-2', C-6', 129.9(d); C-3', C-5', 127.9(d); and C-4', 126.2ppm (d).

Mass Spectrum:

469.2808(M^+, calcd for $C_{28}H_{39}NO_5$, 469.2826), 451, 433, 415, 360, 324, 120, and 91*m/e*.

References

Y. Izawa, T. Hirose, T. Shimizu (nee Tomioka), K. Koyama, and S. Natori; Six New 10-Phenyl[11]cytochalasins, Cytochalasins N-S from *Phomopsis* sp.; Tetrahedron, Vol. 45, pp. 2323-2335(1989).

S. Natori and I. Yahara; Cytochalasins; In Mycotoxins and Phytoalexins; R. P. Sharma, and D. K. Salunkhe (eds.); CRC Press, pp. 291-338(1991).

Common/Systematic Name

Cytochalasin S

(5*S*,6*S*,7*S*,16*S*,18*R*,21*R*)-5,7,18,21-Tetrahydroxy-16,18-dimethyl-10-phenyl-[11]cytochalasa-13(*E*),10(*E*)-dien-1-one

Molecular Formula/Molecular Weight

$C_{28}H_{39}NO_5$; MW = 469.28282

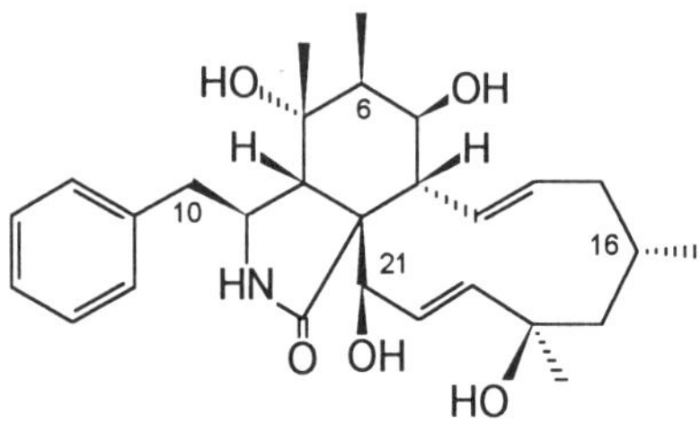

General Characteristics

Colorless powder; mp., 149-151°C (hexane-acetone); $[\alpha]_D^{23}$ -62.9°.

Fungal Source

Phomopsis sp.

Isolation/Purification

The mold was incubated in stationary culture on sterilized wheat at 26°C for 20 days. The moldy wheat was extracted three times with methylene chloride for 24 hrs at room temperature. The extract was chromatographed over silica gel using a gradient system of hexane-acetone as the developing solvent to afford several fractions (1, hexane-acetone, 5:1; 2, 3:1; 3, 2:1; 4, 1:1; and 5, 1:2, v/v). Fraction 5 was chromatographed on columns containing silica gel and eluted with chloroform-methanol (15:1, v/v) followed by hexane-acetone (5:3, v/v) and subjected to HPLC on a Nucleosil 50-5 column with hexane-acetone (5:4, v/v) as the first mobile phase followed by hexane-acetone (5:3, v/v) to give cytochalasins R, S, and Q respectively.

Biological Activity

Biological activity typically that of other cytochalasins (inhibition of a variety of cellular movements) which is based on an interaction with the protein actin.

Spectral Data

UV:

λ_{max}^{MeOH} 208nm (ϵ=13,370).

IR:

(KBr) 3350, 2900, 1680, 1445, 1362, and 960cm^{-1}.

^{1}H NMR:

(DMSO-d_6) H-2, 7.833(s); H-3, 3.557(ddd, $J_{3,4}$=4.7Hz, $J_{3,10a}$=5.2Hz, $J_{10a,b}$=13.8Hz); H-4, 2.078(d); H-6, ca. 1.53($J_{6,12}$=7.3Hz); H-7, 2.851(m, $J_{7,8}$=11.2Hz); H-8, 3.043(dd); H-10a, 2.650(dd); H-10b, ca. 2.90; H-11, 1.130(d); H-12a, 1.030(d); H-13, 5.393(dd, $J_{13,14}$=16.6Hz); H-14, 4.889(ddd, $J_{14,15a}$=3.9Hz, $J_{14,15b}$=11.2Hz); H-15a, ca. 1.53; H-15b, 1.866(ddd); H-16, 1.720(m); H-17a, 1.330(dd); H-17b, 1.592(dd); H-19, 5.578(dd); H-20, 5.666(dd); H-21, 3.243(m); 16-CH_3, 0.920(d); 18-CH_3, 1.102 (s); H-2', H-6', ca. 7.21; H-3', H-5', 7.290(dd); H-4', ca. 7.21; 21-OH, 5.414(d); and 7-OH, 3.877ppm (d, $J_{7,OH}$=5.1Hz).

^{13}C NMR:

(DMSO-d_6) C-1, 174.8(s); C-3, 52.7(d); C-4, 55.5(d); C-5, 72.1(s)*; C-6, 49.0(d); C-7, 72.2(d); C-8, 45.1(d); C-9, 54.7(s); C-10, 42.0(t); C-11, 25.3(q); C-12, 16.9(q); C-13, 127.8(d); C-14, 135.5(d); C-15, 43.0(t); C-16, 28.0(d); C-17, 53.5(t); C-18, 72.3(s)*; C-19, 136.5(d); C-20, 129.8(d); C-21, 74.2(d); C-22, 26.2(q); C-23, 31.9(q); C-1', 136.7(s); C-2', C-6', 130.2(d); C-3', C-5', 127.9(d); and C-4', 126.3ppm (d).

* Assignments may be reversed.

Mass Spectrum:

469.2792(M^+, calcd for $C_{28}H_{39}NO_5$, 469.2826), 451, 433, 415, 378, 360, 324, 306, 288, 270, 242, 216, 120, and 91*m/e*.

References

Y. Izawa, T. Hirose, T. Shimizu (nee Tomioka), K. Koyama, and S. Natori; Six New 10-Phenyl[11]cytochalasins, Cytochalasins N-S from *Phomopsis* sp.; Tetrahedron, Vol. 45, pp. 2323-2335(1989).

S. Natori and I. Yahara; Cytochalasins; In Mycotoxins and Phytoalexins; R. P. Sharma, and D. K. Salunkhe (eds.); CRC Press, pp. 291-338(1991).

Common/Systematic Name

Cytochalasin N_{HYP}

(7*S*,16*S*,18*R*,21*R*,13*E*,19*E*)-21-Acetoxy-5,6-epoxy-7,18-dihydroxy-16,18-dimethyl-10-phenyl[11]cytochalasa-13(*E*),19(*E*)-diene-1,17-dione

Molecular Formula/Molecular Weight

$C_{30}H_{37}NO_7$; MW = 523.25700

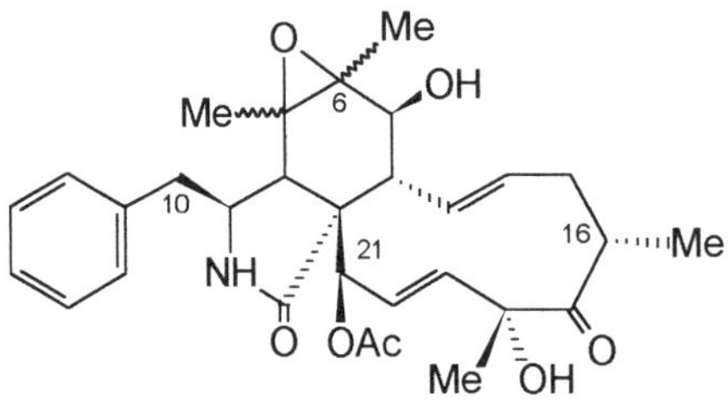

General Characteristics

Hair-like needles from methanol; mp., 272°C; $[\alpha]_D^{23}$ -4° (*c*=0.5, in MeOH).

Fungal Source

Hypoxylon terricola (habitat restricted to dead and decaying coniferous needles; only found in one location in the U.S.A. and in the Atlantic Pyrenees).

Isolation/Purification

The mycelia were extracted with chloroform. Evaporation yielded a solid that was chromatographed using Merck Kieselgel PF. The sample was applied to the column in chloroform-methanol (95:5, v/v) and eluted with the same solvent to yield cytochalasin C and a mixture of cytochalasins C, D, and N which were further purified by flash chromatography using chloroform-butanol (97:3, v/v) as the eluting solvent.

Biological Activity

Marked cytostatic effects on mammalian cells in tissue culture; target protein was actin.

Spectral Data

IR:

(KBr) 3410, 1742, 1705, and 1699cm^{-1}.

^{1}H NMR:

(C_5D_5N) 2-NH, 9.55(s); 3-H, 4.05(ddd, *J*=7.0, 7.0. 2.0); 4-H, 2.88(d, *J*=2.0); 7-H, 4.15(dd, *J*=10.5, 6.0); 8-H, 3.81(dd, *J*=10.5, 10.5); 10-Ha, Hb, 3.16(d, 7.0); 11-H, 1.59(s); 12-H, 1.25(s); 13-H, 6.61(dd, *J*=15.5, 10.5); 14-H, 5.47(ddd, *J*=15.5, 10.5, 4.5); 15-Ha, 1.95(ddd, *J*=11.5, 5.5, 1.0); 15-Hb, 2.58-2.75(m); 16-H, 2.58-2.75(m); 19-H, 5.65(dd, *J*=16.0, 2.5); 20-H, 6.76(dd, *J*=16.0, 2.5); 21-H, 6.22(dd, *J*=2.5, 2.5);

22-H, 1.02(d, *J*=6.5); 23-H, 1.56(s); 21-OAc, 2.38(s); 7-OH, 6.06(d, *J*=6.0); 18-OH, 6.02(s, br); and Ar-5H, 7.29-7.38ppm (m).

^{13}C NMR:
(CH_3) 14.83, 19.40, 20.16, 20.74, and 24.64ppm; (CH_2) 38.70, and 45.43ppm; (CH) 42.42, 44.50, 49.02, 56.76, 70.15, 76.72, 127.04, 128.23, 129.03 x 2, 129.95 x 2, 131.18, 133.41, and 134.05ppm; and (C) 55.57, 63.42, 65.67, 78.45, 138.39, 170.73, 174.89, and 210.90ppm.

Mass Data:
EIMS: 523*m/e*; found: C, 69.1; H, 7.2; N, 2.6, $C_{30}H_{37}NO_7$ requires C, 68.8; H, 7.1: N, 2.7%.

References

R. L. Edwards, D. J. Maitland, and A. J. S. Whalley; Metabolites of the Higher Fungi. Part 24. Cytochalasin N, O, P, Q, and R, New Cytochalasins from the Fungus *Hypoxylon terricola* Mill.; J. Chem. Soc. Perkin Trans. I, pp. 57-65(1989).

S. Natori and I. Yahara; Cytochalasins; In Mycotoxins and Phytoalexins; R. P. Sharma, and D. K. Salunkhe (eds.); CRC Press, pp. 291-338(1991).

Common/Systematic Name

Cytochalasin O_{HYP}

(6*R* or 6*S*,7*S*,16*S*,18*R*,21*R*)-21-Acetoxy-6,7,18-trihydroxy-16,18-dimethyl-10-phenyl-[11]cytochalasa-13(*E*),19(*E*)-diene-1,17-dione

Molecular Formula/Molecular Weight

$C_{30}H_{39}NO_7$; MW = 525.27265

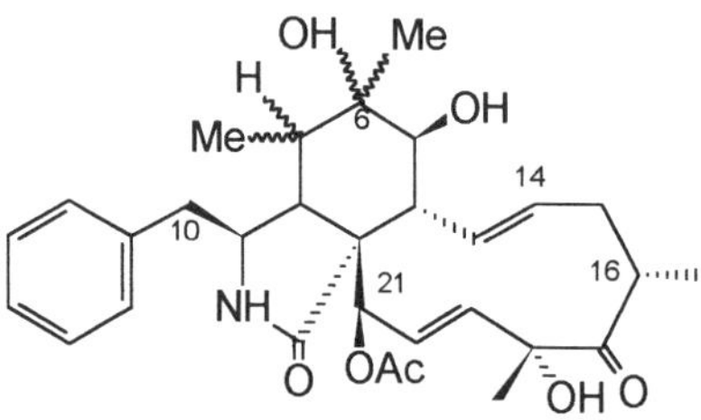

General Characteristics

Needles from toluene-methanol; mp., 258-265°C; $[\alpha]_D^{23}$ -39.3° (*c*=1.0, in MeOH).

Fungal Source

Hypoxylon terricola (habitat restricted to dead and decaying coniferous needles; only found in one location in the U.S.A. and in the Atlantic Pyrenees).

Isolation/Purification

The mycelium was extracted with chloroform; evaporation yielded a solid that was chromatographed using Merck Kieselgel PF. The sample was applied to the column in chloroform-methanol (95:5, v/v) and eluted with the same solvent to give two fractions, one containing cytochalasins C, D, and N and the other containing cytochalasin O.

Biological Activity

Marked cytostatic effects on mammalian cells in tissue culture; target protein was actin.

Spectral Data

IR:

(KBr) 3410, 1741, 1603, and 1691cm^{-1}.

^{1}H NMR:

(C_5D_5N) 2-NH, 9.25(s); 3-H, 3.98(ddd, *J*=7.6, 5.6. 4.6); 4-H, 2.43(dd, *J*=5.3, 4.6); 5-H, 2.6-2.8(m); 7-H, 3.76(d, *J*=11.5); 8-H, 3.55(dd, *J*=10.0, 11.5); 10-Ha, 2.95(dd, 13.5, 5.2); 10-Hb, 2.84(dd, *J*=13.5, 7.6); 11-H3, 1.14(d, J=6.3); 12-H3, 1.44(s); 13-H, 6.32(dd, *J*=15.3, 10.0); 14-H, 5.43(ddd, *J*=15.3, 10.7, 4.7); 15-Ha, 1.97(dd, *J*=12.3, 4.4); 15-Hb, 2.60-2.80(m); 16-H, 2.60-2.80(m); 19-H, 5.64(dd, *J*=15.9, 2.5); 20-H, 6.98(dd, *J*=15.9, 2.5); 21-H, 5.94(dd, *J*=2.5, 2.5); 22-H, 1.04(d, *J*=6.6); 23-H, 1.56(s); 21-OAc, 2.31(s); 6-OH, 5.37(s, br); 7-OH, 6.08(s, br); 18-OH, 5.99(s, br); and Ar-5H, 7.22-7.34ppm (m).

^{13}C NMR:
(CH_3) 13.55, 19.44, 20.53, 24.68, and 25.30ppm; (CH_2) 38.82 and 46.60ppm; (CH) 39.85, 42.59, 44.73, 49.97, 54. 18, 73.42, 78.77, 127.07, 127.46, 129.04 x 2, 130.09 x 2, 131.05, 133.49, and 134.59ppm; and (C) 55.52, 72.56, 78.37, 138.43, 170.36, 175.66, and 211.39ppm.

Mass Data:
EIMS: 525*m/e*; found: C, 68.7; H, 7.6; N, 2.6, $C_{30}H_{39}NO_7$ requires C, 68.5; H, 7.4: N, 2.7%.

References
R. L. Edwards, D. J. Maitland and A. J. S. Whalley; Metabolites of the Higher Fungi. Part 24. Cytochalasin N, O, P, Q, and R, New Cytochalasins from the Fungus *Hypoxylon terricola* Mill.; J. Chem. Soc. Perkin Trans. I, pp. 57-65(1989).

S. Natori and I. Yahara; Cytochalasins; In Mycotoxins and Phytoalexins; R. P. Sharma, and D. K. Salunkhe (eds.); CRC Press, pp. 291-338(1991).

Common/Systematic Name

Cytochalasin P_{HYP}

(6*S* or 6*R*,7*S*,16*S*,18*R*,21*R*)-21-Acetoxy-6,7,18-trihydroxy-16,18-dimethyl-10-phenyl-[11]cytochalasa-13(*E*),19(*E*)-diene-1,17-dione

Molecular Formula/Molecular Weight

$C_{30}H_{39}NO_7$; MW = 525.27265

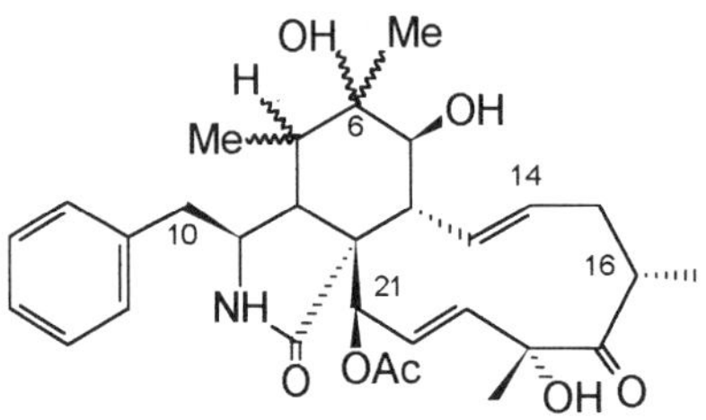

General Characteristics

Needles from acetone-light petroleum; mp., 169-173°C; $[\alpha]_D^{23}$ -35.8° (*c*=1.0, in MeOH).

Fungal Source

Hypoxylon terricola (habitat restricted to dead and decaying coniferous needles; only found in one location in the U.S.A. and in the Atlantic Pyrenees).

Isolation/Purification

The mycelia were extracted with chloroform. Evaporation yielded a solid that was chromatographed using Merck Kieselgel PF. The sample was applied to the column in chloroform-methanol (95:5, v/v) and eluted with the same solvent to give several fractions; one fraction was a viscous yellow gum. The gum was triturated with ethyl acetate, filtered and afforded a mixture containing cytochalasins C, O, and N. Evaporation of the filtrate and crystallization of the residue from acetone-light petroleum gave cytochalasin P as needles.

Biological Activity

Marked cytostatic effects on mammalian cells in tissue culture; target protein was actin.

Spectral Data

IR:

(KBr) 3425, 1747, 1700, and 1697cm^{-1}.

^{1}H NMR:

(C_5D_5N) 2NH, 9.10(s); 3-H, 4.79(ddd, *J*=8.0, 4.5, 4.0); 4-H, 2.3-2.41(m); 5-H, 2.3-2.41(m); 7-H, 4.29(dd, *J*=11.0, 3.0); 8-H, 3.26(dd, *J*=11.0, 10.3); 10-Ha,

2.60-2.85(m); 10-Hb, 3.12(dd, *J*=13.7, 3.4); 11-H, 1.39(d, J=6.9); 12-H, 1.72(s); 13-H, 6.33(dd, *J*=15.0, 9.8); 14-H, 5.47(ddd, *J*=15.0, 10.6, 4.4); 15-Ha, 2.01(dd, *J*=12.5, 4.4); 15-Hb, 2.60-2.85(m); 16-H, 2.60-2.85(m); 19-H, 5.67(dd, *J*=15.9, 2.4); 20-H, 7.06(dd, *J*=15.9, 2.8); 21-H, 5.94(dd, *J*=2.6, 2.6); 22-H, 1.06(d, J=6.8); 23-H, 1.60(s); 21-OAc, 2.43(s); 6-OH, 4.90(under HOD signal); 7-OH, 5.80(d, *J*=3.0); 18-OH, 6.01(s); and Ar-5H, 7.16-7.34ppm (m).

^{13}C NMR:

(CH_3) 13.42, 19.43, 20.63, 23.30 and 24.73ppm; (CH_2) 38.73 and 46.26; (CH) 39.22, 42.72, 47.08, 51.82, 54.62, 76.81, 79.10, 126.67, 127.17, 128.80 x 2, 129.86 x 2, 131.06, 133.66, and 134.98ppm; and (C) 55.72, 76.08, 78.32, 39.04, 170.08, 175.59, and 211.56ppm.

Mass Data:

EIMS: 525*m/e*; found: C, 68.6; H, 7.5; N, 2.7, $C_{30}H_{39}NO_7$ requires C, 68.6; H, 7.4: N, 2.7%.

References

R. L. Edwards, D. J. Maitland and A. J. S. Whalley; Metabolites of the Higher Fungi. Part 24. Cytochalasin N, O, P, Q, and R, New Cytochalasins from the Fungus *Hypoxylon terricola* Mill.; J. Chem. Soc. Perkin Trans. I, pp. 57-65(1989).

S. Natori and I. Yahara; Cytochalasins; In Mycotoxins and Phytoalexins; R. P. Sharma, and D. K. Salunkhe (eds.); CRC Press, pp. 291-338(1991).

Common/Systematic Name

Cytochalasin Q_{HYP}

(6*R*,7*S*,16*S*,18*R*,21*R*)-21-Acetoxy-6,7-epoxy-18-hydroxy-16,18-dimethyl-10-phenyl-[11]-cytochalasa-13(*E*),19(*E*)-diene-1,17-dione

Molecular Formula/Molecular Weight

$C_{30}H_{37}NO_6$; MW = 507.26209

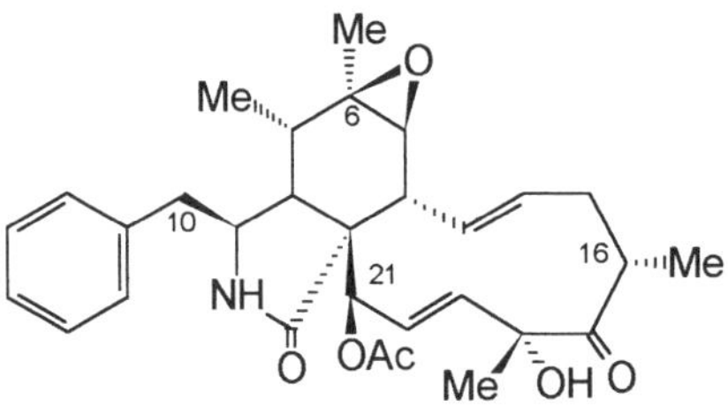

General Characteristics

Fine, silky, acetone solvated needles from acetone-light petroleum; mp., 145-147°C; $[\alpha]_D^{23}$ (solvate) -94.5° (*c*=1.0, in $CHCl_3$).

Fungal Source

Hypoxylon terricola (habitat restricted to dead and decaying coniferous needles; only found in one location in the U.S.A. and in the Atlantic Pyrenees).

Isolation/Purification

The mycelia were extracted with chloroform. Evaporation yielded a solid that was chromatographed using Merck Kieselgel PF. The sample was applied to the column in chloroform-methanol (95:5, v/v) and eluted with the same solvent to give several fractions; one fraction was a viscous yellow gum which was dissolved in ethyl acetate, filtered after 24 hours to yield a mixture containing cytochalasins C, D, O, and N. The mother liquor was evaporated and the gum was redissolved in ethyl acetate, filtered after 24 hours to give large rhombs comprising mainly cytochalasin R. The viscous filtrate containing the bulk of the cytochalasin Q was evaporated and the resulting gum dissolved in a mixture of benzene-ethyl acetate-acetic acid (50:49:1, v/v) and applied to a silica gel column eluted with the same solvent mixture; evaporation gave two fractions, one a gummy yellow foam which yielded fine, silky acetone-solvated needles of cytochalasin Q.

Biological Activity

Marked cytostatic effects on mammalian cells in tissue culture; target protein was actin.

Spectral Data

IR:

(KBr) 3440, 1745, and 17.02cm^{-1}.

^{1}H NMR:

(C_5D_5N) 2NH, 9.50(s); 3-H, 3.92(dd, *J*=6.6, 7.9); 4-H, 2.45(dd, *J*=5.7, 1.8); 5-H, 1.90-2.05(dq, *J*=7.3, 5.7); 7-H, 3.06 (d, *J*=5.8); 8-H, 2.97(dd, *J*=9.9, 5.7); 10-Ha, 2.84(dd, *J*=13.2, 7.9); 10-Hb, 3.09(dd, *J*=13.2, 6.6); 11-H3, 0.74(d, *J*=7.3); 12-H3, 1.21(s); 13-H, 6.46(dd, *J*=15.6, 10.1); 14-H, 5.46(ddd, *J*=15.6, 10.4, 5.2); 15-Ha, 1.90-2.05(m); 15-Hb, 2.64-2.77(m); 16-H, 2.64-2.77(m); 19-H, 5.62(dd, *J*=15.8, 2.4); 20-H, 6.85(dd, *J*=15.8, 2.4); 21-H, 6.24(dd, *J*=2.2, 2.4); 22-H, 1.07(d, *J*=6.2); 23-H, 1.57(s); 21-OAc, 2.38(s); 18-OH, 6.05-6.15(s, br); and Ar-5H, 7.20-7.40ppm (m).

^{13}C NMR:

(CH_3) 12.58, 19.39, 19.63, 20.58, and 24.69ppm; (CH_2) 38.30, and 46.19ppm; (CH) 37.36, 42.49, 46.03, 50.54, 54.49, 63.16, 76.64, 127.05, 128.60, 129.00 x 2, 130.10 x 2, 131.94, 132.14, and 133.03ppm; and (C) 56.11, 78.26, 138.26, 170.66, 175.47, and 210.88ppm.

Mass Data:

EIMS: 507*m/e*; found: C, 70.1; H, 7.3; N, 2.7, $C_{30}H_{37}NO_6$; requires C, 70.1; H, 7.7: N, 2.5%.

References

R. L. Edwards, D. J. Maitland and A. J. S. Whalley; Metabolites of the Higher Fungi. Part 24. Cytochalasin N, O, P, Q, and R, New Cytochalasins from the Fungus *Hypoxylon terricola* Mill.; J. Chem. Soc. Perkin Trans. I, pp. 57-65(1989).

S. Natori and I. Yahara; Cytochalasins; In Mycotoxins and Phytoalexins; R. P. Sharma, and D. K. Salunkhe (eds.); CRC Press, pp. 291-338(1991).

Common/Systematic Name

19,20-Epoxycytochalasin Q
(13*E*)-21-Acetoxy-6,7,19,20-diepoxy-18-hydroxy-16,18-dimethyl-10-phenyl-[11]cytochalasa-13-ene-1,17-dione

Molecular Formula/Molecular Weight

$C_{30}H_{37}NO_7$; MW = 523.25700

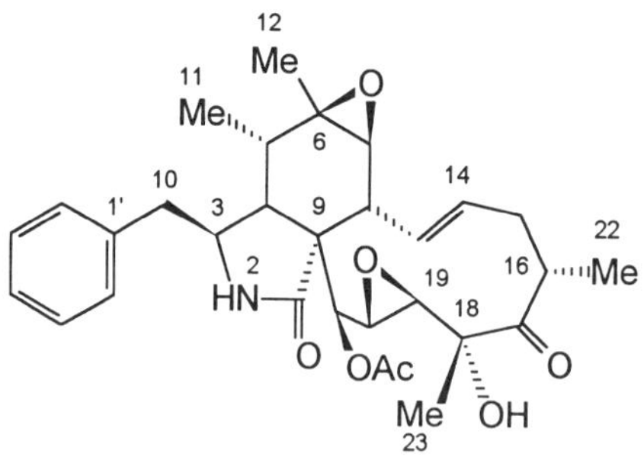

General Characteristics

Crystals; mp., 266-268°C; $[\alpha]_D^{23}$ -73° (*c*=1.1, in $CHCl_3$).

Fungal Source

Fruit bodies of *Xylaria obovata*, a wood inhabiting fungus.

Isolation/Purification

The fungus was cultured on rice; the rice cultures were extracted with chloroform. Purification was achieved by silica gel column chromatography by elution with a hexane-acetone gradient followed by preparative TLC.

Biological Activity

The cytochalasin was lethal to brine shrimp (LC_{50} 2.5μg/ml) and cytotoxic to HL-60 cells at 1μg/ml. It also inhibited mammalian cell growth with high potency as demonstrated in the Vero monkey cell growth inhibition assay (IC_{50} 0.46μg/ml).

Spectral Data

IR:

(KBr) 1220, 1370, 1450, 1690, 1740, 2970, and 3440cm^{-1}.

^{1}H NMR:

(C_5D_5N) NH, 9.58(s); 3-H, 3.92(br t, *J*=7.0; 4-H, 2.52(dd, *J*=5.8, 2.0); 5-H, 1.89(dq, *J*=7.2, 5.8); 7-H, 3.02(d, *J*=5.6); 8-H, 2.75(m); 10-H_a, 2.87(dd, *J*=13.2, 8.0); 10-H_b, 3.08(dd, *J*=13.2, 6.0); 11-H, 0.63(d, *J*=7.2); 12-H, 1.17(s); 13-H, 6.64(dd, *J*=15.2, 10.0); 14-H, 5.83(sept, *J*=15.6, 10.0, 6.0); 15-H_a, 2.00(m); 15-H_b, 2.75(m); 16-H,

3.24(m); 19-H, 3.72(d, *J*=2.0); 20-H, 4.30(dd, *J*=8.0, 2.0); 21-H, 6.18(br s); 22-H, 1.07 (d, *J*=6.8); 23-H, 1.64(s); OAc, 2.18(s); H-2', H-6', 7.40(d, *J*=6.7); H-3', H-5', 7.34(t, *J*=7.8); and H-4', 7.23ppm (d, *J*= 6.7Hz).

^{13}C NMR:

(C_5D_5N) C-1, 175.4(s); C-3, 54.9(d); C-4, 51.2(d); C-5, 37.3(d); C-6, 57.4(s); C-7, 63.1(d); C-8, 45.7(d); C-9, 55.6(s); C-10, 46.1(t); C-11, 12.4(q); C-12, 19.6(q); C-13, 132.5(d); C-14, 131.6(d); C-15, 37.9(t); C-16, 42.2(d); C-17, 216.3(s); C-18, 77.4(s); C-19, 60.8(d); C-20, 53.9(d); C-21, 73.7(d); C-22, 19.2(q); C-23, 22.7(q); C-1', 138.2(s); C-2',6', 130.2(d); C-3',5', 128.9(d); C-4', 127.1(d); $\underline{C}H_3CO$, 20.4(q); and $CH_3\underline{C}O$, 170.8ppm (s).

Mass Spectrum:

HREIMS: 523.2648(M^+, 8%, calcd for $C_{30}H_{37}NO_7$, 523.2569), 495(M^+ - CO, 17), 480, 464, 432, 338, and 91*m/e* (100),

Reference

E. Dagne, A. A. Leslie Gunatilaka, S. Asmellash, D. Abate, D. G. I. Kingston, G. A. Hofmann, and R. K. Johnson; Two New Cytotoxic Cytochalasins from *Xylaria obovata*; Tetrahedron, Vol. 50, pp. 5615-5620(1994).

Common/Systematic Name

19,20-Epoxydeacetylcytochalasin Q

(13*E*)-6,7,19,20-Diepoxy-18,21-dihydroxy-16,18-dimethyl-10-phenyl[11]cytochalasa-13-ene-1,17-dione

Molecular Formula/Molecular Weight

$C_{28}H_{35}NO_6$; MW = 481.24644

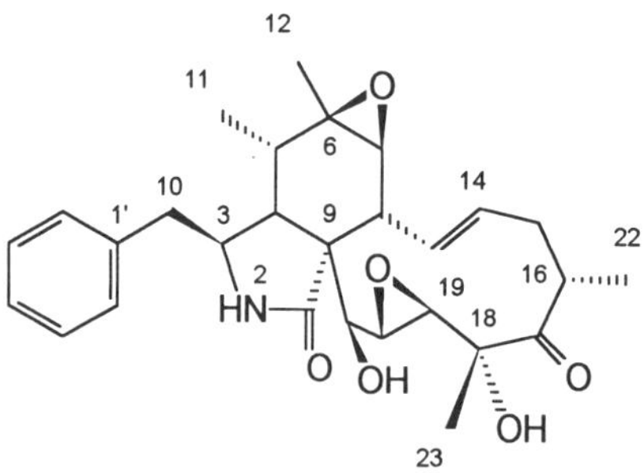

General Characteristics

Crystals; mp., 119-121° C.

Fungal Source

Fruit bodies of *Xylaria obovata*, a wood inhabiting fungus.

Isolation/Purification

The fungus was cultured on rice; the rice cultures were extracted with chloroform. Purification was achieved by silica gel column chromatography by elution with a hexane-acetone gradient followed by preparative TLC.

Biological Activity

The cytochalasin was lethal to brine shrimp (LC_{50} 2.5μg/ml) and cytotoxic to HL-60 cells at 1μg/ml. It also inhibited mammalian cell growth with high potency as demonstrated in the Vero monkey cell growth inhibition assay (IC_{50} 1.9μg/ml)

Spectral Data

IR:

(KBr) 1370, 1450, 1685, 2970, and 3400cm^{-1}.

^{1}H NMR:

(C_5D_5N) NH, 9.25(s); 3-H, 3.91(br t, *J*=7.0; 4-H, 2.10(m); 5-H, 1.96(m); 7-H, 3.09(d, *J*=5.6); 8-H, 2.75(m); 10-H_a, 2.85(dd, *J*=13.2, 7.0); 10-H_b, 3.06 (dd, J = 13.2, 5.8); 11-H, 0.82(d, *J*=7.2); 12-H, 1.20(s); 13-H, 6.66(dd, *J*=15.4, 9.6); 14-H, 5.85(sept, *J*=15.6, 10.0, 4.0); 15-H_a, 1.97(m); 15-H_b, 2.75(m); 16-H, 3.21(m); 19-H, 3.98(d, *J*=2.0); 20-H, 4.27(t, *J*=1.6); 21-H, 4.97(br s); 22-H, 1.06(d, *J*=6.4Hz); 23-H, 1.67(s); and H-4', 7.20ppm (m).

^{13}C NMR:
(C_5D_5N) C-1, 177.2(s); C-3, 54.6(d); C-4, 52.8(d); C-5, 37.5 (d); C-6, 57.6(s); C-7, 63.6(d); C-8, 44.7(d); C-9, 56.7(s); C-10, 46.2(t); C-11, 12.7(q); C-12, 19.8(q); C-13, 132.9(d); C-14, 131.1(d); C-15, 38.1(t); C-16, 42.2(d); C-17, 216.8(s); C-18, 77.7(s); C-19, 60.8(d); C-20, 56.1(d); C-21, 73.3(d); C-22, 19.2(q); C-23, 22.8(q); C-1', 138.3(s); C-2', C-6', 130.1(d); C-3', C-5', 128.9(d); and C-4', 126.1ppm (d).

Mass Spectrum:
HREIMS: 481.2464(M^+, 5%, calcd for $C_{28}H_{35}NO_6$, 481.2467), 390(M^+ - 91, 100%), and 338*m/e* (96).

Reference
E. Dagne, A. A. Leslie Gunatilaka, S. Asmellash. D. Abate, D. G. I. Kingston, G. A. Hofmann, and R. K. Johnson; Two New Cytotoxic Cytochalasins from *Xylaria obovata*; Tetrahedron, Vol. 50, pp. 5615-5620(1994).

Common/Systematic Name

Cytochalasin R_{HYP}

21-Acetoxy-6,7,13,14-diepoxy-18-hydroxy-16,18-dimethyl-10-phenyl[11]cytochalasa-19(*E*)-ene-1,17-dione

Molecular Formula/Molecular Weight

$C_{30}H_{37}NO_7$; MW = 523.25700

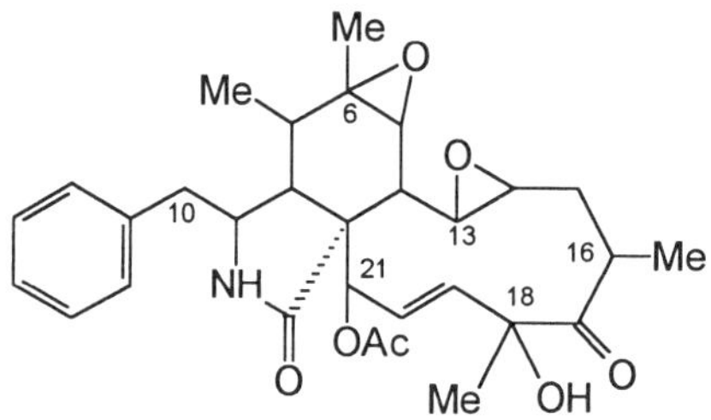

General Characteristics

Glistening solvated rods from methyl cyanide; mp., 159-167°C; $[\alpha]_D^{23}$ (ethyl acetate solvate) -73.1° (*c*=1.0, in $CHCl_3$); $[\alpha]_D^{23}$ MeCN solvate - 49.3° (*c*=1.0, in MeCN).

Fungal Source

Hypoxylon terricola (habitat restricted to dead and decaying coniferous needles; only found in one location in the U.S.A. and in the Atlantic Pyrenees).

Isolation/Purification

The mycelia were extracted with chloroform. Evaporation yielded a solid that was chromatographed using Merck Kieselgel PF. The sample was applied to the column in chloroform-methanol (95:5, v/v) and eluted with the same solvent to give several fractions; one fraction was a viscous yellow gum which was dissolved in ethyl acetate, filtered after 24 hours to yield a mixture containing cytochalasins C, D, O, and N. The mother liquor was evaporated, the gum was redissolved in ethyl acetate and filtered after 24 hours to give large rhombs comprising mainly cytochalasin R.

Biological Activity

Marked cytostatic effects on mammalian cells in tissue culture, target protein was actin.

Spectral Data

IR:

(KBr) 3460, 3315, 1750, 1712, and 1700cm^{-1}.

^{1}H NMR:

(C_5D_5N) 2NH, 9.70(s); 3-H, 3.96(ddd, *J*=7.0, 7.1, 2.0); 4-H, 2.40(dd, *J*=5.7, 2.0); 5-H, 1.85(dq, *J*=7.3, 5.7); 7-H, 3.39(d, *J*=5.7); 8-H, 1.98(dd, *J*=8.6, 5.7); 10-Ha,

2.84(dd, *J*=13.2, 7.7); 10-Hb, 3.11(dd, *J*=13.2, 6.4); 11-H3, 0.71(d, *J*=7.3); 12-H3, 1.20(s); 13-H, 4.37(dd, J=8.6, 2.0); 14-H, 3.0-3.12(m); 15-Ha, 1.95-2.09(m); 15-Hb, 2.12(dd, *J*=12.4, 1.5); 16-H, 3.0-3.12(m); 19-H, 6.22(dd, *J*=12.5, 2.6); 20-H, 7.18(dd, *J*=12.5, 2.6); 21-H, 6.25(s); 22-H, 1.03(d, *J*=6.8); 23-H, 1.62(s); 21-OAc, 2.30(s); 18-OH, 6.54(s); and Ar-5H, 7.20-7.38ppm (m).

^{13}C NMR:
(CH_3) 12.50, 19.55, 20.39, 20.48, and 24.77ppm; (CH_2) 38.79, and 46.16ppm; (CH) 37.45, 38.23, 44.78, 50.79, 54.75, 59.16, 61.79, 62.20, 76.16, 127.11, 129.03 x 2, 130.10 x 2, 130.56, and 132.22ppm; and (C) 55.20, 56.11, 78.76, 138.15, 170.61, 175.45, and 213.21ppm.

Mass Data:
EIMS: 523*m/e*; found: C, 68.1; H, 7.1; N, 5.0, $C_{30}H_{37}NO_7$; requires C, 68.1; H, 7.1: N, 5.0%.

References
R. L. Edwards, D. J. Maitland, and A. J. S. Whalley; Metabolites of the Higher Fungi. Part 24. Cytochalasin N, O, P, Q, and R, New Cytochalasins from the Fungus *Hypoxylon terricola* Mill.; J. Chem. Soc. Perkin Trans. I, pp. 57-65(1989).

S. Natori and I. Yahara; Cytochalasins; In Mycotoxins and Phytoalexins; R. P. Sharma, and D. K. Salunkhe (eds.); CRC Press, pp. 291-338(1991).

Common/Systematic Name

Cytochalasin G

(6*R*,7*S*,16*S*)-6,7-Epoxy-10-(indol-3-yl)-16-methyl[11]cytochalasa-13(*E*)-ene-1,18,21-trione

Molecular Formula/Molecular Weight

$C_{29}H_{34}N_2O_4$; MW = 474.25186

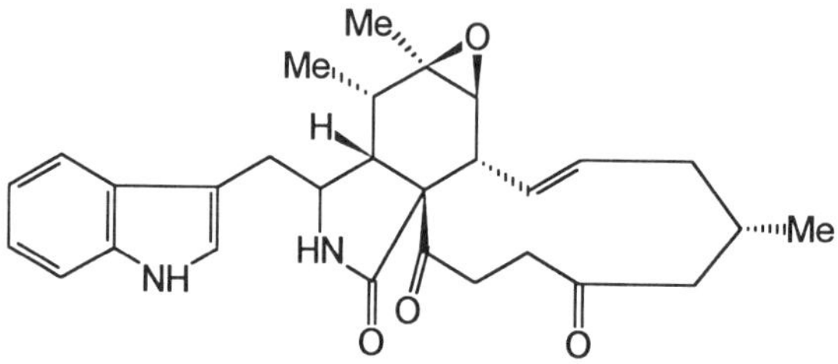

General Characteristics

Needles from methanol; mp, 255-257°C; $[\alpha]_D^{24}$ -99° (*c*=0.35, in MeOH). Colorless crystals; mp, 254-256°C; $[\alpha]_D^{20}$ -100° (*c*=0.3, in MeOH).

Fungal Source

Nigrosabulum spp. and *Pseudeurotium zonatum*.

Isolation/Purification

Extracted twice with ethyl acetate, dried over anhydrous Na_2SO_4 and evaporated to dryness. The dark brown extract was chromatographed on silica gel using increasing amounts of methanol in CH_2Cl_2. Cytochalasin G eluted in the fractions containing 1.25% methanol. Final purification was by crystallization from acetone/hexane.

Spectral Data

UV:

λ_{max}^{MeOH} 222(ε=3,250), and 283nm (535); λ_{max}^{MeOH} 198(log ε=3.95), 219(4.24), 274(3.75), 281(3.77), and 290nm (3.72).

IR:

(Nujol) 3360, 3200, 1716, 1678, 1112, 978, 878, and 740cm^{-1}; (KBr) 3360, 1710, 1675, 1610, 1450, 1420, 1380, 1355, 1290, 1230, 1100, 1080, 1050, and 970cm^{-1}.

^{1}H NMR:

$[(CD_3)_2SO]$ 0.88(d, *J*=8 3H); 0.91(d, *J*=8, 3 H); 1.15(s, 3H); 1.56(m, 2H); 1.79(dxd, *J*=6 and 10, 1H); 1.79(m, 1H); 2.59(d, *J*=6, 2H); 2.69(d, *J*=6, 1H); 2.69(m, 2H); 3.13(m, 1H); 3.72(m, 1H); 4.78(m, 1H); 6.07(dxd, *J*=6, 2H); 2.69(d, *J*=6, 1H); 3.13(m, 1H); 3.72(m, 1H); 4.78(m, 1H); 6.07(dxd, *J*=10 and 15 1H); 7.0-7.5(m, 5H); 8.32(s, 1H, exchangeable with D_2O); and 10.89ppm (s, 1H, exchangeable with D_2O).

^{13}C NMR:

($CDCl_3$) C-1, 173.2 s; C-3, 51.7 d; C-4, 49.1 d; C-5, 35.6 d; C-6, 56.9 s; C-7, 60.7 d; C-8, 47.4 d; C-9, 64.1 s; C-10, 42.1 t; C-11, 12.1 q; C-12, 22.4 q; C-13, 128.4 d; C-14, 132.8 d; C-15, 32.4 t; C-16, 27.4 d; C-17, 36.2 t; C-18, 206.5 s; C-19, 46.1 t; C-20, 46.2 t; C-21, 207.4 s; C-22, 19.0 q; C-2', 120.7 d; C-3', 108.3 s; C-4', 118.4 d; C-5',124.9 d; C-6', 118.4 d; C-7', 111.0 d; C-8', 136.0 s; and C-9', 127.6ppm s.

References

A. F. Cameron, A. Freer, B. Hesp, and C. J. Strawson; Isolation and Crystal and Molecular Structure of Cytochalasin G, an [11]cytochalasin Containing an Indole Group; Chem. Soc., Perkin Trans 2, p. 1741 (1974).

R. J. Cole and R. H. Cox; Handbook of Toxic Fungal Metabolites; Academic Press, New York, p. 272 (1981).

A. Probst and C. Tamm; 19-*O*-Acetylchaetoglobosin B and 19-*O*-Acetylchaetoglobosin D, Two New Metabolites of *Chaetomium globosum*; Helvetica Chimica Acta, Vol. 64, pp. 2056-2064(1981).

S. Natori and I. Yahara; Cytochalasins; In Mycotoxins and Phytoalexins; R. P. Sharma, and D. K. Salunkhe (eds.); CRC Press, pp. 291-338(1991).

Common/Systematic Name

Aspochalasin A

10-Isopropyl-14-methyl[11]cytochalasa-6,13-diene-1,17,18,21-tetrone

Molecular Formula/Molecular Weight

$C_{24}H_{33}NO_4$; MW = 399.24096

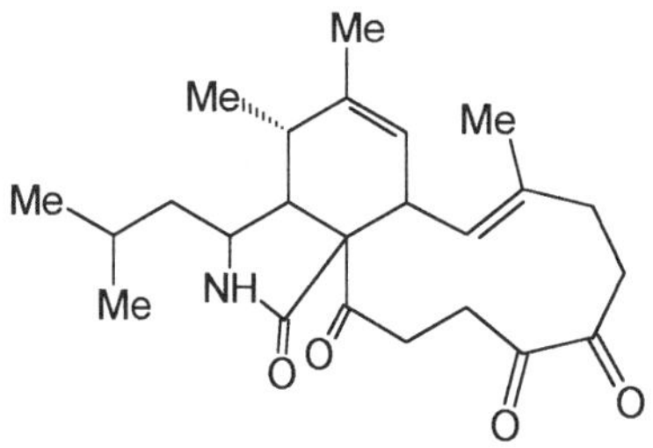

General Characteristics

Bright yellow amorphous powder; $[\alpha]_D^{25}$ -20° (c=0.27, in $CHCl_3$).

Fungal Source

Aspergillus microcysticus.

Spectral Data

UV:

λ_{max}^{EtOH} 265(log ϵ=2.61) and 410nm (log ϵ=1.09).

IR:

(KBr) 1710 and 1690cm^{-1}.

^{13}C NMR:

(25 MHZ, $CDCl_3$): 13.4(qa), 14.7(qa), 19.9(qa), 20.9(qa), 23.7(qa), 24.9(d), 31.2(2t), 35.4(d), 36.5(t), 39.0(t), 43.6 (d), 49.0(t), 51.2(d), 52.0(d), 66.7(s), 124.9(2d), 135.4(s), 140.1(s), 176.2(s), 197.3(s), 202.3(s), and 208.7ppm (s).

Mass Spectrum:

399(M^+, $C_{24}H_{33}NO_4$, 19%), 314(18), 222(100), 194(49), and 177*m/e* (30).

References

W. von Keller-Schierlein, and E. Kupfer; Stoffwechselprodukte von Mikroorganismen: Über die Aspochalasine A, B, C und D; Helvetica Chimica Acta, Vol. 62, Fasc. 5, pp. 1501-1524(1979).

S. Natori and I. Yahara; Cytochalasins; In Mycotoxins and Phytoalexins; R. P. Sharma, and D. K. Salunkhe (eds.); CRC Press, pp. 291-338(1991).

Common/Systematic Name

Aspochalasin B

(17*R*)-17-Hydroxy-10-isopropyl-14-methyl[11]cytochalasa-6,13,19-triene-1,18,21-trione

Molecular Formula/Molecular Weight

$C_{24}H_{33}NO_4$; MW = 399.24096

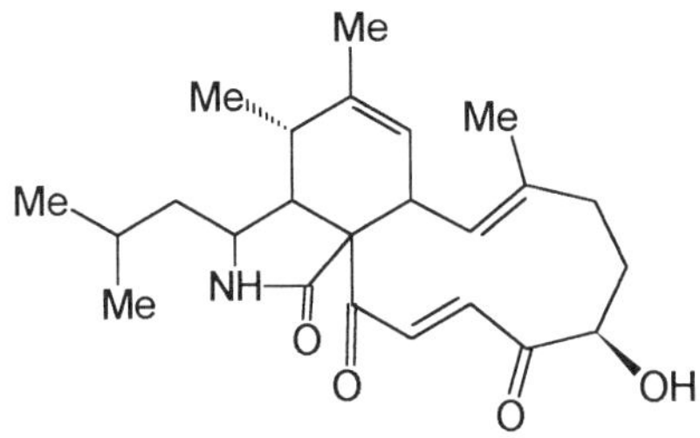

General Characteristics

Pale yellow amorphous powder; $[\alpha]_D^{25}$ -118° (*c*=1.37, in $CHCl_3$). 17-*O*-Acetyl derivative: amorphous powder; $[\alpha]_D^{25}$ -127° (*c*=1.00, in $CHCl_3$).

Fungal Source

Aspergillus microcysticus.

Biological Activity

Antibiotic.

Spectral Data

UV:

λ_{max}^{EtOH} 225nm (log ϵ=3.99).

IR:

($CHCl_3$) 3425, 3200 br, 1740, 1690, and 1620cm^{-1}.

^{1}H NMR:

($CDCl_3$) 0.88(d, *J*=6, 3H); 0.90(d, *J*=6, 3H); 1.22(br, s, 3H); 1.24(d, *J*=6, 3H); 1.25-1.7(m, 2H); 1.80(d, *J*=1, 3H); 1.85-2.05(br, 2H); 2.08(s, 3H); 2.15-3.25(br, 7H); 5.3-5.55(m, H-C(7) and H-C(17)); 6.37(br, d, *J*=11, H-C(13); 6.34 (d *J*=16, 1H); 6.58(br, s, HN); and 8.38ppm (d, *J*=16, 1H).

^{13}C NMR:

25 MHZ, ($CDCl_3$) 13.8(qa), 15.4(qa), 20.2(qa), 23.8(qa), 25.0(qa), 32.3(t), 34.8(d), 39.8(t), 41.5(d), 47.4(d), 48.3(t), 52.0(d), 69.2(s), 74.5(d), 124.5(d), 126.4(2 d), 136.0(s), 138.6(d) 141.5(s), 173.6(s), 195.3(s), and 204.9ppm (s).

Mass Data:

399(M^+, 98%), 381(33), 371(16), 356(11), 342(15), 320(11), 222(36), 220(100), 57(35), 55(81), 43(86), and 41*m/e* (48). $C_{24}H_{33}NO_4$ (399.58), found C, 72.15; H, 8.33; N 3.51% required C 71.96; H 8.38 N 3.35%.

References

W. von Keller-Schierlein, and E. Kupfer; Stoffwechselprodukte von Mikroorganismen: Über die Aspochalasine A, B, C und D; Helvetica Chimica Acta, Vol. 62, Fasc. 5, pp. 1501-1524(1979).

S. Natori and I. Yahara; Cytochalasins; In Mycotoxins and Phytoalexins; R. P. Sharma, and D. K. Salunkhe (eds.); CRC Press, pp. 291-338(1991).

Common/Systematic Name

Aspochalasin C

(17*S*,18*R*)-17,18-Dihydroxy-10-isopropyl-14-methyl[11]cytochalasa-6,13,19-triene-1,21-dione (isomeric with aspochalasin D)

Molecular Formula/Molecular Weight

$C_{24}H_{35}NO_4$; MW = 401.25661

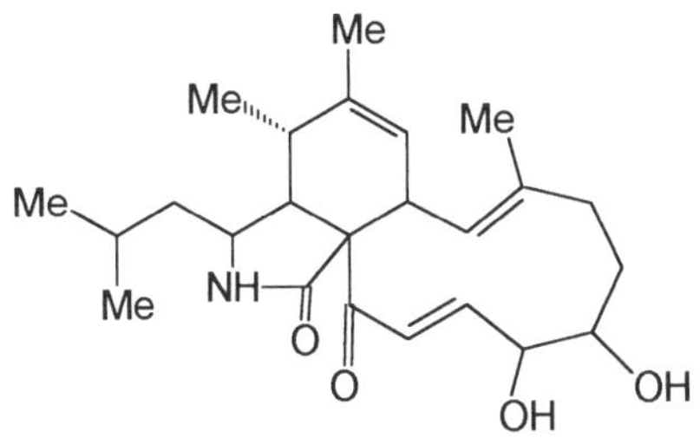

General Characteristics

Colorless, amorphous powder; $[\alpha]_D^{25}$ -86° (*c*=1.37, in $CHCl_3$). 17,18-*O*-Diacetyl derivative: Colorless crystals from benzene-hexane (3:1); mp., 113-114°C (dec.); $[\alpha]_D$ -38° (*c*=1.30, in $CHCl_3$).

Fungal Source

Aspergillus microcysticus.

Spectral Data

UV:

λ_{max}^{EtOH} 240nm (log ϵ = 3.80).

IR:

17,18-*O*-Diacetyl derivative: ($CHCl_3$) 3420, 3180 br, 1735, 1690, and 1630cm^{-1}.

^{1}H NMR:

17,18-*O*-Diacetylaspochalasin C: ($CDCl_3$): 0.95(d J=6, 6H); 1.05-2.65(m, 8 H); 1.25(d *J*=6, 3 H); 1.49(d *J*=1, 3 H); 1.80(br, s, 3 H); 2.05(s, 3 H); 2.10(s, 3H); 2.85(br, d *J*=11, 1 H); 2.9-3.3(m, 2 H); 4.82(m, H-C(17)); 5.30[t, *J*=8, H-C(18)]; 5.40(br, s 1 H); 6.02[br, d *J*=11, H-C(13)]; 6.18[dxd J_1=16, J_2=8, H-C(19)]; 7.25(br, s HN); and 7.45ppm [d *J*=16, H-C(20)].

Mass Spectrum:

401(M^+, $C_{24}H_{35}NO_4$, 10%), 383(8), 365(4), 344(1), 326(2), 262(37), 205(11), 121(100), 57(18), and 55*m/e* (50).

References

W. von Keller-Schierlein and E. Kupfer; Stoffwechselprodukte von Mikroorganismen: Über die Aspochalasine A, B, C und D; Helvetica Chimica Acta, Vol. 62, Fasc. 5, pp. 1501-1524(1979).

S. Natori and I. Yahara; Cytochalasins; In Mycotoxins and Phytoalexins; R. P. Sharma, and D. K. Salunkhe (eds.); CRC Press, pp. 291-338(1991).

Common/Systematic Name

Aspochalasin D

(17*S*,18*S*)-17,18-Dihydroxy-10-isopropyl-14-methyl[11]cytochalasa-6,13,19-triene-1,21-dione

Diastereomer of aspochalasin C (different configuration at C(17) or C(18).

Molecular Formula/Molecular Weight

$C_{24}H_{35}NO_4$; MW = 401.25661

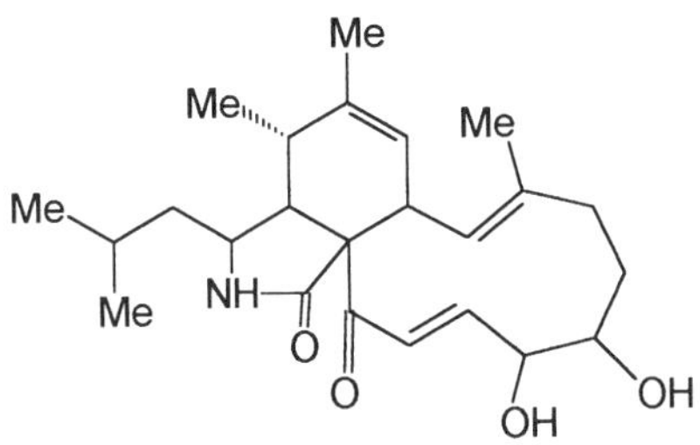

General Characteristics

Colorless needles; mp, 148 °C; $[\alpha]_D^{25}$ -81 ° (*c*=1.43, in EtOH). 17,18-*O*-Diacetyl-aspochalasin D: Amorphous colorless powder; $[\alpha]_D^{25}$ -43 ° (*c*=1.05, in $CHCl_3$).

Fungal Source

Aspergillus microcysticus.

Spectral Data

UV:

λ_{max}^{EtOH} 248nm (log ϵ = 3.92).

^{1}H NMR:

($CDCl_3$) 17,18-*O*-diacetyl derivative: 0.88(d, *J*=6, 3H); 0.90(d, *J*=6, 3H); 1.1-1.8(m, 4H); 1.26(d, *J*=7, 3H); 1.33(br, s, 3H); 1.80(br s, 3H); 1.9-3.3(m, 7H); 2.04(s. 3H); 2.13(s, 3H); 4.79[br, H-C(17)]; 5.43[br, H-C(18)]; 5,72[br, H-C(7)]; 6.10[br, d, *J*=12, H-C(13)]; 6.20[dxd J_1=17, J_2=5, H-C(19)]; 7.11(br, s, HN); and 7.35ppm [dxd J_1= 17, J_2=1.5, H-C(20)].

^{13}C NMR:

($CDCl_3$) 17,18-*O*-diacetyl derivative: 13.5(qa), 15.6(qa), 19.9(qa), 20.9(2qa), 21.2(qa), 23.6(qa), 24.7(d), 28.0(t), 35.1(d), 38.7(t), 43.5(d), 48.5(t), 48.9(d), 51.4(d), 68.4(s), 73.8(d), 78.6(d), 125.2(2d), 130.8(d), 136.3(d), 136.3(s), 140.3(s), 169.5(2s), 174.8(s), and 196.7ppm (s).

Mass Data:

401(M^+, 2%), 383(2), 365(1), 326(2), 316(16), 262(37), 220(3), 178(24), 139(55),

124(69), 121(61), 97(99), 73(80), 69(98), 60(86), 57(69), 55(80), 43(100), and 41*m/e* (96); $C_{24}H_{35}NO_4$ (401.60); found C, 71.79; H, 8.79; N, 3.49%; required C, 71.65; H, 8.84; N, 3.44%.

References

W. von Keller-Schierlein and E. Kupfer; Stoffwechselprodukte von Mikroorganismen: Über die Aspochalasine A, B, C und D; Helvetica Chimica Acta, Vol. 62, Fasc. 5, pp. 1501-1524(1979).

S. Natori and I. Yahara; Cytochalasins; In Mycotoxins and Phytoalexins; R. P. Sharma, and D. K. Salunkhe (eds.); CRC Press, pp. 291-338(1991).

Common/Systematic Name

Cytochalasin E

(6*R*,7*S*,16*S*,18*R*)-6,7-Epoxy-18-hydroxy-16,18-dimethyl-10-phenyl-21,23-dioxa-[13]cytochalasa-13(*E*),19(*E*)-diene-1,17,22-trione

Molecular Formula/Molecular Weight

$C_{28}H_{33}NO_7$; MW = 495.22570

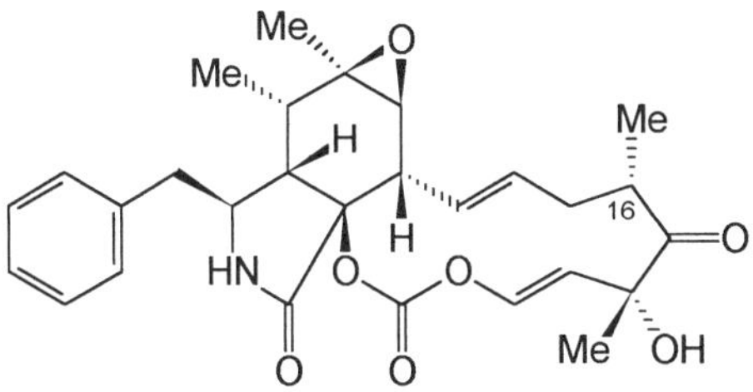

General Characteristics

Crystals from acetone-hexane; mp, 206-208 °C (dec.) $[a]_D^{25}$ -25.6° (in MeOH); mp, 210 °C (from acetone-*n*-hexane). Soluble in dichloromethane, chloroform, acetone, and methanol; sparingly soluble in water. It is unstable in chloroform solution and under acidic conditions.

Fungal Source

Rosellinia necatrix and *Aspergillus clavatus*.

Biological Activity

LD_{50} in rats; oral 9.1mg/kg, IP 2.6mg/kg. Death was due to circulatory collapse caused by massive extravascular effusion of plasma. The LD_{50} values for a single IP dose of cytochalasin E were 1-day-old rats, 0.98mg/kg; adolescent rats, 2.60mg/kg; mice, 4.60mg/kg; and guinea pigs, 0.5-1.5mg/kg. In adolescent rats dosed orally, LD_{50} was 1.3mg/kg. Histopathologic examination showed congestive degenerative changes, necrosis of liver, kidney, spleen, pancreas, and small intestine, brain edema, pulmonary hemorrhages, and injury to vascular walls. Cytochalasin E rarely produced nuclear extrusion typical of other cytochalasins; however, it produced a unique halo around the nuclei.

Spectral Data

UV:

Weak absorptions between 240 and 300nm due in part to the π-π* transition of the monosubstituted aromatic ring.

IR:

($CHCl_3$) 3410, 2970, 1762, 1720, and 1662cm^{-1}.

CD:
(MeOH) Δϵ325 O, Δϵ294 -2.6, Δϵ259 -0.58, Δϵ229 -5.14, and Δϵ218 0.

^{13}C NMR:
C-1, 168.9 s; C-3, 52.1 d; C-4, 45.6 d; C-5, 35.5 d; C-6, 56.1 s; C-7, 58.8 d; C-8, 45.9 d; C-9, 86.9 s; C-10, 42.6 t; C-11, 12.4 q; C-12, 19.8 q; C-13, 127.6 d; C-14, 131.4 d; C-15, 38.5 t; C-16, 39.6 d; C-17, 211.4 s; C-18, 76.5 s; C-19, 121.0 d; C-20, 140.5 d; C-22, 148.8 s; C-24, 19.1 q; C-25, 24.8 q; C-1', 136.1 s; C-2', C-6', 130.1 d; C-3', C-5', 127.9 d; and C-4', 126.3ppm d.

Mass Data:
495*m/e* (M^+); found; C, 67.8; H, 6.85; N, 3.0%. $C_{28}H_{33}NO_7$; requires C, 67.86; H, 6.71; N, 2.83%.

TLC Data

Adsorbent: silica gel GF_{254}; Solvent, acetone-hexane, 2:3, v/v; R_f, 0.25-0.30. Adsorbent: silica gel G-HR; Solvent, A: chloroform-acetone, 93:7, v/v. B: toluene-ethyl acetate-formic acid, 5:4:1, v/v/v. R_f, A: 0.10; B: 0.60. Detection: a dark purple fluorescent spot under UV light after spraying with 50% ethanolic H_2SO_4 and heating.

References

G. Büchi, Y. Kitaura, S. Yuan, H. E. Wright, J. Clardy, A. L. Demain, T. Glinsukon, N. Hunt, and G. N. Wogan; Structure of Cytochalasin E, a Toxic Metabolite of *Aspergillus clavatus*; J. Am. Chem. Soc., Vol. 95, p. 5423-5425(1973).

R. J. Cole and R. H. Cox; Handbook of Toxic Fungal Metabolites; Academic Press, New York, p.266 (1981).

T. Glinsukon, R. C. Shank, G. N. Wogan, and P. M. Newberne; Acute and Subacute Toxicity of Cytochalasin E in Rats; Toxicol Appl. Pharmacol., Vol. 32, p. 135-139 (1975).

S. Natori and I. Yahara; Cytochalasins; In Mycotoxins and Phytoalexins; R. P. Sharma, and D. K. Salunkhe (eds.); CRC Press, pp. 291-338(1991).

P. S. Steyn, F. R. van Heerden, and C. J. Rabie; Cytochalasins E and K, Toxic Metabolites from *Aspergillus clavatus*; J. Chem. Soc. (London), Perkin Trans I, pp. 541-544(1982).

Common/Systematic Name

Rosellichalasin

6,7-Epoxy-10-phenyl-5,6,16,18-tetramethyl-22-oxa[12]cyclochalas-13,19-diene-17,21-dione

Molecular Formula/Molecular Weight

$C_{28}H_{33}NO_5$; MW = 463.23587

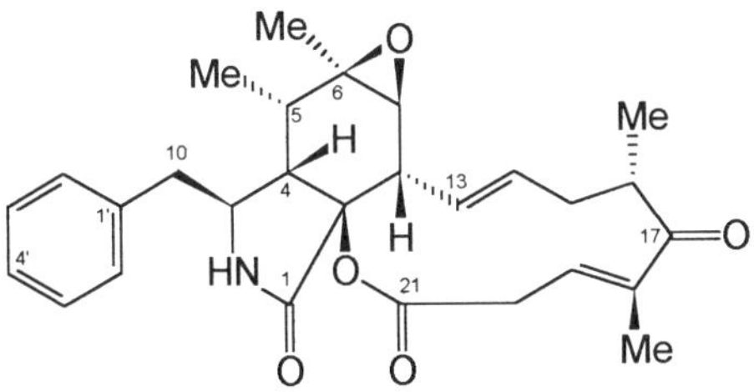

General Characteristics

Colorless needles from *n*-hexane-acetone; mp, 121-123 °C; $[\alpha]_D^{20}$ -2.7° (*c*=1.0, in MeOH).

Fungal Source

Rosellinia necatrix, a plant pathogenic fungus that causes white root rot to several economically important crops.

Isolation/Purification

Mycelial mats were extracted with acetone and purified by a silica gel column with a solvent system of benzene-acetone. Rosellichalasin eluted with benzene-acetone (9:1, v/v) and was crystallized as colorless needles from *n*-hexane-acetone.

Biological Activity

Physiological effects in mammalian cells, microorganisms and plants.

Spectral Data

UV:

λ_{max}^{EtOH} 245nm (ϵ=12,500).

IR:

(KBr) 1665 and 1640cm^{-1}.

^{1}H NMR:

($CDCl_3$) 11-H, 1.00(d, *J*=7.3 Hz); 22-H, 1.13(d, *J*=6.8Hz); 12- H, 1.23(s); 23-H, 1.83(br, s); 5-H, 2.23(dq, *J*=5.4, 7.3 Hz); 15-H, 2.03(m), 2.24(m); 16-H, 3.27(m); 10-H, 2.85(2H, d, *J*=5.4); 4-H, 2.72(dd, *J*=2.0, 5.4 Hz); 8-H, 2.86(dd, *J*=5.4, 10.3

Hz); 3-H, 3.73(m); 7-H, 2.67(d, *J*=5.4 Hz); 19-H, 6.35(br, dd, *J*=6.8, 11.0 Hz); 13-H, 5.83(ddd, 1.5, 10.3, 15.1 Hz); 3', 5'-H, 7.28(m); 2',6'-H, 7.28(m); 14-H, 5.44(ddd, 3.9, 11.2, 15.1 Hz); 20-H, 2.98(dd, 6.8, 12.1 Hz), 3.23(dd, 11.0, 12.1 Hz); and NH, 6.69ppm (br).

^{13}C NMR:

(CDCl$_3$) C-11, 12.4(q); C-22, 17.4(q); C-12, 19.6(q); C-23, 12.8(q); C-5, 36.0(d); C-15, 36.6(t); C-16, 39.8(d); C-10, 44.1(d); C-4, 48.8(d); C-8, 47.0(d); C-3, 53.9(d); C-6, 57.2(s); C-7, 60.3(d); C-18, 143.1(s); C-9, 84.7(s); C-19, 135.1(d); C-4', 125.7(d); C-13, 127.1(d); C-3',5', 128.8(dd); C-2',6', 129.6(dd); C-14, 131.8(d); C-1', 136.6(s); C-20, 39.8(t); C-21, 171.8(s); C-1, 170.1(s); and C-17, 205.4ppm (s).

Mass Spectrum:

EIMS: 463(M$^+$), 372(M$^+$ - 91), 190($C_{11}H_{12}NO_2^+$), 120($C_8H_{10}N^+$), and 91*m/e* (base peak).

References

Y. Kimura, H. Nakajima, and T. Hamasaki; Structure of Rosellichalasin, a New Metabolite Produced by *Rosellinia necatrix*; Agric. Biol. Chem., Vol. 53, pp. 1699-1701 (1989).

S. Natori and I. Yahara; Cytochalasins; In Mycotoxins and Phytoalexins; R. P. Sharma, and D. K. Salunkhe (eds.); CRC Press, pp. 291-338(1991).

Common/Systematic Name

Cytochalasin K_{ASP}

(7*S*,16*S*,18*R*)-7,8-Dihydroxy-16,18-dimethyl-10-phenyl-21,23-dioxa[13]cytochalasa-5,13(*E*),19(*E*)-triene-1,17,22-trione

The same trivial name was given to two different cytochalasins nearly simultaneously (see cytochalasin K from *Chalara microspora*).

Molecular Formula/Molecular Weight

$C_{28}H_{33}NO_7$; MW = 495.22570

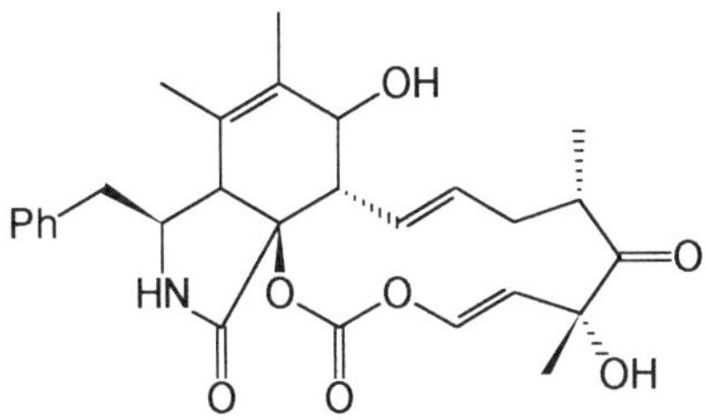

General Characteristics

Cytochalasin K crystallized from hexane-acetone as white crystals; mp, 246-248°C.

Fungal Source

Aspergillus clavatus (MRC 1181). The isolate was obtained from a sample of industrial sorghum malt.

Isolation/Purification

The culture material was extracted with chloroform-methanol (1:1, v:v). The crude extract was partitioned between 90% methanol and hexane, and the methanol extract was evaporated to dryness. The residue was partitioned between chloroform and water and the chloroform extract evaporated to dryness to give a toxic gum. This toxic material was purified by chromatography on silica gel using benzene-acetone (4:1, v:v) to remove lipids. The remaining material was purified by column chromatography on silica gel under pressure (150 kPa) using chloroform-methanol (95:5, v:v) as eluant to give cytochalasins E and K.

Biological Activity

Acutely toxic to ducklings and rats.

Spectral Data

UV:

λ_{max}^{MeOH} 263sh, 257, and 252nm sh (log ϵ=3.44, 3.64, and 3.58).

IR:
(KBr) 3440, 2920, 1765, 1720, and 1662cm^{-1}.

^{1}H NMR:
($CDCl_3$) 7.2-7.04(m, Ph), 6.57(d, *J*=13 Hz, H-20), 6.21-6.05(m, H-13), 5.70(s, NH), 5.67(d, *J*=13Hz, H-19), 5.47-5.20(m, H-14), 4.39(s, OH), 3.87-3.76(m, H-4, H-7), 3.38(t, *J*=8Hz, H-3), 3.0-2.50(m, H-8, H-10, H-15a, H-16), 2.08(m, H-15b), 1.61(s, Me), 1.47(s, Me), 1.44(s, Me), and 1.10ppm (d, *J*=6 Hz, 16-Me).

Mass Data:
495*m/e* (M^+); found: C, 67.2; H, 6.45; N, 2.65%. $C_{28}H_{33}NO_7$; requires C, 67.86; H, 6.71; N, 2.83%.

References

S. Natori and I. Yahara; Cytochalasins; In Mycotoxins and Phytoalexins; R. P. Sharma, and D. K. Salunkhe (eds.); CRC Press, pp. 291-338(1991).

P. S. Steyn, F. R. van Heerden, and C. J. Rabie; Cytochalasins E and K, Toxic Metabolites from *Aspergillus clavatus*; J. Chem. Soc. (London), Perkin Trans. I, pp. 541-544(1982).

Common/Systematic Name

Deoxaphomin
(7*S*,16*R*,20*R*)-7,20-Dihydroxy-5,16-dimethyl-10-phenyl[13]cytochalasa-6(12),13(*E*),21(*E*)-triene-1,23-dione

Molecular Formula/Molecular Weight

$C_{29}H_{37}NO_4$; MW = 463.27226

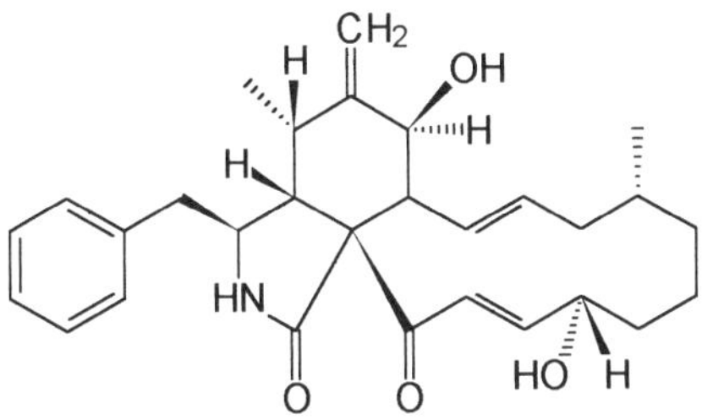

General Characteristics

Amorphous solid; $[\alpha]_D$ -50.8° (*c*=0.178, in $CHCl_3$).

Fungal Source

Phoma exigua var. *exigua* and *Ascochyta heteromorpha.*

Biological Activity

Biological activity comparable to phomin: cytostatic activity (*in vitro*) of P-185 mastocyte cells, ED_{50} 0.29mg/liter; in target cell destruction test treatments of 10, 1, and 0.1μg/liter gave inhibition of 100, 76, and 9%, respectively.

Spectral Data

UV:
λ_{max}^{MeOH} 217(ε=14,100) and 234nm (8,700).

IR:
(CH_2Cl_2) 3590, 3540, 3410, 3060, 3020, 1710, 1670, 1622, 1600, 1490, and 1020cm^{-1}.

^{1}H NMR:
H-2, 6.36; H-3, 2.81; H-4, 3.15; H-5, 3.44; H-7, 3.97; H-8, 2.50; H-10, 2.60; H-11, 0.94; H-12, 5.09, 5.29; H-13, 6.18; H-14, 5.40; H-15-19, 1.0-2.0; H-20, 4.20; H-21, 6.77; H-22, 7.20; H-24, 0.98; H-2'-6', 7.20; and OH, 3.10, 2.35ppm.
LREIMS: 463(8%), 445(15), 372(30), 354(20), 174(18), and 91*m/e* (100).

References

M. Binder and Ch. Tamm; Deoxaphomin, des erst [13]-Cytochalasin, ein möglicher biogenetischer VorLäufer der 24-oxa-[14]-cytochalasane; Helv. Chim. Acta, Vol. 56, p. 966 (1973).

R. Capasso, A. Evidente, G. Ramdazzo, A. Ritieni, A. Bottalico, M. Vurro, and A.Logrieco; Isolation of Cytochalasins A and B from *Ascochyta heteromorpha*; J. Nat., Prod., Vol. 50, p. 989 (1987).

R. Capasso, A. Evidente, A. Ritiewi, G. Ramdazzo, M. Vurro, and A. Bottalico; Ascochalasin, a New Cytochalasin from *Ascochyta heteromorpha*; J. Nat., Prod., Vol. 51, p. 567-571(1988).

S. Natori and I. Yahara; Cytochalasins; In Mycotoxins and Phytoalexins; R. P. Sharma, and D. K. Salunkhe (eds.); CRC Press, pp. 291-338(1991).

Common/Systematic Name

Proxiphomin

(16*R*)-16-Methyl-10-phenyl[13]cytochalasa-6(7),13(*E*),21(*E*)-triene-1,23-dione

Molecular Formula/Molecular Weight

$C_{29}H_{37}NO_2$; MW = 431.28243

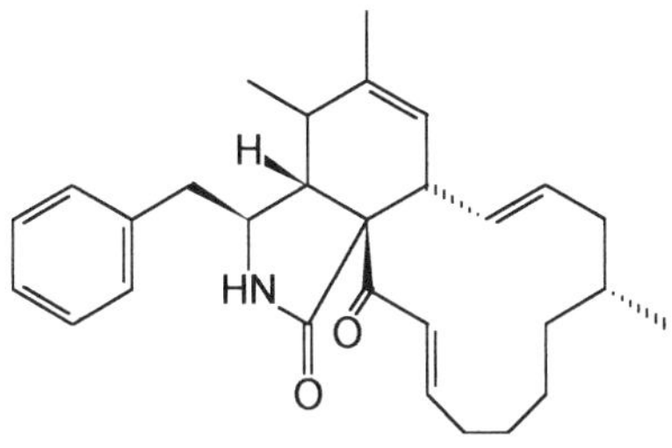

General Characteristics

Amorphous; $[\alpha]_D^{24}$ -140° (*c*=0.156, in $CHCl_3$).

Fungal Source

Phoma exigua var. *exigua*.

Spectral Data

UV:

λ_{max}^{EtOH} 206(ε=22,900), 217(12,300), and 243nm (10,700).

IR:

(CCl_4) 3420, 3200, 3080, 3060, 3020, 1700, 1670, 1610, and 1490cm^{-1}.

^{1}H NMR:

H-2, 5.84; H-3, 3.24; H-4, 3.24; H-7, 5.44; H-10, 2.52, 2.85; H-11, 1.22; H-12, 1.80; H-13, 6.30; H-14, 5.24; H-15-18, 1.0-3.0; H-21, 6.80; H-22, 7.26; H-24, 0.95; and H-2'-6',7.26ppm. Proxiphomin[5,6,16-Trimethyl-10-phenyl[13]cytochalasa-6(7),13,21-trien-1,23-dione].

References

M. Binder and Ch. Tamm; Proxiphomin und Protophomin, zwei neue cytochalasane; Helv. Chim. Acta, Vol. 56, p. 2387 (1973).

S. Natori and I. Yahara; Cytochalasins; In Mycotoxins and Phytoalexins; R. P. Sharma, and D. K. Salunkhe (eds.); CRC Press, pp. 291-338(1991).

Common/Systematic Name

Protophomin

(16*R*)-16-Methyl-10-phenyl[13]cytochalasa-5(6),13(*E*),21(*E*)-triene-1,7,23-trione

Molecular Formula/Molecular Weight

$C_{29}H_{35}NO_3$; MW = 447.27734

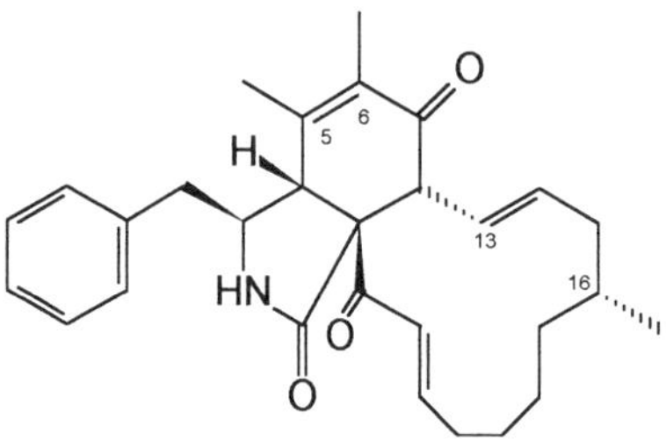

General Characteristics

Crystals from acetone; mp, 252-256°C; $[\alpha]_D^{24}$ -112° (*c*=0.42, in $CHCl_3$).

Fungal Source

Phoma spp.

Spectral Data

UV:

λ_{max}^{EtOH} 207(14,100) and 245nm (13,200).

IR:

(KBr) 3600-3200, 1700, 1680, 1660, 1610, and 1490cm^{-1}.

^{1}H NMR:

H-2, 6.53; H-3, 3.50; H-4, 3.71; H-8, 3.13; H-10, 2.53, 2.70; H-11, 1.53; H-12, 1.70; H-13, 6.24; H-14, 5.09; H-15-19, 1.0-3.0; H-21, 7.07; H-22, 6.73; H-24, 0.84; and H-2'-6', 7.24ppm.

References

M. Binder and Ch. Tamm; Proxiphomin und Protophomin, zwei neue cytochalasane; Helv. Chim. Acta, Vol. 56, p. 2387 (1973).

S. Natori and I. Yahara; Cytochalasins; In Mycotoxins and Phytoalexins; R. P. Sharma, and D. K. Salunkhe (eds.); CRC Press, pp. 291-338(1991).

Common/Systematic Name

Ascochalasin

(7*S*,16*R*,20*R*)-7,20-Dihydroxy-16-methyl-10-phenyl[13]cytochalasa-6(12),13(*E*)-diene-1,23-dione

Molecular Formula/Molecular Weight

$C_{29}H_{39}NO_4$; MW = 465.28791

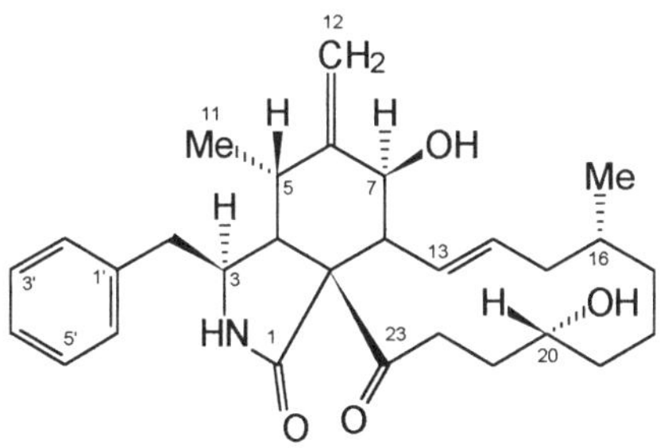

General Characteristics

Ascochalasin was an amorphous solid.

Fungal Source

Ascochyta heteromorpha was isolated in 1985 from oleander (*Nerium oleander*) grown in a nursery near Bari, and deposited in the fungus collection of the Istituto Tossine e Micotossine da Parassiti Vegetali del CNR, Bari, Italy.

Isolation/Purification

The culture filtrates were lyophilized, resuspended in distilled H_2O and extracted with chloroform. The organic extracts were combined, dried (Na_2SO_4) and evaporated under reduced pressure. The residue was chromatographed on a SiO_2 column eluted with chloroform - isopropyl alcohol (9:1, v/v). The first fraction yielded crude cytochalasin A; the successive eluate contained small amounts of cytochalasin A, cytochalasin B and a mixture of products. This mixture was further purified on SiO_2 column eluted with chloroform- isopropyl alcohol (93:7, v/v). Crude cytochalasin B was obtained and a fraction consisting of small amounts of cytochalasin B and a mixture of two products with lower R_f than B. The latter was further purified on SiO_2 plates with chloroform-isopropyl alcohol (93:7, v/v) affording crude cytochalasin B and a crude mixture of two products. The mixture was purified on reversed-phase plates (CH_3CN-H_2O, 6:4, v/v), giving pure ascochalasin and deoxaphomin.

Spectral Data

UV:

λ_{max} <220nm.

IR:

3580-3500, 3400, 1715, and 1605cm^{-1}.

^{1}H NMR:

H-3, 3.30(ddd, $J_{3,4}$=3.3Hz, $J_{3,10}$=5.5Hz, $J_{3,10'}$=3.3Hz); H-4, 3.14(dd, $J_{4,5}$=5.9Hz); H-5, 2.88(dq, $J_{5,11}$=6.6Hz); H-7, 3.94(d, $J_{7,8}$=10.3Hz); H-8, 2.48(dd, $J_{8,13}$=9.6Hz); H-10, 2.74(dd, $J_{10,10'}$=13.6Hz); H-10', 2.50(dd); 3H-11, 1.06(d; H-12, 5.32, brs); H-12', 5.12(brs); H-13, 6.20(ddd, $J_{13,14}$=15.4Hz, $J_{13,15}$=1.8Hz); H-14, 5.42(ddd, $J_{14,15}$=9.6Hz, $J_{14,15'}$=3.3Hz); H-15, 2.15(ddd, $J_{15,15'}$=12.3Hz); 2H-17, 0.85-2.00; H-20, 3.30(m); H-21, 0.85-2.00; H-22, 0.85-2.00; Me-C-16, 0.94; and H-3',5', 7.20ppm.

^{13}C NMR:

C-1, 164.1, s; C-3, 53.2, d; C-4, 45.8, d; C-5, 31.9, d; C-6, 143.9, s; C-7, 70.6, d; C-8, 50.7, d; C-9, 65.7, s; C-10, 44.3, t; C-11, 13.6, q; C-12, 114.1, t; C-13, 127.4, d; C-14, 137.4, d; C-15, 29.6, d; C-16, 33.8, d; C-17,34.7, t; C-18, 25.2, t; C-19, 41.5, t; C-20, 70.3, d; C-21,39.2, t; C-22, 29.6, t; C-23, 191.6, s; 16Me, 22.2, q; C-1', 129.3, s; C-2', 129.1, d; C-3', 128.9, d; C-4', 127.0, d; C-5', 128.9, d; and C-6', 129.1ppm, d.

Mass Spectrum:

HREIMS: 465.2873 (M^+); calcd for $C_{29}H_{39}NO_4$ (465.2869). Other significant peaks were detected at 463.2715 ($C_{29}H_{37}NO_4$), likely formed by loss of H_2 in the source from the molecular ion (465.2873); 372.2191($C_{22}H_{30}NO_4$), and 354.2075($C_{22}H_{28}NO_4$) originated from the ion at 463.2715 by loss of a benzyl group and H_2O, respectively; the ion at *m/z* 270.1496($C_{17}H_{20}NO_2$) arose from the fragment at 354.2075 by losses of H_2O and a cyclopentadienyl moiety. This fragmentation pattern was coincident with that of deoxaphomin except for the loss of two hydrogens.

References

R. Capasso, A. Evidente, A. Ritieni, G. Randazzo, M. Vurro, and A. Bottalico; Ascochalasin, A New Cytochalasin from *Ascochyta heteromorpha*; J. Nat. Prod., Vol. 51, pp. 567-571(1988).

S. Natori and I. Yahara; Cytochalasins; In Mycotoxins and Phytoalexins; R. P. Sharma, and D. K. Salunkhe (eds.); CRC Press, pp. 291-338(1991).

Common/Systematic Name

Cytochalasin K_{CHA}

(6*R*,7*S*,16*S*,19*S*)-19-Acetoxy-6,7-epoxy-16,18-dimethyl-10-phenyl[13]cytochalasa-13(*E*),17(*E*),21(*E*)-triene-1,20,23-trione

The same trivial name was given to two different cytochalasins nearly simultaneously.

Molecular Formula/Molecular Weight

$C_{32}H_{37}NO_6$; MW = 531.26209

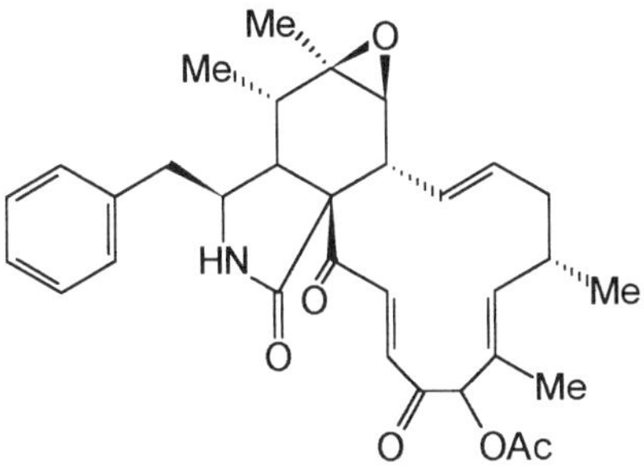

General Characteristics

Cytochalasin K was amorphous; $[\alpha]_D^{25}$ -177° (EtOH).

Fungal Source

Chalara microspora.

Isolation/Purification

Extracted with EtOAc and isolated using reversed-phase chromatography.

Biological Activity

Biological activity not reported but assumed to be similar to the other cytochalasins.

Spectral Data

UV:

$\lambda_{max}^{Abs.\ EtOH}$ 232nm (log ϵ=11,300).

IR:

(KBr) 3380(OH), 1750, and 1700cm^{-1} (broad, C=O).

^{1}H NMR:

($CDCl_3$) NH, 5.85; H-3, 3.66($J_{3\text{-}10a}$=5.5, $J_{3\text{-}10b}$=8.0, $J_{3\text{-}4}$=2.5Hz); H-4, 2.99($J_{4\text{-}5}$=5.5); H-5, 1.83($J_{5\text{-}11}$=6.5); H-7, 2.83($J_{7\text{-}8}$=5.0); H-8, 2.21($J_{8\text{-}13}$=10.0); H-10a, 2.71($J_{10a\text{-}10b}$=13.5); H-10b, 2.53; 3H-11, 1.03; 3H-12, 1.28; H-13, 6.16($J_{13\text{-}14}$=15.5); H-14, 5.27($J_{14\text{-}15a}$=10.2, $J_{14\text{-}15b}$=3.5); H-15a, 2.07($J_{15a\text{-}15b}$=13.5); H-15b, 2.32; H-16,

2.5($J_{16\text{-}16Me}$=7.3, $J_{16\text{-}17}$=9.0); H-17, 5.73; H-19, 5.94; H-21, 7.66($J_{21\text{-}22}$=15.5); H-22, 6.71; 16CH_3, 1.09; 18CH_3, 1.50; -$OOCCH_3$, 2.18; and H-2', H-3' and H-4', 7.1-7.4Hz.

^{13}C NMR:

($CDCl_3$) C-1, 172.9; C-3, 53.7; C-4, 48.0a; C-5, 32.3b; C-6, 58.0; C-7, 62.2; C-8, 46.4a; C-9, 63.0; C-10, 44.3; C-11, 13.1c; C-12, 19.8d; C-13, 128.1e; C-14, 134.1f; C-15, 41.2; C-16, 36.2b; C-17, 133.6f; C-18, 128.1e; C-19, 83.3; C-20, 194.59; C-21, 142.4; C-22, 134.9f; C-23, 196.99; 16-CH_3, 11.5c; 18-CH_3, 20.8d; -$OOCCH_3$, 169.8; -$OOCCH_3$, 20.8d; C-1', 136.2; C-2', 129.4; C-3', 128.9; and C-4', 127.1ppm e.

(a-f: May be interchanged.).

Mass Spectrum:

HRMS: 531.2660*m/e*, $C_{32}H_{37}NO_6$; requires 531.2621.

References

T. Fex; Structures of Cytochalasin K, L and M, Isolated from *Chalara microspora*; Tet. Lett., Vol. 22, pp. 2703-2706(1981).

S. Natori and I. Yahara; Cytochalasins; In Mycotoxins and Phytoalexins; R. P. Sharma, and D. K. Salunkhe (eds.); CRC Press, pp. 291-338(1991).

4

Aflavinines and Related Indoles

Aflavinine
Dihydroxyaflavinine (20,25-Dihydroxyaflavinine)
20-Hydroxyaflavinine
24,25-Dehydro-10,11-dihydro-20-hydroxyaflavinine
10,11-Dihydro-11,12-dihydro-20-hydroxyaflavinine
14-*epi*-14-Hydroxy-10,23-dihydro-24,25-dehydroaflavinine
10,23-Dihydro-24,25-dehydroaflavinine
10,23-Dihydro-24,25-dehydro-21-oxoaflavinine
Aflavazole

Common/Systematic Name
Aflavinine

Molecular Formula/Molecular Weight
$C_{28}H_{39}NO$; MW = 405.30317

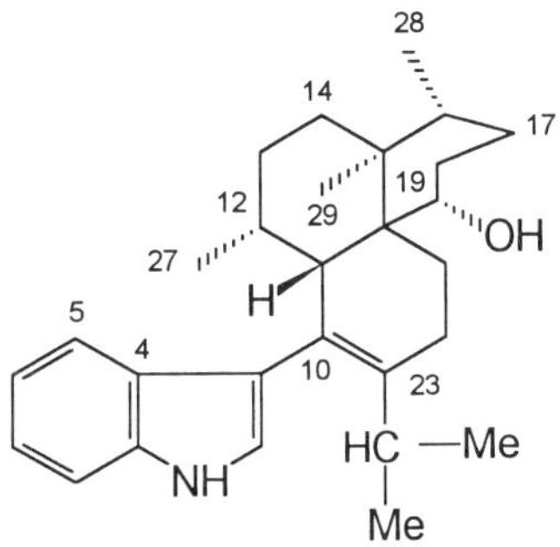

General Characteristics
Aflavinine was obtained as colorless needles from EtOAc; mp., 102-104°C; $[\alpha]_D$ +24.9° (*c*=0.98, in $CHCl_3$).

Fungal Source
Aspergillus flavus and *A. tubingensis.*

Isolation/Purification
Extracted with $CHCl_3$; chromatographed on silica gel with $CHCl_3$-cyclohexane (1:9, v/v) as eluant.

Biological Activity
Antiinsectan activity.

Spectral Data

UV:
λ_{max}^{MeOH} 291(ϵ=2710), 283(3010), and 225nm (18,700).

^{1}H NMR:
($CDCl_3$) H-1, 8.02(br, s); H-2, 6.88(d, *J*=2.2); H-5, 7.42(br d, *J*=7.8); H-6, 7.08(dd, *J*=7.1, 7.8); H-7, 7.17(dd, *J*=7.1, 8.1); H-8, 7.36(br, d, *J*=8.1); H-11, 2.43(br, d, *J*=5.1); H-12, 1.96(m); H-13, 1.14(m), 1.64(m); H-14, 1.18(m), 1.55(m); H-16, 2.03(m); H-17, 1.23(m), 1.69(m); H-18, 1.75(m), 2.06(m); H-19, 4.46(br, s); H-21, 1.73(m), 1.85(m); H-22, 2.10(m), 2.22(m); H-24, (septet, *J*= 7.0); H-25, 0.82(d, *J*=7.1); H-26, 0.96(d, *J*=6.8); H-27, 1.08(d, *J*=7.1); H-28, 0.75(d, *J*=6.8); and H-29, 0.98ppm (s).

^{13}C NMR:

($CDCl_3$) C-2, 121.2; C-3, 118.6; C-4, 127.6; C-5, 119.6; C-6, 118.6; C-7, 121.8; C-8, 111.0; C-9, 135.9; C-10, 125.5; C-11, 43.7; C-12, 31.3; C-13, 25.7; C-14, 27.6; C-15, 38.5; C-16, 29.1; C-17,25.4; C-18, 21.8; C-19, 71.1; C-20, 42.4; C-21, 30.1; C-22, 20.5; C-23, 141.0; C-24, 31.0; C-25, 21.9; C-26, 20.8; C-27, 18.1; C-28, 15.7; and C-29, 18.1ppm.

References

R. T. Gallagher, T. McCabe, K. Hirotsu, and J. Clardy; Aflavinine, a Novel Indole-mevalonate Metabolite from Tremorgen-producing *Aspergillus flavus* Species; Tet. Lett., Vol. 21, pp. 243-246(1980).

M. R. TePaske, J. B. Gloer, D. T. Wicklow, and P. F. Dowd; Three New Aflavinines from The Sclerotia of *Aspergillus tubingensis*; Tetrahedron, Vol. 45, pp. 4961-4968(1989).

Common/Systematic Name

Dihydroxyaflavinine; 20,25-Dihydroxyaflavinine

Molecular Formula/Molecular Weight

$C_{28}H_{39}NO_3$; MW = 437.29299

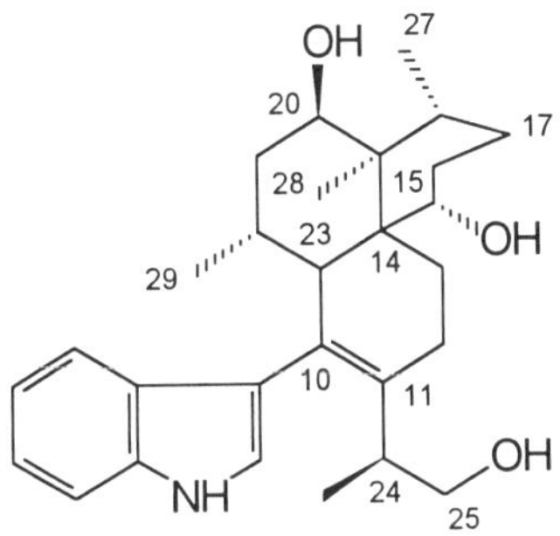

General Characteristics

Crystals suitable for X-ray diffraction experiments formed from methanol with symmetry $P2_1$ with a = 9.448; colorless plates from ethyl acetate; mp., 254-256°C; $[\alpha]_D$ +22.9° (c=0.50, in MeOH).

Fungal Source

Aspergillus flavus (NRRL 3251) and *A. flavus* (NRRL 6541).

Isolation/Purification

The cultures were extracted with hot chloroform; the crude chloroform extract was chromatographed on a silica gel column eluted with benzene, ethyl ether, ethyl acetate, and acetone. Dihydroxyaflavinine crystallized from the ethyl acetate fraction as colorless plates. Hexane and $CHCl_3$ extracts of milled sclerotia were subjected to reversed phase flash chromatography followed by reversed-phase HPLC [5-μm C_{18} column, MeOH-H_2O (70:30, v/v), 2.0mL/min, monitored at 215nm] to afford 20,25-dihydroxyaflavinine, 20-hydroxyaflavinine, 24,25-dehydro-10,11-dihydro-20-hydroxyaflavinine, and 10,11-dihydro-11,12-dehydro-20-hydroxyaflavinine. Retention time for 20,25-dihydroxyaflavinine, 14.4min.

Biological Activity

Antiinsectan but not tremorgenic. Antifeeding activity against *Carpophilus hemiptaerus*.

Spectral Data

UV:

λ_{max}^{MeOH} 225(ε=31,200), 282-284(7,400), and 290nm (6,000), was typical of a 3-substituted indole chromophore.

IR:

The IR spectrum showed absorptions indicating the presence of OH and indole groups (3250, 3450, and 1035cm^{-1}), *gem*-dimethyl groups (doublet 1370, 1380cm^{-1}), and four adjacent aromatic hydrogens (745cm^{-1}).

^{1}H NMR:

The 100-MHZ ^{1}H NMR spectrum showed three doublets (*J*=7Hz) at 0.83, 0.97, and 1.15ppm and a singlet at 1.22ppm for the four methyl groups. In addition to multiplets at 1.2-2.7 and 3.2-4.0ppm, other peaks were observed at 4.3(br s), 6.7-7.2(indole ring protons), and 8.9ppm(N-H).

H-2, 6.91(s); H-5, 7.44(br d, *J*=7.8); H-6, 7.03(dd, *J*=7.8, 6.4); H-7, 7.14(dd, *J*=8.0, 6.4); H-8, 7.40(br d, *J*=8.0); H-12, 2.34(m); 2.16(m); H-13, 2.02(m); 1.75(m); H-15, 4.54(br s); H-16, 2.11(m); 1.78(m); H-17, 1.86(m); 1.09(m); H-18, 2.09(m); H-20, 3.94(dd, *J*=10.0, 2.0); H-21, 1.91(m); 1.42(dd, *J*=12, 2); H-22, 2.21(m); H-23, 2.56(br d, *J*=6.0); H-24, 2.61(br q, *J*=7.0); H-25, 3.51(dd, *J*=11, 7); H-26, 0.81(d, *J*=7.0); H-27, 0.95(d, *J*=7.0); H-28, 1.19(s); and H-29, 1.15ppm (d, *J*=8.0).

^{13}C NMR:

The ^{13}C NMR spectrum showed 10 peaks for the sp^{2} carbons at 137.0(s), 135.8(s), 127.8(s), 126.9(s), 122.1(d), 120.6(d), 118.8(d), 118.3(d), 116.5(s), and 111.1ppm (d).

The hydroxy-bearing carbons appear at 70.5(d), 68.9(d), and 65.7ppm (t). The remainder of the aliphatic carbons have absorptions at 44.2(s), 43.1(s), 38.9, 35.1(t), 31.1(d), 30.3(t), 29.6(d), 27.3(t), 21.8(t), 21.5(t), 19.4(q), 19.2(q), 15.4(q), and 13.1ppm (q). (CD_3OD): 138.5(s), 137.7(s), 129.9(s), 128.4(s), 123.2(d), 122.2(d), 120.0(d), 119.6(d), 118.0(s), 112.2(d), 72.6(d), 71.0(d), 67.3(t), 49.9(d), 45.9(s), 44.7(s), 40.4(d), 35.9(t), 32.5(d), 31.3(t), 31.2(d), 28.6(t), 23.1(t), 22.8(t), 20.1(q), 19.6(q), 15.6(q), and 13.6ppm (q).

Mass Spectrum:

The high-resolution mass spectrum gave a molecular ion peak at 437.2909*m/e* corresponding to a molecular formula of $C_{28}H_{39}NO_3$ (calcd 437.29297*m/e*). In addition to the molecular ion peak in the low-resolution mass spectrum, peaks were observed at 419(M-H_2O), 401(M-2H_2O), 338, and 130*m/e*. EIMS: 437(M^+, rel. int. 12.5%), 419(3.5), 328(3.0), 302(5.4), 288(5.4), 260(18), 234(31), 218(44), 194(47), 180(45), 167(49), 154(30), 144(40), 130(100), and 117(85); HREIMS: obsd 437.2931; calcd for $C_{28}H_{39}NO_3$ 437.2936.

TLC Data

Purified dihydroxyaflavinine was a reddish-purple spot on silica gel 60 F_{254} at R_f=0.44 [toluene-ethyl acetate-formic acid (5:4:1, v/v/v)].

References

R. J. Cole, J. W. Dorner, J. P. Springer, and R. H. Cox; Indole Metabolites from a Strain of *Aspergillus flavus*; J. Agric. & Food Chem., Vol. 29, pp. 293-295(1981).

J. B. Gloer, M. R. TePaske, J. S. Sima, D. T. Wicklow, and P. F. Dowd; Antiinsectan Aflavinine Derivatives from the Sclerotia of *Aspergillus flavus*; J. Organ. Chem., Vol. 53., pp. 5457-5460(1988).

Common/Systematic Name

20-Hydroxyaflavinine

Molecular Formula/Molecular Weight

$C_{28}H_{39}NO_2$; MW = 421.29808

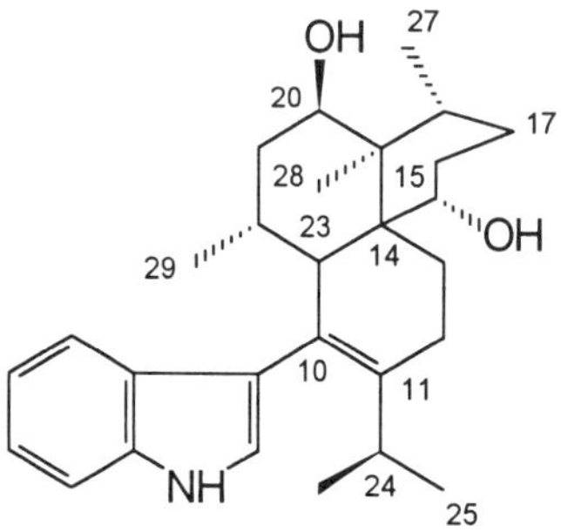

General Characteristics

Melting point 174-176°C dec; $[\alpha]_D$ +23.8° (*c*=0.56, in MeOH).

Fungal Source

Aspergillus flavus (NRRL 6541).

Isolation/Purification

Hexane and $CHCl_3$ extracts of milled sclerotia were subjected to reversed-phase flash chromatography followed by reversed-phase HPLC [5-μm C_{18} column, MeOH-H_2O (70:30, v/v), 2.0mL/min, monitored at 215nm] to afford 20,25-dihydroxyaflavinine, 20-hydroxyaflavinine, 24,25-dehydro-10,11-dihydro-20-hydroxyaflavinine, and 10,11-dihydro-11,12-dehydro-20-hydroxyaflavinine. Retention time for 20-hydroxyaflavinine, 34.2min.

Biological Activity

Antifeeding activity against *Carpophilus hemiptaerus.*

Spectral Data

UV:

λ_{max}^{MeOH} 224(ϵ=14,920), 283(2,760), and 290nm (2,520).

^{1}H NMR:

H-2, 6.89(s); H-5, 7.44(br d, *J*=7.8); H-6, 7.08(dd, *J*=7.8, 6.3); H-7, 7.18(dd, *J*=8.3, 6.3); H-8, 7.36(br d, *J*=8.3); H-12, 2.31(m); 2.21(m); H-13, 1.99(m); 1.67(m); H-15, 4.44(br s); H-16, 2.04(m); 1.63(m); H-17, 1.79(m); 1.11(m); H-18, 2.12(m); H-20, 3.99(dd, *J*=12.8, 2.7); H-21, 1.95(m); 1.46(m); H-22, 2.10(m); H-23, 2.47(br d,

J=5.5); H-24, 2.61(septet, *J*=6.8); H-25, 0.82(d, *J*=6.8); H-26, 0.96(d, *J*=6.8); H-27, 0.99(d, *J*=6.6); H-28, 1.24(s); and H-29, 1.16ppm (d, *J*=7.6).

^{13}C NMR:
(CD_3OD) 141.8(s), 137.7(s), 128.5(s), 127.2(s), 122.8(d), 122.1(d), 120.0(d), 119.5(d), 112.2(d), 112.0(s), 72.6(d), 71.0(d), 49.8(d), 46.0(s), 44.7(s), 36.0(t), 32.5(d), 32.0(d), 31.5(t), 31.2(d), 28.6(t), 23.2(t), 22.1(t), 21.5(q), 21.1(q), 19.9(q), 19.6(q), and 13.6ppm (q).

Mass Spectrum:
EIMS: 421(M^+, 20), 403(2.0), 378(3.1), 360(3.1), 342(4.3), 288(4.4), 234(12), 220(26), 206(22), 194(35), 180(28), 168(62), 154(25), 144(26), 130(100), and 117*m/e*(50); HREIMS: obsd 421.2981; calcd for $C_{25}H_{39}NO_2$, 421.2980.

Reference

J. B. Gloer, M. R. TePaske, J. S. Sima, D. T. Wicklow, and P. F. Dowd; Antiinsectan Aflavinine Derivatives from the Sclerotia of *Aspergillus flavus*; J. Organ. Chem., Vol. 53, pp. 5457-5460(1988).

Common/Systematic Name

24,25-Dehydro-10,11-dihydro-20-hydroxyaflavinine

Molecular Formula/Molecular Weight

$C_{28}H_{39}NO_2$; MW = 421.29808

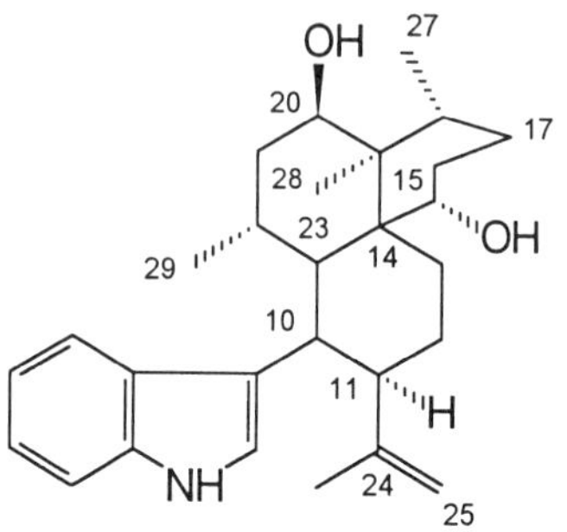

General Characteristics

Melting point 259-262°C dec; $[\alpha]_D$ +0.9° (*c*=0.34, in MeOH).

Fungal Source

Aspergillus flavus (NRRL 6541).

Isolation/Purification

Hexane and $CHCl_3$ extracts of milled sclerotia were subjected to reversed-phase flash chromatography followed by reversed-phase HPLC [5-μm C_{18} column, MeOH-H_2O (70:30, v/v), 2.0mL/min, monitored at 215nm] to afford 20,25-dihydroxyaflavinine, 20-hydroxyaflavinine, 24,25-dehydro-10,11-dihydro-20-hydroxyaflavinine and 10,11-dihydro-11,12-dehydro-20-hydroxyaflavinine. Retention time for 24,25-dehydro-10,11-dihydro-20-hydroxyaflavinine, 25.8 min.

Biological Activity

Antifeeding activity against *Carpophilus hemiptaerus.*

Spectral Data

UV:

λ_{max}^{MeOH} 227(ε=26,260), 284(6,060), and 291nm (5,720).

^{1}H NMR:

H-2, 7.06(s); H-5, 7.46(br d, *J*=7.8); H-6, 6.98(dd, *J*=7.8, 6.3); H-7, 7.06(dd, *J*=8.1, 6.3); H-8, 7.30(br d, *J*=8.1); H-10, 3.66(dd, *J*=13, 6); H-11, 3.22(ddd, *J*=13, 12, 6); H-12, 1.95(m); 1.65(m); H-13, 2.17(m); 1.78(m); H-15, 4.64(br s); H-16, 1.96(m); 1.17(m); H-17, 1.85(m); 1.27(m); H-18, 2.23(m); H-20, 3.92(dd, *J*=12.9, 2.7); H-21,

1.95(ddd, *J*=13, 12, 5.5); 1.21(m); H-22, 1.55(m); H-23, 2.67(dd, *J*=5, 6); H-25, 4.81(br s); H-26, 1.50(br s); H-27, 1.03,(d, *J*=6.6); H-28, 1.28(s); and H-29, 1.32ppm (d, *J*=7.3).

^{13}C NMR:

(CD$_3$OD) 151.7(s), 137.7(s), 128.6(s), 124.6(d), 122.0(d), 119.3(d), 118.7(d), 116.2(s), 112.3(d), 111.6(t), 72.6(d), 69.1(d), 47.4(s), 45.5(s), 44.8(d), 39.5(d), 38.9(t), 35.7(d), 32.6(d), 32.3(d), 31.1(t), 29.2(t), 28.5(t), 25.8(t), 23.1(q), 19.7(q), 18.4(q), and 13.8ppm (q).

Mass Spectrum:

EIMS: 421(M^+; 23), 406(1.5), 403(1.7), 388(1.0), 330(4.3), 302(2.4), 288(1.2), 248(2.0), 220(4.0), 210(10), 196(28), 184(14), 168(28), 143(13), 130(100), and 117*m/e* (16); HREIMS: obsd 421.2975; calcd for $C_{25}H_{39}NO_2$, 421.2980.

Reference

J. B. Gloer, M. R. TePaske, J. S. Sima, D. T. Wicklow, and P. F. Dowd; Antiinsectan Aflavinine Derivatives from the Sclerotia of *Aspergillus flavus*; J. Organ. Chem., Vol. 53, pp. 5457-5460(1988).

Common/Systematic Name

10,11-Dihydro-11,12-dehydro-20-hydroxyaflavinine

Molecular Formula/Molecular Weight

$C_{28}H_{39}NO_2$; MW = 421.29808

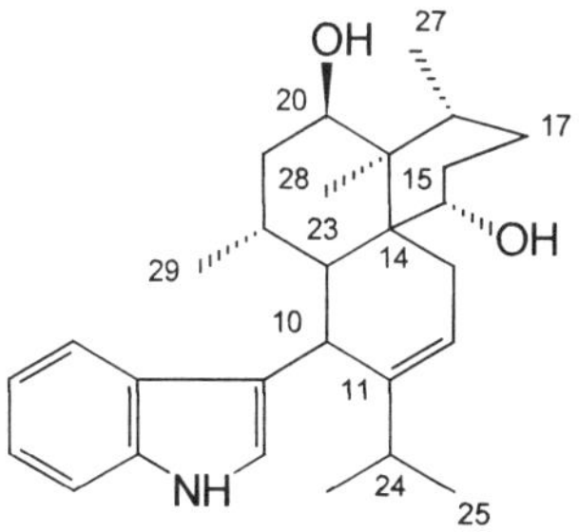

General Characteristics

Melting point 276-278☜C dec; $[\forall]_D$ +1.7☜ (*c*=0.10, in MeOH).

Fungal Source

Aspergillus flavus (NRRL 6541).

Isolation/Purification

Hexane and $CHCl_3$ extracts of milled sclerotia were subjected to reversed-phase flash chromatography followed by reversed-phase HPLC [5-:m C_{18} column, MeOH-H_2O (70:30, v/v), 2.0mL/min, monitored at 215nm] to afford 20,25-dihydroxyaflavinine, 20-hydroxyaflavinine, 24,25-dehydro-10,11-dihydro-20-hydroxyaflavinine, and 10,11-dihydro-11,12-dehydro-20-hydroxyaflavinine. Retention time for 10,11-dihydro-11,12-dehydro-20-hydroxyaflavinine, 35.5 min.

Biological Activity

Antifeeding activity against *Carpophilus hemiptaerus*.

Spectral Data

UV:

8_{max}^{MeOH} 224(,=20,030), 251(3,600), and 285nm (3,380).

^{1}H NMR:

H-2, 7.00(s); H-5, 7.46(br d, *J*=7.8); H-6, 7.02(dd, *J*=7.8, 6.1); H-7, 7.09(dd, *J*=8.0, 6.1); H-8, 7.36(br d, *J*=8.0); H-10, 4.17(d, *J*=5); H-12, 5.66(br d, *J*=5.6); H-13, 2.63(dd, *J*=13.5, 5.6); 2.29(m); H-15, 4.29(br s); H-16, 2.19(m); 1.80(m); H-17, 1.81(m); 1.26(m); H-18, 2.22(m); H-20, 3.95(dd, *J*=12.8, 3.0); H-21, 1.78(m); 1.32(m); H-22, 1.49(m); H-23, 2.53(dd, *J*=5.3, 5); H-24, 2.71(septet, *J*=6.8); H-25, 1.10(d, *J*=6.8); H-26, 0.72(d, *J*=6.8); H-27, 1.02,(d, *J*=6.6); H-28, 1.24(s); and H-29, 1.14ppm (d, *J*=7.1).

^{13}C NMR:
(CD$_3$OD) 144.7(s), 137.5(s), 129.5(s),124.5(d), 122.2(d), 121.6(d), 120.0(s),119.6(d), 118.3(d), 112.3(d), 73.1(d), 70.7(d), 46.1(s), 44.9(s), 40.1(d), 37.9(t), 37.1(d), 31.5(d), 31.4(d), 30.9(t), 30.2(d), 29.0(t), 28.7(t), 23.4(q), 21.1(q), 19.7(q), 17.9(q), and 13.6ppm (q).

Mass Spectrum:
EIMS: 421(M$^+$, 2.8), 403(0.6), 388(0.8), 342(1.6), 274(3.1), 260(4.4), 246(7.7), 232(8.9), 220(14), 210(24), 196(30), 180(32), 168(100), 143(32), 130(95), and 117*m/e* (81); HREIMS: obsd 421.2990; calcd for $C_{25}H_{39}NO_2$, 421.2980.

Reference

J. B. Gloer, M. R. TePaske, J. S. Sima, D. T. Wicklow, and P. F. Dowd; Antiinsectan Aflavinine Derivatives from the Sclerotia of *Aspergillus flavus*; J. Organ. Chem., Vol. 53, pp. 5457-5460(1988).

Common/Systematic Name

14-*epi*-14-Hydroxy-10,23-dihydro-24,25-dehydroaflavinine

Molecular Formula/Molecular Weight

$C_{28}H_{39}NO_2$; MW = 421.29808

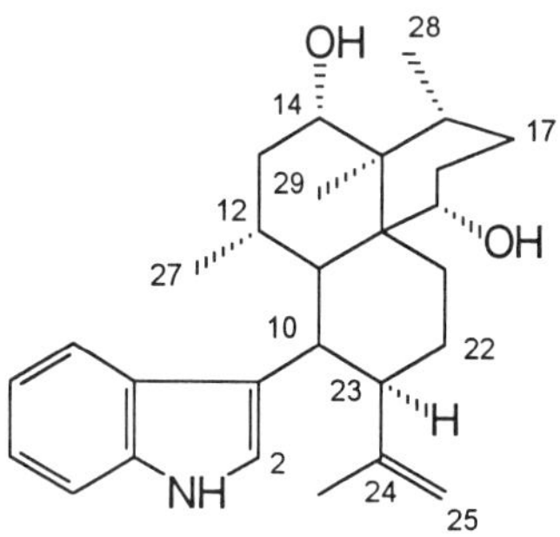

General Characteristics

Melting point, 79-82°C; $[\alpha]_D$ -5.6° (*c*=1.06, in $CHCl_3$).

Fungal Source

Aspergillus tubingensis (NRRL 4700), *A. flavus,* and *A. parasiticus.*

Isolation/Purification

Sclerotia were ground to a powder with a mortar and pestle and extracted with hexane. Filtration and evaporation of solvent afforded a yellow oil. Reversed-phase HPLC of the hexane extract using an Altex reversed-phase semipreparative column (C_{18}-5μm particle size; UV detection at 215nm; 20ml/min; 90:10, v/v, MeOH-H_2O) afforded pure 14-*epi*-14-hydroxy-10,23-dihydro-24,25-dehydroaflavinine along with fractions containing 10,23-dihydro-24,25-dehydroaflavinine and 10,23-dihydro-24,25-dehydro-21-oxo-aflavinine. 10,23-Dihydro-24,25-dehydroaflavinine was isolated by reversed-phase HPLC using a solvent composition of [MeOH-H_2O (85:15, v/v); 2.5ml/min], and 10,23-dihydro-24,25-dehydro-21-oxoaflavinine was isolated by further chromatography on a 10-μm Hamilton PRP-l column (100% MeOH, v/v, 1.0ml/min).

Biological Activity

No antiinsectan activity; mild antibacterial activity against *Bacillus subtilis* at 100μg/disk.

Spectral Data

UV:

λ_{max}^{MeOH} 292(ε=2,100), 284 (2,290), and 226nm (16,400).

^{1}H NMR:

H-1, 8.04(br, s); H-2, 7.08(br s); H-5, 7.52(br, d, *J*=7.6); H-6, 7.11(dd, *J*=7.6, 6.8); H-7, 7.16(dd, *J*=8.1, 6.8); H-8, 7.32(d, *J*=8.1); H-10(dd, *J*=5.9, 12.9); H-11, 2.73(dd, *J*=5.9, 5.8); H-12, 1.42(m); H-13, 0.85(m, 1.68, m); H-14, 4.74(br, s); H-16, 2.18(m); H-17, 1.19(m, 1.68, m); H-18, 1.38(m, 1.78, m); H-19, 4.73(br, m); H-21, 1.74(m, 2.15, m); H-22, 1.62(m, 2.31, m); H-23, 3.38(ddd, *J*=4.6, 13, 13); H-25, 4.77, 4.86(br, s); H-26, 1.44(s); H-27, 1.29(d, *J*=5.8); H-28, 0.78(d, *J*=5.8); and H-29, 1.02ppm (s).

^{13}C NMR:

C-2, 123.4; C-3, 115.9; C-4, 127.5; C-5, 118.3; C-6, 119.0; C-7, 121.6; C-8, 111.1; C-9, 135.7; C-10, 34.8; C-11, 38.0; C-12, 29.3; C-13, 29.9; C-14, 71.7; C-15, 39.3; C-16, 32.2; C-17, 28.5; C-18, 31.4; C-19, 68.8; C-20, 46.9; C-21, 24.9; C-22, 30.9; C-23, 39.5; C-24, 150.0; C-25, 111.4; C-26, 18.1; C-27, 18.1; C-28, 15.9; and C-29, 17.9ppm.

Mass Spectrum:

421(M^+ 40%), 388(0.3), 334(7.2), 306(6.9), 243(3.3), 226(5.1), 196(14), 182(45), 168(43), 159(16), 146(18), 130(100), and 117*m/e* (14); HREIMS: obs. 421.2962; calcd. for $C_{28}H_{39}NO_2$ 421.2980.

<u>Reference</u>

M. R. TePaske, J. B. Gloer, D. T. Wicklow, and P. F. Dowd; Three New Aflavinines From The Sclerotia of *Aspergillus tubingensis*; Tetrahedron, Vol. 45, pp. 4961-4968 (1989).

Common/Systematic Name

10,23-Dihydro-24,25-dehydroaflavinine

Molecular Formula/Molecular Weight

$C_{28}H_{39}NO$; MW = 405.30317

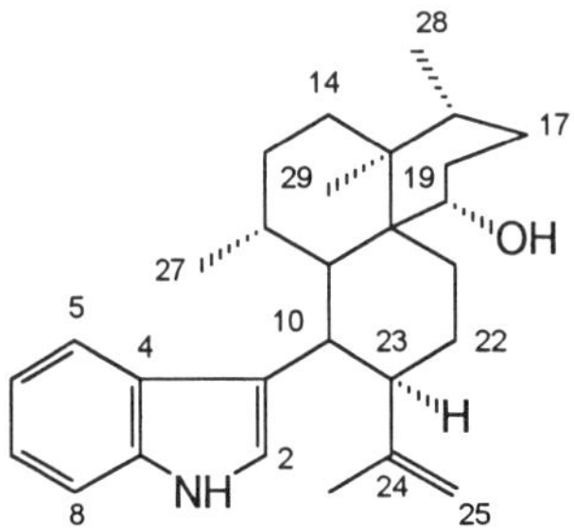

General Characteristics

Melting point 192-194°C; $[\alpha]_D$ -1.2° (*c*=0.5, in $CHCl_3$).

Fungal Source

Aspergillus tubingensis (NRRL 4700), *A. flavus* and *A. parasiticus*.

Isolation/Purification

Sclerotia were ground to a powder with a mortar and pestle and extracted with hexane. Filtration and evaporation of solvent afforded a yellow oil. Reversed-phase HPLC of the hexane extract using an Altex reversed phase semipreparative column [C_{18}-5µm particle size; UV detection at 215nm; 20ml/min; MeOH-H_2O (90:10, v/v)] afforded pure 14-*epi*-14-hydroxy-10,23-dihydro-24,25-dehydroaflavinine along with fractions containing 10,23-dihydro-24,25-dehydroaflavinine and 10, 23-dihydro-24,25-dehydro-21-oxoaflavinine. 10,23-Dihydro-24,25-dehydroaflavinine was isolated by reversed-phase HPLC using a solvent composition of [MeOH-H_2O (85:15, v/v); 2.5ml/min] and 10,23-dihydro-24,25-dehydro-21-oxoaflavinine was isolated by further chromatography on a 10-µm Hamilton PRP-l column (100% MeOH 1.0ml/min).

Biological Activity

No antiinsectan activity; mild antibacterial activity against *Bacillus subtilis* at 100µg/disk.

Spectral Data

UV:

λ_{max}^{MeOH} 291(ϵ=4,100), 284(4,400), and 226nm (31,600).

^{1}H NMR:

H-1, 7.89, br, s; H-2, 7.02, d, *J*=2.2; H-5, 7.52, br, d, *J*=7.8; H-6,7.09, dd, *J*=6.8, 7.8; H-7, 7.16, dd, *J*=6.8, 8.1; H-8, 7.32, d, *J*=8.1; H-10, 3.68, dd, *J*=5.1, 12.9; H-11, 2.62, m; H-12, 1.45, m; H-13, 1.16, m, 1.54, m; H-14, 0.86, m, 1.63, m; H-16, 2.18, m; H-17, 1.36, m, 1.75, m; H-18, 1.86, m, 2.21, m; H-19, 4.84, br, s; H-21, 1.88, m, 2.04, m; H-22, 1.75, m, 1.84, m; H-23, 3.19, m; H-25, 4.64, 4.78, br, s; H-26, 1.51, s; H-27, 1.24, d, *J*=7.1; H-28, 0.77, d, *J*=6.8; and H-29, 0.97ppm, s.

^{13}C NMR:

C-2, 122.8; C-3, 116.7; C-4, 127.4; C-5, 118.4; C-6, 119.0; C-7, 121.6; C-8, 111.1; C-9, 136.0; C-10, 34.6; C-11, 43.6; C-12, 29.8; C-13, 27.9; C-14, 25.3; C-15, 39.3; C-16, 31.4; C-17, 28.2; C-18, 28.9; C-19, 69.0; C-20, 44.0; C-21, 24.6; C-22, 30.1; C-23, 38.7; C-24, 150.3; C-25, 111.0; C-26, 18.4; C-27, 21.9; C-28, 15.8; and C-29, 18.4.

Mass Spectrum:

405(M^+ 22%), 390(1.3), 372(2.6), 330(2.4), 236(1.8), 210(7.8), 196(20), 184(14), 182(14), 168(15), 156(27), 143(17), 130(100), and 115*m/e* (11); obs. 405.3044; calcd. for $C_{28}H_{39}NO$, 405.3032.

Reference

M. R. TePaske, J. B. Gloer, D. T. Wicklow, and P. F. Dowd; Three New Aflavinines From The Sclerotia of *Aspergillus tubingensis*; Tetrahedron, Vol. 45, pp. 4961-4968 (1989).

Common/Systematic Name

10,23-Dihydro-24,25-dehydro-21-oxoaflavinine

Molecular Formula/Molecular Weight

$C_{28}H_{37}NO_2$; MW = 419.28243

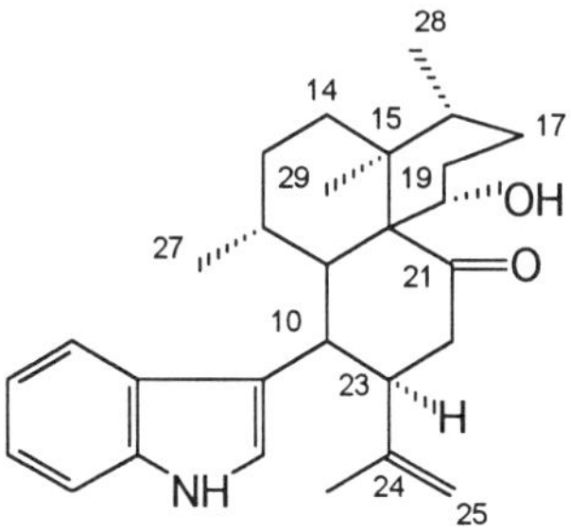

General Characteristics

Melting point 138-141°C; $[\alpha]_D$ -13.5° (*c*=0.72, in $CHCl_3$).

Fungal Source

Aspergillus tubingensis (NRRL 4700), *A. flavus*, and *A. parasiticus.*

Isolation/Purification

Sclerotia were ground to a powder with a mortar and pestle and extracted with hexane. Filtration and evaporation of solvent afforded a yellow oil. Reversed-phase HPLC of the hexane extract using an Altex reversed-phase semipreparative column [C_{18}-5μm particle size; UV detection at 215nm; 20ml/min; MeOH-H_2O (90:10, v/v)] afforded pure 14-*epi*-14-hydroxy-10,23-dihydro-24,25-dehydroaflavinine along with fractions containing 10,23-dihydro-24,25-dehydroaflavinine and 10,23-dihydro-24,25-dehydro-21-oxo-aflavinine. 10,23-Dihydro-24,25-dehydroaflavinine was isolated by reversed-phase HPLC using a solvent composition of [MeOH-H_2O (85:15, v/v); 2.5ml/min] and 10,23-dihydro-24,25-dehydro-21-oxo-aflavinine was isolated by further chromatography on a 10-μm Hamilton PRP-l column (100% MeOH 1.0ml/min).

Biological Activity

Caused a 68% weight reduction in *Heliothis zea* fed at a rate of 125ppm for 1 week; caused a 38% reduction in feeding rate by *Carpophilus hemipterus*; and exhibited mild antibacterial activity against *Bacillus subtilis* at 100μg/disk.

Spectral Data

UV:

λ_{max}^{MeOH} 291(ε=1,750), 283(2,100), 273(1,400), 267(1,200), and 224nm (18,200).

^{1}H NMR:

H-1, 8.00, br, s; H-2, 7.03, br, s; H-5, 7.55, d, *J*=7.8; H-6,7.13, dd, *J*=6.8, 7.8; H-7, 7.19, dd, *J*=6.8, 7.6; H-8, 7.36, d, *J*=7.6; H-10, 4.05, dd, *J*=5.4, 13.2; H-11, 3.00, dd, *J*=5.5, 4.6; H-12, 1.47, m; H-13, 1.54, m, 2.15, m; H-14, 0.93, m, 1.21, m; H-16, 2.08, m; H-17, 1.73, m, 1.96, m; H-18, 1.41, m, 2.32, m; H-19, 5.19, br, s; H-22, 2.42, dd, *J*=6.8, 14.4, 3.08, dd, *J*=12.5, 14.4; H-23, 3.67, ddd, *J*=13, 12.5, 6.8; H-25, 4.68, 4.81, br, s; H-26, 1.60, br, s; H-27, 1.03, d, *J*=6.1; H-28, 0.75, d, *J*=6.8; and H-29, 1.38ppm, s.

^{13}C NMR:

C-2, 122.5; C-3, 114.9; C-4, 127.2; C-5, 118.0; C-6, 119.4; C-7, 122.0; C-8, 112.4; C-9, 136.1; C-10, 34.0; C-11, 43.9; C-12, 29.6; C-13, 29.6; C-14, 28.3; C-15, 38.4; C-16, 31.3; C-17, 24.7; C-18, 30.2; C-19, 72.7; C-20, 58.1; C-21, 214.2; C-22, 44.9; C-23, 47.3; C-24, 146.8; C-25, 111.4; C-26, 18.2; C-27, 18.0; C-28, 14.7; and C-29, 18.1ppm.

Mass Spectrum:

419(M^+ 15%), 401(3.7), 322(2.9), 302(2.7), 265(3.8), 248(3.7), 242(5.3), 232(5.2), 225(7.9), 217(5.2), 208(4.8), 196(28), 182(82), 168(60), 157(70), 146(27), 130(100), and 117*m/e* (17); obs. 419.2839; calcd. for $C_{28}H_{37}NO_2$, 419.2824.

Reference

M. R. TePaske, J. B. Gloer, D. T. Wicklow, and P. F. Dowd; Three New Aflavinines From The Sclerotia of *Aspergillus tubingensis*; Tetrahedron, Vol. 45, pp. 4961-4968 (1989).

Common/Systematic Name

Aflavazole

Molecular Formula/Molecular Weight

$C_{28}H_{35}NO_2$; MW = 417.26678

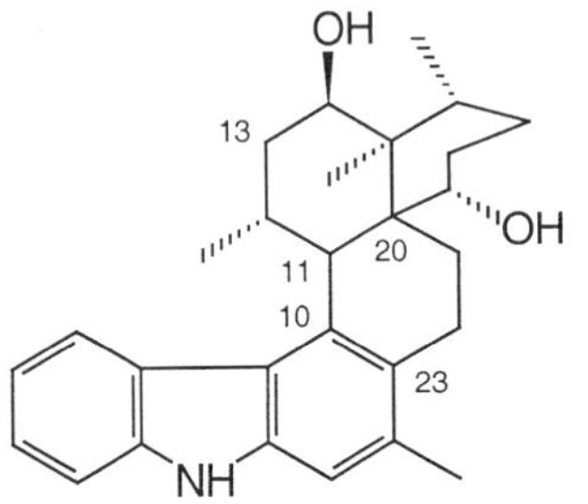

General Characteristics

A light yellow crystalline solid; mp., 156-160°C dec; $[\alpha]_D$ +2.8° (*c*=0.35, in MeOH)

Fungal Source

Aspergillus flavus (NRRL 13462) and *A. parasiticus.*

Isolation/Purification

Ground *A. flavus* sclerotia were exhaustively extracted with hexane, followed by chloroform and the chloroform extract was subjected to flash chromatography on a reversed phase column using a step gradient from 50 to 70% MeOH-H_2O; aflavazole eluted at 60% MeOH-H_2O. Separation of the resulting fraction by reversed phase HPLC; MeOH-H_2O (70:30, v/v) at 2.0mL/min afforded pure aflavazole; HPLC retention time under the above conditions, 25.3min.

Biological Activity

Aflavazole displayed significant antifeedant activity against the fungivorous beetle *Carpophilus hemipterus.*

Spectral Data

UV:

λ_{max}^{MeOH} 341(ε=1600), 327(1,300), 297(7,600), 263(7,500), 243(17,300), and 219nm (15,300).

^{1}H NMR:

($CDCl_3$) H-5, 7.95(br, d, *J*=8.0); H-6, 7.14(br, dd, *J*=8.0, 7.1); H-7, 7.1227(br, dd, *J*=7.8, 7.1); H-8, 7.39(br d, *J*=7.8); H-11, 4.18(br, d, *J*=7.1); H-12, 2.86(m); H-13_{ax}, 2.38(m); H-13_{eq}, 1.68(br, dd, *J*=12.9, 2.2); H-14, 4.22(dd, *J*=12.9, 3.4); H-16,

2.60(m); H-17$_{ax}$, 1.26(m); H-17$_{eq}$, 1.78(m); H-18$_{ax}$, 1.37(br, dd, *J*=12.7, 1.9); H-18$_{eq}$, 1.84(m); H-19, 3.84(br, d, *J*=2.9); H-21, 2.15(m); 2.75(br, dd, *J*=11, 7.1; H-22, 2.89(br, dd, *J*=17.6, 7.1); 2.39(m); H-25, 7.12(br, s); H-26, 2.35(br, s); H-27, 0.64(d, *J*=7.6); H-28, 1.19(d, *J*=6.8); and H-29, 1.33ppm (s).

^{13}C NMR:
(CDCl$_3$) C-2, 140.29; C-3, 119.57: C-4, 123.88: C-5, 122.33; C-6, 119.64; C-7,125.09; C-8, 111.67; C-9, 141.53; C-10, 135.8; C-11, 40.05; C-12, 32.79; C-13, 36.43; C-14, 72.48; C-15, 44.94; C-16, 32.60; C-17, 28.72; C-18, 25.22; C-19, 71.47; C-20, 45.23; C-21, 23.05; C-22, 30.77; C-23, 126.40; C-24, 135.13; C-25, 110.25; C-26, 20.68; C-27, 19.34; C-28, 13.70; and C-29, 19.83.

Mass Spectrum:
EIMS: 417(rel int 100%), 399(37), 381(13), 316(40), 284(8), 272(13), 258(32), 254(16), 244(36), 231(42), 217(62), 204(29), 194(47), 182(20), 168(21), and 130*m/e* (60); HREIMS: obsd 417.2694, calcd for $C_{28}H_{35}NO_2$, 417.2669.

Reference

M. R. TePaske, J. B. Gloer, D. T. Wicklow, and P. F. Dowd; Aflavazole: A New Antiinsectan Carbazole Metabolite from the Sclerotia of *Aspergillus flavus*; J. Organ. Chem., Vol. 55, pp. 5299-5303(1990).

5

Tryptoquivalines

Tryptoquivaline; Tryptoquivaline A; Tryptoquivaline C; FTC
Nortryptoquivalone; Tryptoquivalone; Tryptoquivaline B
Nortryptoquivaline; Tryptoquivaline D; Norisotryptoquivaline; FTD
Deoxytryptoquivaline
Deoxynortryptoquivaline
Tryptoquivaline E; FTE
Tryptoquivaline F
Tryptoquivaline G; FTG
Tryptoquivaline H
Tryptoquivaline I
Tryptoquivaline J; FTJ
Tryptoquivaline L
Tryptoquivaline M
Tryptoquivaline N; Deoxynortryptoquivalone
27-*epi*-Tryptoquivaline
27-*epi*-Nortryptoquivaline

Common/Systematic Name

Tryptoquivaline; Tryptoquivaline A; 'Tryptoquivaline C'; FTC

Molecular Formula/Molecular Weight

$C_{29}H_{30}N_4O_7$; MW = 546.21145

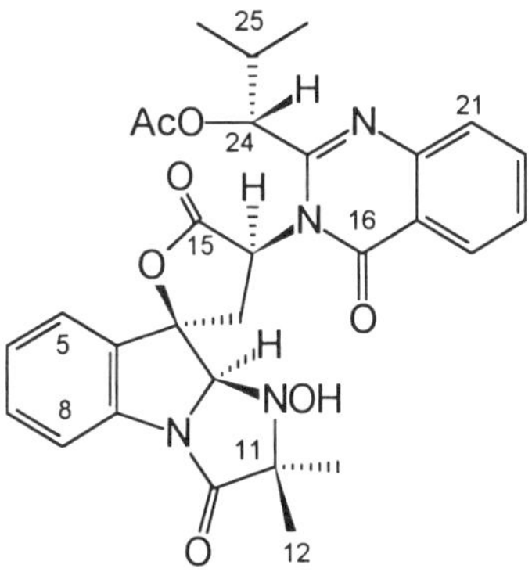

General Characteristics

Colorless prisms from dichloromethane-hexane; mp., 155-157°C; $[\alpha]_D^{25}$ + 130° (*c*=0.22, in $CHCl_3$).

Fungal Source

Aspergillus clavatus (NRRL 5890) and *A. fumigatus*.

Isolation/Purification

See Büchi *et al.*, 1977.

Biological Activity

Tryptoquivaline (dosed IP, up to 50μl DMSO solution) induced persistent tremors in rats.

Spectral Data

UV:

λ_{max}^{EtOH} 228(ϵ=42,200), 232sh (40,200), 252sh (19,500), 268(10,900), 279(9,500), 307(3,700), and 319nm (3,000).

CD:

$\lambda_{max}^{95\%\ EtOH}$ 258(-5.3), 282(0), 305(2.2), and 327nm (0).

^{1}H NMR:

($CDCl_3$) H-2, 5.00; H-5-8, 7.12-7.90; H-11, 1.50; H-12, 1.52; H-13a, 3.10(*J*=10); H-13b, 3.15(*J*=10); H-14, 5.70(*J*=10); H-18, 8.22(*J*=8); H-19-21, 7.12-7.90; H-24, 5.61(*J*=9); H-25, 2.63; H-26, 1.03; H-27, 1.17; CH_3CO, 2.19; and NOH, 3.63, 4.04ppm.

Mass Spectrum:
HREIMS: 546.21554 (100%).

TLC Data

Silica gel GF_{254}, benzene-acetone, 9:1 v/v; R_f not reported. Detection: not reported.

References

G. Büchi, K. C. Luk, B. Kobbe, and J. M. Townsend; Four New Mycotoxins of *Aspergillus clavatus* Related to Tryptoquivaline; J. Org. Chem., Vol. 42, pp. 244-246 (1977).

R. J. Cole and R. H. Cox; Handbook of Toxic Fungal Metabolites; Academic Press, New York, pp. 414-417(1981).

W. B. Turner and D. C. Aldridge; Fungal Metabolites II; Academic Press, New York, New York, p. 434 (1983).

Common/Systematic Name

Nortryptoquivalone; 'Tryptoquivalone'; 'Tryptoquivaline B'

Molecular Formula/Molecular Weight

$C_{26}H_{24}N_4O_6$; MW = 488.16958

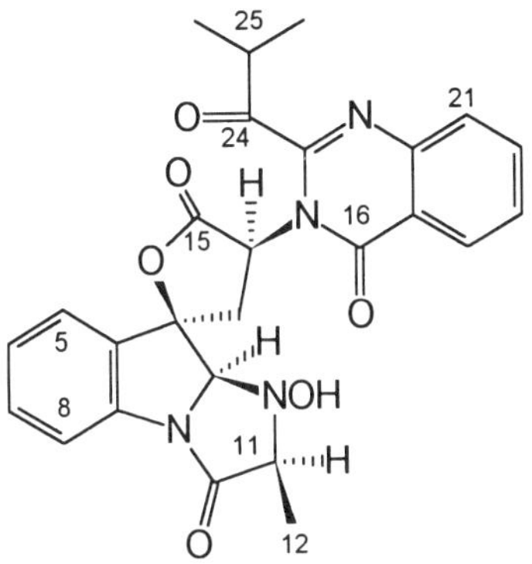

General Characteristics

Colorless prisms from dichloromethane-hexane; mp., 208°-209°C; $[\alpha]_D^{25}$ + 255° (*c*=0.30, in $CHCl_3$).

Fungal Source

Aspergillus clavatus (NRRL 5890).

Biological Activity

Nortryptoquivalone dosed IP (up to 50µl DMSO) induced persistent tremors in rats.

Spectral Data

UV:

λ_{max}^{EtOH} 228(sh) (ϵ = 31,1300), 232(31,800), 253sh (16,900), 278(7,600), 289(6,500), 304(5,400), and 316nm sh (4,500).

CD:

$\lambda_{max}^{95\% EtOH}$ 256(-3.8), 273(0), 298(3.6), and 342nm (0).

^{1}H NMR:

($CDCl_3$) H-2, 5.24; H-5-8, 7.11-7.74; H-11, 1.53; H-12, 1.53; H-13a, 3.06(*J*=10); H-13b, 3.06(*J*=10); H-14, 5.65(*J*=10); H-18, 8.20; H-19-21, 7.11-7.74; H-24, 5.52(*J*=9); H-25, 2.54; H-26, 1.04(*J*=7); H-27, 1.20(*J*=7); and CH_3CO, 2.16ppm.

References

R. J. Cole and R. H. Cox; Handbook of Toxic Fungal Metabolites; Academic Press, New York, p. 418 (1981).

W. B. Turner and D. C. Aldridge; Fungal Metabolites II; Academic Press, New York, New York, p. 434 (1983).

Common/Systematic Name

Nortryptoquivaline; 'Tryptoquivaline D'; Norisotryptoquivaline'; FTD

Molecular Formula/Molecular Weight

$C_{28}H_{28}N_4O_7$; MW = 532.19580

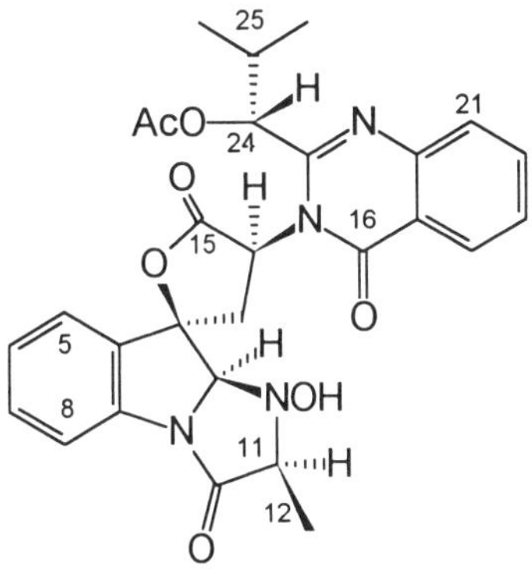

General Characteristics

Colorless prisms from dichloromethane-hexane; mp., 256-258°C; $[\alpha]_D^{25}$ 170° (*c*=0.64, in $CHCl_3$).

Fungal Source

Aspergillus clavatus (NRRL 5890) and *A. fumigatus.*

Biological Activity

Tremorgenic activity not reported in detail; however, metabolite is related to the reported tremorgens, tryptoquivaline and nortryptoquivalone.

Spectral Data

UV:

λ_{max}^{EtOH} 228(ϵ=43,600), 233 sh (42,000), 254 sh (18,700), 267 sh (11,900), 279(10,200), 306(4,500), and 319nm (3,500).

CD:

$\lambda_{max}^{95\%\ EtOH}$ 254(-5.4), 287(0), 307(2.1), and 325 (0).

IR:

3490, 2980, 2940, 2880, 1790, 1728, 1670, 1610, 1485, 1471, and 1410cm^{-1}.

^{13}C NMR:

($CDCl_3$) H-2, 5.10; H-5-8, 7.01-7.79; H-11, 4.28(*J*=7); H-12, 1.58(*J*=7); H-13a,

2.94(J=10,13); H-13b, 3.18(J=10,13); H-14, 5.65(J=10); H-18, 8.12; H-19-21, 7.01-7.79; H-24, 5.54(J=9); H-25, 2.57; H-26, 1.02(J=7); H-27, 1.16(J=7); and CH_3CO, 2.16ppm.

Mass Spectrum:
HREIMS: 532.19525(100%).

References

G. Büchi, K. C. Luk, B. Kobbe, and J. M. Townsend; Four New Mycotoxins of *Aspergillus clavatus* Related to Tryptoquivaline; J. Org. Chem., Vol. 42, pp. 244-246 (1977).

R. J. Cole and R. H. Cox; Handbook of Toxic Fungal Metabolites; Academic Press, New York, p.422 (1981).

W. B. Turner and D. C. Aldridge; Fungal Metabolites II; Academic Press, New York, New York, p. 434 (1983).

Common/Systematic Name

Deoxytryptoquivaline

Molecular Formula/Molecular Weight

$C_{29}H_{30}N_4O_6$; MW = 530.21653

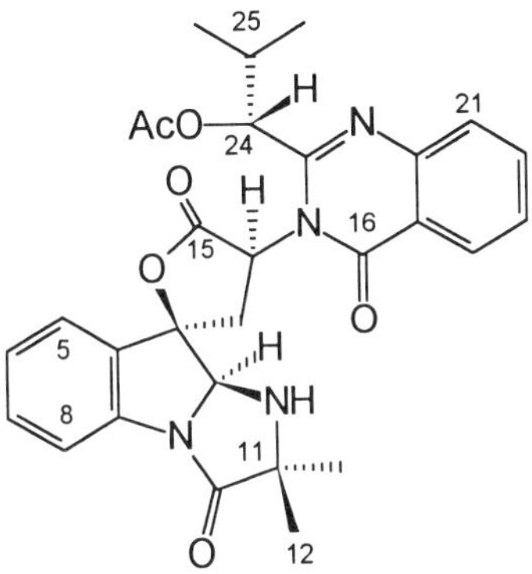

General Characteristics

White needles from dichloromethane-hexane; mp., 150-152°C; $[\alpha]_D^{25}$ +56.8° (*c*=0.78, in $CHCl_3$).

Fungal Source

Aspergillus clavatus.

Biological Activity

Details of tremorgenic activity not reported; however, metabolite is chemically related to known tremorgens, tryptoquivaline and nortryptoquivalone.

Spectral Data

UV:

λ_{max}^{EtOH} 227(ϵ=44,500), 232(sh) (41,900), 252(sh) (18,500), 267(sh) (12,000), 278(sh) (10,300), 304(3,300), and 318nm (sh) (2,700).

IR:

($CHCl_3$) 3360, 3310, 2980, 2935, 2875, 1790, 1720, 1676, 1604, 1483, and 1469cm^{-1}.

^{1}H NMR:

($CDCl_3$) H-2, 5.24; H-5-8, 7.11-7.74; H-11, 1.53; H-12, 1.53; H-13a, 3.06(*J*=10); H-13b, 3.06(*J*=10); H-14, 5.65(*J*=10); H-18, 8.20; H-19-21, 7.11-7.74; H-24, 5.52(*J*=9); H-25, 2.54; H-26, 1.04(*J*=7); H-27, 1.20(*J*=7); and CH_3CO, 2.16ppm.

Mass Spectrum:
HREIMS: 530.21527(100%).

References

G. Büchi, K. C. Luk, B. Kobbe, and J. M. Townsend; Four New Mycotoxins of *Aspergillus clavatus* Related to Tryptoquivaline; J. Org. Chem., Vol. 42, pp. 244-246 (1977).

R. J. Cole and R. H. Cox; Handbook of Toxic Fungal Metabolites; Academic Press, New York, p. 426 (1981).

W. B. Turner and D. C. Aldridge; Fungal Metabolites II; Academic Press, New York, New York, p. 434 (1983).

Common/Systematic Name

Deoxynortryptoquivaline

Molecular Formula/Molecular Weight

$C_{28}H_{28}N_4O_6$; MW = 516.20088

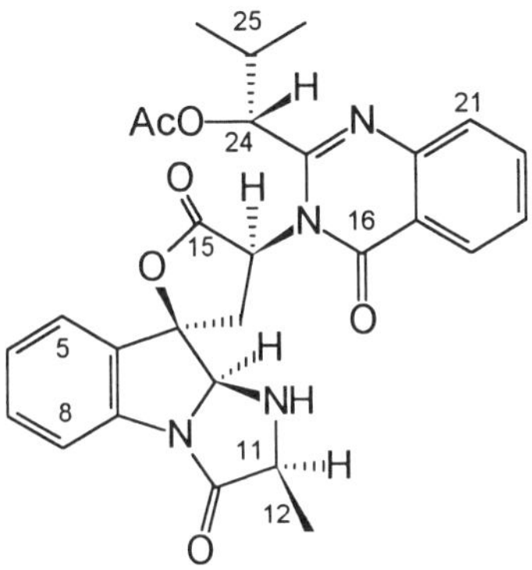

General Characteristics

Colorless prisms from diethyl ether; mp., 158-160°C; $[\alpha]_D^{25}$ 69.5° (c=0.82, in $CHCl_3$).

Fungal Source

Aspergillus clavatus.

Biological Activity

Details of tremorgenic activity not reported; however, the metabolite is related to the reported tremorgens, tryptoquivaline and nortryptoquivalone.

Spectral Data

UV:

λ_{max}^{EtOH} 228(ε=43,900), 233(sh) (40,100), 254(sh) (15,600), 268(11,700), 278(sh) (10,500), 305(4,100), and 317nm (3,300).

IR:

($CHCl_3$) 3360, 2975, 2935, 2880, 1790, 1724, 1676, 1607, and 1483cm^{-1}.

^{1}H NMR:

($CDCl_3$) H-2, 5.22; H-5-8, 7.02-7.74; H-11, 4.12(J=7); H-12, 1.55(J=7); H-13a, 2.86(J=10, 13); H-13b, 3.07(J=10, 13); H-14, 5.65(J=10); H-18, 8.14; H-19-21, 7.02-7.74; H-24, 5.55(J=9), H-25, 2.58; H-26, 1.00(J=7); H-27, 1.15(J=7); and CH_3CO, 2.16ppm.

Mass Spectrum:
HREIMS: 516.20420(100%).

References

G. Büchi, K. C. Luk, B. Kobbe, and J. M. Townsend; Four New Mycotoxins of *Aspergillus clavatus* Related to Tryptoquivaline; J. Org. Chem., Vol. 42, pp. 244-246 (1977).

R. J. Cole and R. H. Cox; Handbook of Toxic Fungal Metabolites; Academic Press, New York, p. 434 (1981).

W. B. Turner and D. C. Aldridge; Fungal Metabolites II; Academic Press, New York, New York, p.435 (1983).

Common/Systematic Name

Tryptoquivaline E; FTE

Molecular Formula/Molecular Weight

$C_{22}H_{18}N_4O_5$; MW = 418.12772

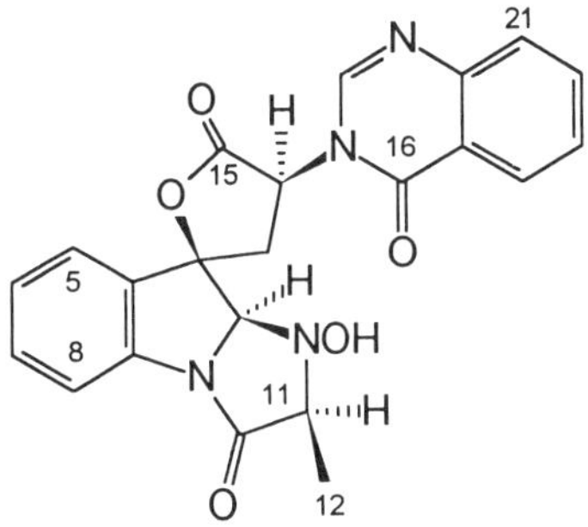

General Characteristics

Colorless feathers from acetone; mp., ~257°C (dec.); $[\alpha]_D^{15.5}$ +257° (c=0.009, in $CHCl_3$).

Fungal Source

Aspergillus fumigatus and *A. clavatus.*

Biological Activity

Related to tremorgen, tryptoquivaline; however, not demonstrated to be tremorgenic.

Spectral Data

UV:

λ_{max}^{MeOH} 225.5(ϵ=32,300), 232(sh) (29,800), 254(sh) (16,000), 265.5(sh) (11,700), 275.5(sh) (8,400), 291(sh) (3,500), 303(3,000), and 315nm (2,600).

IR:

(KBr) 3430, 1780, 1740, 1732, 1677, 1658, and 1614cm^{-1}.

^{1}H NMR:

(pyridine) H-2, 5.42; H-5-8, 6.83-7.80; H-11, 4.26(J=7); H-12, 1.63(J=7); H-13a, 3.38(J=10, 13); H-13b, 3.56(J=10, 13); H-14, 6.48(J=10); H-18, 8.17; H-19-21, 6.83-7.80; H-23, 8.59; and N-OH, 10.42ppm.

References

R. J. Cole and R. H. Cox; Handbook of Toxic Fungal Metabolites; Academic Press, New York, p. 438 (1981).

W. B. Turner and D. C. Aldridge; Fungal Metabolites II; Academic Press, New York, New York, p. 435 (1983).

M. Yamazmki, H. Fujimoto, and E. Okyama; Structure Determination of Six Fungal Metabolites, Tryptoquivaline E, F, G, H, I, and J; Chem. Pharm. Bull., Vol. 26, pp. 111-117(1978).

Common/Systematic Name

Tryptoquivaline F

Molecular Formula/Molecular Weight

$C_{22}H_{18}N_4O_4$; MW = 402.13281

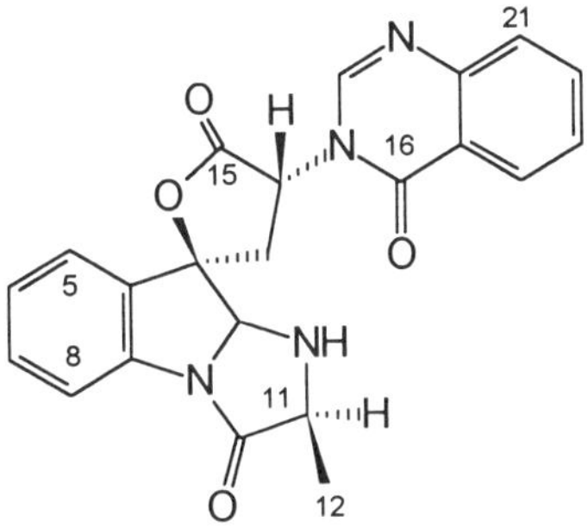

General Characteristics

Colorless fine needles from methanol; mp., ~277°C (dec.); $[\alpha]_D^{15.5}$ -109° (*c*=0.006, in $CHCl_3$).

Fungal Source

Aspergillus fumigatus.

Biological Activity

Reportedly related to tremorgen tryptoquivaline; however, not demonstrated to be tremorgenic.

Spectral Data

UV:

λ_{max}^{MeOH} 226(ϵ=33,400), 232(sh) (31,200), 255(sh) (12,400), 265(sh) (11,101), 276(sh) (8,100), 290(sh) (3,100), 303(2,800), and 315nm (2,200).

IR:

(KBr) 3365, 1775, 1725, 1664, and 160cm^{-1}.

^{1}H NMR:

($CDCl_3$) H-2, 5.65; H-5-8, 7.12-8.07; H-11, 4.4(*J*=7); H-12, 1.63(*J*=7); H-13a, 3.19(*J*=9); H-13b; 3.33(*J*=9,13); H-14, 5.40(*J*=9); H-18, 8.21(*J*=7); H-19-21, 7.12-8.07; H-23 and CH_3CO, 2.15ppm.

References

R. J. Cole and R. H. Cox; Handbook of Toxic Fungal Metabolites; Academic Press, New York, p. 438 (1981).

W. B. Turner and D. C. Aldridge; Fungal Metabolites II; Academic Press, New York, New York, p. 435 (1983).

M. Yamazmki, H. Fujimoto, and E. Okyama; Structure Determination of Six Fungal Metabolites, Tryptoquivaline E, F, G, H, I, and J; Chem. Pharm. Bull., Vol. 26, pp. 111-117(1978).

Common/Systematic Name

Tryptoquivaline G; FTG

Molecular Formula/Molecular Weight

$C_{23}H_{20}N_4O_5$; MW = 432.14337

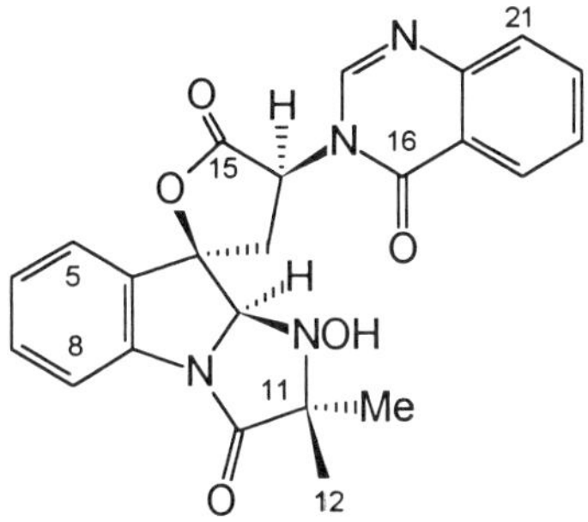

General Characteristics

Colorless prisms from acetone; mp., 240-241.5°C (dec.); $[\alpha]_D^{11}$ +215° (*c*=0.011, in acetone).

Fungal Source

Aspergillus fumigatus.

Biological Activity

Reportedly related to tremorgen tryptoquivaline; however, not demonstrated to be tremorgenic.

Spectral Data

UV:

λ_{max}^{MeOH} 226(ϵ=34,300), 232(sh) (31,700), 253(sh) (17,400), 265(sh) (11,800), 275(sh) (8,200), 291(sh) (3,700), 302(3,000), and 315nm (2,500).

IR:

(KBr) 3470, 1778, 1738, 1662, and 1610cm^{-1}.

^{1}H NMR:

(pyridine) H-2, 5.30; H-5-8, 6.96-7.96; H-11, 4.26(*J*=7); H-12, 1.50, 1.62; H-13a, 3.43(*J*=10, 14); H-13b, 3.64; H-14, 6.56(*J*=10); H-18, 8.23; H-19-21, 6.96-7.96; H-23, 8.66; and N- OH, 10.61ppm.

References

R. J. Cole and R. H. Cox; Handbook of Toxic Fungal Metabolites; Academic Press, New York, p. 438 (1981).

W. B. Turner and D. C. Aldridge; Fungal Metabolites II; Academic Press, New York, New York, p. 435 (1983).

M. Yamazaki, H. Fujimoto, and E. Okyama; Structure Determination of Six Fungal Metabolites, Tryptoquivaline E, F, G, H, I, and J; Chem. Pharm. Bull., Vol. 26, pp. 111-117(1978).

Common/Systematic Name
Tryptoquivaline H

Molecular Formula/Molecular Weight
$C_{22}H_{18}N_4O_5$; MW = 418.12772

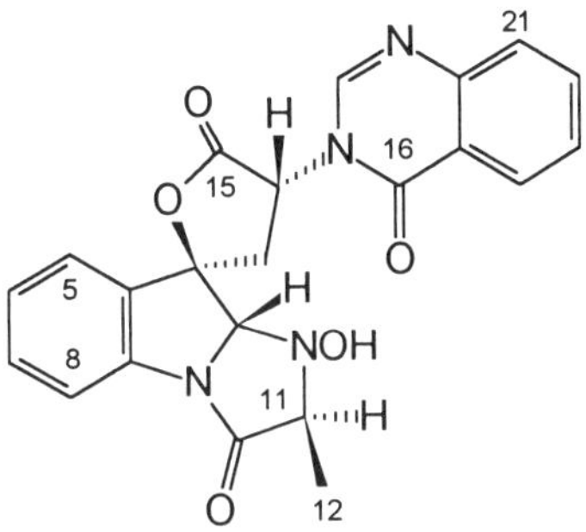

General Characteristics
Colorless fine needles from methanol; mp., ~274°C (dec.); $[\alpha]_D^{11}$ -155° (*c*=0.021, in acetone)

Fungal Source
Aspergillus fumigatus.

Biological Activity
Related to the reported tremorgen tryptoquivaline; however, not demonstrated to be tremorgenic.

Spectral Data

UV:
λ_{max}^{MeOH} 226(ϵ=33,100), 232(sh) (30,900), 255(sh) (16,600), 266(sh) (11,300), 276(sh) (8,500), 291(sh) (3,600), 303(3,100), and 315nm (2,500).

IR:
(KBr) 3430, 1780, 1742, 1734, 1667, and 1609cm^{-1}.

^{1}H NMR:
(pyridine) H-2, 5.25; H-5-8, 6.68-7.88; H-11, 3.98(*J*=8); H-12, 1.45(*J*=8); H-13a, 2.96(*J*=10,13); H-13b, 3.60(*J*=10, 13); H-14, 5.76(*J*=10); H-18, 8.11; H-19-21, 6.68-7.88; H-23, 8.38; and N-OH, 10.6ppm.

References
R. J. Cole and R. H. Cox; Handbook of Toxic Fungal Metabolites; Academic Press, New York, p. 438 (1981).

W. B. Turner and D. C. Aldridge; Fungal Metabolites II; Academic Press, New York, New York, p. 435 (1983).

M. Yamazaki, H. Fujimoto, and E. Okyama; Structure Determination of Six Fungal Metabolites, Tryptoquivaline E, F, G, H, I, and J; Chem. Pharm. Bull., Vol. 26, pp. 111-117(1978).

Common/Systematic Name

Tryptoquivaline I

Molecular Formula/Molecular Weight

$C_{27}H_{26}N_4O_6$; MW = 502.18523

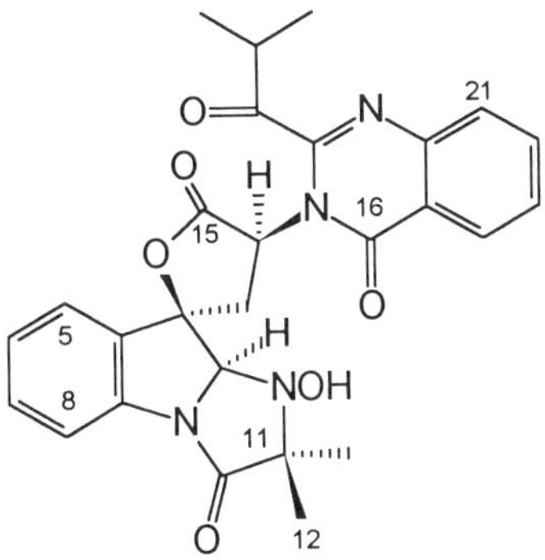

General Characteristics

Colorless leaflets from methylene-methanol; mp., 232-235.5°C (dec.); $[\alpha]_D^{14}$ +239° (*c*=0.16, in $CHCl_3$).

Fungal Source

Aspergillus fumigatus.

Biological Activity

Related to the reported tremorgen tryptoquivaline; however, not demonstrated to be tremorgenic.

Spectral Data

UV:

λ_{max}^{MeOH} 235(ε=31,700), 250(sh) (21,400), 292(9,600), and 321nm (sh) (6,100).

IR:

(KBr) 3480, 1780, 1732, 1710, 1675, and 1609cm^{-1}.

^{1}H NMR:

($CDCl_3$) H-2, 4.99; H-5-8, 7.00-7.94; H-12, 1.49; H-13a, 3.06(*J*=10, 14); H-13b, 3.39(*J*=10, 14); H-14, 5.47(*J*=10); H-18, 8.24(*J*=7); H-19-21, 7.00-7.94; H-25, 4.07(*J*=7); H-26, 1.22; H-27, 1.28; and NOH, 7.01ppm.

References

R. J. Cole and R. H. Cox; Handbook of Toxic Fungal Metabolites; Academic Press, New York, p. 438 (1981).

W. B. Turner and D. C. Aldridge; Fungal Metabolites II; Academic Press, New York, New York, p. 435 (1983).

M. Yamazaki, H. Fujimoto, and E. Okyama; Structure Determination of Six Fungal Metabolites, Tryptoquivaline E, F, G, H, I, and J; Chem. Pharm. Bull., Vol. 26, pp. 111-117(1978).

Common/Systematic Name
Tryptoquivaline J; FTJ

Molecular Formula/Molecular Weight
$C_{22}H_{18}N_4O_4$; MW = 402.13281

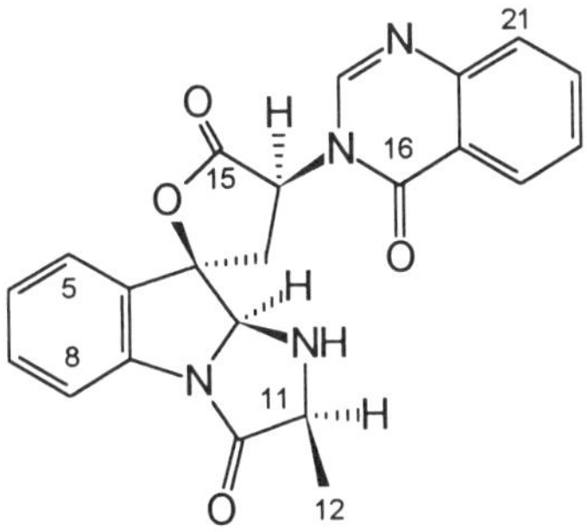

General Characteristics
Colorless fine needles from acetone-methanol; mp., 254-258°C; $[\alpha]_D^{14}$ +135° (c=0.024, in acetone).

Fungal Source
Aspergillus fumigatus.

Biological Activity
Related to the reported tremorgen tryptoquivaline; however, not demonstrated to be tremorgenic.

Spectral Data

UV:
λ_{max}^{MeOH} 225.5(ϵ=41,100), 231(sh) (38,000), 253(sh) (16,200), 264(sh) (12,800), 275(sh) (9,700), 290(sh) (4,200), 302(3,900), and 310nm (3,100).

IR:
(KBr) 3375, 1780, 1713 1670, and 1710cm^{-1}.

^{1}H NMR:
(DMSO) H-2, 5.41(J=6); H-5-8, 7.20-8.02; H-11, 3.87(J=7); H-12, 1.41(J=7); H-13a, 3.08; H-13b, 3.10; H-14, 6.01(J=10); H-18, 8.17; H-19-21, 7.20-8.02; H-23, 8.49; and NH, 3.76ppm.

References

R. J. Cole and R. H. Cox; Handbook of Toxic Fungal Metabolites; Academic Press, New York, p. 438 (1981).

W. B. Turner and D. C. Aldridge; Fungal Metabolites II; Academic Press, New York, New York, p. 435 (1983).

M. Yamazaki, H. Fujimoto, and E. Okyama; Structure Determination of Six Fungal Metabolites, Tryptoquivaline E, F, G, H, I, and J; Chem. Pharm. Bull., Vol. 26, pp. 111-117(1978).

Common/Systematic Name

Tryptoquivaline L

Molecular Formula/Molecular Weight

$C_{23}H_{20}N_4O_5$; MW = 432.14337

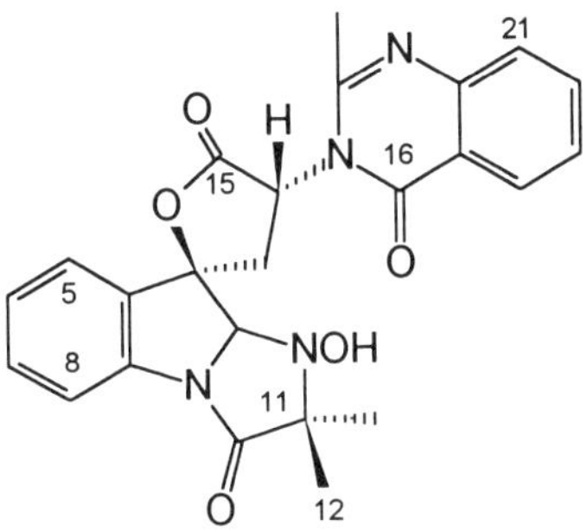

General Characteristics

Colorless leaflets from acetone; mp., 265-268°C; $[\alpha]_D^{23}$ -229° (*c*=0.03, in dimethyl sulfoxide).

Fungal Source

Aspergillus fumigatus.

Spectral Data

UV:

λ_{max}^{MeOH} 216(sh) (ε=33,900), 226(33,000), 231(sh) (30,800), 252(sh) (17,400), 264(sh) (12,300), 274(sh) (8,400), 290(sh) (3,700), 302(3,000), and 315nm (2,400).

IR:

(KBr) 3230, 1784, 1749, 1670, 1616, 1485, 1260, and 1200cm^{-1}.

^{1}H NMR:

(DMSO) H-2, 5.21; H-5-8, 7.24-8.00; H-12, 1.26, 1.36; H-13, 3.03, 3.43; H-14, 5.57; H-18, 8.23; H-19-21, 7.24-8.00; H-23, 8.53; and NOH, 8.74ppm.

References

R. J. Cole and R. H. Cox; Handbook of Toxic Fungal Metabolites; Academic Press, New York, p. 438 (1981).

W. B. Turner and D. C. Aldridge; Fungal Metabolites II; Academic Press, New York, New York, p. 435 (1983).

M. Yamazaki, H. Fujimoto, and E. Okyama; Structure Determination of Six Fungal Metabolites, Tryptoquivaline E, F, G, H, I, and J; Chem. Pharm. Bull., Vol. 26, pp. 111-117(1978).

Common/Systematic Name

Tryptoquivaline M

Molecular Formula/Molecular Weight

$C_{28}H_{28}N_4O_7$; MW = 532.19580

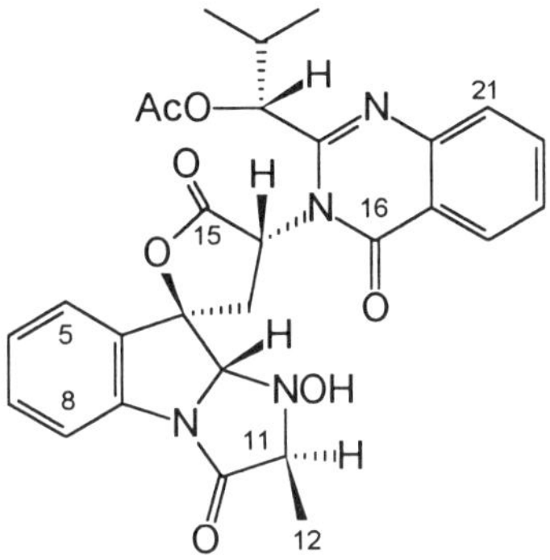

General Characteristics

Colorless plates from methanol-water; mp., 157-164°C; $[\alpha]_D^{24}$ -154° (*c*=0.50, in $CHCl_3$).

Fungal Source

Aspergillus fumigatus.

Spectral Data

UV:

λ_{max}^{MeOH} 228(ϵ=32,700), 232(30,700), 255(15,400), 278(9,300), 305(2,900), and 317nm (2,700).

IR:

(KBr) 3400, 1788, 1725, 1678, 1600, 1480, 1464, and 1210cm^{-1}.

^{1}H NMR:

H-2, 5.22; H-5-8, 7.12-7.88; H-11, 4.15(*J*=7); H-12, 1.55(*J*=7); H-13, 2.68, 3.65(*J*=11,10); H-14, 5.87(*J*=10); H-18, 8.24(*J*=8); H-19-21, 7.12-7.88; H-24, 5.54(*J*=10); H-25, 2.74; H-26, 0.92(*J*=6); H-27, 1.04(*J*=6); CH_3CO, 2.16; and OH, 6.86ppm.

References

R. J. Cole and R. H. Cox; Handbook of Toxic Fungal Metabolites; Academic Press, New York, p. 438 (1981).

W. B. Turner and D. C. Aldridge; Fungal Metabolites II; Academic Press, New York, New York, p. 435 (1983).

M. Yamazaki, H. Fujimoto, and E. Okyama; Structure Determination of Six Fungal Metabolites, Tryptoquivaline E, F, G, H, I, and J; Chem. Pharm. Bull., Vol. 26, pp. 111-117(1978).

Common/Systematic Name

Tryptoquivaline N; Deoxynortryptoquivalone

Molecular Formula/Molecular Weight

$C_{26}H_{24}N_4O_5$; MW = 472.17467

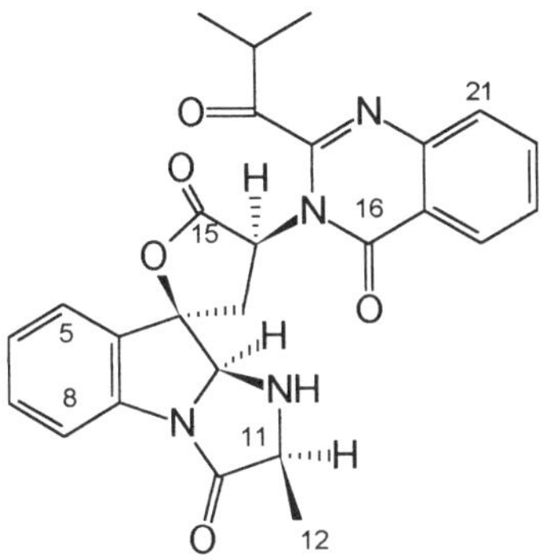

General Characteristics

Colorless needles from methanol; mp., 193-197°C; $[\alpha]_D^{24}$ +127° (*c*=0.66, in dimethyl sulfoxide).

Fungal Source

Aspergillus fumigatus and *A. clavatus.*

Spectral Data

UV:

λ_{max}^{MeOH} 232(ϵ=32,300), 251(sh) (17,900), 291(9,000), and 320nm (sh) (6,100).

IR:

(KBr) 3360, 1780, 1722, 1705, 1680, 1607, 1481, and 1250cm^{-1}.

References

R. J. Cole and R. H. Cox; Handbook of Toxic Fungal Metabolites; Academic Press, New York, p. 438 (1981).

W. B. Turner and D. C. Aldridge; Fungal Metabolites II; Academic Press, New York, New York, p. 435 (1983).

M. Yamazaki, H. Fujimoto, and E. Okyama; Structure Determination of Six Fungal Metabolites, Tryptoquivaline E, F, G, H, I, and J; Chem. Pharm. Bull., Vol. 26, pp. 111-117(1978).

Common/Systematic Name
27-*epi*-Tryptoquivaline

Molecular Formula/Molecular Weight
$C_{29}H_{30}N_4O_7$; MW = 546.21145

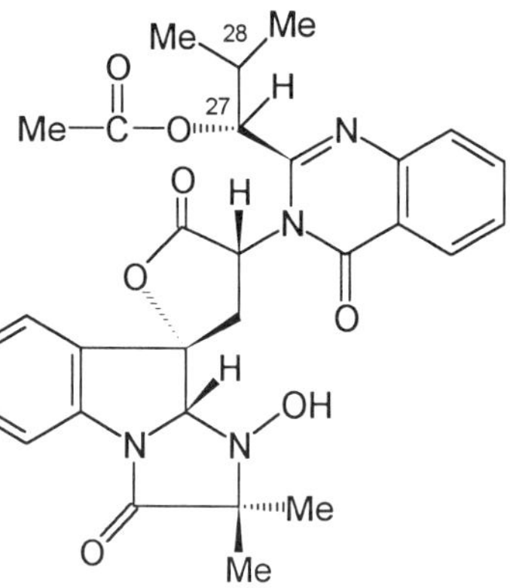

General Characteristics
Colorless needles from MeOH; mp., 225-227°C; $[\alpha]_D^{25}$ -138° (c=0.020, in $CHCl_3$).

Fungal Source
Corynascus setosus (IFM 4648).

Isolation/Purification
Corynascus setosus was cultivated on sterilized rice at 25°C for 17 days. The moldy rice was extracted two times with ethyl acetate with shaking at room temperature for 2 hours, to give a crude extract which was partitioned with *n*-hexane-MeOH (1:1, v/v). The defatted layer was then partitioned with ethyl acetate-H_2O (1:1, v/v) and the ethyl acetate layer was chromatographed on a silica gel column with *n*-hexane-ethyl acetate (2:1, v/v), (1:1, v/v), and (1:2, v/v), ethyl acetate and MeOH two times to give fractions I, II, III, and IV. Fraction III was further chromatographed on silica gel columns with *n*-hexane-ethyl acetate and $CHCl_3$-MeOH repeatedly to afford helvolic acid, helvolinic acid, setosusin, and 2-(1-oxo-2-hydroxyethyl)furan. Fraction I was chromatographed on silica gel columns with *n*-hexane-ethyl acetate repeatedly and on an octadecyl silica gel (ODS) column with acetonitrile-H_2O to furnish 27-*epi*-tryptoquivaline and 27-*epi*-nortryptoquivaline. Fraction II was also chromatographed in a similar manner to afford fiscalin B, previously identified from *Neosartorya fischeri*.

Biological Activity
27-*epi*-Tryptoquivaline and 27-*epi*-nortryptoquivaline caused a weak tremor when administered at 50mg/kg, i.p. The tremor appeared at *ca.* 30 and 120 minutes after injection and continued for *ca.* 120 and 30 minutes, respectively.

Spectral Data

UV:
λ_{max}^{MeOH} 209(sh, log ε=4.67), 289(sh, 3.83), 306(sh, 3.54), and 318nm (sh, 3.44).

CD:
(Δε) 0(325), + 1.8(305), + 3.6(281), 0(260), and - 1.9nm (253) (c= 0.011, in EtOH).

IR:
($CHCl_3$) 3500, 3000, 1790. 1735, 1675, and 1610cm^{-1}.

^{1}H NMR:
($CDCl_3$) 5.05(1H, s, H-2); 41(1H, br d, *J*=7.6Hz, H-5); 7.28(1H, td, *J*=7.6, 1.1Hz, H-6); 7.48(1H, td, *J*=7.6, 1.1Hz, H-7); 7.64(1H, br d, *J*=7.6Hz); 5.88(1H, t-like, *J*=10.0Hz, H-12); 3.12(1H, dd, *J*=13.5, 9.7Hz, H-13); 3.14 (1H, dd, *J*=13.5, 10.1Hz, H-13); 6.99(1H, s, 16-OH); 8.25(1H, dd, *J*=7.2, 1.3Hz, H-20); 7.55(1H, td, *J*=7.2, 1.2Hz, H-21); 7.84(1H, td, *J*=7.2, 1.3Hz, H-22); 7.79(1H, br d, *J*=7.2Hz); 5.65(1H, d, *J*=10.1, H-27); 2.69(1H, m, H-28); 1.06(3H, d, *J*=6.8Hz); 1.17(3H, d, *J*=6.8Hz); 2.22(3H, s, H-33); 1.49(3H, s, H-34); and 1.50ppm (3H, s, H-35).

^{13}C NMR:
($CDCl_3$) 87.6, C-2(d); 83.9, C-3(s); 133.7, C-4(s); 123.7, C-5(d); 125.6, C-6(d); 131.9, C-7(d); 116.1, C-8(d); 138.1, C-9(s); 169.4, C-11(s); 54.7, C-12(d); 34.6, C-13(t); 169.4, C-14(s); 71.4, C-15(s); 161.7, C-18(s); 120.3, C-19(s); 126.8, C-20(d); 128.2, C-21(d); 135.5, C-22(d); 128.0, C-23(d); 146.5, C-24(s); 151.5, C-26(s); 78.9, C-27(d); 31.8, C-28(d); 18.9, C-29(q); 18.9, C-30(q); 170.6, C-32(s); 20.8, C-33(q); 16.9, C-34(q); and 22.8ppm (q).

Mass Spectrum:
HRFAB-MS: 547.2183*m/e* ($C_{29}H_{31}N_4O_7$ requires 547.2193 [$(M+H)^+$]).

Reference

H. Fujimoto, E. Negishi, K. Yamaguchi, N. Nishi, and M. Yamazaki; Isolation of New Tremorgenic Metabolites from an Ascomycete, *Corynascus setosus*; Chem. Pharm. Bull.; Vol. 44, pp. 1843-1848(1996).

Common/Systematic Name

27-*epi*-Nortryptoquivaline

Molecular Formula/Molecular Weight

$C_{28}H_{28}N_4O_7$; MW = 532.19580

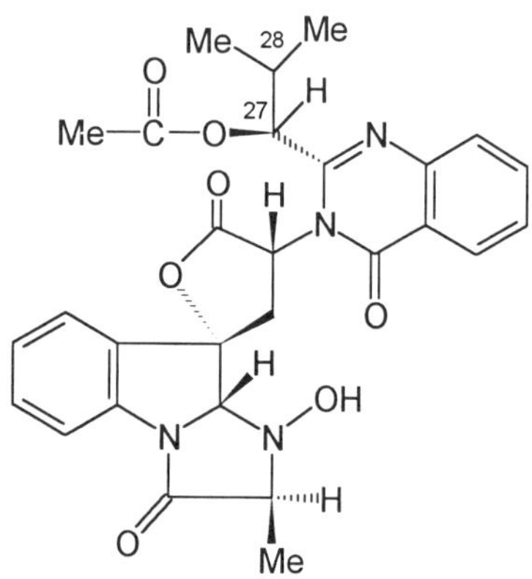

General Characteristics

Colorless needles from MeOH, mp., 236-238°C; $[\alpha]_D^{18}$ + 196° (c=0.292, in $CHCl_3$).

Fungal Source

Corynascus setosus (IFM 4648).

Isolation/Purification

Corynascus setosus was cultivated on sterilized rice at 25°C for 17 days. The moldy rice was extracted two times with ethyl acetate with shaking at room temperature for 2 hours, to give a crude extract which was partitioned with *n*-hexane-MeOH (1:1, v/v). The defatted layer was then partitioned with ethyl acetate-H_2O (1:1, v/v) and ethyl acetate layer was chromatographed on a silica gel column with n-hexane-ethyl acetate (2:1, v/v), (1:1, v/v), and (1:2, v/v), ethyl acetate and MeOH two times to give fractions I, II, III, and IV. Fraction III was further chromatographed on silica gel columns with *n*-hexane-ethyl acetate and $CHCl_3$-MeOH repeatedly to afford helvolic acid, helvolinic acid, setosusin, and 2-(1-oxo-2-hydroxyethyl)furan. Fraction I was chromatographed on silica gel columns with *n*-hexane-ethyl acetate repeatedly and on an octadecyl silica gel (ODS) column with acetonitrile-H_2O to furnish 27-*epi*-tryptoquivaline and 27-*epi*-nortryptoquivaline. Fraction II was also chromatographed in a similar manner to afford fiscalin B, previously identified from *Neosartorya fischeri*.

Biological Activity

27-*epi*-Tryptoquivaline and 27-*epi*-nortryptoquivaline caused a weak tremor when administered at 50mg/kg, i.p. The tremor appeared at *ca.* 30 and 120 minutes after injection and continued for *ca.* 120 and 30 minutes, respectively.

Spectral Data

UV:
λ_{max}^{MeOH} 209(sh, log ϵ = 4.64), 290(sh, 3.80), 307(sh, 3.53), and 318nm (sh, 3.43).

CD:
(Δϵ) 0(325), + 1.9(305), + 4.1(278), 0(259), and - 2.6(252nm) (c= 0.011, in EtOH).

IR:
($CHCl_3$) 3500, 3000, 1780. 1720, 1660, and 1600cm^{-1}.

^{1}H NMR:
($CDCl_3$) 5.23 (1H, s, H-2); 7.41(1H, br d, *J*=7.6Hz, H-5); 7.28(1H, td, *J*=7.6, 1.1Hz, H-6); 7.49(1H, td, *J*=7.6, 1.1Hz, H-7); 7.63(1H, br d, *J*=7.6Hz); 5.87(1H, t-like, *J*=10.1Hz, H-12); 3.09(1H, dd, *J*=13.3. 9.5Hz, H-13); 3.15(1H, dd, *J*=13.3. 10.7Hz, H-13); 4.35(1H, q, *J*=7.2Hz, H-15); 7.16(1H, s, 16-OH); 8.22(1H, dd, *J*=8.4, 1.5Hz, H-20); 7.55(1H, td, *J*=8.4, 1.3Hz, H-21); 7.84(1H, td, *J*=8.4, 1.5Hz, H-22); 7.79(1H, br d, *J*=8.4Hz); 5.66(1H, d, *J*=9.8, H-27); 2.68(1H, m, H-28); 0.98(3H, d, *J*=6.6Hz); 1.16(3H, d, *J*=6.6Hz); 2.21(3H, s, H-33); and 1.59ppm (3H, d, *J*=7.2Hz, H-35).

^{13}C NMR:
($CDCl_3$) 89.9, C-2(d); 83.9, C-3(s); 133.7, C-4(s); 125.7, C-5(d); 125.7, C-6(d); 131.9, C-7(d); 116.1, C-8(d); 137.8, C-9(s); 169.3, C-11(s); 54.6, C-12(d); 34.1, C-13(t); 169.2, C-14(s); 67.9, C-15(s); 161.8, C-18(s); 120.3, C-19(s); 126.7, C-20(d); 128.3, C-21(d); 135.5, C-22(d); 128.0, C-23(d); 146.5, C-24(s); 151.5, C-26(s); 79.0, C-27(d); 31.8, C-28(d); 19.0, C-29(q); 18.9, C-30(q); 170.5, C-32(s); 20.8, C-33(q); and 11.0ppm (q).

Mass Spectrum:
HRFAB-MS: 533.2023*m/e* ($C_{28}H_{29}N_4O_7$ requires 533.2036 [$(M+H)^+$]).

Reference

H. Fujimoto, E. Negishi, K. Yamaguchi, N. Nishi, and M. Yamazaki; Isolation of New Tremorgenic Metabolites form an Ascomycete, *Corynascus setosus*; Chem. Pharm. Bull.; Vol. 44, pp. 1843-1848(1996).

6

Penitrems/Lolitrems

Penitrem A
Penitrem B
Secopenitrem B
10-Oxo-11,33-dihydropenitrem B
Penitrem C
Penitrem D
Penitrem E
Penitrem F
Pennigritrem
PC-M4
Lolitrem B
Lolitrem E (Lolitrem C)
Lolitriol

Common/Systematic Name

Penitrem A

Molecular Formula/Molecular Weight

$C_{37}H_{44}NO_6Cl$; MW = 633.28572

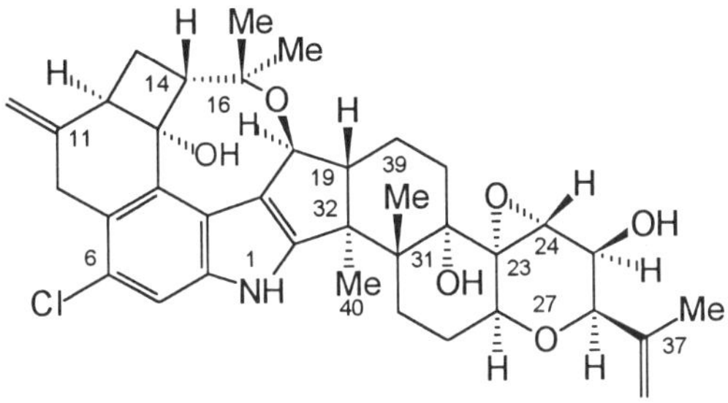

General Characteristics

White amorphous solid.

Fungal Source

Penicillium crustosum.

Isolation/Purification

P. crustosum cultures were filtered and the mycelium macerated with acetone in a Waring blender. The acetone solution was evaporated and the aqueous residue partitioned between dichloromethane and water. The residue from the dichloromethane solution was partitioned between *n*-hexane and 90% methanol. The 90% methanol solution was evaporated and the aqueous residue once again partitioned between dichloromethane and water. The crude extract obtained from the dichloromethane solution was percolated through a short silica-gel column with benzene-acetone (4:1, v/v) to give the mixture of penitrems. Residual material on the column was eluted with benzene-acetone (1:4, v/v) to give the fraction containing crude roquefortine. This material was purified by percolation through an aluminum oxide (activity II-III) column with chloroform-methanol (9:1, v/v) to yield, after crystallization from aqueous methanol, roquefortine, mp., 196-200°C. The mixture of penitrems was separated and purified by column chromatography on silica gel using benzene-acetone (85:15, v/v) to yield the six penitrems in the following order of descending R_f values: penitrem F, B, A, E, C, and D.

Biological Activity

Highly tremorgenic and acutely toxic.

Spectral Data

UV:

λ_{max}^{MeOH} 233 and 295nm (ε=37,000 and 11,600).

IR:
(KBr) 3400, 2930, 1710, and 1650cm^{-1}.

CD:
325, 0; 315, 0.91; 300, 0; 255, 0; 236, -14.09; and 210nm, 0.

^{1}H NMR:
[$(CD_3)_2CO$] The intensities of four of the signals (10.03, s; 4.16, s; 3.40, d, *J*=7.5Hz; and 3.32ppm, s) decreased upon addition of deuterium oxide to the sample as well as through saturation transfer upon irradiation of the water resonance at 2.84ppm. The signal at 10.03ppm was assigned to the NH proton of the indole moiety whereas the remaining signals were attributed to hydroxy protons. The one-proton aromatic singlet at 7.24ppm was assigned to 7-H; five three-proton signals at 1.75, 1.71, 1.40, 1.22, and 1.07ppm were assigned to tertiary methyl groups. The signal at 1.71ppm showed broadening, which was resolved in the resolution enhanced spectrum, due to long-range couplings. The remainder of the ^{1}H-spectrum exhibited extensive fine structure (see de Jesus, *et al.*, 1983).

^{13}C NMR:
[$(CD_3)_2CO$] C-2, 154.36; C-3,120.64; C-4, 133.29; C-5, 125.80; C-6, 124.56; C-7,111.86; C-8, 121.99; C-9, 139.3; C-10, 35.06; C-11, 149.48; C-12,47.01; C-13, 24.67; C-14, 52.71; C-15, 81.01; C-16, 76.09; C-18,72.44; C-19, 58.79; C-20, 18.56; C-21, 30.59; C-22, 78.24; C-23, 66.11; C-24, 61.92; C-25, 66.31; C-26, 74.67; C-28, 71.99; C-29, 28.89; C-30, 26.91; C-31, 43.55; C-32, 50.08; C-33, 107.10; C-34, 20.32; C-35, 31.06; C-36, 19.70; C-37, 143.27; C-38, 111.64, C-39, 18.98; and C-40, 21.35ppm.

Mass Spectrum:
HREIMS showed M^+ at 633.2859, $C_{37}H_{44}NO_6Cl$ requires 633.2857.

Reference

A. E. de Jesus, P. S. Steyn, F. R. van Heerden, R. Vleggaar, P. L. Wessels, and W. E. Hull, Tremorgenic Mycotoxins from *Penicillium crustosum*: Isolation of Penitrems A-F and the Structure Elucidation and Absolute Configuration of Penitrem A; J. Chem. Soc. Perkin Trans. I, pp. 1847-1856(1983).

Common/Systematic Name

Penitrem B

Molecular Formula/Molecular Weight

$C_{37}H_{45}NO_5$; MW = 583.32977

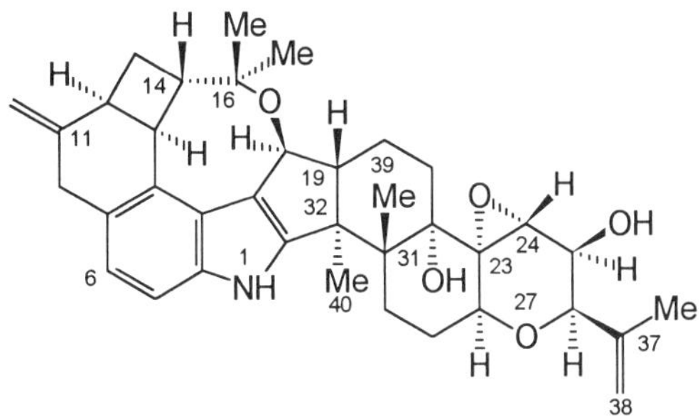

General Characteristics

White amorphous solid.

Fungal Source

Penicillium crustosum.

Isolation/Purification

P. crustosum cultures were filtered and the mycelium macerated with acetone in a Waring blender. The acetone solution was evaporated and the aqueous residue partitioned between dichloromethane and water. The residue from the dichloromethane solution was partitioned between *n*-hexane and 90% methanol. The 90% methanol solution was evaporated and the aqueous residue once again partitioned between dichloromethane and water. The crude extract obtained from the dichloromethane solution was percolated through a short silica-gel column with benzene-acetone (4:1, v/v) to give the mixture of penitrems. Residual material on the column was eluted with benzene-acetone (1:4, v/v) to give the fraction containing crude roquefortine. This material was purified by percolation through an aluminum oxide (activity II-III) column with chloroform-methanol (9:1, v/v) to yield, after crystallization from aqueous methanol, roquefortine; mp., 196-200°C. The mixture of penitrems was separated and purified by column chromatography on silica gel using benzene-acetone (85:15, v/v) to yield the six penitrems in the following order of descending R_f values: penitrem F, B, A, E, C, and D.

Biological Activity

Highly tremorgenic and acutely toxic.

Spectral Data

UV:

220 and 286nm (ϵ=31,900 and 11,900, respectively).

IR:
(KBr) 3400, 2930, 1700, and 1650cm^{-1}.

CD:
305, 0; 285, -2.56; 252, -0.60; and 236nm, -9.50.

^{1}H NMR:
The ^{1}HNMR of penitrem B showed that the structure differed from penitrem A in that both the chlorine atom and the C-15 hydroxy group are replaced by hydrogen atoms. The chemical shifts and coupling constants of rings A-F are similar to those of penitrem D.

^{13}C NMR:
C-2, 152.97; C-3, 119.40; C-4, 128.84; C-5, 128.13; C-6, 120.99; C-7, 110.26; C-8, 123.19; C-9, 139.34; C-10, 38.75; C-11, 150.22; C-12, 35.04; C-13, 26.69; C-14, 52.32; C-15, 39.35; C-16, 75.47; C-18, 72.10; C-19, 59.12; C-20, 18.61; C-21, 30.58; C-22, 78.26; C-23, 66.16; C-24, 61.95; C-25, 66.33; C-26, 74.68; C-28, 72.03; C-29, 28.92; C-30, 26.85; C-31, 43.60; C-32, 49.68; C-33, 105.86; C-34, 18.61; C-35, 28.80; C-36, 19.71; C-37, 143.29; C-38, 111.64, C-39, 18.92; and C-40, 21.24ppm.

Mass Spectrum:
HREIMS: found, M$^+$, 583.3302; $C_{37}H_{45}NO_5$ requires 583.3297.

Reference

A. E. de Jesus, P. S. Steyn, F. R. van Heerden, R. Vleggaar, P. L. Wessels and W. E. Hull; Tremorgenic Mycotoxins from *Penicillium crustosum*: Isolation of Penitrems A-F and the Structure Elucidation and Absolute Configuration of Penitrem A; J. Chem. Soc. Perkin Trans. I, pp. 1847-1856(1983).

Common/Systematic Name

Secopenitrem B

Molecular Formula/Molecular Weight

$C_{37}H_{47}NO_5$; MW = 585.34542

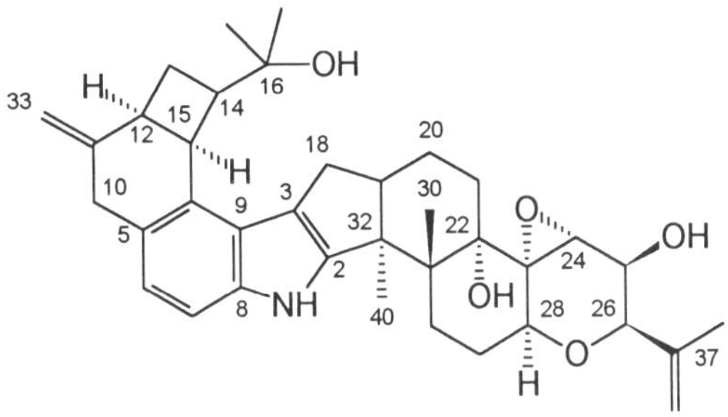

General Characteristics

Orange-brown solid; mp., 185-189°C dec; $[\alpha]_D$ -5.2° (*c*=0.005g/ml, in $CHCl_3$).

Fungal Source

Sclerotia of *Aspergillus sulphureus* (NRRL 4077).

Isolation/Purification

Powdered sclerotia of *A. sulphureus* were sequentially extracted with pentane and CH_2Cl_2 using a Soxhlet apparatus. A portion of the total CH_2Cl_2 extract was fractionated by silica gel column chromatography. A stepwise gradient from 0 to 10% (v/v) MeOH in $CHCl_3$ was employed resulting in the elution and collection of a distinct red band at 4% MeOH. This active fraction was further separated by reversed-phase HPLC (MeOH-H_2O, 89:11, v/v) to yield sulpinines A, B, C, and secopenitrem B (HPLC retention time, 8.5 min) and penitrem B.

Biological Activity

Exhibited potent activity against the lepidopteran crop pest *Helicoverpa zea*.

Spectral Data

^{1}H NMR:

($CDCl_3$) H-6, 6.88(d, *J*=8.1); H-7, 7.07(d, J=8.1); H-10, 3.90(br d, *J*=15.1), 3.40(d, *J*=15.3); H-12, 3.15(dd, *J*=8.9, 8.8); H-13, 2.33(m), 1.85(m); H-14, 2.48(m); H-15, 4.08(dd, *J*=8.5, 8.7); H-18, 2.99(dd, *J*=13.0, 6.1), 2.47(m); H-19, 2.75(m); H-20, 1.89 (m), 1.62 (m); H-21, 1.53(m), 1.50(m); H-24, 3.64(d, *J*=2.3); H-25, 4.03(br s); H-26, 4.10(br s); H-28, 4.30(dd, *J*=9, 9); H-29, 2.36(m), 1.93(m); H-30, 2.67(ddd, *J*=13.6, 13.6, 5.1), 1.33(m); H-33, 4.83(br s), 4.72(br s); H3-34, 1.16(s); H3-35, 1.07(s); H3-36, 1.72(br s); H-38, 5.16(br s), 5.02(br s); H3-39, 1.163(s); and H3-40, 1.175ppm (s).

^{13}C NMR:

(CDCl$_3$) C-2, 152.0; C-3, 116.3; C-4, 131.3; C-5, 129.7; C-6, 121.1; C-7, 109.3; C-8, 123.4; C-9, 138.9, C-10, 37.6; C-11, 149.2; C-12, 36.5; C-13, 25.8; C-14, 52.3; C-15, 37.0, C-16, 71.4; C-18, 29.4; C-19, 49.9; C-20, 20.5; C-21, 30.2; C-22, 78.0; C-23, 65.8; C-24, 61.8; C-25, 64.7; C-26, 73.6; C-28, 71.5; C-29, 27.7; C-30, 27.4; C-31, 42.4; C-32, 50.2; C-33, 108.3; C-34, 26.5; C-35, 27.3; C-36, 19.5; C-37, 141.1; C-38, 112.3; C-39, 18.6; and C-40, 15.6ppm.

Mass Spectrum:

EIMS: 585(M^+, 4), 667(11), 552(17), 531(6), 516(7), 499(84), 484(40), 437(33), 422(35), 369(32), 354(26), 314(70), 301(31), 246(100), 233(37), and 194*m/e* (38); HRFABMS: obsd 586.3589, calcd for $C_{37}H_{47}NO_5$ + H, 586.3532.

Reference

J. A. Laakso, J. B. Gloer, D. T. Wicklow, and P. F. Dowd; Sulpinines A-C and Secopenitrem B: New Antiinsectan Metabolites from the Sclerotia of *Aspergillus sulphureus*; J. Org. Chem., Vol. 57, pp. 2066-2071(1992).

Common/Systematic Name

10-Oxo-11,33-dihydropenitrem B

Molecular Formula/Molecular Weight

$C_{37}H_{45}NO_6$; MW = 599.32469

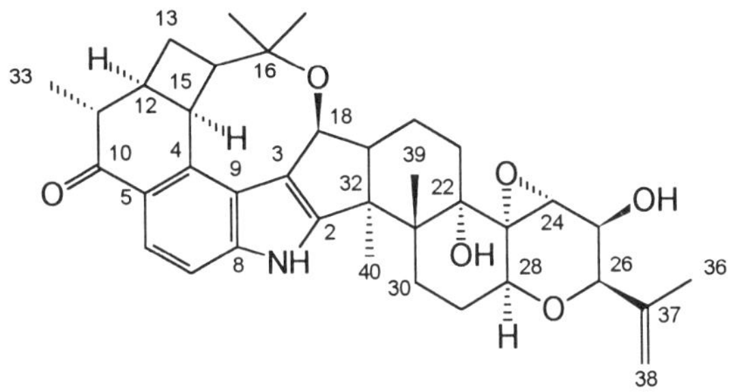

General Characteristics

Obtained as a light yellow solid, $[\alpha]_D$ -78.6° (*c*=0.2 g/dL).

Fungal Source

Sclerotia of *Aspergillus sulphureus* (NRRL 4077).

Isolation/Purification

Sclerotia of *A. sulphureus* (NRRL 4077) were ground with a Tecator mill and sequentially extracted with pentane and CH_2Cl_2 using a Soxhlet apparatus. A portion of the total CH_2Cl_2 extract was fractionated by silica gel column chromatography. A stepwise gradient from 0-10% (v/v) MeOH in $CHCl_3$ was employed, resulting in the elution of a distinct red band at 4% MeOH. The fraction that yielded 10-oxo-11,33-dihydropenitrem B eluted immediately after this distinct band. This fraction was separated further by reversed-phase HPLC (92:8(v/v), MeOH-H_2O; Beckman Ultrasphere ODS column, 5μm particles, 250x10mm, 2.5 mL/min) to give 10-oxo-11,33-dihydropenitrem B as a light yellow solid (HPLC retention time, 8.9 min).

Biological Activity

Exhibited potent activity in dietary assays against the corn earworm, *Helicoverpa zea* and was also moderately effective as a feeding deterrent against the dried fruit beetle, *Carpophilus hemipterus*.

Spectral Data

UV:

λ_{max}^{MeOH} 261(ϵ=28,900) and 289nm (7,310).

IR:
(neat) 3532, 3342, 1660, 1457, 1231, 1038, 934, and 757cm^{-1}.

^{1}H NMR:
(CD_3OD) H-6, 7.38(d, *J*=8.5Hz); H-7, 7.18(d, *J*=8.5Hz); H-11, 2.81(br q, *J*=6.4Hz); H-12, 2.27(m); H-13a, 2.18(m); H-13b, 1.91(m); H-14, 2.77(m); H-15, 3.83(dd, *J*=9.2, 9.2Hz); H-18, 4.89(d, *J*=8.2Hz); H-19, 2.65(m); H-20_{ax}, 1.93(m); H-20_{eq}, 1.77(m); H-21_{ax}, 1.47(ddd, *J*=13.4, 12.7, 4.0Hz); H-21_{eq}, 1.74(m); H-24, 3.49(br, *J*=8Hz); H-25, 4.04(br, s); H-26, 4.03(br, s); H-28, 4.29(dd, *J*=9.2, 8.6Hz); H-29_{ax}, 2.10(m); H-29_{eq}, 2.29(m); H-30_{ax}, 2.61(ddd, *J*=13.8, 13.3, 5.2Hz); H-30_{eq}, 1.62(dd, *J*=13.0, 6.1Hz); H-33, 1.14(d, *J*=6.4Hz); H-34, 1.55(s); H-35, 1.20(s); H-36, 1.71(br, s); H-38a, 5.09(br, s); H-38b, 4.91(br, s); H-39, 1.23(s); and H-40, 1.42ppm (s).

^{13}C NMR:
(CD_3OD) C-2, 155.1; C-3, 120.8; C-4, 136.5; C-5, 125.8; C-6, 118.9; C-7, 111.4; C-8, 143.4; C-9, 122.7; C-10, 203.8; C-11, 46.6; C-12, 34.4; C-13, 28.7; C-14, 50.5; C-15, 35.7; C-16, 77.3; C-18, 73.2; C-19, 59.9; C-20, 18.8; C-21, 30.5; C-22, 78.5; C-23, 66.7; C-24, 62.2; C-25, 66.5; C-26, 75.1; C-27, 72.7; C-28, 29.0; C-30, 27.0; C-31, 44.0; C-32, 50.9; C-33, 12.7; C-34, 19.0; C-35, 28.7; C-36, 19.8; C-37, 143.2; C-38, 111.9; C-39, 19.0; and C-40, 21.2ppm.

Mass Spectrum:
EIMS: 599(M^+, 26%), 493(15), 469(26), 400(9), 265(12), 264(65), 134(26), 133(23), 131(23), 130(100), and 119*m/e* (54); HREIMS: obsd 599.3244*m/e*, calcd for $C_{37}H_{45}NO_6$, 599.3247.

Reference

J. A. Laakso, J. B. Gloer, D.T. Wicklow, and P. F. Dowd; A New Penitrem Analog with Antiinsectan Activity from the Sclerotia of *Aspergillus sulphureus*; J. Agric. Food Chem, Vol. 41, pp. 973-975(1993).

Common/Systematic Name
Penitrem C

Molecular Formula/Molecular Weight
$C_{37}H_{44}NO_4Cl$; MW = 601.29589

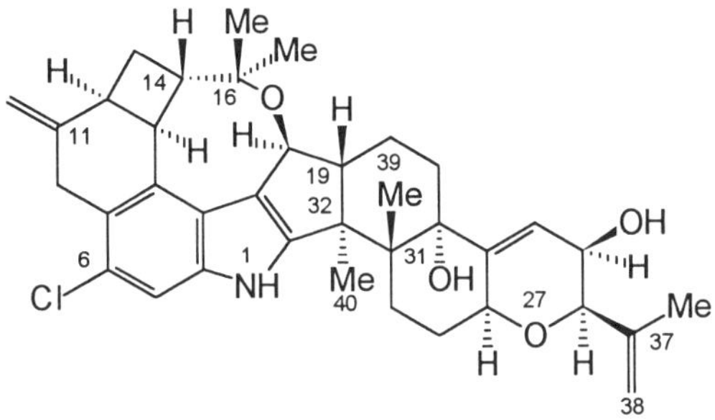

General Characteristics
White amorphous solid.

Fungal Source
Penicillium crustosum.

Isolation/Purification
P. crustosum cultures were filtered and the mycelium macerated with acetone in a Waring blender. The acetone solution was evaporated and the aqueous residue partitioned between dichloromethane and water. The residue from the dichloromethane solution was partitioned between *n*-hexane and 90% methanol. The 90% methanol solution was evaporated and the aqueous residue once again partitioned between dichloromethane and water. The crude extract obtained from the dichloromethane solution was percolated through a short silica-gel column with benzene-acetone (4:1, v/v) to give the mixture of penitrems. Residual material on the column was eluted with benzene-acetone (1:4, v/v) to give the fraction containing crude roquefortine. This material was purified by percolation through an aluminum oxide (activity II-III) column with chloroform-methanol (9:1, v/v) to yield, after crystallization from aqueous methanol, roquefortine, m.p. 196-200°C. The mixture of penitrems was separated and purified by column chromatography on silica gel using benzene-acetone (85:15, v/v) to yield the six penitrems in the following order of descending R_f values: penitrem F, B, A, E, C, and D.

Biological Activity
Highly tremorgenic and acutely toxic.

Spectral Data

UV:
λ_{max}^{MeOH} 232 and 292nm (ϵ=38,200 and 12,500).

IR:
(KBr) 3400, 2930, 1700, and 1650cm^{-1}.

CD:
310, 0; 299, -2.11; 260, -0.40; 235, -13.85; 220, -10.46; and 211nm, -14.27.

^{1}H NMR:
Refer to the reference below for detailed ^{1}H NMR data.

^{13}C NMR:
[$(CD_3)_2CO$] C-2, 154.38; C-3, 119.33; C-4, 130.73; C-5, 125.73; C-6, 125.28; C-7, 110.56; C-8, 122.33; C-9, 138.75; C-10, 35.63; C-11, 148.94; C-12,34.86; C-13, 26.61; C-14, 52.37; C-15, 39.63; C-16, 75.49; C-18, 72.03; C-19, 58.89; C-20, 19.06; C-21, 35.00; C-22, 77.45; C-23, 148.33; C-24, 119.70; C-25, 64.27; C-26, 74.36; C-28, 80.38; C-29, 29.19; C-30, 27.71; C-31, 43.67; C-32, 49.91; C-33, 107.35; C-34, 18.64; C-35, 28.77; C-36, 19.97; C-37, 143.90; C-38, 110.78, C-39, 20.10; and C-40, 21.15ppm.

Mass Spectrum:
HREIMS showed M^+ at 601.2956, $C_{37}H_{44}NO_4Cl$ requires 601.2958.

Reference

A. E. de Jesus, P. S. Steyn, F. R. van Heerden, R. Vleggaar, P. L. Wessels and W. E. Hull; Tremorgenic Mycotoxins from *Penicillium crustosum*: Isolation of Penitrems A-F and the Structure Elucidation and Absolute Configuration of Penitrem A; J. Chem. Soc. Perkin Trans. I, pp. 1847-1856(1983).

Common/Systematic Name

Penitrem D

Molecular Formula/Molecular Weight

$C_{37}H_{45}NO_4$; MW = 567.33486

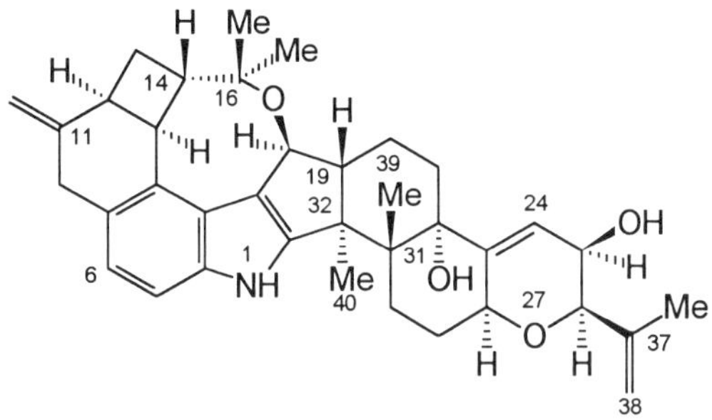

General Characteristics

Penitrem D crystallized from benzene as white needles; mp., >300°C (decomp.).

Fungal Source

Penicillium crustosum.

Isolation/Purification

P. crustosum cultures were filtered and the mycelium macerated with acetone in a Waring blender. The acetone solution was evaporated and the aqueous residue partitioned between dichloromethane and water. The residue from the dichloromethane solution was partitioned between *n*-hexane and 90% methanol. The 90% methanol solution was evaporated and the aqueous residue once again partitioned between dichloromethane and water. The crude extract obtained from the dichloromethane solution was percolated through a short silica-gel column with benzene-acetone (4:1, v/v) to give the mixture of penitrems. Residual material on the column was eluted with benzene-acetone (1:4, v/v) to give the fraction containing crude roquefortine. This material was purified by percolation through an aluminum oxide (activity II-III) column with chloroform-methanol (9:1, v/v) to yield, after crystallization from aqueous methanol, roquefortine; mp., 196-200°C. The mixture of penitrems was separated and purified by column chromatography on silica gel using benzene-acetone (85:15, v/v) to yield the six penitrems in the following order of descending R_f values: penitrem F, B, A, E, C, and D.

Biological Activity

Highly tremorgenic and acutely toxic.

Spectral Data

UV:
λ_{max}^{MeOH} 220 and 286nm (ϵ=34,300 and 11,200).

CD:
310, 0; 282, -1.95; 255, -0.60; 232, -12.85; 223, -9.83; 209, -18.89; and 199nm, 0.

IR:
(KBr) 3400, 1700, and 1650cm^{-1}.

^{1}H NMR:
Refer to de Jesus *et al.*, 1983.

^{13}C NMR:
[$(CD_3)_2CO$] C-2, 153.49; C-3, 119.16; C-4, 128.80; C-5, 128.09; C-6, 120.91; C-7, 110.22; C-8, 123.18; C-9, 139.27 C-10, 38.75; C-11, 150.23; C-12, 35.04; C-13, 26.70; C-14, 52.36; C-15, 39.37; C-16, 75.44; C-18, 72.17; C-19, 58.87; C-20, 19.11; C-21, 35.08; C-22, 77.48; C-23, 148.44; C-24, 119.59; C-25, 64.28; C-26, 74.40; C-28, 80.39; C-29, 29.24; C-30, 27.68; C-31, 43.71; C-32, 49.77; C-33, 105.83; C-34, 18.64; C-35, 28.81; C-36, 19.98; C-37, 143.92; C-38, 110.75, C-39, 20.11; and C-40, 21.32ppm.

Mass Spectrum:
HREIMS showed M^+ at 567.3339; $C_{37}H_{45}NO_4$ requires 567.3348.

Reference

A. E. de Jesus, P. S. Steyn, F. R. van Heerden, R. Vleggaar, P. L. Wessels, and W. E. Hull; Tremorgenic Mycotoxins from *Penicillium crustosum*: Isolation of Penitrems A-F and the Structure Elucidation and Absolute Configuration of Penitrem A; J. Chem. Soc. Perkin Trans. I, pp. 1847-1856(1983).

Common/Systematic Name

Penitrem E

Molecular Formula/Molecular Weight

$C_{37}H_{45}NO_6$; MW = 599.32469

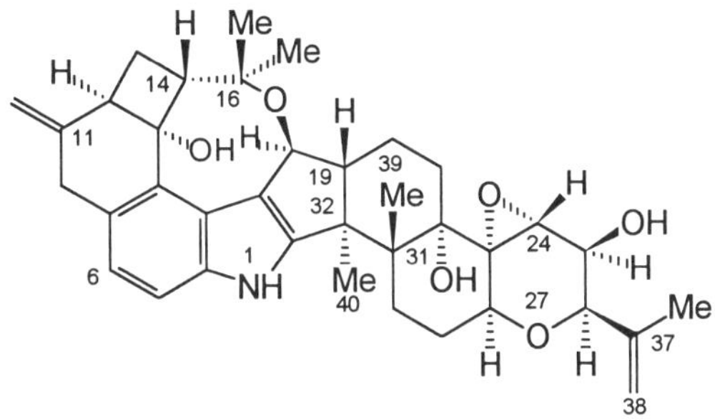

General Characteristics

White amorphous solid.

Fungal Source

Penicillium crustosum.

Isolation/Purification

P. crustosum cultures were filtered and the mycelium macerated with acetone in a Waring blender. The acetone solution was evaporated and the aqueous residue partitioned between dichloromethane and water. The residue from the dichloromethane solution was partitioned between *n*-hexane and 90% methanol. The 90% methanol solution was evaporated and the aqueous residue once again partitioned between dichloromethane and water. The crude extract obtained from the dichloromethane solution was percolated through a short silica-gel column with benzene-acetone (4:1, v/v) to give the mixture of penitrems. Residual material on the column was eluted with benzene-acetone (1:4, v/v) to give the fraction containing crude roquefortine. This material was purified by percolation through an aluminum oxide (activity II-III) column with chloroform-methanol (9:1, v/v) to yield, after crystallization from aqueous methanol, roquefortine, m.p. 196-200°C. The mixture of penitrems was separated and purified by column chromatography on silica gel using benzene-acetone (85:15, v/v) to yield the six penitrems in the following order of descending R_f values: penitrem F, B, A, E, C, and D.

Biological Activity

Highly tremorgenic and acutely toxic.

Spectral Data

UV:

λ_{max}^{MeOH} 220 and 286nm (ϵ=34,200 and 11,200).

IR:

(KBr) 3400, 2930, 1700, and 1650cm^{-1}.

CD:

325, 0; 317, 0.58; 300, 0; 250, 0; 234, -11.28; and 210nm, 0.

^{1}H NMR:

The only major differences between the ^{1}H NMR spectra of penitrem A and E are observed for those protons in close proximity to the chlorine atom. Two ortho-substituted protons were evident from the magnitude of the coupling constant (8.3Hz) observed for resonances at 6.70 and 7.09ppm. The chemical shift difference for the C-10 protons (10-H_a and 10-H_b) was 0.57ppm for penitrem A but -0.26ppm in the case of penitrem E (see de Jesus, *et al.*, 1983 for fine structure in ^{1}H NMR spectrum).

^{13}C NMR:

[$(CD_3)_2CO$] C-2, 153.48; C-3, 120.38; C-4, 131.52; C-5, 128.16; C-6, 120.34; C-7, 111.63; C-8, 122.75; C-9, 140.16; C-10, 38.11; C-11, 150.91; C-12, 47.41; C-13, 24.27; C-14, 52.78; C-15, 81.08; C-16, 76.09; C-18, 72.52; C-19, 58.86; C-20, 18.63; C-22, 78.28; C-23, 66.17; C-24, 61.95; C-25, 66.34; C-26, 74.69; C-28, 72.05; C-29, 28.94; C-30, 26.89; C-31, 43.58; C-32, 49.92; C-33, 105.47; C-34, 20.28; C-35, 31.10; C-36, 19.70; C-37, 143.31; C-38, 111.62, C-39, 18.99; and C-40, 21.53ppm.

Mass Spectrum:

HREIMS showed M^+ at 599.3252; $C_{37}H_{45}NO_6$, requires 599.3246.

Reference

A. E. de Jesus, P. S. Steyn, F. R. van Heerden, R. Vleggaar, P. L. Wessels, and W. E. Hull; Tremorgenic Mycotoxins from *Penicillium crustosum*: Isolation of Penitrems A-F and the Structure Elucidation and Absolute Configuration of Penitrem A; J. Chem. Soc. Perkin Trans. I, pp. 1847-1856(1983).

Common/Systematic Name
Penitrem F

Molecular Formula/Molecular Weight
$C_{37}H_{44}NO_5Cl$; MW = 617.29080

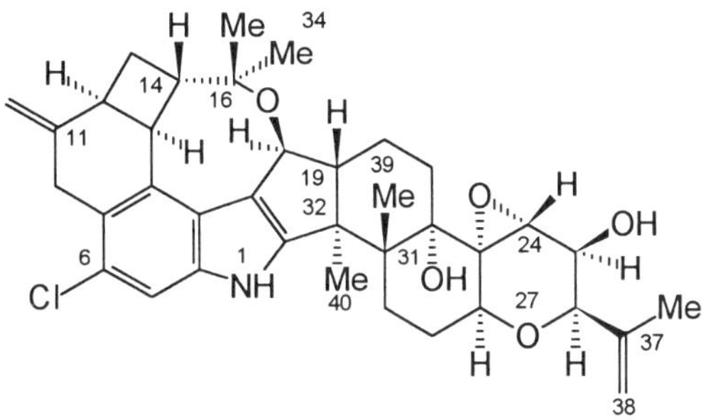

General Characteristics
White amorphous solid.

Fungal Source
Penicillium crustosum.

Isolation/Purification
P. crustosum cultures were filtered and the mycelium macerated with acetone in a Waring blender. The acetone solution was evaporated and the aqueous residue partitioned between dichloromethane and water. The residue from the dichloromethane solution was partitioned between *n*-hexane and 90% methanol. The 90% methanol solution was evaporated and the aqueous residue once again partitioned between dichloromethane and water. The crude extract obtained from the dichloromethane solution was percolated through a short silica-gel column with benzene-acetone (4:1, v/v) to give the mixture of penitrems. Residual material on the column was eluted with benzene-acetone (1:4, v/v) to give the fraction containing crude roquefortine. This material was purified by percolation through an aluminum oxide (activity II-III) column with chloroform-methanol (9:1, v/v) to yield, after crystallization from aqueous methanol, roquefortine, m.p. 196-200°C. The mixture of penitrems was separated and purified by column chromatography on silica gel using benzene-acetone (85:15, v/v) to yield the six penitrems in the following order of descending R_f values: penitrem F, B, A, E, C, and D.

Biological Activity
Highly tremorgenic and acutely toxic.

Spectral Data

UV:
232 and 292nm (ε=35,500 and 11,30, respectively).

IR:
(KBr) 3400, 2930, 1700, and 1650cm^{-1}.

CD:
315, 0; 290, -2.50; 255, 0; 220, -10.10, and 200nm, 0.

^{1}H NMR:
In the ^{1}H NMR spectrum of penitrem F, a new proton signal was observed at 3.87ppm. The presence of additional (H,H) couplings between the cyclobutane protons as well as the changes in their chemical shift values show that the C-15 hydroxyl group in penitrem A is replaced by a hydrogen atom in F. The effect of replacing the C-15 hydroxyl group with a hydrogen atom is especially pronounced for 18-H and the C-34 methyl protons owing to a decrease in steric hindrance as all three of these groups are located below the plane of the eight-membered ring (refer to de Jesus, *et al.*, 1983 below for detailed ^{1}H NMR data).

^{13}C NMR:
C-2, 153.86; C-3, 119.56; C-4, 130.76; C-5, 125.76; C-6, 125.36; C-7, 110.60; C-8, 122.33; C-9, 138.81 C-10, 35.63; C-11, 148.92; C-12, 34.86; C-13, 26.61; C-14, 52.34; C-15, 39.54; C-16, 75.51; C-18,71.97; C-19, 59.13; C-20, 18.55; C-21, 30.49; C-22, 78.23; C-23, 66.10; C-24, 61.93; C-25, 66.31; C-26, 74.67; C-28, 71.97; C-29, 28.88; C-30, 26.89; C-31, 43.55; C-32, 49.82; C-33, 107.36; C-34, 18.62; C-35, 28.75; C-36, 19.70; C-37, 143.26; C-38, 111.65, C-39, 18.91; and C-40, 21.06ppm.

Mass Spectrum:
HREIMS: found, M^{+}, 617.2908; $C_{37}H_{44}NO_5Cl$ requires 617.2907.

Reference

A. E. de Jesus, P. S. Steyn, F. R. van Heerden, R. Vleggaar, P. L. Wessels and W. E. Hull; Tremorgenic Mycotoxins from *Penicillium crustosum*: Isolation of Penitrems A-F and the Structure Elucidation and Absolute Configuration of Penitrem A; J. Chem. Soc. Perkin Trans. I, pp. 1847-1856(1983).

Common/Systematic Name

Pennigritrem

Molecular Formula/Molecular Weight

$C_{37}H_{44}NO_6Cl$; MW = 633.28572

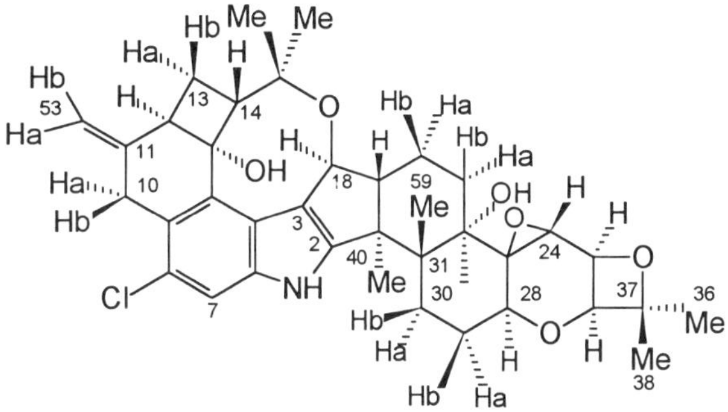

General Characteristics

Pennigritrem was isolated as a white amorphous solid.

Fungal Source

Penicillium nigricans (IMI 228669).

Isolation/Purification

Extracted with acetone, evaporated to dryness and the residue dissolved in acetone-chloroform (1:1, v/v); silica gel 60 (Merck 230-400 mesh) was added and the mixture evaporated and fractionated by flash chromatography using a silica gel column eluted with chloroform-acetone (19:1, v/v). Final purification was with preparative HPLC using Dynamax C_{18} reversed-phase chromatography with MeOH-water (3:1, v/v) at 11ml/min. and detection at 233nm.

Biological Activity

Tremorgenic; albino mice (male) administered a colloidal suspension (4.6mg/300 mm^3, ethanol-dimethyl sulfoxide-water, 1:1:1, v/v/v) produced tremor within 0.5hr. This represents a marked reduction in tremorgenic activity when compared to penitrem A (50μg/200mm^3).

Spectral Data

UV:

λ_{max} 235 and 295nm (ε=35,700 and 10,300).

^1H NMR:

1N-H, 10.0; H-7, 7.24; H-10a, 3.63, H-10b, 3.26; H-12, 2.96; H-13a, 2.41, H-13b,

2.24; H-14, 2.45; OH-15, 4.19; H-16 CH_3, 1.05, 1.74; H-18,4.90; H-19, 2.60; H-20a, 1.94, H-20b, 1.79; H-21a, 2.03, H-21b, 1.62; OH-22, 3.48; H-24, 3.35; H-25, 4.60; (1H, J=4.17Hz); H-26, 3.87(1H, J=4.17Hz); H-28, 3.50(1H, J=4.21Hz and 7.18Hz); H-29a, 2.66(1H, J=4.21Hz); H-29b, 1.93(1H, J=7.18Hz); H-30a, 2.53; H-30b, 1.74; H-31 CH_3, 1.35; H-32 CH_3, 1.43; H-33a, 5.01; and H-37, 2X CH_3, 1.40, and 1.20ppm.

^{13}C NMR:

C-2, 154.11 s; C-3, 120.47 s; C-4, 133.26 s; C-5, 125.76 s; C-6, 124.50 s; C-7, 111.78 d; C-8, 121.97 s; C-9, 139.66 s; C-10, 35.02 t; C-11, 149.42 s; C-12, 46.90 d; C-13, 24.63 t; C-14, 52.63 d; C-15, 80.85 s; C-16, 76.04 s; C-18, 72.59 d; C-19, 58.39 d; C-20, 18.78 t; C-21, 30.65 t; C-22, 77.36 s; C-23, 67.15 s; C-24, 56.52 d; C-25, 70.45 d; C-26, 75.56 s; C-28, 73.79 d; C-29, 27.53 t; C-30, 26.70 t; C-31, 42.89 s; C-32, 50.35 s; C-33, 107.08 t; C-34, 20.26 q; C-35, 31.01 q; C-36, 22.96 q; C-37, 85.93 s; C-38, 21.87 t, q; C-39, 25.71 q; and C-40, 21.46ppm q.

Reference

J. Penn, J. R. Biddle, P. G. Mantle, J. N. Bilton, and R. N. Sheppard; Pennigritrem, a Naturally-Occurring Penitrem A Analogue with Novel Cyclisation in the Diterpenoid Moiety; J. Chem. Soc., Perkin Trans I, pp. 23-26(1991).

Common/Systematic Name
PC-M4

Molecular Formula/Molecular Weight
$C_{37}H_{49}NO_4$; MW = 571.36616

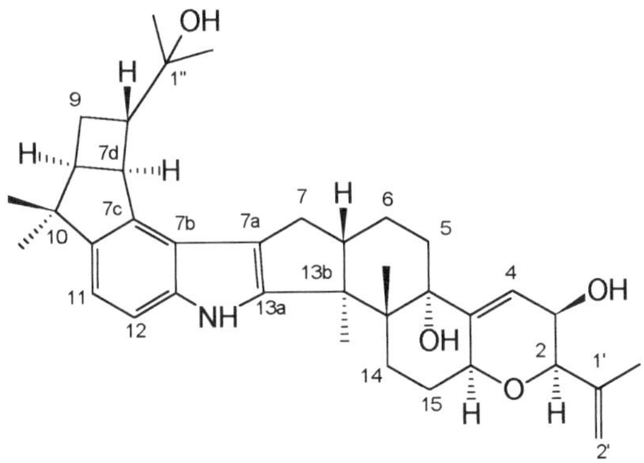

General Characteristics
Crystalline powder, mp., 269-272°C (dec.).

Fungal Source
Penicillium crustosum (strain NHL 6491).

Isolation/Purification
Penicillium crustosum was cultivated at 25°C for 14 days using Czapek-Dox medium supplemented with 0.2% yeast extract. The mycelium was extracted with CH_2Cl_2 at room temperature. The residue obtained by evaporation of the extract was chromatographed on silica gel with C_6H_6-Me_2CO (5:1, v/v) followed by repeated purification by LPLC [C_6H_6-Me_2CO (20:1, v/v) or C_6H_{14}-EtOAc-MeOH (12:6:1, v/v/v to obtain PC-M4 and with C_6H_6-Me_2CO (3:1, v/v)] followed by purification by HPLC using the solvent system C_6H_6-EtOAc (5:2, v/v) to give PC-M5.

Biological Activity
Biological activity not presented but based on structure PC-M4 is probably tremorgenic.

Spectral Data

UV:
λ_{max}^{MeOH} 233(log ε=4.09) and 283nm (3.71).

IR:
(KBr) 3600 and 3400cm^{-1} (NH, OH).

CD:
(c=$4.06x10^{-5}$, MeOH) +1.6(214), -2.0(240), -0.6(271), and -0.5nm (292).

^{1}H NMR:
[$(CD_3)_2SO$] 0.96(6H, s, Me-13C, Me-1"); 1.21(3H, s, Me-13b); 1.23(3H, s, Me-1"); 1.25(3H, s, Me-10); 1.27(3H, s, Me-10); 1.55(1H, brd, *J*=11.5 Hz, H-5a); 1.62(1H, brd, *J*=12.2 Hz, H-6B); 1.67-1.88(5H, m, H-6a, H-14B, H-15B, H2-9); 1.72(3H, brs, Me-1'); 1.93(2H, m, H-5B, H-8); 2.05(1H, m, H-15a); 2.29(1H, dd, J=13.1, 10.5 Hz, H-7a); 2.46(1H, ddd, *J*=12.8, 12.8, 5.8 Hz, H-14a); 2.70(2H, m, H-6a, H-9a); 2.84(1H, dd, *J*=13.1, 5.8 Hz, H-7B); 3.70(1H, brd, *J*=9.0Hz, H-7d); 3.71(1H, brs, H-2); 3.84(1H, brd, *J*=4.7Hz, H-3); 4.50(1H, br dd, *J*=9.2, 7.9Hz, H-15a); 4.85(1H, br s, H-2'); 5.01(1H, brs, H-2'); 5.58(1H, br d, *J*=4.7Hz, H-4); 6.74(1H, d, *J*=8.2Hz, H-11); 7.12(1H, d, *J*=8.2Hz, H-12); and 10.53ppm [1H, br s, H-13 (NH)].

^{13}C NMR:
C-2, 79.1; C-3, 62.6; C-4, 117.7; C-4a, 146.7; C-4b, 75.7; C-5, 33.2; C-6, 21.1; C-6a, 49.3; C-7, 28.3; C-7a, 113.7; C-7b, 121.4; C-7c, 133.7; C-7d, 44.2; C-8, 48.6; C-9, 23.4; C-9a, 49.0; C-10, 44.8; Me-10, 21.7, 32.1; C-l0a, 141.8; C-11, 113.9; C-12, 110.6; C-12a, 139.7; C-13a, 153.0; C-13b, 49.9; Me-13b, 16.2; C-13, 42.1; Me-13c, 19.2; C-14, 26.3; C-15, 27.9; C-15a, 72.9; C-1', 142.9; C-2', 100.0; C-3'(Me), 19.6; C-1", 70.5; and C-Me-1", 27.1, 27.8ppm.

Mass Spectrum:
HRMS: 571.3662(M^+, 17); (calcd for $C_{37}H_{49}NO_4$, 571.3662), 485(100), and 470*m/e* (35).

Reference

T. Yamaguchi, K. Nozawa, T. Hosoe, S. Nakajima, and K. Kawai; Indoloditerpenes Related to Tremorgenic Mycotoxins, Penitrems, from *Penicillium crustosum*; Phytochemistry, Vol. 32, pp. 1177-1181(1993).

Common/Systematic Name

Lolitrem B

Molecular Formula/Molecular Weight

$C_{42}H_{55}NO_7$; MW = 685.39785

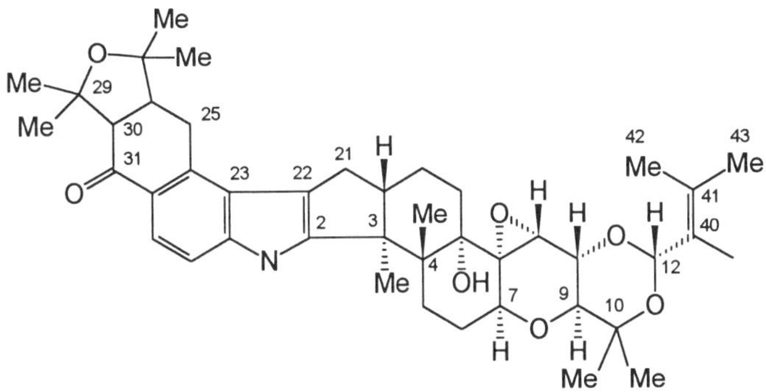

General Characteristics

Crystals; mp., 303-304°C.

Fungal Source

Acremonium lolii, the endophyte of ryegrass (*Lolium perenne* L.).

Isolation/Purification

The lolitrems were extracted from ground endophyte-infected perennial ryegrass seed, containing lolitrem B, by Soxhlet extraction with petroleum spirit (35-60°C) for 11 hours. After concentration *in vacuo*, the filtered petroleum extract was partitioned against ethanol-water (4:1, v/v). The alcoholic extract was diluted by addition of water, extracted with dichloromethane, the extract was dried ($MgSO_4$), and the solvent was removed *in vacuo*. The resulting brown oil contained lolitrem B. This oil was dissolved in petroleum spirit, extracted with acetonitrile-water (13:7, v/v), and the petroleum fraction was discarded. The aqueous acetonitrile extract was washed with petroleum spirit, diluted by addition of water, and extracted with dichloromethane. The extract was dried ($MgSO_4$) and the solvent was removed *in vacuo* to give a brown oil containing lolitrem B. This oil was applied in the minimum volume of dichloromethane to a flash column, packed as a slurry in petroleum spirit. The column was eluted first with petroleum spirit, then with petroleum spirit-dichloromethane (1:1, v/v), dichloromethane, and then with a stepwise gradient of acetonitrile-dichloromethane (1:19, 1:9, 3:17, 1:4, 2:3, and 3:2, v/v). Fractions containing lolitrem B (by HPLC) were concentrated *in vacuo* to give a brown oil containing lolitrem B. This material was purified by flash chromatography using acetonitrile-dichloromethane (3:47, then with 2:23, v/v) to afford a yellow solid containing lolitrem B. The solid was further purified by flash chromatography using acetonitrile-dichloromethane first at 3:97, and then at 3:47, v/v. Fractions containing lolitrem B were concentrated *in vacuo* to give a pale yellow solid containing 62% of lolitrem B. Crystallization from acetonitrile-dichloromethane gave a colorless solid containing lolitrem B and E. The mixture was reacted with acetic anhydride-pyridine (1:1, v/v) and 4-(*N,N*-dimethylamino)-pyridine for 24 hours to acetylate lolitrem E. The mixture was dissolved in dichloromethane, washed with water, dried ($MgSO_4$), and eluted from a flash column with acetonitrile-dichloromethane (3:17, v/v). The residue was crystallized from acetonitrile-dichloromethane to give lolitrem B. The mother liquor from the first crystallization afforded a second crop of colorless crystals containing lolitrem B. From the resulting mother liquor was obtained a third crop, as a pale yellow solid, containing lolitrem B along with lolitrem F. Recrystallization of this material gave a cream colored solid containing lolitrem B. The lolitrem B from the first, second, and third crops was then combined, recrystallized to give lolitrem B as a colorless solid.

Biological Activity

A major agent involved in the etiology of ryegrass staggers, a nervous disorder of sheep, cattle, horses, and deer grazing perennial ryegrass (*Lolium perenne* L.) pastures infected with *Acremonium lolii*. The disorder is characterized by severe incoordination and hypersensitivity to external stimuli and is of considerable importance to agriculture in New Zealand and Australia, with occasional outbreaks also being reported in other countries.

Spectral Data

UV:

λ_{max}^{MeOH} 290(ϵ=6,700) and 267nm (26,800) in the UV spectrum of lolitrem B suggested the presence of a 2,3-disubstituted indole nucleus with a carbonyl group.

IR:

(KCl) 3530, 3480, and 3315cm^{-1}, assigned to OH and NH groups and a carbonyl absorption band at 1664cm^{-1}.

^1H NMR:

($CDCl_3$) A feature of the 500.13 MHZ ^1H NMR spectrum of lolitrem B was the three-proton signals at 1.717(d, *J*=1.3Hz), 1.711(d, *J*=1.3Hz), 1.515, 1.370, 1.301, 1.276, 1.276, 1.266, 1.240, and 1.134ppm assigned to the protons of ten tertiary methyl groups. The remainder of the resonances exhibited extensive fine structure. First-order analyses of these multiplets yielded the values of the proton chemical shifts.

1-NH, 8.313; H-5a, 1.367; H-5b, 2.698; H-6a, 1.749; H-6b, 2.253; H-7, 4.306; H-9, 3.550; H-12, 5.519; H-14, 3.903; H-15, 3.602; H-18a, 1.564; H-18b, 1.423; H-19a, 1.928; H-19b, 1.627; H-20, 2.84; H-21a, 2.617; H-21b, 2.920; H-25a, 3.425; H-25b, 2.961; H-26, 2.660; H-30, 2.763; H-33, 7.831; H-34, 7.194; and H-40, 5.281ppm.

^{13}C NMR:

($CDCl_3$) C-2, 152.77(s); C-3, 50.69(s); C-4, 42.36(s); C-5, 27.38(t); C-6, 27.98(t); C-7, 71.45(d); C-9, 71.21(d); C-10, 74.70(s); C-12, 92.66(d); C-14, 71.11(d); C-15,

61.13(d); C-16, 67.73(s); C-17,78.04(s); C-18, 30.26(t); C-19, 20.49(t); C-20, 50.08(d); C-21, 29.16(t); C-22, 118.58(s); C-23, 125.96(s); C-24, 123.89(s); C-25, 28.28(t); C-26, 49.87(d); C-27, 79.26(s); C-29, 79.93(s); C-30, 59.93(d); C-31, 196.51(s); C-32, 136.97(s); C-33, 120.23(d); C-34, 110.42(d); C-35, 142.00(d); C-36, 15.91(q)*; C-37, 16.59(q)*; C-38, 18.87(q)*; C-39, 25.01(q)*; C-40, 121.96(d); C-41, 139.54(s); C-42, 25.65(q); C-43, 18.63(q); C-44, 25.10(q)*; C-45, 28.28(q)*; C-46, 29.31(q)*; and C-47, 30.63ppm (q)*.

* May be interchanged.

Mass Spectrum:

Molecular ion at *m/e* 685.3974 with an abundant ion at *m/e* 348 arising through cleavage of the C-3, C-4 and C-18, C-19 bonds with transfer of a hydrogen atom to the indole-containing fragment. A similar diagnostic fragmentation was observed for the related tremorgens aflatrem, paspalinine, and penitrem A.

HPLC Data

Zorbax Silica, particle size 5-6μm; solvent, dichloromethane-acetonitrile (80:20, v/v), 1.8ml/min.; fluorescence detection, excitation at 268nm, emission at 440nm; and UV detection at 268nm.

References

R. M. Ede, C. O. Miles, L. P. Meagher, S. C. Munday, and A. L. Wilkins; Relative Stereochemistry of the A/B Rings of the Tremorgenic Mycotoxin Lolitrem B; J. Agric. Food Chem., Vol. 42, pp. 231-233(1994).

R. T. Gallagher, A. D. Hawkes, P. S. Steyn, and R. Vleggaar; Tremorgenic Neurotoxins from Perennial Ryegrass Causing Ryegrass Staggers Disorder of Livestock: Structure Elucidation of Lolitrem B; J. Chem. Soc. Chem. Commun., pp. 614-616(1984).

C. O. Miles, S. C. Munday, A. L. Wilkins, R. M. Ede, and N. R. Towers; Large Scale Isolation of Lolitrem B and Structure Determination of Lolitrem E; J. Agric. Food Chem., Vol. 42, pp. 1488-1492(1994).

Common/Systematic Name

Lolitrem E; Lolitrem C

Molecular Formula/Molecular Weight

$C_{42}H_{57}NO_7$; MW = 687.41350

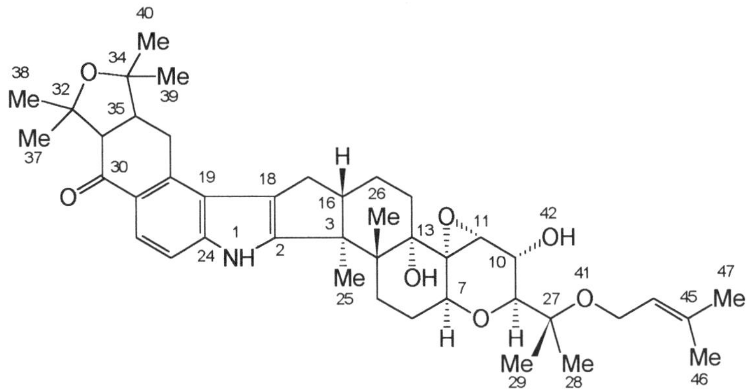

General Characteristics

A colorless solid which decomposed without melting above 150°C.

Fungal Source

Acremonium lolii, the endophyte of ryegrass (*Lolium perenne* L.).

Isolation/Purification

Lolitrem E was isolated from fractions enriched in minor lolitrems obtained during the purification of lolitrem B. These were subjected to repeated flash chromatography, using acetonitrile-dichloromethane. Eluted fractions were monitored by HPLC, and fractions enriched in lolitrem E were pooled for further purification. After 4 flash chromatography purifications, the crude lolitrem E was dissolved in the minimum of dichloromethane and an equal volume of petroleum spirit was added, precipitating most of the lolitrem E; the bulk of the other lolitrems remained in the mother liquor. The precipitate was treated with dilute acidic ethanol to convert contaminating lolitrems into lolitriol (lolitrem E is stable to acid hydrolysis). The residue was then treated briefly with $NaBH_4$ to reduce contaminating ketosterols to diols. Lolitrem E was then easily separated from the more polar lolitriol and dihydroxysterols by flash chromatography to give a colorless solid.

Biological Activity

Chemically related to the agents involved in the etiology of ryegrass staggers, a nervous disorder of sheep, cattle, horses, and deer grazing perennial ryegrass (*Lolium perenne* L.) pastures infected with *Acremonium lolii*. Lolitrem E was not tremorgenic in mice.

Spectral Data

Spectral Data

UV:

Qualitatively, the UV absorbance spectrum was identical to that reported by Gallagher *et al.* (1985) for lolitrem B; λ_{max}^{MeOH} 290 and 267nm.

^{1}H NMR:

(C_5D_5N) 1.34(3H, s, H-40); 1.38(3H, s, H-29); 1.40(3H, s, H-28); 1.45(3H, s, H-26); 1.49(3H, s, H-39); 1.54(3H, s, H-38); 1.58(3H, s, H-47); 1.59(3H, s, H-46); 1.69(3H, s, H-37); 1.75(3H, s, H-25); 2.95(1H, d, *J*=14.1Hz, H-31); 3.59(1H, dd, *J*=15.6, 4.1Hz, H-36); 3.93(1H, d, *J*=9.6Hz, H-9); 3.96(1H, br s, H-11); 4.06(2H, br d, *J*=7.2Hz, H-43); 4.36(1H, d, *J*=8.6Hz, H-10); 4.63(1H, t, *J*=8.5Hz, H-7); 5.36(1H, t, *J*=6.6Hz, H-44); 5.65(1H, m, 10-OH); and 6.37ppm (1H, s, 13-OH).

^{13}C NMR:

(C_5D_5N) C-2, 154.7; C-3, 51.5; C-4, 43.1; C-5, 26.9; C-6, 28.7; C-7, 72.1; C-9, 76.2; C-10, 67.8; C-11, 64.5; C-12, 69.3; C-13, 77.6; C-14, 30.1; C-15, 21.2; C-16, 50.7; C-17, 29.8; C-18, 118.5; C-19, 126.3; C-20, 124.9; C-21, 137.4; C-22, 119.8; C-23, 111.0; C-24, 143.5; C-25, 16.5; C-26, 18.7; C-27, 78.7; C-28, 23.9; C-29, 20.5; C-30, 196.5; C-31, 60.5; C-32, 79.7; C-34, 79.3; C-35, 50.5; C-36, 28.7; C-37, 31.0; C-38, 25.5; C-39, 29.6; C-40, 25.1; C-43, 58.9; C-44, 122.5; C-45, 135.9; C-46, 25.4; and C-47, 17.7ppm.

Mass Spectrum:

EIMS: 688(21%), 687.4101(M^+, 687.4135 for $C_{42}H_{57}NO_7$, 34), 619(18), 604(18), 586(14), 472(19), 471(30), 468(15), 457(16), 456(30), 349(29), 348(100), 336(15), 335(34), 278(14), and 277*m/e* (18).

HPLC Data

Zorbax Silica, particle size 5-6μm; solvent, dichloromethane-acetonitrile (80:20, v/v), 1.8ml/min.; fluorescence detection, excitation at 268nm, emission at 440nm; and UV detection at 268nm.

Reference

C. O. Miles, S. C. Munday, A. L. Wilkins, R. M. Ede, and N. R. Towers; Large Scale Isolation of Lolitrem B and Structure Determination of Lolitrem E; J. Agric. Food Chem., Vol. 42, pp. 1488-1492(1994).

Common/Systematic Name
Lolitriol

Molecular Formula/Molecular Weight
$C_{37}H_{49}NO_7$; MW = 619.35090

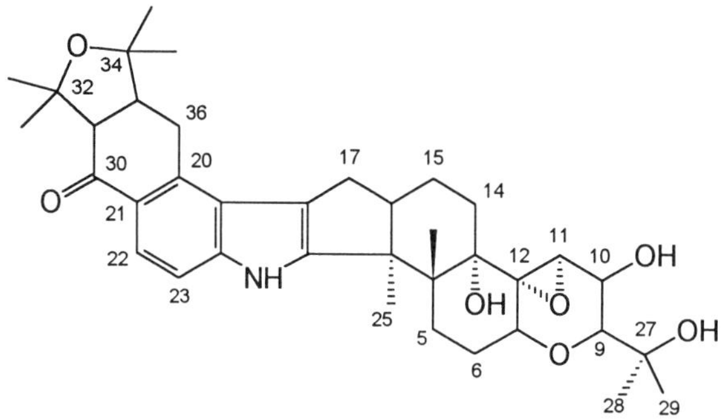

General Characteristics
A pale yellow solid; mp., 322-325°C.

Fungal Source
Acremonium lolii, endophyte on perennial ryegrass.

Isolation/Purification
Extracted with dichloromethane, dried over Na_2SO_4; removal of solvent *in vacuo* afforded a colorless solid. This was purified by flash chromatography using methanol-chloroform, 6:94, v/v, to afford lolitriol as a pale yellow solid.

Biological Activity
Nontremorgenic to mice.

Spectral Data

UV:
$\lambda_{max}^{Acetonitrile}$ 263(log ϵ=4.72) and 290nm (sh).

^{1}H NMR:
(C_5D_5N) H-5, 2.97; H-6, 2.34; H-7, 4.60; H-9, 3.91; H-14, 1.66; H-15, 2.25; H-17, 2.76; H-22, 8.26; H-23, 7.49; H-25, 1.69; H-26, 1.42; H-28, 1.50; H-29, 1.52; H-31, 2.94; H-35, 2.78; H-36, 3.05; H-37, 1.69; H-38, 1.54; H-39, 1.50, and H-40, 1.36ppm.

^{13}C NMR:
(C_5D_5N) C-2, 154.6; C-3, 50.5; C-4, 42.8; C-5, 27.1; C-6, 29.0; C-7, 72.1; C-9, 77.5; C-10, 68.4; C-11, 64.7; C-12, 69.5; C-13, 77.3; C-14, 30.2; C-15; 21.4; C-16, 50.9;

C-17, 29.7; C-18, 118.2; C-19, 125.9; C-20, 124.6; C-21, 137.4; C-22, 120.0; C-23, 111.2; C-24, 143.3; C-25, 16.4; C-26, 18.6; C-27, 72.5; C-28, 24.7; C-29, 28.3; C-30, 196.4; C-31, 60.6; C-32, 79.6; C-34, 79.2; C-35, 50.6; C-36, 28.8; C-37, 30.9; C-38, 25.4; C-39, 29.5; and C-40, 25.0ppm.

Mass Spectrum:
HREIMS: 619.3528*m/e* (M^+, 619.3496 for $C_{37}H_{49}NO_7$, 43%), 604(41), 471(55), 456(44), 348(100), and 335(44).

Reference

C. O. Miles, A. L. Wilkins, R. T. Gallagher, A. D. Hawkes, S. C. Munday, and N. R. Towers; Synthesis and Tremorgenicity of Paxitriols and Lolitriol: Possible Biosynthetic Precursors of Lolitrem B; J. Agric. Food Chem., Vol. 40, pp. 234-238(1992).

7

Paspaline and Related Metabolites

Paspaline
Paspalicine
Paspilinine
Paxilline
α-Paxitriol
β-Paxitriol
3-*O*-Acetoxypaxilline
1'-*O*-Acetylpaxilline
Aflatrem (α,α-Dimethylallylpaspalinine)
β-Aflatrem
Paspalitrem A (3-Methyl-2-butenylpaspalinine)
Paspalitrem B (3-Methyl-3-hydroxy-1-butenylpaspalinine)
Paspalitrem C
Sulpinine A
Sulpinine B
Sulpinine C
PC-M4
PC-M5
PC-M5'
PC-M6

Common/Systematic Name

Paspaline

Molecular Formula/Molecular Weight

$C_{28}H_{39}NO_2$; MW = 421.29808

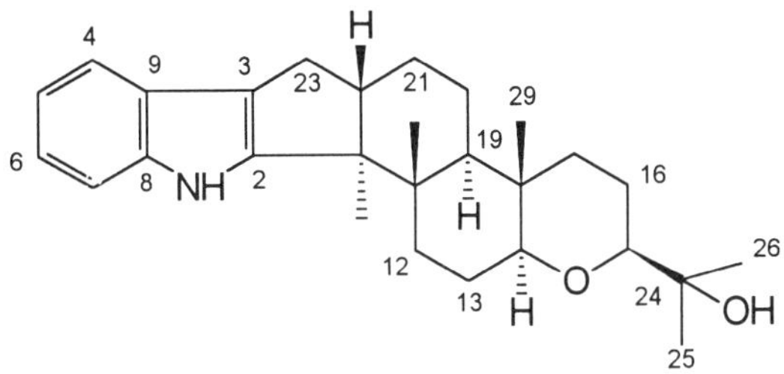

General Characteristics

Crystals from methanol; mp., 254°C; sublimed sample mp., 264°C; $[\alpha]_D$ -23 (*c*=0.36).

Fungal Source

Claviceps paspali.

Biological Activity

Nontremorgenic in mice dosed IP up to 500mg/kg; chemically related to paspalitrem group tremorgens.

Spectral Data

UV:

λ_{max} 228-231(ϵ=25,118), 282(7,943), and 291nm (6,309).

^{13}C NMR:

C-2, 150.7 s; C-3, 118.3 s; C-4, 118.3 d; C-5, 119.4 d; C-6, 120.4 d; C-7, 111.3 d; C-8, 139.9 s; C-9, 125.1 s; C-10, 52.9 s; C-11, 42.2 s; C-12, 21.9 t; C-13, 24.6 t; C-14, 84.7 d; C-15, 85.7 d; C-16, 37.7 t; C-17, 25.2 t; C-18, 36.4 s; C-19, 46.4 d; C-20, 21.9 t; C-21, 27.5 t; C-22, 48.7 d; C-23, 33.8 t; C-24,71.9 s; C-25, 33.7 qt; C-26, 26.1 qt; C-27, 19.9 q; C-28, 14.5 q; and C-29, 12.7ppm q.

TLC Data

Silica gel G-HR; toluene-ethyl acetate-formic acid, 5:4:1, v/v/v; R_f: 0.76. Detection: dull fluorescent spot after spraying with 50% ethanolic H_2SO_4 and heating at 100°C for 5 min.

References

R. J. Cole and R. H. Cox; Handbook of Toxic Fungal Metabolites; Academic Press, New York, pp. 390-393(1981).

J. P. Springer and J. Clardy; Paspaline and Paspalicine, Two Indole-Mevalonate Metabolites from *Claviceps paspali*; Tet. Lett., Vol. 21, pp. 231-234(1980).

Common/Systematic Name

Paspalicine

Molecular Formula/Molecular Weight

$C_{27}H_{31}NO_3$; MW = 417.23039

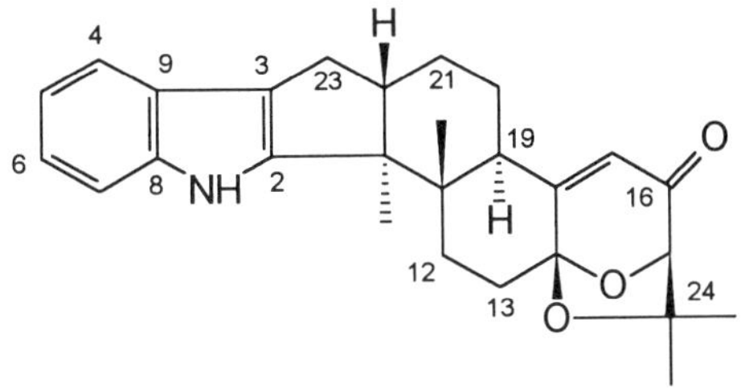

General Characteristics

Large needles from acetone; mp., 240°C (dec.); $[\alpha]_D$ +173° (*c*=0.5); crystals from methanol; mp., 230°C.

Fungal Source

Claviceps paspali.

Biological Activity

Nontremorgenic relative of paspalinine. No clinical signs in mice dosed (IP) up to 500mg/kg.

Spectral Data

UV:

λ_{max} 231(ϵ=47,863), 250(17,782), and 275nm (12,589).

CD:

$\Delta\epsilon$ +11.8

^{13}C NMR:

C-2, 149.4 s; C-3, 118.4 s; C-4, 118.6 d; C-5, 119.9 d; C-6, 120.8 d; C-7, 111.6 d; C-8, 140.2 s; C-9, 125.3 s; C-10, 51.5 s; C-11, 39.9 s; C-12, 2.6 t; C-13, 27.7 t; C-14, 104.4 s; C-15, 88.4 s; C-16, 197.6 s; C-17, 118.4 d; C-18, 171.8 s; C-19, 37.5 d; C-20, 28.6 t; C-21, 29.4 t; C-22, 48.9 d; C-23, 32.1 t; C-24, 78.2 s; C-25, 23.8 q; C-26, 29.0 q; C-27, 23.2 q; and C-28, 14.9ppm q.

TLC Data

Silica gel G-HR; toluene-ethyl acetate-formic acid, 5:4:1, v/v/v; R_f, 0.85. Detection: dark spot with fluorescent halo under UV light after spraying with 50% ethanolic H_2SO_4 and heating at 100°C for 5 min.

References

R. J. Cole and R. H. Cox; Handbook of Toxic Fungal Metabolites; Academic Press, New York, pp. 394-397(1981).

J. P. Springer and J. Clardy; Paspaline and Paspalicine, Two Indole-Mevalonate Metabolites from *Claviceps paspali*; Tet. Lett., Vol. 21, pp. 231-234(1980).

Common/Systematic Name

Paspalinine

Molecular Formula/Molecular Weight

$C_{27}H_{31}NO_4$; MW = 433.22531

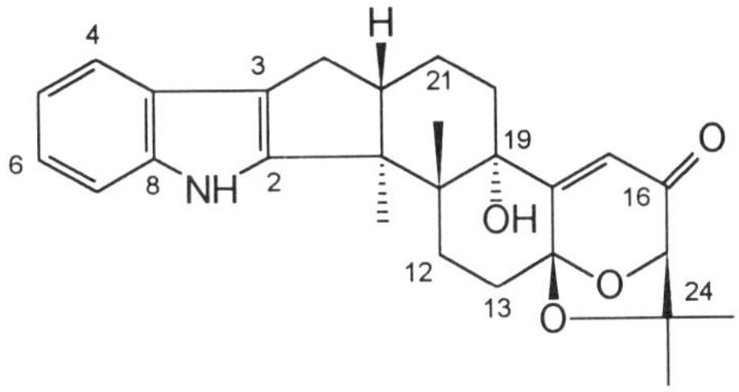

Fungal Source

Claviceps paspali and *Aspergillus flavus* sclerotia.

Isolation/Purification

Extracted with chloroform. The crude extract chromatographed on a silica gel column. Tremorgens eluted with ethyl ether and ethyl acetate. The active fractions were chromatographed on a silica gel column eluted with a linear gradient from benzene to ethyl ether followed by a second gradient from ethyl ether to ethyl acetate. Aflatrem and paspalanine were isolated in the first gradient while dihydroxyaflavinine was isolated during the second gradient elution.

Biological Activity

ED_{50} for tremor >14mg/kg IP in mice. Other clinical signs: uncoordinated movement, diarrhea, rough hair coat and hypersensitivity to sound stimuli. Gross clinical signs very similar to those produced by paxilline.

Spectral Data

UV:

λ_{max}^{MeOH} 232(ϵ=39,800) and 275nm (10,500).

^{13}C NMR:

C-2, 152.1 s; C-3, 117.1 s; C-4, 118.4 d; C-5, 119.5 d; C-6, 120.3 d; C-7, 111.5 d; C-8, 139.9 s; C-9, 125.2; C-10, 51.5 s; C-11, 39.9 s; C-12, 21.1 t; C-13, 26.3 t; C-14, 104.5 s; C-15, 87.9 s; C-16, 197.2 s; C-17, 117.5 d; C-18, 169.9 s; C-19, 77.4 s; C-20, 27.4 t; C-21, 28.2 t; C-22, 48.6 d; C-23, 32.8 t; C-24, 78.6 s; C-25, 23.5 q; C-26, 28.8 q; C-27, 23.0 q; and C-28, 16.3ppm q.

TLC Data

Silica gel G-HR; chloroform-acetone, 93:7, v/v; R_f: 0.52. Detection: blue spot after spraying with 50% ethanolic H_2SO_4 and heating at 100°C for 5 min; fluorescent under UV light.

References

R. J. Cole and R. H. Cox; Handbook of Toxic Fungal Metabolites; Academic Press, New York, pp. 398-401(1981).

R. J. Cole, J. W. Dorner, J. P. Springer, and R. H. Cox; Indole Metabolites from a Strain of *Aspergillus flavus*; J. Agric. Food Chem., Vol. 29, pp. 293-295(1981).

R. T. Gallagher, J. Finer, J. Clardy, A. Leutwiler, F. Weibel, W. Acklin, and D. Arigoni; Paspalanine, A Tremorgenic Metabolite from *Claviceps paspali* Stevens et Hall; Tet. Lett., Vol. 21, pp. 235-238(1980).

Common/Systematic Name
Paxilline

Molecular Formula/Molecular Weight
$C_{27}H_{33}NO_4$; MW = 435.24096

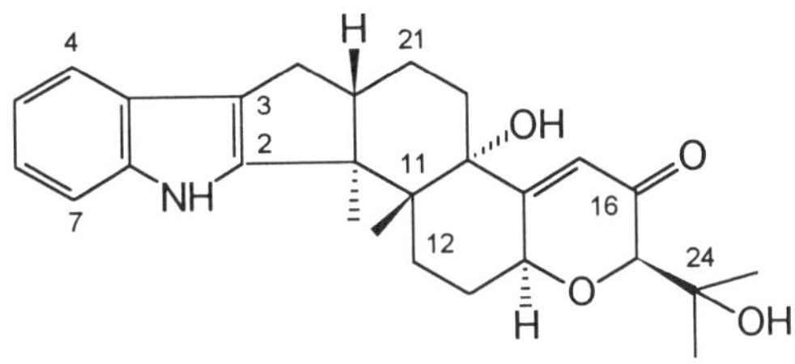

General Characteristics
Clear cubes from acetone; mp., 252°C (paxilline crystallized with 1 molecule of acetone H-bonded to the hydrogen of the indole nitrogen).

Fungal Source
Penicillium paxilli, *Emericella desertorum*, *E. foreolata*, *E. striata*, and *Acremonium lolii*, an endophyte of perennial ryegrass (*Lolium perenne* L.).

Isolation/Purification
The tremorgen was extracted with hot chloroform and the crude extract was chromatographed on a silica gel column; the tremorgen eluted with diethyl ether. The ether fraction was chromatographed on a silica gel column eluted with a linear gradient from toluene to ethyl acetate. Paxilline was crystallized from acetone solution.

Biological Activity
In day-old cockerels dosed orally: at 25mg/kg (1mg/cockerel) tremors were intermittent; at 100mg/kg (4mg/cockerel) tremors were more sustained. Mortality was observed at higher dosage levels. In mice dosed intraperitoneally, intermittent tremors were observed at levels down to 35mg/kg. Tremors were enhanced when the animal tried to move or was forced to move. Mice were noticeably hypersensitive to sound stimuli. No mortality was observed in mice dosed up to 227mg/kg. Mice continued to feed or attempt to feed. Suspected as one of the tremorgens responsible for the clinical signs of ryegrass staggers.

Spectral Data

UV:
λ_{max}^{MeOH} 230(ϵ=41,500) and 281nm (8,000).

IR:
(KBr) 3420, 1650, 1355, 1365, and 740cm^{-1}.

CD:
$\Delta\epsilon$ 335(+ 1.2) and 300nm (+ 3.3).

^{13}C NMR:
C-2, 152.1 s; C-3, 114.5 s; C-4, 117.2 d; C-5, 118.4 d; C-6, 118.8 d; C-7, 111.4 d; C-8, 139.3 s; C-9, 124.1 s; C-10, 50.0 s; C-11, 39.9 s; C-12, 20.6 t; C-13, 25.8 t; C-14, 72.2 d; C-15, 83.1 d; C-16, 196.9 s; C-17, 117.9 d; C-18, 169.9 s; C-19, 75.4 s; C-20, 26.7 t; C-21, 28.1 t; C-22, 49.1 d; C-23, 32.4 t; C-24, 70.8 s; C-25, 25.7 qt; C-26, 25.8 q; C-27, 18.6 q; and C-28, 16.2ppm q.

Mass Data:
435.2422(M^+), 420.2165, 378.2033, 377.1998, 363.1779, and 362.1753*m/e*. (Anal. found: C, 75.29; H, 7.68; N, 3.12; calcd for $C_{27}H_{33}NO_4$; C, 74.48; H, 7.58; N, 3.21; O, 14.70).

TLC Data

Silica gel G-HR; toluene-ethyl acetate-formic acid, 5:4:1 v/v/v; R_f: 0.75. Detection: A dark spot with 50% ethanolic H_2SO_4 spray; a greenish-gray spot with 3% ethanolic phosphomolybdic acid.

References

R. J. Cole and R. H. Cox; Handbook of Toxic Fungal Metabolites; Academic Press, New York, pp. 386-389(1981).

R. J. Cole, J. W. Kirksey, and J. M. Wells; The Structure of Paxilline, a Tremorgenic Metabolite of *Penicillium paxilli* Bainier; Can. J. Microbiol., Vol. 20, pp. 1159-1162(1974).

C. O. Miles, A. L. Wilkins, R. T. Gallagher, A. D. Hawkes, S. C. Munday, and N. R. Towers; Synthesis and Tremorgenicity of Paxitriols and Lolitriol: Possible Biosynthetic Precursors of Lolitrem B; J. Agric. Food Chem., Vol. 40, pp. 234-238(1992).

J. P. Springer, J. Clardy, J. M. Wells, R. J. Cole, and J. W. Kirksey; The Structure of Paxilline, a Tremorgenic Metabolite of *Penicillium paxilli* Bainier; Tet. Lett. pp. 2531-2534(1975).

Common/Systematic Name

α-Paxitriol

Molecular Formula/Molecular Weight

$C_{27}H_{35}NO_4$; MW = 437.25661

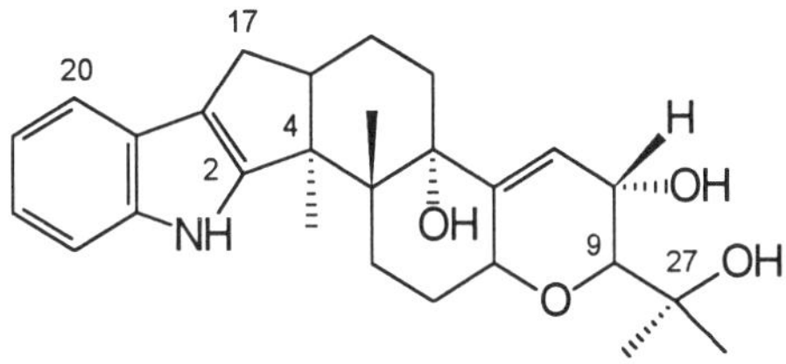

General Characteristics

Colorless solid that decomposed without melting at 250-300°C.

Fungal Source

Acremonium lolii endophyte on perennial ryegrass.

Isolation/Purification

Extracted with dichloromethane and dried over Na_2SO_4 overnight at 4°C in the dark. Removal of solvent *in vacuo* afforded a pale yellow oil. Addition of dichloromethane resulted initially in dissolution of the product, followed by precipitation. After standing at 4°C for 30 min, solvent was removed by decantation. The off-white crystals were washed with fresh solvent to afford pure β-paxitriol. The washings were purified by flash chromatography (acetone-dichloromethane, 3:17, v/v) to give pure α-paxitriol (the less mobile diastereoisomer).

Biological Activity

Nontremorgenic to mice at 100mg/kg; caused lethargy and rough hair coats, and normal activities such as walking, rearing and preening were greatly reduced for several hours.

Spectral Data

UV:

$\lambda_{max}^{Acetonitrile}$ 231(log ϵ=4.53) and 281nm (3.91).

^{1}H NMR:

($CDCl_3$-DMSO) H-5, 2.57; H-6, 2.01; H-7, 4.60; H-9, 3.03; H-11, 5.35; H-14, 1.69; H-15, 2.06; H-17, 2.36; H-20, 7.28; H-21, 6.92; H-22, 6.91; H-23, 7.27; H-25, 1.29; H-26, 0.95; H-28, 1.22; and H-29, 1.26ppm.

^{13}C NMR:

($CDCl_3$-DMSO) C-2, 153.5; C-3, 50.5; C-4, 42.5; C-5, 26.8; C-6, 28.3; C-7, 73.3;

C-9, 81.7; C-10, 64.5; C-11, 120.2; C-12, 144.5; C-13, 75.8; C-14, 33.5; C-15, 21.2; C-16, 49.7; C-17, 27.1; C-18, 115.1; C-19, 124.7; C-20, 117.6; C-21, 118.4; C-22, 119.1; C-23, 111.7; C-24, 139.9; C-25, 16.3; C-26, 19.5; C-27, 72.4; C-28, 24.2; and C-29, 27.8ppm.

Mass Spectrum:
437.2587(M^+, 437.2557 for $C_{27}H_{35}NO_4$, 55%), 422(47), 419(42), 404(28), 343(15), 328(18), 208(9), 182(100), 169(54), and 230*m/e* (56).

Reference

C. O. Miles, A. L. Wilkins, R. T. Gallagher, A. D. Hawkes, S. C. Munday, and N. R. Towers; Synthesis and Tremorgenicity of Paxitriols and Lolitriol: Possible Biosynthetic Precursors of Lolitrem B; J. Agric. Food Chem., Vol. 40, pp. 234-238(1992).

Common/Systematic Name

β-Paxitriol

Molecular Formula/Molecular Weight

$C_{27}H_{35}NO_4$; MW = 437.25661

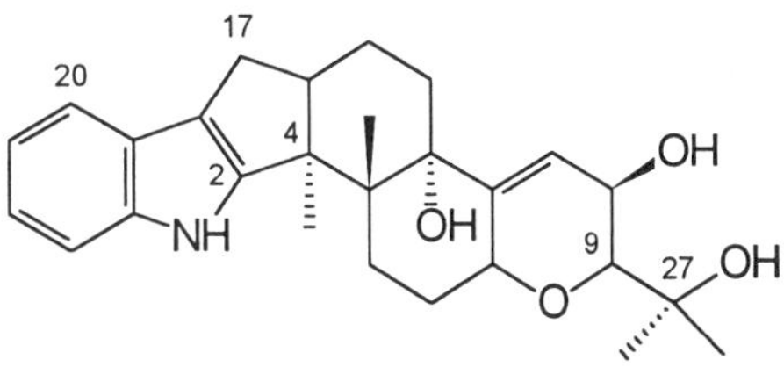

General Characteristics

Colorless solid that decomposed without melting at 250-300°C.

Fungal Source

Acremonium lolii endophyte on perennial ryegrass.

Isolation/Purification

Extracted with dichloromethane and dried over Na_2SO_4 overnight at 4°C in the dark. Removal of solvent *in vacuo* afforded a pale yellow oil. Addition of dichloromethane resulted initially in dissolution of the product, followed by precipitation. After standing at 4°C for 30 min, solvent was removed by decantation. The off-white crystals were then washed with fresh solvent to afford pure β-paxitriol. The washings were purified by flash chromatography (acetone-dichloromethane, 3:17, v/v) to give pure α-paxitriol (the less mobile diastereoisomer).

Biological Activity

Nontremorgenic to mice at 100mg/kg; caused lethargy and rough hair coats, and normal activities such as walking, rearing and preening were greatly reduced for several hours.

Spectral Data

UV:

$\lambda_{max}^{Acetonitrile}$ 231(log ϵ=4.58) and 280nm (3.94).

^{1}H NMR:

(C_5D_5N) H-5, 2.61; H-6, 2.19; H-7, 4.61; H-9, 3.06; H-10, 4.19; H-11, 5.64; H-14, 1.69; H-15, 2.03; H-17, 2.39; H-20, 7.33; H-21, 6.96; H-22, 6.94; H-23, 7.32; H-25, 1.33; H-26, 1.04; H-28, 1.29; and H-29, 1.30ppm.

^{13}C NMR:

(C_5D_5N) C-2, 153.4; C-3, 50.5; C-4, 42.4; C-5, 26.8; C-6, 28.3; C-7, 74.1; C-9, 80.4;

C-10, 63.3; C-11, 117.5; C-12, 147.9; C-13, 76.2; C-14, 33.7; C-15, 21.2; C-16, 49.8; C-17, 27.1; C-18, 115.2; C-19, 124.7; C-20, 117.6; C-21, 118.5; C-22, 119.2; C-23, 111.8; C-24, 139.9; C-25,16.3; C-26, 19.6; C-27, 72.0; C-28, 26.7; and C-29, 27.1ppm.

Mass Spectrum:

437.2558(M^+, 437.2557 for $C_{27}H_{35}NO_4$, 55%), 422(52), 419(15), 343(18), 328(18), 208(17), 182(100), 69(52), and 130*m/e* (57).

Reference

C. O. Miles, A. L. Wilkins, R. T. Gallagher, A. D. Hawkes, S. C. Munday and N. R. Towers; Synthesis and Tremorgenicity of Paxitriols and Lolitriol: Possible Biosynthetic Precursors of Lolitrem B; J. Agric. Food Chem., Vol. 40, pp. 234-238(1992).

Common/Systematic Name
3-*O*-Acetoxypaxilline

Molecular Formula/Molecular Weight
$C_{29}H_{37}NO_5$; MW = 479.26717

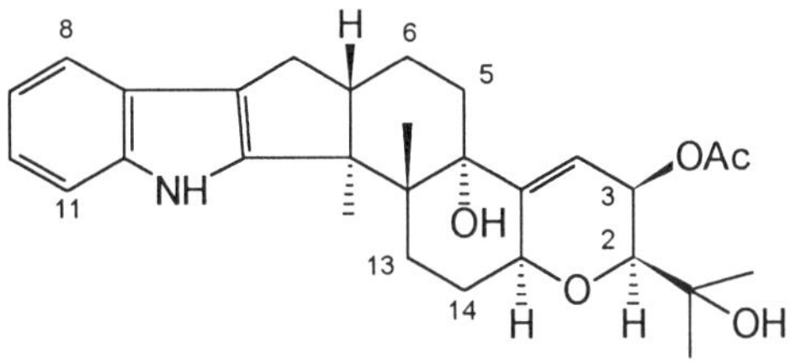

General Characteristics
Colorless crystalline powder; mp., 162-164°C.

Fungal Source
Penicillium crustosum (strain NHL 6491) isolated from mycelia of contaminated bread which had been intended for school lunches in Shinagawa-ku, Tokyo, Japan in 1983.

Isolation/Purification
P. crustosum was cultivated at 25°C for 14 days containing Czapek-Dox medium supplemented with 0.2% yeast extract. The mycelium was extracted with CH_2Cl_2; the residue obtained by evaporation of the extract and chromatography on silica gel with benzene-acetone (100:1, v/v) gave ergosterol; with benzene-acetone (50:1, v/v) followed by purification by LPLC using benzene gave penitrems F and B; with benzene-acetone (20:1, v/v) followed by purification by LPLC using benzene-acetone (100:1, v/v) gave penitrems A and E; with benzene-acetone (10:1, v/v) followed by further purification by LPLC [benzene-acetone (50:1, v/v)] gave penitrem D; with benzene acetone (5:1, v/v) followed by repeated purification by LPLC using benzene-acetone (20:1, v/v) and/or hexane-AcOEt-EtOH gave cyclopenin and 3-*O*-acetoxypaxilline; and with benzene-acetone (3:1, v/v) followed by purification by HPLC using benzene/AcOEt (5:2, v/v) gave dihydrodehydroxypaxilline.

Biological Activity
Probable biosynthetic precursor for the penitrems and probably tremorgenic; however, tremorgenic activity was not reported.

Spectral Data

UV:
λ_{max}^{MeOH} 229(log ε=4.74) and 279nm (4.05).

IR:
(KBr) 3500, 3460, 3400(NH, OH), and 1720cm^{-1} (OAc).

CD:
(c=4.55 x 10^{-5}, MeOH) $[\Theta]^{20}$ -61,000(232), +4,900(286), and +5,000nm (294).

^{1}H NMR:
[$(CD_3)_2CO$] 1.00(3H, s, 12C-Me), 1.20(3H, 5, 2'-Me), 1.26(3H, s, 3'-Me). 1.36(3H, s, 12b-Me), 1.70(3H, m), 1.82(1H, dddd, J=13.5, 13.5, 8.5, 5.2), 1.95(1H, ddd, J=13.5, 13.5, 4.5), 1.99(3H, s, 3-OCOMe), 2.10(1H, m), 2.39(1H, dd, J=13.0, 10.8, 7B-H), 2.67(1H, dd, J=13.0, 6.3, 7a-H), 2.69(1H, ddd, J=13.3, 13.3, 4.8), 2.85(1H, m), 3.32(1H, d, J=1.8, 2-H), 3.48(1H, s, OH), 3.49(1H, s, OH), 4.65(1H, br dd, J=10.5, 7.6, 14a-H), 5.20(1H, ddd, J=5.8, 1.8, 1.8, 3-H), 5.69(1H, dd, J=5.8, 1.8, 4-H), 6.94(2H, m, 9-H, 10-H), 7.28(1H, m, 8-H or 11-H), 7.32(1H, m, 11-H or 8-H), and 9.85ppm [1H, br s, 12-H (NH)].

^{13}C NMR:
[$(CD_3)_2CO$] C-2, 82.56; C-3, 66.01; C-4, 115.21; C-4a, 151.29; C-4b, 77.52; C-5, 34.71; C-6, 22.0; C-6a, 50.67; C-7, 30.56; C-7a, 116.71; C-7b, 126.11; C-8, 118.66; C-9, 119.54; C-10, 120.36; C-11, 112.45; C-11a, 141.23; C-12a, 153.84; C-12b, 51.61; 12b-Me, 16.73; C-12c, 43.53; 12-C-Me, 19.93; C-13, 27.87; C-14, 29.13; C-14a, 75.06; C-1', 71.58; C-2', 25.99; C-3', 27.95; <u>Me</u>COO, 21.28; and Me<u>C</u>OO, 170.69ppm.

Mass Spectrum:
EI-MS: 479.2669(M^+, 479.2670 for $C_{29}H_{37}NO_5$, 63), 464.2433[$(M-Me)^+$, 464.2433 for $C_{28}H_{34}NO_5$, 100], 182(87), and 130m/e (68).

Reference

T. Hosoe, K. Nozawa, S. Udagawa, S. Nakajima, and K. Kawai; Structures of New Indoloditerpenes, Possible Biosynthetic Precursors of the Tremorgenic Mycotoxins, Penitrems, from *Penicillium crustosum*; Chem. Pharm. Bull., Vol. 38, pp. 3473-3475 (1990).

Common/Systematic Name

1'-*O*-Acetylpaxilline

Molecular Formula/Molecular Weight

$C_{29}H_{35}NO_5$; MW = 477.25152

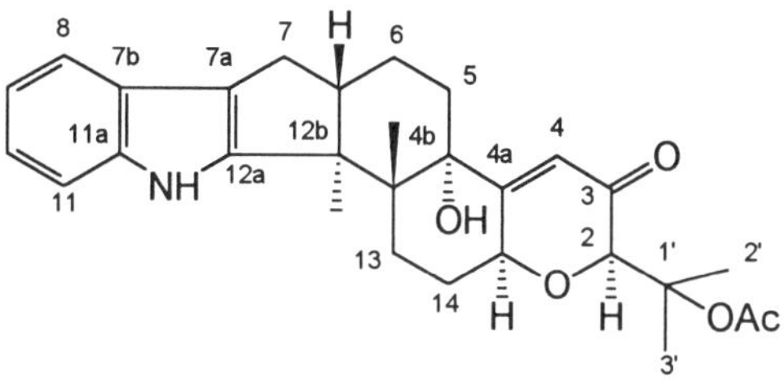

General Characteristics

Colorless needles from ethyl acetate; mp., 262-265°C (sublim.).

Fungal Source

Emericella striata, strain 80-NE-22.

Isolation/Purification

The dried mycelia were extracted with acetone at room temperature. The acetone extract was chromatographed on silica gel with benzene-acetone followed by column chromatography with benzene-ethyl acetate (5:1, v:v). It was further purified by repeated LPLC [hexane-ethyl acetate (10:1, v:v)] to yield 1'-*O*-acetylpaxilline.

Biological Activity

Tremorgenic.

Spectral Data

UV:

λ_{max}^{EtOH} 231(log ϵ=4.62). 280(3.97), and 290nm (sh) (3.92).

IR:

3480, 3400(OH, NH), 1728(OAc), and 1680cm^{-1} (-CO-).

CD:

Θ -80400(244), -1090(268sh), +8260(296), and +3430nm (338).

^{1}H NMR:

($CDCl_3$) 1.02(3H, s, Me); 1.32(3H, s, Me); 1.43(3H, s, Me); 1.50(1H, m); 1.61(1H, s, OH); 1.65(3H, s, Me); 1.55-2.08(6H, m); 2.04(3H, s, OAc); 2.27(1H, m); 2.44(1H, dd *J*=13.1, 10.9Hz); 2.73(1H, dd *J*=13.1, 6.1Hz); 2.80(1H, m); 4.77(1H, brt, *J*=10.0Hz;

CH_2-CH-O-); 4.79(1H, d *J*=1.8Hz, (=CH-O-)); 5.78(1H, d *J*=1.8Hz(=C=CH); 7.07(2H, m); 7.29(1H, m); 7.43(1H, m); and 7.83ppm (1H, brs. NH).

^{13}C NMR:

[$CDCl_3$ plus trace $(CD_3)_2SO$] C-2, 80.43; C-3, 195.31; C-4, 120.07; C-4a, 166.21; C-4b, 77.37; C-5, 28.05; C-6, 28.37; C-6a, 49.54; C-7, 34.23; C-7a, 117.49; C-7b, 125.15; C-8, 118.52; C-9, 119.73; C-10, 120.64; C-11, 111.52; C-11a, 139.81; C-12a, 151.79; C-12b, 50.85; C-12c, 43.14; C-13, 20.94; C-14, 27.22; C-14a, 72.94; C-1', 81.89; C-2', 22.84; C-3', 23.86; 12b-Me, 16.21; 12c-Me, 19.73; O-CO-Me, 22.31; and O-CO-Me, 170.92ppm.

Mass Data:

EI-MS: 477(100% M^+), 462(75 [M-Me]), 417(22 [M^+-AcOH], 402(25[M^+-AcOH-Me]$^-$), 384(20 [M-AcOH-Me-H_2O]), 182(65), and 130(45); anal calcd for $C_{29}H_{35}NO_5$; C, 72.93: H, 7.39: N, 2.93; found: C, 73.07: H, 7.42: N, 2.81 .

Reference

K. Nozawa, Y. Horie, S. Udagawa, K. Kawai, and M. Yamazaki; Isolation of a New Tremorgenic Indoloditerpene, 1'-*O*-Acetylpaxilline, from *Emericella striata* and Distribution of Paxilline in *Emericella* spp.; Chem. Pharm. Bull., Vol. 37, pp. 1387-1389 (1989).

Common/Systematic Name

Aflatrem; α,α-Dimethylallylpaspalinine

Molecular Formula/Molecular Weight

$C_{32}H_{39}NO_4$; MW = 501.28791

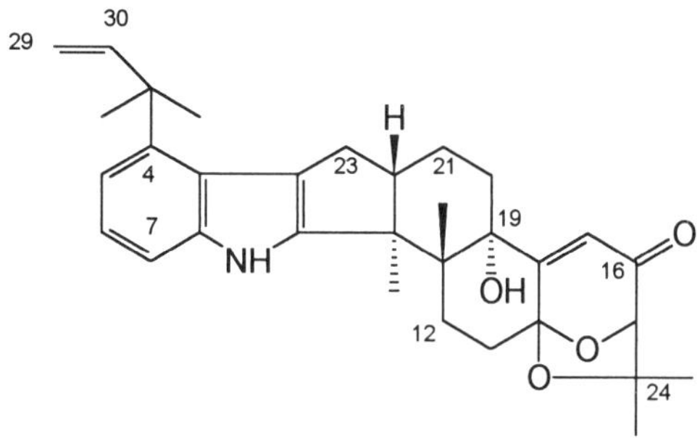

General Characteristics

Colorless needles from ethyl ether-acetone; mp., 222-224°C.

Fungal Source

Aspergillus flavus.

Isolation/Purification

Fungal cultures were extracted with chloroform and the crude extract was chromatographed on a silica gel column. Tremorgens eluted with ethyl ether and ethyl acetate. The active fractions were combined and chromatographed on a silica gel column eluted with a linear gradient from benzene to ethyl ether followed by a second gradient from ethyl ether to ethyl acetate. Aflatrem and paspalanine were isolated in the first gradient.

Biological Activity

Tremorgenic when dosed IP or orally to mice, guinea pigs, and rats. A dose of 1mg of partially purified toxin to mice via stomach tube initially resulted in inactivity but animals responded to auditory and tactile stimuli. Tremors became marked when animals attempted to move. Trembling became more pronounced in 1-2 hr after dosing and continued for several hours. Marked improvement was usually evident the day after treatment with the toxin.

Spectral Data

UV:

λ_{max}^{MeOH} 231(ε=27,750), 282(9,050), and 292nm (sh) (7,850).

^{13}C NMR:

C-2, 151.8 s; C-3, 115.1 s; C-4, 140.6 s; C-5, 115.8 d; C-6, 118.9 d; C-7, 110.6 d; C-8, 139.3 s; C-9, 123.3 s; C-10, 50.5 s; C-11, 39.4 s; C-12, 21.0 t; C-13, 26.4 t; C-14, 104.5 s; C-15, 87.6 d; C-16, 197.0 s; C-17, 116.9 d; C-18, 170.0 s; C-19, 77.6 s; C-20, 28.2 t; C-21, 32.6 t; C-22, 48.0 d; C-23, 33.8 t; C-24, 78.0 s; C-25, 28.8 q; C-26, 22.9 q; C-27, 22.9 q; C-28, 16.0 q; C-29, 111.1 t; C-30, 140.6 d; C-31, 41.3 s; C-32, 29.3 q; and C-33, 29.5ppm q.

TLC Data

Silica gel G-HR; chloroform-acetone, 93:7 (v/v); R_f: 0.65. Detection: blue spot after spraying with H_2SO_4 followed by 1% dimethyl aminobenzaldehyde (ethanolic) and heating at 100°C for 1-2 min.

References

R. J. Cole and R. H. Cox; Handbook of Toxic Fungal Metabolites; Academic Press, New York, pp. 410-413(1981).

R. J. Cole, J. W. Dorner, J. P. Springer, and R. H. Cox; Indole Metabolites from a Strain of *Aspergillus flavus*; J. Agric. Food Chem., Vol. 29, pp. 293-295(1981).

R. T. Gallagher and B. J. Wilson; Aflatrem, the tremorgenic mycotoxin from *Aspergillus flavus*; Tet. Lett., Vol. 21, pp. 239-240(1980).

W. B. Turner and D. C. Aldridge; Fungal Metabolites II; Academic Press, New York, New York, pp. 298-300(1983).

Common/Systematic Name

β-Aflatrem

Molecular Formula/Molecular Weight

$C_{32}H_{39}NO_4$; MW = 501.28791

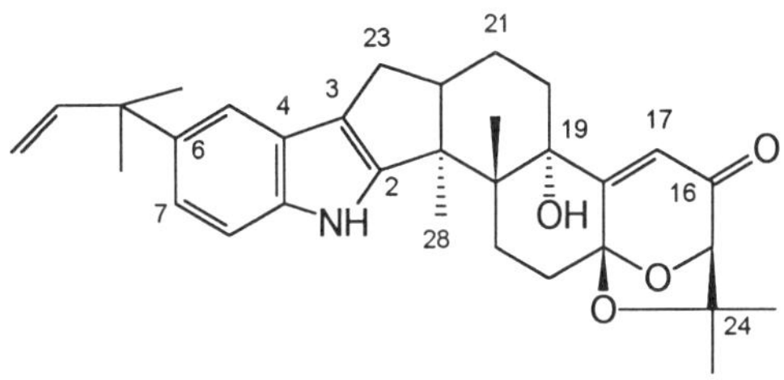

General Characteristics

β-Aflatrem was obtained as a yellow crystalline solid with the following properties: mp., 188-190°C; $[\alpha]_D$ +77.9° (*c*=0.011, in $CHCl_3$).

Fungal Source

Aspergillus flavus (NRRL 13462) sclerotia, *A. parasiticus* (NRRL 6433, 13539), and *A. subolivaceus* (NRRL 4998).

Isolation/Purification

A. flavus (NRRL 13462) sclerotia were subjected to exhaustive extraction with hexane, and this extract was directly subjected to preparative reversed-phase HPLC [8μm C_{18} column, 2.14x25cm, MeOH:H_2O (90:10, v/v) at 8.4ml/min] to afford the following major components: paspalinine (retention time, 17 min), aflatrem (26 min), β-aflatrem (32 min), nominine (34 min), aflavinine (38.5 min), and paspaline (66 min).

Biological Activity

Exhibited significant activity against *Helicoverpa zea*, causing a 57% reduction in weight gain relative to controls when incorporated into a standard diet at a concentration of 100ppm.

Spectral Data

UV:

λ_{max}^{MeOH} 233(ϵ=18,500), 264(6,300), and 296nm (2,700).

IR:

(CH_2Cl_2) 3572, 3468, 3060, 2971, 2937, 1690, 1614, 1455, 1275, and 894cm^{-1}.

^{1}H NMR:

($CDCl_3$) H-1, 7.73, s; H-5, 7.43, d, *J*=1.5; H-7, 7.13, dd, *J*=1.5, 8.8; H-8, 7.27, d,

J=8.8; H-12, 2.26, m, 2.69, m; H-13, 1.75, m, 1.82, m; H-15, 4.32, s; H-17, 5.86, s; H-20, 2.73, m, 2.83, m; H-21, 2.45, dd, *J*=12.5, 10.3, 2.73, m; H-22, 2.83, m; H-23, 1.92, m, 1.97, m; H-25, 1.14, s; H-26, 1.42, s; H-27, 1.19, s; H-28, 1.23, s; H-30, 6.12, dd, *J*=10.5, 17.3; H-31, 5.05, br d, *J*=10.5, 5.09, br d, *J*=17.3; and H-32/33, 1.48ppm, br s.

^{13}C NMR:

($CDCl_3$) C-2, 152.45; C-3, 117.22; C-4, 124.94; C-5, 115.32; C-6, 140.11; C-7, 119.54; C-8, 111.04; C-9, 138.14; C-10, 51.45; C-11, 39.86; C-12, 26.93; C-13, 21.14; C-14, 104.36; C-15, 87.96; C-16, 197.28; C-17, 117.58; C-18, 169.84; C-19, 77.61; C-20, 28.25; C-21, 27.58; C-22, 48.55; C-23, 33.82; C-24, 78.71; C-25, 23.07; C-26, 28.76; C-27, 23.55; C-28, 16.27; C-29, 41.05; C-30, 149.01; C-31, 109.87; and C-32/33, 28.83, 28.76ppm.

Mass Spectrum:

501(M^+, 20), 4.86(21), 483(18), 468(18), 443(10), 428(16), 425(31), 410(48), 387(17), 372(4), 344(5), 250(31), 237(37), 222(23), 198(35), 182(50), 168(37), and 130*m/e* (100); HREIMS: found 501.2877; calcd for $C_{32}H_{39}NO_4$, 501.2881.

Reference

M. R. TePaske, J. B. Gloer, D. T. Wicklow, and P. F. Dowd; Aflavarin and β-Aflatrem: New Anti-Insectan Metabolites From The Sclerotia of *Aspergillus flavus*; J. Natural Products, Vol. 55, pp. 1080-1086(1992).

Common/Systematic Name

Paspalitrem A; 3-Methyl-2-butenylpaspalinine

Molecular Formula/Molecular Weight

$C_{32}H_{39}NO_4$; MW = 501.28791

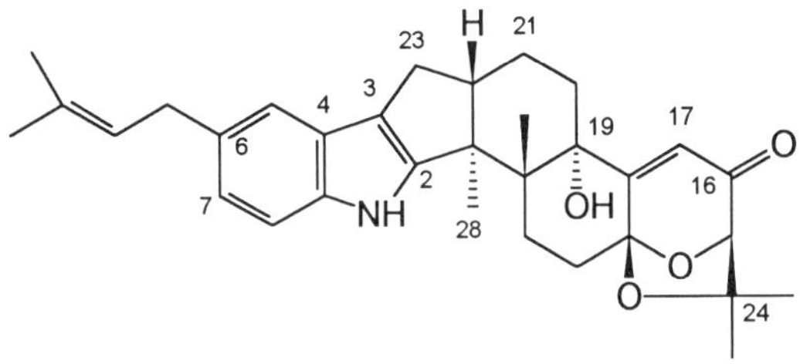

Fungal Source

Claviceps paspali sclerotia (collected from *Paspalum dilatatum* infected plants) and an endophytic *Phomopsis* sp. (MF5670) isolated from the living bark of *Cavendishia pubescens*, a shrub or small tree of dry or exposed slopes and thickets in upland regions of northwest South America. This isolate was from Colombia. A potential ecological role of this metabolite in regard to endophytism of the woody host is possible.

Isolation/Purification

Fungal sclerotia were extracted with chloroform; the chloroform extract was partitioned between hexane and 80% aqueous methanol. The aqueous methanol extract was chromatographed on a silica gel column eluted with a linear gradient from benzene to ethyl ether. The active fractions were chromatographed on a silica gel column eluted with a linear gradient from benzene to 10% ethyl ether/benzene.

Biological Activity

ED_{50} in mice dosed IP was <14.0mg/kg. Clinical signs were intermittent tremors, diarrhea, rough hair coat, and hypersensitivity to sound stimuli. Gross clinical signs very similar to those produced by paxilline.

Spectral Data

UV:

λ_{max}^{MeOH} 234 and 278nm (ϵ max not reported).

^{1}H NMR:

($CDCl_3$) 1.18, 6H, s; 1.35, 3H, s; 1.42, 3H, s; 1.77, 6H, s; 1.8-2.9, 11H, m; 3.62, 2H, m; 4.29, 1H, s; 5.38, 1H, m; 5.73, 1H, s; and 6.8-8.0ppm, 5H, m.

^{13}C NMR:

C-2, 151.2 s; C-3, 116.7 s; C-4, 117.6 d; C-5, 127.9 s; C-6, 120.9 d; C-7, 109.4 d; C-8,

139.8 s; C-9, 124.6 s; C-10, 51.2 s; C-11, 39.9 s; C-12, 21.1 t; C-13, 27.0 t; C-14, 104.4 s; C-15, 88.0 s; C-16, 197.3 s; C-17, 117.6 d; C-18, 169.8 s; C-19, 77.6 s; C-20, 28.3 t; C-21, 29.4 t; C-22, 48.7 d; C-23, 33.8 t; C-24, 78.7 s; C-25, 23.6 q; C-26, 28.9 q; C-27, 23.1 q; C-28, 16.3 q; C-29, 32.0 t; C-30, 123.7 d; C-31, 133.0 s; C-32, 18.0 q; and C-33, 25.8ppm q.

Mass Spectrum:
501.2885*m/e* (M^+) (requires 501.2878)

TLC Data

Silica gel G-HR; chloroform-acetone, 93:7, v/v; R_f=0.60. Detection: blue spot after spraying with 50% ethanolic H_2SO_4 and heating at 100°C for 5 min; fluorescent under UV light.

References

G. F. Bills, R. A. Giscobbe, S. H. Lee, F. Pelaez, and J. S. Tkacz; Tremorgenic mycotoxins, paspalitrem A and C, from a tropical *Phomopsis*; Mycol. Res., Vol. 96, pp. 977-983(1992).

R. J. Cole and R. H. Cox; Handbook of Toxic Fungal Metabolites; Academic Press, New York, p. 402 (1981).

R. J. Cole, J. W. Dorner, J. A. Lansden, R. H. Cox, C. Pape, B. Cunfer, S. S. Nicholson, and D. M. Bedell; Paspalum Staggers: Isolation and Identification of Tremorgenic Metabolites from Sclerotia of *Claviceps paspali*; Agric. Food Chem., Vol. 25, pp. 1197-1201(1977).

Common/Systematic Name

Paspalitrem B, 3-Methyl-3-hydroxy-1-butenylpaspalinine

Molecular Formula/Molecular Weight

$C_{32}H_{39}NO_5$; MW = 517.28282

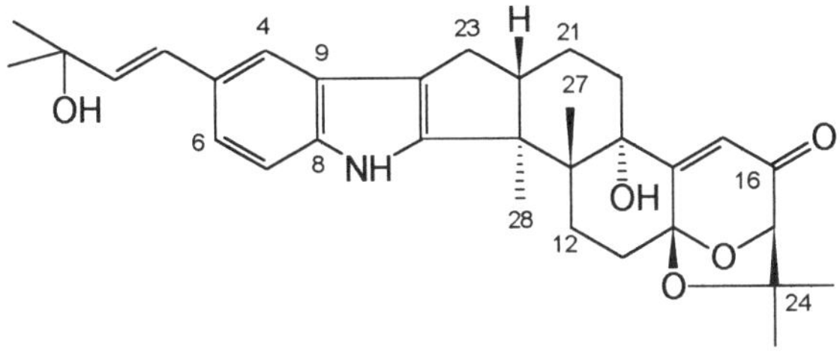

General Characteristics

Paspalitrem B readily formed a methylated derivative in methanol solution and acidic conditions. The methylation occurred with the tertiary hydroxyl group located on the 3-methyl-3-hydroxy-1-butenyl moiety.

Fungal Source

Claviceps paspali sclerotia.

Isolation/Purification

See paspalitrem A.

Biological Activity

ED_{50} for tremorgenic activity was <14mg/kg in mice dosed IP; other clinical signs were diarrhea, rough hair coat, and hypersensitivity to sound stimuli. Gross clinical signs very similar to those produced by paxilline.

Spectral Data

UV:

λ_{max}^{MeOH} 227, 248, 305, and 336nm (ϵ max not reported).

^{1}H NMR:

($CDCl_3$) 1.21, 3H, s; 1.25, 3H, s; 1.41, 3H, s; 1.47, 3H, s; 1.50, 6H, s; 1.90-2.77, 11H, m; 4.32, 1H, s; 5.81, 1H, s; 6.42, 1H, d, *J*=16.0Hz; 7.0-7.30, 4H, m; and 7.76ppm, 1H, s N-H.

^{13}C NMR:

($CDCl_3$) C-2, 152.3 s; C-3, 116.4 s; C-4, 116.0 d; C-5, 128.6 s; C-6, 120.9 d; C-7, 110.5 d; C-8, 140.3 s; C-9, 124.2 s; C-10, 51.2 s; C-11, 39.9 d; C-12, 21.1 t; C-13, 27.0 t; C-14, 104.4 s; C-15, 87.9 s; C-16, 197.3 s; C-17, 117.6 d; C-18, 169.7 s; C-19, s; C-20, 28.3 t; C-21, 29.9 t; C-22, 48.6; C-23, 33.8 t; C- 24, 78.7 s; C-25, 23.6 q; C-26, 28.8 q; C-27, 23.0 q; C-28, 16.3 q; C-29, 124.7 d; C-30, 137.5 d; C-31, 71.2 s; C-32, 29.9 q; and C-33, 29.9ppm q.

TLC Data

Chloroform-acetone, 93:7 (v/v); R_f: 0.20. Detection: spray with 50% ethanolic H_2SO_4 and heat at 100°C for 5 min. Blue-green spot after spraying; turns blue after heating; fluorescent under UV light.

References

R. J. Cole and R. H. Cox; Handbook of Toxic Fungal Metabolites; Academic Press, New York, pp. 406-409 (1981).

R. J. Cole, J. W. Dorner, J. A. Lansden, R. H. Cox, C. Pape, B. Cunfer, S. S. Nicholson, and D. M. Bedell; Paspalum Staggers: Isolation and Identification of Tremorgenic Metabolites from Sclerotia of *Claviceps paspali*; Agric. Food Chem., Vol. 25, pp. 1197-1201(1977).

Common/Systematic Name
Paspalitrem C

Molecular Formula/Molecular Weight
$C_{32}H_{39}NO_4$; MW = 501.28791

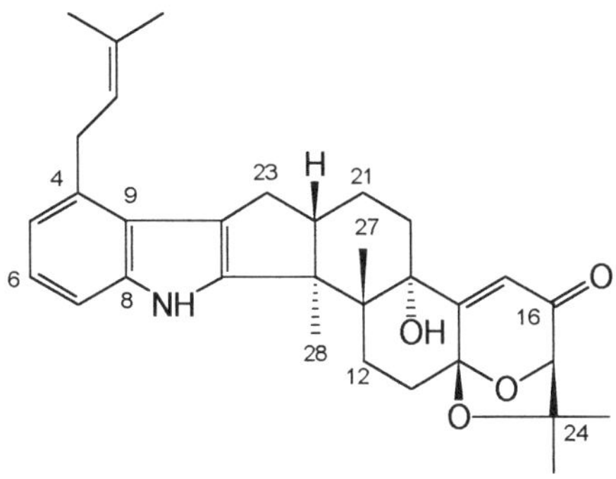

Fungal Source
Claviceps paspali sclerotia and an endophytic *Phomopsis* sp. (MF5670) isolated from the living bark of *Cavendishia pubescens*, a shrub or small tree of dry or exposed slopes and thickets in upland regions of northwest South America. This isolate was from Colombia. A potential ecological role of this metabolite in regard to endophytism of the woody host is possible.

Isolation/Purification
Fungal cultures were extracted three times with methyl ethyl ketone which provided a brown oily residue upon the removal of solvent. After adding methylene chloride to the residue, the mixture was sonicated and filtered through sintered glass. The filter cake was washed twice with portions of fresh methylene chloride. The filtrates were pooled, and the solvent was removed *in vacuo*. The material from methylene chloride was then subjected to silica gel flash chromatography (Silica Gel 60, particle size 0.040-0.063mm, 230-400 mesh ASTM; EM Science). The column was eluted stepwise with methylene chloride-methanol; the effluent was monitored at 240nm. Analysis of fractions by analytical reversed phase HPLC (Whatman Partisil 10 ODS-3, 4-6mm x 25cm; 80% aqueous methanol, isocratic, 1ml per min, ambient temperature) revealed the presence of the major components (paspalitrems A and C). The fractions rich in the major component were recovered and subsequently subjected to preparative reversed-phase HPLC (Whatman Partisil 10 ODS-3; 70% aqueous methanol, isocratic, 10ml/min, ambient temperature) to provide the major component (paspalitrem C) and a minor component (paspalitrem A). The retention times for the two compounds by the analytical HPLC procedure were 20.1 and 21.8 minutes, respectively.

Biological Activity
Tremorgenic in vertebrates and toxic in some insect species.

Spectral Data

UV:

λ_{max}^{MeOH} 236 and 282nm.

^{1}H NMR:

(CD_2Cl_2) 7.83(H-1, 1H, s); 7.13(H-7, 1H, dd, *J*=8.1, 0.6Hz); 6.96(H-6, 1H, dd, *J*=8.1, 7.2Hz); 6.81(H-5, 1H, dd, *J*=7.2, 0.6Hz); 5.83(H-17, 1H, d, *J*=1.2Hz); 5.39(H-30, 1H, tq, *J*=7.2, 1.5Hz); 4.30(H-15, 1H, d, *J*=1.5Hz); 3.59(H-29, 2H, d, *J*=7.2); 2.84(H-22, 1H, m); 2.80, 2.07(H-21, 2H, m); 2.76, 2.07(H-20, 2H, m); 2.03(H-13, 2H, m); 1.93(H-23, 2H, m); 1.81(H-12, 2H, m); 1.77(H-33, 3H, s); 1.75(H-32, 3H, s); 1.43(H-26, 3H, s); 1.38(H-28, 3H, s); 1.24(H-27, 3H, s); and 1.17ppm (H-25, 3H, s).

^{13}C NMR:

(CD_2Cl_2) 197.4(C-16, s); 169.9(C-18, s); 151.7(C-2, s), 140.3(C-8, s); 133.3(C-31, s); 132.0(C-4, s); 124.9(C-9, s); 124.2(C-30, d); 121.1(C-6, d); 119.2(C-5, d); 118.1(C-17, d); 116.9(C-3, s); 109.6(C-7, d); 104.7(C-14, s); 88.4(C-15, d); 79.0(C-24, s); 78.0(C-19, s); 51.6(C-10, s); 49.1(C-22, d); 40.2(C-11, s); 34.2(C-23, t); 32.4(C-29, t); 29.7(C-21, t); 29.0(C-26, q); 28.7(C-20, t); 27.3(C-13, t); 25.8(C-32, q); 23.8(C-27, q); 23.2(C-25, q); 21.4(C-12, t); 18.0(C-33, q); and 16.3ppm (C-28, q).

Mass Spectrum:

HREIMS: 501.2894*m/e* (M^+); calcd. 501.2894.

References

G. F. Bills, R. A. Giscobbe, S. H. Lee, F. Pelaez, and J. S. Tkacz; Tremorgenic mycotoxins, paspalitrem A and C, from a tropical *Phomopsis*; Mycol. Res., Vol. 96, pp. 977-983(1992).

J. W. Dorner, R. J. Cole, R. H. Cox, and B. M. Cunfer; Paspalitrem C, a New Metabolite from Sclerotia of *Claviceps paspali*; J. Agric. and Food Science, Vol. 32, pp. 1069-1071 (1984).

Common/Systematic Name
Sulpinine A

Molecular Formula/Molecular Weight
$C_{32}H_{41}NO_4$; MW = 503.30356

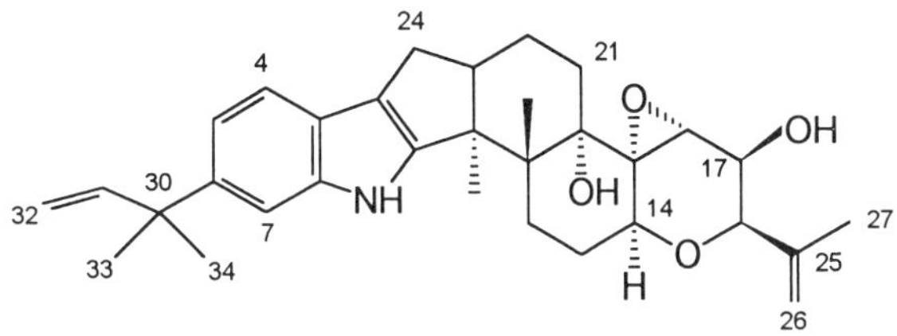

General Characteristics
Sulpinine A was isolated as a yellow-orange solid with the following properties: mp, 149-152°C dec; $[\alpha]_D$ -29.6° (c=0.005, in $CHCl_3$).

Fungal Source
Sclerotia of *Aspergillus sulphureus* (NRRL 4077).

Isolation/Purification
Powdered sclerotia of *A. sulphureus* were sequentially extracted with pentane and CH_2Cl_2 using a Soxhlet apparatus. A portion of the total CH_2Cl_2 extract was fractionated by silica gel column chromatography. A stepwise gradient from 0 to 10% (v/v) MeOH in $CHCl_3$ was employed resulting in the elution and collection of a distinct red band at 4% MeOH. This active fraction was further separated by reversed phase HPLC (MeOH-H_2O, 89:11, v/v) to yield sulpinines A (HPLC retention time 16.0 min), B, and C and secopenitrem B and penitrem B.

Biological Activity
Exhibited potent activity against the lepidopteran crop pest *Helicoverpa zea*.

Spectral Data

UV:
λ_{max}^{MeOH} 235(22,600) and 283nm (5,600).

IR:
3473, 2933, 2873, 1457, 1371, 1043, 911, and 756cm^{-1}.

^{1}H NMR:
(CD_3OD) H-4, 7.20(d, J=8.3); H-5, 6.95(dd, J=8.3, 1.7); H-7, 7.28(d, J=1.3); H-12, 1.63(m), 2.60(m); H-13$_{eq}$, 2.09(m); H-13$_{ax}$, 2.25(m); H-14$_{ax}$, 4.28(br dd, J=9.0, 8.8);

H-16$_{ax}$, 4.04(br s); H-17$_{eq}$, 4.03(br d, *J*=3.1); H-18$_{eq}$, 3.47(br d, *J*=2.0); H-21, 1.37(m), 1.60(m); H-22$_{eq}$, 1.49(dm, *J*=10.0); H-22$_{ax}$, 1.89(dddd, *J*=12, 12, 12, 3); H-23$_{ax}$, 2.69(m); H-24, 2.32(m), 2.56(m); H-26, 4.91(br s), 5.10(br s); H-27, 1.70(br s); H-28, 1.14(s); H-29, 1.26(s); H-31, 6.07(dd, *J*=17.5, 10.6); H-32, 4.97(dd, *J*=10.6, 1.5), 5.07(dd, *J*=17.5, 1.5); H-33, 1.41(s); and H-34, 1.41ppm (s).

^{13}C NMR:

(CD_3OD) C-2, 153.9; C-3, 116.7; C-4, 118.1; C-5, 118.6; C-6, 142.0; C-7, 110.0; C-8, 141.2; C-9, 124.4; C-10, 52.0; C-11, 43.8; C-12, 27.4; C-13, 29.1; C-14, 72.1; C-16, 75.1; C-17, 66.5; C-18, 66.3; C-19, 66.8; C-20, 78.8; C-21, 27.2; C-22, 21.9; C-23, 51.5; C-24, 30.5; C-25, 143.2; C-26, 111.9; C-27, 19.8; C-28, 19.1; C-29, 16.5; C-30, 42.1; C-31, 150.5; C-32, 110.2; C-33, 29.3; and C-34, 29.3ppm.

Mass Spectrum:

EIMS: 503(M^+, 32), 488(43), 467(12), 452(13), 434(10), 397(10), 373(24), 358(29), 250(100), 222(35), 198(33), 182(72), and 167*m/e* (21); HREIMS: obsd 503.3039; calcd for $C_{32}H_{41}NO_4$, 503.3036.

Reference

J. A. Laakso, J. B. Gloer, D. T. Wicklow, and P. F. Dowd; Sulpines A-C and Secopenitrem B: New Antiinsectan Metabolites from the Sclerotia of *Aspergillus sulphureus*; J. Org. Chem., Vol. 57, pp. 2066-2071(1992).

Common/Systematic Name
Sulpinine B

Molecular Formula/Molecular Weight
$C_{32}H_{41}NO_3$; MW = 487.30864

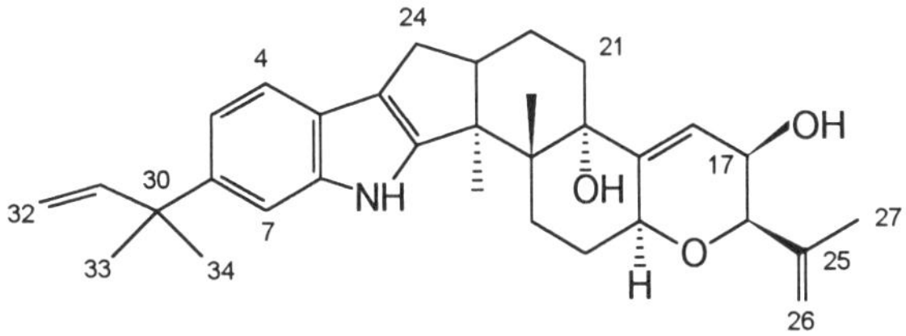

General Characteristics
Sulpinine B was an orange oil; $[\alpha]_D$ -43.2° (*c*=0.003, in $CHCl_3$).

Fungal Source
Sclerotia of *Aspergillus sulphureus* (NRRL 4077).

Isolation/Purification
Powdered sclerotia of *A. sulphureus* were sequentially extracted with pentane and CH_2Cl_2 using a Soxhlet apparatus. A portion of the total CH_2Cl_2 extract was fractionated by silica gel column chromatography. A stepwise gradient from 0 to 10% (v/v) MeOH in $CHCl_3$ was employed resulting in the elution and collection of a distinct red band at 4% MeOH. This active fraction was further separated by reversed phase HPLC (MeOH-H_2O, 89:11, v/v) to yield sulpinines A, B (HPLC retention time, 13.8 min), C and secopenitrem B, and penitrem B.

Biological Activity
Exhibited potent activity against the lepidopteran crop pest *Helicoverpa zea*.

Spectral Data

^1H NMR:
(CD_3OD) H-1, 7.72(br s); H-4, 7.34(d, *J*=8.3); H-5, 7.07(dd, *J*=8.3, 1.5); H-7, 7.28(d, *J*=0.8); H-12, 2.68(dm, *J*=6.0), 1.59(m); H-13, 2.23(m), 1.84(m); H-14, 4.61(br dd, *J*=9.1, 8.8); H-16, 3.86(br s); H-17, 3.96(br d, *J*=5.6); H-18, 5.82(br d, *J*=4.7); H-21, 1.71(m), 1.34(m); H-22, 2.06(m), 2.02(m); H-23, 2.80(m); H-24, 2.65(dm, *J*=4.4), 2.39(dd, *J*=12.9, 12.9); H-26, 5.20(br s), 5.03(br s); H-27, 1.79(br s); H-28, 1.10(s); H-29, 1.28(s); H-31, 6.05(dd, *J*=17.4, 10.6); H-32, 5.06(dd, *J*=17.3, 1.2), 4.99 (dd, *J*=10.6, 1.2); H-33, 1.41(s); and H-34, 1.41ppm (s).

^{13}C NMR:
(CD_3OD) C-2, 152.2; C-3, 116.9; C-4, 117.9; C-5, 118.5; C-6, 141.2; C-7, 108.9; C-8, 139.8; C-9, 123.1; C-10, 50.7; C-11, 42.9; C-12, 28.2; C-13, 29.3; C-14, 73.7;

C-16, 79.1; C-17, 62.8; C-18, 118.7; C-19, 148.1; C-20, 77.7; C-21, 27.3; C-22, 21.1; C-23, 49.7; C-24, 34.7; C-25, 141.6; C-26, 111.7; C-27, 19.8; C-28, 20.2; C-29, 16.2; C-30, 41.1; C-31, 148.8; C-32, 110.0; C-33, 28.6; and C-34, 28.6ppm.

Mass Spectrum:

EIMS: 487(M^+ 21), 472(16), 469(10), 451(26), 436(11), 250(100), 198(34), 182(71), 167(23), 129(45), 115(28), and 105(21); HREIMS: obsd 487.3104; calcd for $C_{32}H_{41}NO_3$, 487.3086.

Reference

J. A. Laakso, J. B. Gloer, D. T. Wicklow, and P. F. Dowd; Sulpines A-C and Secopenitrem B: New Antiinsectan Metabolites from the Sclerotia of *Aspergillus sulphureus*; J. Org. Chem., Vol. 57, pp. 2066-2071(1992).

Common/Systematic Name
Sulpinine C

Molecular Formula/Molecular Weight
$C_{32}H_{41}NO_6$; MW = 535.29339

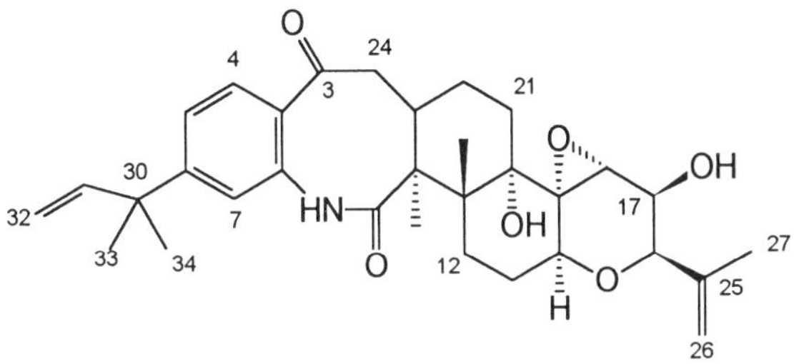

General Characteristics
Yellow oil; $[\alpha]_D$ +17.1° (c=0.003, in $CHCl_3$).

Fungal Source
Sclerotia of *Aspergillus sulphureus* (NRRL 4077).

Isolation/Purification
Powdered sclerotia of *A. sulphureus* were sequentially extracted with pentane and CH_2Cl_2 using a Soxhlet apparatus. A portion of the total CH_2Cl_2 extract was fractionated by silica gel column chromatography. A stepwise gradient from 0 to 10% (v/v) MeOH in $CHCl_3$ was employed resulting in the elution and collection of a distinct red band at 4% MeOH. This active fraction was further separated by reversed phase HPLC (89:11 (v/v), MeOH-H_2O) to yield sulpinines A, B, C (HPLC retention time, 6.0 min), and secopenitrem B and penitrem B.

Biological Activity
Exhibited potent activity against the lepidopteran crop pest *Helicoverpa zea*.

Spectral Data

UV:
λ_{max}^{MeOH} 229(ϵ=25,600) and 262nm (18,200).

IR:
3483, 2965, 2872, 1685, 1647, 1603, 1391, and 756cm^{-1}.

^{1}H NMR:
(CD_3OD) H-1, 7.13(br s); H-4, 7.62(d, J=8.1); H-5, 7.32(dd, J=8.1, 1.8); H-7, 6.99(d, J=1.7); H-12$_{ax}$, 2.41(m); H-12$_{eq}$, 1.89(dm, J=11.4); H-13$_{ax}$, 1.70(m); H-13$_{eq}$, 2.25(m); H-14$_{ax}$, 4.19(dd, J=9.3, 9.0); H-16$_{ax}$, 4.04(br s); H-17$_{eq}$, 3.96(br d, J=1.9);

H-18, 3.47(br d, *J*=2.3); H-20(OH), 1.45(br s); H-21_{ax}, 1.21(m), H-21_{eq}, 1.34(m); H-22_{ax}, 1.76(dd m, *J*=13.4, 3.4); H-22_{eq}, 1.34(m); H-23_{ax}, 2.99(m); H-24a, 3.05(dd, *J*=17.8, 4.4); H-24b, 2.40(dd, *J*=17.8, 4.0); H-26a, 5.13(br s); H-26b, 5.00(d, *J*=1.6); H-27, 1.68(br s); H-28, 0.99(s); H-29, 1.55(s); H-31, 5.93(dd, *J*=17.4, 10.6); H-32a, 5.09(dd, *J*=10.6, 0.9); H-32b, 5.06(dd, *J*=17.4, 0.9); H-33, 1.37(s); and H-34, 1.37ppm (s).

^{13}C NMR:
(CD_3OD) C-2, 176.6; C-3, 202.4; C-4, 129.4; C-5, 125.3; C-6, 154.5; C-7, 125.0; C-8, 136.8; C-9, 131.6; C-10, 57.5; C-11, 43.4; C-12, 24.1; C-13, 27.3; C-14, 71.1; C-16, 73.4; C-17, 64.6; C-18, 61.8; C-19, 65.5; C-20, 77.1; C-21, 28.1; C-22, 24.4; C-23, 36.1; C-24, 47.7; C-25, 140.9; C-26, 112.5; C-27, 19.4; C-28, 18.7; C-29, 16.5; C-30, 41.3; C-31, 146.4; C-32, 112.1; C-33, 28.0; and C-34, 28.0ppm.

Mass Spectrum:
EIMS: 535(M^+, 13%), 254(3), 242(3), 228(3), 214(11), 200(4), 188(100), 172(5), 145(9), 130(9), 115(5), and 105*m/e* (6); HREIMS: obsd 535.2945; calcd for $C_{32}H_{41}NO_6$, 535.2934.

Reference

J. A. Laakso, J. B. Gloer, D. T. Wicklow, and P. F. Dowd; Sulpines A-C and Secopenitrem B: New Antiinsectan Metabolites from the Sclerotia of *Aspergillus sulphureus*; J. Org. Chem., Vol. 57, pp. 2066-2071(1992).

Common/Systematic Name

PC-M4

Molecular Formula/Molecular Weight

$C_{37}H_{49}NO_4$; MW = 571.36616

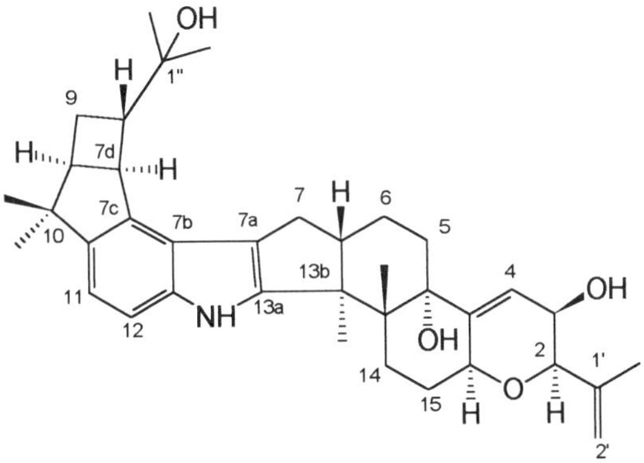

General Characteristics

Crystalline powder, mp., 269-272°C (dec.).

Fungal Source

Penicillium crustosum (strain NHL 6491).

Isolation/Purification

Penicillium crustosum was cultivated at 25°C for 14 days using Czapek-Dox medium supplemented with 0.2% yeast extract. The mycelium was extracted with CH_2Cl_2 at room temperature. The residue obtained by evaporation of the extract was chromatographed on silica gel with C_6H_6-Me_2CO (5:1, v/v) followed by repeated purification by LPLC [C_6H_6-Me_2CO (20:1, v/v) or C_6H_{14}-EtOAc-MeOH [12:6:1, v/v/v to obtain PC-M4 and with C_6H_6-Me_2CO (3:1, v/v)] followed by purification by HPLC using the solvent system C_6H_6-EtOAc (5:2, v/v) to give PC-M5.

Biological Activity

Biological activity not presented but based on structure PC-M4 is probably tremorgenic.

Spectral Data

UV:

λ_{max}^{MeOH} 233(log ϵ=4.09) and 283nm (3.71).

IR:

(KBr) 3600 and 3400cm^{-1} (NH, OH).

CD:
(c=4.06x10^{-5}, MeOH) +1.6(214), -2.0(240), -0.6(271), and -0.5nm (292).

^{1}H NMR:
[$(CD_3)_2SO$] 0.96(6H, s, Me-13C, Me-1"); 1.21(3H, s, Me-13b); 1.23(3H, s, Me-1"); 1.25(3H, s, Me-10); 1.27(3H, s, Me-10); 1.55(1H, brd, *J*=11.5 Hz, H-5a); 1.62(1H, brd, *J*=12.2 Hz, H-6B); 1.67-1.88(5H, m, H-6a, H-14B, H-15B, H2-9); 1.72(3H, brs, Me-1'); 1.93(2H, m, H-5B, H-8); 2.05(1H, m, H-15a); 2.29(1H, dd, J=13.1, 10.5 Hz, H-7a); 2.46(1H, ddd, *J*=12.8, 12.8, 5.8 Hz, H-14a); 2.70(2H, m, H-6a, H-9a); 2.84(1H, dd, *J*=13.1, 5.8 Hz, H-7B); 3.70(1H, brd, *J*=9.0Hz, H-7d); 3.71(1H, brs, H-2); 3.84(1H, brd, *J*=4.7Hz, H-3); 4.50(1H, br dd, *J*=9.2, 7.9Hz, H-15a); 4.85(1H, br s, H-2'); 5.01(1H, brs, H-2'); 5.58(1H, br d, *J*=4.7Hz, H-4); 6.74(1H, d, *J*=8.2Hz, H-11); 7.12(1H, d, *J*=8.2Hz, H-12); and 10.53ppm [1H, br s, H-13 (NH)].

^{13}C NMR:
C-2, 79.1; C-3, 62.6; C-4, 117.7; C-4a, 146.7; C-4b, 75.7; C-5, 33.2; C-6, 21.1; C-6a, 49.3; C-7, 28.3; C-7a, 113.7; C-7b, 121.4; C-7c, 133.7; C-7d, 44.2; C-8, 48.6; C-9, 23.4; C-9a, 49.0; C-10, 44.8; Me-10, 21.7, 32.1; C-l0a, 141.8; C-11, 113.9; C-12, 110.6; C-12a, 139.7; C-13a, 153.0; C-13b, 49.9; Me-13b, 16.2; C-13, 42.1; Me-13c, 19.2; C-14, 26.3; C-15, 27.9; C-15a, 72.9; C-1', 142.9; C-2', 100.0; C-3'(Me), 19.6; C-1", 70.5; and C-Me-1", 27.1, 27.8ppm.

Mass Spectrum:
HRMS: 571.3662(M^{+}, 17); (calcd for $C_{37}H_{49}NO_4$, 571.3662), 485(100), and 470*m/e* (35).

Reference

T. Yamaguchi, K. Nozawa, T. Hosoe, S. Nakajima, and K. Kawai; Indoloditerpenes Related to Tremorgenic Mycotoxins, Penitrems, from *Penicillium crustosum*; Phytochemistry, Vol. 32, pp. 1177-1181(1993).

Common/Systematic Name
PC-M5

Molecular Formula/Molecular Weight
$C_{32}H_{41}NO_4$; MW = 503.30356

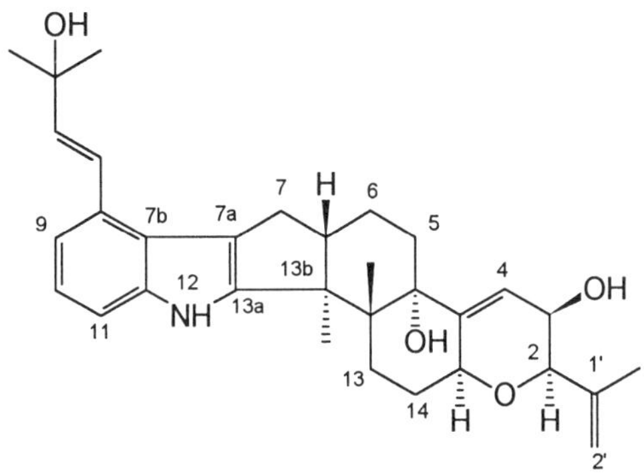

General Characteristics
Pale yellow needles from ethyl acetate; mp., 218-220°C (dec.).

Fungal Source
Penicillium crustosum (strain NHL 6491).

Isolation/Purification
Penicillium crustosum was cultivated at 25°C for 14 days using Czapek-Dox medium supplemented with 0.2% yeast extract. The mycelium was extracted with CH_2Cl_2 at room temp. The residue obtained by evaporation of the extract was chromatographed on silica gel with C_6H_6-Me_2CO (5:1, v/v) followed by repeated purification by LPLC [C_6H_6-Me_2CO (20:1, v/v) or C_6H_{14}-EtOAc-MeOH (12:6:1, v/v/v)] to obtain PC-M4 and with C_6H_6-Me_2CO (3:1, v/v) followed by purification by HPLC using the solvent system C_6H_6-EtOAc (5:2, v/v) to give PC-M5.

Biological Activity
Biological activity not presented but based on the structure of PC-M4 it is probably tremorgenic.

Spectral Data

UV:
λ_{max}^{MeOH} 226sh (log ϵ=4.30), 246(4.22), 305(3.74), and 325nm (3.74).

IR:
(KBr) 3525 and 3400cm^{-1} (NH, OH).

CD:
(C=4.49x10^{-5}, MeOH) -1.3(242), +0.4(259), +0.6(291), and +1.0nm (334).

^{1}H NMR:
[$(CD_3)_2SO$] 1.04(3H, s, Me-12C); 1.38(3H, s, Me-12b); 1.41(6H, s, Me-3" x 2); 1.69(2H, m, H-5, H-6); 1.75(1H, m, H-13B); 1.77(3H, br s, Me-1'); 1.87(2H, m, H-5, H-14); 2.06(1H, ddd, *J*=12.7, 12.7, 3.5Hz, H-13); 2.06(1H, m, H-6); 2.16(1H, m, H-14); 2.60(1H, ddd, *J*=13.5, 12.7, 4.6Hz, H-13a); 2.68(1H, dd, *J*=13.3, 4.6Hz, H-7B); 2.90(2H, m, H-6a, H-7a); 3.15(1H, d, *J*=9.3Hz, OH-3); 3.40(1H, br s, OH); 3.72(1H, br s, OH); 3.80(1H, br s, H-2); 3.909(1H, ddd, *J*=9.3,5.8, 1.8Hz, H-3); 4.62(1H, br dd, *J*=10.2, 8.2Hz, H-14a); 4.87(1H, qd, *J*=1.4, 1.4Hz, H-2'); 5.09(1H, br s, H-2'); 5.76(1H, dd, *J*=5.8, 1.8Hz, H-4); 6.42(1H, d, *J*=15.9Hz, H-2"); 6.92(1H, dd, *J*=8.0, 7.7Hz, H-10); 7.10(1H, d, *J*=15.9Hz, H-l"); 7.14(1H, d, *J*=7.7Hz, H-9); 7.16(1H, d, *J*=8.0Hz, H-ll); and 9.87ppm [1H, br s, H-12 (NH)].

^{13}C NMR:
C-2, 77.8; C-3, 65.3; C-4, 114.5; C-4a, 150.6; C-4b, 77.8; C-5, 34.7; C-6, 22.5; C-6a, 49.5; C-7, 28.7; C-7a, 116.7; C-7b, 122.0; C-7c, 134.4; C-7d, 44.4; C-8, 49.2; C-9, 24.0; C-9a, 49.6; C-10, 45.6; Me-10, 21.9, 32.3; C-10a, 143.7; C-11, 115.6; C-12, 110.7; C-12a, 139.7; C-13a, 152.4; C-13b, 50.5; Me-13b, 16.3; Me-13c, 20.1; C-14, 28.3; C-15, 28.1; C-15a, 73.4; C-1', 141.1; C-2', 111.8; C-3'(Me), 19.6; C-1", 72.9; C-Me-1", 26.6, 28.0ppm; <u>Me</u>COO, 21.1; and Me<u>C</u>OO, 170.9ppm.

Mass Spectrum:
EIMS: 485([M-H_2O]$^+$, 100), 470([M-H_2O]$^+$, 34), 400(16), 382(28), and 248*m/e* (28).

Reference

T. Yamaguchi, K. Nozawa, T. Hosoe, S. Nakajima, and K. Kawai; Indolodíterpenes Related to Tremorgenic Mycotoxins, Penitrems, from *Penicillium crustosum*; Phytochemistry, Vol. 32, pp. 1177-1181(1993).

Common/Systematic Name
PC-M5'

Molecular Formula/Molecular Weight
$C_{29}H_{37}NO_5$; MW = 479.26717

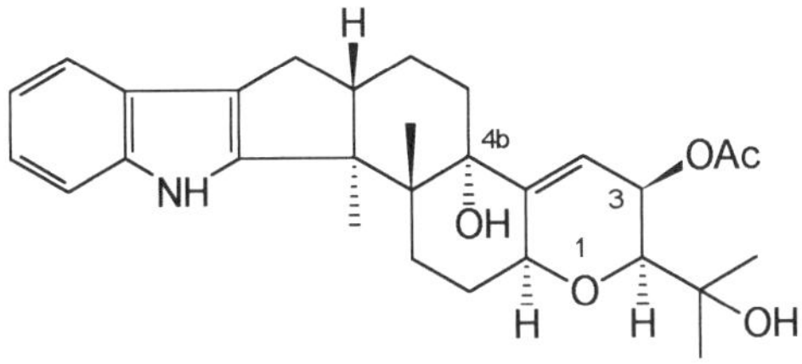

General Characteristics
Colorless crystalline powder; mp, 162-164°C.

Fungal Source
Penicillium crustosum, strain NHL 6491, isolated from contaminated bread which had been intended for school lunches in Shinagawa-ku, Tokyo.

Isolation/Purification
Penicillium crustosum was cultivated at 25°C for 14 days on Czapek-Dox medium supplemented with 0.2% yeast extract. The fresh mycelium was extracted with CH_2Cl_2 at room temperature. The residue obtained by evaporation of the extract was chromatographed on silica gel with benzene-acetone (50:1, v/v) followed by purification by LPLC using benzene to obtain penitrems F and B, with benzene-acetone (20:1, v/v) followed by purification by LPLC using the solvent system of benzene-acetone (100:1, v/v) to give penitrems A and E, with benzene-acetone (10:1, v/v) followed by further purification hy LPLC [benzene-acetone (50:1, v/v)] to obtain penitrem D, with benzene-acetone (5:1, v/v) followed by repeated purification by LPLC [benzene-acetone (20:1, v/v) and/or hexane-AcOEt-EtOH] to give cyclopenin and PC-M5', with benzene-acetone (3:1, v/v) followed by purification by HPLC using the solvent system of benzene-AcOEt (5:2, v/v) to give PC-M6.

Spectral Data

UV:
λ_{max}^{MeOH} 229(log ϵ=4.74) and 279nm (4.05).

IR:
3500, 3460, 3400(NH, OH), and 1720cm^{-1} (AcO).

^{1}H NMR:
[$(CD_3)_2CO$] 1.00(3H, s, 12c-Me); 1.00(3H, s, 2'-Me); 1.26(3H, s, 3-Me); 1.36(3H, s,

12b-Me); 1.70(3H, m); 1.82(1H, dddd, J=13,5, 13.5, 8.5, 5.2Hz); 1.95(1H, ddd, J=13.5, 13.5, 4.5Hz); 1.99(3H, s, 3-OCOMe); 2.10(1H, m); 2.39(1H, dd, J=13.0, 10.8Hz, 7a-H); 2.67(1H, dd, J=13.0, 6.3Hz, 7a-H); 2.69(1H, ddd, J=13.3. 13.3, 4.8Hz); 2.85(1H, m); 3.32(1H, d, J=1.8Hz, 2-H); 3.48(1H, s, OH); 3.49(1H, s, OH); 4.65(1H, br dd, J=10.5, 7.6Hz, 14a-H); 5.20(1H, ddd, J=5.8, 1.8, 1.8Hz, 3-H); 5.69(1H, dd, J=5.8, 1.8Hz, 4-H); 6.94(2H, m, 9-H, 10-H); 7.28(1H, m, 8-H or 11-H); 7.32(1H, m, 11-H or 8-H); and 9.85ppm (1H, br s, 12-H (NH)).

^{13}C NMR:

[$(CD_3)_2CO$] C-2, 82.56; C-3, 66.01; C-4, 115.21; C-4a, 151.29; C-4b, 77.52; C-5, 34.71; C-6, 22.01; C-6a, 50.67; C-7, 30.56; C-7a, 116.71; C-7b, 126.11; C-8, 118.66; C-9, 119.54; C-10, 120.36; C-11, 112.45; C-11a, 141.23; C-12a, 153.84; C-12b, 51.61; C-12b-Me, 16.73; C-12c, 43.53; C-12c-Me, 19.93; C-13, 27.87; C-14, 29.13; C-14a, 75.06; C-1', 71.58; C-2', 25.99; C-3', 27.95; C-MeCOO, 21.28; and MeCOO; 170.69ppm.

Mass Spectrum:

HREIMS: 479.2669*m/e* (M^+), $C_{29}H_{37}NO_5$ requires 479.2670.

Reference

T. Hosoe, K. Nozawa, S. Udagawa, S. Nakajima, and K. Kawai; Structures of New Indoloditerpenes, Possible Biosynthetic Precursors of the Tremorgenic Mycotoxins, Penitrems, from *Penicillium crustosum*; Chem. Pharm. Bull. Vol. 38, pp. 3473-3475 (1990).

Common/Systematic Name

PC-M6

Molecular Formula/Molecular Weight

$C_{27}H_{35}NO_3$; MW = 421.26169

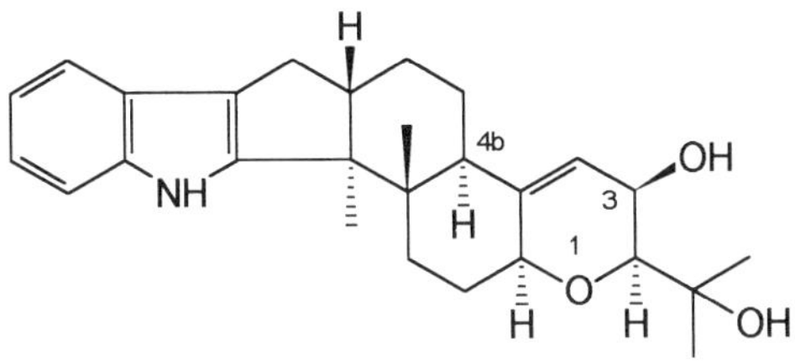

General Characteristics

Colorless crystalline powder; mp. (dec.), 260-263°C.

Fungal Source

Penicillium crustosum, strain NHL 6491, isolated from contaminated bread which had been intended for school lunches in Shinagawa-ku, Tokyo.

Isolation/Purification

Penicillium crustosum was cultivated at 25°C for 14 days on Czapek-Dox medium supplemented with 0.2% yeast extract. The fresh mycelium was extracted with CH_2Cl_2 at room temperature. The residue obtained by evaporation of the extract was chromatographed on silica gel with benzene-acetone (50:1, v/v) followed by purification by LPLC using benzene to obtain penitrems F and B, with benzene-acetone (20:1, v/v) followed by purification by LPLC using the solvent system of benzene-acetone (100:1, v/v) to give penitrems A and E, with benzene-acetone (10:1, v/v) followed by further purification by LPLC [benzene-acetone (50:1, v/v)] to obtain penitrem D, with benzene-acetone (5:1, v/v) followed by repeated purification by LPLC [benzene-acetone (20:1, v/v) and/or hexane-AcOEt-EtOH] to give cyclopenin and PC-M5', with benzene-acetone (3:1, v/v) followed by purification by HPLC using the solvent system of benzene-AcOEt (5:2, v/v) to give PC-M6.

Spectral Data

UV:

λ_{max}^{MeOH} 229(log ϵ=4.64) and 280nm (3.98).

IR:

(KBr) 3560, 3420, and 3270cm^{-1} (NH, OH).

^{1}H NMR:

[$(CD_3)_2SO$] 0.88(3H, s, 12b-Me); 0.98(3H, s, 12c-Me); 1.17(3H, s, 2'-Me); 1.20(3H, s, 3'-Me); 1.46(1H, ddd, *J*=11.5, 11.5, 4.6Hz); 1.54(1H, br d, *J*=12.7Hz); 1.61(1H, m); 1.71(2H, m); 1.80(1H, ddd, *J*=11.5, 11.5, 3.5Hz); 1.84(1H, ddd, *J*=12.7, 12.7, 3.5Hz); 2.03(2H, m); 2.19(1H, br d, *J*=11.5Hz); 2.31(1H, dd, *J*=12.7, 10.4Hz, 7a-H); 2.60(1H, dd, *J*=12.7, 6.9Hz, 7b-H); 2.70(1H, m); 3.00(1H, d, *J*= 1.8Hz, 2-H); 3.92(1H, br dd, *J*= 10.2, 7.2Hz, l4a-H); 4.04(1H, dd, *J*=6.0, 1.8Hz, 3-H); 5.45(1H, d, *J*=6.0Hz, 4-H); 6.90(1H, br t, *J*=7.0Hz, 9-H or 10-H); 6.94(1H, br t, *J*=7.0Hz, 10-H or 9-H); 7.27(2H, dd, *J*=7.0, 1.2Hz, 8-H, 11-H); and 10.70ppm (1H, br s, NH).

^{13}C NMR:

[$(CD_3)_2CO$] C-2, 80.91; C-3, 62.48; C-4, 117.54; C-4a, 144.11; C-4b, 40.50; C-5, 31.32; C-6, 24.17; C-6a, 48.94; C-7, 29.15; C-7a, 115.61; C-7b, 124.32; C-8, 118.34; C-9, 119.13; C-10, 119.27; C-11, 111.75; C-11a, 139.99; C-12a, 150.73; C-12b, 49.62; C-12b-Me, 14.50; C-12c, 40.37; C-12c-Me, 15.41; C-13, 26.15; C-14, 26.87; C-14a, 76.13; C-1', 71.35; C-2', 26.46; and C-3', 27.24ppm.

Mass Spectrum:

HREIMS: 421.2616(M^+), $C_{27}H_{35}NO_3$ requires 421.2616, 406*m/e* (M^+-Me).

Reference

T. Hosoe, K. Nozawa, S. Udagawa, S. Nakajima, and K. Kawai; Structures of New Indoloditerpenes, Possible Biosynthetic Precursors of the Tremorgenic Mycotoxins, Penitrems, from *Penicillium crustosum*; Chem. Pharm. Bull., Vol. 38, pp. 3473-3475 (1990).

8

Janthitrems

- Janthitrem B
- Janthitrem E
- Janthitrem F (10-*O*-Acetyljanthitrem E)
- Janthitrem G

Common/Systematic Name

Janthitrem B

Molecular Formula/Molecular Weight

$C_{37}H_{47}NO_5$; MW = 585.34542

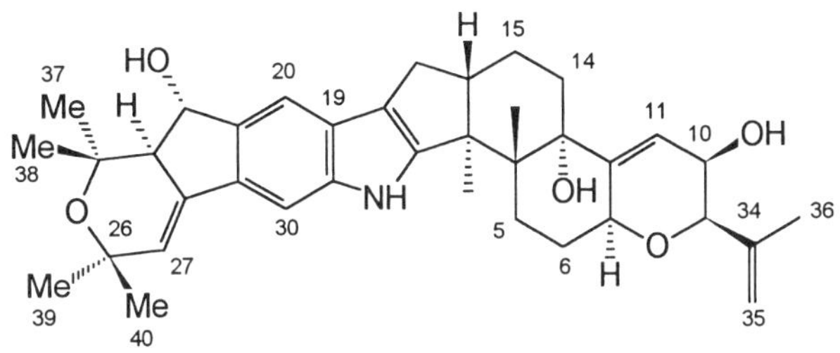

General Characteristics

Obtained as a pale-yellow glass. Gray-green color response to Erhlich's reagent on TLC.

Fungal Source

Penicillium janthinellum.

Isolation/Purification

Purified janthitrem B was obtained as a pale-yellow glass from column chromatography on Mallinckrodt Silic AR CC-7 silica gel following repeated preparatory thin-layer chromatography. Flash chromatography was performed on silica gel (E Merck 9385) using toluene-acetone (17:3, v:v) as the eluent to further purify decomposed samples of janthitrem B from storage.

Biological Activity

Tremorgenic in mouse bioassay. I.P. injection of 200μg of toxin in propylene glycol solution elicited a characteristic tremor response accompanied by incoordination and hypersensitivity to sound and touch.

Spectral Data

UV:

λ_{max}^{MeOH} 228(ϵ=15,420), 258(25,170), 265(27,300), and 329nm (16,600); λ_{max}^{MeOH}
Fluorescence emission: 385nm.

^{1}H NMR:

[$(CD_3)_2CO$] H-5, 2.60, 1.58; H-6, 2.04, 1.79; H-7, 4.58; H-9, 3.77; H-10, 3.91; H-11, 5.69; H-14, 1.58, 1.70; H-15, 2.04, 1.57; H-16, 2.68; H-17, 2.35, 2.65; H-20, 7.374; H-22, 4.90; H-23, 2.65; H-27, 5.97; H-30, 7.366; H-32, 1.32; H-33, 0.89; H-35, 4.86, 5.07; H-36, 1.76; H-37, 1.41; H-38, 1.09; H-39, 1.25; H-40, 1.29; 10-OH, 3.03(d, *J*=9.3 Hz); 13-OH, 3.33(s, br); 22-OH, 4.27(d, *J*=7.6 Hz); and NH, 9.81ppm (s br).

^{13}C NMR:
$(CD_3)_2CO$ C-2, 156.0; C-3, 51.8; C-4, 43.5; C-5, 28.1; C-6, 29.2; C-7, 74.3; C-9, 80.5; C-10, 64.2; C-11, 119.5; C-12, 148.5; C-13, 77.5; C-14, 34.7; C-15, 22.1; C-16, 50.5; C-17, 27.9; C-18, 116.9; C-19, 127.8; C-20, 114.1; C-21, 140.1; C-22, 76.4; C-23, 60.3; C-24, 74.3; C-26, 72.7; C-27, 120.2; C-28, 137.2; C-29, 131.6; C-30, 103.6; C-31, 142.2; C-32, 16.7; C-33, 20.0; C-34, 143.9; C-35, 110.8; C-36, 20.1; C-37, 30.6; C-38, 23.7; C-39, 30.4; and C-40, 32.5ppm.

Mass Spectrum:
ElMS: 585.3422*m/e* (M^+, 585.3442 for $C_{37}H_{47}NO_5$), 568(35), 567(M^+ - H_2O, 71), 553(29), 552(M^+ - H_2O - CH_3, 81), 550(34), 549(69), 535(30), 534(78), 533(21), 532(34), 531(45), 529(24), 525(40), 524(97), 517(25), 516(48), 514(25), 507(42), 506(100), 504(21), 490(22), 489(35), 488(75), 486(44), 464(21), 436 (29), and 330(36).

TLC Data

Thin-layer chromatography was performed on silica gel plates (E. Merck 55543) using toluene-acetone (3:2, v:v) as the eluent. Janthitrems were visualized by their fluorescence when irradiated at 366nm.

Reference

A. L. Wilkins, C. O Miles, R. M. Ede, R. T. Gallagher, and S. C. Munday; Structure Elucidation of Janthitrem B, a Tremorgenic Metabolite of *Penicillium janthinellum*, and Relative Configuration of the A and B Rings of Janthitrems B, E, and F; J. Agric. Food Chem., Vol. 40, pp. 1307-1309(1992).

Common/Systematic Name
Janthitrem E

Molecular Formula/Molecular Weight
$C_{37}H_{49}NO_6$; MW = 603.35599

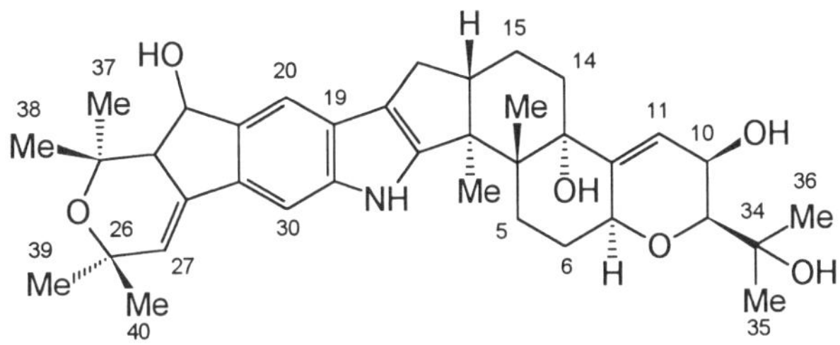

General Characteristics
Colorless amorphous solid.

Fungal Source
Penicillium janthinellum (TDD4).

Isolation/Purification
The cultures of *Penicillium janthinellum* were filtered and the mycelium macerated with acetone in a Waring blender. The acetone solution was evaporated and the aqueous residue partitioned between ethyl acetate and water. The residue of the ethyl acetate solution was partitioned between *n*-hexane and 90% methanol. The 90% methanol solution was evaporated and the aqueous residue once again partitioned between ethyl acetate and water. The crude extract obtained from the ethyl acetate solution was separated by column chromatography on silica gel using benzene-acetone (70:30, v/v) as eluant to yield the three janthitrems in order of descending R_f values: janthitrem G, F, and E.

Biological Activity
Tremorgenic.

Spectral Data

UV:
λ_{max}^{MeOH} 228(ϵ=17,700), 258sh (27,300), 265(30,000), and 330nm (17,000).

IR:
(KBr) 3400, 2900, and 1700cm^{-1}.

^{13}C NMR:

(acetone-d_6) C-2, 155.92 s; C-3, 51.75 s; C-4, 43.39 s; C-5, 27.85 t; C-6, 29.18 t; C-7, 75.03 d; C-9, 81.82 d; C-10, 64.48 d; C-11, 119.15 d; C-12, 148.56 s; C-13, 77.49 s; C-14, 34.51 t; C-15, 22.02 t; C-16, 50.33 d; C-17, 28.04 t; C-18, 116.85 s; C- 19, 127.77 s: C-20, 113.99 d; C-21, 139.92 s; C-22, 76.45 d; C-23, 60.32 d; C-24, 74.26 s; C-26, 72.78 s; C-27, 120.13 d; C-28, 137.11 s; C-29, 131.51 s; C-30, 103.73 d; C-31, 142.11 s; C-32, 16.58 q; C-33, 20.20 q; C-34, 72.65 s; C-35, 27.28 q; C-36, 27.21 q; C-37, 30.43 q; C-38, 23.76 q; C-39, 30.63 q; and C-40, 32.51ppm q.

Mass Spectrum:

Found: M^+, 603.355; $C_{37}H_{49}NO_6$ requires 603.356.

Reference

A. E. de Jesus, P. S. Steyn, F. R. van Heerden, and R. Vleggaar; Structure Elucidation of the Janthitrems, Novel Tremorgenic Mycotoxins from *Penicillium janthinellum*; J. Chem. Soc. Perkin Trans. I, pp. 697-701(1984).

Common/Systematic Name

Janthitrem F; 10-*O*-Acetyljanthitrem E

Molecular Formula/Molecular Weight

$C_{39}H_{51}NO_7$; MW = 645.36655

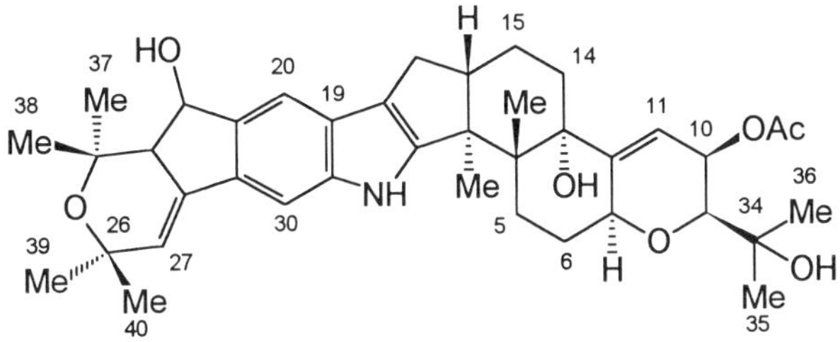

General Characteristics

Colorless amorphous solid.

Fungal Source

Penicillium janthinellum (TDD4).

Isolation/Purification

The cultures of *Penicillium janthinellum* were filtered and the mycelium macerated with acetone in a Waring blender. The acetone solution was evaporated and the aqueous residue partitioned between ethyl acetate and water. The residue of the ethyl acetate solution was partitioned between *n*-hexane and 90% methanol. The 90% methanol solution was evaporated and the aqueous residue once again partitioned between ethyl acetate and water. The crude extract obtained from the ethyl acetate solution was separated by column chromatography on silica gel using benzene-acetone (70:30, v:v) as eluant to yield the three janthitrems in order of descending R_f values: janthitrem G, F, and E.

Biological Activity

Tremorgenic.

Spectral Data

UV:

λ_{max}^{MeOH} 228(ϵ=14,200), 258sh (20,500), 265(22,400), and 330nm (12,200).

IR:

(KBr) 3400, 2900, and 1720cm^{-1}.

^{13}C NMR:

(acetone-d_6) C-2, 155.64 s; C-3, 51.72 s; C-4, 43.37 s; C-5, 27.70 t; C-6, 29.14 t; C-7,

75.03 d; C-9, 82.44 d; C-10, 66.00 d; C-11, 115.14 d; C-12, 151.26 s; C-13, 77.42 S; C-14, 34.50 t; C-15, 21.88 t; C-16, 50.27 d; C-17, 27.85 t; C-18, 116.84 s; C-19, 127.67 s; C-20, 114.08 d; C-21, 139.74 s; C-22, 76.35 d; C-23, 60.10 d; C-24, 74.22 s; C-26, 72.70 s; C-27, 120.13 d; C-28, 136.85 s; C-29, 131.57 s; C-30, 103.36 d; C-31, 142.02 s; C-32, 16.60 q; C-33, 19.87 q; C-34, 71.61 s; C-35, 27.81 q; C-36, 25.95 q; C-37, 30.25 q; C-38, 23.68 q; C-39, 30.61 q; and C-40, 32.40 q; $\underline{C}OCH_3$, 170.86; and $CO\underline{C}H_3$, 21.37ppm.

Mass Spectrum:
Found: 645.367, M^+; $C_{39}H_{51}NO_7$ requires 645.366.

Reference

A. E. de Jesus, P. S. Steyn, F. R. van Heerden, and R. Vleggaar; Structure Elucidation of the Janthitrems, Novel Tremorgenic Mycotoxins from *Penicillium janthinellum*; J. Chem Soc. Perkin Trans. I, pp. 697-701(1984).

Common/Systematic Name

Janthitrem G

Molecular Formula/Molecular Weight

$C_{39}H_{51}NO_6$; MW = 629.37164

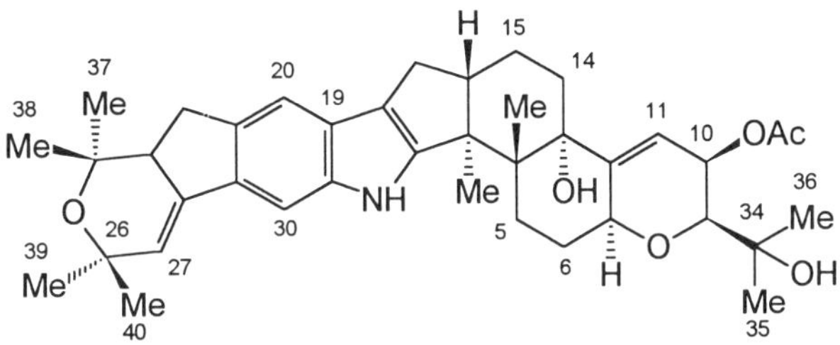

General Characteristics

Colorless amorphous solid.

Fungal Source

Penicillium janthinellum (TDD4).

Isolation/Purification

The cultures of *Penicillium janthinellum* were filtered and the mycelium macerated with acetone in a Waring blender. The acetone solution was evaporated and the aqueous residue partitioned between ethyl acetate and water. The residue of the ethyl acetate solution was partitioned between *n*-hexane and 90% methanol. The 90% methanol solution was evaporated and the aqueous residue once again partitioned between ethyl acetate and water. The crude extract obtained from the ethyl acetate solution was separated by column chromatography on silica gel using benzene-acetone (70:30, v:v) as eluant to yield the three janthitrems in order of descending R_f values: janthitrem G, F, and E.

Biological Activity

Tremorgenic.

Spectral Data

UV:

λ_{max}^{MeOH} 228(ϵ=23,000), 258sh (15,300), 263(15,700), and 331nm (10,080).

IR:

(KBr) 3400, 2900, and 1720cm^{-1}.

^{13}C NMR:

(acetone-d_6) C-2, 155.38 s; C-3, 51.70 s; C-4, 43.45 s; C-5, 27.74 t; C-6, 29.15 t; C-7, 75.06 d; C-9, 82.47 d; C-10, 66.08 d; C-11, 115.16 d; C-12, 151.28 s; C-13, 77.47 s; C-14, 34.56 t; C-15, 21.92 t; C-16, 50.39 d; C-17, 27.87 t; C-18, 116.46 s; C-19, 127.60 s: C-20, 114.11 d; C-21, 136.69 s; C-22, 33.53 d; C-23, 49.79 d; C-24, 74.74 s; C-26, 72.94 s; C-27, 119.53 d; C-28, 140.79 s; C-29, 133.31 s; C-30, 103.96 d; C-31, 141.17 s; C-32, 16.60 q; C-33, 19.86 q; C-34, 71.62 s; C-35, 27.83 q; C-36, 25.94 q; C-37, 29.82 q; C-38, 22.53 q; C-39, 30.49 q; and C-40, 32.30 q; $\underline{C}OCH_3$, 170.69; and $CO\underline{C}H_3$, 21.33ppm.

Mass Spectrum:

Found: 629.372, M^+; $C_{39}H_{51}NO_6$ requires 629.372.

Reference

A. E. de Jesus, P. S. Steyn, F. R. van Heerden, and R. Vleggaar; Structure Elucidation of the Janthitrems, Novel Tremorgenic Mycotoxins from *Penicillium janthinellum*; J. Chem Soc. Perkin Trans. I, pp. 697-701(1984).

9

Miscellaneous Indole Metabolites

2,4-Dimethylindole
4-Hydroxymethyl-2-methylindole
4-Methoxymethyl-2-methylindole
Marcfortine A
Marcfortine B
Marcfortine C
Paraherquamide
Nominine
Aspernomine
Tubingensin A
Tubingensin B
Radarin A
Radarin B
Radarin C
Radarin D

Common/Systematic Name

2,4-Dimethylindole

Molecular Formula/Molecular Weight

$C_{10}H_{11}N$; MW = 145.0891

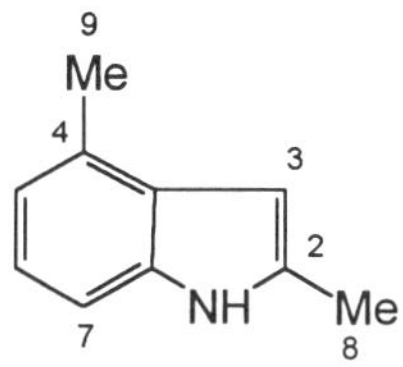

General Characteristics

2,4-Dimethylindole was obtained as a yellow oil.

Fungal Source

Fruit bodies of *Tricholoma sciodes* and *T. virgatum.*

Isolation/Purification

Fruit bodies of *Tricholoma sciodes* were collected in the vicinity of Lund, Sweden. The fruit bodies were ground in a meat grinder, and the mush was extracted with ethyl acetate. The organic phase was separated, dried with Na_2SO_4 and the solvent was evaporated. The fresh fruit bodies of *T. virgatum* were frozen at -20°C, rapidly broken with a hammer and extracted at -20°C with ethyl acetate. The organic phase was dried with $MgSO_4$ and filtered through a short Al_2O_3 column to remove free fatty acids. Final purification from crude extracts was achieved by silica gel column and radial chromatography.

Spectral Data

UV:

λ_{max}^{EtOH} 223(ϵ=19,200), 268 (4,400), 271 (4,400), 273(4,300), and 278nm (2,900).

IR:

(KBr) 3380, 2920, 1690, 1610, 1160, and 770cm^{-1}.

^{1}H NMR:

($CDCl_3$) H-1, 7.82(br s); H-3, 6.24(m); H-5, 6.88(d, *J*=7.2Hz); H-6, 7.03(dd, *J*=7.0, 8.0Hz); H-7, 7.13(d, *J*=8.1Hz); H-8, 2.45(s); and H-9, 2.52ppm (s).

^{13}C NMR:

($CDCl_3$) C-2, 134.3(s); C-3, 98.9(d); C-3a, 128.9(s); C-4, 129.1(s); C-5, 119.8(d); C-6, 121.0(d); C-7, 107.8(d); C-7a, 135.7(s); C-8, 13.7(q); and C-9, 18.8ppm (q).

Mass Spectrum:
HREIMS: 145.0892*m/e* (M^+, 67%, $C_{10}H_{11}N$), requires 145.0891, 144(100), and 130*m/e* (15).

Reference

L. Garlaschelli, Z. Pang, O. Sterner, and G. Vidari; New Indole Derivatives from the Fruit Bodies of *Tricholoma Sciodes* and *T. Virgatum*; Tetrahedron, Vol. 50, pp. 3571-3574 (1994).

Common/Systematic Name
4-Hydroxymethyl-2-methylindole

Molecular Formula/Molecular Weight
$C_{10}H_{11}NO$; MW = 161.08406

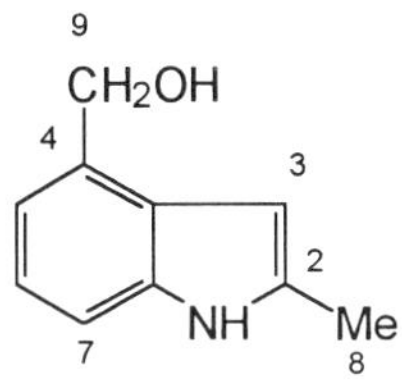

General Characteristics
4-Hydroxymethyl-2-methylindole was obtained as a yellow oil.

Fungal Source
Fruit bodies of *Tricholoma sciodes* and *T. virgatum.*

Isolation/Purification
Fruit bodies of *Tricholoma sciodes* were collected in the vicinity of Lund, Sweden. The fruit bodies were ground in a meat grinder, and the mush was extracted with ethyl acetate. The organic phase was separated, dried with Na_2SO_4 and the solvent was evaporated. The fresh fruit bodies of *T. virgatum* were frozen at -20°C, rapidly broken with a hammer and extracted at -20°C with ethyl acetate. The organic phase was dried with $MgSO_4$ and filtered through a short Al_2O_3 column to remove free fatty acids. Final purification from crude extracts was achieved by silica gel column and radial chromatography.

Spectral Data

UV:
λ_{max}^{EtOH} 222(ϵ=25,400) and 279nm (6,100).

IR:
(KBr) 3380, 2920, 1620, 1570, 1450, 1420, 1400, 1360, 1300, 1200, 1170, 1100, and 780cm^{-1}.

^{1}H NMR:
($CDCl_3$) H-1, 7.91(br s); H-3, 6.34(m); H-5, 7.04(d, *J*=7.1Hz); H-6, 7.08(dd, *J*=7.0, 8.0Hz); H-7, 7.24(d, *J*=7.8Hz); H-8, 2.45(d, *J*=0.6Hz); H-9, 4.72(s); and OCH_3, 3.41ppm (s).

^{13}C NMR:
($CDCl_3$) C-2, 135.2(s); C-3, 98.9(d); C-3a, 128.0(s); C-4, 128.8(s); C-5, 119.3(d); C-6, 120.7(d); C-7, 110.0(d); C-7a, 136.2(s); C-8, 13.7(q); C-9, 64.1(t); and OCH_3, 58.0ppm (q).

Mass Spectrum:

HREIMS: 161.0842*m/e* (M^+, 100%, $C_{10}H_{11}NO$), requires 161.0840, 144(71), 132(58), 117(23), 101(33), 84(50), and 59*m/e* (63).

Reference

L. Garlaschelli, Z. Pang, O. Sterner, and G. Vidari; New Indole Derivatives from the Fruit Bodies of *Tricholoma Sciodes* and *T. Virgatum*; Tetrahedron, Vol. 50, pp. 3571-3574 (1994).

Common/Systematic Name

4-Methoxymethyl-2-methylindole

Molecular Formula/Molecular Weight

$C_{11}H_{13}NO$; MW = 175.09971

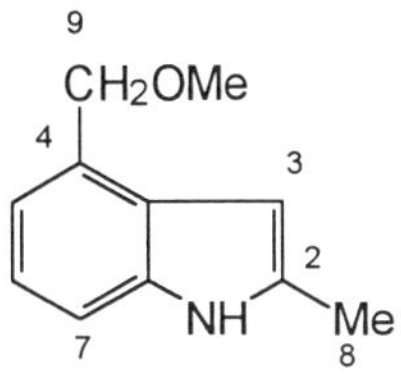

General Characteristics

4-Methoxymethyl-2-methylindole was obtained as a yellow oil.

Fungal Source

Fruit bodies of *Tricholoma sciodes* and *T. virgatum.*

Isolation/Purification

Fruit bodies of *Tricholoma sciodes* were collected in the vicinity of Lund, Sweden. The fruit bodies were ground in a meat grinder, and the mush was extracted with ethyl acetate. The organic phase was separated, dried with Na_2SO_4 and the solvent was evaporated. The fresh fruit bodies of *T. virgatum* were frozen at -20°C, rapidly broken with a hammer and extracted at -20°C with ethyl acetate. The organic phase was dried with $MgSO_4$ and filtered through a short Al_2O_3 column to remove free fatty acids. Final purification from crude extracts was achieved by silica gel column and radial chromatography.

Spectral Data

UV:

λ_{max}^{EtOH} 219(ϵ=22,500), 266 (4,700), and 274nm (5,600).

IR:

(KBr) 3360, 2920, 1440, 1420, 1390, 1340, 1290, 1220, 1060, 1000, and 780cm^{-1}.

^{1}H NMR:

($CDCl_3$) H-1, 8.18(br s); H-3, 6.32(m); H-5, 7.08(d, *J*=7.0Hz); H-6, 7.12(dd, *J*=7.0, 7.0Hz); H-7, 7.21(d, *J*=7.0Hz); H-8, 2.38(s); and H-9, 4.90ppm (s).

^{13}C NMR:

($CDCl_3$) C-2, 135.6(s); C-3, 98.4(d); C-3a, 127.4(s); C-4, 131.4(s); C-5, 118.3(d); C-6, 120.9(d); C-7, 110.2(d); C-7a, 136.3(s); C-8, 13.7(q); and C-9, 64.1ppm (t).

Mass Spectrum:
HREIMS: 175.0999(M^+, 38%, $C_{11}H_{13}NO$), requires 175.0997, 159(10), 144(100), 132(17), and 130*m/e* (21).

<u>Reference</u>

L. Garlaschelli, Z. Pang, O. Sterner, and G. Vidari; New Indole Derivatives from the Fruit Bodies of *Tricholoma Sciodes* and *T. Virgatum*; Tetrahedron, Vol. 50, pp. 3571-3574 (1994).

Common/Systematic Name

Marcfortine A

Molecular Formula/Molecular Weight

$C_{28}H_{35}N_3O_4$; MW = 477.26276

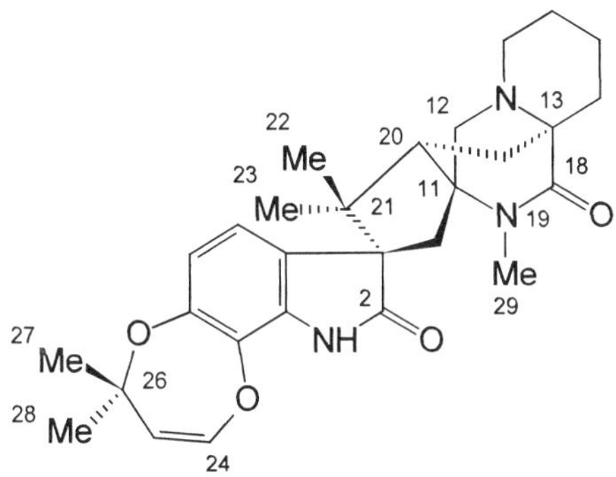

General Characteristics

Crystals; mp., 242-244°C; $[\alpha]_D^{22}$ -5.3° (*c*= 1.14, in $CHCl_3$).

Fungal Source

Penicillium roqueforti.

Isolation/Purification

Marcfortine A was purified by chromatography of the alkaloidal extract obtained from lyophilized mycelium.

Spectral Data

UV:

λ_{max} 226(ε =30,080) and 268nm sh (4,625).

IR:

($CHCl_3$) 3400(NH), 1700, and 1630cm^{-1} (C=O).

^{1}H NMR:

($CDCl_3$) The spectrum revealed an aromatic ring which has two contiguous protons (H-4 and H-5) giving rise to an AB quartet (doublets at 6.79 and 6.61ppm, J_{AB}=8.1Hz); a widely separated olefinic AB quartet (doublet at 6.38ppm and doublet at 4.92, J_{AB}=7.5Hz), assigned to H-24 and H-25, respectively; signals due to four methyl groups [0.84, 1.13 and 1.45ppm (6H)] due to the two isoprene units; and two of the three nitrogen atoms were exchangeable with D_2O (8.7ppm) and one was an N-CH_3 (3.12ppm) group.

^{13}C NMR:
(CDCl$_3$) C-2, 183.3, s; C-3, 60.6, s; C-4, 120.2, d; C-5, 114.9*, d; C-6, 146.2, s; C-7, 132.8**, s; C-8, 135.4**, s; C-9, 124.9, s; C-10, 37.0, t; C-11, 63.1, s; C-12, 61.5, t; C-13, 64.2, s; C-14, 31.7, t; C-15, 20.7, t; C-16, 25.9, t; C-17, 54.5, t; C-18, 173.9, s; C-19, 31.7, t; C-20, 52.9, d; C-21, 46.5, s; C-24, 139.2, d; C-25, 117.2*, d; C-26, 79.8, s; N-ME, 26.4, q; 21-Me, 20.7, q, 25.8***, q; and 26-Me, 29.9ppm, q.

*, **, *** Assignments may be reversed.

Mass Spectrum:
HREIMS: 477.2602(M$^+$) and a base peak at 418.2248*m/e* for $C_{26}H_{30}N_2O_3$ (M$^+$ - MeNHCHO).

Reference

J. Polonsky, M-A. Merrien, T. Prange, C. Pascard, and S. Moreau; Isolation and Structure (X-Ray analysis) of Marcfortine A, a New Alkaloid from *Penicillium roqueforti*; J. C. S. Chem. Commun., pp. 601-602(1980).

Common/Systematic Name
Marcfortine B

Molecular Formula/Molecular Weight
$C_{27}H_{33}N_3O_4$; MW = 463.24711

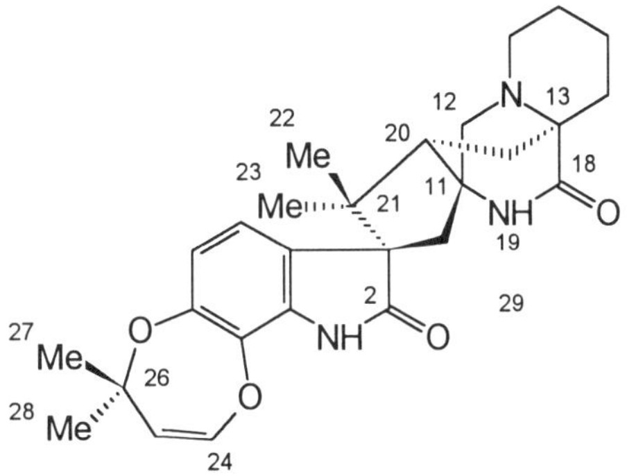

General Characteristics
Crystals from ethyl acetate; mp., 178-180°C; $[\alpha]_D^{22}$ -67.7° (*c*= 1.77, in $CHCl_3$).

Fungal Source
Penicillium roqueforti strain B26.

Isolation/Purification
Marcfortine B was purified by chromatography of the alkaloidal extract obtained from lyophilized mycelium.

Spectral Data

UV:
λ_{max} 229nm (ϵ=20,755)

^{1}H NMR:
($CDCl_3$) H-4, 6.66(d, *J*=8.1Hz); H-5, 6.79(d); H-24, 6.39(d, *J*=7.5Hz); H-25, 4.91(d); H-12, 3.71(*J*=11.2Hz), 2.48(br d); H-17, 2.70(dd, *J*=11.2Hz), 2.48(br, d); 26-Me, 1.45, 1.43; and 21-Me, 1.08, 0.81ppm.

^{13}C NMR:
($CDCl_3$) C-2, 183.1, s; C-3, 61.4, s; C-4, 120.4, d; C-5, 115.0*, d; C-6, 146.1, s; C-7, 132.6**, s; C-8, 135.4**, s; C-9, 124.9, s; C-10, 39.9, t; C-11, 61.4, s; C-12, 61.4, t; C-13, 63.1, s; C-14, 31.1, t; C-15, 20.9, t; C-16, 25.9, t; C-17, 54.6, t; C-18, 177.1, s; C-19, 31.8, t; C-20, 54.2, d; C-21, 46.7, s; C-24, 139.1, d; C-25, 117.8*, d; C-26, 79.8, s; 21-Me, 23.9, q, 25.8***, q; and 26-Me, 30.1ppm, q.

*, **, *** Assignments may be reversed.

Mass Spectrum:
HREIMS: 463.2479*m/e* (M^+) for $C_{27}H_{33}N_3O_4$.

References

J. Polonsky, M-A. Merrien, T. Prange, C. Pascard, and S. Moreau; Isolation and Structure (X-Ray analysis) of Marcfortine A, a New Alkaloid from *Penicillium roqueforti*; J. C. S. Chem. Commun., pp. 601-602(1980).

T. Prange, M.-A. Billion, M. Vuilhorgne, C. Pascard, J. Polonsky, and S. Moreau; Structures of Marcfortine B and C, Alkaloids from *Penicillium roqueforti*; Tet. Lett., Vol. 22, pp. 1977-1980(1981).

Common/Systematic Name
Marcfortine C

Molecular Formula/Molecular Weight
$C_{27}H_{33}N_3O_3$; MW = 447.25219

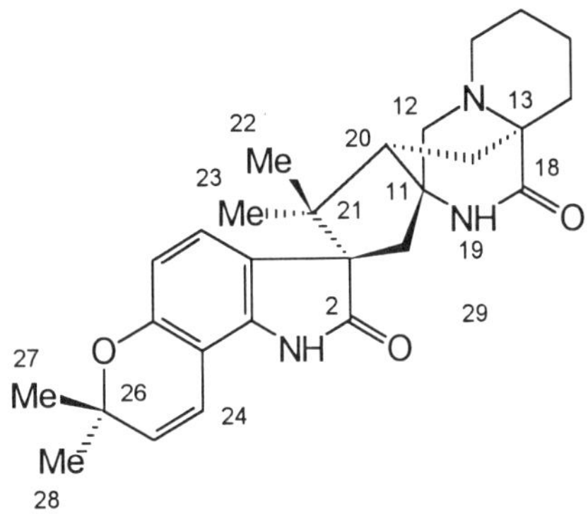

General Characteristics
Colorless prisms from ethyl acetate; mp., 264-267°C; $[\alpha]_D^{22}$ -64.4° (*c*=1.1, in $CHCl_3$).

Fungal Source
Penicillium roqueforti strain B26.

Isolation/Purification
Marcfortine C was purified by chromatography of the alkaloidal extract obtained from lyophilized mycelium.

Spectral Data

UV:
λ_{max} 246nm (ϵ=11,490).

^{1}H NMR:
($CDCl_3$) H-4, 6.86(d, *J*=8.1Hz); H-5, 6.42(d); H-24, 6.44(d, *J*=10Hz); H-25, 5.82(d); H-12, 3.68(d, *J*=11.2Hz), 2.45(br d); H-20,3.08(t, *J*=10Hz); H-17, 2.67(dd, *J*=11.2Hz); 26-Me, 1.45, 1.43; and 21-Me, 1.08, 0.81ppm.

^{13}C NMR:
($CDCl_3$) C-2, 185.5, s; C-3, 61.0, s; C-4, 124.4, d; C-5, 109.4, d; C-6, 153.1, s; C-7, 105.6, s; C-8, 137.8, s; C-9, 121.2, s; C-10, 39.6, t; C-11, 61.2, s; C-12, 61.4, t; C-13, 62.6, s; C-14, 30.8, t; C-15, 20.7, t; C-16, 25.7, t; C-17, 54.5, t; C-18, 177.2, s; C-19, 31.5, t; C-20, 54.3, d; C-21, 46.3, s; C-24, 116.3, d; C-25, 131.4, d; C-26, 76.8, s; 26-Me, 27.8, 27.8; and 21-Me, 23.7, q, 25.8ppm, q.

Mass Spectrum:
LREIMS: 447*m/e* (M^+) for $C_{27}H_{33}N_3O_3$.

References

J. Polonsky, M-A. Merrien, T. Prange, C. Pascard, and S. Moreau; Isolation and Structure (X-Ray analysis) of Marcfortine A, a New Alkaloid from *Penicillium roqueforti*; J. C. S. Chem. Commun., pp. 601-602(1980).

T. Prange, M.-A. Billion, M. Vuilhorgne, C. Pascard, J. Polonsky, and S. Moreau; Structures of Marcfortine B and C, Alkaloids from *Penicillium roqueforti*; Tet. Lett., Vol. 22, pp. 1977-1980(1981).

Common/Systematic Name
Paraherquamide

Molecular Formula/Molecular Weight
$C_{28}H_{35}N_3O_5$; MW = 493.25767

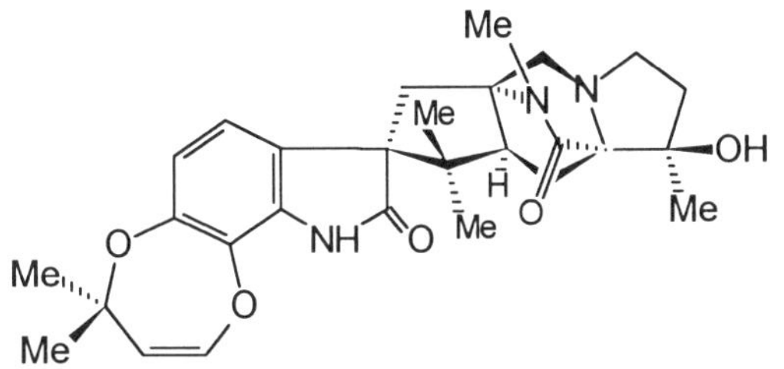

General Characteristics
Colorless prisms from ethyl acetate; mp., 244-247°C (dec.); $[\alpha]_D^{22}$ -28°(*c*=0.43, in MeOH); positive color on Dragendorf's test.

Fungal Source
Penicillium paraherquei.

Biological Activity
Reported to be toxic but details not presented.

Spectral Data

UV:
λ_{max}^{EtOH} 226(ϵ=32,400), 260(6,100), and 290nm (1,600).

IR:
(KBr) 3510, 3430, 3245, 1714, and 1650cm^{-1}.

^{1}H NMR:
($CDCl_3$) 0.86(3H, s); 1.10(3H, s); 1.45(6H, s); 1.65(3H, s); 1.85(1H, d, *J*=15Hz); 1.77-2.40(5H, m); 2.55(1H, d, *J*=11Hz); 2.58(1H, s, disappeared with D_2O); 2.67(1H, d, *J*=15Hz); 2.93-3.25(2H, m); 3.03(3H, s); 3.58(1H, d, *J*=11Hz); 4.87(1H, d, *J*=8Hz); 6.30(1H, d, *J*=8Hz); 6.64(1H, d, *J*=8Hz); 6.78(1H, d, *J*=8Hz); and 8.33ppm (1H, s, disappeared with D_2O).

Mass Spectrum:
LREIMS: 493*m/e* (M^+).

Reference

M. Yamazaki, E. Okuyama, M. Kobayashi, and H. Inoue; The Structure of Paraherquamide, A Toxic Metabolite from *Penicillium paraherquei*; Tet. Lett., Vol. 22, pp. 135-136(1981).

Common/Systematic Name
Nominine

Molecular Formula/Molecular Weight
$C_{28}H_{39}NO$; MW = 405.30317

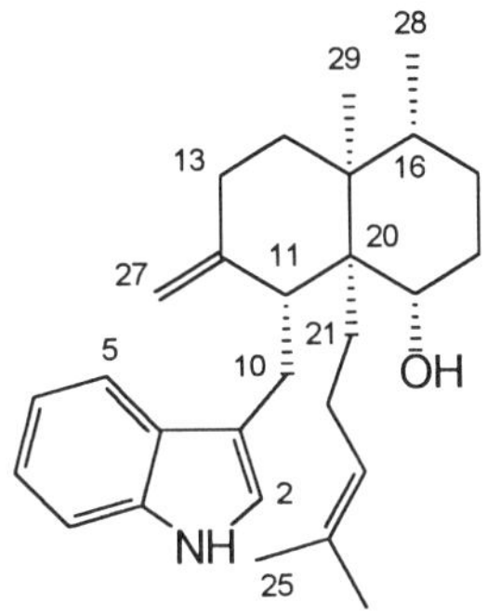

General Characteristics
Melting point, 54-55°C; $[\alpha]_D$ +23.6° (*c*=0.85, in MeOH).

Fungal Source
Sclerotia of *Aspergillus nomius* (NRRL 13137). *A. nomius* is closely related to the aflatoxin-producing fungi, *A. flavus* and *A. parasiticus*, both of which selectively allocate antiinsectan aflavinine derivatives to their sclerotia.

Isolation/Purification
Sclerotia of *A. nomius* were ground with a mortar and pestle and triturated repeatedly with hexane. The combined hexane extracts were filtered and evaporated to afford a light yellow oil which was subjected to reversed-phase semipreparative HPLC [5μm, C_{18} column; 90:10 (v/v) MeOH-H_2O at 2.0mL/min] to afford nominine as an off-white powder.

Biological Activity
Nominine exhibited potent activity against the widespread crop pest *Heliothis zea*, causing 40% mortality and a 97% reduction in weight relative to controls when incorporated into a standard test diet at 100ppm dry weight.

Spectral Data

^{1}H NMR Data:
($CDCl_3$) H-1, 7.88(br, s); H-2, 6.93(br s); H-5, 7.59(br d, *J*= 7.8Hz); H-6, 7.11(dd, *J*=7.1, 7.8); H-7, 7.17(dd, *J*=7.1, 8.1); H-8, 7.32(br d, *J*=8.1); H-10, 3.04(br d, *J*=15.4Hz; 3.10(dd, J=9.0, 15.4Hz); H-11, 3.22(br d, J=9.0Hz; H-13, 2.11(ddd, J=3.2,

3.5, 12.7Hz); 2.21(m); H-14, 1.51(m); 1.68(m); H-16, 2.45(m); H-17, 1.33(m); 1.70(m); H-18, 1.64(m); 1.92(m); H-19, 4.52(br s); H-21, 1.36(m); 1.75(m); H-22, 2.21(m); H-23, 5.17(br t, *J*=7.1Hz); H-25, 1.67(br s); H-26, 1.71(br s); H-27, 4.81(br s); 4.92(br s); H-28, 0.82(d, *J*=6.6Hz); and H-29, 11.01ppm (s).

^{13}C NMR:

(CDCl$_3$) C-2, 121.2(d); C-3, 117.1(s); C-4,127.7(s); C-5, 118.5(d); C-6, 119.1(d); C-7, 121.8(d); C-8, 111.0(d); C-9, 136.0(s); C-10, 21.4(t); C-11, 45.9(d); C-12, 148.9(s); C-13, 33.5(t); C-14, 34.4(t); C-15, 40.9(s); C-16, 31.1(d); C-17, 25.4(t); C-18, 28.8(t); C-19, 70.0(d); C-20, 47.9(s); C-21, 29.2(t); C-22, 23.9(t); C-23, 125.8(d); C-24, 131.2(s); C-25, 17.8(q); C-26, 25.8(q); C-27, 107.7(t); C-28, 16.6(q); and C-29, 18.7ppm (q).

Mass Spectrum:

EIMS: (70 eV) 405(M$^+$; rel intensity 57), 387(100), 318(15), 304(52), 302(70), 288(17), 248(15), 232(15), 196(42), 180(40), 168(28), and 156(16); HREIMS obsd 405.3035; calcd for $C_{28}H_{39}NO$ 405.3031.

Reference

J. B. Gloer, B. L. Rinderknecht, D. T. Wicklow, and P. F. Dowd; Nominine: A New Insecticidal Indole Diterpene from the Sclerotia of *Aspergillus nomius*; J. Org. Chem., Vol. 54, pp. 2530-2532(1989).

Common/Systematic Name
Aspernomine

Molecular Formula/Molecular Weight
$C_{28}H_{39}NO_2$; MW = 421.29808

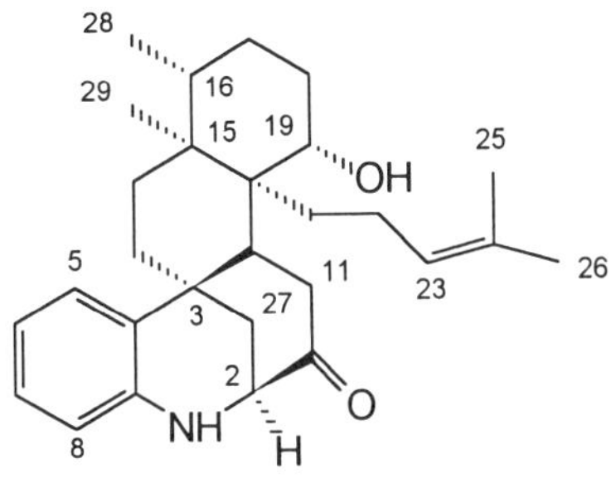

General Characteristics
$[\alpha]_D$ +225° (*c*=0.12 g/dL; MeOH).

Fungal Source
Sclerotial metabolite from *Aspergillus nomius* (NRRL 6552). The strain of *A. nomius* was originally isolated from a pine sawfly (*Diprion similis*).

Isolation/Purification
Sclerotia of *A. nomius* were ground with a mortar and pestle and then extracted with *n*-pentane. Concentration of the resulting *n*-pentane extract afforded a yellow-orange oil. A portion of this extract was subjected to silica gel chromatography using a hexane-ethyl acetate gradient. Aspernomine was obtained as fine white needles from 90% hexane-ethyl acetate. Aspernomine was also purified by reversed-phase HPLC separation of the pentane extract, eluting slightly before nominine with a retention time of 20.9 min, using 90:10(v/v) MeOH-H_2O on a Beckman Ultrasphere 5μm C_{18} column at 2.0 mL/min.

Biological Activity
Exhibited moderate activity against the corn earworm (*Helicoverpa zea*); 100ppm in a standard diet resulted in a 35% reduction in weight gain of test insects relative to controls. Exhibited cytotoxicity toward three human solid tumor cell lines. ED_{50} values were 3.09, 4.93, and 3.08μg/ml (A-549 lung carcinoma, MCF-7 breast adenocarcinoma and HT-29 colon adenocarcinoma).

Spectral Data

UV:
λ_{max}^{MeOH} 333(ε=1,150), 302(2,510), 244(5,760), and 222nm (5,460).

IR:

(neat) 3500, 3360, 2970, 2930, 1698, 1606, 1490, and 750cm^{-1}.

^{1}H NMR:

($CDCl_3$) H-1, 4.35(br s); H-2, 3.75(br s); H-5, 7.43(br d, *J*=7.2Hz); H-6, (ddd, *J*=1.1, 7.2, 7.2); H-7, 7.04(ddd, *J*=1.1, 7.8, 7.8Hz); H-8, 6.51(dd, *J*=1.1, 7.8Hz); H-11a, 2.08(dd, *J*=9.3, 17.6); H-11b, 2.49(d, *J*=17.6); H-12, 2.64(br d, *J*=9.3Hz); H-13$_{eq}$, 1.28(m); H-13$_{ax}$, 2.58(ddd, *J*=4.1, 14.5, 14.5Hz); H-14$_{eq}$, 1.39(m); H14$_{eq}$, 1.68(m); H-16, 2.40(m); H-17a, 1.34(m); 17b, 1.73(m); H-18$_{eq}$, 1.53(br dd, *J*=3.1, 14.0Hz); H-18$_{eq}$, 1.82(m); H-19, 4.01(br s); H-21a, 1.63(m); H-21b, 1.97(m); H-22a, 1.98(m); H-22b, 2.18(m); H-23, 5.01(br t); H-25, 1.60(s); H-26, 1.68(s); H-27a, 1.79(br d, *J*=14.0); H-27b, 2.93(br dd, *J*=3.7, 14.0Hz); H-28, 0.93(d, *J*=7.7Hz); and H-29, 1.09(s).

^{13}C NMR:

($CDCl_3$) C-2, 56.97(d); C-3, 36.30(s); C-4, 130.70(s); C-5, 125.59(d); C-6, 118.37(d); C-7, 127.58(d); C-8, 114.65(d); C-9, 142.70(s); C-10, 209.20(s); C11-a, 37.33(t); C-12, 47.25(d); C-13, 30.62(t); C-14, 28.95(t); C-15, 40.09(s); C-16, 31.33(d); C-17, 24.97(t); C-18,29.92(t); C-19, 69.84(d); C-20, 46.38(s); C-21, 30.20(t); C-22, 23.88(t); C-23, 125.59(d); C-24, 131.72(s); C-25, 17.91(q); C-26, 25.57(q); C-27, 34.63(t); C-28, 15.92(q); and C-29, 18.84(q).

Mass Spectrum:

EIMS: (70 eV) 421(M^+, rel intensity 4), 184(7), 156(100), 143(37), 130(28); HREIMS obsd 421.3024; calcd for $C_{28}H_{39}NO_2$, 421.2981.

Reference

G. M. Staub, J. B. Gloer, D. T. Wicklow, and P. F. Dowd; Aspernomine: A Cytotoxic Antiinsectan Metabolite with a Novel Ring System from the Sclerotia of *Aspergillus nomius*; J. Amer. Chem. Soc., Vol. 114, pp. 1015-1017(1992).

Common/Systematic Name
Tubingensin A

Molecular Formula/Molecular Weight
$C_{28}H_{35}NO$; MW = 401.27186

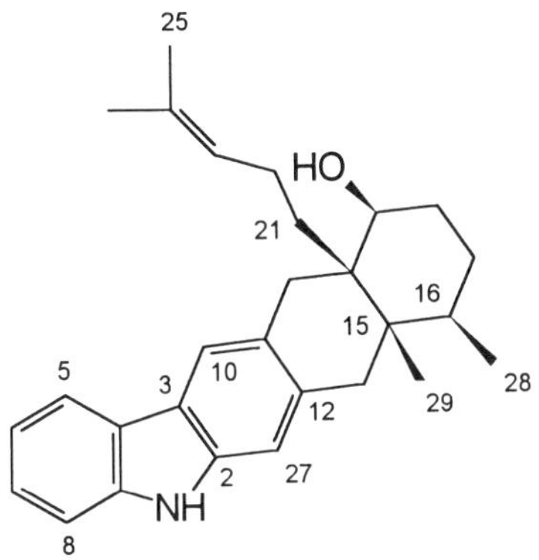

General Characteristics
A light yellow solid from MeOH-H_2O; mp., 95-98°C; $[\alpha]_D$ 13.6° (*c*=1.0, in $CHCl_3$).

Fungal Source
Aspergillus tubingensis (NRRL 4700), a member of the *Aspergillus niger* taxonomic group.

Isolation/Purification
Sclerotia of *A. tubingensis* were ground with a mortar and pestle and triturated repeatedly with hexane. The combined hexane extracts were filtered and evaporated to afford a yellow oil. This residue was subjected to crude preliminary separation by reversed-phase semipreparative HPLC [5-μm C_{18} column; 250x10mm; MeOH-H_2O (90:10, v/v) at 2.0mL/min; HPLC retention time 17.7min] [MeOH-H_2O (90:10, v/v)]. Fractions containing tubingensin A were rechromatographed on the same column at MeOH:H_2O (85:15, v/v) to afford tubingensin A as a light yellow solid.

Biological Activity
Tubingensin A exhibited activity against the widespread crop pest *Heliothis zea* and displayed *in vitro* antiviral activity against *Herpes simplex* virus type 1.

Spectral Data

UV:
λ_{max}^{MeOH} 340(ε=480), 326(480), 302(6,780), 262(6,930), 239(18,200), and 218nm (14,900).

^{1}H NMR:

(CDCl$_3$) H-1, 7.81(br s); H-5, 7.98(br d, *J*=7.8); H-6, 7.18(dd, *J*=3.9, 7.6, 7.8); H-7, 7.34(m); H-8, 7.34(m); H-10, 7.92(s); H-13, 2.99(ddd, *J*=7.3, 12.9, 17.6, H_{ax}); 2.88(br, dd, *J*=6.6, 17.6, H_{eq}); H-14, 1.52(m); 2.01(m); H-16, 1.74(m); H-17, 1.17(m); 1.70(m); H-18, 1.66(m); 2.05(m); H-19, 4.99(br, s); H-21, 1.71(m); 2.08(m); H-22, 1.76(m); 2.06(m); H-23, 5.03(dd, *J*=6.6, 5.9); H-25, 1.43(br, s); H-26, 1.58(br, s); H-27, 7.11(s); H-28, 0.85(d, *J*=5.6); and H-29, 1.21ppm (s).

^{13}C NMR:

(CDCl$_3$) C-2, 137.84(s); C-3, 121.32(s); C-4, 123.78(s); C-5, 119.77(d); C-6, 119.13(d); C-7, 125.27(d); C-8, 110.41(d); C-9, 139.99(s); C-10, 118.45(d); C-11, 132.43(s); C-12, 135.08(s); C-13, 27.06(t); C-14, 29.42(t); C-15, 38.76(s); C-16, 32.58(d); C-17, 25.36(t); C-18, 29.61(t); C-19, 71.35(d); C-20, 47.23(s); C-21, 34.91(t); C-22, 23.10(t); C-23, 125.00(d); C-24, 131.48(s); C-25, 17.62(q); C-26, 25.62(q); C-27, 110.65(d); C-28, 0.85(q); and C-29, 18.35ppm (s).

Mass Spectrum:

EIMS: 401(M^+, 38%), 318(100), 300(52), 260(11), 246(40), 234(21), 232(25), 220(28), 206(51), 180(32), 146(10), and 130*m/e*(5); HREIMS: obsd 401.2698; calcd for $C_{20}H_{38}NO$ 401.2720.

Reference

M. R. TePaske, J. B. Gloer, D. T. Wicklow, and P. F. Dowd; Tubingensin A: An Antiviral Carbazole Alkaloid from the Sclerotia of *Aspergillus tubingensis*; J. Org. Chem., Vol. 54, pp. 4743-4746(1989).

Common/Systematic Name
Tubingensin B

Molecular Formula/Molecular Weight
$C_{28}H_{35}NO$; MW = 401.27186

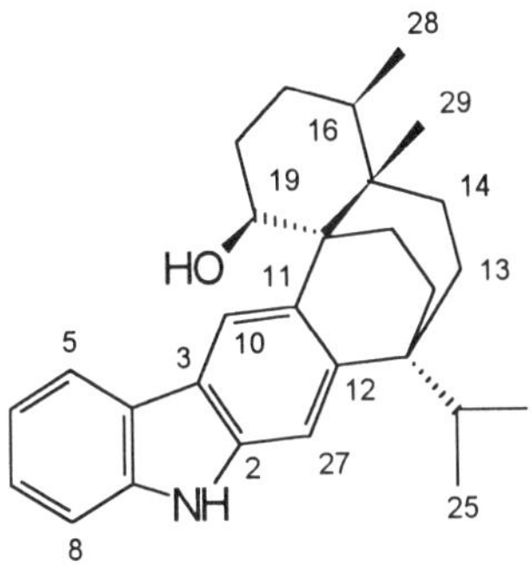

Fungal Source
Aspergillus tubingensis (NRRL 4700).

Isolation/Purification
Sclerotia extracted with hexane and fractionated by C_{18} HPLC (see Tubingensis A).

Biological Activity
Exhibited antiinsectan activity against *Heliothis zea* and antiviral activity against *Herpes simplex*.

Spectral Data

UV:
Characteristic of a carbazole moiety.

^{1}H NMR:
($CDCl_3$) H-1, 7.86(br s); H-5, 7.98(br, d, *J*=7.8); H-6, 7.15(ddd, *J*=1.5, 7.3, 7.8); H-7, 7.32(ddd, *J*=1.1, 6.6, 7.3); H-8, 7.30(dd, *J*=1.5, 6.6); H-10, 8.05(br s); H-13_{eq}, 1.40(m); H-13_{ax}, 1.82(ddd, *J*=4.4, 12.7, 14.1); H-14_{eq}, 1.24(m); H-14_{ax}, 0.17(ddd, *J*=5.0, 13.4, 14.1); H-16, 1.22(m); H-17, 1.31(m), 1.72(m); H-18_{eq}, 2.11(ddd, *J*=3.2, 3.4, 10.7); H-18_{ax}, 2.68m; H-19, 4.36 br t); H-21, 1.76(m); 2.59 (br dd, *J*=3.6, 10.3); H-22, 1.44(m); 1.66(m); H-24, 2.41(qq, *J*=6.6, 6.8); H-25, 1.00(d, *J*=6.6); H-26, 1.09(d, *J*=6.8); H-27, 7.32(br s); H-28, 0.70(d, *J*=6.8); and H-29, 1.15ppm (s).

^{13}C NMR:
($CDCl_3$) C-2, 137.95; C-3, 119.8; C-4, 123.65; C-5, 119.7; C-6, 119.19; C-7, 125.08; C-8, 110.8; C-9, 139.62; C-10, 116.83; C-11, 134.80; C-12, 142.80; C-13, 38.36;

C-14, 38.08; C-15, 40.67; C-16, 38.79; C-17, 25.65; C-18, 33.67; C-19, 76.65; C-20, 47.63; C-21, 27.70; C-22, 25.63; C-23, 42.47; C-24, 35.05; C-25, 19.45; C-26, 17.06; C-27, 107.39; C-28, 16.89; and C-29, 14.08ppm.

Mass Spectrum:

EIMS: 401(M^+; rel. int. 91%), 383(1.0), 358(15), 340(4), 330(1.7), 314(1.4), 300(1.6), 288(36), 260(31), 246(49), 230(34), 218(100), 204(16), 191(5), 180(11), 167(5), 144(7), and 130*m/e* (28); HREIMS, obs. 401.2733; calcd. for $C_{28}H_{35}NO$, 401.2720

Reference

M. R. TePaske, J. B. Gloer, D. T. Wicklow, and P. F. Dowd; The Structure of Tubingensin B: A Cytotoxic Carbazole Alkaloid from the Sclerotia of *Aspergillus tubingensis*; Tet. Lett., Vol. 30, pp. 5965-5968(1989).

Common/Systematic Name
Radarin A

Molecular Formula/Molecular Weight
$C_{28}H_{39}NO_2$; MW = 421.29808

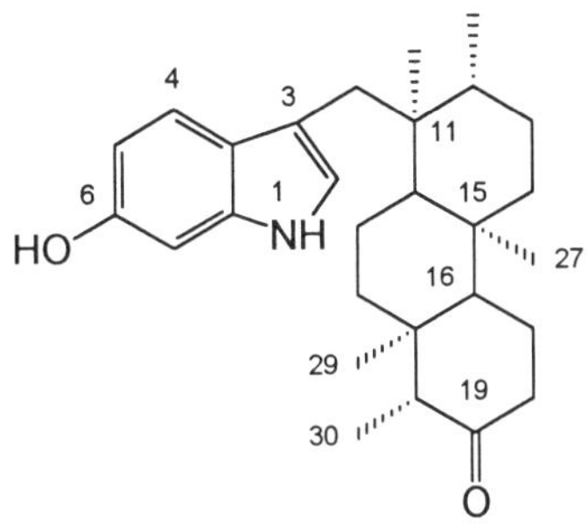

General Characteristics
Radarin A was isolated as a pink oil; $[\alpha]_D$ +11.1° (*c*=0.005, in $CHCl_3$).

Fungal Source
Sclerotia of *Aspergillus sulphureus* (NRRL 4077).

Isolation/Purification
Ground sclerotia of *A. sulphureus* (NRRL 4077) were exhaustively extracted using a Soxhlet apparatus, first with pentane and then with methylene chloride. The methylene chloride extract was subjected to silica gel column chromatography, using a stepwise gradient from 0 to 10% (v/v) MeOH in $CHCl_3$. Fractions of similar composition as determined by TLC were pooled. The resulting active fractions were separated further by reversed-phase HPLC (5μm-Beckman Ultrasphere ODS column; 250x10mm; with detection at 215nm; flow rate 2.0mL/min) using various MeOH-H_2O mixtures to yield pure radarins A-D. Radarin A: HPLC retention time, 25.5 min (MeOH-H_2O, 88:12, v/v).

Biological Activity
Exhibited significant biological activity against the corn earworm *Helicoverpa zea*, as well as cytotoxicity in assays against three human solid tumor cell lines.

Spectral Data

UV:
λ_{max}^{MeOH} 210(ϵ=6,222), 226(6,985), and 290nm (1,512).

IR:
3405, 2925, 2956, 1700, 1628, 1452, and 757cm^{-1}.

CD:
(MeOH) 290(-78.6), 233(-31.9), and 216nm (-34.3).

^{1}H NMR:
(acetone-d_6) H-2, 6.89(br s); H-4, 7.36(d, J=8.6); H-5, 6.63(dd, J=8.6, 2.2); H-7, 6.78(d, J=2.1); H-10a, 2.74(d, J=15.1); H-10b, 2.65(d, J=15.1); H-12$_{ax}$, 1.57(m); H-13$_{ax}$, 1.39(m); H-13$_{eq}$, 1.25(m); H-14$_{ax}$, 0.71(m); H-14$_{eq}$, 1.58(m); H-16$_{ax}$, 1.28(m); H-17$_{ax}$, 1.83(m); H-17$_{eq}$, 1.54(m); H-18$_{ax}$, 2.22(m); H-18$_{eq}$, 2.13(m); H-20$_{ax}$, 2.10(m); H-22$_{ax}$, 1.20(m); H-22$_{eq}$, 1.72(ddd, J=12.9, 3.3, 3.2); H-23$_{ax}$, 1.50(m); H-23$_{eq}$, 1.96(m); H-24$_{ax}$, 1.10(dd, J=11.9,1.9); H-25, 0.82(s); H-26, 1.02(d, J=6.7); H-27, 0.86(s); H-28, 0.74(d, J=6.7); and H-29, 0.68ppm (s).

^{13}C NMR:
(acetone-d_6) C-2, 123.2; C-3, 112.2; C-4, 120.2; C-5, 109.8; C-6, 153.9; C-7, 97.4; C-8, 138.1; C-9, 124.1; C-10, 34.5; C-11, 41.3; C-12, 36.8; C-13, 28.1; C-14, 40.2; C-15, 38.7; C-16, 59.3; C-17, 22.8; C-18, 41.7; C-19, 211.4; C-20, 58.3; C-21, 42.1; C-22, 41.0; C-23, 19.7; C-24, 51.1; C-25, 18.1; C-26, 17.6; C-27, 16.8; C-28, 7.2; and C-29, 15.0ppm.

Mass Spectrum:
EIMS: 421(M$^+$, 4.3%), 189(4.2), 175(2.6), 161(3.7), 146(100), 123(6.6), 121(9.3), 119(5.8), 109(8.0), 107(9.0), and 105*m/e* (7.0); HREIMS: obsd 421.2996; calcd for $C_{28}H_{39}NO_2$, 421.2981.

Reference

J. A. Laakso, J. B. Gloer, D. T. Wicklow, and P. F. Dowd; Radarins A-D: New Antiinsectan and Cytotoxic Indole Diterpenoids from the Sclerotia of *Aspergillus sulphureus*; J. Org. Chem., Vol. 57, pp. 138-141(1992).

Common/Systematic Name
Radarin B

Molecular Formula/Molecular Weight
$C_{28}H_{41}NO_2$: MW = 423.31373

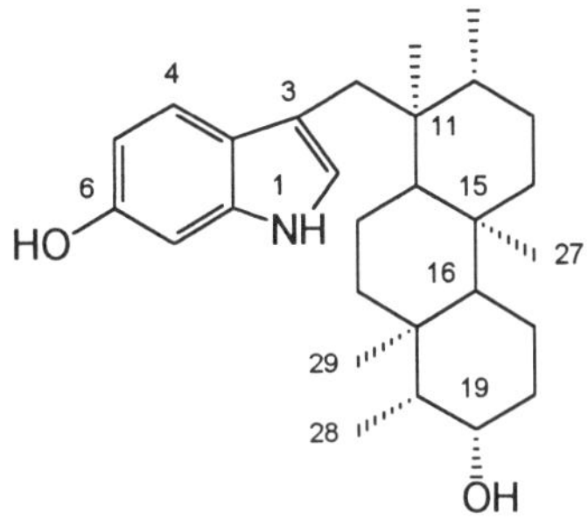

General Characteristics
Radarin B was a yellow solid; mp., 115-118°C (dec); $[\alpha]_D$ +39.4° (*c*=0.003, in $CHCl_3$).

Fungal Source
Sclerotia of *Aspergillus sulphureus* (NRRL 4077).

Isolation/Purification
Ground sclerotia of *A. sulphureus* (NRRL 4077) were exhaustively extracted using a Soxhlet apparatus, first with pentane and then with methylene chloride. The methylene chloride extract was subjected to silica gel column chromatography, using a stepwise gradient from 0 to 10% (v/v) MeOH in $CHCl_3$. Fractions of similar composition as determined by TLC were pooled. The resulting active fractions were separated further by reversed-phase HPLC (5μm-Beckman Ultrasphere ODS column; 250x10mm; with detection at 215nm; flow rate 2.0mL/min) using various MeOH-H_2O mixtures to yield pure radarins A-D. Radarin B: HPLC retention time, 22.2 min (MeOH:H_2O, 86:14, v/v).

Biological Activity
Exhibited biological activity against the corn earworm *Helicoverpa zea*, as well as cytotoxicity in assays against three human solid tumor cell lines.

Spectral Data

IR:
3408, 2927, 2856, 1628, 1453, 1384, and 757cm^{-1}.

CD:
(MeOH) 228nm (-64.2).

^{1}H NMR:

(acetone-d_6) H-2, 6.88(br s); H-4, 7.38(d, J=8.5); H-5, 6.61(dd, J=8.6, 2.2); H-7, 6.80(d, J=2.0); H-l0a, 2.75(d, J=15.2); H-10b, 2.66(d, J=15.1); H-12$_{ax}$, 1.52(m); H-13$_{ax}$, 1.38(m); H-13$_{eq}$, 1.21(m); H-14$_{ax}$, 0.58(dm, J=3.9); H-14$_{eq}$, 1.58(m); H-16$_{ax}$, 0.64(dd, J=11.7, 1.9); H-17$_{ax}$, 1.50(m); H-17$_{eq}$, 1.30(m); H-18$_{ax}$, 1.40(m); H-18$_{eq}$, 1.76(m); H-19$_{eq}$, 3.62(m);H-20$_{ax}$, 1.07(m); H-22$_{ax}$, 0.95(m); H-22$_{eq}$, 1.76(m); H-23$_{ax}$, 1.45(m); H-23$_{eq}$, 1.89(dm, J=13.5); H-24$_{ax}$, 1.04(m); H-25, 0.83(s); H-26, 1.04(d, J=7.5); H-27, 0.89(s); H-28, 0.92(d, J=7.2); and H-29, 1.02ppm (s).

^{13}C NMR:

(acetone-d_6) C-2, 123.0; C-3, 112.2; C-4, 120.2; C-5, 109.7; C-6, 153.8; C-7, 97.3; C-8, 138.1; C-9, 124.2; C-10, 34.3; C-11, 41.3; C-12, 36.7; C-13, 28.2; C-14, 40.2; C-15, 38.3; C-16, 61.9; C-17, 16.6; C-18, 36.5; C-19, 71.8; C-20, 50.3; C-21, 38.4; C-22, 41.7; C-23, 19.1; C-24, 51.3; C-25, 17.9; C-26, 17.7; C-27, 17.1; C-28, 12.2; and C-29, 17.0ppm.

Mass Spectrum:

EIMS: 423(M$^+$, 1.3%), 405(3.8), 243(7.7), 163(11), 147(100), 121(19), 107(22), 91(28), and 81*m/e* (22); HRFABMS: obsd 424.3245; calcd for $C_{28}H_{41}NO_2$ + H, 424.3215.

Reference

J. A. Laakso, J. B. Gloer, D. T. Wicklow, and P. F. Dowd; Radarins A-D: New Antiinsectan and Cytotoxic Indole Diterpenoids from the Sclerotia of *Aspergillus sulphureus*; J. Org. Chem., Vol. 57, pp. 138-141(1992).

Common/Systematic Name

Radarin C

Molecular Formula/Molecular Weight

$C_{28}H_{39}NO$; MW = 405.30317

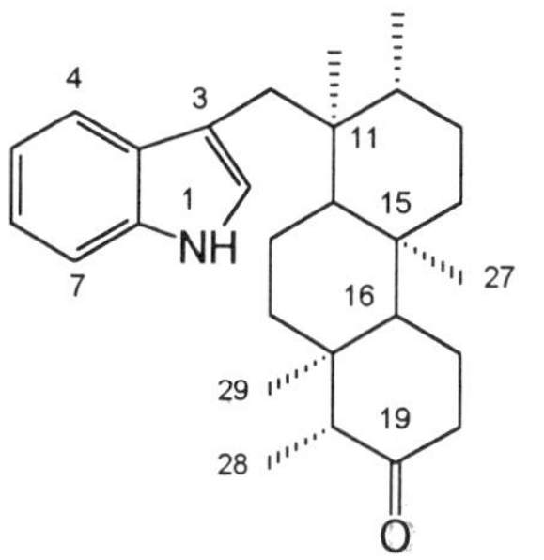

General Characteristics

Radarin C was a yellow oil; $[\alpha]_D$ +6.7° (*c*=0.002, in $CHCl_3$).

Fungal Source

Sclerotia of *Aspergillus sulphureus* (NRRL 4077).

Isolation/Purification

Ground sclerotia of *A. sulphureus* (NRRL 4077) were exhaustively extracted using a Soxhlet apparatus, first with pentane and then with methylene chloride. The methylene chloride extract was subjected to silica gel column chromatography, using a stepwise gradient from 0 to 10% (v/v) MeOH in $CHCl_3$. Fractions of similar composition as determined by TLC were pooled. The resulting active fractions were separated further by reversed-phase HPLC (5μm-Beckman Ultrasphere ODS column; 250x10mm; with detection at 215nm; flow rate 2.0mL/min) using various MeOH-H_2O mixtures to yield radarins A-D. Radarin C: HPLC retention time, 40 min (MeOH-H_2O, 90:10, v/v).

Biological Activity

Exhibited biological activity against the corn earworm *Helicoverpa zea*, as well as cytotoxicity in assays against three human solid tumor cell lines.

Spectral Data

IR:

3410, 2925, 2857, 1707, 1456, 1388, and 741cm^{-1}.

CD:

(MeOH) 298(-58.7), 229(-36.7), and 212nm (+68.4).

^{1}H NMR:
(acetone-d_6) H-2, 7.13(br s); H-4, 7.61(br d, J=8.0); H-5, 7.00(ddd, J=8.0, 7.1, 1.0); H-6, 7.07(ddd, J=8.0, 7.0, 1.0); H-7, 7.38(br d, J=8.0); H-10a, 2.83(d, J=15.0); H-10b, 2.76(d, J=15.2); H-12_{ax}, 1.60(m); H-13_{ax}, 1.42(m); H-13_{eq}, 1.30(m); H-14_{ax}, 0.73(m); H-14_{eq}, 1.62(m); H-16_{ax}, 1.36(m); H-17_{ax}, 1.87(m); H-17_{eq}, 1.56(m); H-18_{ax}, 2.32(m); H-18_{eq}, 2.25(m); H-20_{ax}, 1.07(m); H-22_{ax}, 0.95(m); H-22_{eq}, 1.76(m); H-23_{ax}, 1.45(m); H-23_{eq}, 1.89(dm, J=13.5); H-24_{ax}, 1.04(m); H-25, 0.83(s); H-26, 1.04(d, J=7.5); H-27, 0.89(s); H-28, 0.92(d, J=7.2); and H-29, 0.72ppm (s).

^{13}C NMR:
(acetone-d_6) C-2, 125.0; C-3, 112.2; C-4, 119.8; C-5, 109.3; C-6, 121.7; C-7, 112.1; C-8, 137.0; C-9, 130.1; C-10, 34.3; C-11, 41.3; C-12, 36.8; C-13, 28.1; C-14, 40.2; C-15, 38.4; C-16, 59.3; C-17, 22.8; C-18, 41.7; C-19, 211.5; C-20, 58.2; C-21, 42.1; C-22, 41.0; C-23, 19.7; C-24, 51.2; C-25, 18.1; C-26, 17.6; C-27, 16.7; C-28, 7.1; and C-29, 15.0ppm.

Mass Spectrum:
EIMS: 405(M^+, 2.0%), 137(2.2), 130(100), 121(3.2), 111(3.3), 109(3.2), and 107*m/e* (3.5); HREIMS; obsd 405.3008; calcd for $C_{28}H_{39}NO$, 405.3032.

<u>Reference</u>

J. A. Laakso, J. B. Gloer, D. T. Wicklow, and P. F. Dowd, Radarins A-D: New Antiinsectan and Cytotoxic Indole Diterpenoids from the Sclerotia of *Aspergillus sulphureus*; J. Org. Chem., Vol. 57, pp. 138-141(1992).

Common/Systematic Name

Radarin D

Molecular Formula/Molecular Weight

$C_{28}H_{41}NO$; MW = 407.31882

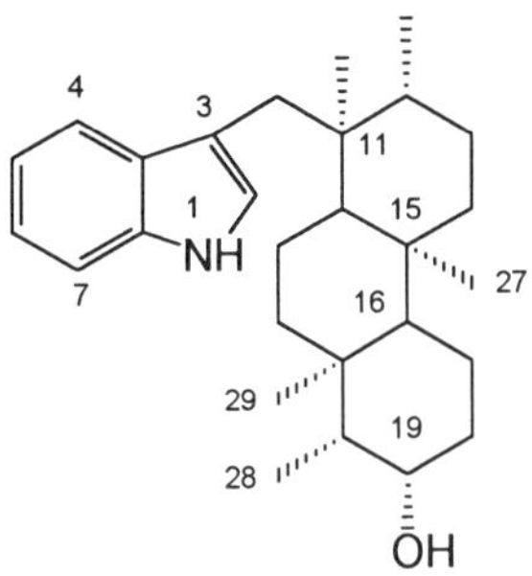

General Characteristics

Radarin D was a yellow oil; $[\alpha]_D$ +31.8° (*c*=0.003, in $CHCl_3$).

Fungal Source

Sclerotia of *Aspergillus sulphureus* (NRRL 4077).

Isolation/Purification

Ground sclerotia of *A. sulphureus* (NRRL 4077) were exhaustively extracted using a Soxhlet apparatus, first with pentane and then with methylene chloride. The methylene chloride extract was subjected to silica gel column chromatography, using a stepwise gradient from 0 to 10% (v/v) MeOH in $CHCl_3$. Fractions of similar composition as determined by TLC were pooled. The resulting active fractions were separated further by reversed-phase HPLC (5µm-Beckman Ultrasphere ODS column; 250x10mm; with detection at 215nm; flow rate 2.0mL/min) using various MeOH-H_2O mixtures to yield radarins A-D. Radarin D: HPLC retention time, 45 min (MeOH-H_2O, 90:10, v/v).

Biological Activity

Exhibited biological activity against the corn earworm *Helicoverpa zea*, as well as cytotoxicity in assays against three human solid tumor cell lines.

Spectral Data

IR:

3414, 2924, 2856, 1456, 1384, and 742cm^{-1}.

CD:

(MeOH) 228(-58.0), 298(-58.7), 229(-36.7), and 212nm (+68.4).

^{1}H NMR:

(acetone-d_6) H-2, 7.08(br s); H-4, 7.60(br d, J=8.0); H-5, 7.05(ddd, J=7.0, 7.0, 1.0); H-6, 7.05(ddd, J=7.0, 7.0, 1.0); H-7, 7.36(d, J=8.1); H-10a, 2.81(d, J=15.2); H-10b, 2.72(d, J=15.1); H-12$_{ax}$, 1.57(m); H-13$_{ax}$, 1.38(m); H-13$_{eq}$, 1.21(m); H-14$_{ax}$, 0.58(ddd, J=13.0, 13.0, 3.8); H-14$_{eq}$, 1.60(m); H-16$_{ax}$, 0.62(dd, J=12.0, 1.8); H-17$_{ax}$, 1.50(m); H-17$_{eq}$, 1.30(m); H-18$_{ax}$, 1.40(m); H-18$_{eq}$, 1.78(m); H-19$_{eq}$, 3.61(dm, J=2.6); H- 20$_{ax}$, 1.06(m); H-22$_{ax}$, 0.95(ddd, J=12.8, 12.8, 3.7); H-22$_{eq}$, 1.76(m); H-23$_{ax}$, 1.45(m); H-23$_{eq}$, 1.89(dm, J=16.6); H-24$_{ax}$, 1.03(dm, J=1.8); H-25, 0.86(s); H-26, 1.05(d, J=6.5); H-27, 0.89(s); H-28, 0.90(d, J=7.1); and H-29, 1.02ppm (s).

^{13}C NMR:

(acetone-d_6) C-2, 124.8; C-3, 112.3; C-4, 119.8; C-5, 119.2; C-6, 121.6; C-7, 112.0; C-8, 136.9; C-9, 130.2; C-10, 34.2; C-11, 41.4; C-12, 36.8; C-13, 28.2; C-14, 40.3; C-15, 38.3; C-16, 62.0; C-17, 16.7; C-18, 36.5; C-19, 71.7; C-20, 50.3; C-21, 38.4; C-22, 41.8; C-23, 19.1; C-24, 51.4; C-25, 17.9; C-26, 17.7; C-27, 17.1; C-28, 12.2; and C-29, 17.1ppm.

Mass Spectrum:

EIMS: 407(M$^+$ 0.5%), 389(1.7), 163(4.3), 149(5.5), 131(100), 121(6.9), 111(7.1), 109(5.1), and 107*m/e* (6.9). HREIMS: obsd 407.3176; calcd for $C_{28}H_{41}NO$, 407.3188.

<u>Reference</u>

J. A. Laakso, J. B. Gloer, D. T. Wicklow, and P. F. Dowd, Radarins A-D: New Antiinsectan and Cytotoxic Indole Diterpenoids from the Sclerotia of *Aspergillus sulphureus*; J. Org. Chem., Vol. 57, pp. 138-141(1992).

10

Loline Alkaloids

Loline; Festuline
N-Formylloline
N-Acetylloline
N-Methylloline
Norloline
N-Formylnorloline
N-Acetylnorloline
Peramine
Festucine

Common/Systematic Name
Loline; Festucine

Molecular Formula/Molecular Weight
$C_8H_{14}N_2O$; MW = 154.11061

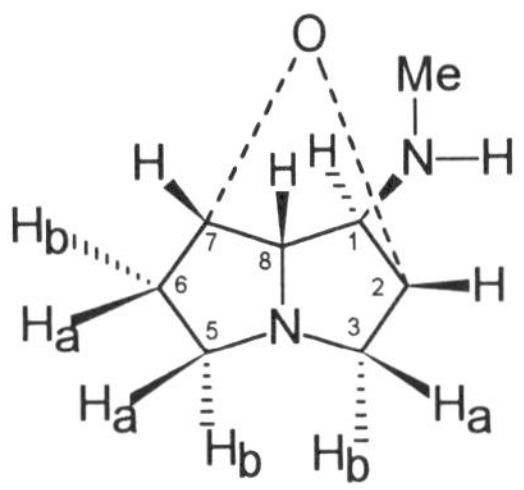

General Characteristics
Colorless, viscous oil.

Fungal Source
Present in caryopses of tall fescue (*Festuca arundinacea*) infected with the endophyte *Acremonium coenophialum*. Also found in *Lolium temulentum*, *L. cuneatum*, and *Adenocarpus decorticans*.

Isolation/Purification
Air dried caryopses were pulverized and extracted with ligroin (Soxhlet method) for 12h followed by cold methanol. The filtrate was evaporated to dryness. The viscous brown residue was suspended in 2.5% HCl and was kept in the refrigerator overnight. After filtration, the aqueous solution was extracted with Et_2O and CH_2Cl_2, respectively. The aqueous solution was evaporated to dryness and a small quantity of methanol was used to suspend the residue; the solution was adjusted to pH 8-10 with 30% NaOH and a crude alkaloid mixture was obtained after column chromatography on alumina. Further purification of loline was accomplished with gas chromatography of the crude alkaloid mixture(column length 2m, diameter 3 mm; 3% SE 30 on Chromosorb PN AW; column temperature 110°C; injection temperature 150°C: flow rate was 50ml N_2/min, retention time = 8.5). Loline was obtained as a colorless oil.

Biological Activity
The loline alkaloids are suspected contributors to several disease syndromes in cattle that consume endophyte-infected tall fescue; however, in tests for central nervous system activity loline•HCl was ineffective in displacing prazosin, serotonin, QNB, bungarotoxin, and flunitrazepam from binding sites.

Spectral Data

IR:

(CHCl$_3$) 2793, 2715, 1476, 1432, 1367, 1311, 1293, 1251, 1218, 1134, 1090, 1044, 1025, 991, and 956cm^{-1}.

^{1}H NMR:

(CDCl$_3$) H-1, 3.03(dd, $J_{1,2}$=1.6Hz); H-2, 3.71(dd, $J_{2,3a}$=<2.0Hz); H-3a, 3.10(dd, $J_{3a,3b}$=11.6Hz); H-3b, 2.10(d); H-5a, 2.62(ddd, $J_{5a,5b}$=12.3Hz, $J_{5a,6a}$=9.8Hz, $J_{5a,6b}$=7.3Hz, $J_{5b,6a}$=3.8Hz, $J_{5b,6b}$=8.3Hz); H-5b, 2.77(ddd); H-6a, 1.65(dddd, $J_{6a,6b}$=14.3Hz, $J_{6a,7}$=4.3Hz); H-6b, 1.74(ddd); H-7, 4.10(dd, $J_{7,8}$=1.9Hz); H-8, 2.84(dd, $J_{8,1}$=1.8Hz); and N-Me, 2.19ppm (s).

(D$_2$O) H-1, 4.23(dd, $J_{1,2}$=<2.0Hz); H-2, 4.79(dd, $J_{2,3a}$=1.0Hz); H-3a, 4.15(dd, $J_{3a,3b}$=13.9Hz); H-3b, 3.55(d); H-5a, 3.73(ddd, $J_{5a,5b}$=12.8Hz, $J_{5a,6a}$=8.2Hz, $J_{5a,6b}$=7.7Hz, $J_{5b,6a}$=5.0Hz, $J_{5b,6b}$=9.6Hz); H-5b, 3.73(ddd); H-6a, 2.28(dddd, $J_{6a,6b}$=14.6Hz, $J_{6a,7}$=4.8Hz); H-6b, 2.37(ddd); H-7, 4.72(dd, $J_{7,8}$=2.2Hz); H-8, 4.79(dd, $J_{8,1}$=1.9Hz); NH, 4.76(bm); and N-Me, 2.79ppm (s).

^{13}C NMR:

(CHCl$_3$) C-1, 67.8(d); C-2, 73.4(d); C-3, 60.6(t); C-5, 54.0(t); C-6, 33.5(t); C-7, 81.0(d); C-8, 69.0(d); and N-Me, 34.7ppm (q).

(D$_2$O) C-1, 65.9(d); C-2, 73.9(d); C-3, 64.2(t); C-5, 58.1(t); C-6, 31.6(t); C-7, 83.2(d); C-8, 72.2(d); and N-Me, 36.5ppm (q).

Mass Spectrum:

EIMS: 154(M$^+$, 3.5), 123(12), 110(34), 95(31), and 82*m/e* (100%).

References

G. Dannhardt and L. Steindl; Alkaloids of *Lolium temulentum*; Isolation, Identification and Pharmacological Activity; Planta Medica, pp. 212-214(1985).

R. J. Petroski, S. G. Yates, D. Weisleder, and R. G. Powell; Isolation, Semi-synthesis, and NMR Spectral Studies of Loline Alkaloids; J. Natural Products, Vol. 52, pp. 810-817 (1989).

R. G. Powell and R. J. Petroski; The Loline Group of Pyrrolizidine Alkaloids; In S. W. Pelletier (Ed.); The Alkaloids: Chemical and Biological Perspectives; Vol. 8, p. 320, Springer-Verlag, New York (1992).

S. G. Yates and H. L. Tookey, Festucine; An Alkaloid from Tall Fescue (*Festuca arundinacea* Schreb.): Chemistry of the Functional Groups; Aust. J. Chem., Vol. 18, pp. 53-60(1965).

Common/Systematic Name
N-Formylloline

Molecular Formula/Molecular Weight
$C_9H_{14}N_2O_2$; MW = 182.10553

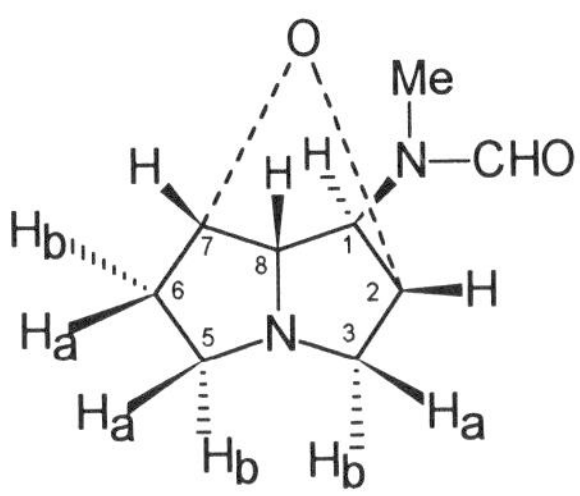

General Characteristics
Clear, viscous oil.

Fungal Source
Present in caryopses of tall fescue (*Festuca arundinacea*) infected with the endophyte *Acremonium coenophialum*; also found in *Lolium cuneatum.*

Biological Activity
The loline alkaloids are suspected contributors to several disease syndromes in cattle that consume endophyte-infected tall fescue. Studies have shown a positive association between endophyte infection, loline alkaloid production and resistance to certain insect pests. *N*-Formylloline was shown to be toxic to the large milkweed bug (*Oncopeltus fasciatus*) (ED_{50} 2μg).

Spectral Data

IR:
($CHCl_3$) 2937, 2880, 1671, 1473, 1386, 1353, 1084, 1050, 1024, and 962cm^{-1}.

^{1}H NMR:
($CDCl_3$) H-1, 3.68(dd, $J_{1,2}$=1.5Hz); H-2, 4.05(dd, $J_{2,3a}$=<2.0Hz); H-3a, 3.09(dd, $J_{3a,3b}$=11.9Hz); H-3b, 2.33(d); H-5a, 2.83(ddd, $J_{5a,5b}$=13.1Hz, $J_{5a,6a}$=9.3Hz, $J_{5a,6b}$=7.1Hz, $J_{5b,6a}$=4.4Hz, $J_{5b,6b}$=7.8Hz); H-5b, 2.91(ddd); H-6a, 1.80(dddd, $J_{6a,6b}$=14.3Hz, $J_{6a,7}$=4.3Hz); H-6b, 1.93(ddd); H-7, 4.34(dd, $J_{7,8}$=1.8Hz); H-8, 3.30(dd, $J_{8,1}$=2.0Hz); N-Me, 2.76(s); and HC=O, 7.25ppm (s).

^{13}C NMR:
($CHCl_3$) C-1, 65.3(d); C-2, 73.9(d); C-3, 60.4(t); C-5, 54.4(t); C-6, 32.8(t); C-7, 81.8(d); C-8, 67.4(d); N-Me, 33.4(q); and HC=O, 162.1ppm (d).

Mass Spectrum:
EIMS: 154(M^+ - 28, 11.0), 123(9), 110(9), 95(24) and 82*m/e* (100%); GC-MS: 182(1), 154(15), 139(1), 123(10), 111(11), 110(12), 96(9), 95(25), 83(17), 82(100), 80(21), 69(16), 55(16), 42(45), and 41*m/e* (22%).

References

R. J. Petroski, S. G. Yates, D. Weisleder, and R. G. Powell; Isolation, Semi-synthesis, and NMR Spectral Studies of Loline Alkaloids; J. Natural Products, Vol. 52, pp. 810-817 (1989).

S. G. Yates, J.C. Fenster, and R. J. Bartelt; Assay of Tall Fescue Seed Extracts, Fractions and Alkaloids Using the Large Milkweed Bug; J. Agric. Food Chem. Vol. 37, pp. 354-357 (1989).

S. G. Yates and H. L. Tookey; Festucine, and Alkaloid from Tall Fescue (*Festuca arundinacea* Schreb.): Chemistry of the Functional Groups; Aust. J. Chem., Vol. 18, pp. 53-60(1965).

Common/Systematic Name
N-Acetylloline

Molecular Formula/Molecular Weight
$C_{10}H_{16}N_2O_2$; MW = 196.12118

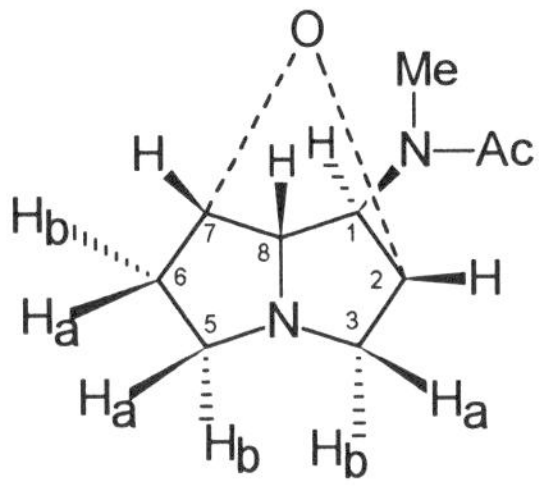

General Characteristics
Clear, viscous oil.

Fungal Source
Present in caryopses of tall fescue (*Festuca arundinacea*) infected with the endophyte *Acremonium coenophialum*; also found in *Lolium cuneatum.*

Biological Activity
The loline alkaloids are suspected contributors to several disease syndromes in cattle that consume endophyte-infected tall fescue. Studies have shown a positive association between endophyte infection, loline alkaloid production, and resistance to certain insect pests.

Spectral Data

IR:
($CHCl_3$) 2937, 2878, 1652, 1472, 1400, 1348, 1023, and 957cm^{-1}.

^{1}H NMR:
($CDCl_3$) H-1, 4.05(dd, $J_{1,2}$=2.7Hz); H-2, 4.38(dd, $J_{2,3a}$=<2.0Hz); H-3a, 3.03(dd, $J_{3a,3b}$=11.7Hz); H-3b, 2.26(d); H-5a, 2.84(ddd, $J_{5a,5b}$=12.8Hz, $J_{5a,6a}$=9.1Hz, $J_{5a,6b}$=7.4Hz, $J_{5b,6a}$=4.2Hz, $J_{5b,6b}$=8.4Hz); H-5b, 2.93(ddd); H-6a, 1.81(dddd, $J_{6a,6b}$=14.2Hz, $J_{6a,7}$=4.3Hz); H-6b, 1.92(ddd); H-7, 4.29(dd, $J_{7,8}$=<2.0Hz); H-8, 3.10(dd, $J_{8,1}$ =<2.0Hz); and N-Me, 3.04(s); MeC=O, 1.96ppm (s).

^{13}C NMR:
($CHCl_3$) C-1, 64.1(d); C-2, 73.4(d); C-3, 61.0(t); C-5, 54.7(t); C-6, 33.0(t); C-7, 80.6(d); C-8, 67.8(d); N-Me, 33.9(q); MeC=O, 171.5(s); and MeC=O, 22.3ppm (q).

Mass Spectrum:

EIMS: 196(M^+, 2.1), 167(5), 153(8), 123(23), 95(43), 82(100), and 42*m/e* (42%).

Reference

R. J. Petroski, S. G. Yates, D. Weisleder, and R. G. Powell; Isolation, Semi-synthesis, and NMR Spectral Studies of Loline Alkaloids; J. Natural Products, Vol. 52, pp. 810-817 (1989).

Common/Systematic Name

N-Methylloline

Molecular Formula/Molecular Weight

$C_9H_{16}N_2O$; MW = 168.12626

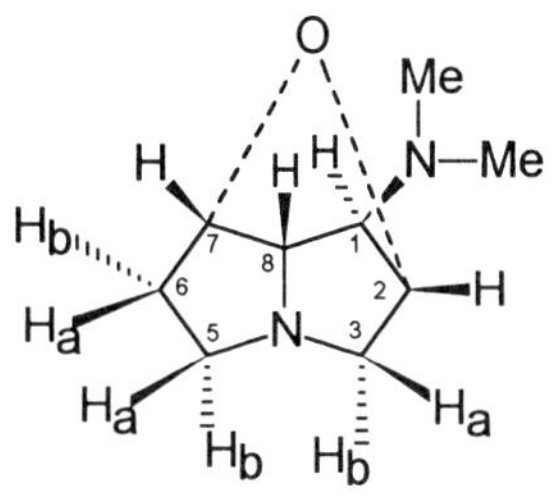

General Characteristics

N-Methylloline-HCl recrystallized from EtOH; mp., 212-216°C.

Fungal Source

Present in endophyte-infected *Lolium cuneatum.*

Biological Activity

The loline alkaloids are suspected contributors to several disease syndromes in cattle that consume endophyte-infected tall fescue. Studies have shown a positive association between endophyte infection, loline alkaloid production, and resistance to certain insect pests.

Spectral Data

IR:

($CHCl_3$) 2942, 2875, 2818, 2768, 1600, 1466, 1367, 1314, 1272, 1184, 1094, 1042, and 960cm^{-1}.

^{1}H NMR:

($CDCl_3$) H-1, 2.53(dd, $J_{1,2}$=1.2Hz); H-2, 3.82(dd, $J_{2,3a}$=1.2Hz); H-3a, 3.36(dd, $J_{3a,3b}$=10.9Hz); H-3b, 2.18(d); H-5a, 2.78(ddd, $J_{5a,5b}$=12.8Hz, $J_{5a,6a}$=9.3Hz, $J_{5a,6b}$=7.2Hz, $J_{5b,6a}$=4.2Hz, $J_{5b,6b}$=8.4Hz); H-5b, 2.89(ddd); H-6a, 1.75(dddd, $J_{6a,6b}$=14.0Hz, $J_{6a,7}$=4.4Hz); H-6b, 1.86(ddd); H-7, 4.25(dd, $J_{7,8}$=1.8Hz); H-8, 3.01(dd, $J_{8,1}$=1.3Hz); NMe, 2.12(s); and N-Me, 2.12ppm (s).

^{13}C NMR:

($CHCl_3$) C-1, 74.1(d); C-2, 74.2(d); C-3, 61.2(t); C-5, 54.3(t); C-6, 33.40(t); C-7, 82.0(d); C-8, 69.2(d); NMe, 44.4(q); and N-Me, 44.4ppm (q).

Mass Spectrum:
EIMS: 168(M^+, 1.7), 123(42), 95(68), and 82*m/e* (100%).

Reference

R. J. Petroski, S. G. Yates, D. Weisleder, and R. G. Powell; Isolation, Semi-synthesis, and NMR Spectral Studies of Loline Alkaloids; J. Natural Products, Vol. 52, pp. 810-817 (1989).

Common/Systematic Name
Norloline

Molecular Formula/Molecular Weight
$C_7H_{12}N_2O$; MW = 140.09496

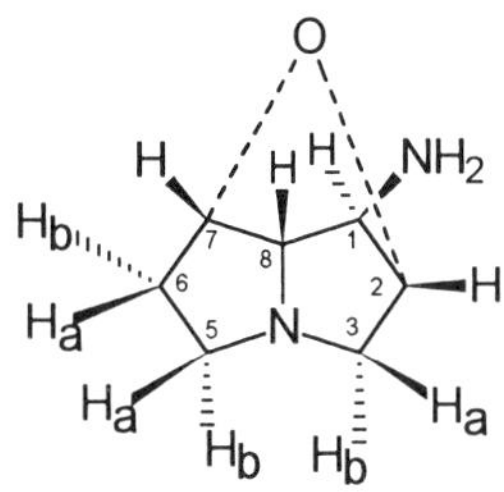

General Characteristics
Clear viscous oil; very soluble in water and very volatile.

Fungal Source
Present in endophyte-infected *Lolium cuneatum*.

Biological Activity
The loline alkaloids are suspected contributors to several disease syndromes in cattle that consume endophyte-infected tall fescue. Studies have shown a positive association between endophyte infection, loline alkaloid production, and resistance to certain insect pests.

Spectral Data

IR:
($CHCl_3$) 3376, 3293, 3181, 2964, 2937, 2876, 1616, 1473, 1293, 1249, 1216, 1174, 1041, 1000, 998, and 974cm^{-1}.

^{1}H NMR:
($CDCl_3$) H-1, 3.48(dd, $J_{1,2}$=<2Hz); H-2, 3.72(dd, $J_{2,3a}$=1.6Hz); H-3a, 3.38(dd, $J_{3a,3b}$=11.7Hz); H-3b, 2.29(d); H-5a, 2.80(ddd, $J_{5a,5b}$=12.8Hz, $J_{5a,6a}$=9.3Hz, $J_{5a,6b}$=7.5Hz, $J_{5b,6a}$=3.8Hz, $J_{5b,6b}$=8.3Hz); H-5b, 2.98(ddd); H-6a, 1.84(dddd, $J_{6a,6b}$=14.3Hz, $J_{6a,7}$=4.4Hz); H-6b, 1.94(ddd); H-7, 4.29(dd, $J_{7,8}$=1.9Hz); and H-8, 2.92ppm(dd, $J_{8,1}$=1.8Hz).

^{13}C NMR:
($CHCl_3$) C-1, 60.5(d); C-2, 76.2(d); C-3, 60.8(t); C-5, 54.5(t); C-6, 34.1(t); C-7, 81.7(d); and C-8, 71.9ppm (d).

Mass Spectrum:

EIMS: 140(M^+, 4.3), 123(24), 111(15), 97(22), 95(15), 82(100), and 69*m/e* (26%).

Reference

R. J. Petroski, S. G. Yates, D. Weisleder, and R. G. Powell; Isolation, Semi-synthesis, and NMR Spectral Studies of Loline Alkaloids; J. Natural Products, Vol. 52, pp. 810-817 (1989).

Common/Systematic Name
N-Formylnorloline

Molecular Formula/Molecular Weight
$C_8H_{12}N_2O_2$; MW = 168.08988

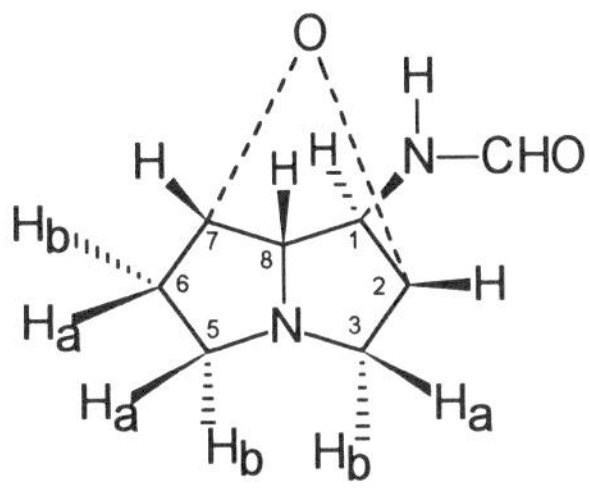

General Characteristics
Clear, viscous oil.

Fungal Source
Present in endophyte-infected *Lolium cuneatum*.

Biological Activity
The loline alkaloids are suspected contributors to several disease syndromes in cattle that consume endophyte-infected tall fescue. Studies have shown a positive association between endophyte infection, loline alkaloid production, and resistance to certain insect pests.

Spectral Data

IR:
($CHCl_3$) 3190, 2972, 2880, 2790, 1681, 1600, 1541, 1388, 1339, 1247, 1105, and 1007cm^{-1}.

^{1}H NMR:
($CDCl_3$) H-1, 4.52(dd, $J_{1,2}$=2.1Hz); H-2, 4.29(dd, $J_{2,3a}$=<2.0Hz); H-3a, 3.43(dd, $J_{3a,3b}$=12.0Hz); H-3b, 2.53(d); H-5a, 3.04(ddd, $J_{5a,5b}$=12.9Hz, $J_{5a,6a}$=9.3Hz, $J_{5a,6b}$=7.5Hz, $J_{5b,6a}$=4.0Hz, $J_{5b,6b}$=8.6Hz); H-b, 3.17(ddd); H-6a, 2.07(dddd, $J_{6a,6b}$=14.3Hz, $J_{6a,7}$=3.9Hz); H-6b, 2.18(ddd); H-7, 4.50(dd, $J_{7,8}$=2.2Hz); H-8, 3.32(dd, $J_{8,1}$=<2.0Hz); and NH, 7.39ppm (bm).

^{13}C NMR:
($CHCl_3$) C-1, 55.8(d); C-2, 73.6(d); C-3, 60.8(t); C-5, 53.7(t); C-6, 31.7(t); C-7, 80.0(d); C-8, 69.7(d); and HC=O, 161.8ppm (d).

Mass Spectrum:

EIMS: 168(M^+, 0.3), 140(3), 123(5), 95(17), 82(100), and 69*m/e* (26%).

Reference

R. J. Petroski, S. G. Yates, D. Weisleder, and R. G. Powell; Isolation, Semi-synthesis, and NMR Spectral Studies of Loline Alkaloids; J. Natural Products, Vol. 52, pp. 810-817 (1989).

Common/Systematic Name
N-Acetylnorloline

Molecular Formula/Molecular Weight
$C_9H_{14}N_2O_2$; MW = 182.10553

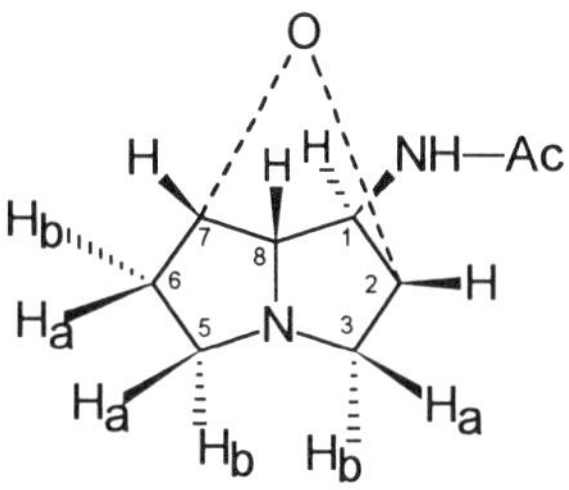

General Characteristics
Clear, viscous oil.

Fungal Source
Present in caryopses of tall fescue (*Festuca arundinacea*) infected with the endophyte *Acremonium coenophialum*; also found in *Lolium cuneatum.*

Biological Activity
The loline alkaloids are suspected contributors to several disease syndromes in cattle that consume endophyte-infected tall fescue. Studies have shown a positive association between endophyte infection, loline alkaloid production, and resistance to certain insect pests.

Spectral Data

IR:
($CHCl_3$) 3284, 2878, 1673, 1542, 1473, 1436, 1374, 1294, 1106, and 962cm^{-1}.

^{1}H NMR:
($CDCl_3$) H-1, 4.41(dd, $J_{1,2}$=2.5Hz); H-2, 4.17(dd, $J_{2,3a}$=1.0Hz); H-3a, 3.29(dd, $J_{3a,3b}$=11.8Hz); H-3b, 2.42(d); H-5a, 2.90(ddd, $J_{5a,5b}$=12.8Hz, $J_{5a,6a}$=9.3Hz, $J_{5a,6b}$=7.4Hz, $J_{5b,6a}$=3.6Hz, $J_{5b,6b}$=8.3Hz); H-5b, 3.10(ddd); H-6a, 1.98(dddd, $J_{6a,6b}$=14.4Hz, $J_{6a,7}$=4.3Hz); H-6b, 2.08(ddd); H-7, 4.44(dd, $J_{7,8}$=1.9Hz); H-8, 3.09(dd, $J_{8,1}$=1.6Hz); and NH, 6.21 and MeC=O, 1.97ppm (s).

^{13}C NMR:
($CHCl_3$) C-1, 57.6(d); C-2, 73.8(d); C-3, 60.9(t); C-5, 54.6(t); C-6, 33.9(t); C-7, 80.9(d); C-8, 69.6; MeC=O, 170.2(s); and MeC=O, 23.1ppm (q).

Mass Spectrum:

EIMS: 153(M^+ - 29, 2.6), 139(1), 123(7), 95(21), 82(100), and 69*m/e* (34%).

Reference

R. J. Petroski, S. G. Yates, D. Weisleder, and R. G. Powell; Isolation, Semi-synthesis, and NMR Spectral Studies of Loline Alkaloids; J. Natural Products, Vol. 52, pp. 810-817 (1989).

Common/Systematic Name

Peramine

3-(3'-Guanidinopropyl)-2-methyl-1,2-dihydropyrrolo[1,2-*a*]pyrazin-1-one

Molecular Formula/Molecular Weight

$C_{12}H_{17}N_5O$; MW = 247.14331

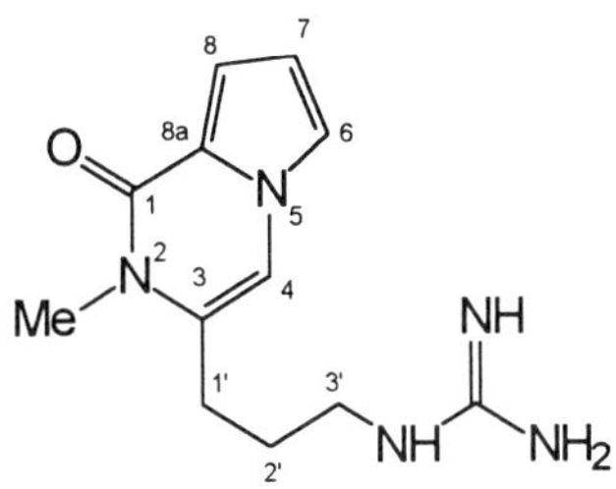

General Characteristics

Peramine gave a positive reaction with the Sakaguchi reagent and no reaction with ninhydrin. Crystalline peramine diacetate had mp. 141-142°C.

Fungal Source

Acremonium loliae infected perennial ryegrass (*Lolium perenne*).

Isolation/Purification

Peramine was obtained as its acetate salt after ethanol extraction of *A. loliae*-infected perennial ryegrass, solvent partitioning and repeated chromatography.

Biological Activity

Perennial ryegrass infected with the endophyte *Acremonium loliae* (Latch, Christensen and Samuels) is resistant to the Argentine stem weevil (*Listronotus bonariensis* Kuschel) as well as to some five other diverse insect species. Resistance against stem weevil is considered to be due to the presence of feeding deterrents which reduce the population of egg-laying adult insects on endophyte-infected plants. Peramine has been identified as the principal feeding deterrent.

Spectral Data

UV:

λ_{max}^{MeOH} 237 and 285nm were similar to those reported for phakellin and its derivatives which contain a pyrrole ring with a carbonyl group at the 2 position.

IR:

(20% MeOH-$CHCl_3$) 3100, 1670, 1615, and 1580cm^{-1} assigned to NH and amide groups.

^{1}H NMR:

(CDCl$_3$) diacetate derivative: ^{1}H NMR showed the two methyl singlets (2.133 and 2.189ppm) and the two NH singlets of the acetylated guanidino moiety, -NH-C(=NAc)NHAc. Connectivities were established by couplings and nuclear Overhauser effect enhancements. The methylene propyl protons showed vicinal couplings ($J_{1',2'}$=7.5, $J_{2',3'}$=~7Hz). The C-3' protons showed a 6Hz coupling to the higher-field guanidino NH singlet and the C-l' protons showed both an allylic coupling (J=0.8Hz) and an nuclear Overhauser effect (7% enhancement) with the *Cis*-olefinic proton H-4. This proton, in turn, showed a long range coupling (J=0.7Hz) to H-8 and an nuclear Overhauser effect enhancement (13%) to H-6 of the pyrrole moiety. The three aromatic protons (H-6, -7, -8) showed couplings ($J_{6,7}$=2.56, $J_{6,8}$=1.52, $J_{7,8}$=3.98Hz) and nuclear Overhauser effect enhancements characteristic of a 1,2-disubstituted pyrrole. Nuclear Overhauser effect enhancements (~3%) were observed between the geminally related heterocyclic amide N-Me and C-1' methylene protons.

^{13}C NMR:

(CDCl$_3$) 25.1(CH$_3$CONH); 27.6(C-2'); 27.9(C-1'); 28.7(CH$_3$CON=); 29.0[N(2)-Me]; 39.7(C-3'); 106.1(C-4); 109.8(C-7); 112.3(C-6); 117.5(C-8); 123.1(C-3); 127.3(C-8a); 155.7(guanidino); 157.1(C-l); 172.8(CH$_3$CONH); and 186.1ppm (CH$_3$CON=).

Reference

D. D. Rowan, M. B. Hunt, and D. L. Gaynor; Peramine, a Novel Insect Feeding Deterrent from Ryegrass Infected with the Endophyte *Acremonium loliae*; J. Chem. Soc., Chem. Commun., pp. 935-936(1986).

Common/Systematic Name

Festucine

Molecular Formula/Molecular Weight

$C_8H_{14}N_2O$; MW = 154.11061

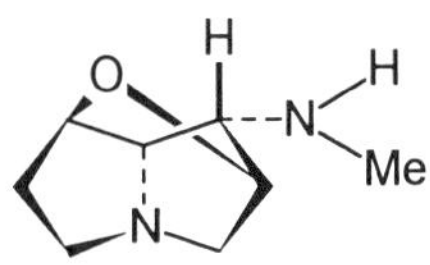

General Characteristics

Free base was a clear volatile oil; the dihydrochloride salt formed as orthorhombic needles which melted with decomposition at 237-242°C, $[\alpha]_D^{25}$ +4.6° (*c*=4.365 in water); pK_a values were 8.25 and 2.5-3.0. Festucine is a positional isomer of loline.

Fungal Source

Found contaminating tall fescue presumed to be of fungal origin by an endophyte *Acremonium* sp.

Isolation/Purification

Alkaloids in tall fescue were extracted with 80% ethanol and then partitioned into chloroform. The hydrochloride salt was separated by paper chromatography (*n*-butanol-acetic acid-water, 10:1:3, v/v; R_f 0.12) and recrystallized from absolute ethanol as the dihydrochloride salt.

Biological Activity

Festucine did not contract isolated guinea pig uterus or intestine. It killed mice when administered intravenously at 400mg/kg, but produced no apparent effects when administered orally at 1000mg/kg.

Spectral Data

UV:

No significant absorption between 220-400nm.

^1H NMR:

($CDCl_3$) 7.53τ (N-CH_3); all values were in the range 5.57-8.15τ; dihydrochloride salt showed N-CH_3 at 6.59τ and all values between 4.51-7.29τ.

Reference

·S. G. Yates and H. L. Tookey; Festucine, an Alkaloid from Tall Fescue (*Festuca arundinacea* Schreb.): Chemistry of the Functional Groups; Aust. J. Chem. Vol. 18, pp. 53-60(1965).

11

Aflatoxins

Aflatoxin B_1
Aflatoxin B_2
Aflatoxin G_1
Aflatoxin G_2
Aflatoxin M_1
Aflatoxin M_2
Aflatoxin P_1
Aflatoxin D_1
Parasiticol (Aflatoxin B_3)
Aflatoxin Q_1
Aflatoxicol A (Ro)
Aflatoxicol B
Aflatoxin B_{2a}
Aflatoxin G_{2a}
Aflatoxicol *O*-ethyl ether A
Aflatoxicol *O*-ethyl ether B

Common/Systematic Name
Aflatoxin B_1

Molecular Formula/Molecular Weight
$C_{17}H_{12}O_6$; MW = 312.06339

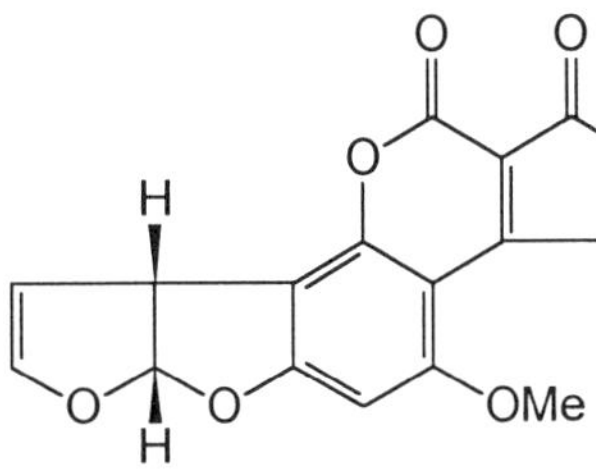

General Characteristics
Crystals from chloroform; mp., 268°-269°C (dec.); $[\alpha]_D$ -480° (*c*=0.1, in dimethylformamide).

Fungal Source
Aspergillus flavus, A. nomius, and *A. parasiticus.*

Biological Activity
The toxic effects of aflatoxin B_1 vary with species, age, sex, and general nutrition. The primary organ affected is the liver with some changes occurring in other organs. The induction of liver lesions, liver carcinoma, and bile duct proliferation by aflatoxin B_1 has been demonstrated in several species of animals. Some species, such as the trout, duckling, rat and pig, are very susceptible to aflatoxicosis, whereas others, such as sheep and cattle, are more tolerant. In Fischer rats and rainbow trout, it was the most potent hepatocarcinogen known. The LD_{50} in 1-day-old rats dosed orally was 0.56mg/kg, in weanling rats, 5.5mg/kg (male), 7.4mg/kg (female); in 100gm male rats, 7.2mg/kg; in 150gm female rats, 17.9mg/kg. The LD_{50} in Macaque monkeys dosed orally was 7.8mg/kg.

Spectral Data

UV:
λ_{max} 223(ϵ=25,600), 265(13,400), and 362nm (21 ,800). Fluorescence emission, 425nm.

^{1}H NMR:
H-4, 2.56; H-5, 3.34; H-9, 6.38; H-13, 6.75(*J*=7.0); H-14, 4.72(*J*=7.0, 3.0); H-15, 5.42(*J*=3.0, 3.0); H-16, 6.40; and H-17, 3.93ppm.

^{13}C NMR:

C-1, 154.7 s; C-2, 117.0 s; C-3, 200.6 s; C-4, 35.0 t; C-5, 29.0 t; C-6, 176.5 s; C-7, 103.7 s; C-8, 161.0 s; C-9, 90.6 d; C-10, 165.3 s; C-11, 107.5 s; C-12, 152.5 s; C-13, 113.2 s; C-14, 47.8 d; C-15, 102.3 d; C-16, 144.8 d; and C-17, 56.4ppm q.

TLC Data

Silica gel G-HR (chloroform-acetone, 93:7, v/v); R_f, 0.33; detected as bright blue fluorescence under UV light.

HPLC Data

Reverse phase Nova-Pak C_{18} (Waters) column, water-MeOH, 40:60 (v/v), 60mg/L KBr, 100µl/L nitric acid. Post column derivatization with bromine (also iodine may be used).

Immunoassay

Numerous immunoassays are commercially available for both qualitative and quantitative analysis.

References

R. J. Cole and R. H. Cox; Handbook of Toxic Fungal Metabolites; Academic Press, New York, pp. 15-19(1981).

J. W. Dorner and R. J. Cole; Rapid Determination of Aflatoxins in Raw Peanuts by Liquid Chromatography with Post column Iodination and Modified Minicolumn Cleanup; J. Assoc. Off. Anal. Chem., Vol. 71, pp. 43-47(1988).

Common/Systematic Name

Aflatoxin B_2

Molecular Formula/Molecular Weight

$C_{17}H_{14}O_6$; MW = 314.07904

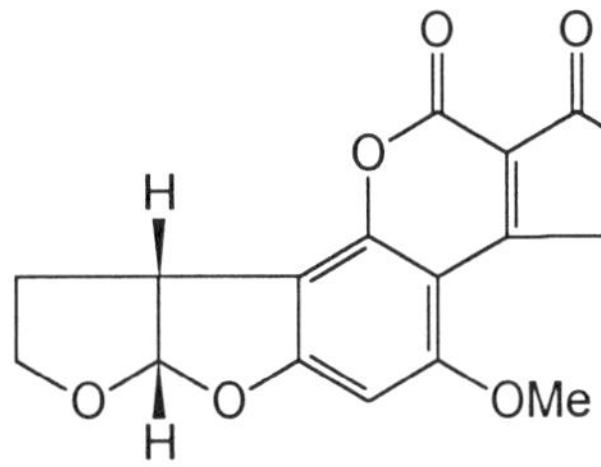

General Characteristics

Crystals from chloroform-pentane; mp., 287-289°C (dec.); $[\alpha]_D$ -430° (*c*=1, in $CHCl_3$).
Crystals from chloroform; mp., 305°C (dec.); $[\alpha]_D$ -490° (*c*=1.0, in $CHCl_3$).

Fungal Source

Aspergillus flavus, A. nomius, and *A. parasiticus.*

Biological Activity

The toxic properties of aflatoxin B_2 were similar to those for aflatoxin B_1; however, potency was markedly reduced compared to aflatoxin B_1. A dosage in ducklings of 50μg of aflatoxin B_2 was required to produce the same degree of bile duct proliferation produced by 3.9μg of aflatoxin B_1.

Spectral Data

UV:

λ_{max}^{MeOH} 220(ε=20,500), 265(12,700), and 363nm (24,000).

^{13}C NMR:

C-1, 155.8 s; C-2, 115.6 s; C-3, 200.0 s; C-4, 34.6 t; C-5, 28.5 t; C-6, 176.6 s; C-7, 105.5 s; C-8, 160.8 s; C-9, 90.0 d; C-10, 165.8 s; C-11, 105.9 s; C-12, 152.0 s; C-13, 113.3 d; C-14, 42.8 d; C-15, 30.6 t; C-16, 66.9 t; and C-17, 56.6ppm q.

TLC Data

Silica gel G-HR (chloroform-acetone, 93:7, v/v); R_f, 0.31; detection as bright blue fluorescence under UV light.

HPLC Data

Reverse phase Nova-Pak C_{18} (Waters) column, water-MeOH, 40:60(v/v), 60mg/L KBr, 100μl/L nitric acid. Postcolumn derivatization with bromine (also iodine may be used). Fluorescence detection-excitation at 365nm, emission at 418nm.

Immunoassay

Numerous immunoassays are commercially available for both qualitative and quantitative analysis.

References

R. J. Cole and R. H. Cox; Handbook of Toxic Fungal Metabolites; Academic Press, New York, pp. 34-37(1981).

J. W. Dorner and R. J. Cole; Rapid Determination of Aflatoxins in Raw Peanuts by Liquid Chromatography with Postcolumn Iodination and Modified Minicolumn Cleanup; J. Assoc. Off. Anal. Chem., Vol. 71, pp. 43-47(1988).

Common/Systematic Name

Aflatoxin G_1

Molecular Formula/Molecular Weight

$C_{17}H_{12}O_7$; MW = 328.05830

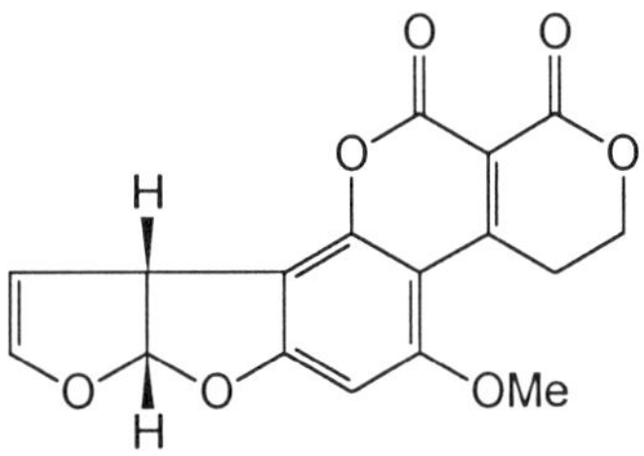

General Characteristics

Crystals from chloroform-methanol; mp., 244- 246°C (dec.); Crystals from acetone; mp., 257-259°C; $[\alpha]_D$ -556° (*c*=1, in $CHCl_3$).

Fungal Source

Aspergillus flavus, *A. nomius*, and *A. parasiticus*.

Biological Activity

The toxicity of aflatoxin G_1 was similar to aflatoxin B_1; acute toxicity was less than B_1 but greater than B_2. The LD_{50} in ducklings was 39.2μg/duckling using dimethylformamide as carrier; 45.7μg/duckling (0.785mg/kg) in another trial using dimethylformamide. The LD_{50} in the rat was twice that of aflatoxin B_1. The lesions induced by G_1 in ducklings are the same as from B_1; in the rat, the zone in the affected liver lobule was the same as in B_1 but the consistent pattern seen with B_1 was absent.

Spectral Data

UV:

λ_{max}^{EtOH} 243(ϵ=11,500), 257(9,900), 264 (10,000), and 362nm (16,100).

^{1}H NMR:

H-4, 4.41; H-5, 3.46; H-9, 6.43; H-13, 6.80(*J*=7.1); H-14, 4.75(*J*=7.1, 2.5); H-15, 5.45(*J*=2.5, 2.5); H-16, 6.47(*J*=2.5); and H-17, 3.95ppm.

^{13}C NMR:

C-1, 154.8 s; C-2, 113.2 s; C-3, 159.9 s; C-4, 64.3 t; C-5, 28.8 t; C-6, 161.1 s; C-7, 106.9 s; C-8, 161.0 s; C-9, 91.0 d; C-10, 164.6 s; C-11, 107.5 s; C-12, 151.7 s; C-13, 113.2 d; C-14, 47.7 d; C-15, 102.3 d; C-16, 144.8 d; and C-17, 56.4ppm q.

TLC Data

Silica gel G-HR (chloroform-acetone, 93:7, v/v) R_f, 0.29; detected as blue-green fluorescence under UV light.

HPLC Data

Reverse phase Nova-Pak C_{18} (Waters) column, water:MeOH, 40:60(v/v), 60mg/L KBr, 100μl/L nitric acid. Postcolumn derivatization with bromine (also iodine may be used). Fluorescence detection excitation at 365nm, emission at 418nm.

Immunoassay

Numerous immunoassays are commercially available for both qualitative and quantitative analysis.

References

R. J. Cole and R. H. Cox; Handbook of Toxic Fungal Metabolites; Academic Press, New York, pp. 25-28(1981).

J. W. Dorner and R. J. Cole; Rapid Determination of Aflatoxins in Raw Peanuts by Liquid Chromatography with Postcolumn Iodination and Modified Minicolumn Cleanup; J. Assoc. Off. Anal. Chem., Vol. 71, pp. 43-47(1988).

Common/Systematic Name

Aflatoxin G_2

Molecular Formula/Molecular Weight

$C_{17}H_{14}O_7$; MW = 330.07395

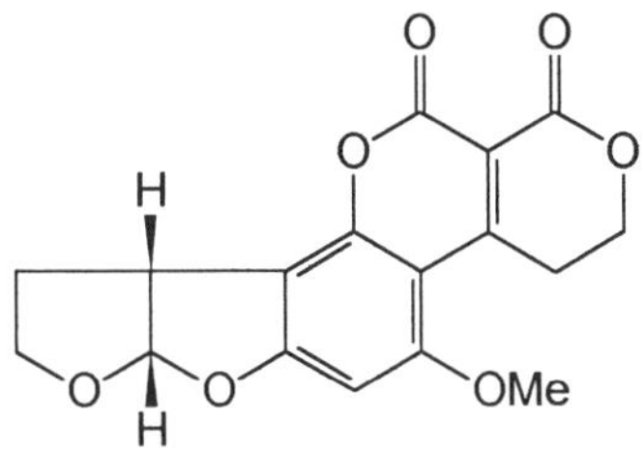

General Characteristics

Crystals from ethyl acetate; mp., 230°C; $[\alpha]_D$ -454° (*c*=1.0, in $CHCl_3$).

Fungal Source

Aspergillus flavus, *A. nomius*, and *A. parasiticus*.

Biological Activity

Aflatoxin G_2 was the least acutely toxic of the 4 major naturally occurring aflatoxins. The LD_{50} in ducklings was 172.5μg/duckling using dimethylformamide as carrier in a 6-day test.

Spectral Data

UV:

λ_{max} 217(ϵ=28,000), 245(12,900), 265(11,200), and 365nm (19,300).

^{1}H NMR:

H-4, 3.46; H-5, 2.30; H-9, 6.34; H-13, 6.47; H-14, 3.60; H-15, 4.16; H-16, 4.42; and H-17, 3.94ppm.

^{13}C NMR:

C-1, 154.9 s; C-2, 113.7 s; C-3, 160.0 s; C-4, 64.3 t; C-5, 28.9 t; C-6, 161.3 s; C-7, 102.1 s; C-8, 161.0 s; C-9, 90.3 d; C-10, 166.1 s; C-11, 106.6 s; C-12, 152.2 s; C-13, 113.7 d; C-14, 43.9 d; C-15, 31.4 t; C-16, 67.7 t; and C-17, 56.4ppm q.

TLC Data

Silica gel G-HR (chloroform-acetone, 93:7, v/v); R_f: 0.27; detected as blue-green fluorescence under UV light.

HPLC Data

Reverse phase Nova-Pak C_{18} (Waters) column, water-MeOH, 40:60(v/v), 60mg/L KBr, 100µl/L nitric acid. Postcolumn derivatization with bromine (also iodine may be used). Fluorescence detection excitation at 365nm, emission at 418nm.

Immunoassay

Numerous immunoassays are commercially available for both qualitative and quantitative analysis.

References

R. J. Cole and R. H. Cox; Handbook of Toxic Fungal Metabolites; Academic Press, New York, pp. 45-48(1981).

J. W. Dorner and R. J. Cole; Rapid Determination of Aflatoxins in Raw Peanuts by Liquid Chromatography with Postcolumn Iodination and Modified Minicolumn Cleanup; J. Assoc. Off. Anal. Chem., Vol. 71, p. 43-47(1988).

Common/Systematic Name

Aflatoxin M_1

Molecular Formula/Molecular Weight

$C_{17}H_{12}O_7$; MW = 328.05830

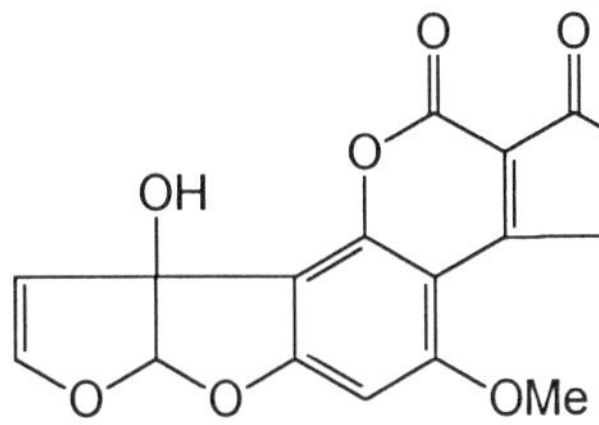

General Characteristics

Crystals from methanol in dimethylformamide; mp., 299°C (dec); $[\alpha]_D$ -280° (*c*=0.1, in dimethylformamide).

Fungal Source

Aspergillus flavus (NRRL 3251), and *A. parasiticus*.

Note: Aflatoxin M_1 is excreted in the milk and urine of animals ingesting aflatoxin B_1. The conversion of B_1 to M_1 occurs in the liver.

Isolation/Purification

Pull milk-water (1:1, v/v) through C_{18} cartridge using slight vacuum; wash with water-CH_3CHOH (95:5, v/v). Place silica gel cleanup column beneath C_{18} cartridge; wash with ether. Elute aflatoxin M_1 from column using CH_2Cl_2-isopropyl alcohol (95:5, v/v); dry gently under nitrogen using heat. Derivative by adding 200µl hexane and 200µl trifluoroacetic acid (TFA); mix and let stand 10 min. at 40°; evaporate to dryness; add 2ml water-CH_3CN (75:25, v/v); mix.

Biological Activity

Aflatoxin M_1 is a hydroxylated metabolite of aflatoxin B_1, secreted in milk of mammals receiving aflatoxin B_1. It is potentially hepatocarcinogenic. The LD_{50} value for aflatoxin M_1 in day old ducklings was 16.6µg/duckling compared to 12µg/duckling for aflatoxin B_1 determined simultaneously. Pathology and clinical signs similar to aflatoxin B_1. Ducklings dosed with aflatoxin M_1 showed liver lesions indistinguishable from those induced by aflatoxin B_1; however, M_1 also induced a renal tubular necrosis not seen with B_1. In rainbow trout and rats, aflatoxin M_1 was slightly less effective than B_1 in inducing hepatic carcinoma.

Spectral Data

UV:

λ_{max}^{EtOH} 226(ε=23,100), 265(11,600), and 357nm (19,000).

TLC Data

Kieselgel G (chloroform-methanol, 97:3, v/v); R_f: 0.34; detection as blue fluorescence under long wave UV light. Adsorbosil-1, isopropyl alcohol-acetone-chloroform, 5:10:85, v/v/v; R_f, 0.46; detection as blue fluorescence under long wave UV light.

HPLC Data

Column: C_{18} bonded silica gel, 0.4 x 25cm, 5μm; mobile phase: water-isopropyl alcohol-CH_3CN (80:12:8, v/v/v); detection: fluorescence at 365nm excitation and >400nm emission.

References

R. J. Cole and R. H. Cox; Handbook of Toxic Fungal Metabolites; Academic Press, New York, pp. 29-33(1981).

K. Helrich, Ed.; AOAC Official Methods of Analysis, 15th Edition, Vol. II; AOAC, Inc., Arlington, VA, pp. 1199-1205(1990)

C. H. Holzapfel, P. S. Steyn, and I. F. H. Purchase; Isolation and Structure of Aflatoxins, M_1 and M_2; Tet. Lett. p. 2799 (1966).

Common/Systematic Name

Aflatoxin M_2

Molecular Formula/Molecular Weight

$C_{17}H_{14}O_7$; MW = 330.07395

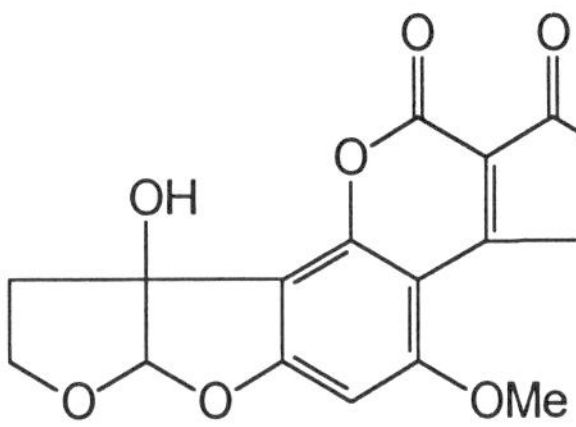

General Characteristics

Crystals from methanol-chloroform; mp., 293 °C (dec.).

Fungal Source

Aspergillus flavus and *A. parasiticus*.

Biological Activity

Aflatoxin M_2 was excreted in the urine and milk of animals ingesting mixed aflatoxins. The LD_{50} value for aflatoxin M_2 was 62μg/day old duckling compared to 12μg for aflatoxin B_1 in the same assay done simultaneously.

Spectral Data

UV:

λ_{max} 221(ε=20,000), 264(10,900), and 357nm (21,000).

IR:

($CHCl_3$) 3350, 1760, and 1690cm^{-1}.

TLC Data

Adsorbosil-1 silica gel, isopropyl alcohol-acetone-chloroform (5:10:85, v/v/v); R_f, 0.42; detection as blue fluorescence under UV light.

References

R. J. Cole and R. H. Cox; Handbook of Toxic Fungal Metabolites; Academic Press, New York, pp. 49-50(1981).

C. W. Holzapfel, P. S. Steyn, and I. F. H. Purchase; Isolation and Structure of Aflatoxins, M_1 and M_2; Tet. Lett., p. 2799 (1966).

Common/Systematic Name

Aflatoxin P_1

Molecular Formula/Molecular Weight

$C_{16}H_{10}O_6$; MW = 298.04774

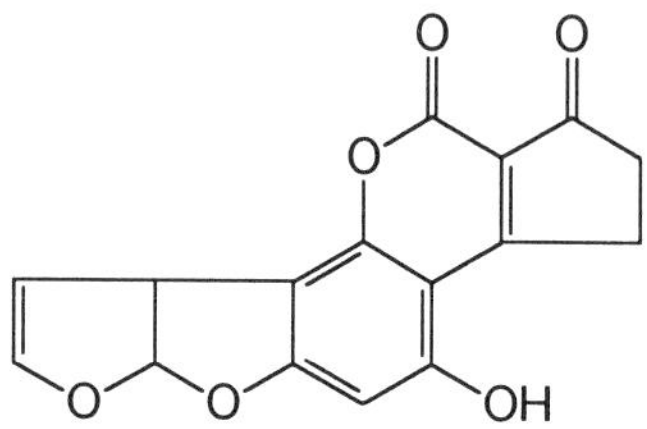

General Characteristics

Pale yellow needles from methanol-benzene-hexane; mp., >320°C; $[\alpha]_D^{20}$ -574° (*c*=0.08, in MeOH).

Source Aflatoxin

P_1 was the principal urinary metabolite of aflatoxin B_1 in rhesus monkeys. It occurred in the urine in unconjugated (3%), sulfate (10%), and glucuronide (50%) forms.

Biological Activity

In a mouse bioassay using IP injection, aflatoxin P_1 showed considerably less toxicity than aflatoxin B_1. At a dosage of 100mg/kg, no mortalities were observed; at 150mg/kg there were 2 mortalities in 15 animals; and at 200mg/kg, no mortalities occurred. Aflatoxin B_1 in the same assay had an LD_{50} of 9.5mg/kg.

Spectral Data

UV:

λ_{max} 226(ϵ=20,400), 267(11,200), 342(14,900), 362(15,400) and 425nm (2,500).

References

G. Buchi, D. Spitzner, S. Paglialunga, and G. N. Wogan; Life Science, Vol. 13, p. 1145 (1973).

R. J. Cole and R. H. Cox; Handbook of Toxic Fungal Metabolites; Academic Press, New York, pp. 3-5 (1981).

J. Dalezios, G. N. Wogan, and S. M. Weinreb; Science, Vol. 171, p. 584 (1971).

Common/Systematic Name

Aflatoxin D_1

Molecular Formula/Molecular Weight

$C_{16}H_{14}O_5$; MW = 286.08412

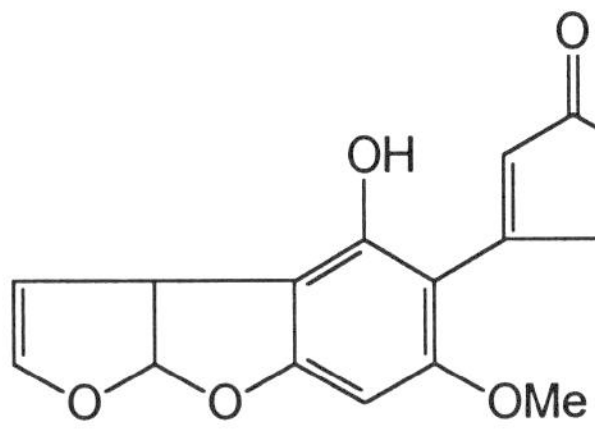

General Characteristics

Sublimed without melting at 220°-290°C; in sealed tube crystals decomposed without melting at 255°-258°C. Acetate derivative; mp., 155-157°C.

Fungal Source

A major product formed from reacting aflatoxin B_1 with ammonium hydroxide at 100°C under pressure.

Biological Activity

Specific toxicity data not known. It has been reported that the nonfluorescent compounds formed in alkaline solutions are strongly toxic (mixture included aflatoxin D_1).

Spectral Data

UV:

λ_{max}^{MeOH} 227(ϵ=20,792) and 324nm (17,074) [corrected from 227(15,920), and 324nm (12,440)].

^{1}H NMR:

H-2, 6.24; H-4, 2.40; H-5, 3.10; H-8, 6.25; H-12, 6.76; H-13, 4.70; H-14, 5.40; H-15, 6.63; and H-16, 3.75ppm.

^{13}C NMR:

C-1, 208.6 s; C-2, 131.5 d; C-3, 170.9 s; C-4, 31.9 t; C-5, 34.2 t; C-6, 106.1 s*; C-7, 159.5 s; C-8, 86.6 d; C-9, 158.6 s; C-10, 106.7 s*; C-11, 151.3 s; C-12, 111.5 d; C-13, 47.6 d; C-14, 103.1 d; C-15, 144.1 d; and C-16, 55.8ppm q.

* Assignment may be reversed.

TLC Data

Silica gel: chloroform-acetone, 95:5, v/v; R_f, 0.31. Detection: turns gray-brown after spraying with 10% $FeCl_3$; orange-yellow with 2,4-dinitrophenylhydrazine. Acetate R_f, 0.78.

References

R. J. Cole and R. H. Cox; Handbook of Toxic Fungal Metabolites; Academic Press, New York, pp. 6-9(1981).

J. B. Stanley, L. S. Lee, A. F. Cucullu, and I. V. deGruy; J. Agric. Food Chem., Vol. 23, p. 447 (1975).

Common/Systematic Name

Parasiticol; Aflatoxin B_3

Molecular Formula/Molecular Weight

$C_{16}H_{14}O_6$; MW = 302.07904

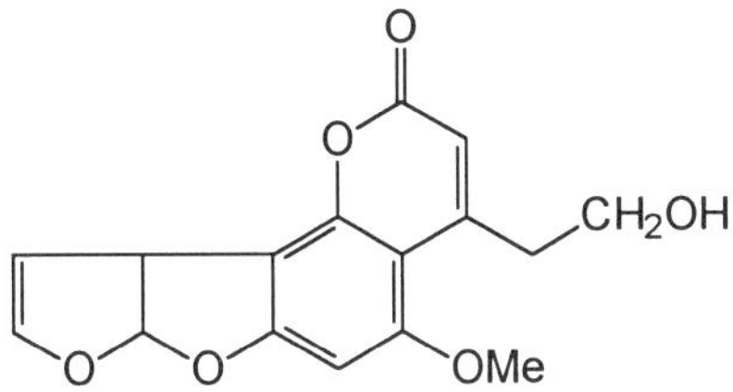

General Characteristics

Crystals from chloroform; mp., 217°C.

Fungal Source

Aspergillus flavus, *A. parasiticus*. Parasiticol appears to be more prominent in older cultures of *A. flavus* and *A. parasiticus*. It was suggested to be the first step in the biological degradation of aflatoxin G_1 and was reported as an intermediate in the biodegradation of aflatoxin G_1 by *Rhizopus* spp.

Biological Activity

Parasiticol had the same acute toxicity to ducklings as aflatoxin B_1, but it had little tendency to cause biliary hyperplasia. It was only 1/100 as toxic as B_1 in chick embryo studies.

Spectral Data

UV:

λ_{max}^{MeOH} 229(sh) (ϵ=10,000), 253(7,300), 262(7,550), and 326nm (9,350); λ_{max} 225(sh) (12,600), 253(6,800), 262(7,400), and 325nm (9,700).

^1H NMR:

H-2, 5.94; H-6, 6.62; H-10, 6.85 (*J*=7.0); H-11, 4.72(*J*=7.0, 3.0); H-12, 5.36 (*J*=3.0, 3.0); H-13, 6.66; H-14, 3.00; H-15, 3.61; H-16, 3.85; and OH, 4.59ppm.

^{13}C NMR:

C-1, 158.6 s*; C-2, 110.8 d; C-3, 154.7 s; C-4, 103.5 s; C-5, 158.8 s*; C-6, 91.0 d; C-7, 160.6 s; C-8, 106.8 s; C-9, 150.7 s; C-10, 112.6 d; C-11, 47.2 d; C-12, 102.0 d; C-13, 145.1 d; C-14, 41.1 t; C-15, 59.9 t; and C-16, 56.4ppm q.

* Assignment may be reversed.

References

R. J. Cole and R. H. Cox; Handbook of Toxic Fungal Metabolites; Academic Press, New York, pp. 10-14(1981).

R. J. Cole and J. W. Kirksey; J. Agric. Food Chem., Vol. 19, p. 222 (1971).

Common/Systematic Name

Aflatoxin Q_1

Molecular Formula/Molecular Weight

$C_{17}H_{12}O_7$; MW = 328.05830

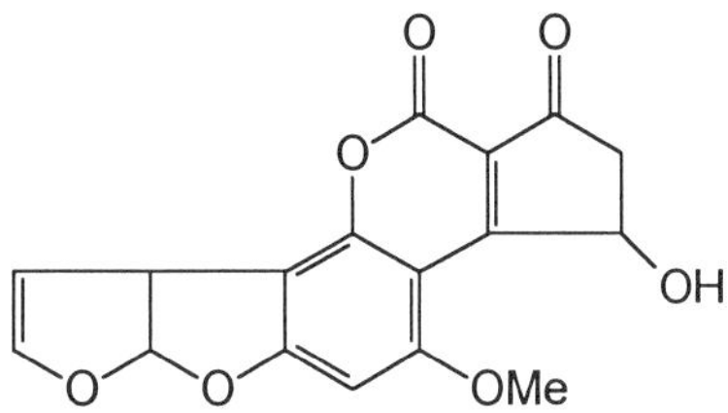

General Characteristics

Colorless needles from methanol-chloroform or hot acetonitrile; mp., 295°C (dec.); crystals from chloroform-hexane; mp., 266°C (dec.).

Fungal Source

Aflatoxin Q_1 was a major metabolite of aflatoxin B_1 metabolism in monkey, rat, and human liver preparations (*in vitro*).

Biological Activity

Aflatoxin Q_1 was approximately 18 times less toxic than aflatoxin B_1 by the air cell route in the chicken embryo test. No mutagenic activity was detected by the bacterial mutagenesis test, using *Salmonella typhimurium* TA 1538 with or without microsomal activities.

Spectral Data

UV:
λ_{max}^{MeOH} 366(ϵ=17,500), 267(11,450), and 223nm (19,030); λ_{max}^{EtOH} 365(18,800), 266(11,700), 242(sh) (10,000), and 224nm (20,500).

TLC Data

Adsorbosil-1 silica gel, chloroform-acetone-*n*-hexane,88:15:20, v/v/v, R_f, 0.23. Detection: intense yellow-green fluorescence under UV light. Silica gel, chloroform-methanol, 20:1, v/v, R_f: 0.25. Detection: yellow fluorescence in 350nm UV light.

References

R. J. Cole and R. H. Cox; Handbook of Toxic Fungal Metabolites; Academic Press, New York, pp. 20-24(1981).

M. S. Masri, W. F. Hadden, R. E. Lundin, and D. P. H. Hsieh; J. Agric. Food Chem., Vol. 22, p. 512 (1974).

Common/Systematic Name

Aflatoxicol A (Ro)

Molecular Formula/Molecular Weight

$C_{17}H_{14}O_6$; MW = 314.07904

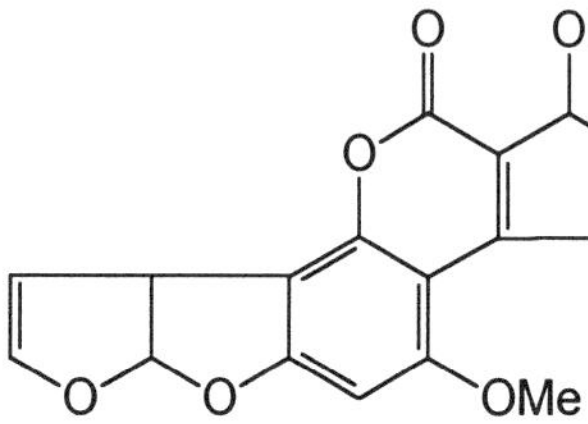

General Characteristics

Crystals from benzene-*n*-hexane; mp., 224-226°C.

Fungal Source

Aflatoxicol A (Ro) is produced from the *in vitro* incubation of aflatoxin B_1 with submitochondrial liver fractions from several animal species. It was also produced from biological reduction of aflatoxin B_1 by *Tetrahymena pyriformis, Dactylium dendroides, Rhizopus* spp., and other microorganisms. It was reported to occur together with a diastereoisomer (aflatoxicol B).

Biological Activity

Reportedly 18 times less toxic than aflatoxin B_1 in the duckling biliary hyperplasia assay.

Spectral Data

UV:

λ_{max}^{EtOH} 332(ϵ=14,100), 261(10,800), and 254nm (6,790). Fluorescence emission, 425nm.

TLC Data

Silica gel G-HR (chloroform-acetone, 93:7, v/v); R_f, 0.30; detection as blue fluorescence under UV light.

References

R. J. Cole and R. H. Cox; Handbook of Toxic Fungal Metabolites; Academic Press, New York, pp. 38-40(1981).

W. B. Turner and D. C. Aldridge; Fungal Metabolites II; Academic Press, New York, New York, 631 pp. (1983).

Common/Systematic Name
Aflatoxicol B

Molecular Formula/Molecular Weight
$C_{17}H_{14}O_6$; MW = 314.07904

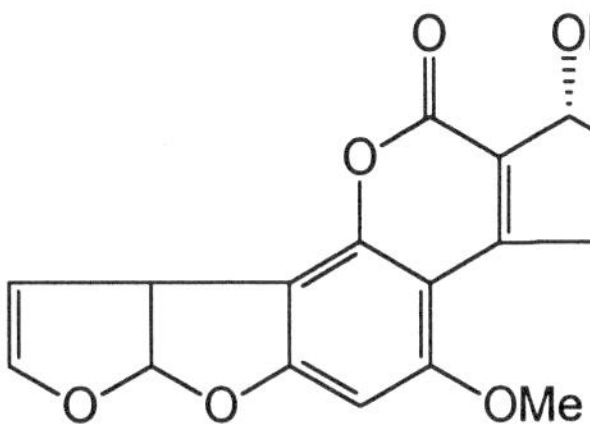

General Characteristics
Crystals from benzene-*n*-hexane, decomposed over broad range, starting at 233°C.

Fungal Source
Aflatoxicol B was obtained from biological reduction of aflatoxin B_1 by *Rhizopus* spp., *Dactylium dendroides, Tetrahymena pyriformis*, and other microorganisms.

Spectral Data

UV:
λ_{max}^{EtOH} 325(ϵ=14,100), 261(10,800), and 254nm (6,790).

TLC Data
Silica gel G-HR (chloroform-acetone, 93:7, v/v); R_f, 0.26; detection as blue fluorescence under UV light.

References
R. J. Cole and R. H. Cox; Handbook of Toxic Fungal Metabolites; Academic Press, New York, pp. 41-44(1981).

W. B. Turner and D. C. Aldridge; Fungal Metabolites II; Academic Press, New York, New York, 631 pp. (1983).

Common/Systematic Name

Aflatoxin B_{2a}

Molecular Formula/Molecular Weight

$C_{17}H_{14}O_7$; MW = 330.07395

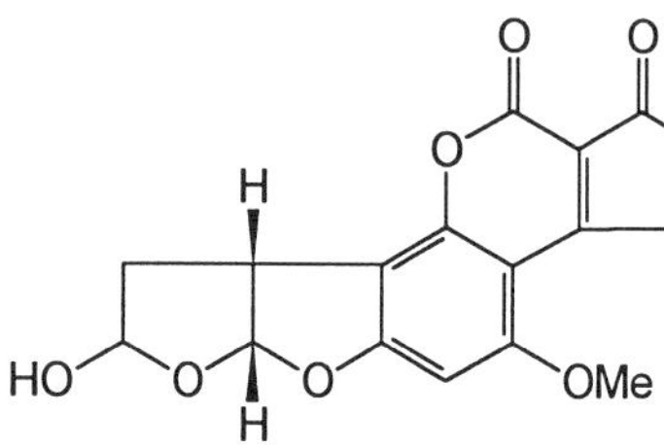

General Characteristics

Melting point, 240°C (dec.).

Fungal Source

Aspergillus flavus and *A. parasiticus*. Also biotransformation product of aflatoxin B_1 by the liver of some animals and forms spontaneously in acidic conditions.

Biological Activity

Aflatoxin B_{2a} was more than 200 times less toxic than aflatoxin B_1 as measured by the initiation of bile duct proliferation in the standard duckling assay. No acute toxicity was noted in Khaki Cambell ducklings (day-old) at levels up to 1200μg/duckling.

Spectral Data

UV:

λ_{max}^{MeOH} 228(ε=17,600), 256(10,300), and 363nm (20,400).

^{13}C NMR:

C-1, 153.9 s; C-2, 117.4 s; C-3, 200.0 s; C-4, 34.6 t; C-5, 28.5 t; C-6, 176.7 s; C-7, 106.9 s; C-8, 160.8 s; C-9, 90.5 d; C-10, 165.3 s; C-11, 108.6 s; C-12, 152.0 s; C-13, 113.6 d; C-14, 41.3 d; C-15, 37.2 t; C-16, 99.7 d; and C-17, 56.6ppm q.

TLC Data

Kieselgel G (chloroform-methanol, 98:2, v/v); R_f, 0.13; detection as blue fluorescence under UV light.

References

R. J. Cole and R. H. Cox; Handbook of Toxic Fungal Metabolites; Academic Press, New York, pp. 51-54(1981).

J. G. Heathcote and J. R. Hibbert; Biochem. Soc. Trans. Vol. 2, p. 301 (1974).

Common/Systematic Name
Aflatoxin G_{2a}

Molecular Formula/Molecular Weight
$C_{17}H_{14}O_8$; MW = 346.06887

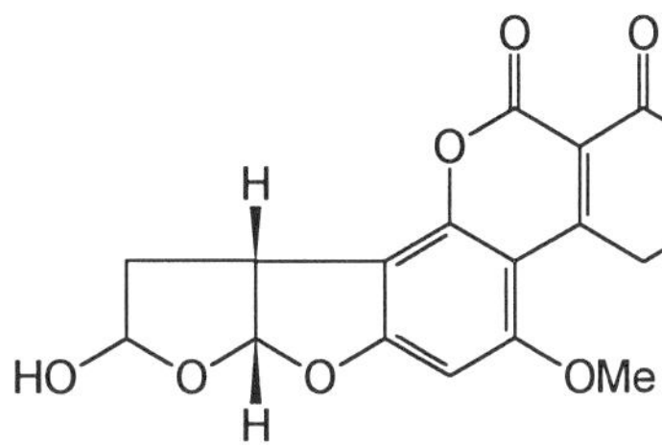

General Characteristics
Melting point, 190°C (dec.).

Fungal Source
Aspergillus flavus and *A. parasiticus*. Also biotransformation product of aflatoxin B_1 by the liver of some animals and forms spontaneously in acidic conditions.

Biological Activity
There were no significant differences in growth and no characteristic liver lesions in day-old Khaki Cambell ducklings dosed up to 1600μg/duckling (LD_{50} of aflatoxin B_1 in same assay was 18.2μg/duckling).

Spectral Data

UV:
λ_{max}^{MeOH} 223(ϵ=18,600), 242(10,100), 262(8,700), and 365nm (18,000).

^{13}C NMR:
C-1, 153.9 s; C-2, 111.0 s; C-3, 159.6 s; C-4, 64.1 t; C-5, 28.4 t; C-6, 161.9 s; C-7, 105.3 s; C-8, 161.6 s; C-9, 91.1 d; C-10, 164.9 s; C-11, 108.6 s; C-12, 151.6 s; C-13, 113.7 d; C-14, 41.9 d; C-15, 41.9 t; C-16, 91.1 d; and C-17, 56.7ppm q.

TLC Data
Kieselgel G (chloroform-methanol, 98:2, v/v); R_f, 0.10; detection as blue fluorescence under UV light.

References
R. J. Cole and R. H. Cox; Handbook of Toxic Fungal Metabolites; Academic Press, New York, pp. 55-58(1981).

J. G. Heathcote and J. R. Hibbert; Biochem. Soc. Trans. Vol. 2, p. 301 (1974).

Common/Systematic Name

Aflatoxicol *O*-ethyl ether A

Molecular Formula/Molecular Weight

$C_{19}H_{18}O_6$; MW = 342.11034

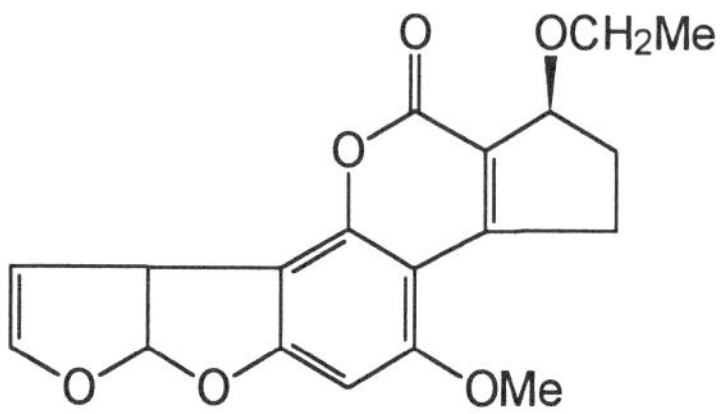

General Characteristics

Colorless crystals from ethanol solution; mp., 198-200°C.

Fungal Source

Produced spontaneously from aflatoxicol A during silica gel column chromatography using chloroform (ethanol preservative) as the eluting solvent.

Spectral Data

UV:

λ_{max}^{EtOH} 332(ϵ=14,200), 261(9,660), and 255nm (8,830).

TLC Data

Silica gel G-HR (chloroform-acetone, 93:7, v/v); R_f, 0.81; detection as blue fluorescence under UV light.

References

R. J. Cole and R. H. Cox; Handbook of Toxic Fungal Metabolites; Academic Press, New York, pp. 59-61(1981).

R. J. Cole, J. W. Kirksey, and B. R. Blankenship; J. Agric. Food Chem., Vol. 20, p. 1100 (1972).

Common/Systematic Name

Aflatoxicol *O*-ethyl ether B

Molecular Formula/Molecular Weight

$C_{19}H_{18}O_6$; MW = 342.11034

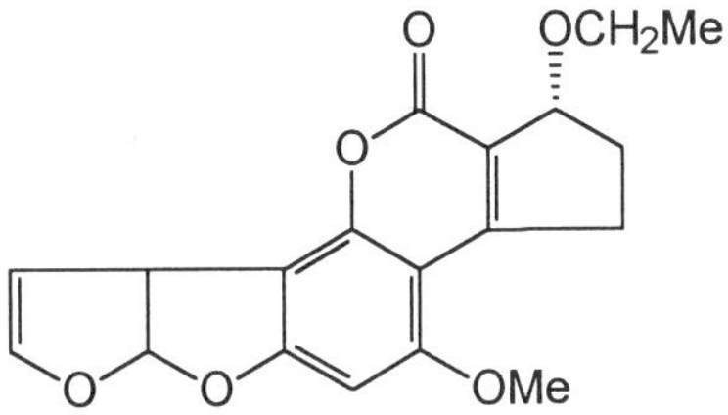

General Characteristics

Colorless crystals from ethanol solution; mp., 194-196°C.

Fungal Source

Produced spontaneously from aflatoxicol B during silica gel column chromatography using chloroform (ethanol preservative) as the eluting solvent.

Spectral Data

UV:

λ_{max}^{EtOH} 331(ϵ=15,750), 261(12,280), and 255nm (11,170).

TLC Data

Silica gel G-HR (chloroform-acetone, 93:7, v/v); R_f, 0.73; detection as blue fluorescence under UV light.

References

R. J. Cole and R. H. Cox; Handbook of Toxic Fungal Metabolites; Academic Press, New York, pp. 62-64(1981).

R. J. Cole, J. W. Kirksey, and B. R. Blankenship; J. Agric. Food Chem., Vol. 20, p. 1100 (1972).

12

Versicolorins

Versicolorin A
Versicolorin B
Versicolorin C
Averufin
Norsolorinic acid
Versiconal hemiacetal acetate
Versiconol acetate
Versiconol
Nidurufin
Dimethylnidurufin
Aversin
O-Methylaversin; Tri-*O*-methylversicolorin B
Versicolorone
Hydroxyversicolorone

Common/Systematic Name
Versicolorin A

Molecular Formula/Molecular Weight
$C_{18}H_{10}O_7$; MW = 338.04265

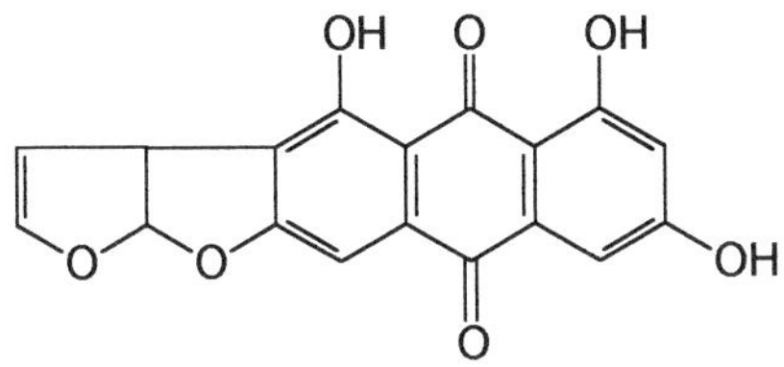

General Characteristics
Orange-yellow needles from chloroform-methanol; mp., 303-306°C; $[\alpha]_D^{18}$ - 354° (*c*=0.75, in dioxane). Trimethyl ether; mp., 241°C. Versicolorin A was soluble in acetone, dioxane, ethyl acetate, ether, and ethanol; sparingly soluble in chloroform and benzene; insoluble in water and aqueous bicarbonate. Versicolorin A is a biosynthetic precursor of the aflatoxins.

Fungal source
Aspergillus versicolor and *A. parasiticus* (mutant strain 1-11-105 wk-1).

Isolation/Purification
The mycelium was harvested after 4-7 days growth on a low salts medium. The pigment was obtained by chloroform-methanol (1:1, v/v) extraction of the mycelium in a Soxhlet apparatus, followed by solvent partition with hexane-90% methanol. The 90% methanol layer contained versicolorin A and was separated by chromatography on silica gel H under pressure (1 kg/cm^2). The column was developed with chloroform-methanol (97:3, v/v). Crystallization from chloroform-methanol gave pure versicolorin A.

Spectral Data

UV:
λ_{max}^{EtOH} 222(ϵ=log 4.45), 255(4.13), 267(4.26), 290(4.40), 326(3.83), and 450nm (3.85).

IR:
(KBr) 3340, 1679, 1625, and 1610cm^{-1}.

^{13}C NMR:
($CDCl_3$) C-1, 158.6, s; C-2, 119.7, s; C-3, 165.1, s; C-4, 100.9, d; C-5, 108.6, d; C-6, 164.8, s; C-7, 107.6, d; C-8, 163.8, s; C-9, 188.4, s; C-10, 180.1, s; C-11, 43.3, t; C-12, 30.0, t; ,C-13, 66.9, d; C-14, 112.9, d; C-1a, 110.4, s; C-4a, 134.2, s; C-5a,

134.8, s; and C-8a, 107.9ppm, s.

TLC Data

Silica gel (benzene-acetic acid. 95:5, v/v); R_f: 0.23; detected as yellow spot in visible light.

References

R. J. Cole and R. H. Cox; Handbook of Toxic Fungal Metabolites; Academic Press, New York, p. 102 (1981).

T. Hamasaki, Y. Hatsuda, N. Terashima, and M. Renbutsu; Studies on the Metabolites of *Aspergillus versicolor* (Vuillemin) Tiraboschi Part V. Isolation and Structures of Three New Metabolites, Versicolorins A, B, and C; Agric. Biol. Chem., Vol. 31, pp. 11-17 (1967).

G. P. Gorst-Allman, P. S. Steyn, P. L. Wessels, and D. B. Scott; Carbon-13 Nuclear Magnetic Resonance Assignments and Biosynthesis of Versicolorin A in Aspergillus parasiticus; J. Chem. Soc., Perkin Trans. 1, pp. 961-964(1978).

Common/Systematic Name

Versicolorin B

Molecular Formula/Molecular Weight

$C_{18}H_{12}O_7$; MW = 340.05830

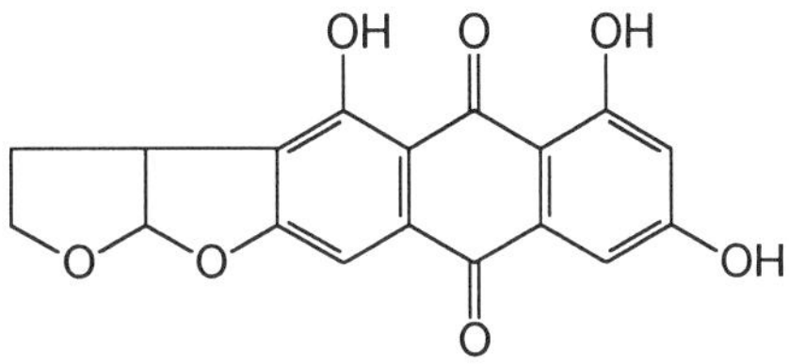

General Characteristics

Fine yellow needles from acetone; mp., 298°C (dec.); trimethyl ether; mp., 216°C; $[\alpha]_D^{25}$ -223° (*c*=0.42, in dioxane). Versicolorin B was soluble in acetone, dioxane, ethyl acetate, ether, and ethanol; sparingly soluble in chloroform and benzene; insoluble in water and aqueous sodium bicarbonate.

Fungal Source

Aspergillus versicolor.

Spectral Data

UV:

λ_{max} 223(ϵ=23,900), 255(13,500), 266(19,500), 291(24,000), 324(12,800), and 450nm (8,700).

TLC Data

Silica gel (benzene-acetic acid, 95:5, v/v); R_f, 0.23; detected as yellow spot in visible light.

References

R. J. Cole and R. H. Cox; Handbook of Toxic Fungal Metabolites; Academic Press, New York, p. 99 (1981).

G. P. Gorst-Allman, P. S. Steyn, P. L. Wessels, and D. B. Scott; J. Chem. Soc., Perkin Trans. 1, p. 961 (1978).

Common/Systematic Name

Versicolorin C

Molecular Formula/Molecular Weight

$C_{18}H_{12}O_7$; MW = 340.05830

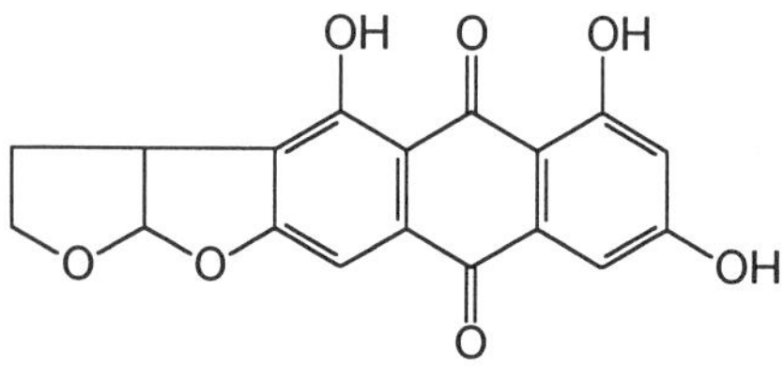

General Characteristics

Orange-red needles from acetone; mp., 310°C; $[\alpha]_D^{25}$ (c=0.44, in dioxane); trimethyl ether; mp., 216°C. Versicolorin C was soluble in acetone, dioxane, ethyl acetate, ether, and ethanol; sparingly soluble in chloroform and benzene; insoluble in water and aqueous bicarbonate. Versicolorin C is a biosynthetic precursor of the aflatoxins.

Fungal Source

Aspergillus versicolor.

Spectral Data

UV:

λ_{max}^{EtOH} 223(ϵ=28,800), 255(15,800), 267(20,400), 292(28,800), 326(10,000), and 450nm (10,700).

^{13}C NMR:

C-1, 158.6 s; C-2, 119.7 s; C-3, 165.1 s; C-4, 100.9 d; C-5, 108.6 d; C-6, 164.8 s; C-7, 107.6 d; C-8, 163.8 s; C-9, 188.4 s; C-10, 180.1 s; C-11, 43.3 t; C-12, 30.0 t; C-13, 66.9 d; C-14, 112.9 d; C-1a, 110.4 s; C-4a, 134.2 s; C-5a, 134.8 s; and C-8a, 107.9ppm s.

TLC Data

Silica gel (benzene-acetic acid. 95:5, v/v); R_f, 0.23; detected as yellow spot in visible light.

References

R. J. Cole and R. H. Cox; Handbook of Toxic Fungal Metabolites; Academic Press, New York, p. 102 (1981).

T. Hamasaki, Y. Hatsuda, N. Terashima, and M. Renbutsu; Agric. Biol. Chem., Vol. 31, p. 11 (1967).

Common/Systematic Name

Averufin

Molecular Formula/Molecular Weight

$C_{20}H_{16}O_7$; MW = 368.08960

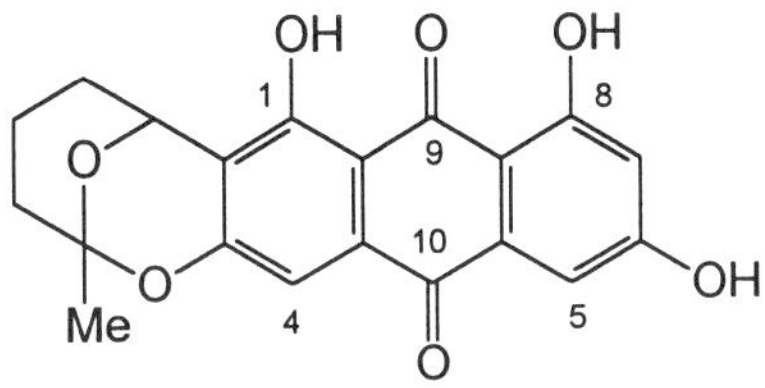

General Characteristics

Bright orange-red laths from acetone; mp., 280-282° (dec.); $[\alpha]_D^{23}$ >1° (*c*=0.30, in EtOH); crystals from acetone; mp., 283-289° (dec.); tri-*O*-acetyl derivative, yellow needles from ethanol; mp., 297-311°C; $[\alpha]_D^{22}$ -15° (5g/liter in chloroform). Averufin is unstable toward alkali; stable toward acid. It is a biosynthetic precursor of aflatoxin B_1.

Fungal Source

Aspergillus versicolor, A. parasiticus (mutant, ATCC 15517), and *A. ustus*.

Spectral Data

UV:

λ_{max}^{EtOH} 223(ε=33,000), 256(sh)(16,500), 265(18,500), 286(sh)(24,800), 294(30,800), 319(12,500), and 454nm (10,500); tri-*O*-acetyl derivative: λ_{max}^{EtOH} 244(ε=18,300), 248(18,300), 281(45,000), 282(45,000), 335(4,900), and 370nm (4,250).

^{1}H NMR:

H-4, 6.98; H-5, 7.08(*J*=2.5); H-7, 6.56(*J*=2.5); H-11, 5.26; H-16, 1.58; and OH's, 11.30, 12.04, 12.42ppm.

^{13}C NMR:

C-1, 158.0 s; C-2, 115.8 s; C-3, 159.7 s; C-4, 107.0 d; C-5, 108.8 d; C-6, 165.1 s; C-7, 107.9 d; C-8, 164.1 s; C-9, 188.6 s; C-10, 180.5 s; C-11, 65.9 d; C-12, 26.8 t; C-13, 15.3 t; C-14, 35.1 t; C-15, 101.1 s; C-16, 27.3 q; C-la, 108.3 s; C-4a, 132.9 s; C-8a, 134.7 s; and C-5a, 108.5ppm s.

TLC Data

Silica gel (Eastman 6060, chloroform-acetone-acetic acid, 97:2:1, v/v/v); R_f, 0.5; detected as a red spot in visible light.

References

R. J. Cole and R. H. Cox; Handbook of Toxic Fungal Metabolites; Academic Press, New York, p. 107 (1981).

J. A. Donkersloot and R. I. Mateles; Biochim. Biophys. Acta., Vol. 86, p. 418 (1964).

Common/Systematic Name
Norsolorinic acid
2-*n*-Hexanoyl-1,3,6,8-tetrahydroxyanthraquinone

Molecular Formula/Molecular Weight
$C_{20}H_{18}O_7$; MW = 370.10525

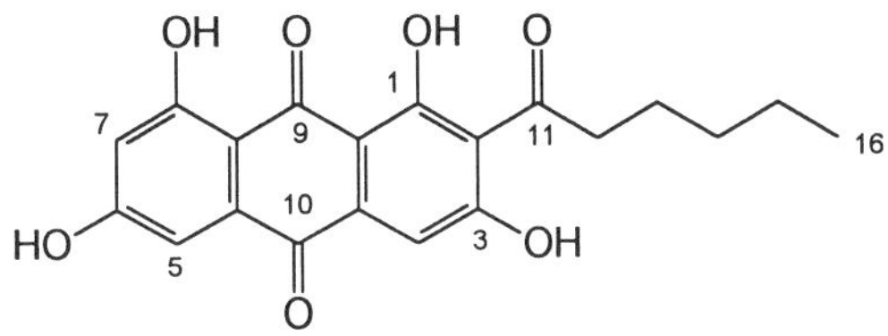

General Characteristics
Red prisms from acetone; mp., 256-257°C (dec.); formed tetramethyl ether; mp.,131-132°C. Norsolorinic acid was sparingly soluble in acetone, ethanol, and methanol; it was insoluble in water, hexane, ether, and sodium bicarbonate; it dissolved in sodium carbonate and sodium hydroxide to give a purple color. Norsolorinic acid is a precursor in aflatoxin biosynthesis.

Fungal Source
Aspergillus versicolor, A. parasiticus (mutant, NRRL, A-27,996), and the lichen *Sorlorina crocea* (L.) Ach.

Spectral Data

UV:
λ_{max}^{EtOH} 235(ε=24,500), 269(16,900), 284(18,600), 297(19,900), 314(22,900), and 465nm (7,760); λ_{max}^{EtOH} 234(ε=23,667), 265(16,650), 283(17,352), 297(sh) (19,872), 313(23,763), and 465nm (7,336).

^{1}H NMR:
($CDCl_3$) H-4, 7.22; H-5, 7.13(*J*=2.5); H-7, 6.61(*J*=2.5); H-12, 2.81; H-13, 1.60; H-14, 1.30; H-15, 1.30; and H-16, 0.88ppm.

^{13}C NMR:
($CDCl_3$) C-1, 161.0, s; C-2, 121.1,s; C-3, 163.0, s; C-4, 108.7, d; C-5, 108.0, d; C-6, 165.0, s; C-7, 107.8, d; C-8, 164.1, s; C-9, 188.0, s; C-10, 181.1, s; C-11, 202.6, s; C-12, 43.5, t; C-13, 22.6, t; C-14, 30.6, t; C-15, 21.8, t; C-16, 13.7, q; C-1a, 108.9, s; C-4a, 134.7, s; C-5a, 134.7, s; C-5a, 134.5, s; and C-8a, 108.0ppm s.

TLC Data
Adsorbosil-l; A: chloroform-acetone-*n*-hexane, 85:15:20 v/v/v. B: ethyl acetate-2-propanol-water, 10:2:1 v/v/v; R_f: A, 0.69; B, 1.0. Detected as orange-red spot in normal light.

References

R. J. Cole and R. H. Cox; Handbook of Toxic Fungal Metabolites; Academic Press, New York, p. 102 (1981).

G. P. Gorst-Allman, P. S. Steyn, P. L. Wessels, and D. B. Scott; Carbon-13 Nuclear Magnetic Resonance Assignments and Biosynthesis of Versicolorin A in *Aspergillus parasiticus*; J. Chem. Soc., Perkin Trans. 1, pp. 961-964 (1978).

T. Hamasaki, Y. Hatsuda, N. Terashima, and M. Renbutsu; Studies on the Metabolites of *Aspergillus versicolor* (Vuillemin) Tiraboschi Part V. Isolation and Structures of Three New Metabolites, Versicolorins A, B, and C; Agric. Biol. Chem., Vol. 31, pp. 11-17 (1967).

Common/Systematic Name

Versiconal hemiacetal acetate

2,3-Tetrafurano-1,6,8-trihydroxy-15-ethyl acetate

Molecular Formula/Molecular Weight

$C_{20}H_{16}O_9$; MW = 400.07943

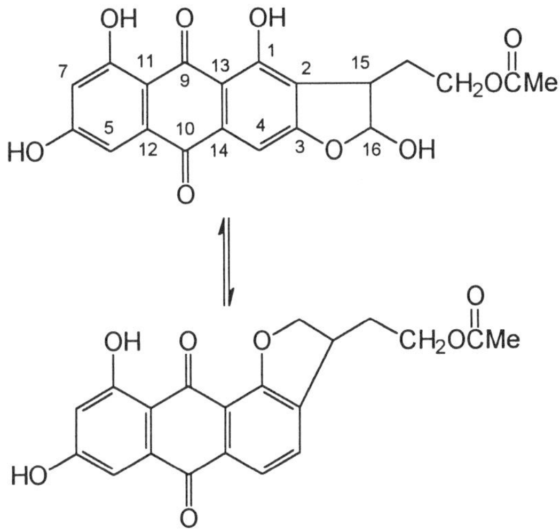

General Characteristics

Orange needles from chloroform-acetone; mp., 216-220°C: from acetone; mp., 234-236°C. In polar solvents, such as dimethyl sulfoxide, versiconal hemiacetal acetate existed as an equilibrium mixture of isomers; in acetone solution, the angular hemiacetal form was absent.

Fungal Source

Versiconal hemiacetal acetate accumulated in cultures of *Aspergillus flavus* and *A. parasiticus* treated with the insecticide dichlorvos, an inhibitor of aflatoxin biosynthesis. It was an intermediate in the biosynthesis of the aflatoxins.

Spectral Data

UV:

λ_{max}^{EtOH} 225(ϵ=23,800), 267(14,000), 298(23,000), 323(11,300), and 480nm.

^{13}C NMR:

C-1, 159.1 s; C-2, 120.5 s; C-3, 164.2 s; C-4, 103; C-5, 108.8 d; C-6, 165.1 s; C-7, 107.0 d; C-8, 164.2 s; C-9, 188.9 s; C-10, 180.9 s; C-11, 134.7 s; C-12, 107.9 s; C-13,

110.0 s; C-14, 134.7 s; C-15, 43 d; C-16, 113.0 d; C-17, 28.9 t; C-18, 61.7 t; C-19, 170.1 s; and C-20, 20.5ppm q.

Mass Spectrum:
Electron-impact mass spectral analysis showed 382.0688*m/e* due to M^+ -H_2O ($C_{20}H_{14}O_8$); chemical-ionization showed distinct 401*m/e* due to $M^+ + H^+$.

TLC Data

Silicar TLC-7G silica gel; A: toluene-ethyl acetate, 27:12, v/v; B: chloroform-acetone, 85:15, v/v; R_f: A, 0.32; B, 0.33. Detected as orange-red spot in normal light.

References

R. J. Cole and R. H. Cox; Handbook of Toxic Fungal Metabolites; Academic Press, New York, p. 115 (1981).

T. Hamasaki, M. Renbutsu, and Y. Harsuda; Agric. Biol. Chem., Vol. 31, p. 1513 (1967).

Common/Systematic Name
Versiconol acetate

Molecular Formula/Molecular Weight
$C_{19}H_{16}O_9$; MW = 388.079432

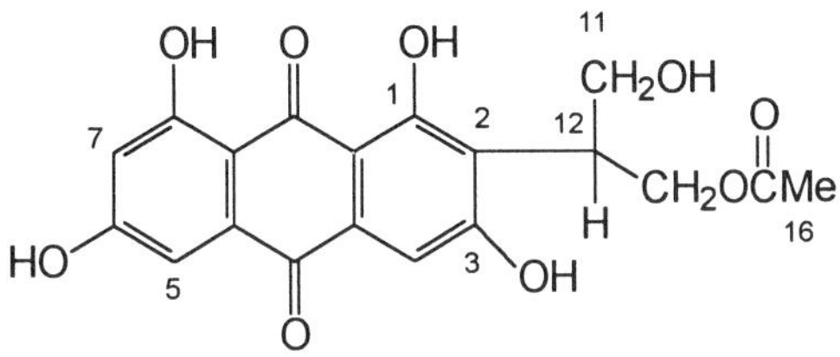

General Characteristics
Isolated as a glass.

Fungal Source
A mutant of *Aspergillus parasiticus*.

Spectral Data

UV:
λ_{max}^{MeOH} 225(ϵ=30,900), 265(sh) (15,800), 294(25,700), 315(12,800), and 453nm (8,500).

IR:
(KBr) 1700(sh), 1620(broad), and 1600cm^{-1}.

^{1}H NMR:
H-4, 7.37; H-5, 7.23(*J*=2.3); H-7, 6.61(*J*=2.3); H-11, 3.83; H-12, NR; H-13, 2.17; H-14, 4.03; H-16, 2.00; 1-OH, 13.02; and 8-OH, 12.31ppm.

^{13}C NMR:
(DMSO, $CDCl_3$, 1:1) C-1, 163.0; C-1a, 108.1; C-2, 121.4; C-3, 163.3; C-4, 108.6; C-4a, 132.2; C-5, 108.6; C-5a, 134.6; C-6, 164.8; C-7, 107.9; C-8, 164.2; C-8a, 108.6; C-9, 188.8; C-10, 181.0; C-11, 62.9; C-12, 35.0; C-13, 27.8; C-14, 62.9; C-15, 169.8; and C-16, 20.8ppm.

References

R. J. Cole and R. H. Cox; Handbook of Toxic Fungal Metabolites; Academic Press, New York, p. 120 (1981).

P. S. Steyn, R. Vleggaar, L. Wessels, R. J. Cole, and D. Scott; J. Chem. Soc., Perkin Trans. I, p. 451 (1979).

Common/Systematic Name
Versiconol

Molecular Formula/Molecular Weight
$C_{18}H_{16}O_8$; MW = 360.08452

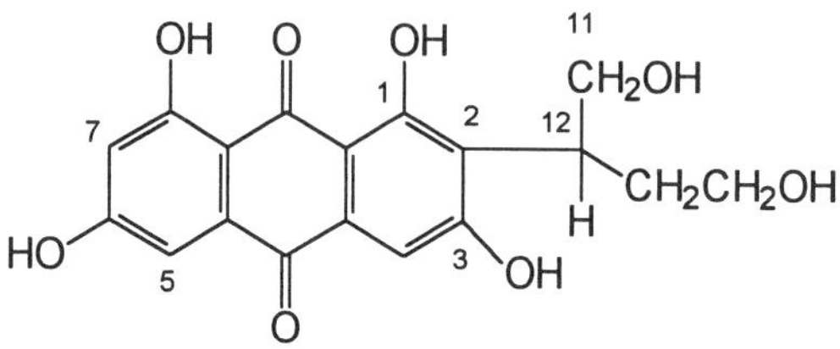

General Characteristics
Crystals from acetone; mp., 257-259°C; Orange-red needles; mp., 265°C (dec.); $[\alpha]_D^{25}$ -35.8° (*c*=0.35, in dioxane).

Fungal Source
A mutant of *Aspergillus parasiticus*.

Spectral Data

UV:
λ_{max}^{MeOH} 224(ε=30,100), 266(14,100), 294(23,900), 315(12,300), and 455nm (7,400);
λ_{max}^{EtOH} 224(ε=44,600), 255(22,300), 265(22,300), 295(33,800), 322(13,800), and 460nm (10,400).

^1H NMR:
(DMSO) H-4, 7.18; H-5, 7.23(*J*=2.3); H-7, 6.54(*J*=2.3); H-11, 3.0-4.0; H-12, 3.0-4.0; H-13, 1.95; H-14, 3.0-4.0; 1-OH, 12.79; and 8-OH, 12.15ppm.

^{13}C NMR:
(DMSO, $CDCl_3$, 1:1) C-1, 162.9; C-1a; 108.1; C-2, 122.9; C-3, 163.1; C-4, 108.9; C-4a, 132.1; C-5, 108.6; C-5a, 134.7; C-6, 164.7; C-7, 107.9; C-8, 164.2; C-8a, 108.6; C-9, 188.8; C-10, 181.0; C-11, 63.2; C-12, 34.9; C-13, 32.5; and C-14, 60.1ppm.

Mass Spectrum:
Electron-impact mass spectral analysis shows 342.0739*m/e* due to M^+ -H_2O.

References
R. J. Cole and R. H. Cox; Handbook of Toxic Fungal Metabolites; Academic Press, New York, p. 121 (1981).

P. S. Steyn, R. Vleggaar, L. Wessels, R. J. Cole, and D. Scott; J. Chem. Soc., Perkin

Trans. I, p. 451 (1979).

W. B. Turner and D. C. Aldridge; Fungal Metabolites II; Academic Press, New York, New York, 631 pp. (1983).

Common/Systematic Name

Nidurufin

Molecular Formula/Molecular Weight

$C_{20}H_{16}O_8$; MW = 384.08452

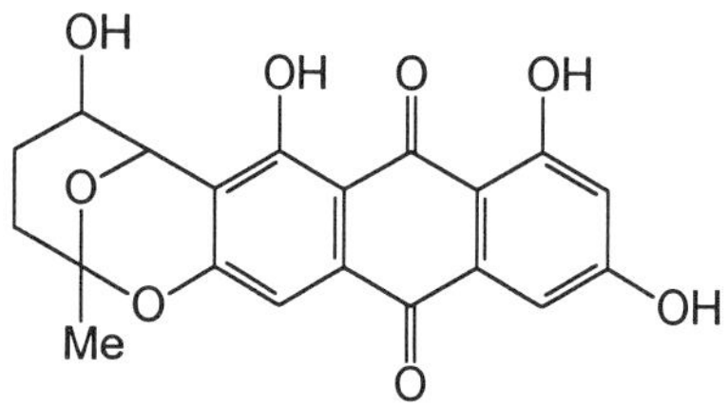

General Characteristics

Crystals from chloroform-methanol; mp., 188°C.

Fungal Source

Aspergillus nidulans.

Spectral Data

UV:

λ_{max}^{EtOH} 223(ε=33,500), 253(15 300), 264(19,000), 291(30,400), 319(10,700), and 450nm (10,000)

IR:

(KBr) 1673 and 1725cm^{-1}.

CD:

Δε 230(-10.4), 240(0), 256(sh) (1.9), 260(2.84), 270(0), 280(0.95), 288(0), 296(-7.6), 308(0), 325(2.8), 348(0), 365(-0.76), 380(-0.57), 400(0), 444(4.17), and 480nm (0.76).

References

P. J. Aucamp and C. W. Holzapfel; J. S. Afr. Chem. Inst., Vol. 23, p. 40 (1970).

R. J. Cole and R. H. Cox; Handbook of Toxic Fungal Metabolites; Academic Press, New York, p. 122 (1981).

W. B. Turner and D. C. Aldridge; Fungal Metabolites II; Academic Press, New York, New York, 631 pp. (1983).

Common/Systematic Name
Dimethylnidurufin

Molecular Formula/Molecular Weight
$C_{22}H_{20}O_8$; MW = 412.11582

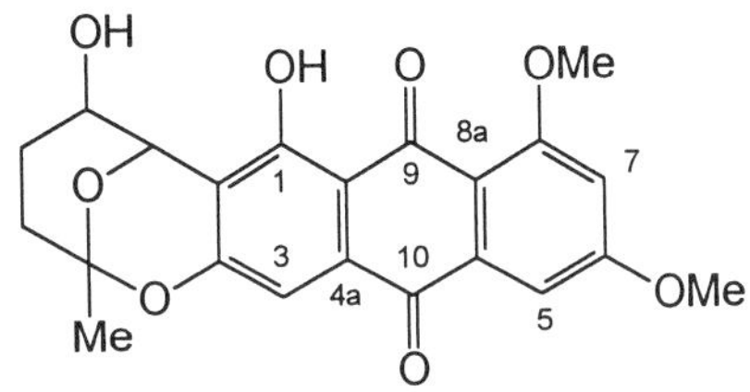

General Characteristics
Crystals from acetone-hexane; mp., 211-213°C; $[\alpha]_D^{25}$ -77° (c=0.15, in $CHCl_3$).

Fungal Source
Aspergillus versicolor.

Spectral Data

UV:
λ_{max}^{EtOH} 224(ε=48,200), 251(19,000), 288(30,900), 314(8,540), and 444nm (8,790).

IR:
(KBr) 3500, 3420, 2940, 1680, 1625, 1600, 1560, 1490, 1460, 1400, 1330, 1300, 1250, 1220, 1170, 1068, 1050, 1000, 970, 890, and 850cm^{-1}.

^{1}H NMR:
($CDCl_3$) H-4, 7.28; H-5, 7.46(J=2.5); H-7, 6.86(J=2.5); H-11, 5.30(J=2.0); H-12, 4.16 m; H-13, 14, 1.6-2.5 m; H-16, 1.64; 12-OH, 1.60; OCH_3, 4.00, 4.16ppm.

References
R. J. Cole and R. H. Cox; Handbook of Toxic Fungal Metabolites; Academic Press, New York, p. 123 (1981).

D. G. I. Kingston, P. N. Chen, and J. R. Vercellotti; Phytochemistry, Vol. 15, p. 1037 (1976).

W. B. Turner and D. C. Aldridge; Fungal Metabolites II; Academic Press, New York, New York, 631 pp. (1983).

Common/Systematic Name

Aversin

Molecular Formula/Molecular Weight

$C_{20}H_{16}O_7$; MW = 368.08960

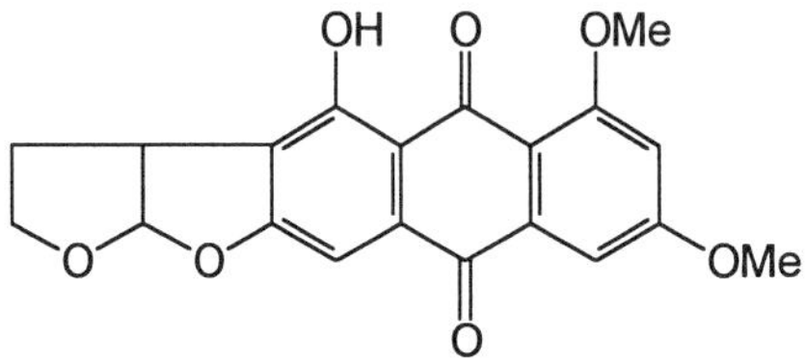

General Characteristics

Slender golden needles from acetone solution; mp., 217°C; $[\alpha]_D^{20}$ -222° (*c*=0.248, in $CHCl_3$).

Fungal Source

Aspergillus versicolor.

Spectral Data

UV:

λ_{max}^{MeOH} 224(ϵ=36,700), 251(13,400), 285(33,600), 313(8,900), 363(4,960), and 440nm (7,830); λ_{max}^{NaOH} 240(ϵ=21,300), 263(34,800), 307(13,800), 355(5,040), 498(6,890), and 501nm (6,890).

IR:

(KBr) 3470, 3090, 2970, 2935, 2880, 2840, 1725, 1665, 1628, 1595, 1558, 1479, 1436, 1423, 1375, 1354, 1329, 1298, 1243, 1210, 1174, 1160, 1118, 1104, 1084, 1076, 1044, 990, 953, 911, 864, 821, 798, 771, 758, and 747cm^{-1}.

References

E. Bullock, D. Kirkaldy, J. C. Roberts, and J. G. Underwood; J. Chem. Soc., p. 829 (1963).

R. J. Cole and R. H. Cox; Handbook of Toxic Fungal Metabolites; Academic Press, New York, p. 125 (1981).

W. B. Turner and D. C. Aldridge; Fungal Metabolites II; Academic Press, New York, New York, 631 pp. (1983).

Common/Systematic Name

O-Methylaversin; Tri-*O*-methylversicolorin B

Molecular Formula/Molecular Weight

$C_{21}H_{18}O_7$; MW = 382.10525

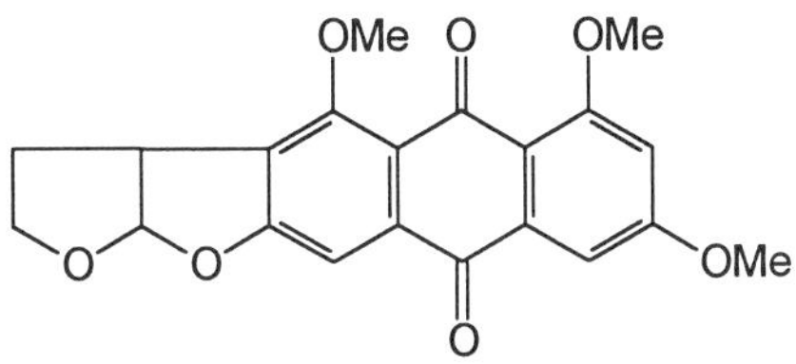

General Characteristics

Fine golden-yellow needles from chloroform-methanol; mp., 216-217°C; $[\alpha]_D^{25}$ -127° (*c*=0.1804, in $CHCl_3$); golden-yellow crystals from methanol; mp., 212-213°C; sublimed sample, mp., 229-230°C.

Fungal Source

Aspergillus versicolor

Spectral Data

UV:

λ_{max}^{EtOH} 222(ε=33,800), 285(39.200), 348(4,700), and 407nm (4,200).

IR:

(KBr) 3460, 3100, 3089, 3053, 3019, 3004, 2986, 2947, 2937, 2880, 2845, 2664, 1673, 1667, 1602, 1572, 1510, 1463, 1440, 1431, 1419, 1357, 1349, 1332, 1323, 1307, 1281, 1255, 1238, 1209, 1201, 1188, 1178, 1163, 1114, 1103, 1085, 1060, 1035, 990, 958, 942, 925, 914, 897, 871, 850, 841, 836, 787, 778, and 753cm^{-1}.

References

R. J. Cole and R. H. Cox; Handbook of Toxic Fungal Metabolites; Academic Press, New York, p. 126 (1981).

G. M. Holmwood and J. C. Roberts; J. Chem. Soc., p. 3899 (1971).

W. B. Turner and D. C. Aldridge; Fungal Metabolites II; Academic Press, New York, New York, 631 pp. (1983).

Common/Systematic Name

Versicolorone

Molecular Formula/Molecular Weight

$C_{20}H_{16}O_7$; MW = 368.08960

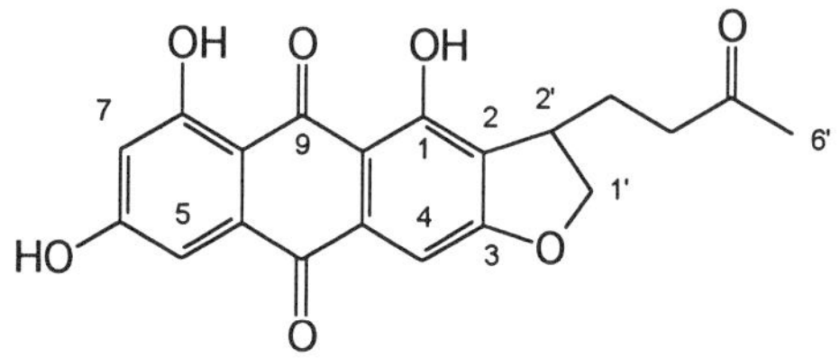

General Characteristics

Recrystallized from acetone-water; mp., 208-210°C. Probable intermediate in the biosynthesis of the aflatoxins.

Fungal Source

Aspergillus parasiticus [Mutant WE-47 (hvn-1)]. Derived from ATCC 15517.

Isolation/Purification

Purification by preparative TLC (40% acetone-hexane) and Chromatotron (50% ethyl acetate-hexane).The product was recrystallized five times from acetone-water and dried under vacuum.

Spectral Data

UV:

λ_{max}^{EtOH} 222(ϵ=26,700), 252(13,300), 264(16,500), 298(17,700), 318(26,400), 468(6,000), and 483nm (6,400).

IR:

($CHCl_3$) 3020, 1700, 1600, 1185, 800, and 670cm^{-1}.

^{1}H NMR:

(DMSO-d_6) 1.94(2H, m, H-3'), 2.06(3H, 8, H-6'), 2.20(1H, dt, *J*=7.4, 17.6, H-4'), 2.34(1-H, dt, *J*=7.8, 17.6Hz, H-4'), 3.38(1H, m, H-2'), 3.68(1H, dd, *J*=6.6, 10.0Hz, H-1'), 3.75(1H, dd, *J*=7.6, 10.0Hz, H-1'), 6.57(1H, d, *J*=2.6Hz, H-7), 7.09(1H d, *J*=2.6Hz, H-5), 7.19(1H, s, H-4), 11.21(1H, brs, 6-OH), 12.18(1H, s, 8-OH); and 12.82ppm (1H, s, 1-OH).

Mass Spectrum:

368(28), 325(6), 310(100), 297(19), and 285*m/e* (6); HRMS: obsd 368.0905, $C_{20}H_{17}O_7$ requires 368.0896.

Reference
C. A. Townsend, K. A. Plavcan, K. Pal, S. W. Brobst, M. S. Irish, E. W. Ely, Jr., and J. W. Bennett; Hydroxyversicolorone: Isolation and Characterization of a Potential Intermediate in Aflatoxin Biosynthesis; J. Org. Chem., Vol. 53, pp. 2472-2477(1988).

Common/Systematic Name
Hydroxyversicolorone

Molecular Formula/Molecular Weight
$C_{20}H_{16}O_8$; MW = 384.08452

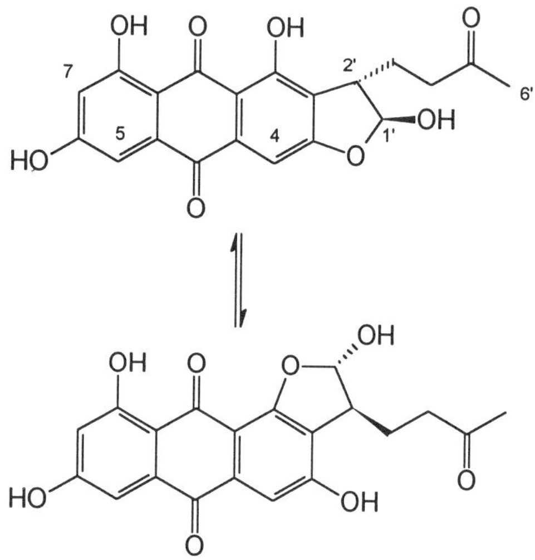

General Characteristics
Obtained as an orange powder from acetone; mp., 247-249°C; $[\alpha]_D^{25}$ 0° (*c*=0.006, in $CHCl_3$).

Fungal Source
Aspergillus parasiticus [(Mutant WE-47 (hvn-1)]. Derived from ATCC 15517. Probable intermediate in the biosynthesis of the aflatoxins.

Isolation/Purification
The mycelia were filtered, washed well with water, and pulverized in a blender with acetone. The residual cells were extracted with acetone until colorless. The solvent was removed, and the material was extracted with pentane. The residue was preadsorbed and chromatographed on silica gel eluted with chloroform-methanol (97:3, v/v). The fraction containing mainly hydroxyversicolorone was recrystallized several times from ethyl acetate-hexane to afford pure hydroxyversicolorone.

Spectral Data

UV:
λ_{max}^{EtOH} 223(ϵ=24,000), 265(20,300), 293(19,500), 316(22,600), 476(5,300), and 528nm (4,000).

IR:

(CHCl$_3$) 3390, 1705, 1600(s) 1440, 1320, and 970cm^{-1}.

^{1}H NMR:

(DMSO-d_6) 1.68(1-H, m, H-3'), 1.94(1-H, m H-3'), 2.06(3-H, 8, H-6'), 2.56(2-H, t, J=6.6Hz, H-4'), 3.09(1-H, dt, J=1.5Hz, H-2'), 5.89(1-H, br dd, J=5.9, 1.5Hz, H-1'), 6.56(½H, d, J=2.2Hz, *H-7), 6.58(½H, d, J=2.2Hz, H-7), 7.06(½H, d, J=2.2Hz, *H-5), 7.10(½H, d, J=2.2 Hz, H-5), 7.11(½H, s, H-4), 7.26(½H, s, *H-4), 7.73 (<1 H, br d, J=5.9Hz, 1'-OH), 11.09(3/2H, br s, 3 (OH)), 12.20(½H, br s, 13.8Hz, OH), 12.53(½H, br s, 17.1Hz, OH), 13.38(½H, s, 17.1Hz, OH); and 13.38ppm (½H, s, 17.1Hz, OH).

* Asterisk denotes angular isomer

^{13}C NMR:

(DMSO-d_6) (Linear form) C-5', 207.7; C-9, 189.0; C-10, 180.8; C-6(164.9, 164.2, 164.1, 164.0); C-3(163.6); C-1, 159.1; C-14(135.2, 134.7, 134.5, 134.4); C-2, 121.5; C-4, 108.7; C-13, 110.5; C-5, 108.7; C-12, 108.4; C-7, 107.9; C-1', 102.4; C-2', 46.2; C-6', 29.8; C-3', 23.9; and C-4' 23.9ppm; (angular form) C-9, 184.7; C- 10, 181.5; C-6(164.9, 164.2, 164.1,164.0); C-3, 160.8; C-1, 159.0; C-14(135.2, 134.7, 134.5, 134.4); C-2, 122.7; C-4, 108.8; C-13, 109.4; C-5, 107.1; C-1', 107.7; and C-2', 45.4ppm.

Mass Spectrum:

CIMS: (NH$_3$) 385m/e (M$^+$ +1, 16), 369(100); HRFABMS: obsd 285.0927m/e (M$^+$ 1)+, $C_{20}H_{17}O_8$ requires 384.0923. EIMS: 384(2), 382(22), 368(28), 367(60), 366(100), 347(21), 340(26), 339(32), 324(97), 313(34), 312(48), 311(92), 310(86), 309(62), 299(46), 298(76), 297(86), 296(78), 285(46), 270(26), 269(22) 245 (20), 155(28), 70(35), and 61m/e (47).

Reference

C. A. Townsend, K. A. Plavcan, K. Pal, S. W. Brobst, M. S. Irish, E. W. Ely, Jr., and J. W. Bennett; Hydroxyversicolorone: Isolation and Characterization of a Potential Intermediate in Aflatoxin Biosynthesis; J. Org. Chem., Vol. 53, pp. 2472-2477(1988).

13

Sterigmatocystin and Related Metabolites

Sterigmatocystin
Dihydrosterigmatocystin
O-Methylsterigmatocystin
Dihydro-*O*-methylsterigmatocystin
Aspertoxin
5-Methoxysterigmatocystin
Dihydrodemethylsterigmatocystin
Dimethoxysterigmatocystin
Sterigmatin

Common/Systematic Name

Sterigmatocystin

3*a*,12*c*-Dihydro-8-hydroxy-6-methoxyfuro[3',2':4,5]furo[3,2-*c*]xanthen-7-one

Molecular Formula/Molecular Weight

$C_{18}H_{12}O_6$; MW = 324.06339

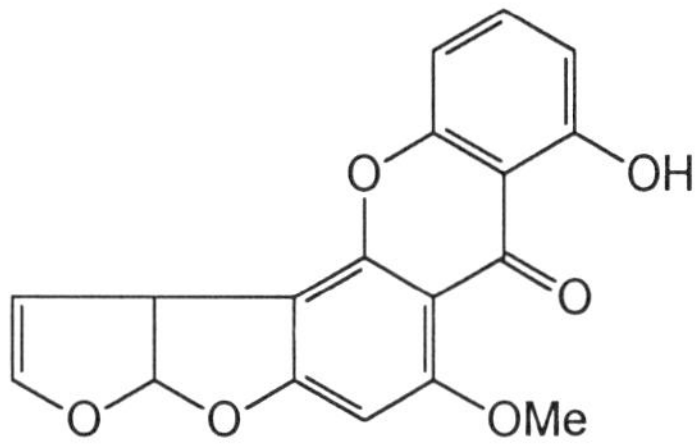

General Characteristics

Pale yellow crystals; mp., 246°C (dec.) of a sublimed sample. Sterigmatocystin was relatively insoluble in most solvents tested; solubility was best in chloroform (7138 mg/100 ml) and pyridine (1815 mg/100 ml); $[\alpha]_D^{20}$ -398° (*c*=1.0, in $CHCl_3$).

Fungal Source

Aspergillus versicolor, A. amstelodami = Erotium amstelodami, A. chevalieri = E. chevalieri, A. ruber = E. rubrum, A. unguis, A. multicolor, A. nidulans, Bipolaris sorokiniana, A. aurantio-brunnel, A. quadrilineatus, A. ustus Bainier, *A. variecolor, Chaetomium thielavioideum,* and *Farrowia* sp. Also an intermediate in biosynthesis of aflatoxins by *A. parasiticus* and *A. flavus.*

Biological Activity

The LD_{50} values for sterigmatocystin in albino rats was 166mg/kg (male rats, per os, dimethylformamide solvent): 60mg/kg (male rats, IP, dimethylformamide solvent); 120mg/kg (female rats, per os, wheat germ oil carrier); 65mg/kg (male rats, IP, wheat germ oil carrier). The LD_{50} in male monkeys was 32mg/kg (dosed IP, with DMSO as carrier). Acute toxicity: caused liver and kidney damage and renal necrosis in rats; it was cirrhogenic; caused hepatic damage in primates. In monkeys, oral administration (20mg/kg) every 14 days for several months caused chronic hepatitis and hyperplasia. It has been hypothesized that sterigmatocystin may be implicated in the etiology of chronic liver disease in humans in Africa.

Spectral Data

UV:

λ_{max}^{EtOH} 208(ϵ=19,000), 235(24,500), 249(27,500), and 329nm (13,100).

^{1}H NMR:

H-1, 6.48(J=2.0, 2.5); H-2, 5.42(J=2.5); H-3, 4.75(J=2.0, 7.25); H-4, 6.79(J=7.25); H-5, 6.35; H-8, 6.78(J=8.25, 1.0); H-9, 7.45(J=8.25); H-10, 6.70(J=8.25, 1.0); and H-18, 3.96ppm.

^{13}C NMR:

C-1, 145.1 d; C-2, 105.7 d; C-3, 47.9 d; C-4, 113.1 d: C-5, 90.4 d; C-6, 163.0 s; C-7, 154.7 s; C-8, 106.4 d; C-9, 135.4 d; C-10, 111.0 d; C-11, 162.1 s; C-12, 108.8 s; C-13, 180.9 s; C-14, 105.7 s; C-15, 153.7 s; C-16, 106.4 s; C-17, 164.3 s; and C-18, 56.6ppm q.

TLC Data

Silica gel (chloroform-methanol, 98:2, v:v); R_f: 0.5; detection as orange-red fluorescent spot under UV light; it exhibited a light yellow fluorescence, if sprayed with acetic acid.

GLC Data

Chromosorb W, Liquid phase: 1.5% SE-30, 220°C; relative retention time 1.21 (relative to cholestane).

References

R. J. Cole and R. H. Cox; Handbook of Toxic Fungal Metabolites; Academic Press, New York, pp. 68-69(1981).

W. B. Turner and D. C. Aldridge; Fungal Metabolites II; Academic Press, New York, New York, 631 pp. (1983).

Common/Systematic Name
Dihydrosterigmatocystin; 1,2-Dihydro-6-methoxy-7-hydroxydifuroxanthone

Molecular Formula/Molecular Weight
$C_{18}H_{14}O_6$; MW = 326.07904

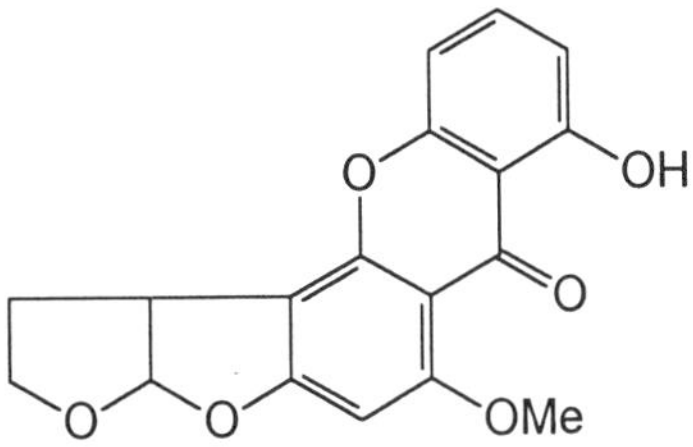

General Characteristics
Pale yellow needles; mp., 230°C (dec.); $[\alpha]_D^{20}$ -311.7° (*c*=0.85, in $CHCl_3$). Yellow plates from ethanol (sublimed sample); mp., 229-230°C.

Fungal Source
Aspergillus versicolor.

Biological Activity
Dihydrosterigmatocystin markedly inhibited mitosis of primary kidney epithelial cells of *Cercopithecus aethiops* but had negligible effects on nucleolar morphology. It also markedly inhibited the incorporation of [^{13}H]thymidine and [^{3}H]uridine, which indicated impaired DNA and RNA synthesis.

Spectral Data

UV:
λ_{max}^{EtOH} 233(ϵ=27,600), 247(32,200), and 325nm (16,600); λ_{max} 208(ϵ=20,400), 232(26,300), 247(30,900), and 325nm (16,300).

^{1}H NMR:
($CDCl_3$) H-1, 4.10; H-2, 2.23; H-3, 3.62(*J*=5.5); H-4, 6.41(*J*=5.5); H-5, 6.25; H-8, 6.72(*J*=8.0, 1.0); H-9, 7.39(*J*=8.0); H-10, 6.64(*J*=8.0, 1.0); H-18, 3.90; and 7-OH, 13.26ppm.

^{13}C NMR:
($CDCl_3$) C-1, 67.6 t; C-2, 31.4 t; C-3, 44.2 d; C-4, 113.1 d; C-5, 89.6 d; C-6, 163.1 s; C-7, 154.6 s; C-8, 105.5 d; C-9, 135.2 d; C-10, 110.7 d; C-11, 161.9 s; C-12, 108.7 s; C-13, 180.8 s; C-14, 105.1 s; C-15, 154.6 s; C-16, 106.7 s; C-17, 165.7 s; and C-18, 56.6ppm q.

TLC Data

Silica gel G-HR (chloroform-acetone, 93:7, v/v); R_f: 0.83; detected as red-orange fluorescent spot under UV light.

References

R. J. Cole and R. H. Cox; Handbook of Toxic Fungal Metabolites; Academic Press, New York, pp. 73-74(1981).

Y. Hatsuda, T. Hamasaki, M. Ishida, K. Matsui, and S. Hara; Agric. Biol. Chem., Vol. 36, p. 521 (1972).

W. B. Turner and D. C. Aldridge; Fungal Metabolites II; Academic Press, New York, New York, p. 631 (1983).

Common/Systematic Name

O-Methylsterigmatocystin; 6,7-Dimethoxydifuroxanthone

Molecular Formula/Molecular Weight

$C_{19}H_{14}O_6$; MW = 338.07904

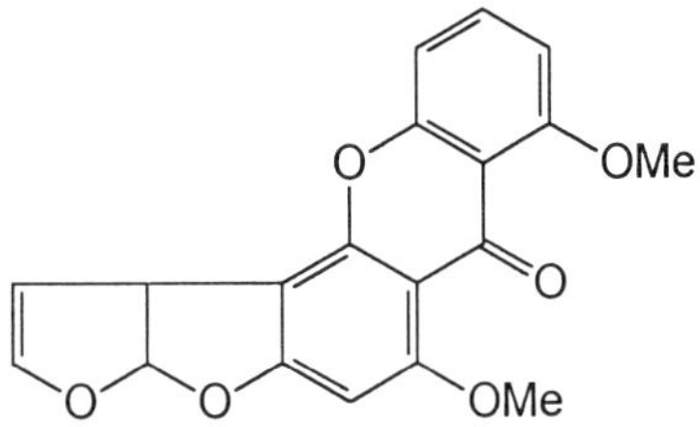

General Characteristics

Colorless prisms from ethanol; mp., 274°C (synthetic compound); crystals from methanol and chloroform-heptane; mp., 265°C (dec.); faint yellow, slender rods from methanol; mp., 265-267°C.

Fungal Source

Aspergillus flavus, *A. parasiticus*, *Chaetomium thielavioideum*, and *Farrowia* sp.

Spectral Data

UV:

λ_{max}^{MeOH} 236(ε=40,700) and 310nm (16,500).

^{1}H NMR:

($CDCl_3$) H-1, 6.48(*J*=2.5. 2.0); H-2, 5.43(*J*=2.5); H-3, 4.76(*J*=7.1, 2.0); H-4, 6.78(*J*=7.1); H-5, 6.36; H-7, 6.92(*J*=8.3, 1.0); H-8, 7.48(*J*=8.3); H-9, 6.74(*J*=8.3, 1.0); H-18, 3.95; and H-19, 3.91ppm.

^{13}C NMR:

($CDCl_3$) C-1, 145.0 d; C-2, 102.6 d; C-3, 48.1 d; C-4, 112.9 d; C-5, 90.3 d; C-6, 162.8 s; C-7. 156.5 s; C-8, 106.2 d; C-9, 133.4 d; C-10, 108.9 d; C-11, 160.4 s; C-12, 106.2 s; C-13, 174.6 s; C-14, 105.6 s; C-15, 152.9 s; C-16, 106.2 s; C-17, 162.7 s; C-18, 56.3 q; and C-19, 56.3ppm q.

TLC Data

Silica gel G-HR (chloroform-acetone, 93:7, v/v); R_f, 0.38; detected as blue fluorescent spot under UV light; turns to yellow fluorescent spot after spraying with 50% ethanolic H_2SO_4.

References

R. J. Cole and R. H. Cox; Handbook of Toxic Fungal Metabolites; Academic Press, New York, p. 77 (1981).

W. B. Turner and D. C. Aldridge; Fungal Metabolites II; Academic Press, New York, New York, 631 pp. (1983).

S. Udagawa, T. Muroi, H. Kurata, S. Sekita, K. Yoshihira, S. Natori, and M. Umeda; Can. J. Microbiol., Vol. 25, p. 170 (1979).

Common/Systematic Name
Dihydro-*O*-methylsterigmatocystin; 1,2-Dihydro-6-methoxy-7-hydroxydifuroxanthone

Molecular Formula/Molecular Weight
$C_{19}H_{16}O_6$; MW = 340.09469

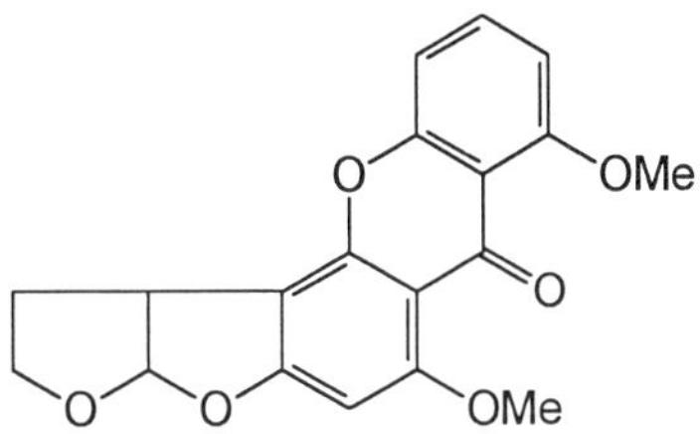

General Characteristics
Colorless rods from methanol; mp., 282-283 °C; colorless needles from chloroform-methanol; mp., 281-282 °C.

Fungal Source
Aspergillus flavus and *A. parasiticus.*

Biological Activity
The toxicity of dihydro-*O*-methylsterigmatocystin, as evaluated in primary cell culture (primary kidney epithelial cells of *Cercopithecus aethiops*) showed negligible effects on mitosis and nucleolar morphology; also negligible effects on the incorporation of [^{3}H]thymidine and [^{3}H]uridine, indicating no inhibition on DNA and RNA synthesis.

Spectral Data

UV:
λ_{max}^{MeOH} 238 and 313nm (ϵ max not reported); λ_{max} 203(26,300), 237(38,900), and 311nm (17,300).

^{1}H NMR:
H-1, 4.20; H-2, 2.34; H-3, 3.72; H-4, 6.48(*J*=6.0); H-5, 6.34; H-8, 6.97(*J*=8.0, 1.0); H-9, 7.52 (J=8.0); H-10, 6.78(*J*=8.0, 1.0); H-18, 4.00; and H-19, 3.96ppm.

^{13}C NMR:
C-1, 67.5 t; C-2, 31.4 t; C-3, 44.3 d; C-4, 112.8 d; C-5, 89.5 d; C-6, 162.7 s; C-7, 156.3 s; C-8, 106.0 d; C-9, 133.1 d; C-10, 108.7 d; C-11, 160.3 s; C-12, 106.0 s; C-13, 156.3 s; C-14, 104.2 s; C-15, 153.2 s; C-16, 106.0 s; C-17, 164.1 s; C-18, 56.3 q; and C-19, 56.3ppm q.

TLC Data

Silica gel G-HR (chloroform-acetone, 93:7, v:v); R_f, 0.32; detected as blue fluorescent spot under UV light changing to yellow fluorescent after spraying with 50% ethanolic H_2SO_4.

References

W. B. Turner and D. C. Aldridge; Fungal Metabolites II; Academic Press, New York, New York, 631 pp. (1983).

R. J. Cole and R. H. Cox; Handbook of Toxic Fungal Metabolites; Academic Press, New York, pp. 81-82(1981).

R. J. Cole, J. W. Kirksey, and H. W. Schroeder; Tet. Lett., p. 3109 (1970).

Common/Systematic Name

Aspertoxin; 3-Hydroxy-6,7-dimethoxydifuroxanthone

Molecular Formula/Molecular Weight

$C_{19}H_{14}O_7$; MW = 354.07395

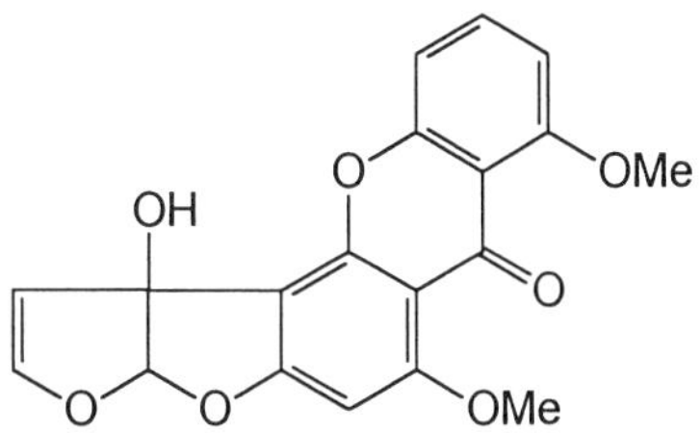

General Characteristics

Crystals from dioxane/H_2O; mp., 240-280°C (dec.); from dimethylformamide; mp., 325-327°C; $[\alpha]_D^{27}$ -140° (*c*=0.015, in dimethylformamide). Aspertoxin is insoluble in most organic solvents.

Fungal Source

Aspergillus flavus.

Biological Activity

In developing chicken embryo, injections of 2.0μg/egg (yolk or air sac) killed 100% of the embryos; while 0.7μg/egg killed 50% of the embryos. Microscopically, the embryos showed beak malformations, generalized edema, loss of muscle tone and hemorrhage from the umbilical vessels.

Spectral Data

UV:

λ_{max}^{MeOH} 241(ϵ=33,900) and 310nm (12,100).

^{1}H NMR:

H-1, 6.72; H-2, 5.76; H-4, 6.38; H-5, 6.56; H-8, 7.05; H-9, 7.61; H-10, 6.95; H-18, 3.93; and H-19, 3.93ppm.

TLC Data

Silica gel (chloroform-acetic acid, 9:1 v:v); R_f=0.55-0.60; detected as blue fluorescent spot under UV light.

References

R. J. Cole and R. H. Cox; Handbook of Toxic Fungal Metabolites; Academic Press, New York, p. 85 (1981).

W. B. Turner and D. C. Aldridge; Fungal Metabolites II; Academic Press, New York, New York, 631 pp. (1983).

Common/Systematic Name

5-Methoxysterigmatocystin

Molecular Formula/Molecular Weight

$C_{20}H_{16}O_7$; MW = 368.08960

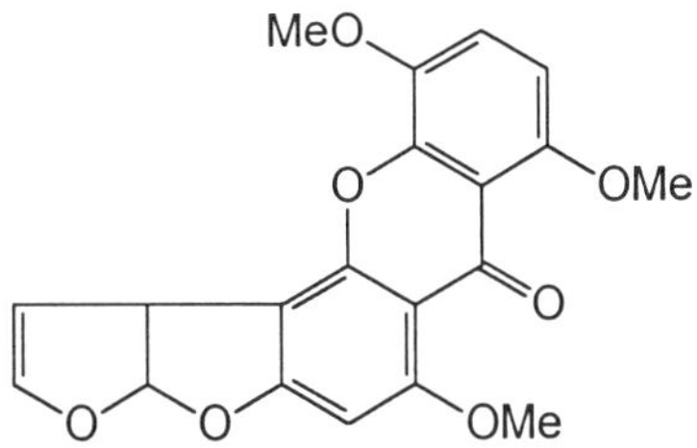

General Characteristics

Pale yellow needles from sublimed sample; mp., 223°C (dec.); $[\alpha]_D^{20}$ -360° (*c*=0.238, in $CHCl_3$).

Fungal Source

Aspergillus versicolor.

Spectral Data

UV:

λ_{max}^{EtOH} 232(ϵ=24,100), 248(26,800), 279(11,200), and 331nm (12,100).

^{1}H NMR:

Similar to sterigmatocystin except for two coupled aromatic protons at 6.71 and 7.18ppm.

IR:

(KBr) 3447, 3383, 3121, 3096, 3016, 2971, 2927, 2853, 1662, 1634, 1618, 1595, 1559, 1498, 1462, 1444, 1419, 1398, 1360, 1345, 1339, 1302, 1285, 1262, 1248, 1233, 1223, 1199, 1187, 1168, 1148, 1140, 1099, 1078, 1060, 1042, 1017, 979, 960, 930, 881, 853, 825, 788, 767, 744, 737, and 724cm^{-1}.

References

R. J. Cole and R. H. Cox; Handbook of Toxic Fungal Metabolites; Academic Press, New York, p. 89 (1981).

W. B. Turner and D. C. Aldridge; Fungal Metabolites II; Academic Press, New York, New York, 631 pp. (1983).

Common/Systematic Name

Dihydrodemethylsterigmatocystin

Molecular Formula/Molecular Weight

$C_{17}H_{12}O_6$; MW = 312.06339

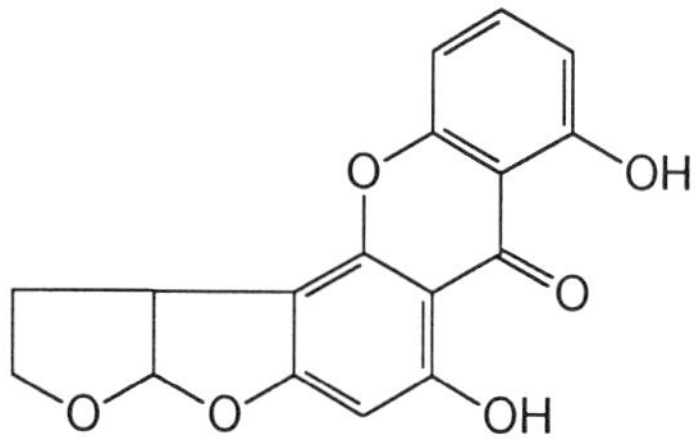

General Characteristics

Pale yellow needles from acetone; mp., 202°C (dec.); $[\alpha]_D^{25}$ -376.6° (*c*=0.90, in $CHCl_3$); green ferric reaction in ethanol.

Fungal Source

Aspergillus versicolor.

Spectral Data

UV:

λ_{max}^{EtOH} 233(ε=26,800), 250(33,100), 259(30,300), and 335nm (19,400).

IR:

(KBr) 1659, and 1625cm^{-1}.

References

R. J. Cole and R. H. Cox; Handbook of Toxic Fungal Metabolites; Academic Press, New York, p. 91 (1981).

W. B. Turner and D. C. Aldridge; Fungal Metabolites II; Academic Press, New York, New York, 631 pp. (1983).

Common/Systematic Name

Dimethoxysterigmatocystin; 6,9,10-Trimethoxy-7-hydroxydifuroxanthone

Molecular Formula/Molecular Weight

$C_{20}H_{16}O_8$; MW = 384.08452

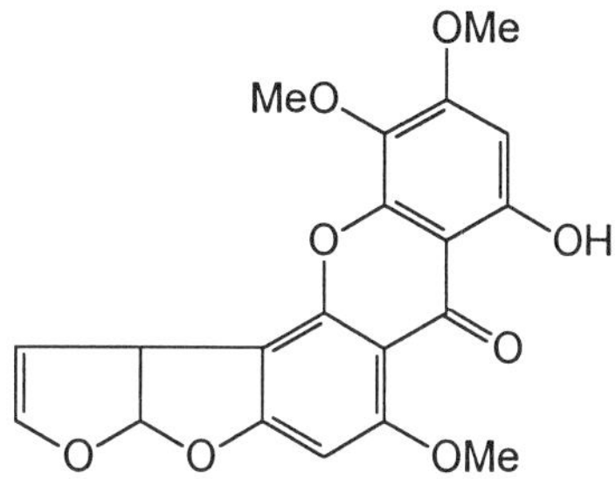

General Characteristics

Pale yellow needles from acetone; mp., 253-254°C; dihydro derivative; mp., 241-242°C: acetate derivative; mp., 188-189°C; monomethyl ether derivative; mp., 257-258°C.

Fungal Source

Aspergillus versicolor.

Spectral Data

UV:

λ_{max}^{EtOH} 233(ε=27,200), 275(sh) (7,700), 284(34,000), and 330nm (19,200).

IR:

(KBr) 3125, 1655, 1635, and 1610cm^{-1}.

^{1}H NMR:

($CDCl_3$) H-1, 6.64(*J*=2, 2.5); H-2, 5.41(*J*=2, 2.5); H-3, 4.80(*J*=2, 2.5, 7); H-4, 6.75(*J*=7); H-5*, 6.28; H-8*, 6.32; 7-OH, 13.20; OCH_3, 3.91, 3.94, and 3.98ppm.

* Assignments may be reversed.

References

R. J. Cole and R. H. Cox; Handbook of Toxic Fungal Metabolites; Academic Press, New York, p. 92 (1981).

W. B. Turner and D. C. Aldridge; Fungal Metabolites II; Academic Press, New York, New York, 631 pp. (1983).

Common/Systematic Name

Sterigmatin

Molecular Formula/Molecular Weight

$C_{17}H_{10}O_6$; MW = 310.04774

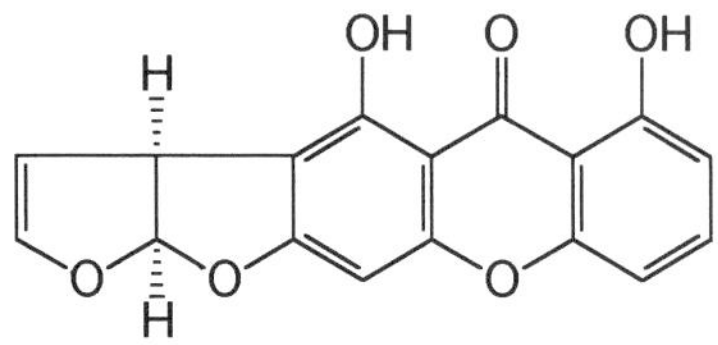

General Characteristics

Pale yellow needles from acetone; mp., 253°C; $[\alpha]_D^{20}$ -377° (*c*=0.50, in $CHCl_3$); gave a green ferric reaction in ethanol.

Fungal Source

Aspergillus versicolor.

Isolation/Purification

Mycelium extracted with acetone and extract chromatographed on silica gel column chromatography. Recrystallized from acetone to give pale yellow needles.

Spectral Data

UV:

λ_{max}^{EtOH} 225(ϵ=23,400), 250(33,800), 259(23,800), 268(20,000), and 324nm (16,900).

IR:

(KBr) 1670, 1640, and 1610cm^{-1}.

^{1}H NMR:

($CDCl_3$) 11.85 and 12.11ppm (2 x OH protons, s); 6.44(1H, s); 6.76(1H, dd, *J*=1 and 8.5Hz); 6.85(1H, dd, J=1 and 8.5 Hz); 7.55(1H, t, *J*=8.5Hz); 4.68(1H, dt, *J*=2.5 and 7Hz); 5.44(1H, t, *J*=2.5Hz); 6.46(1H, t, *J*=2.5Hz); and 6.77ppm (1H, d, *J*=7.0Hz, dihydro furan ring system).

Mass Spectrum:

EIMS: 310*m/e* (M^+)

References

K. Fukuyama, T. Tsukihara, Y. Katsube, T. Hanasaki, Y. Hatsuda, N. Tanaka, T. Ashida, and M. Kakudo; The Crystal and Molecular Structure of Sterigmatin, A Metabolite of *Aspergillus versicolor*; Bull. Chem. Soc. Japan, Vol. 48, pp. 1639-1640(1975).

T. Hamasaki, K. Matsui, K. Isono, and Y. Hatsuda; A New Metabolite from *Aspergillus versicolor*; Agric. Biol. Chem. Vol. 37, pp. 1769-1770(1973).

14

Chokols

Chokol A
Chokol B
Chokol C
Chokol D
Chokol E
Chokol F
Chokol G

Common/Systematic Name

Chokol A

4-(3-Hydroxy-2,3-dimethylcyclopentyl)penta-4-en-1-ol

Molecular Formula/Molecular Weight

$C_{12}H_{22}O_2$; MW = 198.16198

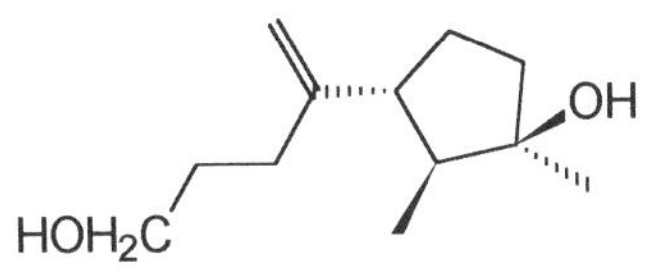

General Characteristics

Colorless syrup; $[\alpha]_D^{24}$ -45.5° (*c*=0.4, in MeOH).

Fungal Source

Epichloë typhina on *Phleum pratense*.

Isolation/Purification

Timothy chokes were extracted with 70% ethanol, partitioned between *n*-hexane and water and subsequently between ethyl acetate and water. The ethyl acetate extract was chromatographed on a silica gel ($CHCl_3$-MeOH, 95:5, v/v) followed by several chromatographies on silica gel (*n*-hexane-EtOAc gradient system), Sephadex LH-20 ($CHCl_3$-MeOH, 1:1, v/v) and silica gel (twice, $CHCl_3$-MeOH, 95:5, v/v) and cyclohexane-EtOAc, 1:1, v/v). Final purification was achieved by HPLC (μBondapak C_{18}; H_2O-CH_3CN, 4:1, v/v).

Biological Activity

Moderate fungitoxic activity (TLC plate bioassay using *Cladosporium herbarum*); minimal inhibition was about 25μg/spot.

Spectral Data

IR:

(film) 3350, 3050, 2920, 1730, 1640, 1440, 1380, 1150, 1050, and 880cm^{-1}.

^{1}H NMR:

($CDCl_3$) 4.79(1H, s, H-14a); 4.78(1H, d, *J*=1.5Hz, H-14b); 3.67(2H, t, *J*=6.6, H-10); 2.39(1H, ddd, *J*=11.3, 9.2, 9.2Hz, H-6); 2.06(2H, br. t, *J*=7.8Hz, H-8); 1.98(1H, m, H-5a); 1.76(2H, t, *J*=7.8Hz, H-4); 1.71-1.78(2H, m, H-9); 1.56(1H, dq, *J*=11.3, 6.8Hz, H-2); 1.42(1H, m, H-5b); 1.28(3H, s, H-13); and 0.87ppm (3H, d, *J*=6.8Hz, H-1).

^{13}C NMR:

($CHCl_3$) 10.7(C-1), 47.6(C-2), 80.3(C-3), 39.9(C-4), 28.8(C- 5), 51.7(C-6), 151.3(C-7), 30.2(C-8), 31.1(C-9), 62.7(C-10), 26.5(C-13) and 108.2ppm (C-14).

Mass Spectrum:

FI-MS: 198*m/e* (M^+, 31%), and 181(M^+-OH, 100); EI-MS: 198.1628(M^+, $C_{12}H_{22}O_2$, calcd 198.1620, 0.4%), 180.1502(M^+-H_2O, $C_{12}H_{20}O$; calcd. 180.1503, 0.2), 136(36), 121(34), 71(43), and 43*m/e* (100).

Reference

H. Koshino, S. Togiya, S. Terada, T. Yoshihara, S. Sakamura, T. Shimanuki, T. Sato, and A. Tajimi; New Fungitoxic Sesquiterpenoids, Chokols A-G, from Stromata of *Epichloë typhina* and the Absolute Configuration of Chokol E; Agric. Biol. Chem., Vol. 53, pp. 789-796(1989).

Common/Systematic Name

Chokol B

6-(3-Hydroxy-2,3-dimethylcyclopentyl)-2-methylhepta-1,6-dien-3-ol

Molecular Formula/Molecular Weight

$C_{15}H_{26}O_2$; MW = 238.19328

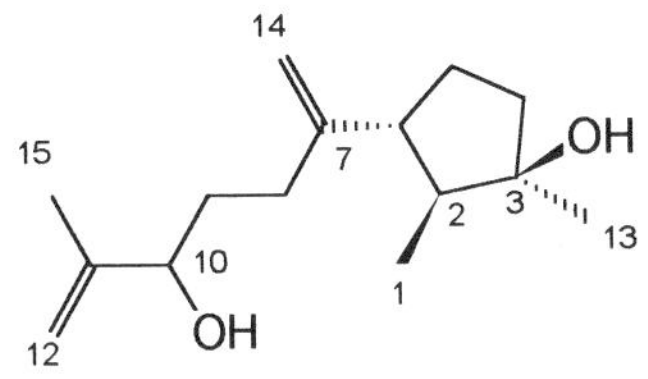

General Characteristics

Colorless syrup.

Fungal Source

Epichloë typhina on *Phleum pratense*.

Isolation/Purification

Timothy chokes were extracted with 70% ethanol, partitioned between *n*-hexane and water and subsequently between ethyl acetate and water. The hexane extract was chromatographed on a silica gel ($CHCl_3$-MeOH, 95:5, v/v) followed by several chromatographies on silica gel ($CHCl_3$-MeOH and benzene-EtOAc gradient system), Sephadex LH-20 ($CHCl_3$-MeOH, 1:1, v/v), and silica gel (cyclohexane-EtOAc, 75:25, v/v).

Biological Activity

Inhibited the growth of *Cladosporium herbarum* at the amount of more than 5µg/spot (TLC plate bioassay).

Spectral Data

IR:

(film) 3370, 3080, 2920, 1720, 1640, 1445, 1380, 1080, and 880cm^{-1}.

^{1}H NMR:

($CDCl_3$) 4.95(1H, br. s, H-12a); 4.85(1H, br. s, H-12b); 4.79(1H, d, *J*=1.0Hz, H-14a); 4.78(1H, d, *J*=1.0Hz, H-14b); 4.09(1H, dd, *J*=6.8, 5.9Hz, H-10); 2.39(1H, ddd, *J*=11.2, 9.3, 8.8Hz, H-6); 2.09(1H, dddd, *J*=9.3, 6.4, 5.9 1.0Hz, H-8a); 1.92-2.02(2H, m, H-5a and 8b); 1.77(2H, t, *J*=7.8Hz, H-4); 1.74(3H, s, H-15); 1.63-1.78(2H, m, H-9); 1.56(1H, dq, *J*=11.2, 6.8Hz, H-2); 1.44(1H, m, H-5b); 1.28(3H, s, H-13); and 0.87ppm (3H, d, *J*=6.8Hz, H-1).

^{13}C NMR:

($CHCl_3$) 10.7(C-1), 47.7(C-2), 80.3(C-3), 40.0(C-4), 28.8(C-5), 51.9(C-6), 151.5(C-7), 33.5*(C-8), 30.0*(C-9), 75.8(C-10), 147.6(C-11), 110.0(C-12), 26.6(C-13), 108.2(C-14), and 17.6ppm (C-15).

* Assignments may be exchanged.

Mass Spectrum:

FD-MS: 239*m/e* (MH^+); EI-MS: 220.1834(M^+-H_2O, $C_{15}H_{24}O$; calcd 220.1827), 205(M^+-Me-H_2O), 202(M^+-2H_2O, 4.0%), and 43*m/e* (base peak).

Reference

H. Koshino, S. Togiya, S. Terada, T. Yoshihara, S. Sakamura, T. Shimanuki, T. Sato, and A. Tajimi; New Fungitoxic Sesquiterpenoids, Chokols A-G, from Stromata of *Epichloë typhina* and the Absolute Configuration of Chokol E; Agric. Biol. Chem., Vol. 53, pp. 789-796(1989).

Common/Systematic Name

Chokol C

6-(3-Hydroxy-2,3-dimethylcyclopentyl)-2-methylhepta-2(*E*),6-dien-1-ol

Molecular Formula/Molecular Weight

$C_{15}H_{26}O_2$; MW = 238.19328

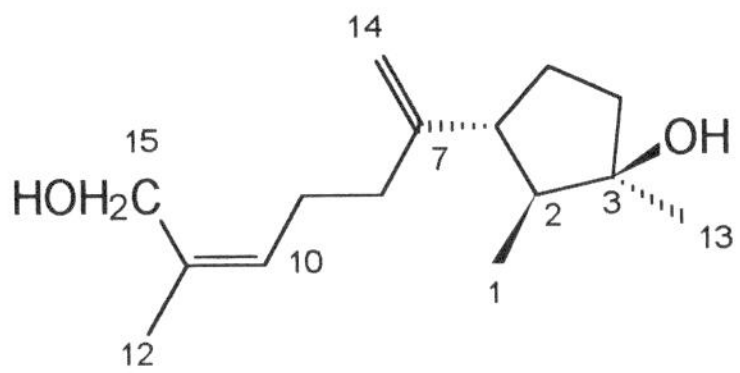

General Characteristics

Colorless needles; mp., 51.0-53.0°C; $[\alpha]_D^{22}$ -32.0° (*c*=0.25, in EtOH).

Fungal Source

Epichloë typhina on *Phleum pratense*.

Isolation/Purification

Timothy chokes were extracted with 70% ethanol, partitioned between *n*-hexane and water and subsequently between ethyl acetate and water. The hexane extract was chromatographed on silica gel ($CHCl_3$-MeOH, 95:5, v/v) followed by several chromatographies on silica gel ($CHCl_3$-MeOH and benzene-EtOAc gradient system), Sephadex LH_{20} ($CHCl_3$-MeOH, 1:1, v/v) and silica gel (cyclohexane-EtOAc, 75:25, v/v). Final purification was achieved by HPLC (μBondapak C_{18}; H_2O-CH_3CN, 7:3, v/v).

Biological Activity

Inhibited the growth of *Cladosporium herbarum* at the amount of more than 5μg/spot (TLC plate bioassay).

Spectral Data

IR:

(KBr) 3340, 3080, 2970, 1650, 1370, 1230, 1170, 1020, and 890cm^{-1}.

^{1}H NMR:

($CDCl_3$) 5.43(1H, tq, *J*=7.0, 1.3Hz, H-10); 4.79(1H, s, H-14a); 4.76(1H, d, *J*=1.5Hz, H-14b); 4.00(2H, s, H-12); 2.39(1H, ddd, *J*=11.3, 9.4, 9.0Hz, H-6); 2.20(2H, dt, *J*=7.0, 7.3Hz, H-9); 2.05(2H, dt, *J*=3.7, 7.3Hz, H-8); 1.96(1H, dddd, *J*=13.3, 9.4, 8.2, 7.6Hz, H-5a); 1.76(2H, dd, *J*=8.2, 7.6Hz, H-4); 1.68 (3H, s, H-15); 1.55(1H, dq, *J*=11.3, 7.0Hz, H-2); 1.42(1H, dddd, *J*=13.3, 9.0, 8.2, 7.6Hz, H-5b); 1.28(3H, s, H-13); and 0.87ppm (3H, d, *J*=7.0Hz, H-1).

^{13}C NMR:
(CHCl$_3$) 10.7(C-1), 47.6(C-2), 80.3(C-3), 40.0(C-4), 28.7(C-5), 51.8(C-6), 151.4(C-7), 33.6(C-8), 26.4(C-9), 125.9(C- 10), 134.9(C-11), 68.8(C-12), 26.6(C-13), 108.2(C-14) and 13.8ppm (C-15).

Mass Spectrum:
FD-MS: 238*m/e* (M^+, 68%); EI-MS: 238(M^+, 0.2%), 220.1864(M^+-H_2O, $C_{15}H_{24}O$, calcd. 220.1827, 2.0), 202(20), 187(25), 159(18), 133(20), 121(37), 107(61), 95(59), 93(42), 79(41), and 43*m/e* (100).

Reference

H. Koshino, S. Togiya, S. Terada, T. Yoshihara, S. Sakamura, T. Shimanuki, T. Sato, and A. Tajimi; New Fungitoxic Sesquiterpenoids, Chokols A-G, from Stromata of *Epichloë typhina* and the Absolute Configuration of Chokol E; Agric. Biol. Chem., Vol. 53, pp. 789-796(1989).

Common/Systematic Name

Chokol D

6-(3-Hydroxy-2,3-dimethylcyclopentyl)-2-methylhepta-2,6-dien-1-ol

Molecular Formula/Molecular Weight

$C_{15}H_{26}O_2$; MW = 238.19328

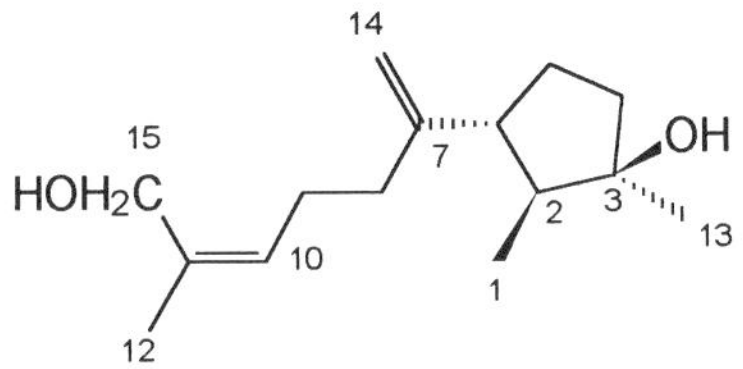

General Characteristics

Colorless syrup; $[\alpha]_D^{22}$ -44.4° (*c*=0.054, in EtOH).

Fungal Source

Epichloë typhina on *Phleum pratense*.

Isolation/Purification

Timothy chokes were extracted with 70% ethanol, partitioned between *n*-hexane and water and subsequently between ethyl acetate and water. The hexane extract was chromatographed on a silica gel ($CHCl_3$-MeOH, 95:5, v/v) followed by several chromatographies on silica gel ($CHCl_3$-MeOH and benzene-EtOAc gradient system), Sephadex LH_{20} ($CHCl_3$-MeOH, 1:1, v/v) and silica gel (cyclohexane-EtOAc, 75:25, v/v). Final purification was achieved by HPLC (μBondapak C_{18}; H_2O-CH_3CN, 7:3, v/v).

Biological Activity

Inhibited the growth of *Cladosporium herbarum* at the amount of more than 5μg/spot (TLC plate bioassay).

Spectral Data

IR:

(film) 3370, 3080, 2970, 1730, 1645, 1450, 1375, 1200, 1100, 1005, 920, and 885cm^{-1}.

^{1}H NMR:

($CDCl_3$) 5.31(1H, t, *J*=7.1Hz, H-10); 4.79(1H, s, H-14a); 4.75(1H, d, *J*=1.5Hz, H-14b); 4.12(2H, s, H-15); 2.38(1H, ddd, *J*=11.2, 9.0, 8.3Hz, H-6); 2.22(2H, dt, *J*=7.1, 7.3Hz, H-9); 2.01(2H, dt, *J*=3.4, 7.3Hz, H-8); 1.96(1H, dddd, *J*=13.2, 9.0, 7.8, 7.8Hz, H-5a); 1.80(3H, d, *J*=1.0Hz, H-12); 1.76(2H, t, *J*=7.8Hz, H-4); 1.55(1H, dq, *J*=11.2, 6.6Hz, H-2); 1.41(1H, dddd, *J*=13.2, 8.3, 7.8 7.8Hz, H-5b); 1.28(3H, s, H-13); and 0.87ppm (3H, d, *J*=6.6Hz, H-1).

^{13}C NMR:
($CHCl_3$) 10.7(C-1), 47.6(C-2), 80.3(C-3), 40.0(C-4), 28.7(C-5), 51.8(C-6), 151.4(C-7), 34.1(C-8), 26.3(C-9), 128.2(C- 10), 134.6(C-11), 21.3(C-12), 26.6(C-13), 108.3(C-14), and 61.7ppm (C-15).

Mass Spectrum:
FD-MS: 239(MH^+, 54%), 238(M^+, 55), and 220*m/e* (M^+-H_2O, 100); EI-MS: 238(M^+, 0.1%), 220.1795(M^+-H_2O, $C_{15}H_{24}O$, calcd 220.1827, 1.3), 202(9.0), 187(13), 162 (11), 161(10), 133(15), 121(20), 107(35), 95(27), and 43*m/e* (100).

Reference

H. Koshino, S. Togiya, S. Terada, T. Yoshihara, S. Sakamura, T. Shimanuki, T. Sato, and A. Tajimi; New Fungitoxic Sesquiterpenoids, Chokols A-G, from Stromata of *Epichloë typhina* and the Absolute Configuration of Chokol E; Agric. Biol. Chem., Vol. 53, pp. 789-796(1989).

Common/Systematic Name

Chokol E

(3*R*)-6-[(1*R*,2*S*,3*R*)-3-Hydroxy-2,3-dimethylcyclopentyl]-2-methylhepta-6-ene-2,3-diol

Molecular Formula/Molecular Weight

$C_{15}H_{28}O_3$; MW = 256.20384

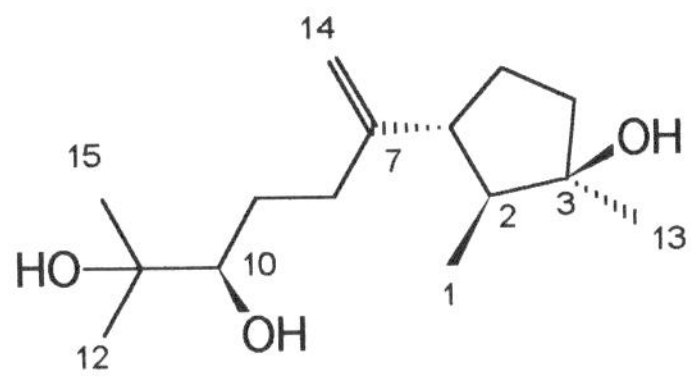

General Characteristics

Colorless syrup; $[\alpha]_D^{20}$ -15.8° (*c*=0.67, in EtOH).

Fungal Source

Epichloë typhina on *Phleum pratense*.

Isolation/Purification

Timothy chokes were extracted with 70% ethanol, partitioned between *n*-hexane and water and subsequently between ethyl acetate and water. The ethyl acetate extract was chromatographed on silica gel ($CHCl_3$-MeOH, 95:5, v/v) followed by silica gel ($CHCl_3$-acetone gradient system), Sephadex LH-20 ($CHCl_3$-MeOH, 1:1, v/v), and silica gel (twice, cyclohexane-EtOAc, 3:7, v/v, and benzene-EtOAc, 3:7, v/v) chromatographies.

Biological Activity

Relatively weak fungitoxic activity (TLC plate bioassay using *Cladosporium herbarum*); minimum amount of inhibition was about 50μg/spot.

Spectral Data

IR:

(film) 3400, 3080, 2970, 1730, 1650, 1460, 1380, 1160, and 1080cm^{-1}.

CD:

($CHCl_3$, Eu(*fod*)3) 305(-3.8 Δε), 290(0), and 285nm (+1.5).

^{1}H NMR:

($CDCl_3$) 4.82(1H, s, H-14a); 4.78(1H, s, H-14b); 3.40(1H, br. d, *J*=10.7Hz, H-10); 2.41(1H, ddd, *J*=11.7, 8.8, 8.8Hz, H-6); 2.28(1H, ddd, *J*=15.1, 9.5, 4.9Hz, H-8a); 2.06(1H, ddd, *J*=15.1, 10.0, 6.4Hz, H-8b); 1.98(1H, dddd, *J*=13.2, 8.8, 7.8 7.8Hz, H-

5a); 1.77(2H, t, *J*=7.8Hz, H-4); 1.67(1H, dddd, *J*=13.3, 9.5, 6.4, 2.0Hz, H-9a); 1.55(1H, dq, *J*=11.7, 6.8Hz, H-2); 1.48(1H, dddd, *J*=13.3, 10.7, 10.0, 4.9Hz, H-9b); 1.45(1H, dddd, *J*=13.2, 8.8, 7.8, 7.8Hz, H-5b); 1.29(3H, s, H-13); 1.23(3H, s, H-12); 1.18(3H, s, H-15); and 0.88ppm (3H, d, *J*=6.8Hz, H-1).

^{13}C NMR:
($CHCl_3$) 10.7(C-1), 47.8(C-2), 80.3(C-3), 39.9(C-4), 28.8(C-5), 51.9(C-6), 151.7(C-7), 31.1(C-8), 30.0(C-9), 78.4(C- 10), 73.1(C-11), 26.5*(C-12), 26.5(C-13), 108.2(C-14), and 23.3*ppm (C-15).

* Assignments may be exchanged.

Mass Spectrum:
FD-MS: 257*m/e* (MH^+); EI-MS: 256.2083(M^+, $C_{15}H_{28}O_3$, calcd 256.2038, 0.3%), 238(M^+-H_2O, 3.0), 220(M^+-$2H_2O$, 4.0), 205(2.9), 202(2.1), 180(5.2), 161(7.5), 136(34), 121(52), 107(30), 95(49), 81(28), 71(40), 59(100), and 43*m/e* (74).

Reference

H. Koshino, S. Togiya, S. Terada, T. Yoshihara, S. Sakamura, T. Shimanuki, T. Sato, and A. Tajimi; New Fungitoxic Sesquiterpenoids, Chokols A-G, from Stromata of *Epichloë typhina* and the Absolute Configuration of Chokol E; Agric. Biol. Chem., Vol. 53, pp. 789-796(1989).

Common/Systematic Name
Chokol F

Molecular Formula/Molecular Weight
$C_{14}H_{24}O_3$; MW = 240.17254

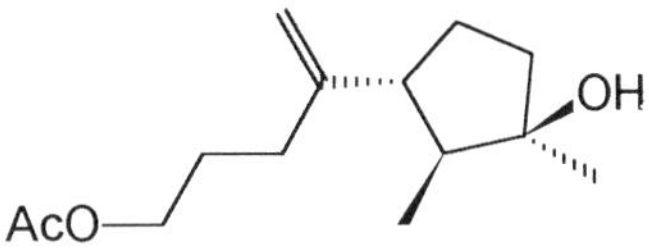

General Characteristics
Colorless syrup; $[\alpha]_D^{24}$ -48.8° (*c*=0.32, in EtOH).

Fungal Source
Epichloë typhina on *Phleum pratense*.

Isolation/Purification
Timothy chokes were extracted with 70% ethanol, partitioned between *n*-hexane and water and subsequently between ethyl acetate and water. The ethyl acetate extract was chromatographed on silica gel (*n*-hexane-EtOAc gradient system), Sephadex LH_{20} ($CHCl_3$-MeOH, 1:1, v/v), silica gel (twice, $CHCl_3$-acetone, 99:1, v/v) and cyclohexane-EtOAc, 9:1, v/v) and silica gel (preparative TLC, *n*-hexane-EtOAc, 7:3, v/v). Final purification was achieved by HPLC (μ-Porasil, *n*-hexane-EtOH, 9:1, v/v).

Spectral Data

IR:
(film) 3470, 3070, 2950, 2925, 1745, 1640, 1445, 1370, 1245, 1040, 920, and 885cm^{-1}.

^{1}H NMR:
($CDCl_3$) 4.81(1H, s, H-14a); 4.76(1H, d, *J*=1.0Hz, H-14b); 4.08(2H, t, *J*=6.6Hz, H-10); 2.38(1H, ddd, *J*=11.2, 9.3, 9.3Hz, H-6); 2.05(3H, s. H-Ac); 2.02-2.07(2H, m, H-8); 1.98(1H, dddd, *J*=12.2, 9.3, 7.8, 7.8Hz, H-5a); 1.78-1.83(2H, m, H-9); 1.76(2H, t, *J*=7.8Hz, H-4); 1.55(1H, dq, *J*=11.2, 6.8Hz, H-2); 1.41(1H, dddd, *J*=12.2, 9.3, 7.8, 7.8Hz, H-5b); 1.29(3H, s, H-13); and 0.87ppm (3H, d, *J*=6.8Hz, H-1).

Mass Spectrum:
EI-MS: 222.1621(M^+-H_2O, $C_{14}H_{22}O_2$; calcd 222.1619, 5.1%), 201(2.5), 180(3.1), 162(8.7), 155(13), 147(16), 122(20), 121(21), 109(26), 107(24), 95(33), 93(31), 81(33), 67(34), 55(41) and 43*m/e* (100).

Reference

H. Koshino, S. Togiya, S. Terada, T. Yoshihara, S. Sakamura, T. Shimanuki, T. Sato, and A. Tajimi; New Fungitoxic Sesquiterpenoids, Chokols A-G, from Stromata of *Epichloë typhina* and the Absolute Configuration of Chokol E; Agric. Biol. Chem., Vol. 53, pp. 789-796(1989).

Common/Systematic Name

Chokol G

3-(3-Hydroxy-2,3-dimethylcyclopentyl)but-3-en-1-ol

Molecular Formula/Molecular Weight

$C_{11}H_{20}O_2$; MW = 184.14633

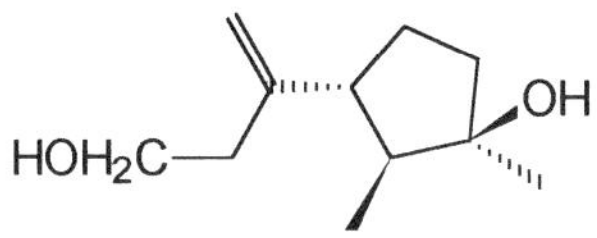

General Characteristics

Colorless syrup; $[\alpha]_D^{24}$ -43.3° (*c*=0.24, in MeOH).

Fungal Source

Epichloë typhina on *Phleum pratense*.

Isolation/Purification

Timothy chokes were extracted with 70% ethanol, partitioned between *n*-hexane and water and subsequently between ethyl acetate and water. The ethyl acetate extract was chromatographed on silica gel ($CHCl_3$-MeOH, 95:5, v/v) followed by several chromatographies on silica gel (*n*-hexane-EtOAc gradient system), Sephadex LH_{20} ($CHCl_3$-MeOH, 1:1, v/v) and silica gel (twice, $CHCl_3$-MeOH, 95:5, v/v and cyclohexane-EtOAc, 1:1, v/v). Final purification was achieved by HPLC (μBondapak C_{18}; H_2O-CH_3CN, 4:1, v/v).

Biological Activity

Relatively weak fungitoxic activity (TLC plate bioassay using *Cladosporium herbarum*); minimal inhibition was about 50μg/spot.

Spectral Data

IR:

(film) 3370, 3070, 2950, 1720, 1640, 1440, 1370, 1040, 920, and 880cm^{-1}.

^{1}H NMR:

($CDCl_3$) 4.91(1H, s, H-14a); 4.84(1H, dd, *J*=2.6, 1.5Hz, H-14b); 3.75(2H, t, *J*=6.6Hz, H-9); 2.40(1H, ddd, *J*=11.4, 9.0, 9.0Hz, H-6); 2.28(2H, t, *J*=6.6Hz, H-8); 2.00(1H, dddd, *J*=13.9, 9.0, 7.7, 7.7Hz, H-5a); 1.77 (2H, t, J=7.7Hz, H-4); 1.56(1H, dq, *J*=11.4, 6.6Hz, H-2); 1.43(1H, dddd, *J*=13.9, 9.0, 7.7, 7.7Hz, H-5b); 1.29(3H, s, H-13); and 0.88ppm (3H, d, J=6.6Hz, H-1).

^{13}C NMR:

($CHCl_3$) 10.6(C-1), 47.6(C-2), 80.2(C-3), 39.9(C-4), 28.7(C-5), 51.7(C-6), 148.1(C-7), 37.1(C-8), 60.9(C-9), 26.6(C-13); and 108.9ppm (C-14).

Mass Spectrum:
FIMS: 184(M^+, 16%), 167(M^+-OH, 100), and 166*m/e* (M^+- H_2O, 75); EIMS: 166.1349(M^+-H_2O, $C_{11}H_{18}O$, calcd 166.1358, 19%), 151(12), 148(9), 135(40), 121(33), 107(32), 105(34), 95(54), and 43*m/e* (100).

Reference

H. Koshino, S. Togiya, S. Terada, T. Yoshihara, S. Sakamura, T. Shimanuki, T. Sato, and A. Tajimi; New Fungitoxic Sesquiterpenoids, Chokols A-G, from Stromata of *Epichloë typhina* and the Absolute Configuration of Chokol E; Agric. Biol. Chem., Vol. 53, pp. 789-796(1989).

15

Enaminomycins and Related Metabolites

Enaminomycin A (Antiphenicol)
Enaminomycin B
Enaminomycin C
Antibiotic G7063-2
Epoformin (Desoxyepoxydon)
(±)-Epoxydon
Acetylepoformin
(±)-Epoxydon monoacetate
(±)-Desoxyepiepoxydon
(±)-Epiepoxydon [(±)-Isoepoxydon]
Coriloxin

Common/Systematic Name

Enaminomycin A; Antiphenicol

2-Amino-3-carboxy-1,4-benzoquinone 5,6-epoxide; 4-Amino-2,5-dioxo-7-oxabicyclo[4.1.0]hept-3-ene-3-carboxylic acid

Molecular Formula/Molecular Weight

$C_7H_5NO_5$; MW = 183.01677

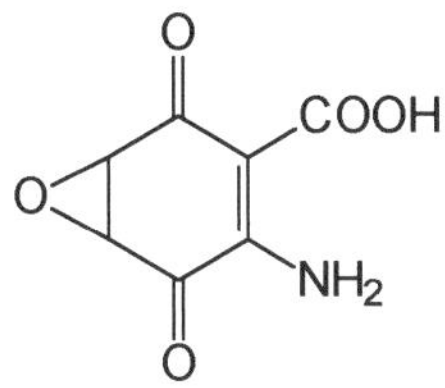

General Characteristics

Enaminomycin A (antiphenicol) is an acidic, lipophilic, white amorphous powder; mp., 105°C (dec.); $[\alpha]_D^{20}$ -20.9° (*c*=0.83, in MeOH). Crystallized from ethyl acetate to give yellow needles, mp 153-155°C (dec.); pK_a 6.1 and 9.7. Antiphenicol was positive to 2,4-dinitrophenylhydrazine. It decolorized aqueous potassium permanganate solution and becomes brown with ninhydrin, orange-red with sodium nitroprusside and grayish violet with isatine, respectively. It is soluble in water, methanol, ethanol, acetone and ethyl acetate and insoluble in benzene and chloroform.

Fungal Source

Streptomyces fulvoviolaceus No.851 and *S. baarnensis* No. 13120.

Isolation/Purification

The cultured broth was filtered and the filtrate was adjusted to pH 6 and extracted with ethyl acetate. The extract was concentrated and applied to a column of silicic acid. Active fractions eluted with ethyl acetate were collected and concentrated to remove the solvent. The concentrate was applied onto a silica gel column. The active substance was eluted with benzene-ethyl acetate (95:5, v/v). The active fractions were concentrated and yielded a yellowish powder. Antiphenicol was recrystallized from ethyl acetate as yellow needles.

Biological Activity

Showed noticeable antagonistic action against chloramphenicol in *Escherichia coli*. Antiphenicol antagonized the activities of antibiotics such as chloramphenicol, thiamphenicol, lincomycin and erythromycin, all of which have effects on the ribosome 50S subunit of *E. coli*. The enaminomycins are active against Gram-positive and Gram-negative bacteria as well as against some species of fungi. Enaminomycin A is also active against L1210 mouse leukemia cells *in vitro*.

Spectral Data

UV:
λ_{max}^{MeOH} 244(ϵ=9,150), 292 (15,200), and 349nm (660).

IR:
(KBr) 3350, 3250, 2730, 1700, 1590, 1500, 1440, 1370, 1250, 1050, 990, 880, 750, and 570cm^{-1}.

CD:
(MeOH) [θ]25, +25,600(250), +27,900(253), +65,800(273), -79,200(300), and -900(250).

^{1}H NMR:
(acetone-d_6) 4.02(1H, d, *J*=1Hz); 4.22(1H, d, *J*=4Hz); 8.6(1H, broad); 10.0(1H, broad); and 13.2ppm (1H, broad).

^{13}C NMR:
(acetone-d_6) 53.2(d, *J*=52.4Hz); 55.4(d, *J*=52.7Hz); 96.4(s); 155(s); 168.7(s); 187.4(s); and 192.8ppm (s).

Mass Spectrum:
HREIMS: 183.0146*m/e* (M^+); calcd. for $C_7H_5NO_5$ 183.0167.

References

Y. Imagawa, S. Shima, A. Hirota, and H. Sakai; Isolation and Structure Elucidation of Antiphenicol, An Antagonist of Chloramphenicol; Agric. Biol. Chem., Vol. 43, pp. 2437-2440(1979).

Y. Itoh, T. Haneishi, M. Arai, T. Hata, K. Aiba, and C. Tamura; New Antibiotics, Enaminomycins, B and C. III. The Structures of Enaminomycins A, B and C; J. Antibiot., Vol. 31, pp. 838-846(1978).

Common/Systematic Name

Enaminomycin B

2-Oxo-4-amino-5-hydroxy-5-acetonyl-7-oxabicyclo[4.1.0]hept-3-ene-3-carboxylic acid

Molecular Formula/Molecular Weight

$C_{10}H_{11}NO_6$; MW = 241.05864

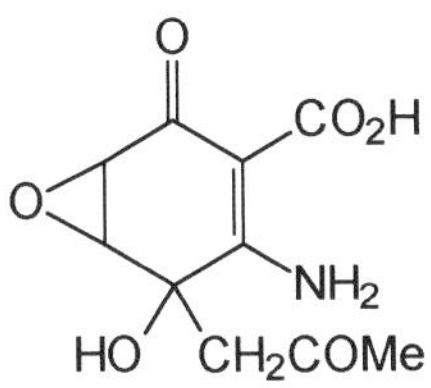

General Characteristics

Enaminomycin B is an acidic, lipophilic, colorless crystalline substance; mp., 160°C (dec.), $[\alpha]_D^{20}$ + 60.1° (*c*=0.99, in MeOH).

Fungal Source

Streptomyces fulvoviolaceus No.851 and *S. baarnensis* No. 13120.

Biological Activity

The enaminomycins are active against Gram-positive and Gram-negative bacteria as well as against some species of fungi.

Spectral Data

UV:

λ_{max}^{MeOH} 244(ϵ=315) and 293nm (580).

IR:

(KBr) 3500-2500, 1720, 1670, and 1650cm^{-1}.

CD:

(MeOH) 296(-80400) and 269nm (+94400).

^{1}H NMR:

(acetone-d_6) The NMR spectrum exhibited a methyl singlet at 2.20, a methylene singlet at 3.15 and a hydroxy singlet at 5.22, in addition to two epoxide protons at 3.60(*J*=4.5Hz) and 4.10ppm (*J*=4.5Hz).

Mass Spectrum:

241*m/e* (M^+).

Reference

Y. Itoh, T. Haneishi, M. Arai, T. Hata, K. Aiba, and C. Tamura; New Antibiotics, Enaminomycins A, B and C. III. The Structures of Enaminomycins A, B and C; J. Antibiot., Vol. 31, pp. 838-846(1978).

Common/Systematic Name

Enaminomycin C

2-Oxo-4-amino-5-hydroxy-7-oxabicyclo[4.1.0]hept-3-ene-3-carboxylic acid

Molecular Formula/Molecular Weight

$C_7H_7NO_5$; MW = 185.03242

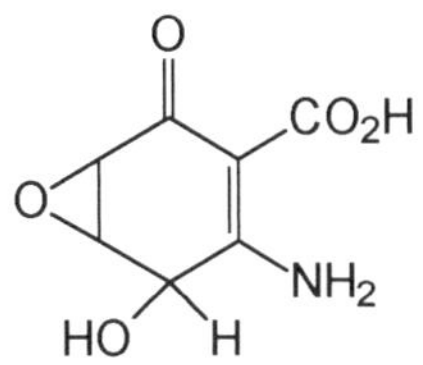

General Characteristics

Enaminomycin C is an acidic, lipophilic, colorless crystalline substance; mp., 173 °C (dec.); $[\alpha]_D^{20}$ +31.4° (*c*=0.14, in MeOH). Treatment of enaminomycin C with diazomethane in methanol gave a biologically active substance, which showed the same R_f value as enaminomycin A on silica gel TLC.

Fungal Source

Streptomyces baarnensis No. 13120.

Biological Activity

The enaminomycins are active against Gram-positive and Gram-negative bacteria as well as against some species of fungi.

Spectral Data

UV:

λ_{max}^{MeOH} 245(ϵ=436) and 290nm (930).

IR:

3500-2500, 1680, and 1605cm^{-1}.

CD:

(MeOH) 294(-78000) and 268nm (+64200).

^{1}H NMR:

(DMSO-d_6) The NMR spectrum exhibited two protons at 3.63(*J*=4.5Hz) and 3.82(*J*=4.5Hz) corresponding to epoxide protons, a proton giving a broad double doublet at 4.81(*J*=8.5, 2.0Hz) and an exchangeable proton giving doublet at 6.56ppm (*J*=8.5Hz). One of the epoxide protons was coupled to a proton (4.81ppm) on the carbon linked to the hydroxy group.

Mass Spectrum:
185*m/e* (M^+).

Reference

Y. Iyoh, T. Haneishi, M. Arai, T. Hata, K. Aiba, and C. Tamura; New Antibiotics, Enaminomycin A, B and C. III.The Structures of Enaminomycin A, B and C; J. of Antibiot., Vol. 31, pp. 838-846(1978).

Common/Systematic Name

Antibiotic G7063-2

4-Amino-7-oxabicyclo[4.1.0]hept-3-ene-2,5-dione-3-carboxamide

Molecular Formula/Molecular Weight

$C_7H_6N_2O_4$; MW = 182.03276

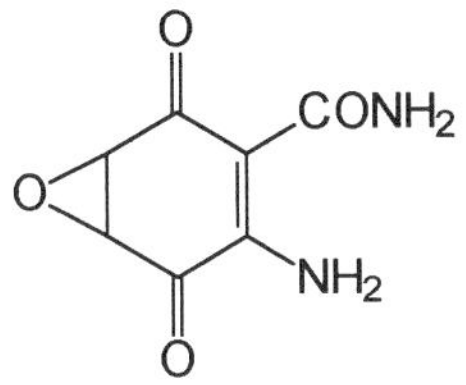

General Characteristics

G7063-2 is a yellow crystalline antibiotic (decomposes >180°C); soluble in water, methanol, dimethyl sulfoxide, and acetone and slightly soluble in chloroform. It turns red with the loss of antibiotic activity in sodium carbonate solution at pH 10.

Fungal Source

Streptomyces sp. (NCIB-11306).

Isolation/Purification

The fungal broth was adjusted to pH 7 with sulfuric acid and centrifuged to separate aqueous solution from mycelium. The aqueous solution was extracted with 3 one-third volumes of ethyl acetate and the combined ethyl acetate extracts were evaporated to dryness. The residue was extracted with *n*-butanol-methanol-water (4:1:2, v/v/v), filtered to remove inactive solid and the extract fractionated on a column of Sephadex LH_{20} in the same solvent mixture. Fractions active against both *Staphylococcus aureus* and *Escherichia coli* were separated from fractions active only against *Staphylococcus aureus*. The fractions with activity against both organisms were combined and evaporated to dryness. The residue was extracted with ethyl acetate and filtered. The filtrate was evaporated to 30ml and applied to a column of Sephadex LH_{20} packed in chloroform-ethyl acetate (1:2, v/v). Elution was with the same solvent and active fractions were combined, evaporated to 70ml and kept at -20°C. After 3 days yellow crystals were collected, washed with cold ethyl acetate and dried under reduced pressure to give pure G7063-2.

Biological Activity

G7063-2 had moderate activity against a wide range of Gram-positive and Gram-negative bacteria; weak to moderate activity against fungi; and an LD_{50} IP to mice was about 17mg/kg body weight.

Spectral Data

UV:

λ_{max}^{Water} 248(ϵ=430), 292(740), and 358nm (72); $\lambda_{max}^{0.1N\ HCl}$ 249(450), 292(690), and 358nm (75); $\lambda_{max}^{0.1N\ NaOH}$ 249sh (870) and 260nm (1010).

IR:

(Nujol mull) showed peaks at 3440 and 3300 (-NH_2) and at 1720, 1630, and 1555cm^{-1} [NH_2CO-C(CO-R)=C-COR].

^{1}H NMR:

(acetone-d_6) Spectrum of G7063-2 showed signals centered at 5.92τ (d, 4Hz, 1H) and 6.13(d, 4Hz, 1H) for vicinally coupled epoxide protons, at τ 1.40 and 3.42τ (2H) for amide protons and at 0.60τ for amine protons (2H).

^{13}C NMR:

(DMSO-d_6) Showed seven carbon resonances at 52.5; 55.0; 97.6; 154.7; 169.4; 188.5; and 188.8ppm.

Mass Data:

The mass spectrum showed a base peak-molecular ion at *m/e* 182; an accurate mass measurement for this peak gave a value of 182.0326 indicating a molecular formula of $C_7H_6N_2O_4$. Fragmentation peaks at 137 and 109*m/e* corresponded with the loss of CH_3NO and $C_2H_3NO_2$ moieties; elemental analysis gave: C, 46.2; H, 3.4; N, 15.2; $C_7H_6N_2O_4$ requires C, 46.2; H, 3.3; N, 15.4%.

TLC Data

Samples were applied to either layers of cellulose containing fluorescent indicator or to layers of Kieselgel $60F_{254}$ (E. Merck, Darmstadt, Germany). Development was with butanol-methanol-water (4:1:2, v/v/v) for cellulose plates and with ethyl acetate for silica plates. After development at 24°C sheets were air-dried, examined under UV light (254 and 356nm). R_f values were 0.80 and 0.67, respectively.

Reference

M. Noble, D. Noble, and R. B. Sykes; G7063-2, A New Nitrogen-containing Antibiotic of The Epoxydon Group, Isolated from the Fermentation Broth of A Species of *Streptomyces;* J. Antibiot., Vol. 30, pp. 455-459(1977).

Common/Systematic Name

Epoformin; Desoxyepoxydon

2,3-Epoxy-4-hydroxy-6-methyl-5-cyclohexen-1-one

Molecular Formula/Molecular Weight

$C_7H_8O_3$; MW = 140.04734

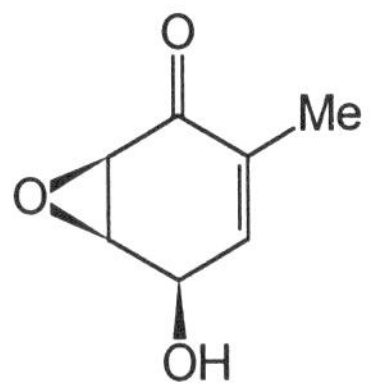

General Characteristics

Colorless needles; mp., 75-77°C; $[\alpha]_D^{22}$ +114.3° (*c*=1.0, in EtOH); recrystallized from benzene (mp., 89-91°C).

Fungal Source

Penicillium claviforme and *Penicillium patulum* (NRRL 2159A) = *P. griseofulvum.*

Isolation/Purification

Culture filtrate was extracted with ethyl acetate, dried and subjected to preparative TLC: silica gel GF_{254}, chloroform-EtOH (8:2, v/v), R_f 0.46.

Biological Activity

Weak antimicrobial activity; strong cytotoxicity against PS-cells; and LD_{50} in mice, ca. 100 mg/kg (IV).

Spectral Data

UV:

λ_{max}^{EtOH} 240nm (ε=5540); λ_{max}^{MeOH} 242nm (ε=4700).

IR:

($CHCl_3$) 3550(OH), 1680(conjugated C=O), 1650(-C=C-),1230, and 880cm^{-1} (epoxide); (KBr) 3410, 2950, and 1655cm^{-1}.

ORD:

365 = +114°; 335 = 0°; 312.5 = -70°; 290= 0°; 260 = +263°; and 250 =0°.

^{1}H NMR:

($CDCl_3$) 6.25(1H, m); 4.63(1H, m, *J*=3.0, 2.5, 2.0Hz); 3.80(1H, dt, *J*=4.0, 3.0, 2.5Hz); 3.47(1H, d, *J*=4.0Hz); 1.83(3H, t, *J*=2.0, 2.0); and 3.07ppm (broad singlet, exchangeable with D_2O).

Mass Data:
Calcd $C_7H_8O_3$; C, 59.99; H, 5.75 found C, 59.88, 59.86; H, 5.70, 5.70.

References

A. I. Scott, L. Zamir, G. T. Phillips, and M. Yalpani; The Biosynthesis of Patulin; Bioorganic Chemistry, Vol. 2, pp. 1124-1139(1973).

I. Yamamoto, E. Mizuta, T. Henmi, T. Yamano, and S. Yamatodani; Epoformin, A New Antibiotic Produced by *Penicillium claviforme* Bainier; J. Takeda Res. Lab. Vol..32, pp. 532-538(1973).

Common/Systematic Name

(±)-Epoxydon

Molecular Formula/Molecular Weight

$C_7H_8O_4$; MW = 156.04226

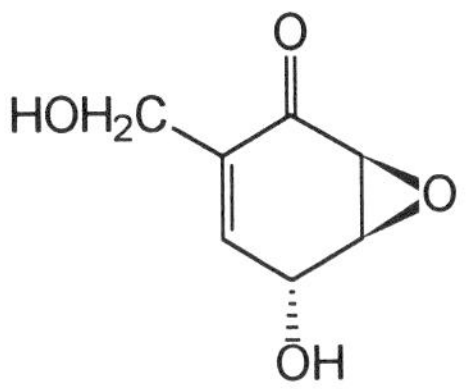

General Characteristics

Oil; $[\alpha]_D^{23}$ 91.9° (*c*=0.123, in EtOH); $[\alpha]_D^{24}$ +105° (*c*=0.98, in EtOH).

Fungal Source

Penicillium claviforme, *P. patulum* = *P. griseovulvum*, *Ascochyta chrysanthemi*, *Mycosphaerella ligulicola*, and *Phoma chrysanthemi*.

Isolation/Purification

Cultures were extracted with ethyl acetate, dried over sodium sulfate and evaporated to dryness. The crude extract was chromatographed by preparative TLC on silica gel, containing 1% KH_2PO_4 using hexane-ethyl acetate (1:1, v/v) and chloroform-methanol, 19:1(v/v) as eluants to give purified (±)-epoxydon and its monoacetate.

Biological Activity

Phytotoxic; cytotoxic PS-cells, 3.1; LD_{50} in mice (IV), 110-219mg/kg body wt.

Spectral Data

UV:

λ_{max}^{EtOH} 238nm (ε=4900).

^{1}H NMR:

(DMSO-d_6) 3.42(1H, d, *J*=5.0Hz, H-2); 3.76(1H, m, H-3); 4.03(2H, -CH_2OH); 4.70(1H, m, H-4); 4.97(1H, OH); 5.78(1H, d, *J*=5.0Hz, OH); and 6.42ppm (1H, m, H-5).

Mass Data:

Anal calcd $C_7H_8O_4$; C, 53.83; H, 5.16; Mol. Wt., 156.13; found: C, 53.96, 53.57; H, 5.18, 5.04; Mol. Wt. 151 (V.P.O.).

References

G. Assante, L. Camarda, L. Merlini, and G. Nasini; Secondary Metabolites from *Mycosphaerella ligulicola*; Phytochem., Vol. 20, pp. 1955-1957(1981).

I. Yamamoto, E. Mizuta, T. Henmi, T. Yamano, and S. Yamatodani; Epoformin, A New Antibiotic Produced by *Penicillium claviforme* Bainier; J. Takeda Res. Lab., Vol., 32, pp. 532-538(1973).

Common/Systematic Name
Acetylepoformin

Molecular Formula/Molecular Weight
$C_9H_{10}O_4$; MW = 182.05791

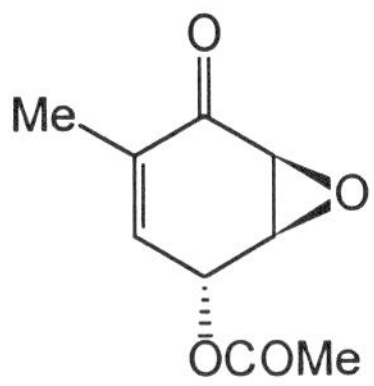

General Characteristics
Crystals; mp., 62-63°C; $[\alpha]_D^{22}$ +113.4° (*c*=1.0, in EtOH).

Fungal Source
Penicillium claviforme, *Ascochyta chrysanthemi, Mycosphaerella ligulicola,* and *Phoma chrysanthemi*.

Spectral Data

UV:
λ_{max}^{EtOH} 237nm (ϵ=6,680).

^{1}H NMR:
($CDCl_3$) 6.15, C5-H(1H, m, *J*=2.5, 2.5, 1.5Hz); 3.85, C3-H (double triplet, *J*=4.0, 2.5, 2.5Hz); 3.48, C2-H(1H, d, *J*=4.0); 1.83(3H, t, *J*=1.5, 2.0Hz); and 5.74ppm, C4-H(1H, m, *J*=2.0, 2.5, 2.5Hz).

Mass Data:
Anal calcd $C_9H_{10}O_4$; C, 59.36; H, 5.49; found: C, 58.90; H, 5.04.

Reference
I. Yamamoto, E. Mizuta, T. Henmi, T. Yamano, and S. Yamatodani; Epoformin, A New Antibiotic Produced by *Penicillium claviforme* Bainier; J. Takeda Res. Lab., Vol. 32, pp. 532-538(1973).

Common/Systematic Name
(±)-Epoxydon monoacetate

Molecular Formula/Molecular Weight
$C_9H_{10}O_5$; MW = 198.05282

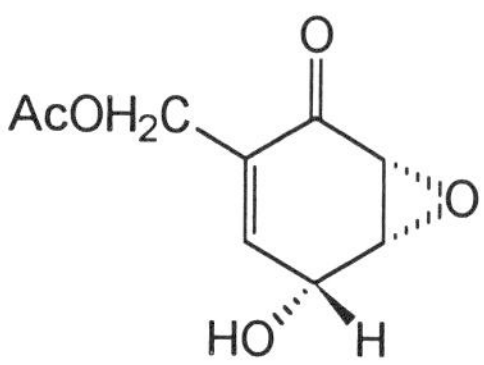

General Characteristics
Needles; mp., 60-62°C; $[\alpha]_D^{23}$ +90.4° (c=0.125, in EtOH); $[\alpha]_D^{24}$ + 105° (c=0.98, in EtOH).

Fungal Source
Ascochyta chrysanthemi, Mycosphaerella ligulicola (CBS 367 67), and *Phoma chrysanthemi.*

Isolation/Purification
Cultures were extracted with ethyl acetate, dried over sodium sulfate and evaporated to dryness. The crude extract was chromatographed by preparative TLC on silica gel, containing 1% KH_2PO_4 using hexane-ethyl acetate (1:1, v/v) and chloroform-methanol, 19:1 (v/v) as eluants to give purified (±)-epoxydon and its monoacetate.

Biological Activity
Phytotoxic.

Spectral Data

IR:
(Nujol) 3430(OH), 1725(acetate C=O), and 1670cm^{-1} (conjugated CO).

^{1}H NMR:
($CDCl_3$) 2.07(3H, s, COMe); 3.15(1H, Br, s, OH); 3.52(1H, d, J=3Hz, H-2); 3.85(1H, m, H-3); 4.72(3H, s, -CH_2-O- and H-4); and 6.53ppm (1H, m, H-5).

Mass Data:
198(M$^+$), 166, 156, 138, and 127*m/e*.

Reference
G. Assante, L. Camarda, L. Merlini, and G. Nasini; Secondary Metabolites from *Mycosphaerella ligulicola*; Phytochem., Vol. 20, pp. 1955-1957(1981).

Common/Systematic Name

(±)-Desoxyepiepoxydon

Molecular Formula/Molecular Weight

$C_7H_8O_3$; MW = 140.04734

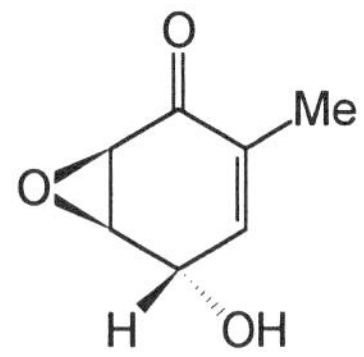

General Characteristics

An amorphous solid; $[\alpha]_D$ +221° (c=0.83, in EtOH).

Fungal Source

Isolated from the culture filtrate of an unidentified fungus, which was separated from the diseased leaf of crepe-myrtle (*Lagerstroemia indica* L.).

Isolation/Purification

The culture filtrate was extracted with ethyl acetate and fractionated into the neutral, acidic and basic fractions. The neutral fraction showed marked inhibition against germination of lettuce seeds, *Lactuca sativa* L. Purification was monitored using the lettuce seed bioassay. The neutral fraction was applied onto a silica gel column eluted stepwise with a mixture of benzene and ethyl acetate. The effluent containing 10% ethyl acetate-benzene was subjected to preparative TLC on silica gel GF_{254} developed with benzene-ethyl acetate (1:1, v/v) and the extract corresponding to R_f 0.40 gave desoxyepi-epoxydon as an amorphous solid. The fraction eluted with 70% ethyl acetate-benzene from the silica gel column was further fractionated with preparative TLC on silica gel GF_{254} developed with benzene-ethyl acetate (1:3, v/v) and the extract (R_f 0.52) yielded (±)-epiepoxydon as an amorphous solid.

Biological Activity

In the bioassay using lettuce seeds, it completely inhibited the germination at a concentration of 50ppm.

Spectral Data

UV:

λ_{max}^{EtOH} 237nm (ϵ=4,440); $\lambda_{max}^{EtOH + 10\% NaOH}$ 32(sh) (6,670), 262(3,440), and 324nm (sh) (870). UV absorption in ethanol was irreversibly changed by addition of alkaline solution, suggesting that desoxyepiepoxydon was labile in an alkaline conditions.

IR:
(film) 3440(OH), 1668(C=O), 1282, 1042(C-O), 830, and 727cm^{-1}.

CD:
(c=0.01, in dioxane) $[\Theta]^{25}$(nm): 0(385), +6,300(340), +140(282), and +11,600(254).

^{1}H NMR:
($CDCl_3$) 6.40(lH, m, -C=CH-); 4.61(1H, broad s, -CHOH); 3.73(1H, m); 3.46(1H, d, J=4Hz); 2.20(1H, broad s, -OH); and 1.82ppm (3H, s, -C=C-CH_3). The NMR spectrum was quite similar to those of epoformin and desoxyepoxydon. However, slight differences were observed in the chemical shifts of signals due to -C=CH- and -CHOH. From these facts, it was concluded that desoxyepiepoxydon has the structural feature similar to epoformin and that the difference may lie in the relative configuration of hydroxyl group at C-4 and oxyran ring.

Mass Spectrum:
HREIMS: 140.0448(M$^+$, 140.0472, calcd for $C_7H_8O_3$), 112, 111, 97, 83, 71, and 69m/e.

Reference

H. Nagasawa, A. Suzuki, and S. Tamura; Isolation and Structure of (+)-Desoxyepi-epoxydon and (±)-Epiepoxydon, Phytotoxic Fungal Metabolites; Agric. Biol. Chem., Vol. 42, pp. 1303-1304(1978).

Common/Systematic Name

(±)-Epiepoxydon; (±)-Isoepoxydon

Molecular Formula/Molecular Weight

$C_7H_8O_4$; MW = 156.04226

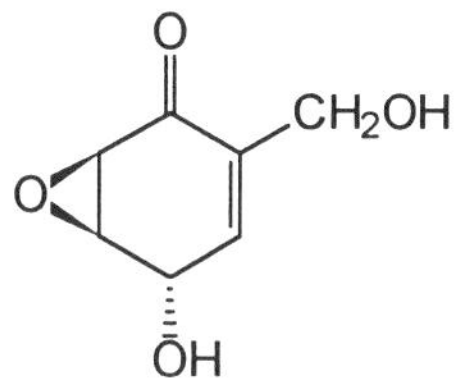

General Characteristics

An amorphous solid; $[\alpha]_D^{24}$ +194° (*c*=1.57, in EtOH).

Fungal Source

Isolated from the culture filtrate of an unidentified fungus, which was separated from the diseased leaf of crepe-myrtle (*Lagerstroemia indica* L.).

Isolation/Purification

The culture filtrate was extracted with ethyl acetate and fractionated into the neutral, acidic and basic fractions. Only the neutral fraction showed the marked inhibition against the germination of lettuce seeds, *Lactuca sativa* L. Purification was monitored using the lettuce seed bioassay. The neutral fraction was applied onto a silica gel column eluted stepwise with the mixture of benzene and ethyl acetate. The effluent with benzene containing 10% ethyl acetate was subjected to preparative TLC on silica gel GF_{254} plates developed with benzene-ethyl acetate (1:1, v/v) and the extract corresponding to R_f 0.40 gave (+)-desoxyepiepoxydon as an amorphous solid. The fraction eluted with benzene containing 70% ethyl acetate from the silica gel column was further fractionated with PTLC on silica gel GF_{254} plate developed with benzene-ethyl acetate (1:3, v/v) and the extract (R_f 0.52) yielded (±)-epioxydon as an amorphous solid.

Biological Activity

In the bioassay using lettuce seeds, it showed 30% inhibition at a concentration of 300ppm.

Spectral Data

IR:

(film) 3340(OH), 1675(C=O), 1397, 1240, 1113, 1031(C-O), 1012(C-O), and 825cm^{-1}.

CD:

(*c*=0.01, dioxane) $[\alpha]^{25}$(nm): 0(390), +7,800(341), +470(282), and +13,300(256).

^{1}H NMR:

($CDCl_3$) 6.65(1H, m), 4.80(1H, broad s, -OH), 4.62(1H, broad s), 4.18(2H, AB quartet, *J*=17Hz, -CH_2OH), 4.05(1H, broad s, -OH), 3.75(1H, m), and 3.38ppm (1H, d, *J*=4Hz). The ^{1}H NMR spectrum was identical with that of authentic (±)-epiepoxydon.

Mass Spectrum:

156*m/e* (M^+, $C_7H_8O_4$). Short communication.

Reference

H. Nagasawa, A. Suzuki, and S. Tamara; Isolation and Structure of (+)-Desoxyepiepoxydon and (±)-Epiepoxydon, Phytotoxic Fungal Metabolites; Agric. Biol. Chem., Vol. 42, pp. 1303-1304(1978).

Common/Systematic Name

Coriloxin

5,6-Epoxy-4-hydroxy-3-methoxy-5-methyl-2-cyclohexen-1-one

Molecular Formula/Molecular Weight

$C_8H_8O_4$; MW = 168.04226

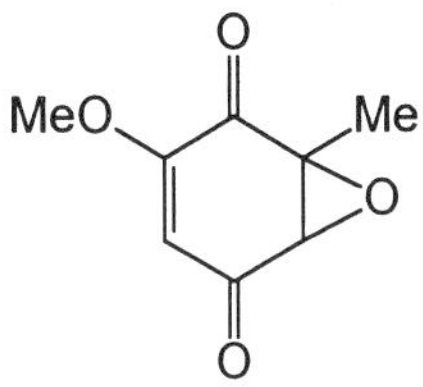

Fungal Source

Coriolus vernicipes.

Reference

Nissan Chem. Ind, Co. Ltd., Japanese Patent J5 5089 274.

16

Boviquinones and Related Metabolites

Common/Systematic Name

Boviquinone-3
2,5-Dihydroxy-3-farnesyl-1,4-benzoquinone

Molecular Formula/Molecular Weight

$C_{21}H_{28}O_4$; MW = 344.19876

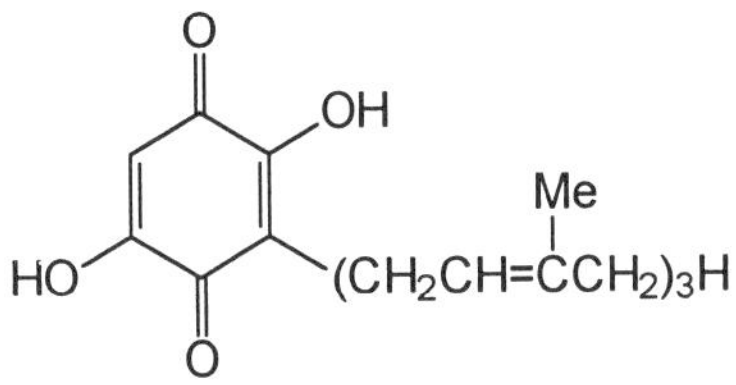

General Characteristics

Boviquinone-3 crystallized from acetic acid as yellow needles turning orange in air; mp., 90-92°C.

Fungal Source

Gomphidius rutilus, Chroogomphus helveticus, and *C. rutilus.*

Isolation/Purification

Freshly collected fruiting bodies of *G. rutilus* were sliced and steeped in cold ethanol for 2 hr. The bright red solution was decanted and the mushrooms were extracted overnight with fresh alcohol. Treatment of the combined extracts with an excess of aqueous lead acetate solution yielded the blue-green lead salt which was filtered off and washed twice with water and then twice with methanol. Methanolic hydrogen chloride was added dropwise to the stirred suspension of the lead salt in methanol. The mixture was filtered and the filtrate was evaporated at 35°C to yield a red gum. Boviquinone-3 was crystallized from acetic acid.

Spectral Data

UV:

λ_{max}^{EtOH} 288nm (log ϵ=4.27).

IR:

(KBr) 3290, 2960, 2915, 2850, 1615, and 1335cm^{-1}; ($CHCl_3$) 3360, 2920, 1645, and 1370cm^{-1}.

^{1}H NMR:

(CCl_4) 2.9(1H); 4.77-5.18(3H); 6.79(d, *J*=7Hz, 2H); 7.74(6H); 7.77(6H); 8.02(8H); 8.33(6H); and 8.42τ (6H).

Mass Data:

LREIMS: 314m/e (M^+); Leucotetraacetate ($C_{29}H_{30}O_8$): 514, 472, 430, 388, 346, 320, 294, 277, 252, 239, 154, 81, and 69*m/e* (100%); found: C, 73.4; H, 8.4; $C_{21}H_{28}O_4$ requires C, 73.3; H, 8.1%.

Reference

P. C. Beaumont and R. L. Edwards; Constituents of The Higher Fungi. Part XI. Boviquinone-3,(2,5-Dihydroxy-3-farnesyl-1,4-benzoquinone), Diboviquinone-3,4, Methylenediboviquinone-3,3, and Xerocomic Acid from *Gomphidius rutilus* Fr. and Diboviquinone-4,4 from *Boletus (Suillus) bovinus* (Linn ex Fr.) Kuntze; J. Chem. Soc. (C), pp. 2582-2585(1971).

Common/Systematic Name

Bovinone

2,5-Dihydroxy-3-geranylgeranyl-1,4-benzoquinone

Molecular Formula/Molecular Weight

$C_{26}H_{36}O_4$; MW = 412.26136

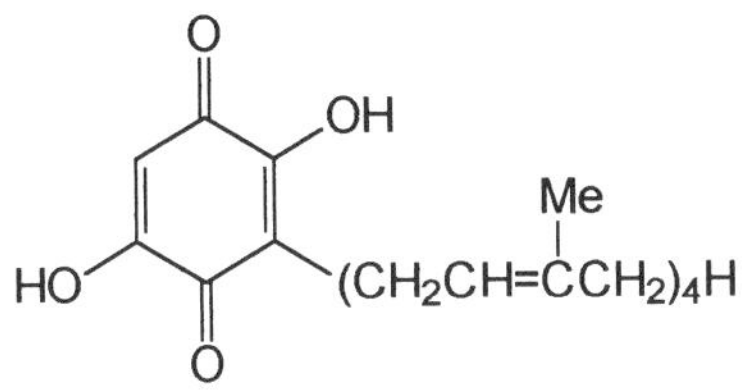

General Characteristics

Crystallized from acetic acid as yellow needles which turned orange when dried in air. It was readily soluble in organic solvents but insoluble in water. The quinonoid nature of bovinone was indicated by the reversible reduction and oxidation of its aqueous alcoholic solution and dithionite and air; yellow needles from glacial acetic acid; mp., 84-85°C.

Fungal Source

Boletus (*Suillus*) *bovinus*.

Isolation/Purification

Bovinone was best obtained by acid decomposition of its insoluble olive-green lead salt. The freshly collected sporophores of *Boletus bovinus* were sliced and steeped in cold ethanol for 1 hr. The bright red solution was decanted and the mushrooms were extracted overnight with fresh, cold alcohol. The combined extracts were treated with an excess of aqueous lead acetate solution; the dark olive-green precipitate was filtered off and washed twice with water and twice with methanol. A suspension of the lead salt in methanol was treated dropwise with 5% methanolic hydrogen chloride until it was completely decomposed. During the decomposition, the mixture was filtered periodically and the red filtrates were evaporated at 35°C under reduced pressure until a red solid precipitated; this was recrystallized from glacial acetic acid as yellow needles.

Spectral Data

UV:

λ_{max}^{EtOH} 287nm (log ϵ=4.31).

IR:

(KBr) 3300, 2959, 2909, 2848, 1610, and 858cm^{-1}; ($CHCl_3$) 3360, 2960, 2919, 2853,1640, 1360, and 850cm^{-1}.

Mass Data:

LREIMS: 414(M + 2), 413(M + 1), 412(M^+), 343(M - 69), 275(M - 69-68), 207(M - 9-2 x 68), 153, 154, and 155*m/e* (benzylium ions), 81, 69(base), 55, 41, and 28*m/e*; HREIMS: 412.2617*m/e* (M^+), requires 412.2614; found: C, 75.5; H 3.4; calcd for $C_{26}H_{36}O_4$, C 75.7; H 8.7%.

Reference

P. C. Beaumont, and R. L. Edwards; Constituents of The Higher Fungi. Part XI. Boviquinone-3, (2,5-dihydroxy-3-farnesyl-1,4-benzoquinone), Diboviquinone-3,4-Methylenediboviquinone-3,3, and Xerocomic Acid from *Gomphidius rutilus* Fr. and Diboviquinone-4,4 from *Boletus (Suillus) bovinus* (Linn ex Fr.) Kuntze; J. Chem. Soc. (C), pp. 2582-2585(1971).

Common/Systematic Name

Methylenediboviquinone-3,3

Molecular Formula/Molecular Weight

$C_{43}H_{56}O_8$; MW = 700.39752

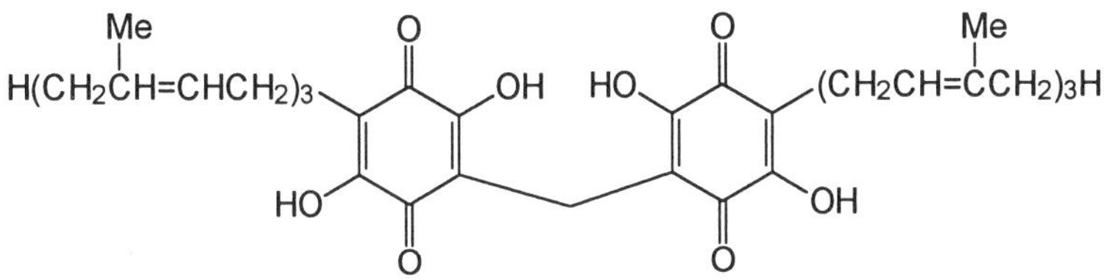

General Characteristics

Recrystallization from acetic acid gave yellow fatty needles; mp., 197-201°C.

Fungal Source

Gomphidius rutilus.

Isolation/Purification

Freshly collected fruiting bodies of *G. rutilus* were sliced and steeped in cold ethanol for 2 hr. The bright red solution was decanted and the mushrooms were extracted overnight with fresh alcohol. Treatment of the combined extracts with an excess of aqueous lead acetate solution yielded the blue-green lead salt which was filtered off and washed twice with water and then twice with methanol. Methanolic hydrogen chloride was added dropwise to the stirred suspension of the lead salt in methanol. The mixture was filtered and the filtrate was evaporated at 35°C to yield a red gum. The gum was dissolved in acetic acid and set aside for three days. Filtration and recrystallization of the yellow residue six times from acetic acid gave methylenediboviquinone-3,3 as yellow fatty needles.

Spectral Data

UV:

λ_{max}^{EtOH} 288nm (log ε=4.40); $\lambda_{max}^{EtOH+NaOH}$ 327nm (log ε=4.56).

IR:

(KBr) 3305, 2965, 2923, 2850, 1620, and 1048cm^{-1}.

^{1}H NMR:

($CDCl_3$) 2.25-2.48(4H); 4.68-5.05(6H); 6.41(2H); 6.86(d, *J*=7Hz, 4H); 7.99(16H); 8.27(6H); 8.30(6H); 8.40(12H); (CCl_4) 2.9(1H); 4.77-5.18(3H); 6.79(d, *J*=7Hz, 2H); 7.74(6H); 7.77(6H); 8.02(8H); 8.33(6H); and 8.42τ (6H).

Mass Data:

700(M^+), 546, 358, and 344*m/e* (M^+ boviquinone-3); found: C, 73.6; H, 8.25; $C_{43}H_{56}O_8$ requires C, 73.7; H, 8.0%.

Reference

P. C. Beaumont, and R. L. Edwards; Constituents of The Higher Fungi. Part XI. Boviquinone-3, (2,5-dihydroxy-3-farnesyl-1,4-benzoquinone), Diboviquinone-3,4-Methylene-diboviquinone-3,3, and Xerocomic Acid from *Gomphidius rutilus* Fr. and Diboviquinone-4,4 from *Boletus (Suillus) bovinus* (Linn ex Fr.) Kuntze; J. Chem. Soc. (C), pp. 2582-2585(1971).

Common/Systematic Name

Diboviquinone-3,4

Molecular Formula/Molecular Weight

$C_{47}H_{62}O_8$; MW = 754.44447

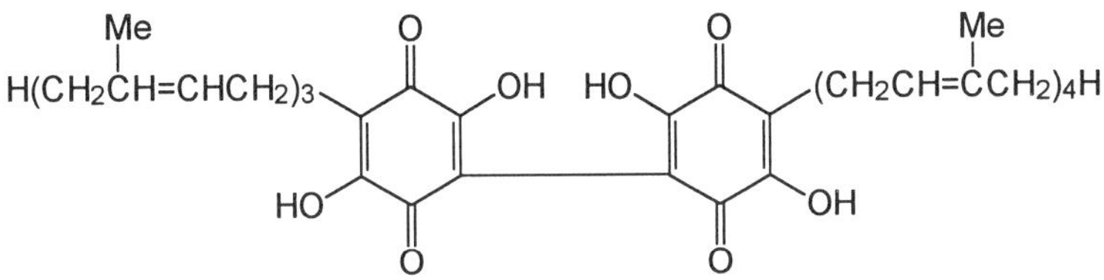

General Characteristics

Clusters of small orange-yellow fatty needles from acetic acid; mp., 137-139°C.

Fungal Source

Gomphidius rutilus.

Isolation/Purification

Freshly collected fruiting bodies of *G. rutilus* were sliced and steeped in cold ethanol for 2 hr. The bright red solution was decanted and the mushrooms were extracted overnight with fresh alcohol. Treatment of the combined extracts with an excess of aqueous lead acetate solution yielded the blue-green lead salt which was filtered off and washed twice with water and then twice with methanol. Methanolic hydrogen chloride was added dropwise to the stirred suspension of the lead salt in methanol. The mixture was filtered and the filtrate was evaporated at 35°C to yield a red gum; boviquinone-3,4 was recrystallized five times from acetic acid.

Spectral Data

UV:

λ_{max}^{EtOH} 288nm (log ϵ=4.46); $\lambda_{max}^{EtOH+NaOH}$ 326nm (log ϵ=4.63).

IR:

(KBr) 3305, 2955, 2923, 2850, 1620, and 1050cm^{-1}.

^{1}H NMR:

($CDCl_3$) 2.03-2.40(4H); 4.67-5.13(7H); 6.88(d, *J*=7Hz, 4H); 8.02(20H); 8.27(6H); 8.32(6H); 8.41(15H); (CCl_4) 2.9(1H); 4.77-5.18(3H); 6.79(d, *J*=7Hz, 2H); 7.74(6H); 7.77(6H); 8.02(8H); 8.33(6H); and 8.42τ (6H).

Mass Data:

LREIMS: 684, 616, 548, 529, 461, 412(M$^+$, boviquinone-4), and 344*m/e* (M$^+$ Boviquinone-3); found: C, 74.5; H, 8.15. $C_{47}H_{62}O_8$ requires C, 74.8; H, 8.2%.

Reference

P. C. Beaumont and R. L. Edwards; Constituents of The Higher Fungi. Part XI. Boviquinone-3,(2,5-dihydroxy-3-farnesyl-1,4-benzoquinone), Diboviquinone-3,4-Methylenediboviquinone-3,3, and Xerocomic Acid from *Gomphidius rutilus* Fr. and Diboviquinone-4,4 from *Boletus (Suillus) bovinus* (Linn ex Fr.) Kuntze; J. Chem. Soc.(C), pp. 2582-2585(1971).

Common/Systematic Name

Diboviquinone-4,4

Molecular Formula/Molecular Weight

$C_{52}H_{70}O_8$; MW = 822.50707

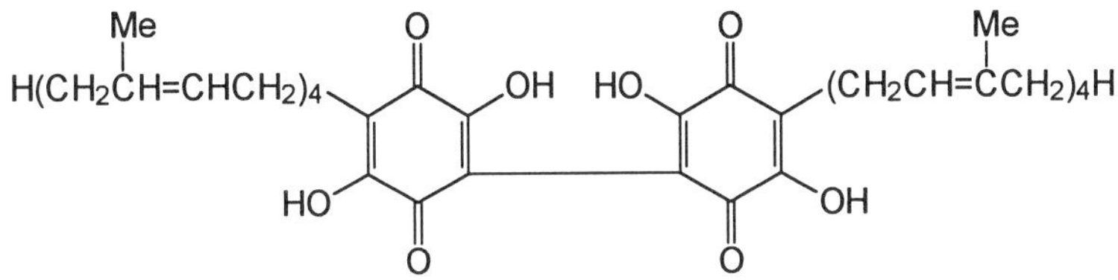

General Characteristics

Recrystallization from acetic acid gave small orange-red needles; mp., 132.5-134°C.

Fungal Source

Boletus (Suillus) bovinus and *Gomphidius rutilus.*

Isolation/Purification

Freshly collected fruiting bodies of *B. bovinus* were sliced and steeped in cold ethanol for 2 hr. The extract was treated with an excess of aqueous lead acetate solution yielded the blue-green lead salt which was filtered off and washed twice with water and then twice with methanol. Methanolic hydrogen chloride was added dropwise to the stirred suspension of the lead salt in methanol. The mixture was filtered and the filtrate was evaporated to yield an orange solid. The solid was recrystallized from acetic acid to give small orange-red needles.

Spectral Data

UV:

λ_{max}^{EtOH} 287nm (log ϵ=4.53); $\lambda_{max}^{EtOH + NaOH}$ 253inf and 325nm.

IR:

(KBr) 3320, 2970, 2920, 2860, 1620, and 1320cm^{-1}; ($CHCl_3$) 3340, 2960, 2920, 2850, 1640, and 1355cm^{-1}.

^{1}H NMR:

($CDCl_3$) 4.69-5.12(8H); 6.86(d, *J*=7Hz, 4H); 7.98(24H); 8.28(6H); 8.38(6H); and 8.68τ (18H).

Mass Data:

LREIMS: 684, 616, 529, and 412*m/e* (M$^+$, boviquinone-4); found: C, 76.4; H, 8.50, $C_{52}H_{70}O_8$ requires C, 76.0; H, 8.5%.

Reference

P. C. Beaumont, and R. L. Edwards; Constituents of The Higher Fungi. Part XI. Boviquinone-3, (2,5-dihydroxy-3-farnesyl-1,4-benzoquinone), Diboviquinone-3,4-Methylenediboviquinone-3,3, and Xerocomic Acid from *Gomphidius rutilus* Fr. and Diboviquinone-4,4 from *Boletus (Suillus) bovinus* (Linn ex Fr.) Kuntze; J. Chem. Soc. (C), pp. 2582-2585(1971).

Common/Systematic Name

Amitenone; Methylenebis(2,5-dihydroxy-4-all-*trans*-gerangeranyl-3,6-benzoquinone); Methylenediboviquinone-4,4

Molecular Formula/Molecular Weight

$C_{53}H_{72}O_8$; MW = 836.52272

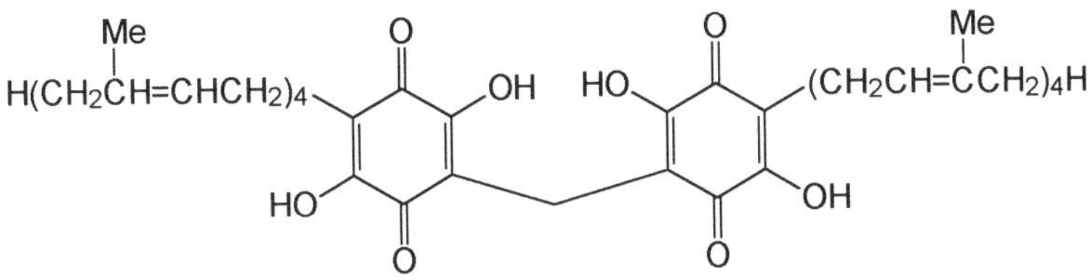

General Characteristics

Yellow orange crystals; mp., 187-188°C.

Fungal Source

Amitake mushroom and *Suillus bovinus*.

Isolation/Purification

Extracted with acetone; purification not described.

Spectral Data

UV:

λ_{max}^{EtOH} 288(log ϵ=4.45); $\lambda_{max}^{EtOH+NaOH}$ 323nm.

IR:

(KBr) 3290(quinone), 1300, 1050, 840, 770, 690; (in $CHCl_3$), 3358(OH), 1646(quinone) deuterium substituted (in $CHCl_3$), 2490(OD).

^1H NMR:

($CDCl_3$) 2.42(4H, s; exchangeable by D_2O; Q-OH), 4.85-5.05(8H); 6.48(2H, s); 6.93(4H, d); 7.85-8.15(24H); 8.30(6H, s); 8.35(6H, s); and 8.43τ (18H, s).

Mass Data:

EIMS: 426.279, 412.258, 343, 275, 207, 81, 69(base), 55, 41, and 28*m/e*; calcd for $C_{53}H_{72}O_8$; C, 76.04% H, 8.67%; found C, 75.84%, H, 8.44%.

Reference

K. Minami, K. Asawa, and M. Sawada; The Structure of Amitenone; Tet. Lett., No. 49, pp. 5067-5070(1968).

17

Fusicoccins

Fusicoccin; Fusicoccin A
Allofusicoccin
Monodeacetylfusicoccin; 3'-Deacetylfusicoccin; F/IV
Dideacetylfusicoccin; F/VII
Isofusicoccin; F/III
12-*O*-Acetyldideacetylfusicoccin
12-*O*-Acetylfusicoccin
12-*O*-Acetylisofusicoccin
16-*O*-Demethyl-19-deoxydideacetyl-3-epifusicoccin; F-V/1
19-Deacetylallofusicoccin; F-V/2
19-Deacetylisofusicoccin; F-VI
19-Deacetylfusicoccin; F-VIII
19-Deoxydideacetylfusicoccin; Fusicoccin J
19-Deoxy-3α-hydroxydideacetylfusicoccin; F-V/3

Common/Systematic Name

Fusicoccin; Fusicoccin A

Molecular Formula/Molecular Weight

$C_{36}H_{56}O_{12}$; MW = 680.37718

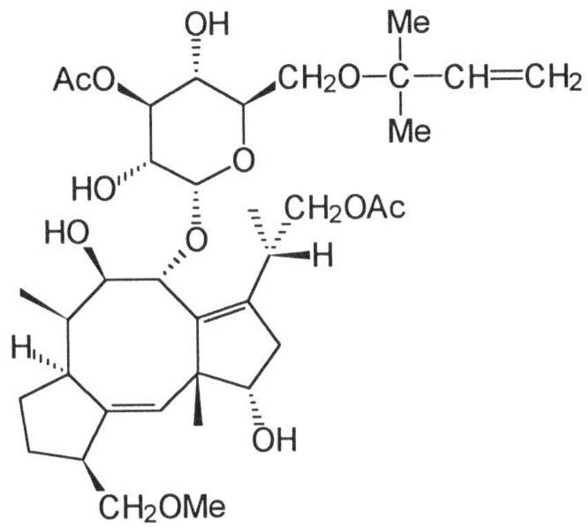

General Characteristics

Crystallization from acetone-light petroleum (bp., 40-60°C) afforded fusicoccin as colorless prisms; mp., 152-154°C containing approximately a 0.5 molar equivalent of acetone. After 24 hr. at 50°C/0.2mm, the acetone of solvation was completely removed to give fusicoccin; mp., 151-153°C; $[\alpha]_D^{30}$ +70.5 (*c*=0.8, in $CHCl_3$). Fusicoccin aglycone; mp., 161-162°C.

Fungal Source

Fusicoccum amygdali, the fungus responsible for a common wilting disease of peach and almond trees in southern Europe.

Isolation/Purification

The original purification of fusicoccin was as follows: the phytotoxic metabolite was exhaustively extracted with butyl acetate and evaporated to dryness; the residue was taken up in $CHCl_3$ and the insoluble fraction discarded; the residue from the $CHCl_3$ extract was taken up in methanol (insoluble fraction discarded); the residue from the methanol extract was washed with hexane to remove lipid impurities and taken up in ethyl ether (insoluble fraction discarded); and the residue from the ether extract was dissolved in about 10 times the volume of chloroform containing 3% acetone and passed through a Florisil column on which the active material was firmly adsorbed. The column was washed with about three column volumes of the same solvent. Fractional elution was effected with chloroform containing 6-10% acetone. The fractionation was followed at first by biological assay and later by thin-layer chromatography with chloroform-isopropanol (92:8), using a sulfuric acid spray.

Spectral Data

IR:
(Nujol) 3400(OH), and 1745cm^{-1} (C=O).

^{1}H NMR:
4.24(dd, 1H, *J*=10, 17Hz); 6.71(s, 3H); 7.89(s, 3H); 7.96(s, 3H); 8.77(6H, s); 8.82(s, 3H); 8.89(d, 3H, *J*=6.5Hz); and 9.16ppm (d, 3H, *J*=7.0Hz).

Mass Data:
LREIMS: 680*m/e* (M^+), $C_{36}H_{56}O_{12}$ molecular wt., 680; minor ion at 722*m/e* presumed due to thermally induced transacetylation; Found: C, 63.55; H, 8.25, $C_{36}H_{56}O_{12}$ requires C, 63.5; H, 8.3%.

References

A. Ballio, M. Brufani, C. G. Casinovi, S. Cerrini, W. Fedeli, R. Pellicciari, B. Santurbano, and A. Vaciago; The Structure of Fusicoccin A; Experientia, Vol. 24, pp. 631-635(1968).

A. Ballio, E. B. Chain, P. De Leo, B. F. Erlanger, M. Mauri, and A. Tonolo; Fusicoccin: a New Wilting Toxin Produced by *Fusicoccum amygdali* Del.; Nature, Vol. 203, p. 297 (1964).

K. D. Barrow, D. H. R. Barton, E. Cha, C. Conlay, T. C. Smale, R. Thomas, and E. S. Waight; Fusicoccin. Part 1. The Nature of the Substituent Groups; J. Chem. Soc.(C), pp. 1259-1264 (1971).

K. D. Barrow, D. H. R. Barton, E. Chain, U. F. W. Ohnsorge, and R. Thomas, Fusicoccin. Part II. The Constitution of Fusicoccin, pp. 1265-1274(1971).

Common/Systematic Name

Allofusicoccin

Molecular Formula/Molecular Weight

$C_{36}H_{56}O_{12}$; MW = 680.37718

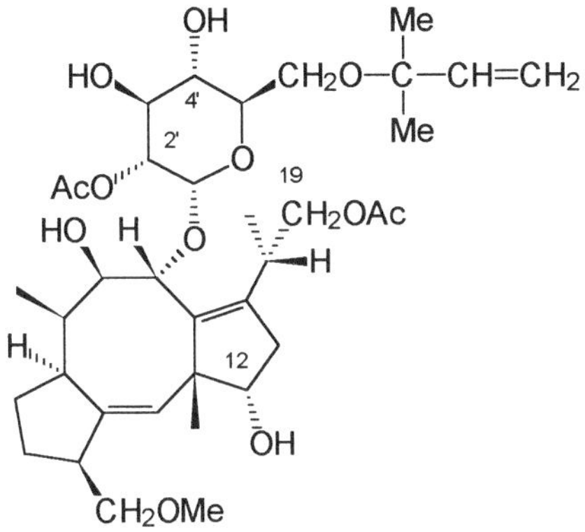

General Characteristics

Allofusicoccin was obtained as a partially crystalline substance by precipitation with light petroleum from acetone solution; mp., 83-86°C; $[\alpha]_D^{25}$ + 35° (*c*=1.26).

Fungal Source

Culture filtrates of *Fusicoccum amygdali*. Allofusicoccin formed (during the production phase) when fusicoccin was incubated at room temperature at the same pH as the culture brew. Therefore it might arise nonenzymatically from fusicoccin during the course of the fermentation.

Isolation/Purification

Allofusicoccin was obtained by chromatographic fractionation of the residue left in ethyl acetate after crystallization of fusicoccin. In particular, repeated fractionations on silica gel columns (Kieselgel S-HR, Machery and Nagel) yielded chromatographically pure allofusicoccin, which was eventually obtained as a partially crystalline substance by precipitation with light petroleum (bp., 30-50°C) from an acetone solution.

Biological Activity

Phytotoxic.

Spectral Data

IR:

The IR spectrum in the region 850-3700cm^{-1} was superimposable upon that of fusicoccin, whereas it was different in the range 500-850cm^{-1}.

^1H NMR:

($CDCl_3$) The NMR spectrum clearly indicated the same features observed in fusicoccin and isofusicoccin, namely a vinyl on a quaternary carbon, an olefinic proton on a trisubstituted double bond, 1 *O*-Me, 2 *O*-Ac, 2 secondary and 3 tertiary C-Me groups. Unambiguous assignment of the acetylated position for each isomer was attained through NMR- and NMDR-spectra. Allofusicoccin dissolved in acetone-d_6 showed a dd centered at 4.6ppm (1 H) with splittings (3.5 and 10Hz) consistent with 1'(eq)-2'(ax) and 2' (ax)- 3'(ax) couplings, as expected for an α-glucopyranoside esterified at C-2'. The dd collapsed to a d centered at 4.65ppm (J=10Hz) on irradiation of the d at 4.99ppm (J=3.6Hz, anomeric proton) and to a d centered at 4.70ppm (J=3.5Hz) on irradiation at 3.96ppm (which therefore must correspond to the chemical shift of CH-3'). Thus, allofusicoccin has a structure differing from fusicoccin by the location of one acetoxy group on C-2' instead of C-3'.

Mass Spectrum:

The mass spectrum was also very similar to that fusicoccin, showing the molecular ion at 680*m/e* and characteristic ions at 408(aglycone), 205(monoacetylglucosyl), 69($C_5H_9^+$), and 43*m/e* (CH_3CO^+).

Reference

A. Ballio, C.G. Casinovi, M. Framondino, G. Grandolini, F. Menichini, G. Randazzo, and C. Rossi; The Structures of Isofusicoccin and Allofusicoccin; Experientia, Vol. 15, pp. 126-127(1972).

Common/Systematic Name
Monodeacetylfusicoccin; F/IV

Molecular Formula/Molecular Weight
$C_{34}H_{54}O_{11}$; MW = 638.36661

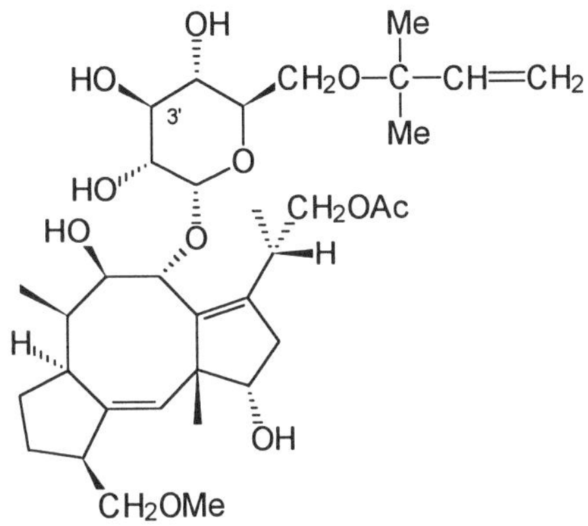

General Characteristics
$[\alpha]_D^{25}$ +18.5 (*c*=0.12, in EtOH).

Fungal Source
Produced in submerged cultures of the phytopathogenic fungus *Fusicoccum amygdali*. Also, formed when dilute solutions of fusicoccin are incubated at room temperature in buffer having the same pH (about 7.0) as the culture brew during the production phase; therefore, probably arises nonenzymatically from fusicoccin during the course of the fermentation.

Isolation/Purification
The brown oily residue left in ethyl acetate after crystallization of fusicoccin was dissolved in chloroform and fractionated on a Florisil column by extended elution with chloroform. Each fraction was tested by thin-layer chromatography (silica gel G, 8% 2-propanol in chloroform; sulfuric acid spray). After fusicoccin (F/I), which emerged first, a very small amount of F/II appeared, followed by isofusicoccin (F/III) and monodeacetylfusicoccin (F/IV), and finally by a mixture of F/V, F/VI and dideacetylfusicoccin (F/VII), separated from isofusicoccin and dideacetylfusicoccin. Appropriate fractions were pooled; those containing mixtures of isofusicoccin and monodeacetylfusicoccin were further fractionated by chromatography under the same conditions described above, whereas dideacetylfusicoccin was obtained pure after repeated chromatography on silica gel (Machery and Nagel S-HR, 50% benzene in acetone). By these procedures monodeacetylfusicoccin was obtained chromatographically pure.

Biological Activity

While isofusicoccin is nearly as phytotoxic as fusicoccin in the assay with tomato plants, monodeacetylfusicoccin and dideacetylfusicoccin are respectively 12 and 100 times less active.

Spectral Data

UV:

λ_{max} <215nm.

IR:

The IR spectrum was very similar to that of fusicoccin.

^{1}H NMR:

The NMR spectrum indicated the occurrence of the same groups observed in fusicoccin, with the only difference that a single O-Ac group was present. This was corroborated by the observation that monodeacetylfusicoccin, contrary to fusicoccin, was oxidizable with periodate. NMR spectra also yielded evidence that the O-Ac group cannot be located on either of the secondary alcoholic functions of the aglycone moiety.

Mass Spectrum:

That a single O-Ac was present was confirmed by the mass spectrum which showed the molecular ion peak at 638*m/e*. Furthermore, the aglycone peak at 408*m/e* was still present, thus indicating that the missing acetyl group was on the glucosyl moiety.

Reference

A. Ballio, C. G. Casinovi, G. Randazzo, and C. Rossi; Characterization of By-products of Fusicoccin in Culture Filtrates of *Fusicoccum amygdali* Del.; Experientia, Vol. 26, pp. 349-351(1970).

Common/Systematic Name

Dideacetylfusicoccin; F/VII

Molecular Formula/Molecular Weight

$C_{32}H_{52}O_{10}$; MW = 596.35605

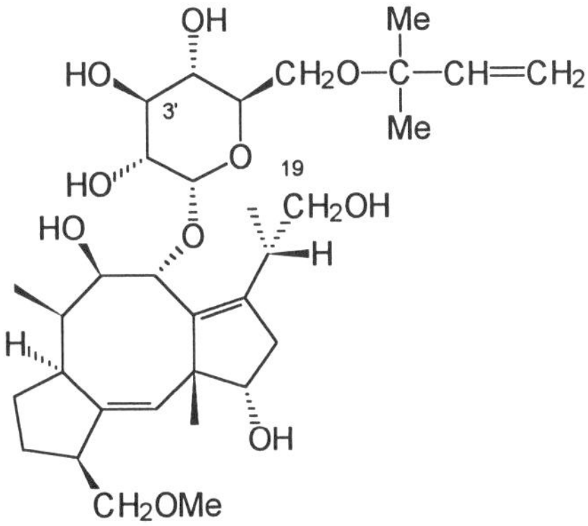

General Characteristics

$[\alpha]_D^{25}$ +9 (*c*=0.90, in EtOH).

Fungal Source

Produced in submerged cultures of the phytopathogenic fungus *Fusicoccum amygdali*. Also formed when dilute solutions of fusicoccin were incubated at room temperature in buffer having the same pH (about 7.0) as the culture brew during the production phase, therefore probably arises nonenzymatically from fusicoccin in the course of the fermentation.

Isolation/Purification

The brown oily residue left in ethyl acetate after crystallization of fusicoccin was dissolved in chloroform and fractionated on a Florisil column by extended washing with chloroform. Each fraction was tested by thin layer chromatography (silica gel G, 8% 2-propanol in chloroform, sulfuric acid spray). After fusicoccin (F/I), which emerged first, a very small amount of F/II appeared, followed by isofusicoccin (F/III) and monodeacetylfusicoccin (F/IV), and finally by a mixture of F/V, F/VI, and dideacetylfusicoccin (F/VII), separated from isofusicoccin and dideacetylfusicoccin. Appropriate fractions were pooled; those containing mixtures of isofusicoccin and monodeacetylfusicoccin were further fractionated by chromatography under the same conditions described. Dideacetylfusicoccin was obtained pure after repeated chromatography on silica gel (Machery and Nagel S-HR, 50% benzene in acetone). By these procedures dideacetylfusicoccin was obtained chromatographically pure.

Biological Activity

While isofusicoccin was nearly as phytotoxic as fusicoccin in the assay with tomato plants, monodeacetylfusicoccin and dideacetylfusicoccin were respectively 12 and 100 times less active.

Spectral Data

UV:

λ_{max} <215nm.

IR:

The IR spectrum showed the absence of O-Ac groups.

^{1}H NMR:

The NMR spectrum indicated similar features observed in the spectrum of fusicoccin and confirmed the absence of O-Ac groups.

Mass Spectrum:

The mass spectrum showed the molecular ion peak at 596*m/e* and strong signals at 366*m/e* (deacetylaglycone) and 69*m/e* ($C_5H_9^+$).

Reference

A. Ballio, C. G. Casinovi, G. Randazzo, and C. Rossi; Characterization of By-products of Fusicoccin in Culture Filtrates of *Fusicoccum amygdali* Del., Experientia, Vol. 26, pp. 349-351(1970).

Common/Systematic Name
Isofusicoccin; F/III

Molecular Formula/Molecular Weight
$C_{36}H_{56}O_{12}$; MW = 680.37718

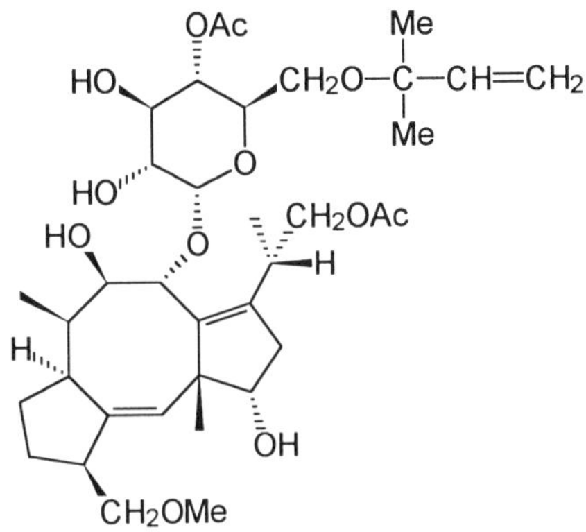

General Characteristics
$[\alpha]_D^{25}$ +11 (*c*=0.15, in EtOH).

Fungal Source
Isofusicoccin was produced in submerged cultures of the phytopathogenic fungus *Fusicoccum amygdali*. It also formed when dilute solutions of fusicoccin were incubated at room temperature in buffer having the same pH (about 7.0) as the culture brew during the production phase; therefore, it probably arises nonenzymatically from fusicoccin during the course of the fermentation.

Isolation/Purification
The brown oily residue left in ethyl acetate after crystallization of fusicoccin was dissolved in chloroform and fractionated on a Florisil column by extended washing with chloroform. Each fraction was tested by thin-layer chromatography (silica gel G, 8% 2-propanol in chloroform, sulfuric acid spray). After fusicoccin (F/I), which emerged first, a very small amount of F/II appeared, followed by isofusicoccin (F/III) and monodeacetylfusicoccin (F/IV), and finally by a mixture of F/V, F/VI, and dideacetylfusicoccin (F/VII), separated from isofusicoccin and dideacetylfusicoccin. Appropriate fractions were pooled; those containing mixtures of isofusicoccin and monodeacetylfusicoccin were further fractionated by chromatography under the same conditions described above. Dideacetylfusicoccin was obtained pure after repeated chromatography on silica gel (Machery and Nagel S-HR, 50% benzene in acetone). By these procedures isofusicoccin was obtained chromatographically pure.

Biological Activity

Isofusicoccin was a highly active phytotoxic metabolite produced in submerged cultures of the phytopathogenic fungus *Fusicoccum amygdali*. Isofusicoccin was nearly as phytotoxic as fusicoccin in the assay with tomato plants.

Spectral Data

UV:

λ_{max} <215nm.

IR:

The IR spectrum in the region 850-3700cm^{-1} was superimposable upon that of fusicoccin, whereas it was quite different in the region 720-850cm^{-1}.

^{1}H NMR:

The NMR spectrum clearly indicated the same features observed in fusicoccin, namely a vinyl on a quaternary carbon, an olefinic proton on a trisubstituted double bond, an O-Me, two O-Ac, 2 secondary and 3 tertiary C-Me groups.

Mass Spectrum:

The mass spectrum was also very similar to that of fusicoccin, showing the molecular ion peak at 680*m/e* and strong signals at 408(aglycone), 205(monoacetylglucosyl), 69($C_5H_9^+$), and 43*m/e* (CH_3CO^+).

Reference

A. Ballio, C. G. Casinovi, G. Randazzo, and C. Rossi; Characterization of By-products of Fusicoccin in Culture Filtrates of *Fusicoccum amygdali* Del.; Experientia, Vol. 26, pp. 349-351(1970).

Common/Systematic Name

12-*O*-Acetyldideacetylfusicoccin; F-V/4

Molecular Formula/Molecular Weight

$C_{34}H_{54}O_{11}$; MW = 638.36661

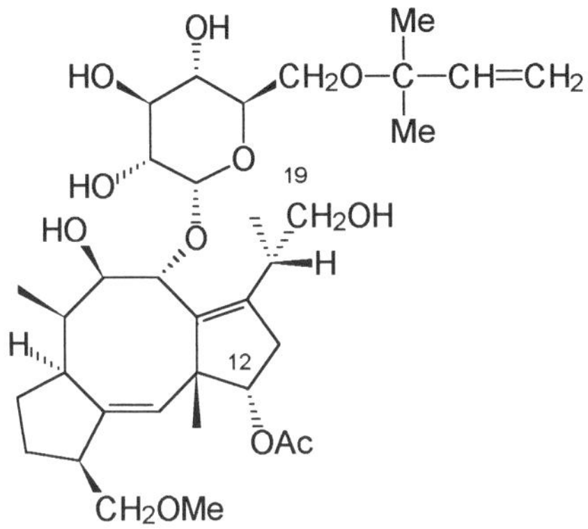

General Characteristics

Crystals from acetone; mp., 186-188°C; $[\alpha]_D^{25}$ +11.5 (*c*=0.49, in $CHCl_3$).

Fungal Source

Fusicoccum amygdali.

Isolation/Purification

Purified by extensive chromatographic fractionations on silica gel columns (Kieselgel S-HR, Macherey and Nagel) of the ethyl acetate mother liquor from the crystallization of fusicoccin.

Biological Activity

Phytotoxic.

Spectral Data

^{1}H NMR:

(acetone-d_6) Spectrum showed the signal expected for the CH-OAc at 4.91ppm as a *m* partially overlapping the AB part of the ABX system due to CH_2-CH- and clearly affected on irradiation at 2.33ppm. This value corresponded to the center of the AB system (2 out of 8 lines were covered by the signals of acetone) of an ABX system which can be attributed to $C(CH_3)_2$=$C(CH_3)$-CH_2-CH(OAc)-$C(CH_3)_3$. This was further supported in the spectrum of the dihydro derivative; (pyridine-d_5) which showed separate signals for the anomeric proton (5.44ppm, *d*, *J*=3.5Hz, collapsed to an *s* upon irradiation at 4.05ppm) and for the acetylated function (1H, 5.27ppm, *dd*, collapsed to a *d*, *J*=5.0Hz upon irradiation at 2.88Hz; the latter two frequencies each corresponded to the center of a four line system, which gave rise to a *d*, *J*=16.0Hz, upon irradiation at 5.27ppm).

Mass Spectrum:
638(M^+), 408(acetate on aglycone), 366(aglycone), and 205*m/e* (monoacetylglucosyl).

Reference

A. Ballio, C. G. Casinovi, M. Framondino, G. Grandolini, G. Randazzo, and C. Rossi; The Structures of Three Isomers of Monodeacetylfusicoccin; Experientia, Vol. 28, pp. 1150-1151(1972).

Common/Systematic Name

12-*O*-Acetylfusicoccin

Molecular Formula/Molecular Weight

$C_{38}H_{58}O_{13}$; MW = 722.38774

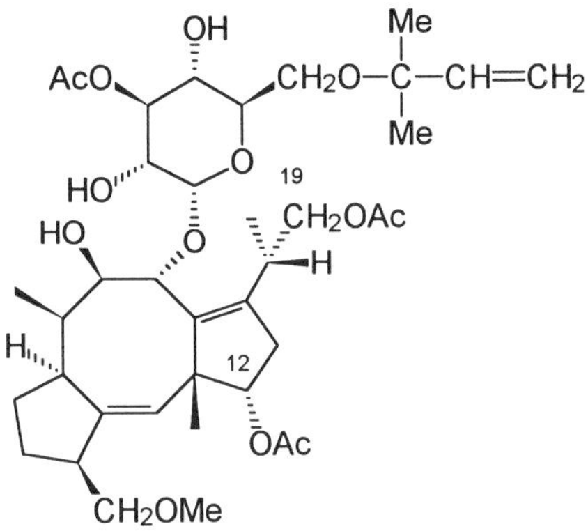

General Characteristics

12-*O*-Acetylfusicoccin crystallized from ethyl ether-light petroleum (40-70°C); mp., 82-83°C and $[\alpha]_D^{25}$ +30.0° (*c*=0.9, in $CHCl_3$).

Fungal Source

Fusicoccum amygdali.

Isolation/Purification

Isolated by repeated column and thin-layer chromatography on silica gel of fractions obtained by chromatographic fractionation of the ethyl acetate mother liquor after crystallization of fusicoccin. It was crystallized from ethyl ether-light petroleum.

Biological Activity

Phytotoxic.

Spectral Data

^1H NMR:

NMR spectra ($CDCl_3$) demonstrated besides other features characteristic of fusicoccin and related compounds, the presence of 3 O-Ac groups. Both 12-*O*-acetylfusicoccin and 12-*O*-acetylisofusicoccin contained O-Ac groups on C-12 and C-19 of the aglycone moiety; in the former the third O-Ac was located on C-2' while in the latter it was located on C-4' on the sugar moieties. Since 12-*O*-acetylfusicoccin was not oxidized by periodate it was located on C-2' in contrast to 12-*O*-acetylisofusicoccin.

Mass Spectrum:

Mass spectra showed 12-*O*-acetylfusicoccin to be isomeric with 12-*O*-acetyliso-fusicoccin with a molecular ion at 722(M^+) for each, resulting in a molecular formula of $C_{38}H_{58}O_{13}$ for each metabolite; each with daughter ions at 405 and 205*m/e* which corresponded to the 2 O-Ac groups in the aglycone and 1 in the sugar moiety.

Reference

A. Ballio, C. G. Casinovi, G. Grandolini, G. Randazzo, C. Rossi, and M. Sorrentino; 12-*O*-Acetylfusicoccin and 12-*O*-Acetylisofusicoccin, Two New Minor Metabolites of *Fusicoccum amygdali* Del.; Experientia, Vol. 30, pp. 1108-1109(1974).

Common/Systematic Name
12-*O*-Acetylisofusicoccin

Molecular Formula/Molecular Weight
$C_{38}H_{58}O_{13}$; MW = 722.38774

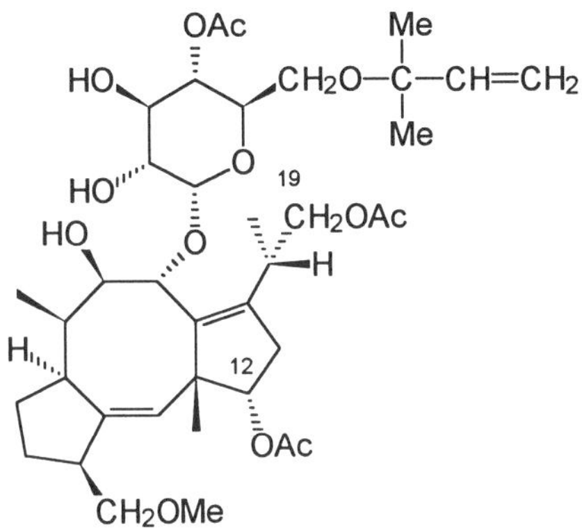

General Characteristics
12-*O*-Acetylisofusicoccin crystallized from ethyl ether-light petroleum (40-70°C); mp., 59°C and $[\alpha]_D^{25}$ +35.1° (*c*=1.4, in $CHCl_3$).

Fungal Source
Fusicoccum amygdali.

Isolation/Purification
Isolated by repeated column and thin-layer chromatography on silica gel of fractions obtained by chromatographic fractionation of the ethyl acetate mother liquor after crystallization of fusicoccin. It was crystallized from ethyl ether-light petroleum.

Biological Activity
Phytotoxic.

Spectral Data

^{1}H NMR:
NMR spectra ($CDCl_3$) demonstrated,besides other features characteristic of fusicoccin and related compounds, the presence of 3 O-Ac groups. Both 12-*O*-acetylfusicoccin and 12-*O*-acetylisofusicoccin contained O-Ac groups on C-12 and C-19 of the aglycone moiety; they differed in the position of the O-Ac on the sugar moiety. NMR data indicated that the third O-Ac group in 12-*O*-acetylisofusicoccin was located on C-4'. Irradiation around 3.90ppm (a value compatible with CH-3' and CH-5') resulted in a triplet centered around 4.72ppm collapsing to a broad singlet; multiplicity and splitting are compatible with values found for CH(4')OAc in isofusicoccin.

Mass Spectrum:

Mass spectra showed it to be isomeric with 12-*O*-acetylfusicoccin with a molecular ion at 722(M^+) for a molecular formula of $C_{38}H_{58}O_{13}$; with daughter ions at 405 and 205*m/e* which corresponded to the 2 O-Ac groups in the aglycone and 1 in the sugar moiety.

Reference

A. Ballio, C. G. Casinovi, G. Grandolini, G. Randazzo, C. Rossi, and M. Sorrentino; 12-*O*-Acetylfusicoccin and 12-*O*-Acetylisofusicoccin, Two New Minor Metabolites of *Fusicoccum amygdali* Del.; Experientia, Vol. 30, pp. 1108-1109(1974).

Common/Systematic Name

16-*O*-Demethyl-19-deoxydideacetyl-3-epifusicoccin; F-V/1

Molecular Formula/Molecular Weight

$C_{31}H_{15}O_9$; MW = 531.07161

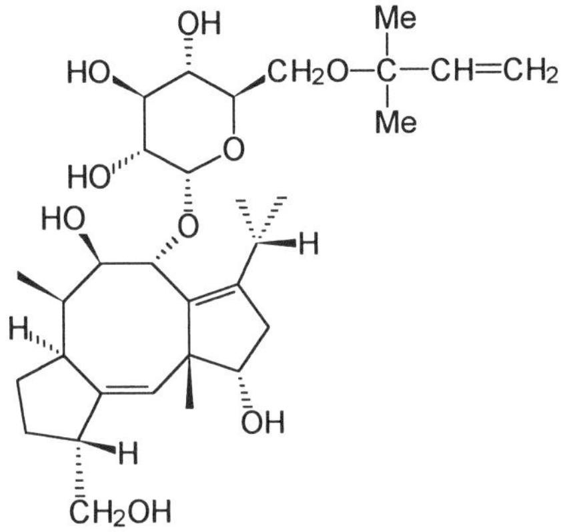

General Characteristics

16-*O*-Demethyl-19-deoxydideacetyl-3-epifusicoccin was obtained as white crystals from acetone; mp., 129-130°C, $[\alpha]_D^{25}$ -10.2° (*c*=1.05, in EtOH). Aglycone was crystallized from ethyl acetate as white crystals; mp., 194-197°C; $[\alpha]_D^{25}$ - 94° (*c*=1.0, in EtOH).

Fungal Source

The phytopathogenic fungus *Fusicoccum amygdali*.

Isolation/Purification

Partially purified fraction further purified by chromatography on silica gel (benzene followed by benzene-acetone, 8:2, v/v). It was finally purified by crystallization as white crystals from acetone. Aglycone was isolated after silica gel chromatography (benzene with increasing amounts of methanol) as white crystals from ethyl acetate.

Biological Activity

Phytotoxic.

Spectral Data

UV:

λ_{max}^{EtOH} <220nm.

Mass Spectrum:

566(M^+), 336(aglycone, $C_{20}H_{32}O_4$), and 69*m/e* (C_5H_9). Aglycone, 336*m/e* (M^+).

Reference

A. Ballio, C. G. Casinovi, G. Grandolini, M. Pomponi, G. Randazzo, and C. Rossi; XIX/16-*O*-Demethyl-19-deoxydideacetyl-3-epifusicoccin; Gazzetta Chimica Italiana, Vol. 105, pp. 647-650(1975).

Common/Systematic Name

19-Deacetylallofusicoccin; F-V/2

Molecular Formula/Molecular Weight

$C_{34}H_{54}O_{11}$; MW = 638.36661

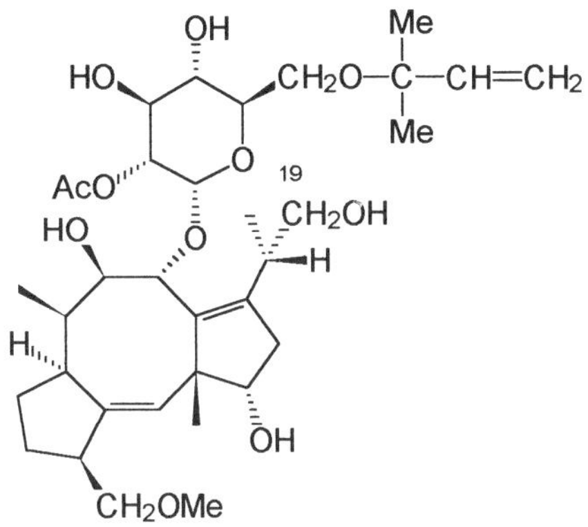

General Characteristics

Crystals; mp., 87-90°C; $[\alpha]_D^{25}$ +15.0 (*c*=0.65, in $CHCl_3$).

Fungal Source

Fusicoccum amygdali.

Isolation/Purification

Purified by extensive chromatographic fractionations on silica gel columns (Kieselgel S-HR, Machery and Nagel) of the ethyl acetate mother liquor from the crystallization of fusicoccin.

Biological Activity

Phytotoxic.

Spectral Data

^{1}H NMR:

(acetone-d_6) Spectrum showed dd(1H) centered at 4.70ppm with (eq)(ax) and (ax)(ax) couplings (*J*=4 and 9Hz), which collapsed to a *d* on irradiation at 4.91ppm (1H, d, *J*=4Hz; anomeric proton, partially overlapping the AB part of the ABX system due to CH_2=CH-). The *dd* can be attributed to the CH(2') OAc of 19-deacetylfusicoccin.

Mass Spectrum:

LREIMS: 638(M^+), 366(aglycone), and 205*m/e* (monoacetylglucosyl).

Reference

A. Ballio, C. G. Casinovi, M. Framondino, G. Grandolini, G. Randazzo, and C. Rossi; The Structures of Three Isomers of Monodeacetylfusicoccin; Experientia, Vol. 28, pp. 1150-1151(1972).

Common/Systematic Name

19-Deacetylisofusicoccin; F-VI

Molecular Formula/Molecular Weight

$C_{34}H_{54}O_{11}$; MW = 638.36661

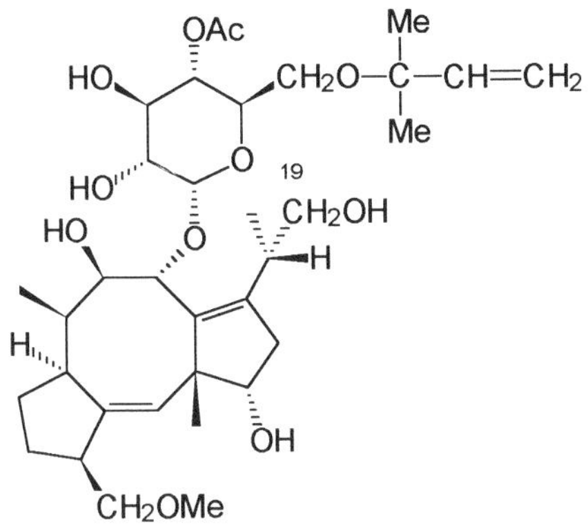

General Characteristics

Crystals from ethyl acetate; mp., 211-213°C; $[\alpha]_D^{25}$ +8.0 (c=0.50, in $CHCl_3$).

Fungal Source

Fusicoccum amygdali.

Isolation/Purification

Purified by extensive chromatographic fractionations on silica gel columns (Kieselgel S-HR, Machery and Nagel) of the ethyl acetate mother liquor from the crystallization of fusicoccin.

Biological Activity

Phytotoxic.

Spectral Data

^{1}H NMR:

($CDCl_3$) Spectrum of dihydro derivative showed the anomeric proton, partially overlapping the AB part of the ABX proton as a *d* (J=3.5Hz) at 5.12ppm, coupled to a proton centered at 3.69ppm (overlapped by other resonances), a frequency which does not affect the *t* (1H, J=9.0Hz) resonating at 4.86ppm; the latter collapses to a broad *s* on irradiation around 3.86ppm, a value compatible with CH-3' and CH-5'.

Mass Spectrum:
638(M^+), 366 (aglycone), and 205*m/e*(monoacetylglucosyl).

Reference

A. Ballio, C. G. Casinovi, M. Framondino, G. Grandolini, G. Randazzo, and C. Rossi; The Structures of Three Isomers of Monodeacetylfusicoccin; Experientia, Vol. 28, pp. 1150-1151(1972).

Common/Systematic Name
19-Deacetylfusicoccin; F-VIII

Molecular Formula/Molecular Weight
$C_{34}H_{54}O_{11}$; MW = 638.36661

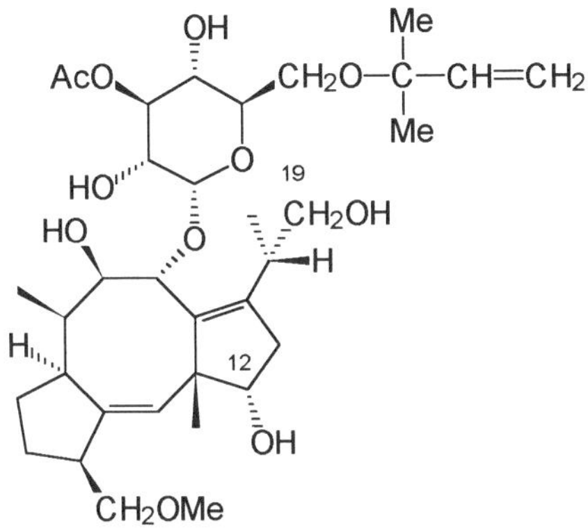

General Characteristics
Crystals from cyclohexane-ethyl acetate; mp., 112-114°C; $[\alpha]_D^{25}$ +36.6 (*c*=0.42, in $CHCl_3$); not oxidizable with periodate.

Fungal Source
Fusicoccum amygdali; originally reported as a product of alkaline isomerization of either 19-deacetylisofusicoccin or dideacetylfusicoccin.

Isolation/Purification
Purified by extensive chromatographic fractionations on silica gel columns (Kieselgel S-HR, Machery and Nagel) of the ethyl acetate mother liquor from the crystallization of fusicoccin.

Biological Activity
Phytotoxic.

Spectral Data

^{1}H NMR:
NMR and NMDR spectra yielded the same type information about the position of the acetoxy group as with allofusicoccin and isofusicoccin.

Mass Spectrum:
638(M^+), 366(deacetylaglycone), 205(monoacetylglucosyl), 69($C_5H_9^+$), and 43*m/e* (CH_3CO^+).

References

A. Ballio, C. G. Casinovi, M. Framondino, G. Grandolini, F. Menichini, G. Randazzo, and C. Rossi; The Structures of Isofusicoccin and Allofusicoccin; Experientia, Vol. 28, pp. 126-127(1972).

A. Ballio, C. G. Casinovi, G. Grandolini, G. Randazzo, C. Rossi, and M. Sorrentino; 12-*O*-Acetylfusicoccin and 12-*O*-Acetylisofusicoccin, Two New Minor Metabolites of *Fusicoccum amygdali* Del.; Experientia, Vol. 30, pp. 1108-1109(1974).

Common/Systematic Name

19-Deoxydideacetylfusicoccin; Fusicoccin J

Molecular Formula/Molecular Weight

$C_{32}H_{52}O_9$; MW = 580.36113

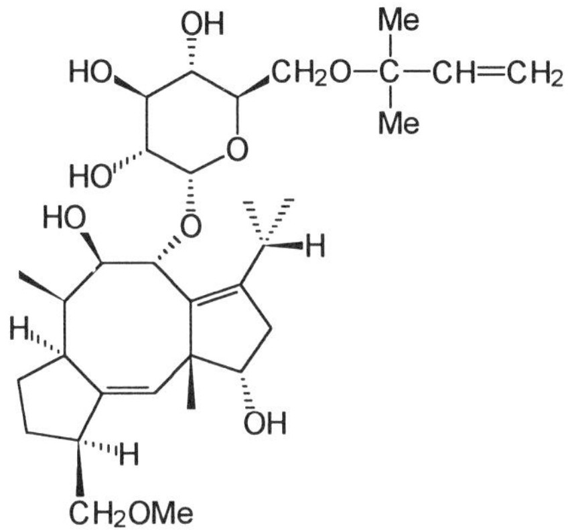

General Characteristics

Crystals from ethyl acetate-light petroleum ether (30-50°); mp., 91°C; $[\alpha]_D^{25}$ +21 (*c*=0.3, in $CHCl_3$). Aglycone: $C_{21}H_{34}O_4$ (M^+ 350); amorphous solid; $[\alpha]_D^{25}$ +4 (*c*=1.0, in $CHCl_3$).

Fungal Source

Fusicoccum amygdali.

Isolation/Purification

19-Deoxydideacetylfusicoccin was purified by silica gel chromatography followed by treatment with 0.1N NaOH for thirty minutes, extraction with 1-butanol and chromatography on a silica gel column. 19-Deoxydideacetylfusicoccin was eluted from the column with chloroform-methanol (8:2, v/v) and crystallized from ethyl acetate-light petroleum ether. Aglycone prepared by treatment of periodate reaction product with alkali; isolated by silica gel column chromatography. Aglycone eluted with chloroform-2-propanol, 95:5 (v/v) as an amorphous solid.

Biological Activity

Phytotoxic.

Spectral Data

UV:

λ_{max}^{EtOH} <220nm.

IR:
(CHCl$_3$) 3500(OH), 1630(olefinic), and 920cm^{-1} (vinyl).

^{1}H NMR:
(CDCl$_3$-pyridine-d_5) Spectrum very similar to dideacetylfusicoccin but with signals for 3 secondary C-methyl groups; 2 being part of an isopropyl group whose CH resonated at 3.22ppm.

Mass Spectrum:
LREIMS: 580(M$^+$), 512(M$^+$ - 68), 350(aglycone), and 69*m/e* ($C_5H_9^+$).

Reference

A. Ballio, C. G. Casinovi, V. D'Alessio, G. Grandolini, G. Randazzo, and C. Rossi; 19-Deoxydideacetylfusicoccin, a Minor Metabolite of *Fusicoccum amygdali* Del.; Experientia, Vol. 30, pp. 844-845(1974).

Common/Systematic Name

19-Deoxy-3α-hydroxydideacetylfusicoccin; F-V/3

Molecular Formula/Molecular Weight

$C_{32}H_{52}O_{10}$; MW = 596.35605

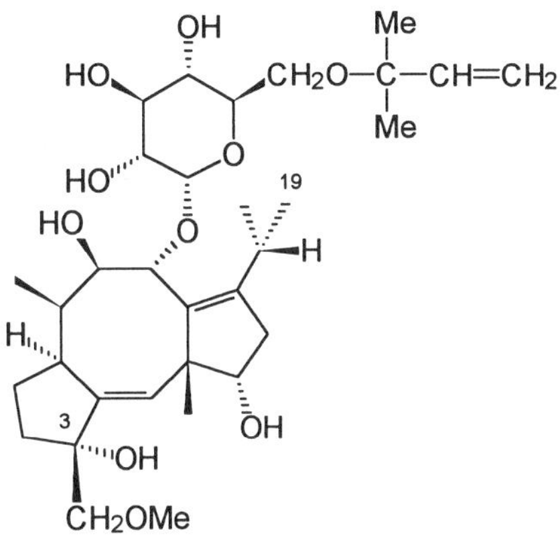

General Characteristics

Obtained as white crystals; mp., 137-138°C (from AcOEt); $[\alpha]_D^{25}$ +22.0 (*c*=0.26, in $CHCl_3$).

Fungal Source

Fusicoccum amygdali.

Isolation/Purification

19-Deoxy-3α-dideacetylfusicoccin was purified by repetitive silica gel column chromatography. Acid hydrolysis yielded approximately one mole of D-glucose (glucose oxidase).

Biological Activity

Phytotoxic.

Spectral Data

UV:

λ_{max}^{EtOH} <220nm.

IR:

($CHCl_3$) 3500(OH), 1630(olefinic), and 920cm^{-1} (vinyl).

^{1}H NMR:

(C_5D_5N) Spectrum was similar to that of 19-deoxy-3α-dideacetylfusicoccin with the following differences: proton H-C (1) appeared as a doublet (J=2Hz) instead of a triplet; in the region where the protons H-C (3) and H-C (6) resonate, only one proton rather than two was present; the C(16)H_2 group gave signals typical of an AB system instead of an ABX system.

^{13}C NMR:

(C_5D_5N) Spectrum very similar to that of deoxydideacetylfusicoccin except for C(2), C(3), and C(4), which were shifted to higher frequencies (4.2, 33.8, and 4.4ppm, respectively).

Mass Spectrum:

Whereas in the electron impact mass spectrum the highest detectable peak was at m/e=578 ($C_{32}H_{50}O$, by high-resolution measurements), the spectrum obtained by the field ion-desorption technique contained a peak at m/e=596 thus suggesting that the molecular formula of 19-deoxy-3α-hydroxydideacetylfusicoccin is $C_{32}H_{52}O_{10}$. Furthermore, the electron impact mass spectrum showed losses of CH_4O (confirmed by metastable peaks) and C_5H_8, as well as the signal expected for the aglycone ($C_{21}H_{34}O_5$, m/e=366); the base peak was at m/e=69 ($C_5H_9^+$).

Reference

A. Ballio, C. G. Casinovi, G. Grandolini, M. Marta, and G. Randazzo; XXIX/ 19-Deoxy-3α-hydroxydideacetylfusicoccin; Gazzetta Chimica Italiana, Vol. 105, pp. 1325-1328(1975).

18

Altenuene and Related Metabolites

(±)-Altenuene
(±)-Dehydroaltenusin
Botrallin
Alternariol Monomethyl Ether
Alternariol
Altenuisol (Altertenuol)
Altenusin
Dehydroaltenusin
Altenuic Acid I
(±)-Altenuic Acid II
Altenuic Acid III

Common/Systematic Name

(±)-Altenuene

2',3',4',5'-Tetrahydro-3,3',4'-trihydroxy-5-methoxy-6'-methyldibenzo[a]pyrone

Molecular Formula/Molecular Weight

$C_{15}H_{16}O_6$; MW = 292.09469

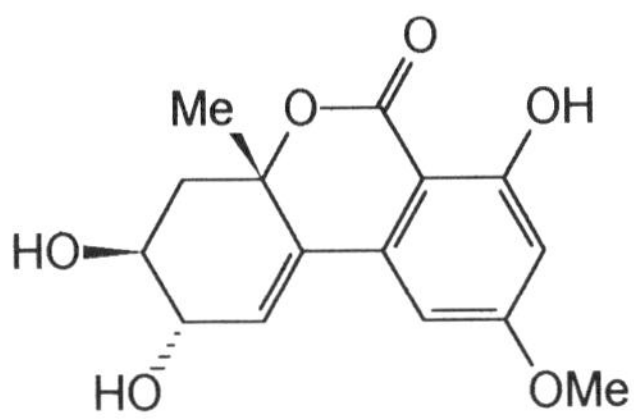

General Characteristics

The metabolite crystallized from acetone-hexane mixtures as colorless needles that melted sharply at 190-191 °C (corr.); produced an intense purple color with addition of ethanolic $FeCl_3$. Altenuene dissolved readily in acetone, 1M NaOH, methanol, pyridine, and tetrahydrofuran. It was slightly soluble in diethyl ether and chloroform and insoluble in benzene, hexane, 1M HCl, saturated aqueous $NaHCO_3$, and water.

Fungal Source

The isolate of *Alternaria tenuis* (NRRL L5872; 5873) was obtained from naturally infected tobacco in 1965.

Isolation/Purification

The rice culture was extracted with acetone-water (7:3, v/v) and allowed to stand for 15-20 min. The slurry was filtered, evaporated to dryness, and repeatedly extracted with hot tetrahydrofuran. The altenuene was purified from the crude tetrahydrofuran extract by column chromatography on silica gel G.

Biological Activity

The compound showed cytotoxic activity against five bacteria tested by the paper disc agar plate method: *Bacillus mycoides* (ATTC 6462), *B. subtilis* (ATTC 6633), *Neisseria gonorrhoeae* (ATTC 23050), *Sarcinia lutea* (ATTC 9341), and *Staphylococcus aureus* (ATTC 6538P).

Spectral Data

UV:

$\lambda_{max}^{95\%\ EtOH}$ 319(6,600), 278(10,000), and 240nm (30,000).

IR:

(KBr) 1635cm^{-1}.

^{1}H NMR:

C-4 H, 6.66 or 6.42, *J*(4,6)=2.5; C-6 H, 6.42 or 6.66, *J*(6,4)=2.5; C-2'H, 6.27, *J*(2',3')=2.5; C-3 H, 4.10, *J*(3',2')=2.5;(3,4)=5.5; C-4'H, 3.86, *J*(4',3')=5.5, *J*(4',5'a)=8.5, *J*(4',5b')=4.0; C-5a, 1.97, *J*(5a',5b')=15, *J*(5a',4)'=8.5; C-5b, 2.40, *J*(5b',5a')=15, *J*(5b',4')=4.0; C-3 OH, 11.39; C-3' OH, 2.98; C-4' OH, 2.98; C-5 OCH_3, 3.90; and C-6'CH_3, 1.52ppm.

^{13}C NMR:

C-4, 100.4(d); C-6, 102.4(d); C-7, 165.7(s); C-8, 55.5(q); C-2', 81.0(s); C-3', 40.2(t); C-4', 69.6(d); C-5', 72.4(d); C-6', 132.5(d); C-7', 27.8(d); 130.9(s); 139.1(s); 143.6(s); 165.7(s); and 168.7ppm (s).

Mass Spectrum:

High resolution mass spectrometry indicated a parent ion with mol. wt. 292.0930, with a molecular formula of $C_{16}H_{16}O_6$.

TLC Data

Silica gel G; (A) benzene-ethanol, 95:5, v/v; (B) chloroform-methanol, 95:5, v/v; R_f (A) 0.14, (B) 0.13; detected as blue fluorescent spot under UV light.

GLC Data:

Solid support: Gas Chrom Q; liquid phase OV-17 (3%); column temp, 100°-250°C at 8°/min rise; injector temp, 300°C; detector temp, 300°C; retention time, about 24 min.

References

R. J. Cole and R. H. Cox; Handbook of Toxic Fungal Metabolites; Academic Press, New York, pp. 628-634(1981).

R. W. Pero, R. G. Owens, S. W. Dale, and D. Harvan; Isolation and Identification of a New Toxin, Altenuene, from the Fungus *Alternaria tenuis*; Biochimica et Biophysica Acta, 230, 170-179(1971).

Common/Systematic Name
(±)-Dehydroaltenusin

Molecular Formula/Molecular Weight
$C_{15}H_{12}O_6$; MW = 288.06339

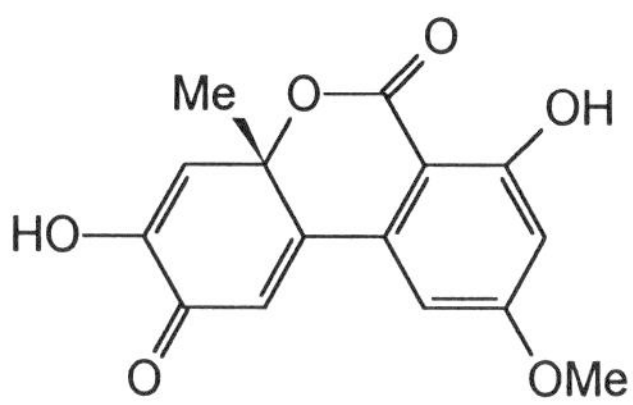

General Characteristics
Dehydroaltenusin crystallized from ethanol as yellow needles; mp., 189-190°C (decomp.); also crystallized from acetone as plates; mp., 190-193°C; dehydroaltenusin is only slightly soluble in water. Aqueous $NaHCO_3$ readily extracted the compound from ethyl acetate solution but dissolves the solid only slowly; the bicarbonate solution is colored yellow. In aqueous NaOH the color is yellow-green, soon changing to yellow. An ethanolic solution gives an intense brown color (with $FeCl_3$), identical with that produced by the action of excess $FeCl_3$ on altenusin; the color is essentially unchanged by the addition of water. An ethanolic solution yields a red precipitate with Brady's reagent.

Fungal Source
Alternaria tenuis and other *Alternaria* spp.

Isolation/Purification
Dehydroaltenusin was initially isolated by column chromatography of the ether extracts by a gradient elution technique. Subsequently, it was extracted with chloroform, redissolved in acetone and left standing for several days after which dehydroaltenusin crystallized out as plates (mp., 190-193°C).

Spectral Data

UV:
λ_{max} 217(log ϵ=4.53), 249(4.10), and 300nm (3.88).

IR:
(KCl Disc) 3380, 1655, 1645sh, 1625, 1580, 1275, 1230, 1210, 1165, 1080, 1032, 975, 865, 800, and 750cm^{-1}.

^{1}H NMR:
(acetone-d_6) Three-proton singlets at 1.76 and 4.00ppm; one-proton singlets at 6.23 and 6.85ppm; one-proton doublets (J=2.5Hz) at 6.68 and 7.05; and two exchangeable protons at 8.00(broad) and 11.32ppm (sharp).

Mass Data:

LREIMS: 288*m/e* (M^+); (Found: C, 62.4, 62.3; H, 4.4, 4.5; OMe, 11.1, 11.1. $C_{15}H_{12}O_6$ requires C, 62.5; H, 4.2; OMe, 10.8 %).

References

R. G. Coombe, J. J. Jacobs, and T. R. Watson; Metabolites of Some *Alternaria* Species. The Structures of Altenusin and Dehydroaltenusin; Aust. J. Chem., Vol. 23, pp. 2343-2351(1970)

D. Rogers and D. J. Williams; The crystal structure of (+)-dehydroaltenusin; Chem. Commun., pp. 390-393(1971).

T. Rosett, R. H. Sankhala, C. E. Stickings, M. E. U. Taylor, and R. Thomas; Studies in the Biochemistry of Micro-organisms; Biochem. J., Vol 67 , pp. 390-399(1957).

Common/Systematic Name
Botrallin

Molecular Formula/Molecular Weight
$C_{16}H_{14}O_7$; MW = 318.07395

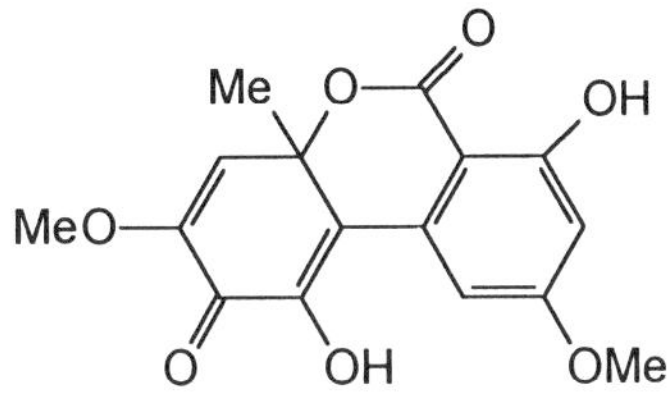

General Characteristics
Yellow prisms from ethanol; mp., 165-185°C (decomp.).The compound showed no sharp melting point. At about 165°C decomposition started, at 185°C the crystals were fully transformed into a dark brown tar. Botrallin was unstable in alkaline solutions. In dilute ammonia a red color was observed which rapidly changed through brown into yellow. The compound dissolved in aqueous sodium bicarbonate with a violet-red color. This color was more stable. It took several hours before the color changed to brown. An alcoholic solution of botrallin gave a violet-brown color with ferric chloride. Reduction of an ethyl acetate solution by shaking with aqueous sodium dithionite led to a slightly yellow solution which did not give a color with aqueous sodium bicarbonate. Evaporation of this solution exposed to the air yielded a residue which again gave the color reaction with alkali. The supposed quinonoid character of the compound was confirmed by a positive Craven test 2. The reddish solution in alcoholic ammonia turned to an intense green upon addition of a drop of ethyl cyanoacetate.

Fungal Source
Botrytis allii, strain Walker, obtained from the Centraal Bureau voor Schimmelcultures, Baarn, the Netherlands

Isolation/Purification
Botrallin was extracted from fungal cultures with ethyl acetate. The residue obtained on evaporating the ethyl acetate was extracted with boiling benzene. Evaporation of the benzene yielded a solid residue which was recrystallized as yellow prisms from ethanol.

Biological Activity
Botrallin in a concentration of 100ppm had no inhibitory effect on the growth of the fungi *Botrytis allii, Penicillium italicum, Cladosporium cucumerinum,* and *Aspergillus niger* and the bacteria *Escherichia coli* and *Bacillus subtilis.* Since *Botrytis allii* is a parasite of onions, it was tested to see if botrallin had a toxic effect on onion scales; however, no effect was observed.

Spectral Data

UV:

λ_{max}^{EtOH} 238(log ϵ=4.36), 273(4.20), and 370nm (3.95).

IR:

(KBr) 1656, 1629, and 1580cm^{-1}.

^{1}H NMR:

The NMR spectrum of botrallin, taken in $CDCl_3$, led to the conclusion that the compound was a benzoquinone with three substituents. One of these substituents was a triply substituted phenyl group. Taking into consideration the formula $C_{16}H_{14}O_7$ the following assignments were made: quinone Me at 1.77ppm (singlet, 3 H); OMe groups at 3.80 and 3.90ppm (singlets, each 3 H); quinone proton at 6.14ppm (singlet, 1 H); two meta-coupled aromatic protons at 6.54 and 7.34ppm (doublets *J*=2.4Hz, each 1 H); OH at 7.23ppm (singlet, 1 H, exchangeable with D_2O); and COOH at 11.36ppm (singlet, 1 H, exchangeable with D_2O).

Mass Data:

HREIMS: 318.07321*m/e* (M^+) (calcd, 318.07394); found C 60.4%; H 4.6%; O 34.8%; calcd for $C_{16}H_{14}O_7$, C 60.38; H 4.43; O 35.19.

References

K. Kameda, H. Aoki, M. Namimi, and J. C. Overeem; An Alternative Structure For Botrallin A Metabolite of *Botrytis allii;*, Tetrahedron Letter, No. 1, pp. 103-106 (1974).

J. C. Overeem and A. Van Dijkman; Botrallin, A Novel Quinone Produced By *Botrytis allii;* Recueil, Vol. 87, pp. 940-944(1968).

Common/Systematic Name

Alternariol monomethyl ether

3,4'-Dihydroxy-5-methoxy-6'-methyldibenzo[a]pyrone

Molecular Formula/Molecular Weight

$C_{15}H_{12}O_5$; MW = 272.06847

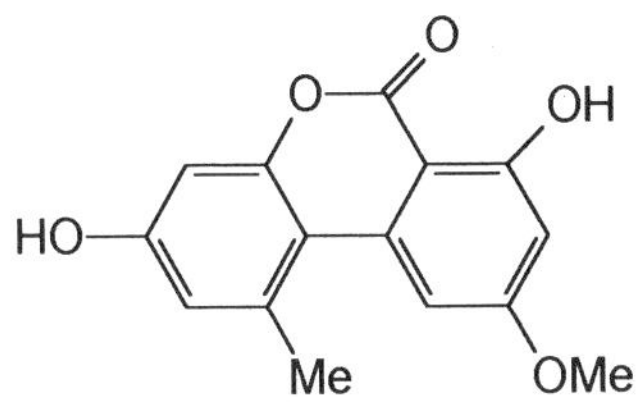

General Characteristics

Crystals from ethanol; mp., 266-267°C (dec.); sublimed without decomposition at 180-200°C in high vacuum; $[\alpha]_D^{20}$ 0° (*c*=0.8, in EtOH).

Fungal Source

Alternaria tenuis (NRRL 5831), *A. dauci,* and *A. cucumerina*. Alternariol monomethyl ether and alternariol have also been found in tobacco, grain sorghum, and pecans.

Isolation/Purification

Alternariol and alternariol monomethyl ether were extracted with methanol-water (80:20, v/v). The crude extract was first separated on columns containing Baker 3405 silica gel. These columns were packed with 3% acetone in chloroform and developed with the same solvent system. An easily visualized component fluorescing blue under long-wavelength UV was recognized during the monitoring of fractions of the first separations of the crude extract. A compound with similar fluorescent characteristics but with a lower R_f was also observed, but appeared to be present in smaller amounts. These two compounds were further purified by a consecutive series of column separations on columns containing E. M. Laboratories silica gel 60 (particle size less than 0.063mm) developed with 1.75% methanol in benzene. The extracts were concentrated and yielded high purity crystals of alternariol and alternariol monomethyl ether, respectively.

Biological Activity

Alternariol monomethyl ether showed cytotoxic activity to bacteria and mammalian cells. Inhibition to *Bacillus mycoides* was observed at 500µg/disc; the ID_{50} to HeLa cells was 8-14µg/ml. In mice dosed IP (DMSO carrier) at 400mg/kg, 1 of 10 mice died; mice were often sedated within a few minutes of dosing, and the eyes of the mice were dull; there were occasional stomach spasms and periodic panting.

Spectral Data

UV:

λ_{max} 335-342(broad), 301, 290, 257, and 230nm (ϵ max not reported).

^{1}H NMR:

H-4, 6.29; H-6, 7.12; H-8, 3.84; H-3', 7.60; H-5', 6.60; and H-8', 2.68ppm.

^{13}C NMR:

C-2, 98.7 s; C-4, 98.5 d; C-6, 103.4 d; C-7, 165.0 s; C-8, 55.4 q; C-3', 101.9 d; C-5', 117.5 d; C-6', 137.8 s; C-8', 25.4 q; 137.9 s; 146.7 s; 152.6 s; 158.2 s; 164.4 s; and 166.0ppm s.

Mass Spectrum:

LREIMS showed a molecular ion at nominal mass 272*m/e*; HREIMS showed a molecular ion at 272.0699*m/e*; calcd for $C_{15}H_{12}O_5$ is 272.0684.

TLC Data

Silica gel G, (A) benzene-ethanol, 95:5, v/v ; (B) chloroform-methanol, 95:5, v/v. R_f (A) 0.39; (B) 0.54. Detection: blue fluorescent spot under UV light.

GLC Data

Solid support: Gas Chrom Q; Liquid phase: OV-17 (3%); Column temp: 100-250°C at 8° min rise; detector temp: 300°C; injector temp: 300°C; retention time: approximately 31 min.

References

R. J. Cole and R. H. Cox; Handbook of Toxic Fungal Metabolites; Academic Press, New York, pp. 615-627(1981).

H. W. Schroeder and R. J. Cole; Natural Occurrence of Alternariol in Discolored Pecans; Agric. Food Chem.; Vol. 25, pp. 204-206(1977).

Common/Systematic Name

Alternariol

3,4',5-Trihydroxy-6'-methyl-dibenzo[a]pyrone

Molecular Formula/Molecular Weight

$C_{14}H_{10}O_5$; MW = 258.05282

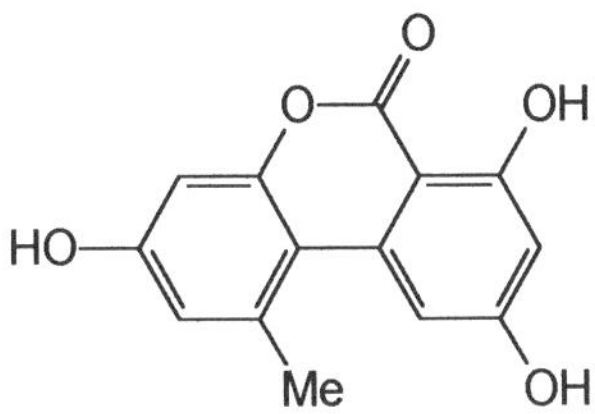

General Characteristics

Crystals from ethanol; mp., 350°C (dec.). Sublimed without decomposition at 250°C in a high vacuum. $[\alpha]_D^{20}$ 0° (*c*=0.8, in EtOH). Triacetate from ethanol; mp., 167-169°C.

Fungal Source

Alternaria tenuis (NRRL 5255; 5872; 5873), *A. dauci*, and *A. cucumerina*. Alternariol and alternariol monomethyl ether have been found in tobacco, grain sorghum, and pecans.

Isolation/Purification

Alternariol and alternariol monomethyl ether were extracted with methanol-water, 80:20. The crude extract was first separated on columns containing Baker 3405 silica gel. These columns were packed with 3% acetone in chloroform and developed with the same solvent system. An easily visualized component fluorescing blue under long-wavelength UV was recognized during the monitoring of fractions of the first separations of the crude extract. A compound with similar fluorescent characteristics but with a lower R_f was also observed, but appeared to be present in smaller amounts. These two compounds were further purified by a consecutive series of column separations on columns containing E. M. Laboratories silica gel 60 (particle size less than 0.063mm) developed with 1.75% methanol in benzene. The extracts were concentrated and yielded high purity crystals of alternariol monomethyl ether and alternariol, respectively.

Biological Activity

Alternariol completely suppresses growth of *Staphylococcus aureus* at concentration of 1:40,000; *E. coli* at concentration of 1:20,000. The ID_{50} to HeLa cells was 6μg/ml. In mice dosed IP (DMSO carrier) at 200mg/kg, 3 of 10 mice died; mice were often sedated within a few minutes of dosing; the eyes of mice recovering were dull; there were occasional stomach spasms and periodic panting.

Spectral Data

UV:

λ_{max}^{EtOH} 218, 258(ϵ=38,000), 302, and 330nm.

IR:

(KBr) 3460(OH), 3100(intramolecular hydrogen-bonded OH), 1672(lactone shifted downfield due to H-bonding with OH), 1590, 1430(phenyl nucleus), 1365(CH_3), 1200(phenolic OH), and 850cm^{-1} (isolated H on aromatic ring).

^{1}H NMR:

H-4, 6.30(*J*=2.0); H-6, 7.14(*J*=2.8); H-3', 7.65; H-5', 6.58; and H-8', 2.66ppm.

^{13}C NMR:

C-2, 97.6 s; C-4, 100.9 d; C-6, 104.2 d; C-7, 165.0 s; C-3', 101.7 d; C-5', 117.3 d; C-6', 137.8 s; C-8', 25.4 q; 128.6 s; 138.2 s; 152.6 s; 158.0 s; 164.3 s; and 165.0ppm s.

Mass Spectrum:

LREIMS showed molecular ion at nominal mass 258*m/e*.

TLC Data

Silica gel G; A: benzene-ethanol, 95:5 v/v; B: chloroform-methanol, 95:5 v/v; R_f: A: 0.21, B: 0.19. Detection: blue fluorescent spot under UV light.

GLC Data

Gas Chrom Q; Liquid phase OV-17 (3%); Column temp. 100-250°C at 8° min rise; Injector temp. 300°C; Detector temp. 300°C; and retention time, about 30 min.

References

R. J. Cole and R. H. Cox; Handbook of Toxic Fungal Metabolites; Academic Press, New York, p. 615 (1981).

H. W. Schroeder and R. J. Cole; Natural Occurrence of Alternariol in Discolored Pecans; Agric. Food Chem.; Vol. 25, pp. 204-206(1977).

Common/Systematic Name

Altenuisol; Altertenuol

3,5,5'-Trihydroxy-4'-methoxydibenzo[a]pyrone

Molecular Formula/Molecular Weight

$C_{14}H_{10}O_6$; MW = 274.04774

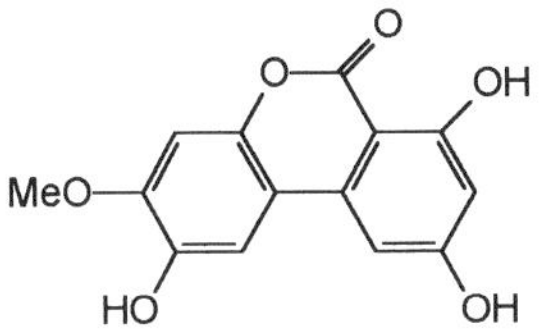

General Characteristics

Altenuisol crystallized from hot acetic acid as slender needles; mp., 277-282°C. It was soluble in acetone, ethanol, and ethyl acetate; only slightly soluble in chloroform and diethyl ether; and insoluble in benzene and hexane.

Fungal Source

Alternaria tenuis.

Isolation/Purification

Altenuisol was extracted with 70% acetone, chromatographed on silica gel G, eluted with increasing tetrahydrofuran in benzene, and further purified on silica gel G using ethyl acetate as eluant.

Biological Activity

The ID_{50} dose with HeLa cells was 8μg/ml and zones of inhibition were noted with *Bacillus mycoides* from 5-200μg/assay disc.

Spectral Data

UV:

λ_{max}^{EtOH} 216, 256, 278nm sh (ϵ=9,000, 11,000, and 3,500, respectively).

IR:

(KBr) 3380, 3280, 1653, 1620, 1600, 1560, 1530, 1510, 1440, 1370, 1275, 1200, 1180, 1170, 1160, 1095, 1035, 985, 915, 857, 830, 815, and 780cm^{-1}.

^{1}H NMR:

Tetrahydrofuran-d_8: singlet 7.38, doublet, 6.92, singlet 6.70, doublet 6.47, and three methoxy protons at 3.89ppm; chemical shift at 11.62ppm H-bonded OH group.

Mass Spectrum:
274.0495*m/e* (M^+); calcd for $C_{14}H_{10}O_6$, 274.0476.

TLC Data

Altenuisol had an R_f of 0.33 in 20% tetrahydrofuran in benzene using silica gel G and fluorescence detection under both short and long wave ultraviolet light.

Reference

R. W. Pero, D. Harvan, and M. C. Blois; Isolation of the Toxin Altenuisol From the Fungus, *Alternaria tenuis* Auct.; Tet. Lett., pp. 945-948(1973).

Common/Systematic Name

Altenusin

Molecular Formula/Molecular Weight

$C_{15}H_{14}O_6$; MW = 290.07904

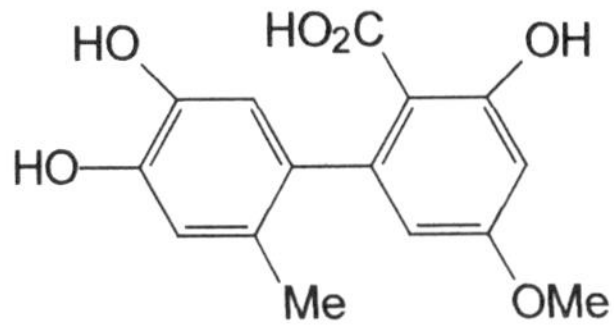

General Characteristics

Altenusin crystallized from $CHCl_3$ in colorless prisms. After drying at 100° C under reduced pressure, it melted at 202-203° C with effervescence to a yellow liquid; undried crystals melted at about 95° C, resolidified, and remelted at the higher temperature. Altenusin can also be crystallized from benzene or water. It was readily soluble in ether, ethanol and methanol; it also dissolved in aqueous $NaHCO_3$. Its ethanolic solution, treated with ethanolic $FeCl_3$, gave a pale-gray color, turning to deep brown with excess. Altenusin does not reduce Fehling's solution in the cold, though the solution turns green; on boiling reduction takes place. Tetramethylaltenusin was a pale-brown gum that recrystallized several times from methanol to gave colorless prisms, mp., 116-117°C.

Fungal Source

Alternaria tenuis, A. citri, A. dauci, A. alternata, Corynespora smithii.

Isolation/Purification

Continuous ethyl ether extraction followed by crystallization from chloroform yielded crystalline material that melted at 201.5-203°C.

Spectral Data

UV:

λ_{max} 217, 247sh, and 290nm.

IR:

(KCl disc) 3350(broad), 1635, 1607, 1520, 1460, 1440, 1365, 1255, 1230, 1205, 1185, 1075, 1040, 980, 875, 860, and 800cm^{-1}.

^{1}H NMR:

(DMSO-d_6) Three-proton singlets at 1.88 and 3.77ppm; one-proton doublet (J=2.5Hz) at 6.15; one proton singlet at 6.85ppm and two-proton singlet at 6.46ppm; three exchangeable protons at 8.60ppm (very broad) and one exchangeable in region 5-6ppm.

Mass Data:

290*m/e* (M^+); found, after drying at 100°C in a high vacuum: C, 62.1; H, 5.2; OMe, 10.4; C-Me, 5.2. $C_{15}H_{14}O_6$ required C, 62.1; H, 4.9; OMe, 10.7; C-Me, 6.2 %.

References

R. G. Coombe, J. J. Jacobs, and T. R. Watson; Metabolites of Some *Alternaria* Species. The Structures of Altenusin and Dehydroaltenesin; Aust. J. Chem., Vol. 23, pp. 2343-2351(1970).

T. Rosett, R. H. Sankhala, C. E. Stickings, M. E. U. Taylor, and R. Thomas; Studies in the Biochemistry of Micro-organisms; Biochem. J., Vol. 67, pp. 390-399(1957).

Common/Systematic Name
Dehydroaltenusin

Molecular Formula/Molecular Weight
$C_{15}H_{12}O_6$; MW = 288.06339

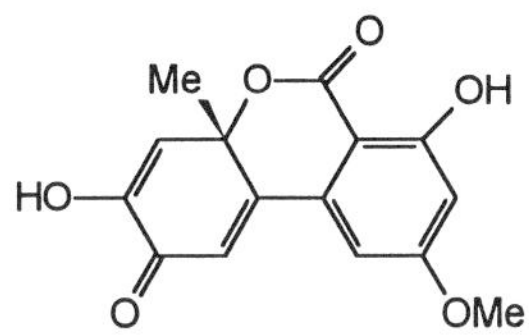

General Characteristics
Yellow plate crystals from acetone; mp., 190-193°C (dec.).

Fungal Source
Alternaria tenuis, A. dauci, A. cucumerina, and *A. alternata.*

Spectral Data

UV:
λ_{max}^{EtOH} 217(ε=33,800), 249(12,600), and 300nm (7,500).

IR:
(KBr) 3380, 1655, 1645(sh), 1625, 1580, 1275, 1230, 1210, 1165, 1080, 1032, 975, 856, 800, and 750cm^{-1}.

^{1}H NMR:
(acetone-d_6) H-4, 6.68(J=2.5); H-6, 7.05(J=2.5); H-8, 4.00; H-3', 6.23; H-6', 6.85; H-7', 1.76; OH, 8.00; and 11.32ppm.

Reference
R. J. Cole and R. H. Cox; Handbook of Toxic Fungal Metabolites; Academic Press, New York, pp. 634 (1981).

Common/Systematic Name

Altenuic acid I

Molecular Formula/Molecular Weight

$C_{15}H_{14}O_8$; MW = 322.06687

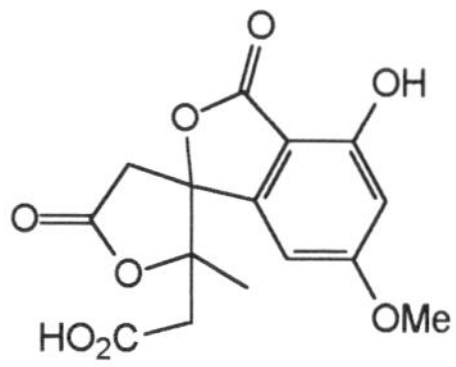

General Characteristics

Altenuic acid I crystallized from water or ethanol as colorless needles; mp., 183-184°C with effervescence; if heated further, it reset at about 200°C and remelted at 224-230°C with further decomposition. The compound retained solvent even when dried to constant weight at 100°C in high vacuum. To obtain solvent-free material, it was necessary to dry for 8 hr. at 120°C in a high vacuum. It dissolved on heating in methanol, ethanol, dioxane, acetic acid and water, but was not very soluble in the cold. An ethanolic solution gave a pale purple-brown color on addition of ethanolic $FeCl_3$, essentially unchanged on addition of water. Its aqueous solution gave no precipitate with Brady's reagent. Altenuic acid I, II, and III are readily interconverted under basic conditions.

Fungal Source

Alternaria tenuis.

Isolation/Purification

Isolated by adsorption on charcoal, followed by elution with ethanol. The isolated crystalline compound was a colorless acidic substance.

Reference

T. Rosett, R. H. Sankhala, C. E. Stickings, M. E. U. Taylor, and R. Thomas; Metabolites of *Alternaria tenuis* Auct.; Culture Filtrate Products, Vol. 67, pp. 390-399(1957).

Common/Systematic Name

(±)-Altenuic acid II

Molecular Formula/Molecular Weight

$C_{15}H_{14}O_8$; MW = 322.06887

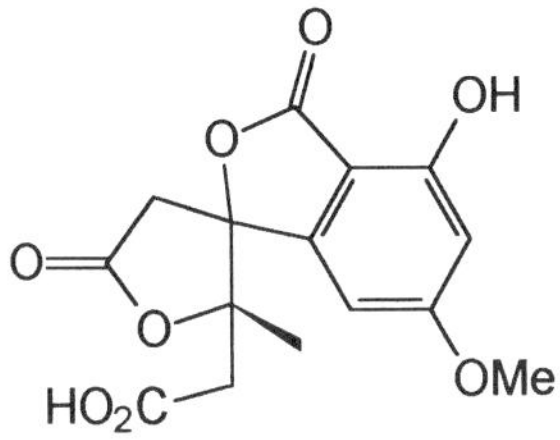

General Characteristics

Altenuic acid II crystallized from aqueous dioxane in small colorless rectangular plates; mp., 245-246°C (decomp.) (uncorr.). It also crystallized from aq. acetic acid. Altenuic acid II was very sparingly soluble in water and the commoner organic solvents. A solution in dioxane/ethanol (1:1, v/v) gave a pale-brown ferric color, essentially unchanged on addition of water. Readily interconvertible with its isomers altenuic I and III under basic conditions.

Fungal Source

Alternaria tenuis.

Isolation/Purification

Isolated by adsorption on charcoal, followed by elution with ethanol, which gave a colorless acidic compound called altenuic acid II.

References

T. Rosett, R. H. Sankhala, C. E. Stickings M. E. U. Taylor, and R. Thomas; Metabolites of *Alternaria tenuis* Auct.; Culture Filtrate Products, Biochem. J., Vol 67, pp. 390-399 (1957).

D. J. Williams; The Crystalline Structure of (±)-Altenuic Acid II; Tet. Lett., pp. 639-640 (1973).

Common/Systematic Name
Altenuic acid III

Molecular Formula/Molecular Weight
$C_{15}H_{14}O_8$; MW = 322.06687

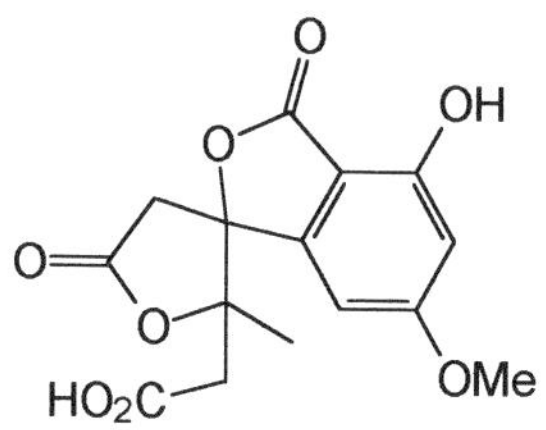

General Characteristics
Altenuic acid III crystallized from aq. methanol or acetic acid in colorless prisms. The melting point was variable; crystals from aqueous methanol usually melted around 185°C with effervescence followed by resetting, complete about 195°C; a further melt occurred between 215 and 235°C, with effervescence. Crystals from acetic acid melted first in the range 198-202°C with effervescence, reset immediately and remelted at about 225°C with effervescence. Altenuic acid III was readily soluble in ethanol and methanol, sparingly soluble in ether, and less soluble in chloroform, benzene or light petroleum. An ethanolic solution gave a pale-wine ferric color, deepening to an intense purple on addition of water. Readily interconvertible with its isomers altenuic I and II under basic conditions. Forms a colorless dimethyl derivative; mp., 143.5-144.5°C.

Fungal Source
Alternaria tenuis.

Isolation/Purification
Mixtures of altenuic acids I and III were difficult to separate. Separation on a preparative scale was achieved by means of counter-current distribution using ethyl acetate-water and extraction from ethyl acetate containing fractions after acidification.

Reference
T. Rosett, R. H. Sankhala, C. E. Stickings, M. E. U. Taylor, and R. Thomas; Metabolites of *Alternaria tenuis* Auct.; Culture Filtrate Products, Biochem. J., Vol 67, pp. 390-399 (1957)

19

Viridin and Related Metabolites

Viridin
Desmethoxyviridin
Viridiol
Desmethoxyviridiol
Wortmannin
11-Desacetoxywortmannin

Common/Systematic Name

Viridin

1β-Hydroxy-2β-methoxy-18-norandrosta-5,8,11,13-tetraeno[6,5,4-*bc*]furan-3,7,17-trione

Molecular Formula/Molecular Weight

$C_{20}H_{16}O_6$; MW = 352.09467

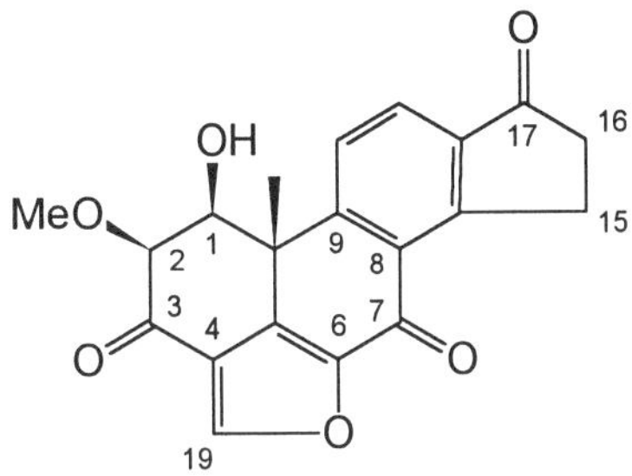

General Characteristics

Prisms from benzene; mp., 245°C (dec.); needles from acetone; mp., 222-224°C; plates from methanol; mp., 140°C; hemimethanolate, 242°C (dec.); $[\alpha]_D^{19}$ -224°; acetyl derivative: microcrystalline solid; mp., 121-126°C; $[\alpha]_D^{17}$ -176°; soluble in water, and chloroform; sparingly soluble in carbon disulfide and carbon tetrachloride.

Fungal Source

Gliocladium virens and *Trichoderma viride.*

Biological Activity

Viridin possesses strong antifungal activity; minimum concentration preventing germination of *Botrytis allii* conidia, 0.005μg/ml.

Spectral Data

UV:

λ_{max} 242(ε=30,900) and 300nm (16,500).

IR:

(Nujol) 3390, 3145, 1692, 1675, 1622, 1587, 1532, 1126, 1090, 1070, 1032, 1019, 1005, 983, and 970cm^{-1}; (hemimethanolate) 3450, 3105, 1709, 1675, 1622, 1587, 1532, 1120, 1085, 1064, 1015, 1001, 982, and 970cm^{-1}.

^{1}H NMR:

H-1, 4.45(*J*=5); H-2, 3.95; H-11, 8.10(*J*=8); H-12, 8.80; H-15, 2.90; H-16, 3.80; H-18, 1.73; H-19, 8.45; and H-20, 3.75ppm.

Mass Data:

C, 68.18%; H, 4.58%; O, 27.24%.

References

R. J. Cole and R. H. Cox; Handbook of Toxic Fungal Metabolites; Academic Press, New York, p.747 (1981).

J. F. Grove, P. McClosky, and J. S. Moffatt; The Structure of Viridin; Chem. Commun., pp. 343-344(1965).

Common/Systematic Name
Desmethoxyviridin

Molecular Formula/Molecular Weight
$C_{19}H_{14}O_5$; MW = 322.08412

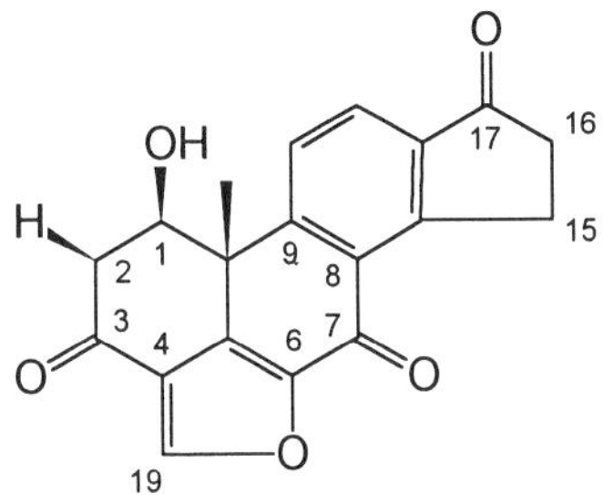

General Characteristics
Melting point variable depending on solvent of crystallization; two ranges were 145-160°C (dec.) or 220-240°C (dec.); crystals from acetone; mp., 230-240°C.

Fungal Source
Nodulisporium hinnuleum (ATCC 24911), an unidentified fungus (ACC 3199), and *Apiospora camptospora*.

Isolation/Purification
Extracted with hot $CHCl_3$. The $CHCl_3$ extract was evaporated to dryness and the residue applied to a silica gel column packed in a slurry of hexane and eluted sequentially with *n*-hexane, Et_2O, $CHCl_3$, EtOAc, Me_2CO, and MeOH. Biological activity, as measured by acute toxicity to orally dosed day-old cockerels, was found in the EtOAc fraction,which was further purified on a second silica gel column eluted with a linear gradient from $CHCl_3$ to EtOAc. The nonpolar fraction contained desmethoxyviridin.

Biological Activity
Desmethoxyviridin was toxic to day-old cockerels, but the level of toxicity was not determined.

Spectral Data

UV:
λ_{max} 243(ϵ=27,000) and 303nm (11,600).

^{13}C NMR:
C-1, 70.8 d; C-2,46.5 t; C-3, 189.9 s; C-4, 122.9 s; C-5, 144.3 s; C-6, 145.6 s; C-7, 172.5 s; C-8, 156.9 s; C-9, 136.3 s; C-10, 41.5 s; C-11, 126.2 d; C-12, 128.4 d; C-13, 156.2 s; C-14, 129.6 s; C-15, 28.1 t; C-16, 35.7 t; C-17, 205.4 s; C-18, 25.2 q; and C-19, 149.3ppm d.

^{1}H NMR:

H-l, 4.33(J=6.0); H-2, 2.72(J=6.0); H-11, 7.83(J=8.5); H-12, 8.58(J=8.5); H-15, 2.75; H-16, 3.58; H-18, 1.58; H-19, 8.75; and 1-OH, 6.12ppm.

TLC Data

Adsorbent: silica gel G-HR; solvent: toluene-ethyl acetate-formic acid, 5:4:1, v/v/v; R_f 0.57. Detection: orange spot after spraying with 50% H_2SO_4 and heating for 5 min.

References

R. J. Cole and R. H. Cox; Handbook of Toxic Fungal Metabolites; Academic Press, New York, pp. 739-742(1981).

R. J. Cole, J. W. Kirksey, J. P. Springer, J. Clasrdy, H. G. Cutler, and K. H. Garren; Desmethoxyviridiol, A New Toxin from *Nodulisporium hinnuleum*; Phytochemistry, Vol. 14, pp. 1429-1432 (1975).

Common/Systematic Name

Viridiol

Molecular Formula/Molecular Weight

$C_{20}H_{18}O_6$; MW = 354.11034

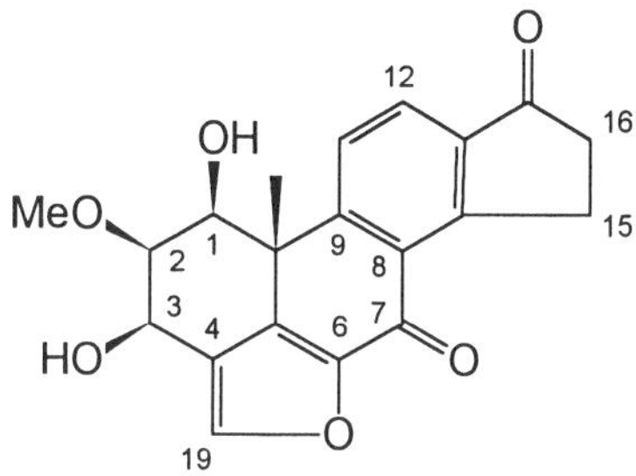

General Characteristics

Crystals; mp., 198-201°C (dec.).

Fungal Source

Trichoderma viride (NRRL 1828) and *Gliocladium virens* (ACC 213).

Spectral Data

UV:

λ_{max} 250(log ε=29,500) and 317nm (11,700).

IR:

(Nujol) 1680 and 1695cm^{-1}; ($CHCl_3$) 1673 and 1712cm^{-1}.

^{13}C NMR:

C-1, 71.7 d; C-2, 81.7 d; C-3, 61.6 d; C-4, 121.9 s; C-5, 142.2 s; C-6, 142.2 s; C-7, 173.1 s; C-8, 158.4 s; C-9, 136.7 s; C-10, 42.2 s; C-11, 127.0 d; C-12, 127.0 d: C-13, 157.6 s; C-14, 127.0 S; C-15, 28.4 t; C-16, 36.4 t; C-17, 206.2 s; C-18, 30.5 q; C-19, 145.3 d; and C-20, 60.5ppm q.

^{1}H NMR:

H-1, 4.32; H-2, 3.60; H-3, 5.12; H-11, 7.93(*J*=8.0Hz); H-12, 8.25(*J*=8.0Hz); H-15, 2.71; H-16, 3.64; H-18, 1.74; H-19, 7.77; and H-20, 3.75ppm.

Mass Spectrum:

LREIMS: 354*m/e* (M^+) with losses of 18, 33, 46, and 74*m/e* mass units.

TLC Data

Adsorbent, silica gel G; solvent, chloroform-methanol, 9:1, v/v; R_f 0.36; detection, green fluorescence under UV light; red-brown after $AgNO_3$ spray.

References

R. J. Cole and R. H. Cox; Handbook of Toxic Fungal Metabolites; Academic Press, New York, pp. 748-752(1981).

J. S. Moffatt, J. D. Bu'Lock, and T. H. Yuen; Viridiol, A Steroid-like Product from *Trichoderma viride*; Chem. Commun., p. 839 (1969).

Common/Systematic Name

Desmethoxyviridiol

Molecular Formula/Molecular Weight

$C_{19}H_{16}O_5$; MW = 324.09977

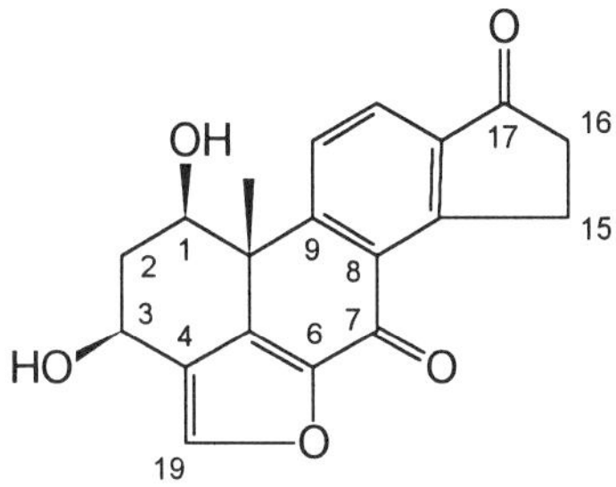

General Characteristics

Crystals from ethyl acetate; mp., 155-157°C; soluble in ethyl ether, chloroform, ethyl acetate, and acetone; moderately soluble in toluene, methanol, and ethanol; insoluble in hexane and water.

Fungal Source

Nodulisporium hinnuleum (ATCC 24911) and an unidentified fungus (ACC 3199).

Isolation/Purification

Extracted with hot $CHCl_3$. The $CHCl_3$ extract was evaporated to dryness and the residue applied to a silica gel column packed in a slurry of hexane and eluted sequentially with *n*-hexane, Et_2O, $CHCl_3$. EtOAc, Me_2CO, and MeOH. Biological activity, as measured by acute toxicity to orally dosed day-old cockerels, was found in the EtOAc fraction, which was further purified on a second silica gel column eluted with a linear gradient from $CHCl_3$ to EtOAc. The polar fraction was crystallized from EtOAc at room temperature.

Biological Activity

Desmethoxyviridiol had an oral LD_{50} of 4.2mg/kg in day-old cockerels. It also produced plant-growth regulating and phytotoxic effects in plant assay systems .

Spectral Data

UV:

λ_{max}^{EtOH} 251(ϵ=30,000) and 322nm (16,000); λ_{max}^{EtOH} 249(ϵ=23,500) and 319nm (11,400).

^{13}C NMR:

($CDCl_3$) C-1, 70.3 d; C-2, 41.8 t; C-3, 59.4 d; C-4, 129.6 s; C-5, 143.9 s; C-6, 143.9

s; C-7, 172.2 s; C-8, 157.4 s; C-9, 135.7 s; C-10, 41.8 s; C-11, 125.5 d; C-12, 127.6 d; C-13, 154.4 s; C-14, 129.6 s; C-15, 27.9 t; C-16, 35.6 t; C-17, 205.7 s; C-18, 27.4 q; and C-19, 146.0ppm d.

^{1}H NMR:
H-1, 4.00; H-2, 2.12; H-3, 4.78(*J*=6.0); H-11, 7.76(*J*=8.0); H-12, 8.56(*J*=8.0); H-15, 2.60; H-16, 3.55; H-18, 1.50; H-19, 7.97; and OH's, 5.46, 5.70ppm.

TLC Data

Adsorbent; silica gel G-HR, solvent; toluene-ethyl acetate-formic acid, 5:4:1, v/v/v; R_f: 0.66; detection: gray-blue spot after spraying with 50% ethanolic H_2SO_4 and heating at 110°C for 5 min.

Reference

R. J. Cole, J. W. Kirksey, J. P. Springer, J. Clardy, H.G. Cutler, and K. H. Garren; Desmethoxyviridiol, A New Toxin from *Nodulisporium hinnuleum*; Phytochemistry, Vol. 14, pp. 1429-1432(1975).

Common/Systematic Name
Wortmannin

Molecular Formula/Molecular Weight
$C_{23}H_{24}O_8$; MW = 428.14712

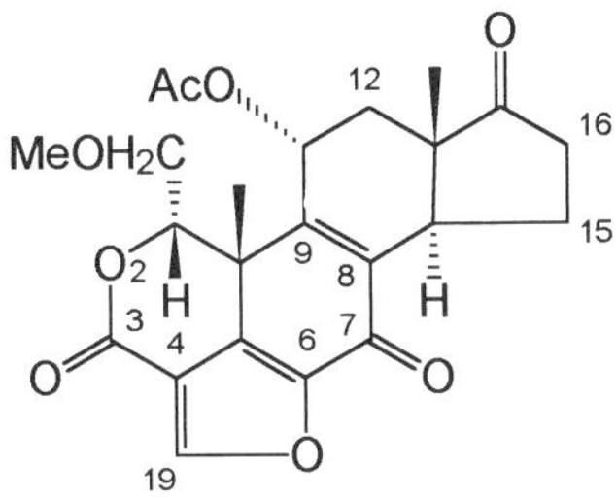

General Characteristics
Crystallized from methanol or benzene to give needles; mp., 238-239°C; $[\alpha]_D^{26}$ +89° (*c*=1.1, in $CHCl_3$); the mono-2,4-dinitrophenylhydrazone crystallized from acetic acid as yellow needles; mp., 266-268°C.

Fungal Source
Penicillium wortmannii and *Myrothecium roridum*.

Spectral Data

UV:
λ_{max} 257 and 292nm (ϵ=11,770 and 7,700).

IR:
(KBr) 3112, 1751, 1732, 1684, 1656, and 1547cm^{-1}; ($CHCl_3$) 3150, 1750, 1683, 1653, and 1553cm^{-1}.

^1H NMR:
($CDCl_3$) H-1, 5.25; H-2, 6.52, 7.02; H-11, 3.90; H-12, 7.30, 8.0; H-14, 7.15; H-20, 1.78; H-18, 9.06; H-19, 8.29; 2-OMe, 6.87; and 11-AOAc, 7.91τ (15 protons at 6.80 and 7.80τ). Coupling constants: *J*1,2=2.0; *J*1,2'=7.0; *J*2,2'=11.0; *J*11,12=8.0; *J*11,12'=8.0; *J*12,12'=12.5; *J*11,14=3.0; *J*14,15=6.0 and *J*14,15=12.2Hz. The four three-proton singlets were assigned to the 13-methyl (9.06), the 10 methyl (8.29), the acetoxy (7.91) and the methoxy (6.87) protons. The one proton singlet at 1.78τ was of similar chemical shift to the furanoid proton in the acid and was assigned to the 20proton. An ABX-system at 7.02, 6.52, and 5.25 with *J*AB 11, *J*AX 2, and *J*BX 6Hz was assigned to the protons at C-2 and C-1. A double triplet at 3.9ppm was assigned to the C-11 proton, which showed an 8Hz coupling to each of the C-12 protons at 7.3 and 8.4τ (*J*12A,12B, 12.5Hz). In addition, the 11proton showed a homoallylic

coupling of 3Hz to the C-14 methine proton at 7.15τ. The 15-proton signals were located at 6.8 and 7.8τ and those of the 16-protons at 7.4 and 7.9τ.

Mass Data:

EIMS: 428.145(M^+, 0.1%), 413(8.0), 385(19), 368(46.0), 354(68), 323(94), 294(32), 268(55), 266(100), 239(41), 238(62), 223(40), 45(37),44(45), and 43*m/e* (55); found after crystallization from methanol and drying *in vacuo* at 100°C for 15 h; C, 63.5, 64.1, 63.9; H, 5.6, 5.9, 5.9%. Found after crystallization from benzene and drying *in vacuo* at 100°C for 6 h: C, 64.8, 65.0, 65.4, 64.3; H, 5.7, 5.7, 5.6, 5.9%; found after sublimation: C, 63.8, 63.6; H, 5.8, 5.8%; $C_{23}H_{24}O_8$ requires C, 64.5; H, 5.6%.

References

J. MacMillan, A. E. Vanstone, and S. K. Yeboah; Fungal Products. Part III. Structure of Wortmannin and Some Hydrolysis Products; J. Chem. Soc. Perkin I, pp. 2898-2903 (1972).

J. MacMillan, T. J. Simpson, and S. K. Yeboah; Absolute Stereochemistry of the Fungal Product, Wortmannin; J.Chem. Soc. Chem Commun., p. 1063 (1972).

T. J. Petcher, H. -P. Weber, and Z. Kis; Crystal Structure and Absolute Configuration of Wortmannin and of Wortmannin *p*-Bromobenzoate; J. Chem. Soc., Chem. Commun., pp. 1061-1062(1972).

Common/Systematic Name

11-Desacetoxywortmannin

Molecular Formula/Molecular Weight

$C_{21}H_{22}O_6$; MW = 370.14164

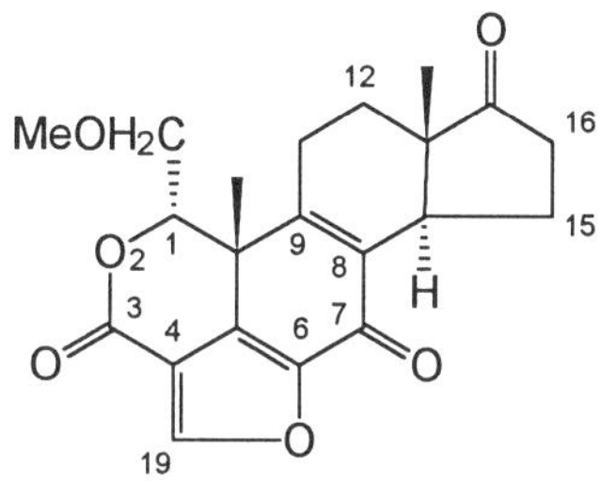

General Characteristics

Crystallized from methylene chloride-ethyl ether; mp., 178-180°C; $[\alpha]_D^{20}$ + 104° (c=0.967, in $CHCl_3$).

Fungal Source

Penicillium funiculosum , *P. wortmannii*, and *Aspergillus janus.*

Biological Activity

Antiinflammatory metabolite.

Spectral Data

UV:

$\lambda_{max}^{Chloroform}$ 258.5(log ε=4.08) and 293.5nm (3.86).

IR:

(CH_2Cl_2) 3140, 1755, 1745, 1680, 1650, and 1510cm^{-1}.

^{1}H NMR:

($CDCl_3$) 0.90 s (3H), 1.71 s (3H), 3.11 s (3H), 3.15 m (2H), 4.82 t(J=5 Hz; 1H), and 8.22τ s (1H).

Mass Data:

LREIMS: 370(100%), 325(85), 312(48), 297(43), 296(48), 281(43), 268(33), and 240*m/e* (67); HREIMS: $C_{21}H_{22}O_6$, 370.401*m/e*; obsd, C, 68.1; H, 6.0; O, 25.9%; required C, 67.9; H, 5.8; O, 26.3%.

Reference

von W. Haefliger and D. Hauser; Isolierung und Strukturaufklarung von 11-Desacetoxy-wortmannin; Helvetica Chimica Acta, Vol. 56, pp. 2901-2903(1973).

20

Cercosporin and Related Metabolites

Cercosporin
Amphicercosporin
Protocercosporin
Hypocrellin
2'-Acetylcercosporin
2',2"-Diacetylcercosporin
2',2"-Dibenzoylcercosporin
Neosporin (Neocercosporin)
Elsinochrome D
Pleichrome

Common/Systematic Name

Cercosporin

1,12-(2-Hydroxypropyl)-2,11-dimethoxy-4,9-dihydroxy-6,7-methylenedioxyperylene-3,10-quinone

Molecular Formula/Molecular Weight

$C_{29}H_{26}O_{10}$; MW = 534.15260

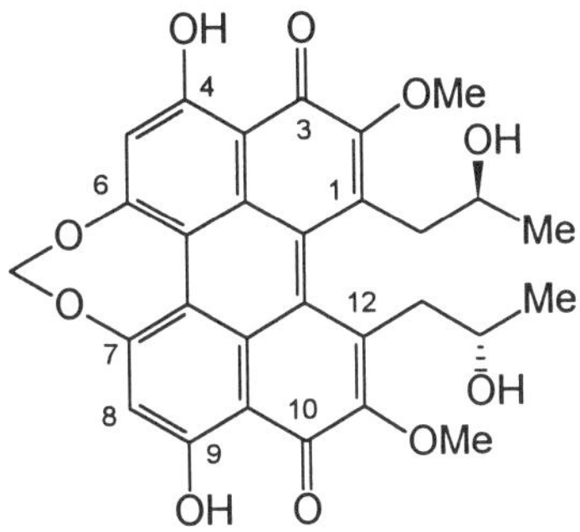

General Characteristics

The pigment melted at 241°C without sublimation or decomposition. Cercosporin was optically active and showed a rotation of $[\alpha]^{20}_{7000}$ +470° which changed on heating in a high boiling solvent, such as toluene, or fusing the crystals at the melting point to a value of -152°C.

Fungal Source

Produced by the mold *Cercosporina kikuchii* responsible for the disease called purple speck disease of Japanese soy beans; *Cercospora hayii*, the causal organism of brown spot of banana fruit. There is widespread distribution of cercosporin producing ability in the genus *Cercospora.* Assante *et al.* (1977) showed that 24 of 61 species tested produced cercosporin. These include *C. ariminiensis, C. bertoreae, C. beticola, C. bizzozeriana, C. canescena, C. carotae, C. chenopodii, C. cistinearum, C. cladosporioides, C. diazu, C. dulcamarae, C. erysimi, C. kikuchii, C. malvacearum, C. malvicola, C. medicaginis, C. nicotianae, C. oryzae, C. personata, C. plantaginis, C. setariae, C. unamunoi,* and *C. violae.*

Isolation/Purification

The pigment was purified by silicic acid column chromatography (acid treated Florisil, 100/200 mesh), packed in an acetone slurry and eluted with chloroform,or it could be obtained by extraction with ethyl ether followed by crystallization from ether to give dark red crystals.

Biological Activity

Phytotoxic.

Spectral Data

UV:

λ_{max}^{EtOH} 223, 260, 271, 275, and 470nm.

IR:

(KBr) 3400m, 2940m, 1619vs, 1585vs, 1554vs, 1455m, 1428m, 1395w, 1348w, 1315m, 1268s, 1223m, 1170s, 1145m, 1113m, 1075m, 1055m, 1017m, 978w, 938w, 921w, and 860cm^{-1} m; bands in the 1700-1550cm^{-1} region ($CHCl_3$), 1614vs; 1583s, and 1551cm^{-1}; (tetrahydrofuran) 1615, 1585, and 1651cm^{-1}.

^{1}H NMR:

The extreme sharpness of the *peri*-hydroxy, the aromatic, the methylenedioxy, the methoxy, and the side-chain hydroxy protons (2.94, 4.24, 5.79, and 8.42ppm), integrating in the ratios 2:2:2:2:6:2, is consistent with a symmetrical arrangement of the substituents on the parent ring system. A methyl doublet(*J*=6Hz) and an ABX-type multiplet, both representing six protons, appeared at 9.37 and 6.7ppm, respectively, and represent the side-chain protons. The assignment of the methoxy groups at C-2 and C-11, rather than at C-5 and C-8, is based upon the position of their NMR resonance, which is comparable to the corresponding groups in the spectrum of elsinochrome A. Moreover, the methoxy resonance failed to undergo an appreciable solvent shift ($CDCl_3$, C_6D_6), which is compatible with the position of the methoxy groups on the parent ring system. The position of the side-chains at C-1 and C-12 is evident from the results of zinc dust distillation which yielded a hydrocarbon with an electronic absorption spectrum closely resembling that of benzo[*ghi*]perylene.

Mass Spectrum:

Major ions in the mass spectrum were 534.1466(M+), 516.1380, 503.1359, 490.1230, 475.1030, 471.1103, 459.1093, 445.0880, 431.0777, 415.0854, 401, 387, 371, 360, 344, 330, and 313*m/e*.

TLC Data

Supelcosil 12A, benzene-MeOH, 1:1, v/v , R_f 0.70; Chromatogram Sheet, chloroform-MeOH, 18:1, v/v, R_f 0.87.

References

G. Assante, R. Locci, L. Camarda, L. Merlini, and G. Masini; Screening of the Genus *Cercospora* for Secondary Metabolites; Phytochemistry, Vol. 16, pp. 243-247(1977).

R. J. J. Ch. Lousberg, U. Weiss, C. A. Salemink, A. Arnone, L. Metlini, and G. Nasini; The Structure of Cercosporin, a Naturally Occurring Quinone; Chem. Comm., pp. 1463-1464(1971).

R. O. Mumma, F. L. Lukezic, and M. G. Kelly; Cercosporin from *Cercospora hayii*; Phytochemistry, Vol. 12, pp. 917-922(1973).

Common/Systematic Name

Amphicercosporin

4,8-Dihydroxy-1,12-(2-hydroxypropyl)-2,11-dimethoxy-6,7-(methylenedioxy)perylene-3,10-quinone

Molecular Formula/Molecular Weight

$C_{29}H_{26}O_{10}$; MW = 534.15260

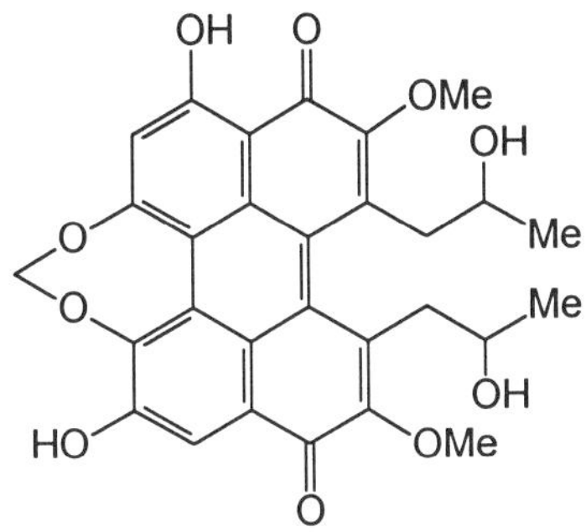

General Characteristics

Reddish purple needles; mp., 195-196°C.

Fungal Source

Cercospora kikuchii.

Spectral Data

UV:

λ_{max}^{EtOH} 260(log ε=4.42), 315-325(3.48), 475(4.23), and 565nm (3.77).

IR:

(Kbr) Showed characteristic absorptions at 1705 and 1630cm^{-1} (nonchelated and chelated carbonyl, respectively).

^{1}H NMR:

($CDCl_3$) showed signals at 1.05(6H, d, *J*=7.2Hz, 2Me); 1.50(2H, s, 2OH); 2.80(2H, dd, *J*=7.2 and 12Hz; 3.45(2H, m); 3.74(2H, m); 4.28(3H, s, MeO); 4.30(3H, s, MeO); 5.82(2H, s); 7.10(H, s, Ph-H); 7.12(1H, s, Ph-H); 11.80(1H, s, free Ph-OH); and 14.60ppm (H, s, chelated Ph-OH).

Reference

S. Matsueda, K. Takagaki, M. Shimoyama, T. Imaizumi, and M. Koreeda; Structure of Amphicercosporin and Protocercosporin; Chem. Ind. (London), p. 58 (1982).

Common Name/Systematic Name

Protocercosporin

Molecular Formula/Molecular Weight

$C_{27}H_{20}O_9$; MW = 488.11073

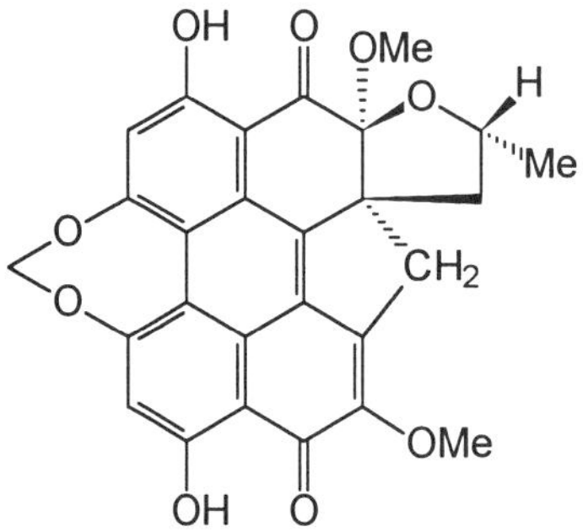

General Characteristics

Orange orthorhombic crystals; mp., 260°C (sub.); protocercosporin is chemically stable and not photosensitive.

Fungal Source

Cercospora kikuchii.

Spectral Data

UV:

λ_{max} 237(log ϵ=4.06), 266(4.06), 298sh (3.64), 340-360(3.55), and 413nm (3.91) showed the extended quinone skeleton.

IR:

The infrared spectrum (KBr) of protocercosporin showed absorption at 1625cm^{-1} (chelated carbonyl).

^{1}H NMR:

($CDCl_3$) Showed signals at 1.55(3H, d, *J*=6Hz, C-15 linked Me); 2.00 and 2.55(1H, dd, *J*=3, 13, 5Hz and 1H, dd, *J*=10, 13.5Hz, respectively, C-14 CH_2); 3.45 and 4.25(1H, d, *J*=17Hz and 1H, d, *J*=17Hz, respectively, C-13 CH_2); 4.40(1H, m, C-15 linked H); 3.48(3H, s, C-2 linked OMe); 4.16(3H, s, C-11 linked OMe); 5.75(2H, dd, *J*=6, 12Hz, -O-CH_2-O-); 12.00(1H, s, C-4 linked OH); and 13.45ppm (1H, s, C-9 linked OH).

Reference

S. Matsueda, K. Takagaki, M. Shimoyama, T. Imaizumi, and M. Koreeda; *Chem. Ind.* (London), p. 58 1982.

Common/Systematic Name

Hypocrellin

Molecular Formula/Molecular Weight

$C_{30}H_{26}O_{10}$; MW = 546.15260

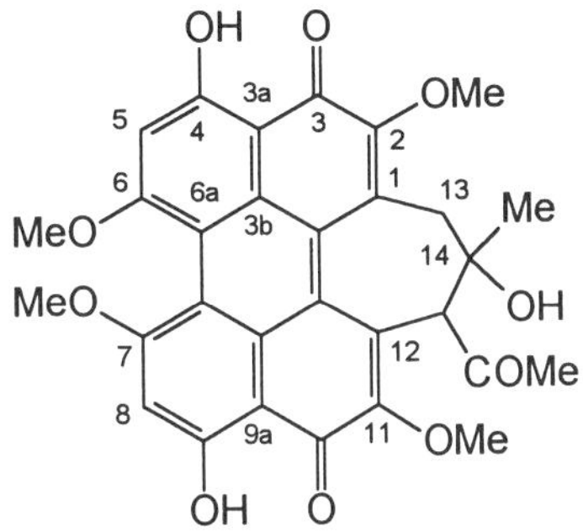

General Characteristics

Dark red crystals from acetone; mp., 209-210°C.

Fungal Source

Hypocrella bambusae.

Biological Activity

Photodynamic activity toward microorganisms.

Spectral Data

UV:

λ_{max}^{EtOH} 215(log ϵ=4.78), 268(4.60), 283(4.59), 342(3.50), 367(3.40), 465(4.48), 539(4.04), 581(4.13), 608nm (3.80); λ_{max}^{NaOH} 217(4.56), 251(4.22), 285(4.30), 473(3.19), 581(4.13) and 608nm (4.15).

IR:

(KBr) 3500(OH), 1720(=C-O), 1620, 1610, 1574, and 1525cm^{-1} (aromatic ring).

^{1}H NMR:

($CDCl_3$) H-5, 6.52(s); H-8, 6.56(s); H-13, 3.53(HA), 2.64(HB, *J*=12Hz); H-15, 3.74(s); H-16, 1.71(s); H-18, 1.90(s); 2-OCH_3, 4.12(s); 6-OCH_3, 4.07(s); 7-OCH_3, 4.08(s); 11-OCH_3, 4.07; 1.68; 15.08; and 1509ppm (3 X D_2O exchangeable protons).

^{13}C NMR:

C-1, 133.2; C-1a, 127.7; C-2, 150.9; C-3, 181.9; C-3a, 106.7; C-3b, 167.5; C-4, 179.7; C-5, 102.4; C-6, 172.0; C-6a, 124.8; C-7, 171.0; C-7a, 124.8; C-7b, 167.5; C-8, 102.4;

C-9, 180.1; C-9a, 106.7; C-10, 179.7; C-11, 150.7; C-12, 134.0; C-12a, 127.7; C-13, 42; C-14, 78.8; C-15, 61.7; C-16, 27.0; C-17, 207.5; C-18, 30.1; C-2-OCH_3, 62.1; C-6-OCH_3, 56.6; C-7-OCH_3, 60.9 and C-11-OCH_3, 56.5ppm.

Mass Spectrum:
EIMS: 546(M^+), 528, 515, 503, 497, 489, 471, 457, 446, 429, and 415*m/e*.

Reference

C. Wei-shin, C. Yuan-teng, W. Xiand-yi, E. Friedrich, H. Puff, and E. Breitmaier; Die Struktur des Hypocrellins und seines Photooxidationsproduktes Peroxyhypocrellin; Liebigs Ann. Chem., pp. 1880-1885(1981).

Common/Systematic Name
2'-Acetylcercosporin

Molecular Formula/Molecular Weight
$C_{31}H_{28}O_{11}$; MW = 576.16316

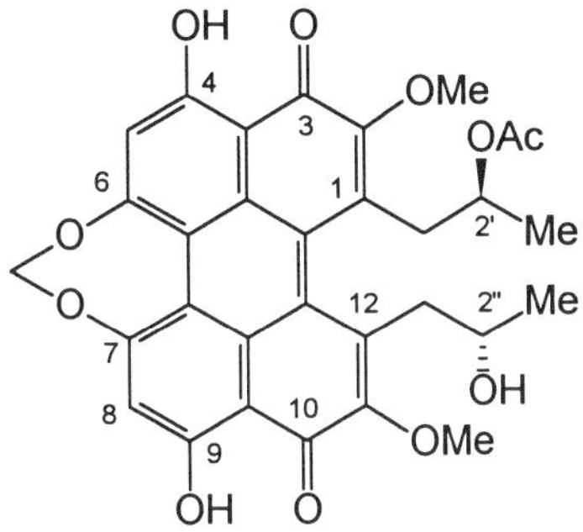

General Characteristics
2'-Acetylcercosporin crystals; mp., 133-134°C.

Fungal Source
Cercospora setariae.

Isolation/Purification
Cercospora setariae cultures were extracted with EtOAc and the crude extract was evaporated to dryness. 2'-Acetylcercosporin was isolated from the crude extract by preparative TLC with benzene-ethyl ether-formic acid (50:50:1, v/v/v).

Biological Activity
Phytotoxic.

Spectral Data

UV:
λ_{max}^{EtOH} 253, 291, 299sh, 480, 590sh, and 640nm (ϵ=15,500, 23,000, 23,300, 14,100, 5,000, and 6,200, respectively).

IR:
(Nujol) 3450(OH), 1740(acetate), and 1620cm^{-1} (conjugated C=O).

CD:
(in EtOH, *c*=0.9 x 10^{-2} g/100ml) 240, 297, 352, and 410nm (Δϵ +23.6, -42.2, +1.92, and -8.00).

^1H NMR:

($CDCl_3$): 0.56 and 0.64(d, 2 Methyls); 1.66(Acetate); 2.80-3.80(m, -CH_2-O and 2-CH_2-CH-O); 4.24 and 4.22ppm (O-Methoxyl groups); 4.64(m,-CH_2-CH-OAc); 5.76(s, O-CH_2-O); 7.04(s, 2 aromatic H's); 14.82 and 14.76ppm (2 chelated OH's).

Mass Spectrum:

EIMS: 576*m/e* (M^+) .

Reference

G. Assante, R. Locci, L. Camarda, L. Merlini, and G. Nasini; Screening of The Genus *Cercospora* for Secondary Metabolites, Phytochemistry, Vol. 16, pp. 243-247(1977).

Common/Systematic Name
2',2"-Diacetylcercosporin

Molecular Formula/Molecular Weight
$C_{33}H_{30}O_{12}$; MW = 618.17373

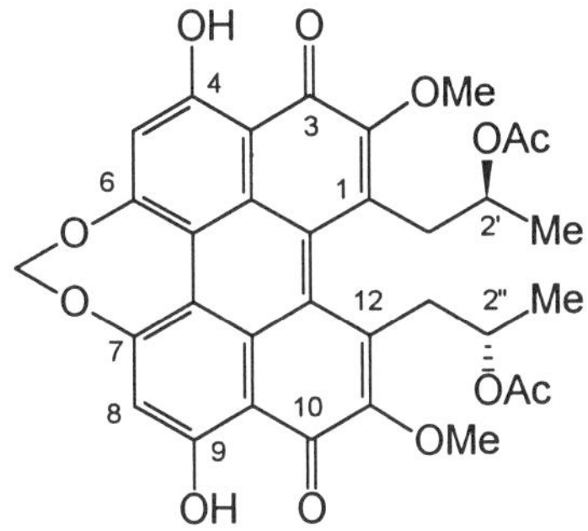

General Characteristics
2',2"-Diacetylcercosporin was obtained as an orange-red powder; mp., 80-82°C.

Fungal Source
Cercospora setariae.

Isolation/Purification
Cercospora setariae cultures were extracted with EtOAc and the crude extract was evaporated to dryness. 2',2"-Diacetylcercosporin was isolated from the crude extract by preparative TLC with benzene-ethyl ether-formic acid (50:50:1, v/v/v).

Biological Activity
Phytotoxic.

Spectral Data

UV:
λ_{max}^{EtOH} 290, 297sh, 485, 600, and 640nm (ϵ=32,700, 32,400, 21,800, 8,600, and 12,000, respectively).

IR:
(Nujol) 1740(acetate) and 1620cm^{-1} (conjugated C=O).

CD:
(in EtOH, c=2.1 x 10^{-2} g/100ml) 246, 297, 320, 352, and 410nm (Δϵ +23.5, -43.5, -7.95, +2.94, and -7.35).

^{1}H NMR:

(CDCl$_3$) 0.55(d, 2 methyls, J=6Hz); 1.70(2 acetates); 3.73 and 3.0ppm (m, 2-CH$_2$-CH-O); 4.28(2 O-methoxy groups); 4.68(m, 2-CH$_2$-CH-OAc); 5.8(s, O-CH$_2$-O); 7.04(s, 2 aromatic H's); and 14.76ppm (2 chelated OH's).

Mass Data:

EIMS: 618*m/e* (M$^+$); found: C, 63.17; H, 4.50; $C_{33}H_{30}O_{12}$ requires C, 64.07; H, 4.89%).

<u>Reference</u>

G. Assante, R. Locci, L. Camarda, L. Merlini, and G. Nasini; Screening of The Genus *Cercospora* for Secondary Metabolites, Phytochemistry, Vol. 16, pp. 243-247

Common/Systematic Name
2',2"-Dibenzoylcercosporin

Molecular Formula/Molecular Weight
$C_{43}H_{34}O_{12}$; MW = 742.20503

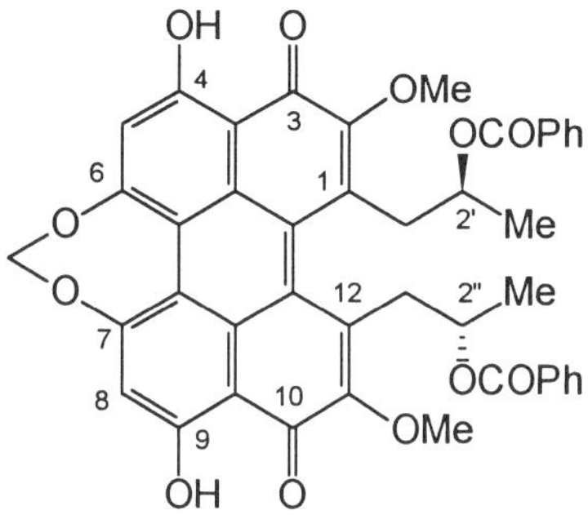

General Characteristics
2',2"-Dibenzoylcercosporin was obtained as a red solid; mp., 120-123°C.

Fungal Source
Cercospora setariae.

Isolation/Purification
Cercospora setariae cultures were extracted with EtOAc and the crude extract was evaporated to dryness. 2',2"-Dibenzoylcercosporin was isolated from the crude extract by preparative TLC with benzene-ethyl ether-formic acid (50:50:1, v/v/v).

Biological Activity
Phytotoxic.

Spectral Data

UV:
λ_{max}^{EtOH} 224, 270, 475, and 565nm (ϵ=36,700, 16,300, 11,800, and 4,300 respectively).

IR:
(Nujol) 1715(OCOPh) and 1620cm^{-1} (conjugated C=O).

CD:
(in EtOH, c= 1.23 x 10^{-2} g/100ml) 240, 297, 318, and 410nm ($\Delta\epsilon$ +21, -24.2, -6.95, and -3.62).

^{1}H NMR:

($CDCl_3$): 0.83(d, 2 methyl's); 3.40-3.86(m, 2-CH_2-CH-O); 4.32(2 methoxy groups); 5.0-5.2(m, 2 -CH_2-CH-OCOPh); 5.62(s, O-CH_2-O); 6.80(s, 2 aromatic H's); 7.0-7.40(10 aromatic H's); and 14.70ppm (2 chelated OH's).

Mass Data:

EIMS: 742*m/e* (M^+); found: C, 68.76; H, 4.60, $C_{43}H_{34}O_{12}$ requires: C, 69.6: H, 4.62.

Reference

G. Assante, R. Locci, L. Camarda, L. Merlini, and G. Nasini; Screening of The Genus *Cercospora* for Secondary Metabolites, Phytochemistry, Vol. 16, pp. 243-247(1977).

Common/Systematic Name
2'-Acetyl-2"-benzoylcercosporin

Molecular Formula/Molecular Weight
$C_{38}H_{32}O_{12}$; MW = 680.18938

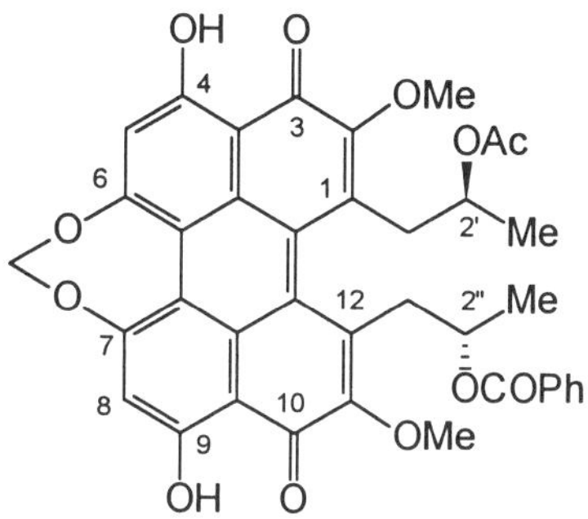

General Characteristics
2'-Acetyl-2"-benzoylcercosporin was obtained as red crystals; mp., 153-155°C.

Fungal Source
Cercospora setariae.

Isolation/Purification
Cercospora setariae cultures were extracted with EtOAc and the crude extract was evaporated to dryness. 2'-Acetyl-2"-benzoylcercosporin was isolated from the crude extract by preparative TLC with benzene-ethyl ether-formic acid (50:50:1, v/v/v).

Biological Activity
Phytotoxic.

Spectral Data

UV:
λ_{max}^{EtOH} 223, 273, 380sh, 480, 570 and 620nm (ε=41,500, 24,400, 4,500, 18,700, 5,850, and 4,000 respectively).

IR:
(Nujol) 1740(acetate), 1720(OCOPh), and 1620cm^{-1} (conjugated C=O).

CD:
(in EtOH, *c*=3.21 x 10^{-2} g/100ml): 240, 298, 320, 360, and 410nm (Δε +16.2, -20.0, -4.86, +0.42, and -3.82).

^1H NMR:
(CDCl$_3$) 0.53 and 0.82ppm (d, methyl); 1.61(acetate); 2.92-3.88(m, 2-CH$_2$-CH-O); 1.28 and 4.30ppm (methoxy); 4.65(m, CH$_2$-CH-OAc); 5.07(m, CH$_2$-CH-OCOPh); 5.70(d, O-CH$_2$-O, J = 7.0Hz); 6.85 and 7.06ppm (s, 2 aromatic protons); 7.16-7.50(C$_6$H$_6$); 14.66 and 14.80ppm (2 /chelated OH's).

Mass Data:
EIMS: 680*m/e* (M^+); found: C, 67.00; H, 4.74, $C_{38}H_{32}O_{12}$ requires: C, 67.05: H, 4.75.

Reference

G. Assante, R. Locci, L. Camarda, L. Merlini, and G. Nasini; Screening of The Genus *Cercospora* for Secondary Metabolites, Phytochemistry, Vol. 16, pp. 243-247(1977).

Common /Systematic Name

Neosporin; Neocerosporin
5,8-Dihydroxy-1,12-(2-hydroxypropyl)-2,11-dimethoxy-6,7-(methylenedioxy) perylene-3,10-quinone

Molecular Formula and Molecular Weight

$C_{29}H_{26}O_{10}$; MW = 534.15260

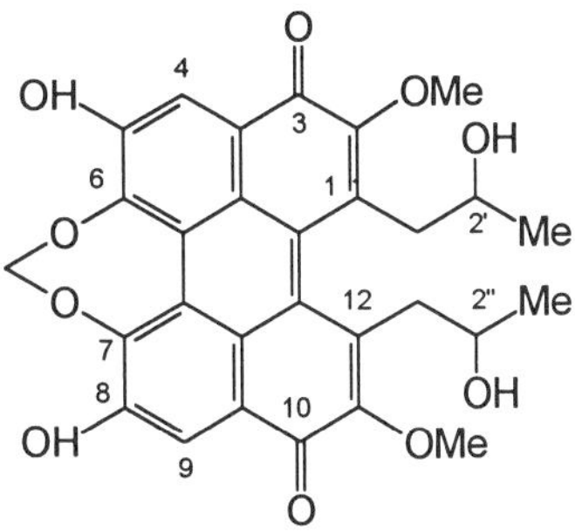

General Characteristics

The novel fungal pigment; mp., 237°C, was isolated together with cercosporin; reddish violet orthorhombic crystals.

Fungal Source

Cercosporina kikuchii.

Spectral Data

UV:

Spectrum showed the skeleton of neosporin was like that of cercosporin;
λ_{max}^{MeOH} 222(ε=49,000), 270(31,500), 475(23,500), and 562nm (8500).

IR:

(KBr) Showed absorption at 1710cm^{-1} (non-chelated carbonyl), which was the characteristic different feature from that of cercosporin.

^{1}H NMR:

The ^{1}H NMR spectrum ($CDCl_3$) of neosporin showed signals at 0.90(6H, d, *J*=6H$_2$, 2Me); 1.40(2H, s, 2OH); 2.9(2H, dd, *J*=6H$_2$ and 12); 4.15(6H, s, 2MeO); 5.65(2H, s, O-CH_2-O-); 6.95(2H, s, 2Ph-H); and 11.2ppm (2H, s, 2Ph-OH).

Mass Spectrum:

The mass spectrum showed the main fragments as follows: 534(M^+ - $C_{29}H_{26}O_{10}$), 516(M^+ - H_2O), 502(M^+ - CH_3OH), 490(M^+ - C_2H_4O), 475(M^+ - C_3H_7O), 458(M^+ - $C_3H_8O_2$), 431(base peak, M^+ -$C_5H_{11}O_2$), 415(M^+ - $C_5H_{11}O_3$), and 401(M^+ - $C_6H_{13}O_3$).

Reference

S. Matsueda; Structure of Neosporin; Chem. Ind., pp. 233-234(1978).

Common/Systematic Name

Elsinochrome D

Molecular Formula/Molecular Weight

$C_{27}H_{15}O_7(OCH_3)_3$; MW = 544.13695

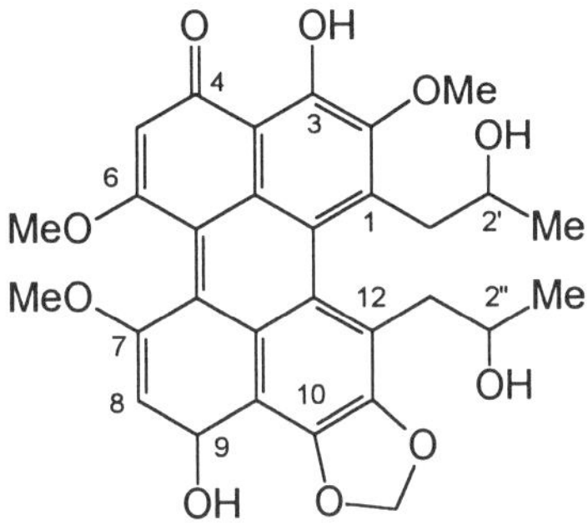

General Characteristics

Elsinochrome D is a monoether of a *peri*-dihydroxyquinone. Recrystallized from *n*-hexane-chloroform (8:1, v/v), the orange crystals of elsinochrome D were dried for 48 hr. at 70°C and 0.1mm; mp., 159-161°C; soluble in most organic solvents, slightly soluble in hot hexane, and very slightly soluble in water; and the solution in aqueous alkali is brownish-green. The brownish-green solution of elsinochrome D in weak alkali turned pink on addition of a few drops of 1N sodium dithionite. When zinc was added to the deep orange solution in acetic acid, the color changed quickly to yellow with green fluorescence. In both cases, the original color was rapidly restored on aeration.

Fungal Source

Elsinoe annonae.

Isolation/Purification

The filtered mycelium was extracted several times with ethyl acetate, the combined extracts were evaporated *in vacuo*, and the residue was taken up in chloroform, washed several times with aqueous sodium hydrogen carbonate, dried ($MgSO_4$) and evaporated to dryness. The residue was chromatographed over calcium hydrogen phosphate with chloroform-ethyl acetate (1:1, v/v) as eluant. The fraction containing mainly elsinochrome D was evaporated *in vacuo* and redissolved in methanol. A white precipitate (amorphous) was filtered off, and the orange solution was evaporated. The residue was taken up in carbon tetrachloride and chromatographed first over calcium hydrogen phosphate, with chloroform as eluant, and subsequently over calcium hydrogen phosphate (activated), with chloroform-acetone-ethanol (131.2:8.7:2, v/v/v) as eluant. The fraction which contained mainly elsinochrome D was evaporated and the residue was recrystallized several times consecutively from *n*-pentane-chloroform (5:1, v/v), *n*-hexane-methanol (10:1, v/v), and *n*-hexane-chloroform (8:1, v/v).

Spectral Data

UV:

λ_{max}^{EtOH} 224, 253, 267, 348, 463, 526, and 560nm (log ϵ 4.70, 4.50, 4.46, 3.66, 4.28, 4.05, and 3.15).

IR:

(KBr) 3400, 1634, 1620, 1600, 1460, 1360, 1145, 1090, and 925cm^{-1}.

^{1}H NMR:

8.91(d) and 8.83(d) (each CH-CH_3); 8.00(OH); 6.17; 6.06; and 5.80(OMe); 6.15(m) and 6.07(m) (CH-CH-OH); 3.90 and 3.77ppm (quinonoid H); 3.67 and 3.73(each 1H, d, *J*=0.5Hz, O-CH_2-O); and 6.00ppm (OH). The positions of the signals at 6.15 and 6.07τ was determined from a spectrum of elsinochrome D in [^{2}H]chloroform-[$^2H_6$]benzene, and may not correspond exactly with the positions of these multiplets in the spectrum of elsinochrome D in pure $CDCl_3$.

Mass Data:

Found: C, 65.7; H, 5.1-OMe, 15.5%; MW, 546.1530 $C_{27}H_{15}O_7(OMe)_3$ requires C, 65.9; H, 4.8; OMe, 17.0%; M, 546.1523.

Reference

R. J. J. Ch. Lousberg, C. A. Salemink, and U. Weiss; Pigments of *Elsinoe* Species. Part V. The Structure of Elsinochrome D; J. Chem Soc., pp. 2159-2162(1970).

Common/Systematic Name

Phleichrome

1,12-Bis(2-hydroxypropyl)-2,6,7,11-tetramethoxy-4,9-dihydroxyperylene-3,10-quinone

Molecular Formula/Molecular Weight

$C_{30}H_{30}O_{10}$; MW = 550.18390

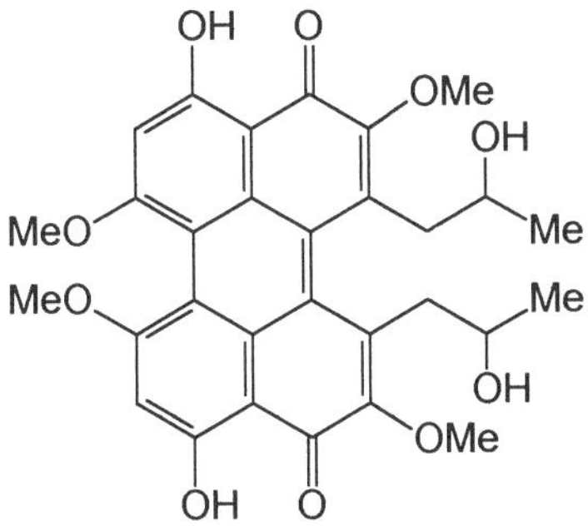

General Characteristics

Obtained as a red pigmented powder. The color in alkaline solution changed from red to green.

Fungal Source

Cladosporium phlei, which causes a leaf spot disease of timothy (*Phleum pratense*). It forms a characteristic eye spot of light grayish-fawn centers with purplish margins on the plant leaves.

Isolation/Purification

The culture filtrates were concentrated *in vacuo* and then extracted with ethyl ether. The extract was dried on Na_2SO_4, concentrated to dryness, and then chromatographed on a polyamide column with water-methanol (1:1, v/v). Its homogeneity was confirmed by TLC on silica gel with 2% oxalic acid solution; R_f 0.56 (reference compound, elsinochrome A, 0.59) in acetone and 0.14 (0.50) in benzene-ethyl acetate (1:1, v/v).

Biological Activity

Phytotoxic.

Spectral Data

UV:

λ_{max} 226(sh) (ϵ=52,600), 260(sh) (32,200), 274(33,900), 474(22,800), 540(sh) (11,400), and 584nm (11,800).

IR:

Absorption bands at 1610(extended quinone system), 1110 (secondary alcohol), and 839cm^{-1} (hexasubstituted phenyl).

ORD:

(c=0.28 x 10^{-3} g/ml in MeOH) [Θ] (nm); -29,400(600), -23,520(589), +13,720(490), -47,040(380), +3,920(330), and +9,800(304).

^{1}H NMR:

(acetone-d_6) assignments as follows: CH_3- at 0.35(d, J=5Hz); -CH_2- and HC- at 2.7-3.2(m) and 3.3-3.9(m); CH_3O- at 4.21(s) and 4.23(s); and Ar-H at 6.80 and Ar-OH at 15.1-16.3ppm (br).

Mass Spectrum:

(Tetraacetate) 718*m/e*.

Reference

T. Yoshihara, T. Shimanuki, T. Araki, and S. Sakamura; A New Phytotoxic Compound Produced by *Cladosporium phlei*; Agr. Biol. Chem., Vol. 39, pp. 1683-1684(1975).

21

Cyathanes

Cyathin A_3
Cyathin A_4
Cyathin B_2
Cyathin B_3
Cyathin C_3 (1,2-Dehydrocyathin B_3)
Cyathin C_5
Allocyathin B_2
Allocyathin B_3
Neoallocyathin A_4
Cyafrin A_4
Cyafrin B_4
Cyafrin A_5
Allocyafrin B_4
Cyathatriol
11-*O*-Acetylcyathatriol
15-*O*-Acetylcyathatriol
11,15-*O*,*O*-Diacetylcyathatriol
Sarcodonin A
Sarcodonin G
Striatin A
Striatin B
Striatin C

Common/Systematic Name

Cyathin A_3

Molecular Formula/Molecular Weight

$C_{20}H_{30}O_3$; MW = 318.21950

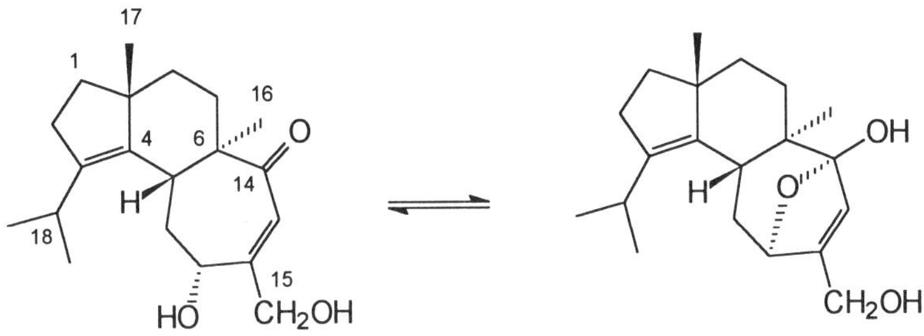

General Characteristics

In the solid state cyathin A_3 existed and crystallized in the internal hemiketal form. Acetylation gave the diacetyl derivative of the hydroxyketone form, whereas treatment with methanolic HCl gave an internal ketal.

Fungal Source

Metabolite of the bird's nest fungus *Cyathus helenae* and *C. africanus*.

Isolation/Purification

The original isolation procedure was based mainly on a combination of column and thin-layer chromatography on the ethyl acetate extract obtained from the culture broth. A material with R_f 0.4 (silica gel G, chloroform-methanol, 9:1, v/v) which appeared chromatographically pure was obtained and called cyathin A_3. However, careful inspection of the NMR spectrum of the acetyl derivative indicated that this material consisted of two components: allocyathin B_3 and its dihydro derivative cyathin A_3. The metabolites were separated and purified using TLC. The plates were developed with Skellysolve B-acetone 2:3, sprayed with a 0.2% solution of 2',7'-dichlorofluorescein in ethanol, and viewed under longwave UV light to locate the zones containing allocyathin B_3 and cyathin A_3. The zones were scraped off and eluted with ether to obtain, after evaporation, allocyathin B_3 and cyathin A_3. Cyathin A_3 was crystallized after trituration with acetone and further purified by recrystallization from benzene or benzene-cyclohexane mixtures.

Biological Activity

The metabolite possessed antibiotic activity.

Spectral Data

UV:

$\lambda_{max}^{Isooctane}$ 323(ϵ=130), and shoulder at 225nm (8,700) (assigned to n-π* and π-π* transitions of the α,β-unsaturated carbonyl system).

IR:

Solid phase IR spectrum lacked absorption in the 1750-1650cm^{-1} region. In solution an IR maximum at 1670cm^{-1} (medium intensity) suggested that in solution cyathin A_3 existed as an equilibrium mixture of the tautomeric forms.

CD:

Maximum at 330nm ($\Delta\epsilon$ +0.73).

^{1}H NMR:

O,O-Diacetylcyathin A_3 derivative: H-1, H-7, and H-8, 1.9-1.1(u); H-2, 2.3(u); H-5b, 2.78(dd, *J*=10 and 2.5Hz); H-10a, 2.05(ddd, *J*=14, 10 and 7Hz); H-10b, 2.53(ddd, *J*=14,6 and 2.5Hz); H-11b, 5.36(ddddd, *J*=7,6, 0.5, 0.5 and 0.5Hz); H-13a or b, 6.13(ddd, *J*=1.5, 0.5 and 0.5 Hz); H-15a, 4.75(ddd, *J*=14, 1.5 and 0.5Hz); H-15b, 4.63(ddd, 14,1.5 and 0.5Hz); H-16 and H-17, 1.15 and 1.06(s, s); H-18, 2.84(qq, *J*=7 and 7Hz); and H-19, H-20, 1.00 and 0.99ppm (d, d, *J*=7 and 7Hz).

Reference

W. A. Ayer and H. Taube; Metabolites of *Cyathus helenae*. A New Class of Diterpenoids; Can. J. Chem., Vol. 51, pp. 3842-3854(1973).

Common/Systematic Name

Cyathin A_4

Molecular Formula/Molecular Weight

$C_{20}H_{30}O_4$; MW = 334.21441

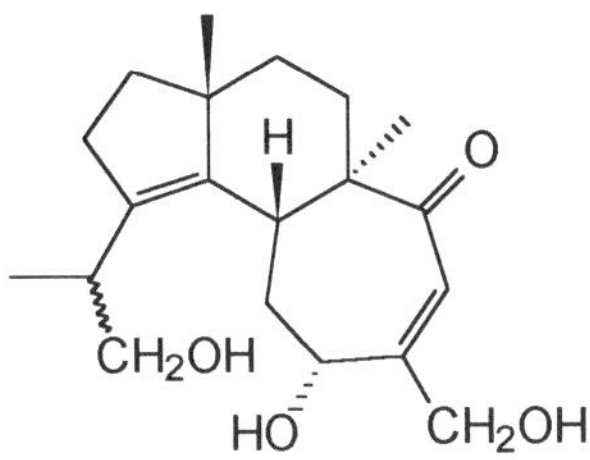

General Characteristics

Evaporative distillation at 220°C/0.2mm gave a clear oil; cyathin A_4 was further characterized as its crystalline tri-*p*-bromobenzoate; crystallization from methylene chloride-methanol gave tri-*p*-bromobenzoylcyathin A_4; mp., 188-189°C.

Fungal Source

Cyathus helenae strain 1500-102.

Isolation/Purification

The active constituents of the culture broth were extracted with ethyl acetate. Examination of the crude extract (referred to as cyathin) by TLC revealed the presence of at least eight components. A solution of the crude cyathin complex was analyzed by preparative TLC, developed with benzene-dioxane-acetic acid (100:25:1, v/v/v). Under UV, bands were detected at R_f 0.54 (cyathin C_5), 0.51 (2,4,5-trihydroxybenzaldehyde), 0.27 (cyathin A_3), and 0.06 (cyathin A_4). Cyathin A_4 was isolated by subjecting crude cyathin from which most of the trihydroxybenzaldehyde has been removed (by treatment with chloroform) to preparative TLC using benzene-acetone-acetic acid (75:25:1, v/v/v) as the developing system; cyathin A_4 R_f 0.10 gave a brown oil, which on further chromatography gave cyathin A_4 as a white foam. Tri-*p*-bromobenzoate: purified by preparative TLC, developed with benzene-acetone (49:1, v/v).

Biological Activity

A paper disc-agar plate method for the assay of antibiotic substances was used. Gram-positive as well as gram-negative bacteria were sensitive to cyathin, but the former were the more sensitive. All species of *Micrococcus* tested proved to be sensitive. *Staphylococcus aureus* 'penicillin-sensitive' as well as 'penicillin-resistant' strains were found to be sensitive. However, *E. coli, Serratia* sp., and *Proteus mirabilis* showed little sensitivity. Among pathogenic forms, only *Pneumococcus multocida, Corynebacterium diphtheriae, Clostridium welchii, Diplococcus pneumoniae, Streptococcus pyogenes,*

Neisseria meningitidis, and *Haemophilus parainfluenzae* were sensitive. None of these pathogenic forms, however, exhibited large zones of inhibition. On the other hand, *Agrobacterium tumefaciens* (the cause of crown gall disease of many horticultural plants) was found to be the most sensitive of all the organisms screened. All fungi tested against cyathin were sensitive to some degree. Most of the sensitive fungi belong to the class Deuteromycetes. The most striking examples of fungi sensitive to cyathin included species of *Aspergillus, Penicillium, Fusarium, Trichoderma, Chaetomium,* and *Gliocladium*. However, none of the Phycomycetes proved to be sensitive to cyathin. The same was true of yeasts. Of the six 'dermatophytes' tested, all showed some degree of sensitivity to cyathin. The most striking examples were *Microsporum canis, Trichophyton rubrum,* and *T. terrestre*.

Spectral Data

IR:

($CHCl_3$) 3600, 3400, 1700(w), 1650(m), and 1375cm^{-1}. Tri-*p*-bromobenzoate: ($CHCl_3$) 1715 1680, 1580, and 1480cm^{-1}.

^{1}H NMR:

($CDCl_3$) 4.02(1H, narrow m); 5.6(1H, m); 5.79(2H, narrow m); 6.0(3H, disappeared on D_2O exchange); 6.62(2H, m); 9.02(3H, s); 9.04(3H, s); and 9.07ppm (3H, d, splitting 6Hz).

Tri-*p*-bromobenzoate ($CDCl_3$) 2.0-2.5(12H, aromatic protons); 3.70(1H, narrow m); 4.22(1H, t); 5.04(2H, m); 5.80(2H, AB part of ABX system); 6.72(1H, q); 7.0-8.0 (several multiplets); 8.0-8.7(complex); 8.84(3H, s); 8.96(3H, d, splitting 7Hz); and 9.02ppm (3H, s).

Mass Data:

HREIMS: 334.2146*m/e*; anal. calcd for $C_{20}H_{30}O_4$ 334.2144; C, 71.82, H, 9.04; found: C, 72.06, H, 8.53.

Tri-*p*-bromobenzoate: anal. calcd for $C_{41}H_{39}O_7Br_3$: C, 55.72; H, 4.45; O, 12.67; Br, 27.16; found: C, 56.00; H, 4.49; O, 12.72; Br, 27.25.

Reference

A. D. Allbutt, W. A. Ayer, H. J. Brodie, B. N. Johri, and H. Taube; Cyathin, a new antibiotic complex produced by *Cyathus helenae*; Can. J. Microbiol., Vol. 17, pp. 1401-1407(1971).

Common/Systematic Name

Cyathin B_2

Molecular Formula/Molecular Weight

$C_{20}H_{28}O_2$; MW = 300.20893

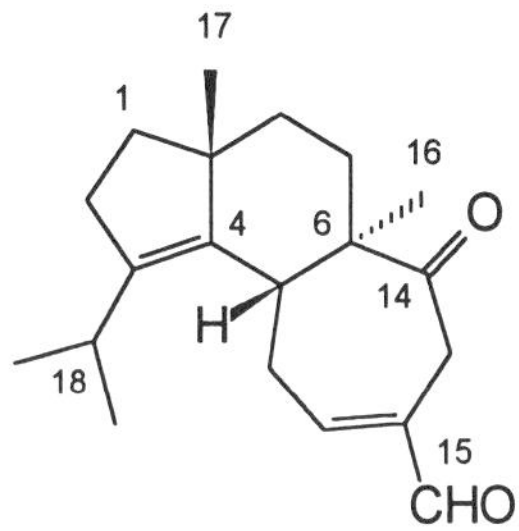

General Characteristics

Cyathin B_2 was obtained as a viscous syrup.

Fungal Source

Cyathus earlei is a tropical or subtropical species of bird's nest fungus which is known to occur in Cuba, Puerto Rico, Mexico, and Hawaii.

Isolation/Purification

The mycelium was extracted with ethyl acetate after 65 days growth on Brodie medium which gave six compounds belonging to the "cyathin" group of diterpenoids. The ethyl acetate extract was washed with water, dried over sodium sulfate, and concentrated to a viscous brown oil. The crude extract was subjected to silica gel column chromatography eluted with Skellysolve B-benzene to give cyathin B_2.

Biological Activity

Moderate antibiotic activity against *Staphylococcus aureus.*

Spectral Data

UV:

λ_{max}^{MeOH} 228nm (ϵ=6,100).

IR:

(CCl_4) 2710, 1710, 1698, and 1645cm^{-1}.

^1H NMR:

(CCl_4) 0.99(s, 3H); 1.02(d, *J*=6Hz, 6H); 1.10(s, 3H); 3.32(d, *J*=14Hz, H on C-13); 3.64(dd, *J*=14 and 1Hz, H on C-13); 6.60(m, C-11, H); and 9.38ppm (s, 1H).

Mass Spectrum:
HREIMS: 300.2092*m/e* (M^+); exact mass calcd for $C_{20}H_{28}O_2$ 300.2090.

Reference

W. A. Ayer and S. P. Lee; Metabolites of bird's nest fungi. Part II. Diterpenoid metabolites of *Cyathus earlei* Lloyd; Can. J. Chem., Vol. 57, pp. 3332-3337(1979).

Common/Systematic Name

Cyathin B_3

Molecular Formula/Molecular Weight

$C_{20}H_{28}O_3$; MW = 316.20384

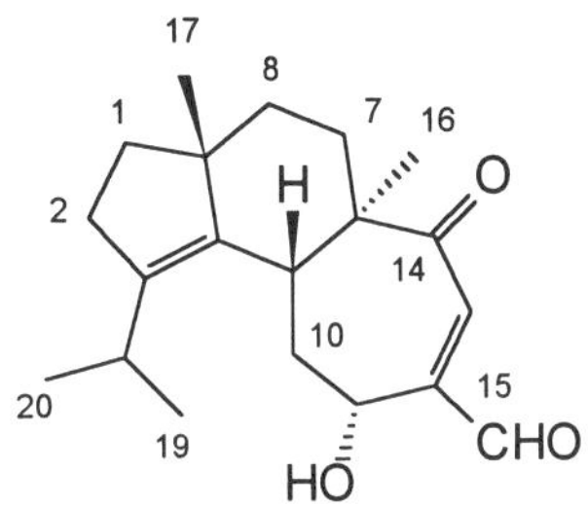

General Characteristics

Colorless needles from ether-pentane; mp., 130-132°C.

Isolation/Purification

The ethyl acetate soluble metabolites of *Cyathus helenae* were chromatographed on a column containing silicic acid containing electronic phosphor using chloroform (0.75% EtOH) as eluent. The progress of the separation was monitored with a short wavelength UV lamp. Crystals of the mixture were applied to TLC plates coated with silica gel-10% $AgNO_3$ and developed with Skellysolve B-acetone (3:2, v/v). Two overlapping bands were detected by UV. These were removed from the plates in 3 fractions; the top and bottom fractions were rechromatographed on silica gel. In this way, it was possible to obtain cyathin B_3 only slightly contaminated with cyathin C_3 (as judged by NMR and MS).

Cyathin B_3 methyl ketal was purified from cyathin C_3 methyl ketal by preparative TLC using silica gel - 10% $AgNO_3$ (solvent system, Skellysolve B-acetone (3:1, v/v), R_f values 0.58 cyathin B_3 methyl ketal and 0.51 cyathin C_3 methyl ketal). Neither could be induced to crystallize.

Biological Activity

The fungus *Cyathus helenae* grown on liquid culture produced a mixture of substances showing antibiotic activity, including cyathin B_3.

Spectral Data

Optical Rotation:

$[\alpha]_D^{24}$ -105°C (c= 0.1, in isooctane).

UV:

$\lambda_{max}^{Isooctane}$ 233nm (ϵ 5,300)

CD:
(c= 0.1, in isooctane) $\Delta\epsilon_{346}$ -0.97 and $\Delta\epsilon_{235}$ -2.78.

IR:
(CCl_4) 2850, 2720, 1692(s), and 1625cm^{-1}.

^{1}H NMR:
(CCl_4) 9.88(s, H-15); 7.00(s, H-13); 4.97(br s, H-11); 3.26(s, methoxyl); 2.93(septet, H-18, J=7Hz); 2.3-1.1(complex); 0.98(d, J=7Hz, one isopropyl methyl), 0.94(s, 3H, H-16 or -17); 0.90(s, 3H, H-17 or -16); and 0.89ppm (d, J=7Hz, one isopropyl methyl).

Mass Spectrum:
LREIMS: 330(24%), 315(14), 301(20), 299(23), 255(21), 227(23), 204(21), 199(21), 189(100), 175(31), 161(33), 133(35), 119(47), 105(63), 91(65), 55(67), and 41*m/e* (86); exact mass measurement 330.2184 (calcd for $C_{21}H_{30}O_3$, 330.2195). Appropriate parent peak at *m/e* 330 and no M^+ -2 peak.

Reference

William A. Ayer and Leslie L. Carstens; Diterpenoid Metabolites of *Cyathus helenae*, Cyathin B_3 and Cyathin C_3, Can. J. Chem., Vol. 51, pp. 3157-3160(1973).

Common/Systematic Name

Cyathin C_3; 1,2-Dehydrocyathin B_3

Molecular Formula/Molecular Weight

$C_{20}H_{26}O_3$; MW = 314.18819

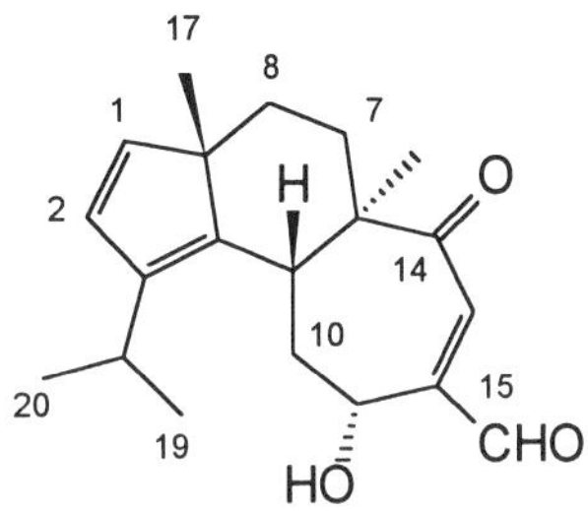

General Characteristics of Mixture (Cyathin C_3 and Cyathin B_3)

Colorless needles from ether-pentane; mp., 131-133°C.

Fungal Source

The bird's nest fungus *Cyathus helenae*.

Isolation/Purification

Ethyl acetate soluble metabolites of *Cyathus helenae* were chromatographed on a column containing silicic acid containing electronic phosphor using chloroform (0.75% EtOH) as eluent. The progress of the separation was monitored with a short wavelength UV lamp. Crystals of the mixture were applied to TLC plates coated with silica gel-10% $AgNO_3$ and developed with Skellysolve B-acetone (3:2, v/v). Two overlapping bands were detected by UV. These were removed from the plates in 3 fractions; the top and bottom fractions were rechromatographed on silica gel. In this way, it was possible to obtain cyathin B_3 only slightly contaminated with cyathin C_3 (as judged by NMR and MS).

Biological Activity

The fungus *Cyathus helenae* grown on liquid culture produced a mixture of substances showing antibiotic activity, including cyathin C_3.

Spectral Data (Cyathin C_3 and Cyathin B_3 mixture)

UV:

$\lambda_{max}^{Dioxane}$ 233nm (ϵ=6,800).

IR:

(CCl_4) 3585, 3350(br), 3050(w), 2810, 2710, 1692(v.s.), and 1625cm^{-1} (w).

^{1}H NMR:

($CDCl_3$) 9.91(s), 9.61(s), 7.01(s), 6.6-6.2(complex), and 5.01ppm (m), methyl region complex.

Mass Spectrum:

314(11), 301(22), 299(5), 273(11), 255(12), 204(23), 203(23), 201(21), 189(58), 187(21), 175(14), 173(10), 161(28), 159(17), 119(37), 105(39), 91(46), 55(57), and 41*m/e* (100%).

Cyathin C_3 methyl ketal:

The spectroscopic properties are similar to those of cyathin B_3 except for those attributable to the cyclopentadiene moiety.

Optical Rotation:

$[\alpha]_D^{24}$ -89°C (*c*=0.043, in isooctane).

UV:

$\lambda_{max}^{isooctane}$ 236(ϵ=7,400) and 257nm (sh) (4,300).

IR:

(CCl_4) Characteristic olefinic C-H stretching bands appeared at 3050, 2850, 2810, 2720, 1693(s), and 1625cm^{-1}.

CD:

(*c*=0.043, in isooctane) $\Delta\epsilon_{356}$ -1.23, $\Delta\epsilon_{258}$ -4.31, and $\Delta\epsilon_{235}$ -9.23.

^{1}H NMR:

(CCl_4) 9.92(s, H-15); 7.03(s, H-13); 6.20 and 6.10(AB quartet, H-1 and -2, *J*=5.5Hz); 5.05(m, H-11); 3.29(s, methoxyl); 2.95(septet, H-18, *J*=7Hz); 2.5-21(complex, 2H); 1.8-1.1(complex); 1.09 and 1.03(two nonequivalent isopropyl methyls, *J*'s=7Hz); 0.88(s, 3H, H-16 or -17); and 0.77ppm (s, 3H, H-17 or H-16). The olefinic protons at C-1 and C-2 appear as an AB quartet (*J*=5.5Hz) centered at 6.15ppm.

Mass Spectrum:

328(39), 313(13), 299(25), 295(21), 253(25), 225(20), 202(27), 187(100), 173(28), 159(23), 145(32), 133(20), 119(24), 105(22), 101(45), 91(25), 75(77), 55(16), and 41*m/e* (29); exact mass measurement 328.2042 (calcd for $C_{21}H_{28}O_3$, 328.2039).

Reference

William A. Ayer and Leslie L. Carstens; Diterpenoid Metabolites of *Cyathus helenae*, Cyathin B_3 and Cyathin C_3; Can. J. Chem., vol. 51, pp. 3157-3160(1973).

Common/Systematic Name

Cyathin C_5

Molecular Formula/Molecular Weight

$C_{20}H_{26}O_5$; MW = 346.17802

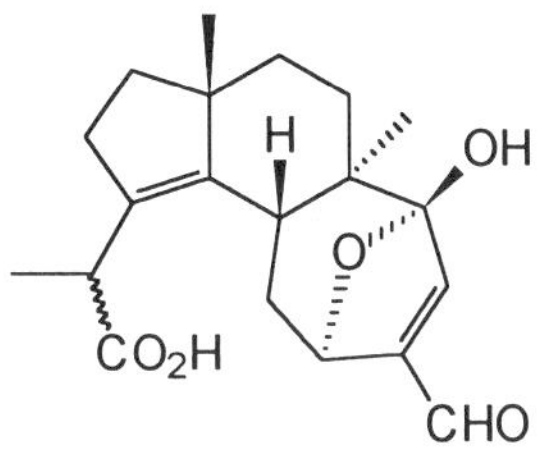

General Characteristics

Colorless crystals from ethyl ether-pentane; mp., 225-226°.

Fungal Source

Cyathus helenae.

Isolation/Purification

The active constituents of the culture broth were extracted with ethyl acetate. Examination of the crude extract (referred to as cyathin) by TLC revealed the presence of at least eight components. A solution of the crude cyathin complex was analyzed by preparative TLC, developed with benzene-dioxane-acetic acid (100:25:1, v/v). Under UV, bands were detected at R_f 0.54 (cyathin C_5), 0.51 (2,4,5-trihydroxybenzaldehyde), 0.27 (cyathin A_3), and 0.06 (cyathin A_4). The material with R_f 0.54 was eluted from the adsorbent with ether-methanol (10:1, v/v) to give a brown oil. Further purification by preparative TLC yielded a material which crystallized from ether-pentane to give colorless crystals of cyathin C_5.

Biological Activity

Gram-positive as well as gram-negative bacteria were sensitive to cyathin, but the former were more sensitive. All species of *Micrococcus* tested proved to be sensitive. *Staphylococcus aureus* 'penicillin-sensitive' as well as 'penicillin-resistant' strains were found to be sensitive. However, *E. coli, Serratia* sp., and *Proteus mirabilis* showed little sensitivity. Among pathogenic forms, only *Pneumococcus multocida, Corynebacterium diphtheriae, Clostridium welchii, Diplococcus pneumoniae, Streptococcus pyogenes, Neisseria meningitidis,* and *Haemophilus parainfluenzae* were sensitive. None of these pathogenic forms, however, exhibited large zones of inhibition. On the other hand, *Agrobacterium tumefaciens* (the cause of crown gall disease of many horticultural plants) was found to be the most sensitive of all the organisms screened. All fungi tested against cyathin were sensitive to some degree. Most of the sensitive fungi belonged to the class Deuteromycetes. The most striking examples of fungi sensitive to cyathin included species of *Aspergillus, Penicillium, Fusarium, Trichoderma, Chaetomium,* and *Gliocladium.*

However, none of the Phycomycetes proved to be sensitive to cyathin. The same was true of yeasts. Of the six 'dermatophytes' tested, all showed some degree of sensitivity to cyathin. The most striking examples were *Microsporum canis, Trichophyton rubrum,* and *T. terrestre*.

Spectral Data

IR:
(Nujol) 3400, 3200, 1695, 1675, 1235, and 1220cm^{-1}.

^{1}H NMR:
(acetone-d_6) 0.1(1H, s); 5.16(2H, m); 5.9-6.6(5-7H, m); 8.92(3H, d, splitting 7Hz); 9.05(3H, s); and 9.15ppm (3H, s).

Mass Data:
HREIMS: 346.1774*m/e*; anal calcd for $C_{20}H_{26}O_5$, 346.1780: C, 69.34; H, 7.57; O, 23.09; found: C, 68.85; H, 7.66; O, 23.47; (Tri-*p*-bromobenzoate) anal calcd for $C_{41}H_{39}O_7Br_3$: C, 55.72; H, 4.45; O, 12.67; Br, 27.16; found: C, 56.00; H, 4.49; O,12.72; Br, 27.25.

Reference

A. D. Allbutt, W. A. Ayer, H. J. Brodie, B. N. Johri, and H. Taube; Cyathin, a new antibiotic complex produced by *Cyathus helenae;* Can. J. Microbiol., Vol. 17, pp. 1401-1407(1971).

Common/Systematic Name
Allocyathin B_2

Molecular Formula/Molecular Weight
$C_{20}H_{28}O_2$; MW = 300.20893

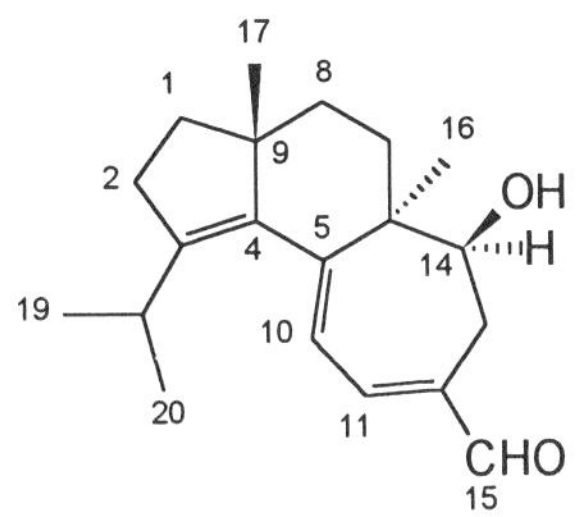

General Characteristics
Allocyathin B_2 was obtained as a yellow syrup which showed a single spot on TLC; $[\alpha]_D^{25}$ + 87.1° (c=0.95, in CH_3OH).

Fungal Source
Cyathus earlei is a tropical or subtropical species of bird's nest fungus which is known to occur in Cuba, Puerto Rico, Mexico, and Hawaii.

Isolation/Purification
The mycelium was extracted with ethyl acetate after sixty-five days growth on Brodie medium which gave a crude extract containing six compounds belonging to the "cyathin" group of diterpenoids. The ethyl acetate extract was washed with water, dried over sodium sulfate, and concentrated to a viscous brown oil. The crude extract was subjected to column chromatography over silica gel by elution with benzene which afforded allocyathin B_2.

Biological Activity
Moderate antibiotic activity against *Staphylococcus aureus*.

Spectral Data

UV:
λ_{max}^{Hexane} 266(ϵ=5,150) and 325nm (12,100).

IR:
(CCl_4) 3600, 2720, 1675, and 1570cm^{-1}.

^1H NMR:
(CCl_4) 0.96 and 1.05(each 3H, d, J=6Hz); 0.97(s, 3H); 1.01(s, 3H); 2.80(heptet, J=6Hz, H on C-18); 3.09(dd, J=18 and 6Hz, 1H on C-13); 3.63(dd, J's 6 and 1Hz, H

on C-14); 5.84(d, J=8Hz, H on C-10); 6.68(dd, J=8 and 1Hz, H on C-11); and 9.37ppm (s, 1H).

Mass Data:

HREIMS: 300.2092; exact mass calcd. for $C_{20}H_{28}O_2$ 300.20893; anal. calcd. for $C_{20}H_{28}O_2$: C 80.02, H 9.40; found: C 80.04, H 9.70.

Reference

W. A. Ayer and S. P. Lee; Metabolites of bird's nest fungi. Part II. Diterpenoid metabolites of *Cyathus earlei* Lloyd; Can. J. Chem., Vol. 57, pp. 3332-3336(1979).

Common/Systematic Name
Allocyathin B_3

Molecular Formula/Molecular Weight
$C_{20}H_{28}O_3$; MW = 316.20384

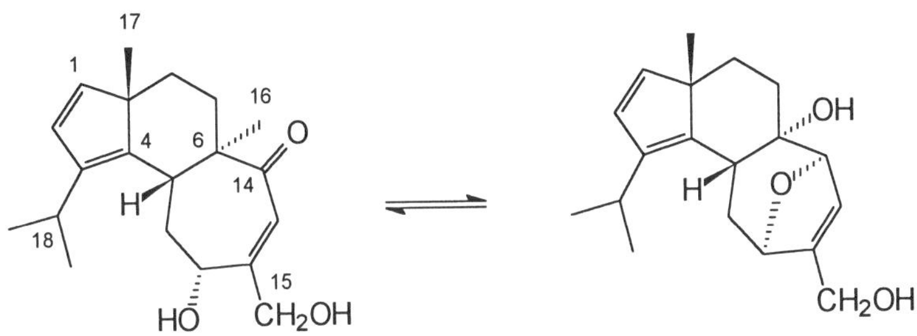

General Characteristics
In the solid state allocyathin B_3 existed in the hydroxyketone form. Acetylation gave the diacetyl derivative of the hydroxyketone form, whereas treatment with methanolic HCl gave an internal ketal. Allocyathin B_3 could only be crystallized after it had been subjected to an acetylation-deacetylation procedure. Recrystallization from Skellysolve B-benzene; mp., 143-144°C.

Fungal Source
The bird's nest fungus, *Cyathus helenae* and *C. africanus*.

Isolation/Purification
The original isolation procedure was based on a combination of column and TLC of the ethyl acetate extract of the culture broth. A material with R_f 0.4 which appeared chromatographically pure was obtained and designated cyathin A_3. Careful inspection of the NMR spectrum of the acetyl derivative indicated that this material consisted of two components, allocyathin B_3 and its dihydro derivative cyathin A_3. Chromatography on silica gel impregnated with 10% silver nitrate separated the two components (solvent Skellysolve B-acetone, 2:3, v/v, R_f 0.51).

Biological Activity
Possessed antibiotic activity.

Spectral Data

UV:
The UV spectrum has a somewhat unsymmetrical maximum at 235nm (MeOH), ϵ=5,000 resulting from two overlapping chromophores.
Acetylated allocyathin B_3: The UV spectrum (isooctane) showed maxima at 325(ϵ=140), 254(4800), and 225nm (9,000).

IR:

Spectrum in chloroform displayed hydroxyl absorption and a broad band of medium intensity at 1650cm^{-1}. This band was assigned to an α,β-unsaturated carbonyl group and it appeared in the same position in the solid-phase spectrum but was much stronger and sharper; other absorptions were 3580 and 3400cm^{-1}.

Acetyl derivative: 1745, 1685, and 1655(sh) cm^{-1} attributed to an α,β-unsaturated carbonyl system.

CD:

Spectrum displayed a positive maximum at 327nm with a dichroic absorption + 1.6, assigned to an α,β-unsaturated carbonyl group.

^{1}H NMR:

The NMR spectrum had one readily analyzable feature: an AB quartet centered at 6.26ppm, *J*=5Hz; the remainder of the spectrum was poorly defined (tautomerism?) and of limited value in structural studies.

Allocyathin B_3 diacetyl derivative ($CDCl_3$): H-1, 6.34, d, *J*=5.5Hz; H-2, 6.31, d, *J*=5.5Hz; H-13, 6.15, ddd, 1.5, 1.5, 0.5Hz; H-11, 5.39, ddd, 6.5, 6.5, 0.5Hz; H-15a, 4.75, dd, *J*=14.5 and 1.5Hz; H-15b, 4.68, dd, *J*=14.5 and 1.5Hz; H-18, 2.96, qq, *J*=7.0 and 7.0; H-5, 2.87, qq, *J*=10.5 and 3.0Hz; H-10a, 2.56, ddd, *J*=14, 6.5, and 3.0; H-10b, 2.27, ddd, *J*=14, 10.5, and 6.5Hz; H-7, H-8, 1.9-1.1, u; H-16, H-17, 1.04, 1.00, s, s; H-19, H-20, 1.12, 1.10, d, d, *J*=7 and 7Hz; C-11 or C-15 OAC, 2.12 or 2.05ppm, s, s.

Mass Spectrum:

Composition $C_{20}H_{28}O_3$ was determined by high resolution mass spectrometry; calcd, 316.2039; found, 316.2031.

<u>TLC Data</u>

R_f 0.4 using chloroform-methanol, 9:1(v/v), on 10% silver nitrate silica gel.

<u>Reference</u>

W. A. Ayer and H. Taube; Metabolites of *Cyathus helenae*: A New Class of Diterpenoids; Cand. J. Chem., Vol. 51, pp. 3842-3854(1973).

Common/Systematic Name
Neoallocyathin A_4

Molecular Formula/Molecular Weight
$C_{20}H_{30}O_4$; MW = 334.21441

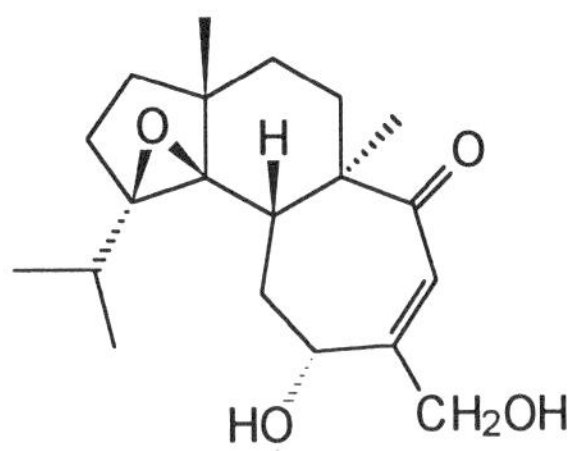

General Characteristics
Neoallocyathin A_4 acetonide, $C_{23}H_{34}O_4$; mp., 144.5-146°C (from ether-pentane).

Fungal Source
Cyathus helenae.

Isolation/Purification
(Neoallocyathin A_4 acetonide) The crude metabolites of *C. helenae* were chromatographed over silicic acid using 1.5% MeOH in $CHCl_3$ as eluant. All fractions showing peaks at 334*m/e* were combined and subjected to TLC on silica gel G (E. Merck) (containing 5% added inorganic phosphor) using acetone-Skellysolve B (7:3, v/v) as the solvent system. The band centered at R_f 0.66 was removed and eluted with ether to give a clear oil. The latter material was again subjected to TLC with silica gel G impregnated with 10% $AgNO_3$ developed with acetone-Skellysolve B (7:3, v/v). After drying, the plate was sprayed lightly with 2',7'-dichlorofluorescein and observed under long wave UV light. Neoallocyathin A_4 acetonide appeared at R_f 0.49.

Spectral Data (Acetonide)

UV:
λ_{max}^{MeOH} 232(ϵ=12,000) and 322nm (100).

IR:
($CHCl_3$) 1685(sh) and 1635cm^{-1}; (neat) 3400 br, and 1642cm^{-1} br.

CD:
(*c*=0.001 M in MeOH) ϵ_{300} -0.18 and ϵ_{270} -0.23.

^{1}H NMR:

(CDCl$_3$) 1.01(s, 3H, C-16, CH$_3$); 1.06(d, 3H, *J*=7Hz) and 1.10(d, 3H, *J*=7Hz, isopropyl methyls); 1.24(s, 3H, C-17 CH$_3$); 4.0-4.5(m, 3H, C-11 and C-15 H's); and 6.03ppm (bs, 1H, C-13 H): (acetonide) (CDCl$_3$) 1.03(s, 3H, C-16, CH$_3$); 1.08(apparent t, 6H, isopropyl CH$_3$'s); 1.24(s, 3H, C-17, CH$_3$); 1.40, 1.50(each 3H singlets, acetonide methyls); 4.15-4.35(m, 3H, C-15 and C-11 H's); and 7.25ppm (bs, 1H, C-13 H).

Mass Spectrum:

HREIMS: 334.2138; exact mass calcd for $C_{20}H_{30}O_4$ 334.2144: Neoallocyathin A$_4$ acetonide 374.7452*m/e*; exact mass calcd for $C_{23}H_{34}O_4$ 374.2457; LREIMS: 374 (M^+, 45%), 359(11), 189(26), 149(21), 79(25), 61(30), and 43*m/e* (100).

TLC Data (Neoallocyathin A$_4$ acetonide)

Subjected to TLC on silica gel G impregnated with 10% $AgNO_3$ using acetone-Skellysolve B (7:3, v/v). After drying, the plate was sprayed lightly with 2',7'-dichlorofluorescein and observed under long wave UV light. It appeared at R_f 0.49.

Reference

W. A. Ayer, L. M. Browne, J. R. Mercer, D. R. Taylor, and D. E. Ward; Metabolites of bird's nest fungi. Part 8. Some minor metabolites of *Cyathus helenae* and some correlations among the cyathins; Can. J. Chem., Vol. 56, pp. 717-721(1978).

Common/Systematic Name

Cyafrin A_4

Molecular Formula/Molecular Weight

$C_{20}H_{30}O_4$; MW = 334.21441

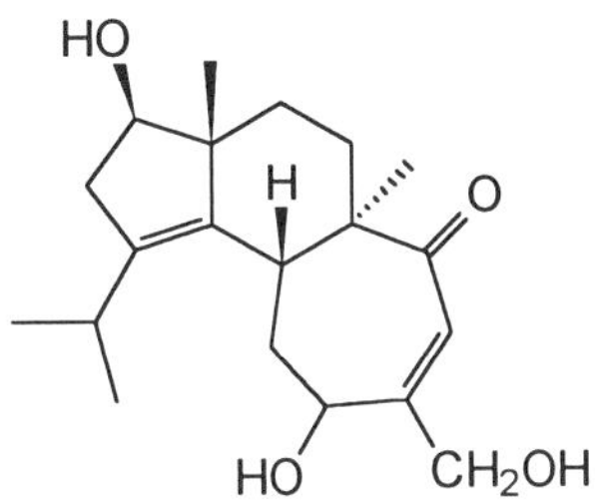

General Characteristics

Cyafrin A_4 crystallized from methanol-benzene as colorless needles; mp., 200-201°C; $[\alpha]_D^{25}$ -125° (*c*=0.4, in MeOH).

Fungal Source

Cyathus africanus (Nidulariaceae).

Isolation/Purification

The crude extract was chromatographed over silicic acid (MN-Kieselgel) using chloroform-methanol (19:1, v/v) as eluant. Fractions were monitored by TLC (solvent system B). Fractions 101-110 contained a mixture of cyathin A_3 and allocyathin B_3 which was separated into its components by preparative TLC over 10% $AgNO_3$-silica gel (solvent system A). Fractions 123-130 contained cyafrin B_4 and allocyafrin B_4. Separation by preparative TLC (solvent system D) gave cyafrin B_4 (R_f 0.6) and allocyafrin B_4 (R_f 0.5). Fractions 228-254 yielded crude cyafrin A_4 which was purified by recrystallization from acetone. Fractions 255-276 gave a mixture of cyafrin A_4 and cyafrin A_5, which was separated by preparative TLC (solvent system C triple elution). Cyafrin A_5 was purified by recrystallization from acetone-benzene. Preparative TLC was carried out on 0.75mm layers of silica gel G (W. Merck, Darmstadt) containing 1% electronic phosphor (General Electric, Cleveland). The solvent systems used were: A, Skellysolve B-acetone (3:1, v/v), B, benzene-acetone-acetic acid (75:25:1, v/v); C, chloroform-acetonitrile (3:2, v/v); and D, benzene-methanol-acetic acid (18:2:1, v/v).

Spectral Data

UV:

λ_{max} 230nm (sh) (ϵ=1500).

IR:
(KBr) 3300(br) and no carbonyl.

^{1}H NMR:
(pyridine) Indicated a mixture of hydroxyketone and hemiacetal forms.

Mass Spectrum:
334.2152*m/e* (M^+); exact mass calcd for $C_{20}H_{30}O_4$, 334.2144.

Reference

W. A. Ayer, T. Yoshida, and D. M. J. Van Schie; Metabolites of bird's nest fungi. Part 9. Diterpenoid metabolites of *Cyathus africanus* Brodie; Can. J. Chem., Vol. 56, pp. 2113-2120(1978).

Common/Systematic Name

Cyafrin B_4

Molecular Formula/Molecular Weight

$C_{20}H_{28}O_4$; MW = 332.19876

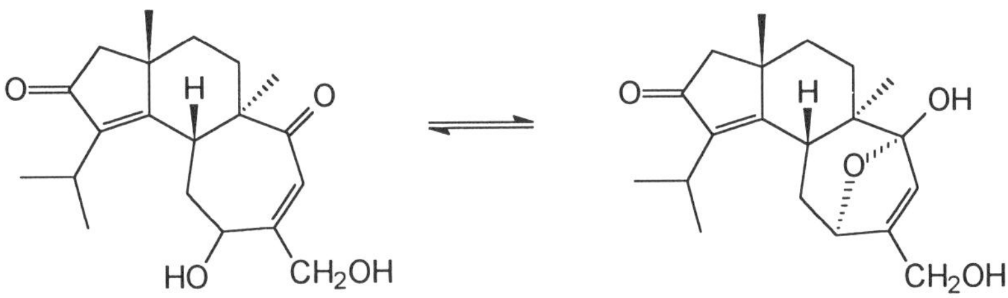

General Characteristics

Cyafrin B_4 was obtained as a colorless syrup; $[\alpha]_D^{25}$ -156.5° (*c*=0.34, in $CHCl_3$).

Fungal Source

Cyathus africanus.

Isolation/Purification

The crude extract was chromatographed over silicic acid (MN-Kieselgel) using chloroform-methanol (19:1, v/v) as eluant. Fractions were monitored by TLC (solvent system B). Fractions 101-110 contained a mixture of cyathin A_3 and allocyathin B_3 which was separated into its components by preparative TLC over 10% $AgNO_3$-silica gel (solvent system A). Fractions 123-130 contained cyafrin B_4 and allocyafrin B_4. Separation by preparative TLC (solvent system D) gave cyafrin B_4 (R_f 0.6) and allocyafrin B_4 (R_f 0.5). Fractions 228-254 yielded crude cyafrin A_4 which was purified by recrystallization from acetone. Fractions 255-276 gave a mixture of cyafrin A_4 and cyafrin A_5, which was separated by preparative TLC (solvent system C triple elution). Cyafrin A_5 was purified by recrystallization from acetone-benzene. Preparative TLC was carried out on 0.75mm layers of silica gel G (W. Merck, Darmstadt) containing 1% electronic phosphor (General Electric, Cleveland). The solvent systems used were: A, Skellysolve B-acetone (3:1, v/v), B, benzene-acetone-acetic acid (75:25:1, v/v); C, chloroform-acetonitrile (3:2, v/v); and D, benzene-methanol-acetic acid (18:2:1, v/v).

Spectral Data

UV:

λ_{max} 241nm (ϵ=11,000).

IR:

($CHCl_3$) 3630, 3420, 1695, and 1623cm^{-1}.

^1H NMR:
Poorly resolved (tautomeric equilibrium).

Mass Spectrum:
332.1983*m/e* (M^+); exact mass calcd for $C_{20}H_{28}O_4$, 332.1988.

Reference

W. A. Ayer, T. Yoshida, and D. M. J. Van Schie; Metabolites of bird's nest fungi. Part 9. Diterpenoid metabolites of *Cyathus africanus* Brodie; Can. J. Chem., Vol. 56, pp. 2113-2120(1978).

Common/Systematic Name
Cyafrin A_5

Molecular Formula/Molecular Weight
$C_{20}H_{30}O_5$; MW = 350.20932

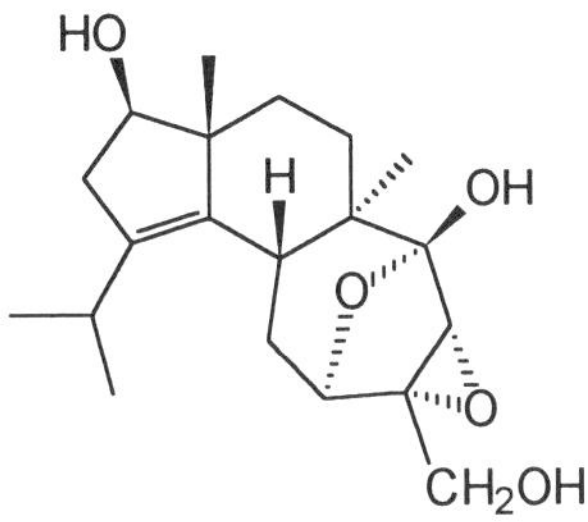

General Characteristics
Cyafrin A_5, was obtained as colorless needles from acetone-benzene; mp., 208-209°C; $[\alpha]_D^{25}$ -77.9° (*c*=0.154, in MeOH).

Fungal Source
Cyathus africanus.

Isolation/Purification
The crude extract was chromatographed over silicic acid (MN-Kieselgel) using chloroform-methanol (19:1, v/v) as eluant. Fractions were monitored by TLC (solvent system B). Fractions 101-110 contained a mixture of cyathin A_3 and allocyathin B_3 which was separated into its components by preparative TLC over 10% $AgNO_3$-silica gel (solvent system A). Fractions 123-130 contained cyafrin B_4 and allocyafrin B_4. Separation by preparative TLC (solvent system D) gave cyafrin B_4 (R_f 0.6) and allocyafrin B_4 (R_f 0.5). Fractions 228-254 yielded crude cyafrin A_4 which was purified by recrystallization from acetone. Fractions 255-276 gave a mixture of cyafrin A_4 and cyafrin A_5, which was separated by preparative TLC (solvent system C triple elution). Cyafrin A_5 was purified by recrystallization from acetone-benzene. Preparative TLC was carried out on 0.75mm layers of silica gel G (W. Merck, Darmstadt) containing 1% electronic phosphor (General Electric, Cleveland). The solvent systems used were: A, Skellysolve B-acetone (3:1, v/v), B, benzene-acetone-acetic acid (75:25:1, v/v); C, chloroform-acetonitrile (3:2, v/v); and D, benzene-methanol-acetic acid (18:2:1, v/v).

Spectral Data

IR:
(film) 3350(br) and 1703cm^{-1} (w).

^{1}H NMR:

($C_5D_5N + D_2O$) 0.88 and 0.99ppm (each 3H, d, J=7Hz, isopropyl methyls); 1.34(s, 3H); 1.36(s, 3H); 4.18(s, 1H); 4.20 and 4.30(dd, J=18Hz); 4.22(t, 1H, J=8Hz); and 4.75ppm (m, 1H).

^{13}C NMR:

(CD_3OD) 12.3; 17.0; 21.2; 22.5(CH_3); 28.5; 29.6; 35.6; 37.1; 58.8(CH_2); 26.4; 40.8; 56.9; 74.0; 82.4(CH); 43.7; 49.6; 63.9; 164.3(C); 136.5; and 138.0ppm (C=C).

Mass Spectrum:

HREIMS 350.2093*m/e* (M^+); exact mass calcd. for $C_{20}H_{30}O_5$, 350.2092.

Reference

W. A. Ayer, T. Yoshida, and D. M. J. Van Schie; Metabolites of bird's nest fungi. Part 9. Diterpenoid metabolites of *Cyathus africanus* Brodie; Can. J. Chem., Vol. 56, pp. 2113-2120(1978).

Common/Systematic Name

Allocyafrin B_4

Molecular Formula/Molecular Weight

$C_{20}H_{28}O_4$; MW = 332.19876

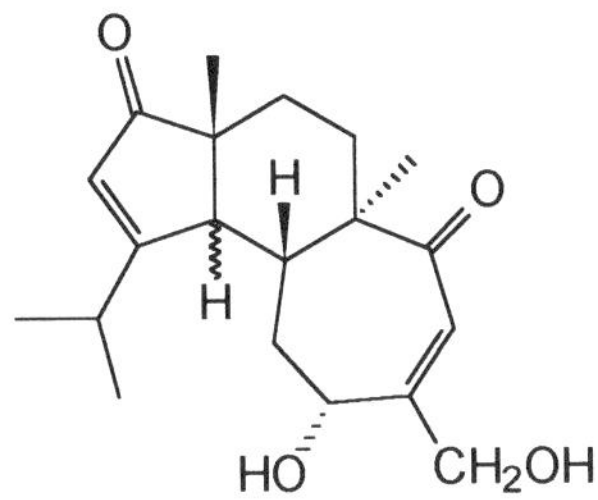

General Characteristics

Allocyafrin B_4 was obtained as a colorless syrup; $[\alpha]_D^{25}$ -157.8° (*c*=0.27, in $CHCl_3$).

Fungal Source

Cyathus africanus.

Isolation/Purification

The crude extract was chromatographed over silicic acid (MN-Kieselgel) using chloroform-methanol (19:1, v/v) as eluant. Fractions were monitored by TLC (solvent system B). Fractions 101-110 contained a mixture of cyathin A_3 and allocyathin B_3 which was separated into its components by preparative TLC over 10% $AgNO_3$-silica gel (solvent system A). Fractions 123-130 contained cyafrin B_4 and allocyafrin B_4. Separation by preparative TLC (solvent system D) gave cyafrin B_4 (R_f 0.6) and allocyafrin B_4 (R_f 0.5). Fractions 228-254 yielded crude cyafrin A_4 which was purified by recrystallization from acetone. Fractions 255-276 gave a mixture of cyafrin A_4 and cyafrin A_5, which was separated by preparative TLC (solvent system C triple elution). Cyafrin A_5 was purified by recrystallization from acetone-benzene. Preparative TLC was carried out on 0.75 mm layers of silica gel G (W. Merck, Darmstadt) containing 1% electronic phosphor (General Electric, Cleveland). The solvent systems used were: A, Skellysolve B-acetone (3:1, v.v); B, benzene-acetone-acetic acid (75:25:1); C, chloroform-acetonitrile (3:2); and D, benzene-methanol-acetic acid (18:2:1).

Spectral Data

UV:

λ_{max} 239nm (ϵ=16,400).

IR:
($CHCl_3$) 3600, 3440, 1700, 1680 (sh), and 1600cm^{-1}.

^{1}H NMR:
($CDCl_3$) 1.08(s, 3H); 1.12(s, 3H); 1.22 and 1.26(each 3H, d, *J*=7Hz); 4.42(m, 3H); 5.98(bs, 1H); and 6.04ppm (bs, 1H).

Mass Spectrum:
HREIMS: 332.1985*m/e* (M^+); exact mass calcd for $C_{20}H_{28}O_4$, 332.1988.

Reference

W. A. Ayer, T. Yoshida, and D. M. J. Van Schie; Metabolites of bird's nest fungi. Part 9. Diterpenoid metabolites of *Cyathus africanus* Brodie; Can. J. Chem., Vol. 56, pp. 2113-2120(1978).

Common/Systematic Name
Cyathatriol

Molecular Formula/Molecular Weight
$C_{20}H_{32}O_3$; MW = 320.23515

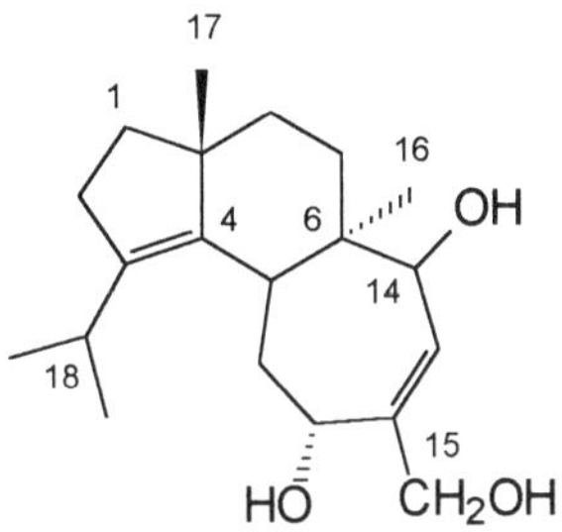

General Characteristics
Cyathatriol was obtained as a white powder which crystallized from acetone; mp., 172-173°C.

Fungal Source
Cyathus earlei is a tropical or subtropical species of bird's nest fungus which is known to occur in Cuba, Puerto Rico, Mexico, and Hawaii.

Isolation/Purification
The ethyl acetate extract of fungal mycelium after sixty-five days growth on Brodie medium gave six compounds belonging to the "cyathin" group of diterpenoids. The ethyl acetate extract was washed with water, dried over sodium sulfate, and concentrated to a viscous brown oil. The crude extract was subjected to silica gel column chromatography eluted with ether-benzene (2:3, v/v) which gave cyathatriol.

Biological Activity
Moderate antibiotic activity against *Staphylococcus aureus*.

Spectral Data

IR:
(film) 3300cm^{-1}.

^{1}H NMR:
(acetone-d_6) 0.80(s, 3H); 0.94(d, *J*=6Hz, 3H); 0.95(d, *J*=6Hz, 3H); 1.07(s, 3H); 3.00(m, H's on C-5 and C-18); 3.76(d, *J*=6Hz, H on C-14); 4.12(s, 2H on C-15); 4.85(ddd, *J*=8, 4, and 1Hz, H on C-11); and 5.87ppm (dd, *J*=6 and 1Hz, H on C-13).

Mass Data:

HREIMS: 320.2336*m/e*; exact mass calcd for $C_{20}H_{32}O_3$ 320.2351; anal. calcd for $C_{20}H_{32}O_3$: C 74.94, H, 10.07; found: C 74.67, H 10.14%.

Reference

W. A. Ayer and S. P. Lee; Metabolites of bird's nest fungi. Part II. Diterpenoid metabolites of *Cyathus earlei* Lloyd; Can. J. Chem., Vol. 57, pp. 3332-3337(1979).

Common/Systematic Name

11-*O*-Acetylcyathatriol

Molecular Formula/Molecular Weight

$C_{22}H_{34}O_4$; MW = 362.24571

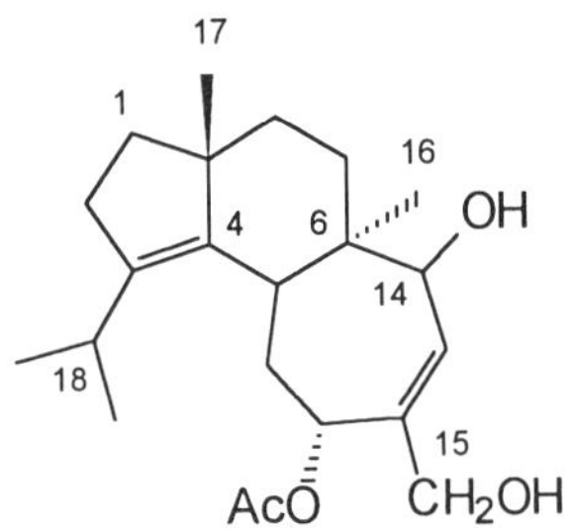

General Characteristics

11-*O*-Acetylcyathatriol crystallized from ether; mp., 165-166°C.

Fungal Source

Cyathus earlei is a tropical or subtropical species of bird's nest fungus which is known to occur in Cuba, Puerto Rico, Mexico, and Hawaii.

Isolation/Purification

The ethyl acetate extract of the fungal mycelium after 65 days growth on Brodie medium gave six compounds belonging to the "cyathin" group of diterpenoids. The ethyl acetate extract was washed with water, dried over sodium sulfate, and concentrated to a viscous brown oil. The crude extract was subjected to silica gel column chromatography eluted with ether-benzene (1:4, v/v) to give 11-*O*-acetylcyathatriol.

Biological Activity

Moderate antibiotic activity against *Staphylococcus aureus*.

Spectral Data

IR:

(CCl_4): 3500 and 1710cm^{-1}.

^{1}H NMR:

($CDCl_3$) 0.80(s, 3H); 0.97(d, *J*=6Hz, 6H); 1.10(s, 3H); 2.10(s, 3H); 3.02(br d, *J*=10Hz, H on C-5); 3.90(d, *J*=6Hz, H on C-14); 4.06(s, 2H on C-15); 5.86(dd, *J*=6 and 1Hz, H on C-13); and 5.95ppm (m, H on C-11).

Mass Data:

HREIMS: found: 362.2496*m/e*; exact mass calcd for $C_{22}H_{34}O_4$, 362.2457; anal calcd for $C_{22}H_{34}O_4$: C 72.87, H 9.45; found: C 72.51, H 9.54.

Reference

W. A. Ayer and S. P. Lee; Metabolites of bird's nest fungi. Part II. Diterpenoid metabolites of *Cyathus earlei* Lloyd; Can. J. Chem. Vol. 57, pp. 3332-3337(1979).

Common/Systematic Name

15-*O*-Acetylcyathatriol

Molecular Formula/Molecular Weight

$C_{22}H_{34}O_4$; MW = 362.24571

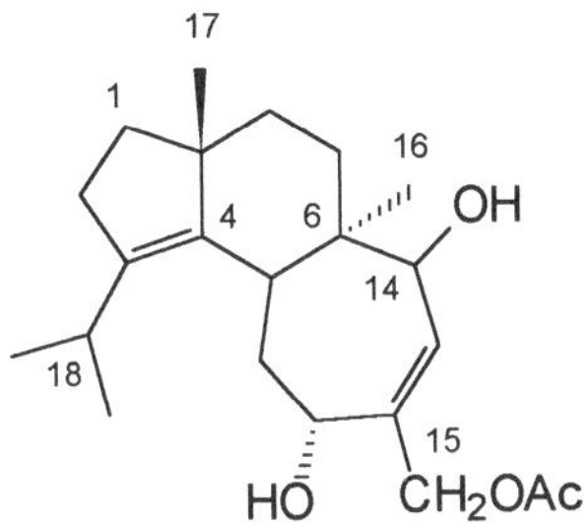

General Characteristics

15-*O*-Acetylcyathatriol was obtained as a viscous oil.

Fungal Source

Cyathus earlei is a tropical or subtropical species of bird's nest fungus which is known to occur in Cuba, Puerto Rico, Mexico, and Hawaii.

Isolation/Purification

The ethyl acetate extract of the fungal mycelium gave six compounds belonging to the "cyathin" group of diterpenoids. The ethyl acetate extract was washed with water, dried over sodium sulfate, and concentrated to a viscous brown oil. The crude extract was subjected to silica gel column chromatography eluted with ether-benzene (1:9, v/v) which gave 15-*O*-acetylcyathatriol.

Biological Activity

Moderate antibiotic against *Staphylococcus aureus*.

Spectral Data

IR:

(CCl_4) 3600, 3500, and 1745cm^{-1}.

^{1}H NMR:

(CCl_4) 0.75(s, 3H); 0.98(d, *J*=6Hz, 6H); 1.07(s, 3H); 2.05(s, 3H); 3.00(m, 2H, H's on C-5 and C-18); 3.82(d, *J*=6Hz, H on C-14); 4.60(s, 2H on C-15); 4.70(m, H on C-11); and 5.65ppm (d, *J*=6Hz, H on C-13) .

Mass Data:

HREIMS: 362.2479*m/e*; exact mass calcd for $C_{22}H_{34}O_4$ 362.2457; anal calcd for $C_{22}H_{34}O_4$: C 72.87, H 9.45; found: C 72.58, H 9.48.

Reference

W. A. Ayer and S. P. Lee; Metabolites of bird's nest fungi. Part II. Diterpenoid metabolites of *Cyathus earlei* Lloyd; Can. J. Chem., Vol. 57, pp. 3332-3337(1979).

Common/Systematic Name
11,15-*O,O*-Diacetylcyathatriol

Molecular Formula/Molecular Weight
$C_{24}H_{36}O_5$; MW = 404.25627

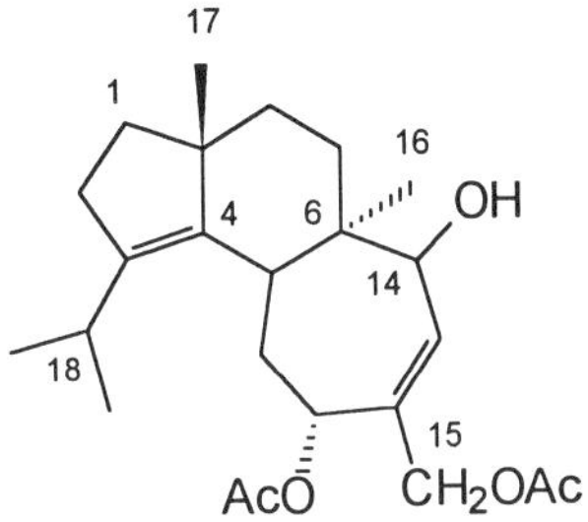

General Characteristics
11,15-*O,O*-Diacetylcyathatriol crystallized from Skellysolve B-ether; mp., 123-124°C.

Fungal Source
Cyathus earlei is a tropical or subtropical species of bird's nest fungus which is known to occur in Cuba, Puerto Rico, Mexico, and Hawaii.

Isolation/Purification
The ethyl acetate extract of the mycelium after sixty-five days growth on Brodie medium gave six compounds belonging to the "cyathin" group of diterpenoids. The ethyl acetate extract was washed with water, dried over sodium sulfate, and concentrated to a viscous brown oil. The crude extract was subjected to silica gel column chromatography; elution with ether-benzene (1:9, v/v) gave 15-*O*-acetylcyathatriol followed by 11,15-*O,O*-diacetylcyathatriol.

Biological Activity
Moderate antibiotic activity against *Staphylococcus aureus*.

Spectral Data

IR:
(CCl_4) 3600, 3500, and 1745cm^{-1}.

^{1}H NMR:
(CCl_4) 0.70(s, 3H); 0.95(d, *J*=6Hz, 6H); 1.10(s, 3H); 1.98(s, 3H); 2.00(s, 3H); 2.90(heptet, *J*=6Hz, H on C-18); 3.00(dd, *J*=10 and 1Hz, H on C-5); 3.70(d, *J*=6Hz, 1H); 4.34(dd, *J*=14 and 1Hz, H on C-15); 4.54(dd, *J*=14 and 1Hz, H on C-15); 5.82(dd, *J*=6 and 1Hz, H on C-13); and 5.85ppm (m, H on C-11).

Mass Data:

The highest peak in the mass spectrum corresponded to the molecular ion-H_2O; exact mass calcd for $C_{24}H_{34}O_4$ (M^+-H_2O): 386.2457; found: 386.2454*m/e*; anal calcd for $C_{24}H_{36}O_5$; C 71.25, H 8.96; found: C 70.96, H 9.07(%).

<u>Reference</u>

W. A. Ayer and S. P. Lee; Metabolites of bird's nest fungi. Part II. Diterpenoid metabolites of *Cyathus earlei*; Can. J. Chem., Vol. 57, pp. 3332-3337(1979).

Common/Systematic Name

Sarcodonin A

Molecular Formula/Molecular Weight

$C_{20}H_{28}O_3$; MW = 316.20384

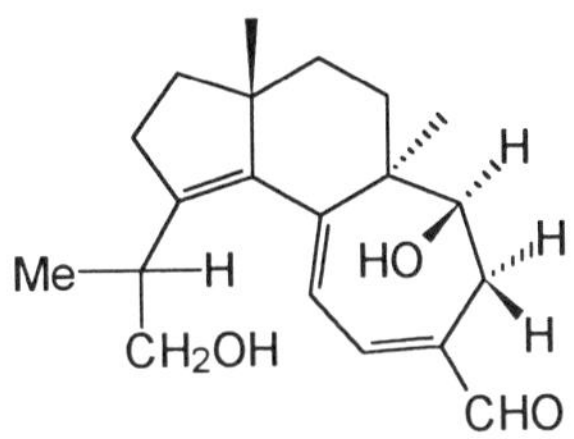

General Characteristics

Yellow syrup; $[\alpha]_D^{21}$ +917° (*c*=0.1, in $CHCl_3$); intense bitterness; threshold value was $3.1 \bullet 10^{-6}$ M. Gave 2,4-dinitrophenylhydrazone, a red amorphous solid; mp., 220-222°C.

Fungal Source

Sarcodon scabrosus.

Isolation/Purification

Dried fruiting bodies of the fungus were extracted with methylene chloride. The neutral fraction was chromatographed on silica gel repeatedly (methanol-chloroform or benzene-ethyl acetate).

Spectral Data

UV:

λ_{max} 338nm (ϵ=46,000).

IR:

(KBr) 3400, 2950-2850, 2700, 1670, 1620, 1580, 1440, 1420, 1380, 1170, and $1040cm^{-1}$.

^1H NMR:

($CDCl_3$) 9.45(1H, s); 6.83(1H, dd, *J*=8.2, 2.3Hz); 6.19(1H, d, *J*=8.2Hz); 3.73(1H, d, *J*=5.8Hz); 3.58(2H, d, *J*=7.2Hz); 3.15(1H, dd, *J*=18.2, 5.8Hz); 2.95(1H, sextet, *J*=7.2Hz); 2.53(1H, d, *J*=18.4Hz); 2.52(1H, m); 2.41(2H, m); 1.72(4H, m); 1.35(1H, dt, *J*=13.9, 3.3Hz); 1.03(3H, s); 0.96(3H, s); and 0.95ppm (3H, d, *J*=7.2Hz).

^{13}C NMR:

($CDCl_3$) 194.3, 154.2, 146.5, 144.5, 141.1, 138.1, 119.8, 74.0, 66.4, 49.6, 48.3, 38.3, 36.4, 35.2, 33.6, 29.4, 29.3, 26.5, 24.3, and 15.9ppm.

Mass Spectrum:

HRMS: 316.2073*m/e* (M^+, calcd. for $C_{20}H_{28}O_3$, 316.2037); EIMS: 316(M^+, 100), 300(10), 298(15), 285(85), 211(48), and 91*m/e* (88).

Reference

H. Shibata, T. Tokunaga, D. Karasawa, A. Hirota, M. Nakayama, H. Nozaki, and T. Tada; Isolation and Characterization of New Bitter Diterpenoids from the Fungus *Sarcodon scabrosus*; Agric. Biol. Chem., Vol. 53, pp. 3373-3375(1989).

Common/Systematic Name
Sarcodonin G

Molecular Formula/Molecular Weight
$C_{20}H_{28}O_3$; MW = 316.20384

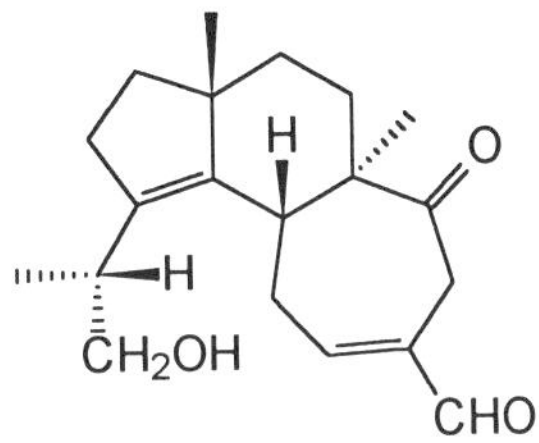

General Characteristics
Colorless prisms; mp., 158-161°C; $[\alpha]_D^{21}$ -64.9° (*c*=0.2, $CHCl_3$). Intense bitterness; threshold value, $3.1 \bullet 10^{-5}$ M.

Fungal Source
Sarcodon scabrosus.

Isolation/Purification
Dried fruiting bodies of the fungus were extracted with methylene chloride. The neutral fraction was chromatographed on silica gel repeatedly (methanol-chloroform or benzene-ethyl acetate).

Spectral Data

UV:
λ_{max} 220nm.

IR:
(KBr) 3400, 2900-2850, 2700, 1705, 1660, 1640, 1450, 1420, 1380, 1280, 1090, and $1050cm^{-1}$.

^1H NMR:
($CDCl_3$) 9.31(1H, s); 6.71(1H, m); 3.72(1H, br, d, *J*=13.6Hz); 3.45(2H, d, *J*=7.3Hz); 3.42(1H, d, *J*=13.9Hz); 3.34(1H, d, *J*=12.0Hz); 3.16(1H, dd, *J*=13.4 and 6.4Hz); 3.02(1H, sextet, *J*=7.3Hz); 2.74(1H, m); 2.31(3H, m); 1.94(1H, dt, *J*=13.3 and 5.3Hz); 1.59(4H, m); 1.24(1H, dt, *J*=13.2 and 3.9Hz); 1.12(3H, s); 1.01(3H, s); and 0.96ppm (3H, d, *J*=7.3Hz).

^{13}C NMR:
($CDCl_3$) 210.6, 192.4, 153.5, 141.1, 135.9, 135.8, 65.8, 55.3, 49.8, 39.5, 37.7, 35.5, 35.2, 34.1, 32.7, 32.1, 28.6, 24.8, 15.6, and 12.7ppm.

Mass Spectrum:
HRMS: 316.2059*m/e* (M^+, calcd. for $C_{20}H_{28}O_3$ 316.2038); EIMS: 316(M^+, 55), 300(58), 284(35), 266(38), 255(36), 174(85), 121(98), 91*m/e* (100%).

Reference

H. Shibata, T. Tokunaga, D. Karasawa, A. Hirota, M. Nakayama, H. Nozaki, and T. Tada; Isolation and Characterization of New Bitter Diterpenoids from the Fungus *Sarcodon scabrosus*; Agric. Biol. Chem., Vol. 53, pp. 3373-3375(1989).

Common/Systematic Name
Striatin A

Molecular Formula/Molecular Weight
$C_{28}H_{40}O_8$; MW = 504.27232

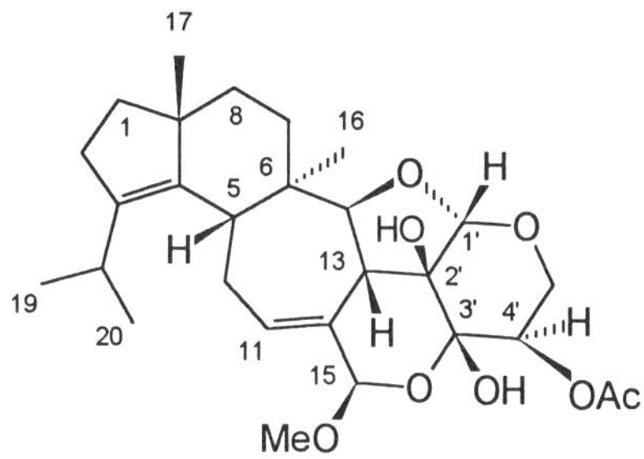

General Characteristics
Colorless crystals from MeOH; mp., 144-145°C; they were soluble in methanol, ethanol, ethyl acetate, and chloroform, and were poorly soluble in water and cyclohexane. Striatin A crystallized with one molecule of methanol, forming a system of hydrogen bonds with the angular OH groups at C(2') and C(3'). The striatins give positive reactions with $KMnO_4$, and a modified Kagi-Miescher reagent. Upon standing in solution the striatins undergo rapid transformation into several new compounds, some of which show antibiotic activity. All striatins were very sensitive to water in the presence of traces of acid resulting in typical changes which were in accord with the formation of ketoaldehydes.

Fungal Source
Cyathus striatus.

Isolation/Purification
The mycelium was extracted with methanol-acetone (2:1, v/v). The combined extracts were evaporated to dryness, the residue dissolved in methanol, and applied to a Sephadex LH-20 column and eluted with the same solvent. The fractions containing the striatins were pooled, concentrated to 1/10 of the original volume, and kept at 4°C. After 2-3 days the crystals of striatin A were removed, and the mother liquid evaporated to dryness. The residue containing the striatins B and C was dissolved in chloroform and applied to a column with silica gel (Mallinckrodt). Striatins B and C were eluted with chloroform-ethanol (99:1, v/v) and chloroform-ethanol-methanol (97:1:2, v/v/v) and crystallized from chloroform (striatin B) and ethanol (striatin C).

Biological Activity
The striatins are highly active against fungi imperfecti and a variety of gram-positive bacteria, as well as against some gram-negative bacteria.

Spectral Data

UV:

The UV spectra of the striatins in ethanol showed no absorption maxima up to 220nm.

^{1}H NMR:

($CDCl_3$) The 5'-H_2 and 4'-H formed an ABX-pattern (3.49, 3.93, and 4.98; *J*=11, 9, and 5Hz); l'-H and 15-H singlets (5.00 and 5.25); 14-H a doublet (4.19, *J*=10Hz); and 11-H, 13-H, and 10-H_2 multiplets (6.04, 3.04, and 2.50). In striatin B an additional hydroxy group was attached to C(10). This followed from the NMR spectrum in which 10-H appeared at 4.84 as a doublet due to 8 Hz coupling to 11-H. The pseudoaxial orientation of this OH-group was deduced from the low field shift of 14-H (0.42), 18-H(0.49), and 16-Me (0.23) induced by the nearby oxygen atom. As a consequence the dihedral angle between 5-H and 10-H became 90° and no vicinal coupling was observed. Striatin C differed from B in lacking the acetyl group (2.15) which led to increased shielding of 4'-H (3.98).

Mass Spectrum:

472*m/e* (M^+ -32) with prominent ion at M^+-47 and a characteristic fragment ion at 203*m/e* ($C_{15}H_{23}$).

TLC Data

Merck silica gel plates: Benzene-methanol-ethyl acetate, 17:2:1, v/v/v; striatin A R_f, 0.51; B, 0.39; and C, 0.24. cyclohexane-ethyl acetate, 1:1, v/v; R_f, A, 0.38; B, 0.30; and C, 0.16. Benzene-acetone-acetic acid, 70:30:1, v/v/v; R_f, A, 0.55; B, 0.47; and C, 0.26.

References

T. Anke, F. Oberwinkler, W. Steglich, and G. Hofle; The Striatins - New Antibiotics from the Basidiomycete *Cyathus striatus* (Huds. ex Pers.) Willd.; J. Antibiot., Vol. 30, pp. 221-225(1977).

H. Hecht, G. Hofle, W. Steglich, T. Anke, and F. Oberwinkler; Striatin A, B, and C: Novel Diterpenoid Antibiotics from *Cyathus striatus*; X-Ray Crystal Structure of Striatin A; J. Chem. Soc., Chem. Commun., pp. 665-666(1978).

Common/Systematic Name

Striatin B

Molecular Formula/Molecular Weight

$C_{28}H_{40}O_9$; MW = 520.26723

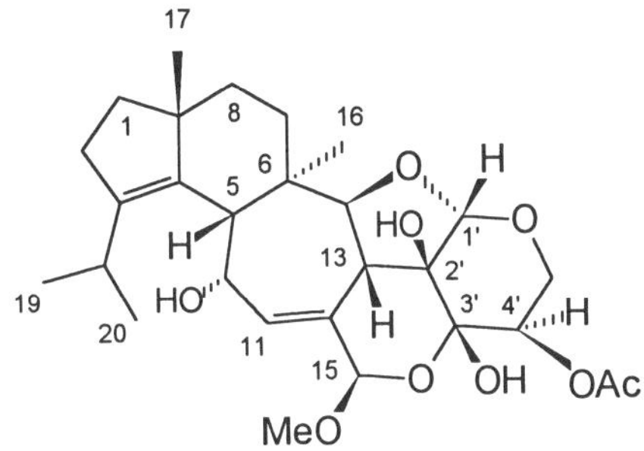

General Characteristics

Colorless crystals from MeOH; mp., 143-144°C; soluble in methanol, ethanol, ethyl acetate, and chloroform, and poorly soluble in water and cyclohexane. Striatin B gave positive reactions with $KMnO_4$, and a modified Kagi-Miescher reagent. Upon standing in solution it rapidly transformed into several new compounds, some of which showed antibiotic activity. All striatins were very sensitive to water in the presence of traces of acid resulting in typical changes which were in accord with the formation of ketoaldehydes.

Fungal Source

Cyathus striatus.

Isolation/Purification

The mycelium was extracted with methanol-acetone (2:1, v/v). The combined extracts were evaporated to dryness; the residue was dissolved in methanol, applied to a Sephadex LH-20 column,and eluted with the same solvent. The fractions containing the striatins were pooled, concentrated to 1/10 of the original volume, and kept at 4°C. After 2-3 days the crystals of striatin A were removed, and the mother liquid evaporated to dryness. The residue containing the striatins B and C was dissolved in chloroform and applied to a column with silica gel (Mallinckrodt). Striatins B and C were eluted with chloroform-ethanol (99:1, v/v) and chloroform-ethanol-methanol (97:1:2, v/v/v) and crystallized from chloroform (striatin B) and ethanol (striatin C).

Biological Activity

The striatins are highly active against fungi imperfecti and a variety of gram-positive bacteria, as well as against some gram-negative bacteria.

Spectral Data

UV:

The UV spectra of the striatins in ethanol showed no absorption maxima up to 220nm.

^{1}H NMR:

($CDCl_3$) The 5'-H_2 and 4'-H formed an ABX-pattern (3.49, 3.93, and 4.98; *J*=11, 9, and 5Hz); 1'-H and 15-H singlets (5.00 and 5.25); 14-H a doublet (4.19, *J*=10Hz); and 11-H, 13-H, and 10-H_2 multiplets (6.04, 3.04, and 2.50). In striatin B an additional hydroxy group was attached to C(10). This followed from the NMR spectrum in which 10-H appeared at 4.84 as a doublet due to 8Hz coupling to 11-H. The pseudoaxial orientation of this OH-group was deduced from the low field shift of 14-H (0.42), 18-H (0.49), and 16-Me (0.23) induced by the nearby oxygen atom. As a consequence the dihedral angle between 5-H and 10-H became 90°, and no vicinal coupling was observed.

Mass Spectrum:

488*m/e* (M^+ -32) with prominent ion at M^+-47 and a characteristic fragment ion at 203*m/e* ($C_{15}H_{23}$).

TLC Data

Merck silica gel plates: Benzene-methanol-ethyl acetate, 17:2:1, v/v/v; striatin A: R_f, 0.51; B, 0.39; and C, 0.24. Cyclohexane-ethyl acetate, 1:1, v/v; R_f, A, 0.38; B, 0.30; and C, 0.16. Benzene-acetone-acetic acid, 70:30:1, v/v/v; R_f, A, 0.55; B, 0.47; and C, 0.26.

References

T. Anke, F. Oberwinkler, W. Steglich, and G. Hofle; The Striatins - New Antibiotics from the Basidiomycete *Cyathus striatus* (Huds. ex Pers.) Willd.; J. Antibiot., Vol. 30, pp. 221-225(1977).

H. Hecht, G. Hofle, W. Steglich, T. Anke; and F. Oberwinkler; Striatin A, B, and C: Novel Diterpenoid Antibiotics from *Cyathus striatus*; X-Ray Crystal Structure of Striatin A; J. Chem. Soc., Chem. Commun., pp. 665-666(1978).

Common/Systematic Name
Striatin C

Molecular Formula/Molecular Weight
$C_{26}H_{38}O_8$; MW = 478.25667

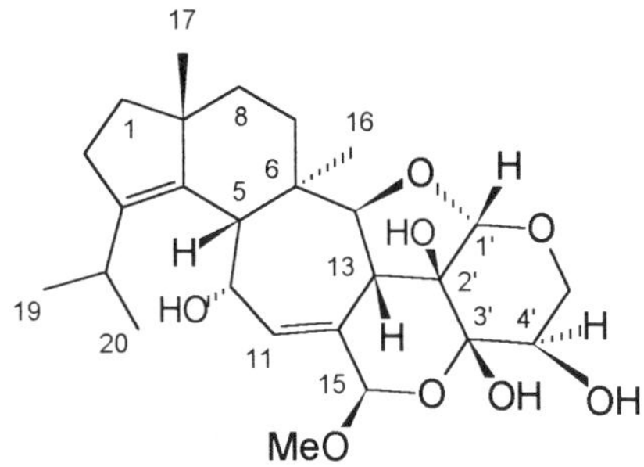

General Characteristics
Colorless crystals from MeOH; mp., 144-145°C; soluble in methanol, ethanol, ethyl acetate, and chloroform, and poorly soluble in water and cyclohexane. The antibiotic gave positive reactions with $KMnO_4$, and a modified Kagi-Miescher reagent. Upon standing in solution the striatins undergo rapid transformation into several new compounds, some of which show antibiotic activity. All striatins were very sensitive to water in the presence of traces of acid resulting in typical changes which were in accord with the formation of ketoaldehydes.

Fungal Source
Cyathus striatus.

Isolation/Purification
The mycelium was extracted with methanol-acetone (2:1, v/v). The combined extracts were evaporated to dryness, the residue dissolved in methanol, applied to a Sephadex LH-20 column,and eluted with the same solvent. The fractions containing the striatins were pooled, concentrated to 1/10 of the original volume, and kept at 4°C. After 2-3 days the crystals of striatin A were removed, and the mother liquid evaporated to dryness. The residue containing the striatins B and C was dissolved in chloroform and applied to a column with silica gel (Mallinckrodt). Striatins B and C was eluted with chloroform-ethanol (99:1, v/v) and chloroform-ethanol-methanol (97:1:2, v/v/v) and crystallized from chloroform (striatin B) and ethanol (striatin C).

Biological Activity
The striatins are highly active against fungi imperfecti and a variety of gram-positive bacteria, as well as against some gram-negative bacteria.

Spectral Data

UV:

The UV spectra of the striatins in ethanol showed no absorption maxima up to 220nm.

^{1}H NMR:

($CDCl_3$) The 5'-H_2 and 4'-H formed an ABX-pattern (3.49, 3.93, and 4.98; *J*=11, 9, and 5Hz); l'-H and 15-H singlets (5.00 and 5.25); 14-H a doublet (4.19, *J*=10Hz); and 11-H, 13-H, and 10-H_2 multiplets (6.04, 3.04, and 2.50). In striatin B an additional hydroxy group was attached to C(10). This followed from the NMR spectrum in which 10-H appeared at 4.84 as a doublet due to 8Hz coupling to 11-H. The pseudoaxial orientation of this OH-group was deduced from the low field shift of 14-H (0.42), 18-H(0.49), and 16-Me (0.23) induced by the nearby oxygen atom. As a consequence the dihedral angle between 5-H and 10-H became 90° and no vicinal coupling was observed. Striatin C differs from striatin B in lacking the acetyl group (2.15ppm) which leads to increased shielding of 4'-H (3.98ppm).

Mass Spectrum:

446*m/e* (M^+ -32) with prominent ion at M^+-47 and a characteristic fragment ion at 203*m/e* ($C_{15}H_{23}$).

TLC Data

Merck silica gel plates: Benzene-methanol-ethyl acetate, 17:2:1, v/v/v; striatin A: R_f, 0.51; B, 0.39; and C, 0.24. Cyclohexane-ethyl acetate, 1:1, v/v; R_f, A, 0.38; B, 0.30; and C, 0.16. Benzene-acetone-acetic acid, 70:30:1, v/v/v; R_f, A, 0.55; B, 0.47; and C, 0.26.

References

T. Anke, F. Oberwinkler, W. Steglich, and G. Hofle; The Striatins - New Antibiotics from the Basidiomycete *Cyathus striatus* (Huds. ex Pers.) Willd.; J. Antibiot., Vol. 30, pp. 221-225(1977).

H. Hecht, G. Hofle, W. Steglich, T. Anke; and F. Oberwinkler; Striatin A, B, and C: Novel Diterpenoid Antibiotics from *Cyathus striatus*; X-Ray Crystal Structure of Striatin A; J. Chem. Soc., Chem. Commun., pp. 665-666(1978).

22

Alliacolide and Related Metabolites

Alliacolide
Alliacide
Alliacol A (Alliacolide II)
Alliacol B (12-Hydroxydehydroalliacolide)
11-Hydroxyalliacolide
12-Hydroxyalliacolide
12-Noralliacolide

Common/Systematic Name
Alliacolide

Molecular Formula/Molecular Weight
$C_{15}H_{22}O_4$; MW = 266.15181

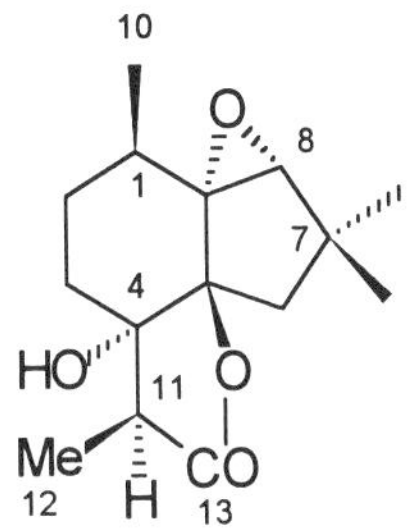

General Characteristics
Crystals from ethyl acetate-light petroleum; mp., 192-194°C (corr.) (sealed capillary) (193°C); $[\alpha]_D^{20}$ - 35° (589), -62°(431), and -80° (365nm) (*c*= 0.1, in $CHCl_3$); $[\alpha]_D$ - 33° (*c*= 0.8, in $CHCl_3$).

Fungal Source
Marasmius alliaceus.

Isolation/Purification
Isolated from the ether extract of the culture broth by a combination of sublimation (the compound sublimes readily), silica gel chromatography, and crystallization (ethyl acetate-light petroleum).

Spectral Data

UV:
End absorption.

IR:
$\lambda_{max}^{Carbon\ tetrachloride}$ 3590, 3450, and 1785cm^{-1}.

^{1}H NMR:
($CDCl_3$) H-1, 1.85; H-6, 1.29, 1.96($J_{6,6'}$=14Hz); H-8, 3.22; H-10, 1.14(d, *J*=7.0Hz); H-11, 2.69(q, *J*=7.0Hz); H-12, 1.18; and H-14 and H-15, 1.12ppm.

^{13}C NMR:
($CDCl_3$) C-1, 31.4; C-2, 25.3; C-3, 28.2; C-4, 77.2; C-5, 92.6; C-6, 40.8; C-7, 38.5; C-8, 68.2; C-9, 68.6; C-10, 24.3; C-11, 45.0; C-12, 7.6; C-13, 176.1; C-14, 23.9*; and C-15, 17.4ppm*.

*Assignments may be reversed.

Mass Spectrum:
HREIMS: 266.1518*m/e* (M^+); LREIMS 266(M^+, 25%), 238(15), 211(11), 210(11), 193(100), 182(46), 151(26), 142(42), and 125*m/e* (39).

References

I. A. Farrell, T. G. Halsall, and V. Thaller; Structures of Some New Sesquiterpenoid Metabolites of *Marasmius alliaceus*; J. C. S. Perkin Trans I, pp. 1790-1793(1981).

T. J. King, I. W. Farrell, T. G. Halsall, and V. Thaller; A New Bicyclic Sesquiterpene Epoxy-lactone with a Novel Carbon Skeleton from Cultures of the Fungus *Marasmius alliaceus*; J.C.S. Chem. Comm., pp. 727-728(1977).

Common/Systematic Name

Alliacide

Molecular Formula/Molecular Weight

$C_{15}H_{22}O_3$; MW = 250.15689

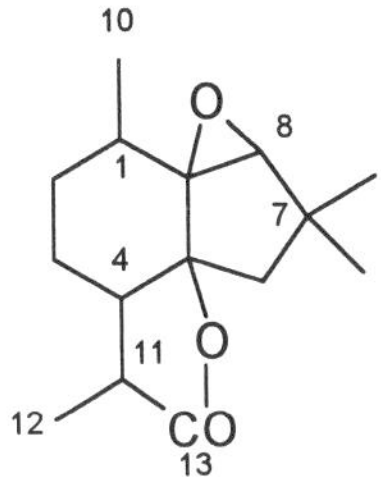

General Characteristics

Needles from light petroleum; mp., 168-171°C.

Fungal Source

Marasmius alliaceus, a wood rotting fungus.

Isolation/Purification

Extracted from the culture broth with ethyl acetate and purified by chromatography on silica gel with chloroform-ethyl acetate-acetic acid, 40:10:1, v/v/v as eluent. Rechromatographed on silica gel column chromatography using 10% ethyl acetate-petroleum ether; final purification was by crystallization from petroleum ether as needles.

Spectral Data

IR:

(Nujol) 1770cm^{-1}

^{1}H NMR:

($CDCl_3$) H-8, 3.25; H-10, 1.30(d, *J*=7.0Hz); H-12, 1.50; and H-14, H-15, 1.18ppm

^{13}C NMR:

($CDCl_3$) C-1, 31.6; C-2, 26.7; C-3, 19.7; C-4, 31.6; C-5, 90.6; C-6, 46.8; C-7, 38.6; C-8, 69.5; C-9, 67.9; C-10, 24.3; C-11, 42.5; C-12, 9.6; C-13, 178.0; C-14, 23.8; and C-15, 17.0ppm.

Mass Data:

HREIMS: 250.1571(M^+ ; found C, 72.1; H, 8.7%); $C_{15}H_{22}O_3$ requires 250.1569; C, 72; H, 8.9%; LREIMS: 250(M^+, 27%), 235(25), 222(12), 195(50), 194(36), 193(21), 182(36), 180(34), 179(32), 177(69), 165(100), 125(55), and 97nm (63).

References

T. Anke, W. H. Watson, B.M. Giannetti, and W. Steglich; New Antibiotics from the Basidiomycete *Marasmius alliaceus*; Planta Med., Vol. 39, p. 194 (1980).

I. A. Farrell, T. G. Halsall, and V. Thaller; Structures of Some New Sesquiterpenoid Metabolites of *Marasmius alliaceus*; J. C. S. Perkin Trans I, pp. 1790-1793(1981).

Common/Systematic Name

Alliacol A; Alliacolide II

Molecular Formula/Molecular Weight

$C_{15}H_{20}O_4$; MW = 264.13616

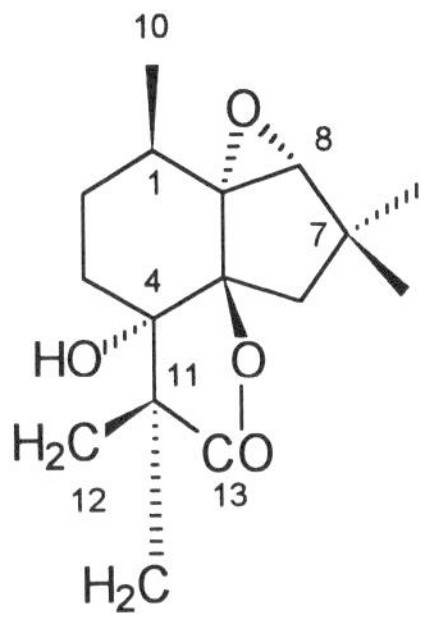

General Characteristics

Crystallized from ethyl acetate-light petroleum as needles; mp., 156-158°C; $[\alpha]_D$ 10° (*c*=0.95, in $CHCl_3$).

Fungal Source

Marasmius alliaceus, a wood rotting fungus.

Isolation/Purification

Isolated from the ether extract of the culture broth by a combination of sublimation (the compound sublimes readily at 140°C, 0.3mm Hg), silica gel chromatography, and crystallization (ethyl acetate-light petroleum).

Biological Activity

Both alliacol A and B showed weak antibacterial and antifungal activity; the growth of sensitive bacteria and fungi were inhibited by concentrations of 25-50μg/ml Both strongly inhibited DNA synthesis in cells of the ascitic form of Ehrlich carcinoma at 5μg/ml whereas RNA synthesis was somewhat less affected. No inhibition of protein synthesis was observed at concentrations up to 20μg/ml.

Spectral Data

UV:

End absorption.

IR:

$\lambda_{max}^{\text{Carbon tetrachloride}}$ 3580, 3450, 1775, 1680, 1125, and 900cm^{-1}.

^{1}H NMR:
(CDCl$_3$) H-6, 1.30, 2.00($J_{6,6'}$=14Hz); H-8, 3.20; H-10, 1.20(d, J=7.0Hz); H-12, 5.9, 6.35; and H-14 and H-15, 1.20ppm.

^{13}C NMR:
(CDCl$_3$) C-1, 31.5; C-2, 26.3; C-3, 38.6; C-4, 76.5; C-5, 95.1; C-6, 41.7; C-7, 39.2; C-8, 67.1; C-9, 69.6; C-10, 24.4; C-11, 142.9; C-12, 124.7; C-13, 168.8; C-14, 24.0; and C-15, 19.4ppm.

Mass Spectrum:
LREIMS: 264(M$^+$, 30%), 249(29), 247(20), 236(45), 193(70), 151(75), and 83*m/e* (100).

References

T. Anke, W. H. Watson, B.M. Giannetti, and W. Steglich; New Antibiotics from the Basidiomycete *Marasmius alliaceus*; Planta Med., Vol. 39, p. 194 (1980).

I. A. Farrell, T. G. Halsall, and V. Thaller; Structures of Some New Sesquiterpenoid Metabolites of *Marasmius alliaceus*; J. C. S. Perkin Trans I, pp. 1790-1793 (1981).

Common/Systematic Name

Alliacol B; 12-Hydroxydehydroalliacolide

Molecular Formula/Molecular Weight

$C_{15}H_{20}O_4$; MW = 264.13616

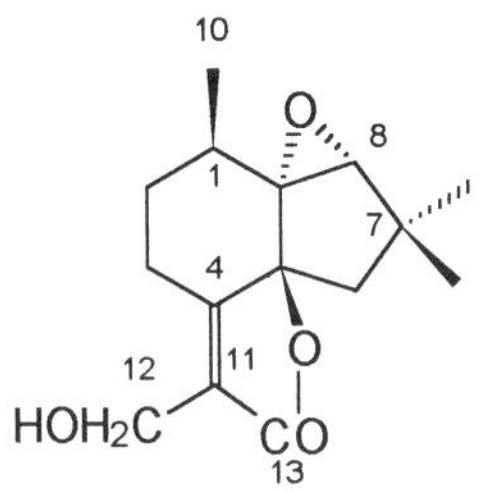

Fungal Source

Marasmius alliaceus, a wood rotting fungus.

Isolation/Purification

Extracted from the culture broth with ethyl acetate and purified by chromatography on silica gel with chloroform-ethyl acetate-acetic acid, 40:10:1 (v/v/v) as eluent. Final purification was by preparative TLC, using chloroform-methanol, 20:1 (v/v).

Biological Activity

Both alliacol A and B showed weak antibacterial and antifungal activity; the growth of sensitive bacteria and fungi was inhibited by concentrations of 25-50μg/ml. Both strongly inhibited DNA synthesis in cells of the ascitic form of Ehrlich carcinoma at 5μg/ml whereas RNA synthesis was somewhat less affected. No inhibition of protein synthesis was observed at concentrations up to 20μg/ml.

Spectral Data

IR:

(Nujol) 3520, 3440, 1735, and 1665cm^{-1}.

^{1}H NMR:

($CDCl_3$) H-6, 1.20, 1.87($J_{6,6'}$=14Hz); H-8, 3.25; H-10, 1.00(d, J=7.0Hz); H-12, 4.43; and H-14 and H-15, 1.20ppm.

^{13}C NMR:

($CDCl_3$) C-1, 31.4; C-2, 23.1; C-3, 35.3; C-4,170.4; C-5, 94.7; C-6, 43.8; C-7, 41.4; C-8, 67.8; C-9, 68.2; C-10, 24.2; C-11, 127.0; C-13, 173.6; C-14, 23.1; and C-15, 19.2ppm.

References

T. Anke, W. H. Watson, B.M. Giannetti, and W. Steglich; New Antibiotics from the Basidiomycete *Marasmius alliaceus*; Planta Med., Vol. 39, p. 194 (1980).

I. A. Farrell, T. G. Halsall, and V. Thaller; Structures of Some New Sesquiterpenoid Metabolites of *Marasmius alliaceus*; J. C. S. Perkin Trans I, pp. 1790-1793(1981).

Common/Systematic Name

11-Hydroxyalliacolide

Molecular Formula/Molecular Weight

$C_{15}H_{22}O_5$; MW = 282.14672

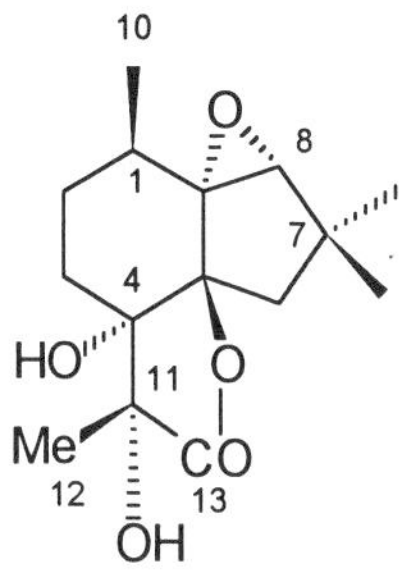

General Characteristics

Crystallized from ethyl acetate in polymorphic form; mp., 199-201.5°C and 228-229°C; $[\alpha]_D$ -8.6° (*c*=0.56, in $CHCl_3$).

Fungal Source

Marasmius alliaceus, a wood rotting fungus.

Isolation/Purification

Isolated from the ether extract of the culture broth by a combination of silica gel column chromatography, preparative thin-layer chromatography (chloroform-methanol, 20:1, v/v), and crystallization from ethyl acetate solution.

Biological Activity

Chemically related to alliacol A and B; both showed weak antibacterial and antifungal activity; both strongly inhibited DNA synthesis in cells of the ascitic form of Ehrlich carcinoma; RNA synthesis was somewhat less affected; and no inhibition of protein synthesis was observed with either metabolite.

Spectral Data

UV:

End absorption.

IR:

(Nujol) 3470, 3350, and 1755cm^{-1}.

^{1}H NMR:

($CDCl_3$) H-6, 1.50, 2.00($J_{6,6'}$=14Hz); H-8, 3.22; H-10, 1.18(d, J=7.0Hz); H-12, 1.42; and H-14 and H-15, 1.18ppm

^{13}C NMR:
(CDCl$_3$) C-1, 31.5; C-2, 25.3; C-3, 28.9; C-4, 76.6; C-5, 94.1; C-6, 42.6; C-7, 38.6; C-8, 67.3; C-9, 68.6; C-10, 24.2; C-11, 74.4; C-12, 17.4*; C-13, 174.9; C-14, 24.1; and C-15, 18.0*ppm.

* Assignments may be interchanged.

Mass Spectrum:
LREIMS: 282(M^+, 10%), 211(16), 205(7), 193(100), 179(18), 165(20), 151(26), 147(15), and 143*m/e* (35).

Reference

I. A. Farrell, T. G. Halsall, and V. Thaller; Structures of Some New Sesquiterpenoid Metabolites of *Marasmius alliaceus*; J. C. S. Perkin Trans I, pp. 1790-1793(1981).

Common/Systematic Name
12-Hydroxyalliacolide

Molecular Formula/Molecular Weight
$C_{15}H_{22}O_5$; MW = 282.14672

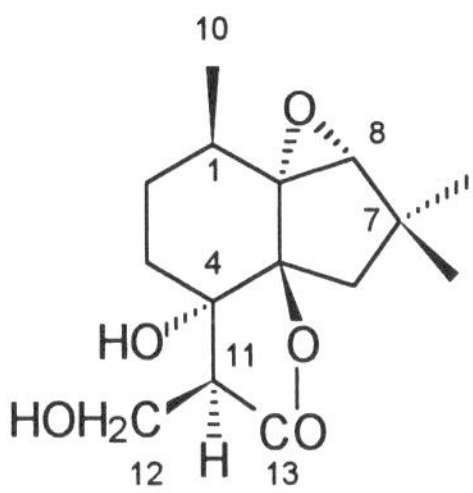

General Characteristics
Crystallized from ethyl acetate-light petroleum as needles; mp., 191-193°C; $[\alpha]_D$ -32.0° (*c*=0.47, in $CHCl_3$).

Fungal Source
Marasmius alliaceus, a wood rotting fungus.

Isolation/Purification
Isolated from the ether extract of the culture broth by a combination of silica gel column chromatography, preparative thin-layer chromatography (chloroform-methanol, 20:1, v/v), sublimation, and crystallization from ethyl acetate solution.

Biological Activity
Chemically related to alliacol A and B; both showed weak antibacterial and antifungal activity; both strongly inhibited DNA synthesis in cells of the ascitic form of Ehrlich carcinoma; RNA synthesis was somewhat less affected; and no inhibition of protein synthesis was observed with either metabolite.

Spectral Data

IR:
(Nujol) 3470 and 1745cm^{-1}.

^{1}H NMR:
($CDCl_3$) H-1, 1.83; H-6, 1.29, 1.98($J_{6,6'}$=14Hz); H-8, 3.23; H-10, 1.20(d, J=7.0Hz); H-11, 2.91; H-12, 4.05; and H-14 and H-15, 1.12ppm

^{13}C NMR:
($CDCl_3$) C-1, 31.4; C-2, 25.5; C-3, 28.9; C-4, 77.0; C-5, 93.1; C-6, 40.8; C-7, 38.6;

C-8, 68.1; C-9, 68.3; C-10, 24.3; C-11, 51.7; C-12, 57.6; C-13, 174.5; C-14, 23.9; and C-15, 17.5ppm.

Mass Spectrum:
LREIMS: 282(M^+, 1%), 267(5), 249(5), 211(20), and 193*m/e* (100).

Reference

I. A. Farrell, T. G. Halsall, and V. Thaller; Structures of Some New Sesquiterpenoid Metabolites of *Marasmius alliaceus*; J. C. S. Perkin Trans I, pp. 1790-1793(1981).

Common/Systematic Name

12-Noralliacolide

Molecular Formula/Molecular Weight

$C_{14}H_{20}O_4$; MW = 252.13616

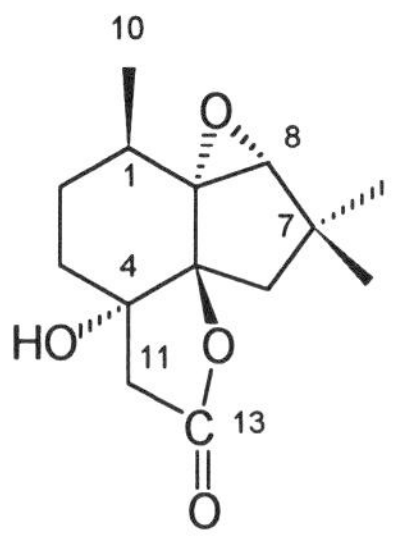

General Characteristics

Crystallized as needles; mp., 198 °C.

Fungal Source

Marasmius alliaceus, a wood rotting fungus.

Isolation/Purification

Isolated from the ether extract of the culture broth by a combination of silica gel column chromatography, preparative thin-layer chromatography (chloroform-methanol, 20:1), and crystallization.

Biological Activity

Chemically related to alliacol A and B; both showed weak antibacterial and antifungal activity; both strongly inhibited DNA synthesis in cells of the ascitic form of Ehrlich carcinoma; RNA synthesis was somewhat less affected; and no inhibition of protein synthesis was observed with either metabolite.

Spectral Data

IR:

(Nujol) 3410 and 1755cm^{-1}.

^{1}H NMR:

([^{2}H]pyridine) H-6, 1.47, 2.37($J_{6,6'}$=14Hz); H-8, 3.25; H-10, 1.18(d, J=7.0Hz); H-11, 2.75, 3.15(d, J=17Hz); H-14, 1.13; and H-15, 1.09ppm

^{13}C NMR:

([^{2}H]pyridine) C-1, 32.4; C-2, 27.0; C-3, 32.4; C-4, 75.2; C-5, 96.3; C-6, 42.1; C-7, 39.1; C-8, 67.1; C-9, 69.1; C-10, 24.9; C-11, 44.4; C-13, 174.2; C-14, 24.2; and C-15, 19.2ppm.

Mass Spectrum:
LREIMS: 252.136(M^+), 237(11%), 210(10), 193(25), 182(37), 167(18), 151(19), 142(46), 140(42), 125(23), 113(25), 109(18), 97(31), and 83*m/e* (100).

Reference

I. A. Farrell, T. G. Halsall and V. Thaller; Structures of Some New Sesquiterpenoid Metabolites of *Marasmius alliaceus*; J. C. S. Perkin Trans I, pp. 1790-1793(1981).

23

Botrydial and Related Metabolites

Botrydial
O-Methyldihydrobotrydial
Deacetyl-*O*-methyldihydrobotrydialone
Dihydrobotrydial
Botryaloic Acid
Botryaloic Acid Acetate
Botryoloic Acid
Norbotryal Acetate
Botrydienal
Dehydrobotrydienal
Deacetyldihydrotrydial

Common/Systematic Name
Botrydial

Molecular Formula/Molecular Weight
$C_{17}H_{26}O_5$; MW = 310.17802

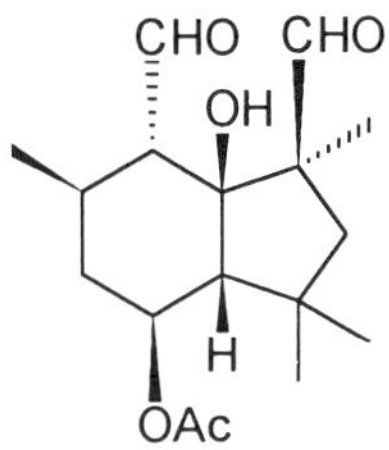

General Characteristics
Crystals from petroleum ether; mp., 108-110°C; $[\alpha]_D^{20}$ +34° (*c*=0.14, in $CHCl_3$).

Fungal Source
Botrytis cinerea.

Biological Activity
Antibiotic with activity against fungi and gram-positive bacteria.

Spectral Data

CD:
(dioxane) + 1.2(308) and - 1.1(220nm).

IR:
(CCl_4) 3465, 1735(OAc), 1717(CH=O-), and 1240cm^{-1} (OAc).

^{1}H NMR:
($CDCl_3$) 0.96(d, *J*=6.0Hz, CH-CH_3); 1.10; 1.29; 1.35(je, s, 3 CH_3); 2.05(s, AcO); 5.08(X part of ABCX system, J_{AX}=4.5, J_{BX}=J_{CX}=11.5Hz, 4H); 9.62(s, CH=O); and 9.80ppm (d, *J*=2.5Hz, CH-CH=O).

Mass Spectrum:
310(M^+, 2%), 250(M^+ - OAc, 14), 204($C_{14}H_{20}O^+$, 87), 180($C_{11}H_{16}O_2^+$, 32), 179($C_{11}H_{15}O_2^+$, 33), 175($C_{13}H_{19}^+$, 100), 119($C_9H_{11}^+$, 55); and 112*m/e* ($C_7H_{12}O^+$, 30).

TLC Data:
R_f 0.3 with Kieselgel-G, PF_{254} using petroleum ether-acetone, 10:3, v/v as solvent.

Reference

H. -W. Fehlhaber, R. Geipel, H. -J. Mercker, R. Tschesche, and K. Welmar; Botrydial, ein Sesquiterpen-Antibiotikum aus der Nährlösung des Pilzes *Botrytis cinerea*; Chem. Ber., Vol. 107, pp. 1720-1730(1974).

Common/Systematic Name

O-Methyldihydrobotrydial

Molecular Formula/Molecular Weight

$C_{18}H_{30}O_5$; MW = 326.20932

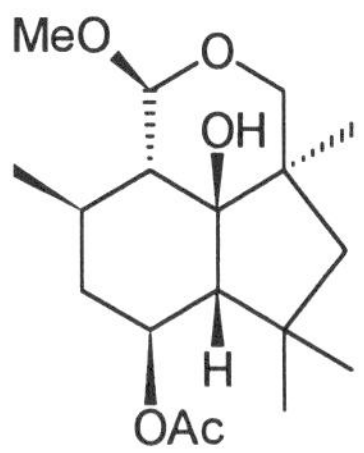

General Characteristics

Crystals from *n*-hexane; mp., 93°C; $[\alpha]_D^{20}$ +85 (*c*=1.0, in MeOH).

Fungal Source

Botrytis squamosa.

Isolation/Purification

The fungus was statically cultured in an onion extract medium. The culture filtrate was adsorbed onto active charcoal at pH 2.0 with HCl and subsequently eluted with acetone. After evaporating the solvent, the residual brown syrup was purified by silica gel column chromatography, eluting with benzene. The eluate gave *O*-methyldihydrobotrydial which was recrystallized from *n*-hexane.

Biological Activity

Biological activity was examined using lettuce seedlings. *O*-Methyldihydrobotrydial inhibited the hypocotyl elongation by approximately 70% at a dose of 10mg/L. However, it accelerated the root growth in proportion to concentrations from 3mg/L to 100mg/L. At a dose of 100mg/L, the root growth was increased by 70% over the control seedlings. On the other hand,deacetyl-*O*-methyldihydrobotrydialone inhibited the hypocotyl elongation by 50%, even at a dose of 300 mg/L,and root growth was hardly influenced by deacetyl-*O*-methyldihydrobotrydialone at concentrations from 1mg/L to 1000mg/L.

Spectral Data

IR:

(KBr) 3520, 1740, 1250, 1120, 1080, and 1050cm^{-1}.

^{1}H NMR:

H-1, 1.60 d(*J*=11Hz); H-2, 1.83 qddd(*J*=2.5, 5.5, 11.0, 11.0); H-3, 1.11 ddd(*J*=9.8. 11.0, 11.0Hz), 2.05 ddd(*J*=2.5, 4.5, 11.0Hz); H-4, 5.09 ddd(*J*=4.5. 9.8. 9.8Hz); H-5,

1.92 d(J=9.8Hz); H-7, 1.05 d(J=10.5Hz), 1.86 d(J=10.5Hz); H-10, 4.82 s; H-11, 0.93 d(J=5.5Hz); H-12, 1.30 s; H-13, 1.10 s; H-14, 1.25 s; H-15, 3.22 d(J=9.5Hz), 3.96 d(J=9.5Hz); 4 CH_3COO-, 2.03 s; and 10 CH_3O-, 3.37ppm s.

^{13}C NMR:

C-1, 54.8 d; C-2, 28.6 d; C-3, 40.0 t; C-4, 72.8 d; C-5, 59. 5 d; C-6, 38.9 s; C-7, 50.4 t; C-8, 45.5 s; 82.6 s; C-10, 98.7 s; C-11, 20.1 q; C-12, 35.6 q; C-13, 27.3 q; C-14, 25.3 q; C-15, 67.5 t; 4 CH_3COO-, 21.5 q; 4 CH_3COO-, 170.5 s; and CH_3O-, 55.0 q.

Mass Data:

EIMS: 308*m/e* (M^+ -18); found: C, 66.19; H, 9.81; calcd. for $C_{18}H_{30}O_5$: C, 66.23; H, 9.26%.

Reference

Y. Kimura, H. Fujioka, H. Nakajima, T. Hamasaki, and A. Isogai; Isolation and Structures of *O*-Methyldihydrobotrydial and Deacetyl-*O*-methyldihydrobotrydialone Produced by *Botrytis squamosa*; Agric. Biol. Chem., Vol. 52 (7), pp. 1845-1847(1988).

Common/Systematic Name

Deacetyl-*O*-methyldihydrobotrydialone

Molecular Formula/Molecular Weight

$C_{16}H_{26}O_5$; MW = 298.17802

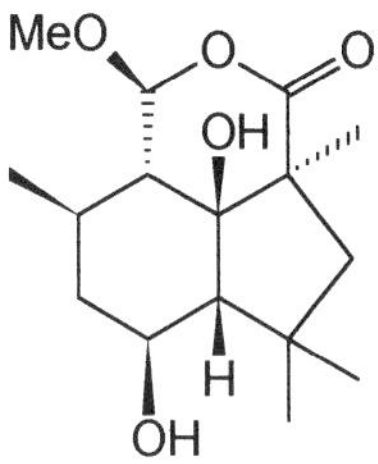

General Characteristics

Crystals from methanol; mp., 236-237°C; $[\alpha]_D^{20}$ +106 (*c*=0.49, in MeOH).

Fungal Source

Botrytis squamosa.

Isolation/Purification

The fungus was statically cultured in an onion extract medium. The culture filtrate was adsorbed onto active charcoal at pH 2.0 with HCl and subsequently eluted with acetone. After evaporating the solvent, the residual brown syrup was purified by silica gel column chromatography, eluting with benzene-acetone (49:1, v/v). The metabolite was applied to a Sephadex LH_{20} column and eluted with methanol. Final purification was by preparative TLC (silica gel HF_{254}; benzene-ethyl acetate, 6:4, v/v) followed by recrystallization from methanol.

Biological Activity

See *O*-methyldihydrobotrydial.

Spectral Data

IR:

(KBr) 3450, 1765, 1285, and 1200cm^{-1}.

^{1}H NMR:

H-1, 1.71 dd(*J*=5.0, 12.0Hz); H-2, 1.61 qddd(*J*=3.0, 6.0, 12.0, 12.0Hz); H-3, 1.22 ddd(*J*=12.0, 12.0, 12.0Hz), 1.90 ddd(*J*=3.0, 4.5, 12.0Hz); H-4, 3.80 ddd(*J*=4.5. 10.5, 12.0Hz); H-5, 1.65 d(*J*=10.5Hz); H-7, 1.50 d(*J*=13.0Hz), 2.46 d(*J*=13.0Hz); H-10, 5.19 d(*J*=5.0Hz); H-11, 0.99 d(*J*=6.0Hz); H-12, 1.29 s; H-13, 1.25 s; H-14, 1.33; and 10-CH_3O-, 3.58ppm s.

^{13}C NMR:
C-1, 55.6 d; C-2, 32.6 d; C-3, 43.1 t; C-4, 69.5 d; C-5, 64.55 d; C-6, 40.0 s; C-7, 49.0 t; C-8, 53.8 s; C-9, 84.4 s; C-10, 108.0 d; C-11, 20.4 q; C-12, 36.3 q; C-13, 27.3 q; C-14, 20.4 q; C-15, 173.9 s; and 10 CH_3O-, 57.0ppm q.

Mass Data:
EIMS: 280(M^+ -18), 266, 252, 238, 222, 195, and 180*m/e*; CIMS: 299(M^+ +1); found: C, 62.96; H, 8.70; calcd. for $C_{16}H_{26}O_5$ + ½ H_2O: C, 62.54; H, 8.79%.

Reference

Y. Kimura, H. Fujioka, H. Nakajima, T. Hamasaki, and A. Isogai; Isolation and Structures of *O*-Methyldihydrobotrydial and Deacetyl-*O*-methyldihydrobotrydialone Produced by *Botrytis squamosa*; Agric. Biol. Chem., Vol. 52 (7), pp. 1845-1847(1988).

Common/Systematic Name
Dihydrobotrydial

Molecular Formula/Molecular Weight
$C_{17}H_{28}O_5$; MW = 312.19367

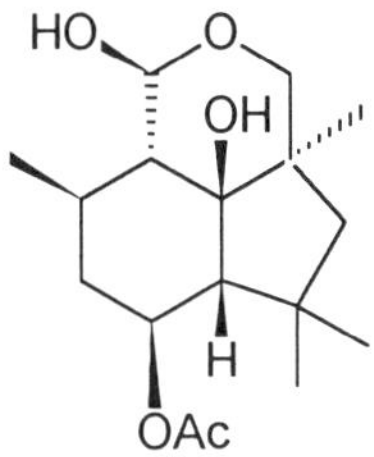

General Characteristics
Crystals from petroleum ether; mp., 158-160°C; $[\alpha]_D^{22}$ + 56° (*c*=0.94, in petroleum ether).

Fungal Source
Botrytis cinerea.

Biological Activity
Antibiotic with activity against fungi and gram-positive bacteria.

Spectral Data

IR:
(CCl_4) 3595, 3535(OH), 1730, and 1235cm^{-1} (OAc).

^{1}H NMR:
($CDCl_3$) 0.98(d, *J*=6.0Hz, CH-CH_3); 1.14(s, CH_3); 1.28(s, 2CH_3); 2.03(s, AcO); 3.25, and 4.20(AB-system, J_{AB}=10Hz, CH_2O); 5.12(X part of ABCX system, J_{AX}=4.5, J_{BX}=J_{CX}=11.5Hz, 4H); and 5.36ppm (s, 10H).

^{13}C NMR:
($CDCl_3$) C-11, 20.0(q), 21.4(q); C-14, 25.4(q); C-13, 27.2(q); C-2, 28.6(d); C-12, 35.9(q); C-6, 38.8(s); C-3, 39.9(t); C-8, 45.4(s); C-7, 50.4(t); C-1, 55.0(d); C-5, 59.8(d); C-15, 67.4(t); C-4, 72.7(d); C-9, 84.4(s); and C-10, 92.2(d), 170.3ppm (s).

Mass Spectrum:
294(M^+ - H_2O, 26%), 234(M^+ - H_2O - HOAc, 50), 175($C_{13}H_{19}^+$, 77), and 96*m/e* (100).

TLC Data
R_f 0.35 with Kieselgel-G, PF_{254} using petroleum ether-acetone, 10:3, v/v as solvent.

References

H. -W. Fehlhaber, R. Geipel, H. -J. Mercker, R. Tschesche, and K. Welmar; Botrydial, ein Sesquiterpen-Antibiotikum aus der Nährlösung des Pilzes *Botrytis cinerea*; Chem. Ber., Vol. 107, pp. 1720-1730(1974).

Y. Kimura, H. Fujioka, H. Nakajima, T. Hamasaki, M. Irie, K. Fukuyama, and A. Isogai; Isolation, X-Ray Structure and Biological Activity of Deacetyldihydrobotrydial Produced by *Botrytis squamosa*; Agric. Biol. Chem., Vol. 50, pp. 2123-2125(1986).

Common/Systematic Name

Botryaloic acid (Isolated as methyl botryaloate)

Molecular Formula/Molecular Weight

$C_{15}H_{24}O_5$; MW = 284.16237

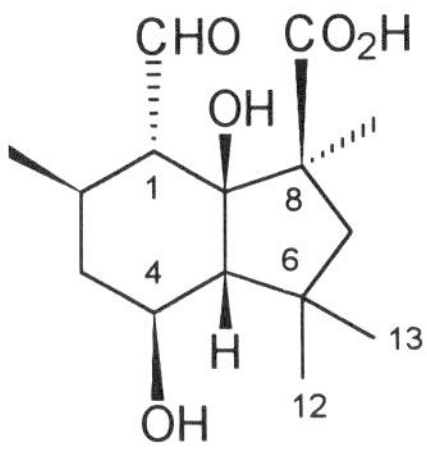

General Characteristics

Methyl botryaloate: Crystallized from ether as needles; mp., 115-117°C; $[\alpha]_D$ +67° (c=0.43, in $CHCl_3$).

Fungal Source

Botrytis cinerea.

Isolation/Purification

The culture broth was saturated with sodium chloride and acidified to pH 2 with hydrochloric acid. The culture broth was extracted with ethyl acetate and the extracts were shaken with aqueous sodium hydrogen carbonate; the sodium hydrogen carbonate extracts were acidified to pH 2 with 6N hydrochloric acid and extracted with ethyl acetate. These extracts were dried and the solvent evaporated to give an oil which was dissolved in ether and treated with an excess of diazomethane. The solvent and excess of reagent were evaporated to give an oil which was chromatographed on a dry column of silica (Merck). Elution with 20% ethyl acetate-light petroleum gave methyl acetylbotryaloate which crystallized from ether as needles. Further elution with 25-30% ethyl acetate-light petroleum gave methyl botryaloate which crystallized from ether as needles. Fractions eluting with 40% ethyl acetate-light petroleum were rechromatographed on preparative TLC using chloroform-ethyl acetate-acetic acid (40:10:1, v/v) to yield methyl botryoloate.

Spectral Data (Methyl botryaloate)

IR:

(Nujol mull) 3460, 3360, 2750, 1730, and 1710 cm^{-1}.

^1H NMR:

($CDCl_3$) 0.90(3H, d, J=5Hz); 1.33(9H, s); 3.68(3H, s, OMe); 3.95(1H, sextet, 14.5, 11, and 11 Hz); and 9.86ppm (1H, d, J=3Hz).

^{13}C NMR:
(CDCl$_3$) C-1, 68.5; C-2, 28.5; C-3, 43.5; C-4, 70.0; C-5, 66.3; C-6, 38.6; C-7, 54.9; C-8, 55.1; C-9, 88.2; C-10, 204.1; C-11, 20.7; C-12, 27.8; C-13, 36.2; C-14, 20.7; C-15, 179.0; and OMe, 52.5ppm.

Mass Data:
Found: C, 64.35; H, 8.8; $C_{16}H_{26}O_5$ requires C, 64.4; H, 8.8%.

Reference

A. P. W. Bradshaw and J. R. Hanson; Three New Sesquiterpenoid Metabolites of *Botrytis cinerea*; J. Chem. Soc., Perkin Trans I, pp. 741-743(1980).

Common/Systematic Name

Botryaloic acid acetate (Isolated and purified as methyl acetyl botryaloate)

Molecular Formula/Molecular Weight

$C_{17}H_{26}O_6$; MW = 326.17294

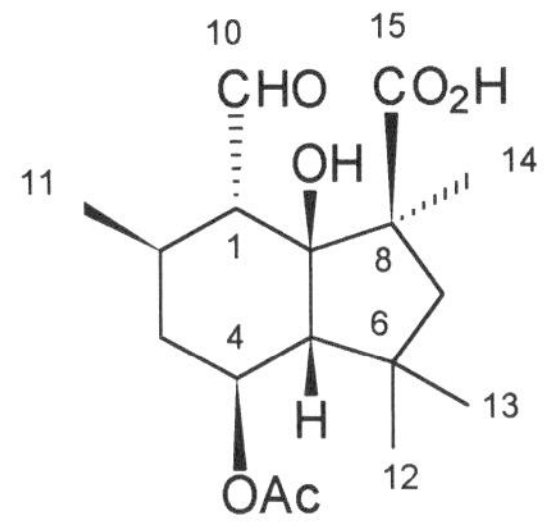

General Characteristics

Methyl acetyl botryaloate: crystallized from ether as needles; mp., 106-108°C; $[\alpha]_D$ +81° (*c*=0.46, in $CHCl_3$).

Fungal Source

Botrytis cinerea.

Isolation/Purification

The culture broth was saturated with sodium chloride and acidified to pH 2 with hydrochloric acid. The culture broth was extracted with ethyl acetate and the extracts were shaken with aqueous sodium hydrogen carbonate; the sodium hydrogen carbonate extracts were acidified to pH 2 with 6N hydrochloric acid and extracted with ethyl acetate. These extracts were dried and the solvent evaporated to give an oil which was dissolved in ether and treated with an excess of diazomethane. The solvent and excess of reagent were evaporated to give an oil which was chromatographed on a dry column of silica (Merck). Elution with 20% ethyl acetate-light petroleum gave methyl acetyl botryaloate which crystallized from ether as needles. Further elution with 25-30% ethyl acetate-light petroleum gave methyl botryaloate which crystallized from ether as needles. Fractions eluting with 40% ethyl acetate-light petroleum were rechromatographed on preparative TLC using chloroform-ethyl acetate-acetic acid (40:10:1, v/v/v) to yield methyl botryoloate.

Spectral Data (Methyl acetyl botryaloate)

IR:

(Nujol mull) 3445, 2760, 2720, 1740, and 1710cm^{-1}.

^{1}H NMR:

($CDCl_3$) 0.86(3H, d, *J*=5Hz); 1.06, 1.30, 1.36, 2.03, and 3.70(each 3H, s); 5.06(1H, sextet *J*=4.5, 11, and ll Hz); and 9.86ppm (1H, d, *J*=3Hz).

^{13}C NMR:
($CDCl_3$) C-1, 68.3; C-2, 28.2; C-3, 38.6; C-4, 72.9; C-5, 61.7; C-6, 38.6; C-7, 55.0; C-8, 55.0; C-9, 88.0; C-10, 203.5; C-11, 20.9*; C-12, 27.5; C-13, 35.7; C-14, 20.5*; C-15, 178.9; OMe, 52.6; and OAc, 21.4, 170.3ppm.

* Assignments may be interchanged.

Mass Data:
Found: C, 63.5; H, 8.3. $C_{18}H_{28}O_6$ requires C, 63.5; H, 8.3%.

Reference

A. P. W. Bradshaw and J. R. Hanson; Three New Sesquiterpenoid Metabolites of *Botrytis cinerea*; J. Chem. Soc., Perkin Trans I, pp. 741-743(1980).

Common/Systematic Name

Botryoloic acid

Molecular Formula/Molecular Weight

$C_{17}H_{28}O_6$; MW = 328.18859

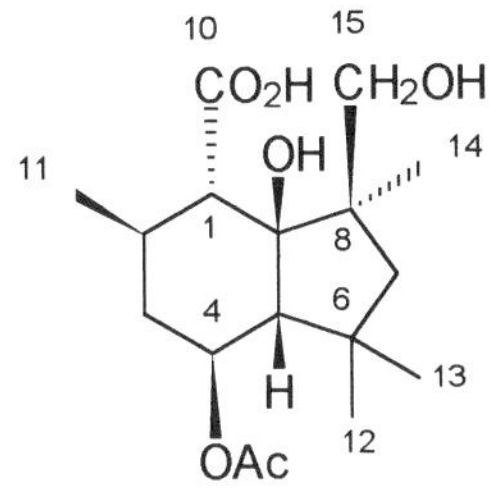

General Characteristics

Methyl botryoloate: Crystallized from methanol as plates; mp., 123-125°C; $[\alpha]_D$ +34° (*c*=0.24, in $CHCl_3$).

Fungal Source

Botrytis cinerea.

Isolation/Purification

The culture broth was saturated with sodium chloride and acidified to pH 2 with hydrochloric acid. The culture broth was extracted with ethyl acetate and the extracts were shaken with aqueous sodium hydrogen carbonate; the sodium hydrogen carbonate extracts were acidified to pH 2 with 6N hydrochloric acid and extracted with ethyl acetate. These extracts were dried and the solvent evaporated to give an oil which was dissolved in ether and treated with an excess of diazomethane. The solvent and excess of reagent were evaporated to give an oil which was chromatographed on a dry column of silica (Merck). Elution with 20% ethyl acetate-light petroleum gave methyl acetyl botryaloate which crystallized from ether as needles. Further elution with 25-30% ethyl acetate-light petroleum gave methyl botryaloate which crystallized from ether as needles. Fractions eluting with 40% ethyl acetate-light petroleum were rechromatographed on preparative TLC using chloroform-ethyl acetate-acetic acid (40:10:1, v/v/v) to yield methyl botryoloate.

Spectral Data (Methyl botryoloate)

IR:

(Nujol mull) 3560, 3480(sh), 3230(br), 1725, and 1705cm^{-1}.

^{1}H NMR:

($CDCl_3$) 0.92(3H, d, *J*=6Hz); 1.04, 1.10, 1.31, and 2.08ppm (each 3H, s); 3.28 and 3.60ppm (each 1H, d, *J*=13Hz); 3.80(3H, s); and 5.10ppm (1H, sextet, *J*=4, 11, and 11Hz).

Mass Data:
Found: C, 63.5; H, 8.3. $C_{18}H_{28}O_6 \bullet 5H_2O$ requires C, 63.5; H, 8.3%.

Reference

A. P. W. Bradshaw and J. R. Hanson; Three New Sesquiterpenoid Metabolites of *Botrytis cinerea*; J. Chem. Soc., Perkin Trans I, pp. 741-743(1980).

Common/Systematic Name
Norbotryal acetate

Molecular Formula/Molecular Weight
$C_{16}H_{24}O_3$; MW = 264.17254

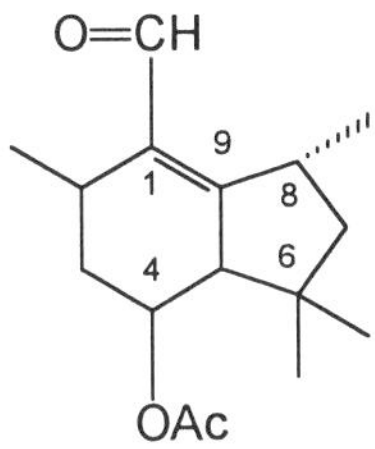

General Characteristics
An unstable oil; $[\alpha]_D^{20}$ +102° (c=0.2, in $CHCl_3$): bp., 84°/ 0.5mm.

Fungal Source
Botrytis cinerea (GCRI strain 216).

Isolation/Purification
The fungal broth was extracted with EtOAc and separated into acidic and neutral fractions with aqueous $NaHCO_3$. The neutral fraction was chromatographed on silica gel, deactivated with 12% water. Elution with 15% EtOAc-petrol gave a fraction which was further purified by TLC on silica gel in EtOAc-petrol (1:4, v/v) to afford norbotryal acetate as an unstable oil. The material had R_f 0.53 in the above system and gave a pink coloration with a MeOH-H_2SO_4 spray.

Spectral Data

UV:
λ_{max} 253nm (ϵ=10,300).

IR:
2740, 1735, 1670, 1625, and 1235cm^{-1}.

^1H NMR:
($CDCl_3$) H-2, 2.85(m); H-3, 1.38 and 2.14 =(m); H-4, 4.75(octet, J=3, 9, 10Hz); H-5, 2.54(q, J=2 and 9Hz); H-7, 1.8(m); H-8, 3.2(m); H-10, 10.0(s); H-11, 1.12(d, J=6Hz); H-12, 1.25(s); H-13, 0.75(s); H-14, 1.28(d, J=7Hz); and Me, 2.00ppm (s).

^{13}C NMR:
($CDCl_3$) C-1, 135.8; C-2; 32.5; C-3, 37.5; C-4, 70.2; C-5, 56.0; C-6, 40.9; C-7, 49.3; C-8, 29.1; C-9, 169.0; C-10, 190.4; C-11, 21.9; C-12, 28.3; C-13, 20.6; C-14, 24.2; C=O, 170.1; and C-Me, 21.3ppm.

Mass Spectrum:

LREIMS: 264(M^+), 204(base peak), 189, metastable 175.1 (for 204-189), 161, 119, 105, 43, and 41*m/e*. HREIMS: 204.15148*m/e*; $C_{14}H_{20}O^+$ (M^+ - $MeCO_2H$) requires 204.151407.

Reference

O. Cuevas and J. R. Hanson; Norbotryal Acetate, A Nor-Sesquiterpenoid Aldehyde from *Botrytis cinerea;* Phytochemistry, Vol. 16, pp. 1061-1062(1977).

Common/Systematic Name
Botrydienal

Molecular Formula/Molecular Weight
$C_{15}H_{20}O_2$; MW = 232.14633

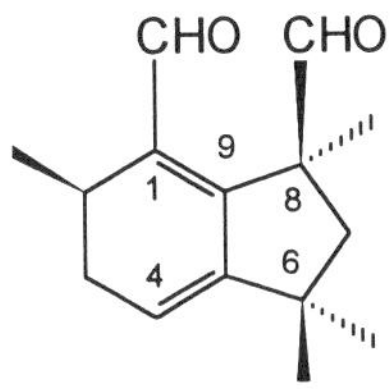

General Characteristics
Colorless needles; mp., 69-70°C; $[\alpha]_D^{30}$ +190° (*c*=0.18, in *n*-hexane).

Fungal Source
Botryotinia squamosa (IFO 9432).

Isolation/Purification
The mycelia of *B. squamosa* and agar medium were macerated with acetone. The acetone extract evaporated to an aqueous residue, which was extracted with ethyl acetate at pH 9. Purification was monitored by a turnip seedling bioassay. The phytotoxin was purified by column chromatography on silica gel followed by preparative TLC (silica gel) and HPLC (Develosil C_8), affording botrydienal as the active principle of the cultured material. Two related metabolites, dehydrobotrydienal and deacetyldihydrobotrydial, also were isolated from the same cultured material of *B. squamosa.*

Biological Activity
Phytotoxic to turnip seedlings. The respective 50% inhibitory concentrations (IC_{50}) of botrydienal, dehydrobotrydienal and deacetyldihydrobotrydial were 10, 40, and 1000µg/ml. Botrydienal and dehydrobotrydienal also showed anti-bacterial activity, the respective MICs against *Escherichia coli* B 110 being 10 and 20µg/ml, and those against *Staphylococcus aureus* IFO 12732 50 and 50µg/ml.

Spectral Data

UV:
λ_{max}^{EtOH} 245(sh, ϵ=2,670) and 324nm (6,940).

IR:
(KBr) 1720, 1660, and 1635cm^{-1}.

^{1}H NMR:
(CDCl$_3$) 0.92(d, $J_{2\,11}$=7.1Hz, 11-CH$_3$); 1.06, 1.25, 1.54(s, 12-, 13- and 14-CH$_3$); 1.63, 2.24(d, J_{gem}=13.9Hz, 7-CH$_2$); 2.17, 2.48(ddd, $J_{2,\,3a}$=8.1, $J_{a,\,4}$=3-2, $J_{2,3B}$=2.0, $J_{3B,4}$=6.1 and J_{gem}=18Hz, 3a-, 3b-H); 2.98(m, 2-H); 5.87(ddd, $J_{2,\,4}$=0.5, J_{3a4}=3.2 and $J_{3B,4}$=6.1Hz, 4-H); and 9-67, 9.74ppm (s, 15- and 10-CHO).

^{13}C NMR:
(CDCl$_3$) 18.3; 25.3; 28.7; 30.5(q, CH$_3$ x 4); 30.5; 50.4(t, CH$_2$ x 2); 24.2(d, CH); 40.4; 56.3(s, quaternary C x 2); 123.5(d, -CH=); 135.7; 149.2; 154.9(s, -C= x 3); 189.5; and 199.5(s, CHO x 2).

Mass Spectrum:
HREIMS: 232.1479*m/e* (M$^+$); calcd. for $C_{15}H_{20}O_2$, 232.1469.

Reference
T. Kimata, M. Natsume, and S. Marumo; Botrydienal, A New Phytotoxin, and its Related Metabolites, Dehydrobotrydienal and Deacetyldihydrobotrydial Produced by *Botryotinia squamosa*; Tetrahedron Letters, Vol. 26, pp. 2097-2100(1985).

Common/Systematic Name
Dehydrobotrydienal

Molecular Formula/Molecular Weight
$C_{15}H_{20}O_2$; MW = 230.13063

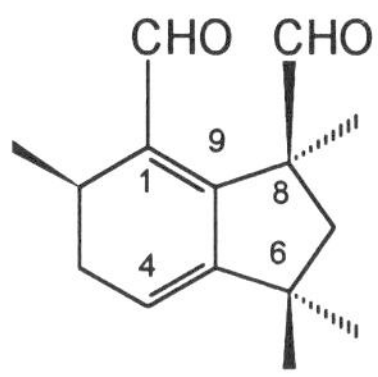

General Characteristics
Colorless oil; $[\alpha]_D^{30}$ -22° (*c*=0.14, in *n*-hexane).

Fungal Source
Botryotinia squamosa (IFO 9432).

Isolation/Purification
See botrydienal.

Biological Activity
See botrydienal.

Spectral Data

UV:
λ_{max}^{EtOH} 260(sh ϵ=6,390) and 315nm (2,080).

IR:
(KBr) 1725, 1685, and 1585cm^{-1}.

^1H NMR:
($CDCl_3$) 1.32, 1.33, 1.55, and 2.68ppm (4 X CH_3; positioned on C-6(2), C-8, and C-2, respectively; 9.60 and 10.40ppm (2 X CHO); 7.22(*J*=7.8Hz on C-3); 7.32(*J*=7.8, 15Hz on C-4); and 1.86, 2.21ppm (2H on C-7, *J*=13.5Hz).

^{13}C NMR:
($CDCl_3$) 19.2; 22.1; 30.5; 31.4(q, CH_3 x 4); 51.3(t, CH_2); 42.4; 57.9(s, quaternary-C x 2); 128.3; 132.2(d, -CH= x 2); 129.7; 140.8; 141.2; 153.1(s, -C= x 4); 191.3; and 200.5ppm (d, CHO x 2).

Reference
T. Kimata, M. Natsume, and S. Marumo; Botrydienal, A New Phytotoxin, and its Related Metabolites, Dehydrobotrydienal and Deacetyldihydrobotrydial Produced by *Botryotinia squamosa*; Tetrahedron Letters, Vol. 26, pp. 2097-2100(1985).

Common/Systematic Name

Deacetyldihydrobotrydial

Molecular Formula/Molecular Weight

$C_{15}H_{26}O_4$; MW = 270.18311

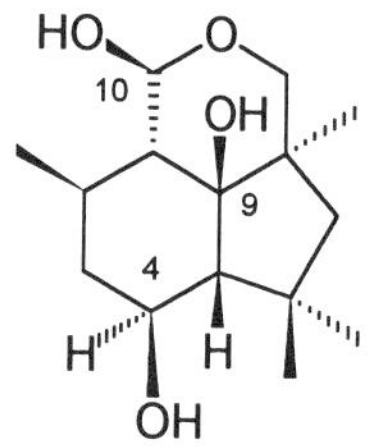

General Characteristics

Colorless prisms; mp., 163-165°C; $[\alpha]_D^{28}$ +22.4° (*c*=1.2, in MeOH).

Fungal Source

Botryotinia squamosa (IFO 9432).

Isolation/Purification

See botrydienal.

Biological Activity

See botrydienal.

Spectral Data

IR:

(KBr) 3460, 3370, and 1000cm^{-1}.

^{1}H NMR:

The presence of three OH groups was shown by D_2O exchangeable signals at 5.60, 5.82, and 8.31ppm.

^{13}C NMR:

In the ^{13}C NMR spectrum measured with a coaxial dual tube of CD_3OD/CD_3OH, the upfield shifted carbons at 70.3, 84.7, and 93.3ppm were assigned to the three respective OH-bearing carbons at 4-C, 9-C, and 10-C. The two carbons vicinal to the OH-bearing carbons at 1-C and 5-C (57.3 and 64.9ppm or vice versa) showed large upfield values (0.136 and 0.141, respectively), clearly indicative that they are sandwiched between the two OH-bearing carbons; 20.6, 26.0, 36.5, and 27.9ppm (4 methyl groups); 46.0, 51.8, and 68.4ppm (3 CH_2 groups); 39.8 and 46.5ppm (2 quaternary carbons); and 57.3, 30.1, 70.3, 64.9, and 93.3ppm (5 methine carbons).

References

T. Kimata, M. Natsume, and S. Marumo; Botrydienal, A New Phytotoxin, and its Related Metabolites, Dehydrobotrydienal and Deacetyldihydrobotrydial Produced by *Botryotinia squamosa*; Tetrahedron Letters, Vol. 26, pp. 2097-2100(1985).

M. Irie, K. Fukuyama, and A. Isogai; Isolation, X-Ray Structure and Biological Activity of Deacetylhydrobotrydiol Produced by *Botrytis squamosa*; Agric. Biol. Chem.; Vol. 50, pp. 2123-2125(1986).

Herbarin and Related Metabolites

24

Herbarin
Dehydroherbarin
O-Methylherbarin
Anhydrofusarubin
8-*O*-Methylfusarubin
O-Ethylfusarubin
Dihydrofusarubin
Dihydrofusarubin (S-form)
Hydroxydihydrofusarubin
O-Ethyldihydrofusarubin
8-*O*-Methylbostrycoidin
Fusarubin (Oxyjavanicin)
Fusarubin Methyl Ether
Javanicin
Norjavanicin
8-*O*-Methyljavanicin
8-*O*-Methylsolaniol
Marticin
Isomarticin
5,8-Dihydroxy-6-methoxy-3-methyl-2-aza-9,10-anthracenedione
rel-(3*R*,4a*R*)-5,10-Dioxo-3,4,4a,5,10,10a-hexahydro-7-methoxy-3-methyl-3,6,9-trihydroxy-1*H*-naphtho[2,3-*c*]pyran
rel-(3*R*,4a*R*,10a*S*)-5,10-Dioxo-3,4,4a,5,10,10a-hexahydro-7-methoxy-3-methyl-3,6,9-trihydroxy-1*H*-naphtho[2,3-*c*]pyran
rel-(3*R*,4a*R*,10a*R*)-5,10-Dioxo-3,4,4a,5,10,10a-hexahydro-3,7-dimethoxy-3-methyl-6,9-dihydroxy-1*H*-naphtho[2,3-*c*]pyran
Anhydrofusarubin Lactone
1,5,10-Trihydroxy-7-methoxy-3-methyl-1*H*-naphtho[2,3-*c*]pyran-6,9-dione
5,10-Dihydroxy-1,7-dimethoxy-3-methyl-1*H*-naphtho[2,3-*c*]pyran-6,9-dione
2,3-Dihydro-5,8-dihydroxy-6-methoxy-2-hydroxymethyl-3-(2-hydroxypropyl)-1,4-naphthalenedione
2,3-Dihydro-5-hydroxy-4-hydroxymethyl-8-methoxynaphtho[1,2-*b*]furan-6,9-dione
5,8-Dihydroxy-2-methoxy-6-hydroxymethyl-7-(2-hydroxypropyl)-1,4-naphthalenedione
2,5,8-Trihydroxy-6-methoxy-3-(2-oxypropyl)-1,4-naphthoquinone
Nectriafurone
8-*O*-Methyl ether nectriafurone

Common/Systematic Name
Herbarin

Molecular Formula/Molecular Weight
$C_{16}H_{16}O_6$; MW = 304.09469

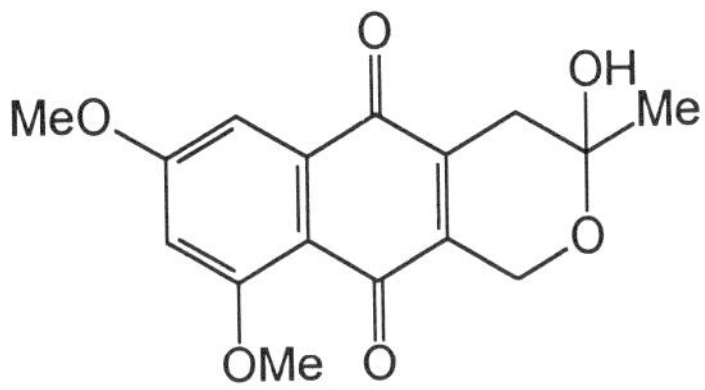

General Characteristics
Herbarin crystallized from methanol as long, bright yellow needles; mp., 192-193°C. It was insoluble in aqueous sodium hydroxide and gave no color with ethanolic ferric chloride. In concentrated sulfuric acid a blood red color developed which on standing turned brown.

Fungal Source
Torula herbarum, a dermataceous fungus regularly associated with dry leaves and twigs of *Felia microphylla*.

Isolation/Purification
Fungal cultures were extracted (pH 4.5-5.0, unacidified) with ethyl acetate, washed twice with water and reduced in volume. A highly pigmented crystalline material separated after standing at -5°C overnight. Herbarin was purified by column chromatography or by preparative thin-layer chromatography and crystallized from methanol solution as long, bright yellow needles.

Biological Activity
Herbarin showed weak antibacterial and antifungal activity. The pigment mixture containing herbarin also showed antiamoebic activity against *Entamoeba histolytica* at a concentration of 20µg/ml.

Spectral Data

UV:
λ_{max}^{EtOH} 415, 266, and 216nm (log ϵ=3.48, 4.18, and 4.83, respectively); infl. 350, 285, and 237nm (log ϵ=3.15, 3.94, and 3.91, respectively).

IR:
(KBr) 3325(OH), 1678, 1650(C=O), 1607, 1572, and 1567cm^{-1} (C=C).

CD:

Optical activity; in ethanolic solution herbarin showed negligible rotation at D line, but ORD showed a negative Cotton effect at 345nm.

^{1}H NMR:

(pyridine-d_5) 2.61(1H, d, J=2.5); 3.18(1H, d, J=2.5); 4.9-5.0(2H, m); 5.4(1H, broad singlet); 6.17(3H, s); 6.21(3H, s); 6.86(1H, m, J=18); 7.33(1H, m, J=18Hz); and 8.26ppm (3H, s).

Mass Data:

Molecular weight determination by osmometric method gave 299. HREIMS showed 304.0905(M^+) $C_{12}H_{16}O_6$ requires 304.0947; 286.0846, M^+ - H_2O; 276.1028, M^+ - CO ; and 271.0643, M^+ -H_2O,-CH_3. Anal. C, 62.9; H, 5.15; calcd for $C_{16}H_{16}O_6$, C, 63.15; H, 5.26.

Reference

M. V. Kadkol, K. S. Gopalkrishnan, and N. Narasimhachari; Isolation and Characterization of Naphthaquinone Pigments from *Torula herbarum* (Pers.) Herbarin and Dehydroherbarin; J. Antibiot., Vol. 24, pp. 245-248(1971).

Common/Systematic Name

Dehydroherbarin

Molecular Formula/Molecular Weight

$C_{16}H_{14}O_5$; MW = 286.08412

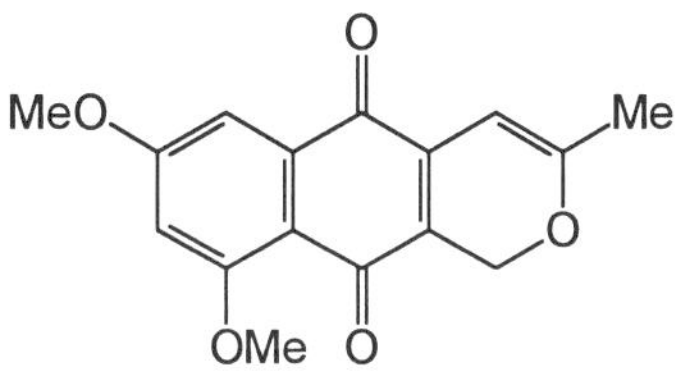

General Characteristics

Dehydroherbarin crystallized from methanol as bright red glistening needles; mp., 186-188°C. It was soluble in ethyl acetate, chloroform, diethyl ether, and insoluble in water; was insoluble in aqueous sodium hydroxide, and did not give color with ethanolic ferric chloride.

Fungal Source

Torula herbarum, a dermataceous fungus regularly associated with dry leaves and twigs of *Felia microphylla.*

Isolation/Purification

Fungal cultures were extracted (pH 4.5-5.0, unacidified) with ethyl acetate, washed twice with water and reduced in volume. Dehydroherbarin was separated by silica gel column chromatography and crystallized from methanol.

Biological Activity

Dehydroherbarin showed weak antibacterial and antifungal activity. The pigment mixture containing dehydroherbarin also showed antiamoebic activity against *Entamoeba histolytica* at a concentration of 20μg/ml.

Spectral Data

UV:

λ_{max}^{EtOH} 485, 400, 335, 272, 250, and 217nm (log ϵ=3.15, 3.15, 3.28, 3.85, 3.85, and 4.12, respectively).

IR:

(KBr) 1675, 1667(C=O), 1632, 1610, 1600, and 1565cm^{-1} (C=C).

^{1}H NMR:

($CDCl_3$) 2.75(1H, d, *J*=2.5); 3.30(1H, d, *J*=2.5); 4.18(1H, d, *J*=1.0Hz); 4.88(2H, s); 6.05(3H, s); 6.07(3H s); and 8.02ppm (3H, s).

Mass Data:

HREIMS showed M^+ 286.0821($C_{16}H_{14}O_5$, 286.0841), M^+ -CH_3, 271.0561, and M^+ -CO, 258.0888*m/e*. Anal: C, 67.3; H, 5.0; calcd for $C_{16}H_{14}O_5$, C, 67.51; H, 4.90.

Reference

M. V. Kadkol, K. S. Gopalkrishnan, and N. Narasimhachari; Isolation and Characterization of Naphthaquinone Pigments from *Torula herbarum* (Pers.) Herbarin and Dehydroherbarin; J. Antibiot., Vol. 24, pp. 245-248(1971).

Common/Systematic Name

O-Methylherbarin

Molecular Formula/Molecular Weight

$C_{17}H_{18}O_6$; MW = 318.11034

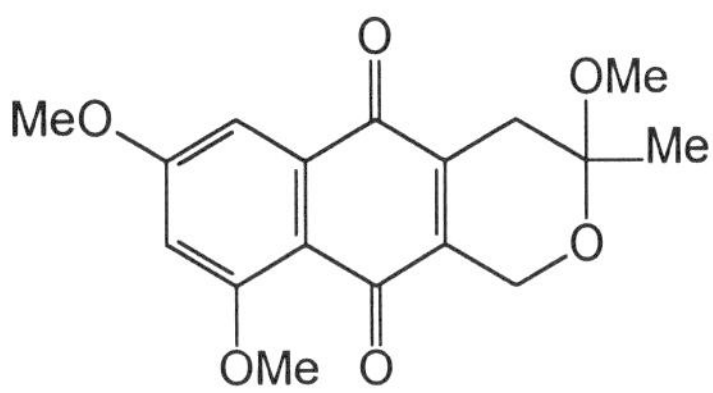

General Characteristics

O-Methylherbarin was crystallized from ethyl acetate as yellow needles and prisms which melted at 188-190°C.

Fungal Source

Torula herbarum, a dermataceous fungus regularly associated with dry leaves and twigs of *Felia microphylla*.

Isolation/Purification

Purified by preparative thin-layer chromatography and crystallized from ethyl acetate as yellow needles and prisms.

Spectral Data

UV:

λ_{max}^{EtOH} 218, 267, 285, and 415nm.

IR:

($CHCl_3$) Spectrum very similar to herbarin except no hydroxyl absorption observed.

^{1}H NMR:

($CDCl_3$) 6.06 and 6.08(aromatic OCH_3); 6.72 (OCH_3); 8.52 (CH_3); 2.73 and 3.29 (aromatic protons); H-9_{eq}, 5.25; H-9_{ax}, 5.65; H-12_{eq}, - 7.2; and H-12_{ax} -7.55τ.

Mass Spectrum:

318(M^+), 303, 286, 271, 244(base peak), and 243*m/e*.

Reference

M. V. Kadkol, K. S. Gopalkrishnan, and N. Narasimhachari; Isolation and Characterization of Naphthaquinone Pigments from *Torula herbarum* (Pers.) Herbarin and Dehydroherbarin; J. Antibiot., Vol. 24, pp. 245-248(1971).

Common/Systematic Name

Anhydrofusarubin

Molecular Formula/Molecular Weight

$C_{15}H_{12}O_6$; MW = 288.06339

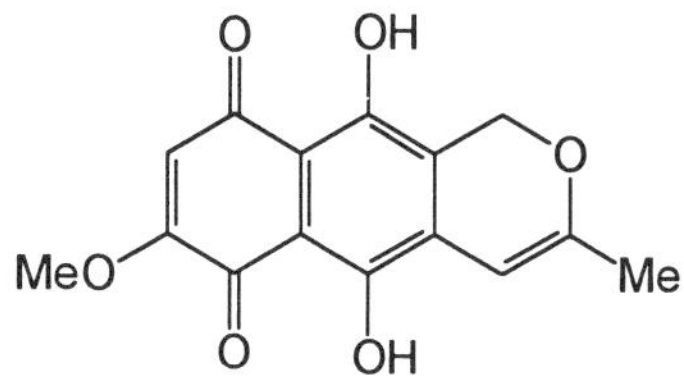

General Characteristics

Crystallized from benzene-methylene chloride; mp., 197-198 °C uncorr.

Fungal Source

Fusarium solani isolated from diseased citrus roots.

Isolation/Purification

Culture filtrates were extracted three times with ethyl acetate; the combined extracts were dried with anhydrous sodium sulfate and reduced in volume. The extract was evaporated to dryness, dissolved in acetone, and fractionated by preparative TLC on silica gel HF_{254} (type 60) plates. Plates were developed with benzene-acetone (85:15, v/v). Seven bands were collected and eluted from the gel with acetone; any remaining colored material was eluted with ethanol. Both acetone and ethanol eluates were diluted and assayed for toxicity in a root growth test. Compounds possessing toxic activity were further purified by TLC with hexane-acetone (75:25, v/v) or hexane-chloroform-ether (1:1:1, v/v/v). Anhydrofusarubin was crystallized from benzene-methylene chloride.

Biological Activity

Phytotoxin that disrupts plant metabolism by inhibiting anaerobic and oxidative decarboxylation reactions. Suspected to be involved in root rot diseases of herbaceous plants and citrus blight, a complex of symptoms also called young tree decline. Anhydrofusarubin was effective in reducing root growth of germinating rough lemon seeds.

Spectral Data

UV:

λ_{max}^{EtOH} 207, 234, 292, 544, and 578nm.

^1H NMR:

($CDCl_3$) 2.04(3H, s, CH_3); 3.94(3H, s, CH_3-O); 5.24(2H, s, CH_2); 6.02(1H, s, CH); 6.15(1H, s, H-6); 12.70(s, OH); and 13.05ppm (s, OH).

Mass Spectrum:
288, 272, 244, and 217*m/e*.

TLC Data

A, C_6H_6-nitromethane-HOAc (75:25:2, v/v/v); B, $CHCl_3$-EtOAc-hexane-HOAc (10:5:5:0.3, v/v/v); C, hexane-Me_2CO-HOAc (15:5:0.3, v/v/v); D, C_6H_6-EtOAc-iso-PrOH-HOAc (145:50:5:1, v/v/v); E, C_6H_6-hexane-Me_2CO (9:9:2, v/v/v) or (3:6:1, v/v/v); F, C_6H_6-Me_2CO (17:3, v/v): G, hexane-Me_2CO-HOAc (15:5:0.1, v/v/v); H, C_6H_6-EtOAc-iso-PrOH-HOAc (16:3:1:0.1, v/v/v). R_f for anhydrofusarubin: A=0.54; B=0.57; C=0.37, and D=0.61. Systems E-H were used for isolation by preparative TLC.

References

R. A. Baker, J. H. Tatum, and S. Nemec, Jr.; Toxin Production by *Fusarium solani* from Fibrous Roots of Blight-Diseased Citrus; Physiology and Biochemistry, Vol. 71, pp. 951-953(1981).

J. H. Tatum and R. A. Baker; Naphthoquinones Produced by *Fusarium solani* Isolated from Citrus; Phytochemistry, Vol. 22, pp. 543-547(1983).

Common/Systematic Name
8-*O*-Methylfusarubin

Molecular Formula/Molecular Weight
$C_{16}H_{16}O_7$; MW = 320.08960

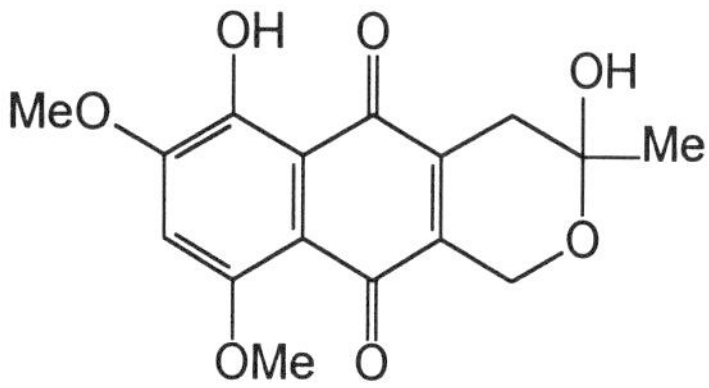

General Characteristics
Crystals from methanol; mp., 138-139°C.

Fungal Source
Fusarium moniliforme (strain MRC 602). The toxicogenic strain of *F. moniliforme* (MRC 602) was isolated from moldy ears of corn in the Transkei, S.A.

Isolation/Purification
Metabolite was extracted with chloroform and partitioned between hexane-90% aqueous methanol; aqueous methanol fraction concentrated and partitioned between chloroform-water. The crude extract was chromatographed on formamide-impregnated cellulose powder eluted with benzene-CH_3COOEt (1:1, v/v); following that, Merck silica type H column chromatography eluted with chloroform-methanol (95:5, v/v) gave 8-*O*-methylfusarubin.

Spectral Data

UV:
λ_{max} 226, 282.5, 484, 510, and 550nm (sh) (log ϵ=4.48, 4.05, 3.83, 3.80, and 3.49, respectively).

IR:
($CHCl_3$) 1600cm^{-1}.

^{1}H NMR:
[$CDCl_3$-$(CD_3)_2SO$, 1:1] H-1, 4.66, ABX_2, J_{ab}=18Hz; H-4, 2.5, 2.78, J_{AX}=J_{BX}=2.7Hz; H-7, 6.85; H-15, 1.56; OCH_3, 4.01; OCH_3, 4.05; and OH, 13.16ppm.

^{13}C NMR:
[$CDCl_3$-$(CD_3)_2SO$, 1:1] C-1, 57.7; C-3, 93.1; C-4, 31.7; C-5, 147.6; C-6, 155.0; C-7, 103.0; C-8, 155.3; C-9, 179.0; C-10, 188.7; C-11, 113.7; C-12, 108.9; C-13, 144.6; C-14, 136.8; C-15, 28.3; 6-OCH_3, 56.1; and 8-OCH_3, 56.1.

Mass Data:

8-*O*-Methylfusarubin failed to give a molecular ion in its mass spectrum upon electron ionization. The compound was converted into a monoacetate which exhibited the appropriate molecular ion in its mass spectrum at 362.099*m/e*. Found: C, 56.88; H, 5.39% $C_{16}H_{16}O_7.H_2O$ requires C, 56.80; H, 5.33%.

Reference

P. S. Steyn, P. L. Wessels, and W. F. O. Marasas; Pigments from *Fusarium moniliforme* Sheldon: Structure and ^{13}C Nuclear Magnetic Resonance Assignments of an Azaanthraquinone and Three Naphthoquinones; Tetrahedron, Vol. 35, pp. 1551-1555 (1979).

Common/Systematic Name
O-Ethylfusarubin

Molecular Formula/Molecular Weight
$C_{17}H_{18}O_7$; MW = 334.10525

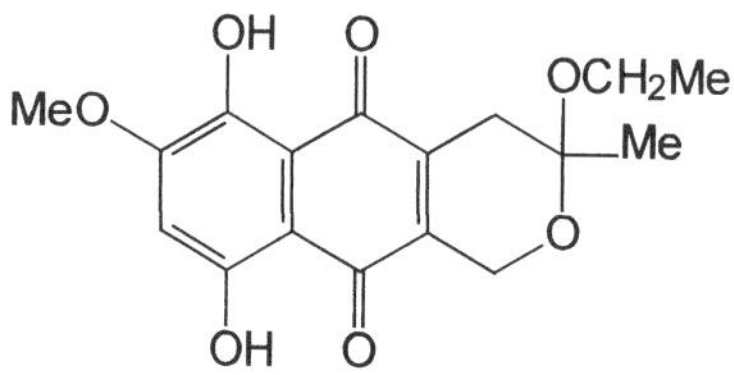

General Characteristics
Reversibly decolorized by sodium hydrosulfite. Readily converted to fusarubin.

Fungal Source
Fusarium solani.

Isolation/Purification
Extracted from acidified fungal broth with chloroform. Separated by column chromatography using Mallinckrodt CC-4, 100-200 mesh and elution with chloroform and increasing concentrations of ethyl acetate.

Biological Activity
Antibiotic activity.

Spectral Data

UV:
λ_{max} 301, 472, 485(sh), 498, 522(small), and 535nm.

IR:
1600, 1580 sh, 1210 s, 1170 s, 1150 s, 1100 s, 1080 s, 1055 s, 970, 950, 840, 810 s, 665, 650, 580, 540, 510, 445, 410, 390cm^{-1}.

^{1}H NMR:
($CDCl_3$) 4.0(OCH_3); 12.7 and 13.0(phenolic OH); 6.2(aromatic H); 1.3(CH_3); 3.7, q; 1.3 t, *J*=5.0 (OEt); and 4.7ppm br, d (CH_2-C).

Reference
N. N. Gerber and M. S. Ammar; New Antibiotic Pigments Related to Fusarubin from *Fusarium solani* (Mart.) SACC., II. Structure Elucidations; J. Antibiot., Vol.32, pp. 685-688(1979).

Common/Systematic Name

Dihydrofusarubin

rel-(3*R*,4a*R*,10a*R*)-5,10-Dioxo-3,4,4a,5,10,10a-hexahydro-7-methoxy-3-methyl-3,6,9-trihydroxy-1*H*-naphtho[2,3-*c*]pyran

Molecular Formula/Molecular Weight

$C_{15}H_{16}O_7$; MW = 308.08960

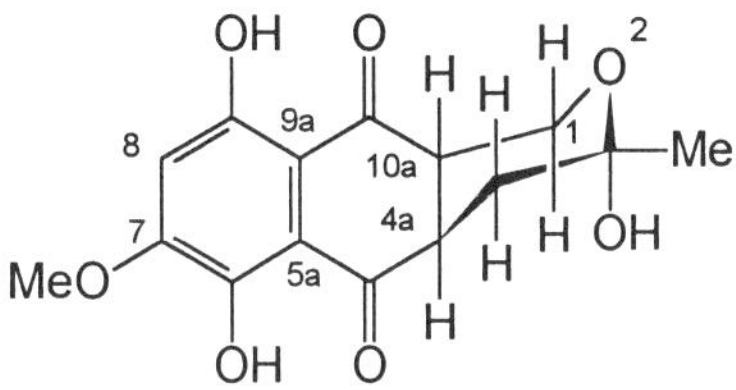

General Characteristics

Reddish-orange needles from CH_2Cl_2; mp., 153-154°C; $[\alpha]_D^{20}$ + 145.4° (*c*=0.31, in acetone).

Fungal Source

Fusarium solani.

Isolation/Purification

Cultures of *F. solani* grown on a maltose ammonium tartrate- salt medium were harvested at 2 days when the pH had dropped to 3 from an initial value of 5. An ethyl acetate extract of the filtrate was taken to dryness and the residue chromatographed on silicic acid. Elution with a 5:1 (v/v), benzene-ethyl acetate mixture gave dihydrofusarubin; *rel*-(3*R*,4a*R*,10a*R*)-5,10-dioxo-3,4,4a,5,10,10a-hexahydro-7-methoxy-3-methyl-3,6,9-trihydroxy-1*H*-naphtho[2,3-*c*]pyran. Decreasing the benzene-ethyl acetate ratio to 3:1, v/v, gave *rel*-(3*R*,4a*R*,10a*S*)-5,10-dioxo-3,4,4a,5,10,10a-hexahydro-7-methoxy-3-methyl-3,6,9-trihydroxy-1*H*-naphtho[2,3-*c*]pyran.

Biological Activity

Antibiotic.

Spectral Data

UV:

$\lambda_{max}^{95\%\ EtOH}$ 213, 243, 273, 300, and 391nm (log ϵ=4.17, 4.30, 3.87, 3.71, and 3.94, respectively).

^{1}H NMR:

The signals for the methyl and methoxy groups of (3*R*,4a*R*,10a*R*)-5,10-dioxo-3,4,4a,5,10,10a-hexahydro-7-methoxy-3-methyl-3,6,9-trihydroxy-1Hnaphtho[2,3-*c*]pyran and (3*R*,4a*R*,10a*S*)-5,10-dioxo-3,4,4a,5,10,10a-hexahydro-7-methoxy-3-methyl-3,6,9-trihydroxy-1*H*-naphtho[2,3-*c*]pyran were readily assigned. Resonances for the ketal and intra-molecularly hydrogen-bonded phenolic hydroxyl groups were temperature dependent and removed by exchange with D_2O. H-8 was deshielded relative to its counterpart fusarubin (6.36ppm) and was, therefore, present in a phenolic rather than a quinone ring. From the chemical shifts and spin-spin coupling constants the ketal ring systems giving rise to the coupled six-spin systems had the conformations shown, with H-4a and H-10a antiperiplanar in the *R* form and synclinal in the *S* form. Conformational free energy calculations indicated that the hydroxyl group at C-3 in both diastereoisomers were axially orientated, assuming a methyl group has a stronger 1,3-diaxial interaction with hydrogen than a hydroxyl group and the 'anomeric effect' favors the epimer with an axial hydroxyl group.

Mass Spectrum:
308.0905*m/e* (M^+); calcd for $C_{15}H_{16}O_7$: 308.08961.

Reference

I. Kurobane, L. C. Vining, A. G. McInnes, and D. G. Smith; Diastereoisomeric 4a,10a-Dihydrofusarubins: True Metabolites of *Fusarium solani*; Can. J. Chem., Vol. 56, pp. 1593-1594(1978).

Common/Systematic Name

Dihydrofusarubin (*S* form)
rel-(3*R*,4a*R*,10a*S*)-5,10-Dioxo-3,4,4a,5,10,10a-hexahydro-7-methoxy-3-methyl-3,6,9-trihydroxy-1*H*-naphtho[2,3-*c*]pyran

Molecular Formula/Molecular Weight

$C_{15}H_{16}O_7$; MW = 308.08960

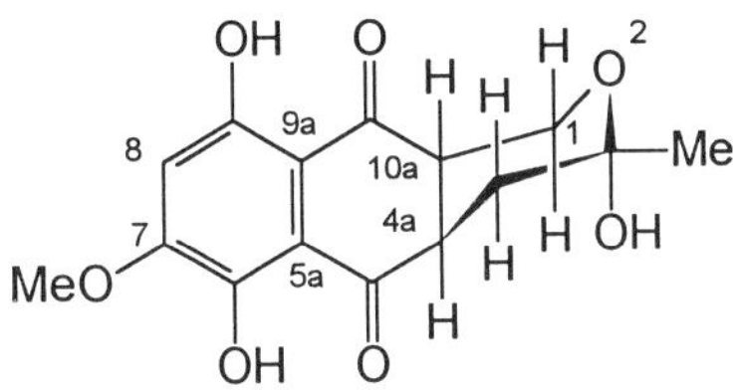

General Characteristics

Pale yellow needles from methanol; mp., 117-118°C; $[\alpha]_D^{20}$ +23.3° (*c*=0.31, in acetone).

Fungal Source

Fusarium solani.

Isolation/Purification

Cultures of *F. solani* grown on a maltose ammonium tartrate-salt medium were harvested at 2 days when the pH had dropped to 3 from an initial value of 5. An ethyl acetate extract of the filtrate was taken to dryness and the residue chromatographed on silicic acid. Elution with a 5:1 (v/v) benzene-ethyl acetate mixture gave dihydrofusarubin, *rel*-(3*R*,4a*R*,10a*R*)-5,10-dioxo-3,4,4a,5,10,10a-hexahydro-7-methoxy-3-methyl-3,6,9-trihydroxy-1*H*-naphtho[2,3-*c*]pyran. Decreasing the benzene-ethyl acetate ratio to 3:1, v/v, gave *rel*-(3*R*,4a*R*,10a*S*)-5,10-dioxo-3,4,4a,5,10,10a-hexahydro-7-methoxy-3-methyl-3,6,9-trihydroxy-1*H*-naphtho[2,3-*c*]pyran.

Biological Activity

Antibiotic

Spectral Data

UV:

$\lambda_{max}^{95\%\ EtOH}$ 213, 243, 273, 300, and 391nm (log ε= 4.15, 4.31, 3.89, 3.70 and 3.96, respectively).

^{1}H NMR:

The signals for the methyl and methoxy groups of *rel*-(3*R*,4a*R*,10a*R*)-5,10-dioxo-3,4,4a,5,10,10a-hexahydro-7-methoxy-3-methyl-3,6,9-trihydroxy-1*H*-naphtho[2,3-*c*]pyran and *rel*-(3*R*,4a*R*,10a*S*)-5,10-dioxo-3,4,4a,5,10,10a-hexahydro-7-

methoxy-3-methyl-3,6,9-trihydroxy-1*H*-naphtho[2,3-*c*]pyran were readily assigned. Resonances for the ketal and intramolecularly hydrogen-bonded phenolic hydroxyl groups were temperature dependent and removed by exchange with $2H_2O$. H-8 was deshielded relative to its counterpart fusarubin (6.36ppm) and was, therefore, present in a phenolic rather than a quinone ring. From the chemical shifts and spin-spin coupling constants the ketal ring systems giving rise to the coupled six-spin systems had the conformations shown, with H-4a and H-10a antiperiplanar in the *R* form and synclinal in the *S* form. Conformational free energy calculations indicated that the hydroxyl group at C-3 in both diastereoisomers were axially orientated, assuming a methyl group has a stronger 1,3-diaxial interaction with hydrogen than a hydroxyl group and the 'anomeric effect' favors the epimer with an axial hydroxyl group.

Mass Spectrum:

M^+ peak too small for mass measurement, M - 18 (also observed in the mass spectrum of *R* form) at 290.0784*m/e;* calcd for $C_{15}H_{14}O_6$, 290.07904.

Reference

I. Kurobane, L. C. Vining, A. G. McInnes, and D. G. Smith; Diastereoisomeric 4a,10a-Dihydrofusarubins: True Metabolites of *Fusarium solani*; Can. J. Chem., Vol. 56, pp. 1593-1594(1978).

Common/Systematic Name

Hydroxydihydrofusarubin

Molecular Formula/Molecular Weight

$C_{15}H_{16}O_8$; MW = 324.08452

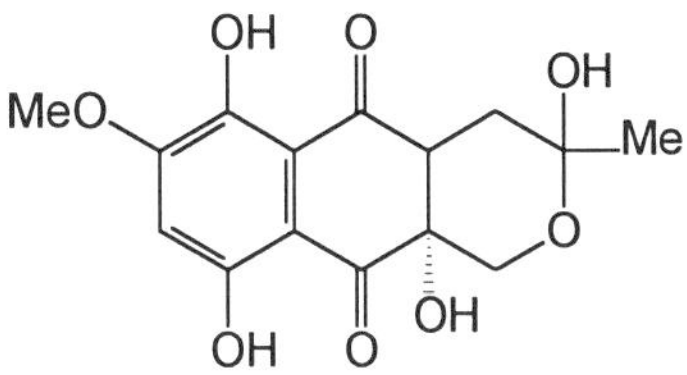

General Characteristics

A yellow pigment reversibly decolorized by sodium hydrosulfite; readily converted to fusarubin; exhibited a strong bluish fluorescence.

Fungal Source

Fusarium solani

Isolation/Purification

Extracted from acidified fungal broth with chloroform. Separated by column chromatography using Mallinckrodt CC-4, 100-200 mesh and elution with chloroform and chloroform with increasing concentrations of ethyl acetate.

Biological Activity

Antibiotic activity.

Spectral Data

UV:

λ_{max} 272, 300(weak), and 388nm.

IR:

3600w, 1730w, 1635s, 1465-1480, 1440, 1410, 1310, 1270, 1170, and 1005cm^{-1}.

^{1}H NMR:

($CDCl_3$) 4.0(OCH_3); 12.1 and 12.2(phenolic OH); 6.75(aromatic H); 1.5(CH_3); 4.2 dd; 1.57 m; and 2.3ppm m.

Reference

N. N. Gerber and M. S. Ammar; New Antibiotic Pigments Related to Fusarubin from *Fusarium solani*, II. Structure Elucidations; J. Antibiot., Vol.32, pp. 685-688(1979).

Common/Systematic Name

O-Ethyldihydrofusarubin

(Diastereoisomeric-3-*O*-ethyl ether derivatives ofdihydrofusarubin, R and S forms)

Molecular Formula/Molecular Weight

$C_{17}H_{20}O_7$; MW = 336.1209

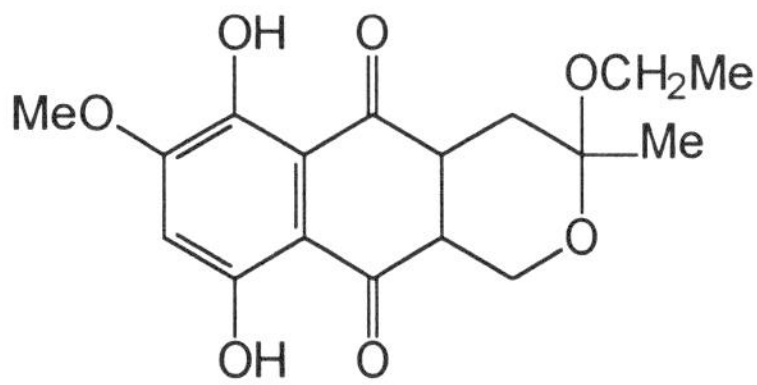

General Characteristics

Yellow pigments that form during crystallization of the parent diastereoisomers from ethanol. The possibility that they are laboratory artifacts cannot be excluded.

Fungal Source

Fusarium solani (cholesterol-metabolizing strain PP 96); probably form non-enzymatically in the culture broth or during purification.

Biological Activity

Antibiotic activity.

Spectral Data (Spectral characteristics corresponded closely those of dihydrofurarubins.)

Mass Spectrum:

CIMS with methane as carrier gas gave five peaks: 377(1.5%, M^+ 41), 365(23, M^+), 337(100, M^+ +1), 319(19, M^+ +1 - H_2O), and 291*m/e* (93, M^+ +1 - EtOH).

References

N. N. Gerber and M. S. Ammar; New Antibiotic Pigments Related to Fusarubin from *Fusarium solani* (Mart.) SACC., II. Structure Elucidations; J. Antibiot., Vol. 32, pp. 685-688(1979).

I. Kurobane, L. C. Vining, A. G. McInnes, and N. N. Gerber; Metabolites of *Fusarium solani* Related to Dihydrofusarubin; J. Antibiot., Vol. 33, pp. 1376-1379(1980).

Common/Systematic Name

8-*O*-Methylbostrycoidin

6,8-Dimethoxy-5-hydroxy-methyl-2-azaanthraquinone

Molecular Formula/Molecular Weight

$C_{16}H_{13}NO_5$; MW = 299.07937

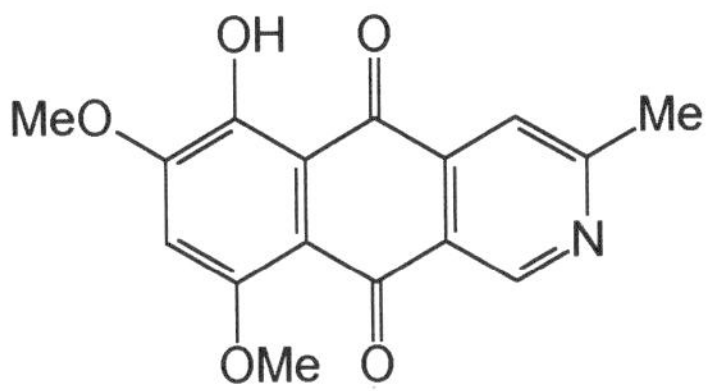

General Characteristics

8-*O*-Methylbostrycoidin was the major pigment from cultures of this strain of *F. moniliforme* (MRC 601). Crystals from chloroform-methanol; mp., 215-216°C. Treatment of 8-*O*-methylbostrycoidin with Zn^{+2} in acetic acid led to a change in the color from dark-red to light pink, however, upon removal of the Zn by filtration, the material was readily oxidized to starting material which indicated that the metabolite was a quinone. 8-*O*-Methylbostrycoidin formed blue alkali-metal salts and exhibited strong chelating properties with e.g. Ca^{+2} and Mg^{+2}. Acetylation of gave a fluorescent light-yellow monoacetate; mp., 254-246°C

Fungal Source

Fusarium moniliforme (strain MRC 602). The toxicogenic strain of *F. moniliforme* (MRC 602) was isolated from moldy ears of maize in the Transkei, S.A.

Isolation/Purification

Metabolite was extracted with chloroform and partitioned between carbon tetrachloride-water. The crude extract was chromatographed on the following systems: (1) formamide-impregnated cellulose powder eluted with benzene-CH_3COOEt followed by (2) Merck silica type H column chromatography eluted with chloroform-methanol (96:4, v/v) and (3) preparative TLC using silica gel H_{254} (chloroform-methanol; 96:4, v/v). R_f for 8-*O*-methylbostrycoidin was 0.51.

Spectral Data

UV:

λ_{max}^{MeOH} (log ϵ) 247.5(4.50), 318(3.92), and 480nm (3.83); $\lambda_{max}^{Acidic\ MeOH}$ 227(4.32), 262(4.20), 310(3.88), and 510nm (3.73); $\lambda_{max}^{Basic\ MeOH}$ 259(4.44), 306(3.82), and 546nm.

IR:
$(CHCl_3)$ 1641, 1591, 1311, and 1265cm^{-1}.

^{1}H NMR:
$(CDCl_3)$ C-1, 1H, 9.44; C-4, 1H, 7.85; C-7, 1H, 6.86; C-15, 1H, 2.76; OCH_3 X 2= 4.05; and OH, 13.19ppm.

Mass Data:
299.080*m/e*, calcd 299.083; found: C 63.75, H 4.39, N 4.63%; requires C 64.2, H 4.35, N 4.68%.

Reference

P. S. Steyn, P. L. Wessels, and W. F. O. Marasas; Pigments from *Fusarium moniliforme* Sheldon: Structure and ^{13}C Nuclear Magnetic Resonance Assignments of an Azaanthraquinone and Three Naphthoquinones; Tetrahedron, Vol. 35, pp. 1551-1555 (1979).

Common/Systematic Name

Fusarubin; Oxyjavanicin

Molecular Formula/Molecular Weight

$C_{15}H_{14}O_7$; MW = 306.07395

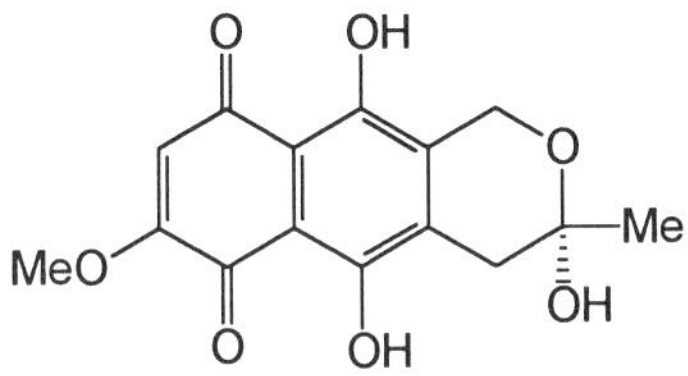

General Characteristics

Red prisms from benzene; mp., 196-198 °C (uncorrected); charring about 200 °C, but mp. 218 °C. Soluble in glacial acetic acid, tetrahydrofuran, acetone, dioxane, pyridine; slightly soluble in cold chloroform, cold alcohol, ether; practically insoluble in carbon disulfide, cyclohexane, cold benzene. Dissolves in dilute NaOH with a violet color; practically insoluble in bicarbonate solution.

Fungal Source

Fusarium solani isolated from diseased citrus roots, and *F. javanicum*.

Isolation/Purification

Culture filtrates were extracted three times with ethyl acetate; the combined extracts were dried with anhydrous sodium sulfate and reduced in volume. The extract was evaporated to dryness, dissolved in acetone, and fractionated by preparative thin-layer chromatography (TLC) on silica gel HF_{254} (type 60) plates. Plates were developed with benzene-acetone (85:15, v/v). Seven bands were collected and eluted from the gel with acetone; any remaining colored material was eluted with ethanol. Both acetone and ethanol eluates were diluted and assayed for toxicity in a root growth test. Compounds possessing toxic activity were further purified by TLC with hexane-acetone (75:25, v/v) or hexane-chloroform-ether (1:1:1, v/v/v). Fusarubin was crystallized from benzene.

Biological Activity

Phytotoxin that disrupts plant metabolism by inhibiting anaerobic and oxidative decarboxylation reactions. Suspected to be involved in root rot diseases of herbaceous plants and citrus blight, a complex of symptoms also called young tree decline. Fusarubin was effective in reducing root growth of germinating rough lemon seeds.

Spectral Data

UV:

λ_{max}^{Ether} 535 and 499nm.

^{1}H NMR:

($CDCl_3$) 1.68(3H, s, CH_3), 2.27(d, *J*=2, OH, disappears on addition of D_2O), 2.72(1H, dd, *J*=18, *J*=2, CH_2), 3.05(1H, d, *J*=18, CH_2), 3.94(3H, s, CH_3-O), 4.90(2H, s, -CH_2-O-), 6.18 (1H, s, H-6), 12.69(s, OH), and 12.95ppm (s, OH).

Mass Data:

306, 288, 273, 259, and 246*m/e*; C 58.82%, H 4.61%, O 36.57%.

TLC Data

Solvent system A, C_6H_6-nitromethane-HOAc (75:25:2, v/v/v); B, $CHCl_3$-EtOAc-hexane-HOAc (10:5:5:0.3, v/v/v); C, hexane-Me_2CO-HOAc (15:5:0.3, v/v/v); D, C_6H_6-EtOAc-iso-PrOH-HOAc (145:50:5:1, v/v/v); E. C_6H_6-hexane-Me_2CO (9:9:2, v/v/v) or (3:6:1, v/v/v); F, C_6H_6-Me_2CO, (17:3, v/v): G, hexane-Me_2CO-HOAc (15:5:0.1, v/v/v); H, C_6H_6-EtOAc-iso-PrOH-HOAc (16:3:1:0.1, v/v/v). R_f for fusarubin: A=0.23; B=0.29; C=0.23, and D=0.39. Systems E-H were used for isolation (preparative TLC).

References

R. A. Baker, J. H. Tatum, and S. Nemec, Jr.; Toxin Production by *Fusarium solani* From Fibrous Roots of Blight-Diseased Citrus; Physiology and Biochemistry, Vol. 71, pp. 951-953(1981).

J. H. Tatum and R. A. Baker; Naphthoquinones Produced by *Fusarium solani* Isolated from Citrus; Phytochemistry, Vol. 22, pp. 543-547(1983).

Common/Systematic Name
Fusarubin methyl ether

Molecular Formula/Molecular Weight
$C_{16}H_{16}O_7$; MW = 320.08960

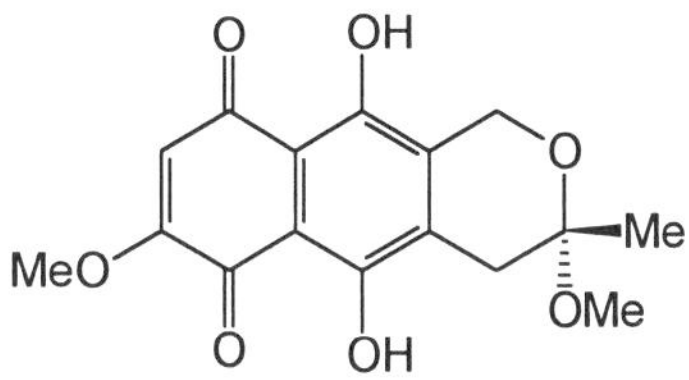

General Characteristics
Red crystals from EtOAc; mp., 188-190° (lit. 190°C).

Fungal Source
Fusarium solani isolated from diseased citrus roots.

Isolation/Purification
Culture filtrates were extracted with ethyl acetate; the combined extracts were dried with anhydrous sodium sulfate and reduced in volume. The extract was evaporated to dryness, dissolved in acetone, and fractionated by preparative thin-layer chromatography (TLC) on silica gel HF_{254} (type 60) plates. Plates were developed with benzene-acetone (85:15, v/v). Seven bands were collected and eluted from the gel with acetone; any remaining colored material was eluted with ethanol. Both acetone and ethanol eluates were diluted assayed for toxicity in a root growth test. Compounds possessing toxic activity were further purified by TLC with hexane-acetone (75:25, v/v) or hexane-chloroform-ether (1:1:1, v/v/v). The methyl ether of fusarubin was crystallized from EtOAc.

Biological Activity
Suspected to be phytotoxic and may be involved in the etiology of citrus decline.

Spectral Data

UV:
λ_{max}^{EtOH} 228, 306, 475, 499, and 534nm.

^{1}H NMR:
($CDCl_3$) 1.55(3H, s, CH_3); 2.66(dt, *J*=18.0, 4eq and 2.0Hz); 3.02(dd, *J*=18.0 (4ax) and 1.5Hz); 3.33(OMeO); 3.94(s, 7-OMe); 4.65(dt, *J*=18.0 (1eq) and 2.7Hz); 4.88(dd, *J*=18.0 (1ax) and 1.5Hz); 6.18(H-8); 12.69(OH); and 12.95ppm (OH).

Mass Spectrum:
320*m/e* (M^+).

TLC Data

Solvent system A, C_6H_6 nitromethane-HOAc (75:25:2, v/v/v); B, $CHCl_3$-EtOAc-hexane-HOAc (10:5:5:0.3, v/v/v); C, hexane-Me_2CO-HOAc (15:5:0.3); D, C_6H_6-EtOAc-iso-PrOH-HOAc (145:50:5:1, v/v/v); E, C_6H_6-hexane-Me_2CO (9:9:2, v/v/v) or (3:6:1, v/v/v); F, C_6H_6-Me_2CO (17:3, v/v); G, hexane-Me_2CO-HOAc (15:5:0.1, v/v/v); H, C_6H_6-EtOAc-iso-PrOH-HOAc (16:3:1:0.1, v/v/v). R_f for methyl ether of fusarubin: A=0.43; B=0.50; C=0.36, and D=0.55. Systems E-H were used for isolation (preparative TLC).

Reference

J. H. Tatum and R. A. Baker; Naphthoquinones Produced by *Fusarium solani* Isolated from Citrus; Phytochemistry, Vol. 22, pp. 543-547(1983).

Common/Systematic Name

Javanicin

2-Acetonyl-3-methyl-7-methoxynaphthazarin

Molecular Formula/Molecular Weight

$C_{15}H_{14}O_6$; MW = 290.07904

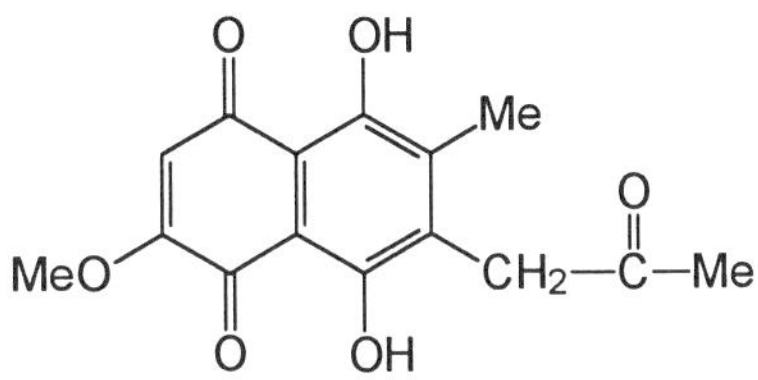

General Characteristics

Crystallized from benzene; mp., 207-208°C uncorr. (lit. 207-208°C).

Fungal Source

Fusarium solani isolated from diseased citrus roots.

Isolation/Purification

Culture filtrates were extracted three times with ethyl acetate; the combined extracts were dried with anhydrous sodium sulfate and reduced in volume. The extract was evaporated to dryness, dissolved in acetone, and fractionated by preparative TLC on silica gel HF_{254} (type 60) plates. Plates were developed with benzene-acetone (85:15, v/v). Seven bands were collected and eluted from the gel with acetone; any remaining colored material was eluted with ethanol. Both acetone and ethanol eluates were diluted and assayed for toxicity in a root growth test. Compounds possessing toxic activity were further purified by TLC with hexane-acetone (75:25, v/v) or hexane-chloroform-ether (1:1:1, v/v/v). Javanicin was crystallized from benzene.

Biological Activity

Phytotoxin that disrupts plant metabolism by inhibiting anaerobic and oxidative decarboxylation reactions. Suspected to be involved in root rot diseases of herbaceous plants and citrus blight, a complex of symptoms also called young tree decline. Javanicin was effective in reducing root growth of germinating rough lemon seeds.

Spectral Data

UV:

λ_{max}^{EtOH} 227, 305, 478, 504, and 541.

^1H NMR:

($CDCl_3$) 2.22(3H, s, CH_3), 2.28(2H, s, CH_2), 3.88(2H, s, CH_2), 3.91(3H, s, CH_3), 6.18 (1H, s, H-6), 12.82(s, OH), and 13.21ppm (s, OH).

Mass Spectrum:
290, 248, 230, 219, 205, and 43*m/e*.

TLC Data

Solvent system A, C_6H_6-nitromethane-HOAc (75:25:2, v/v/v); B, $CHCl_3$-EtOAc-hexane-HOAc (10:5:5:0.3, v/v/v); C, hexane-Me_2CO-HOAc (15:5:0.3, v/v/v); D, C_6H_6-EtOAc-iso-PrOH-HOAc (145:50:5:1, v/v/v); E. C_6H_6-hexane-Me_2CO (9:9:2, v/v/v) or (3:6:1, v/v/v); F, C_6H_6-Me_2CO (17:3, v/v): G, hexane-Me_2CO-HOAc (15:5:0.1, v/v/v); H, C_6H_6-EtOAc-iso-PrOH-HOAc (16:3:1:0.1, v/v/v). R_f for javanicin A=0.36; B=0.45; C=0.30, and D=0.51. Systems E-H were used for isolation (preparative TLC).

References

R. A. Baker, J. H. Tatum, and S. Nemec, Jr.; Toxin Production by *Fusarium solani* from Fibrous Roots of Blight-Diseased Citrus; Physiology and Biochemistry, Vol. 71, pp. 951-953(1981).

J. H. Tatum and R. A. Baker; Naphthoquinones Produced by *Fusarium solani* Isolated from Citrus; Phytochemistry, Vol. 22, pp. 543-547(1983).

Common/Systematic Name

Norjavanicin

2-Acetonyl-7-methoxynaphthazarin

Molecular Formula/Molecular Weight

$C_{14}H_{12}O_6$; MW = 276.06339

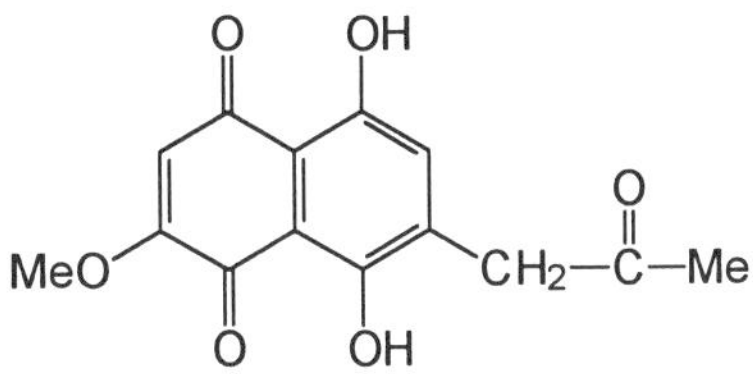

General Characteristics

Red needles from CH_2Cl_2-MeOH; mp., 195-200°C.

Fungal Source

Fusarium solani isolated from diseased citrus roots.

Isolation/Purification

Culture filtrates were extracted with ethyl acetate; the combined extracts were dried with anhydrous sodium sulfate and reduced in volume. The extract was evaporated to dryness, dissolved in acetone, and fractionated by preparative thin-layer chromatography (TLC) on silica gel HF_{254} (type 60) plates. The extract was developed in solvent system F and norjavanicin was isolated as a minor component and crystallized from methylene chloride-methanol to give red crystals.

Biological Activity

Phytotoxic. Suspected to be involved in root rot diseases of herbaceous plants and citrus blight, a complex of symptoms also called young tree decline.

Spectral Data

UV/Visible:

λ_{max}^{EtOH} 225, 299, 477, 503, and 540nm.

^1H NMR:

($CDCl_3$): 2.31, 3H, s; 3.81, 2H, s; 7.18, H-10a; 3.93, 7-OMe; 6.18, H-8; 12.55, OH; and 12.59ppm, OH.

Mass Spectrum:

276*m/e* (M^+).

TLC Data

Solvent system A, C_6H_6-nitromethane-HOAc (75:25:2, v/v/v); B, $CHCl_3$-EtOAc-hexane-HOAc (10:5:5:0.3, v/v/v); C, hexane-Me_2CO-HOAc (15:5:0.3, v/v/v); D, C_6H_6-EtOAc-iso-PrOH-HOAc (145:50:5:1, v/v/v); E, C_6H_6-hexane-Me_2CO (9:9:2, v/v/v) or (3:6:1, v/v/v); F, C_6H_6-Me_2CO (17:3, v/v): G, hexane-Me_2CO-HOAc (15:5:0.1, v/v/v); H, C_6H_6-EtOAc-iso-PrOH-HOAc (16:3:1:0.1, v/v/v). R_f for norjavanicin: A=0.33; B=0.35; C=0.28, and D=0.41.

Reference

J. H. Tatum and R. A. Baker; Naphthoquinones Produced by *Fusarium solani* Isolated from Citrus; Phytochemistry, Vol. 22, pp. 543-547(1983).

Common /Systematic Name

8-*O*-Methyljavanicin

Molecular Formula / Molecular Weight

$C_{16}H_{16}O_6$; MW = 304.09467

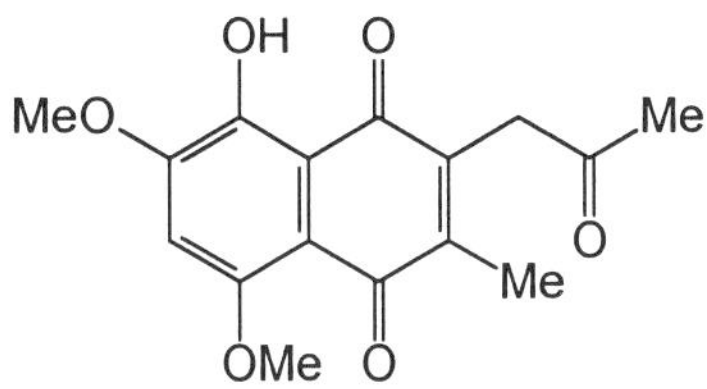

General Characteristics

Recrystallized from acetone to yield red needles; mp., 196-198°C; 8-*O*-methyljavanicin was positive to ferric chloride solution and 2,4-dinitrophenylhydrazine solution.

Fungal Source

Fusarium moniliforme and *F. solani* isolated from rice.

Isolation/Purification

The culture broth was filtered and extracted twice with ethyl acetate at pH 6.5. The combined extracts were concentrated under reduced pressure below 40°C to give a dark brown residue. The residue was dissolved in acetone and mixed with acid-washed Celite. After drying under reduced pressure, the impregnated Celite was charged onto a SilicAR CC-4 column which was eluted with ethyl acetate. After evaporation, the solid was subjected to SilicAR CC-4 column chromatography eluted with benzene and ethyl acetate; solid obtained from above 20% and 30% ethyl acetate fractions was applied onto a LH_{20} column eluted with methanol. After evaporation of the solvent, the residue was applied onto a SilicAR CC-4 column. The active substance eluted with benzene-acetone (49:1, v/v). Fractions with the biological activity were combined and evaporated to dryness to afford red crystals.

Biological Activity

A growth inhibitor on lettuce seedlings and on the root growth of lettuce seedlings (subjected to the growth assay of lettuce seedlings according to the method of Frankland and Wareing). In the bioassay using lettuce seeds at a concentration of 500mg/1iter showed a weak inhibitory effect on germination when observed after 24 hr. However, the activity at doses of 1-500mg/liter revealed approximately the same extent as that of controls after 48 hr. Suppression of hypocotyl elongation of lettuce seedlings was observed at a concentration of 10mg/liter, although at the same concentration it did not inhibit the root growth; at a concentration of 500mg/liter it inhibited the root growth with accompanying necrosis. Biological activities to rice seedlings were examined according to the method of Murakami at doses of 1-1000mg/liter; it did not inhibit the growth of the second leaf sheath of rice.

Spectral Data

UV:

λ_{max} 283(ϵ=31,300), 486(18,600), 510(sh, 16,900), and 550nm (sh, 7,300); λ_{max}^{MeOH} 226, 282.5, 482, 510, and 550nm (sh) (log ϵ=4.56, 4.04, 3.80, 3.75, and 3.80).

IR:

(KBr) 3300-3400(OH), 1715(C=O), 1635(C=O), 1620, 1595, 1480, 1435, 1395, 1315, 1280, 1260, 1220, 1080, 1035, 943, 900, and 830cm^{-1} (indicated the presence of naphthoquinone moiety).

^{1}H NMR:

($CDCl_3$) Exhibited signals at 2.10(3H, s, CH_3); 2.29(3H, s, CH_3); 3.74(2H, s, CH_2); 3.96(3H, s, OCH_3); 3.98(3H, s, OCH_3); 6.72(1H, s, ArH); and 13.0ppm (1H, s, OH).

^{13}C NMR:

($CDCl_3$) C-1, 13.9; C-3, 203.1; C-4, 41.1; C-5, 147.9; C-6, 155.1; C-7, 102.9; C-8, 155.6; C-9, 181.2; C-10, 189.4; C-11, 114.3; C-12, 110.6; C-13, 150.0; C-14, 137.8; C-15, 30.2; 6-OCH_3, 56.4; and 8-OCH_3, 57.0ppm.

References

Y. Kimura, T. Hamasaki, and H. Nakajima; Isolation, Identification and Biological Activities of 8-*O*-Methyljavanicin Produced by *Fusarium solani*; Agric. Biol. Chem., Vol. 45, pp. 2653-2654(1981).

P. S. Steyn, P. L. Wessels, and W. F. O. Marasas; Pigments from *Fusarium moniliforme* Sheldon: Structure and ^{13}C Nuclear Magnetic Resonance Assignments of an Azaanthraquinone and Three Naphthoquinones; Tetrahedron, Vol. 35, pp. 1551-1555 (1979).

Common/Systematic Name

8-*O*-Methylsolaniol

Molecular Formula/Molecular Weight

$C_{16}H_{18}O_6$; MW = 306.11034

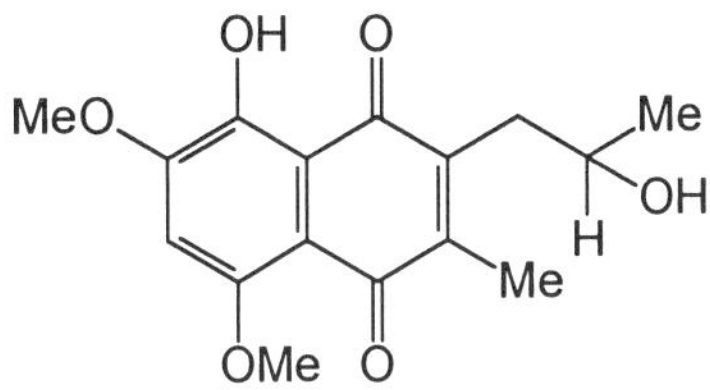

General Characteristics

Crystals from methanol; mp., 152-154°C.

Fungal Source

Fusarium moniliforme (strain MRC 602); the toxicogenic strain of *F. moniliforme* isolated from moldy ears of maize in the Transkei, S.A.

Isolation/Purification

Metabolite was extracted with chloroform and partitioned between hexane-90% aqueous methanol; aqueous methanol fraction concentrated and partitioned between chloroform-water; the crude extract was chromatographed on formamide-impregnated cellulose powder eluted with benzene-CH_3COOEt (1:1, v/v) followed by Merck silica type H column chromatography eluted with chloroform-methanol (98:2, v/v) which gave an 8-*O*-methylsolanion-containing fraction. This was separated by chromatography on Merck pre-coated TLC plates Si gel F_{254}, thickness 2mm, developed in $CHCl_3$-MeOH (94:6, v/v).

Spectral Data

UV:

λ_{max}^{MeOH} 226, 285, 476, and 510nm (sh) (log ϵ=4.49, 4.025, 3.82, and 3.69, respectively).

IR:

($CHCl_3$) 1628, 1470, 1435, and 1272cm^{-1}.

^1H NMR:

($CDCl_3$) H-1, 2.12; H-3, 4.18; H-4, 2.62, 2.82; H-7, 6.49; H-15, 1.36(d, *J*=7Hz); OCH_3, 3.87; OCH_3, 3.92; OH, 3.41(d); and OH, 13.22ppm.

^{13}C NMR:

($CDCl_3$) C-1, 13.9; C-3, 67.2; C-4, 36.7; C-5, 147.4; C-6, 154.7; C-7, 101.8; C-8,

155.0; C-9, 181.3; C-10, 190.5; C-11, 114.1; C-12, 109.9; C-13, 149.6; C-14, 141.4; C-15, 23.9; 6-OCH_3, 56.2; and 8-OCH_3, 56.5ppm.

Mass Data:
Found: 306.111*m/e*; $C_{16}H_{18}O_6$ requires 306.110.

Reference
P. S. Steyn, P. L. Wessels, and W. F. O. Marasas; Pigments from *Fusarium moniliforme* Sheldon: Structure and ^{13}C Nuclear Magnetic Resonance Assignments of an Azaanthraquinone and Three Naphthoquinones; Tetrahedron, Vol. 35, pp. 1551-1555 (1979).

Common/Systematic Name

Marticin

Molecular Formula/Molecular Weight

$C_{18}H_{16}O_9$; MW = 376.07943

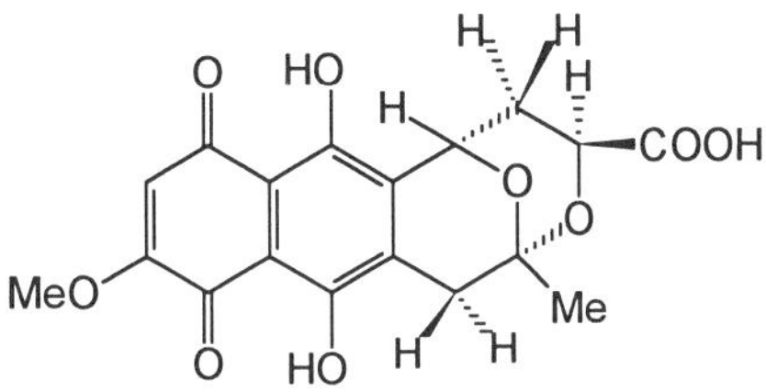

General Characteristics

Red crystals from benzene; 180-182°C.

Fungal Source

Fusarium solani isolated from diseased citrus roots.

Isolation/Purification

Culture filtrates were extracted with ethyl acetate; the extract was dried with anhydrous sodium sulfate and reduced in volume. The extract was fractionated by preparative TLC on silica gel HF_{254} (type 60) plates. Marticin was crystallized from benzene.

Biological Activity

Phytotoxic.

Spectral Data

UV:

λ_{max}^{EtOH} 229, 304, 474, 501, and 536nm.

^1H NMR:

($CDCl_3$) 1.68(s, 3-Me); 2.73(d, *J*=19.0Hz, H-4eq); 3.12(d, *J*=19.0Hz, H-4ax); 2.10(m, H-11eq); 2.86(m, H-11ax); 5.42(d, H-12ax, 9.0Hz (H-11ax); 3.94(7-OMe); 4.58(m, H 1eq); 6.18(H-8); 12.53(OH); and 12.93ppm (OH).

Mass Spectrum:

376*m/e* (M^+).

TLC Data

Solvent system A, C_6H_6-nitromethane-HOAc (75:25:2, v/v/v); B, $CHCl_3$-EtOAc-hexane-HOAc (10:5:5:0.3, v/v/v); C, hexane-Me_2CO-HOAc (15:5:0.3, v/v/v); D, C_6H_6-EtOAc-iso-PrOH-HOAc (145:50:5:1, v/v/v); E. C_6H_6-hexane-Me_2CO (9:9:2, v/v/v) or (3:6:1, v/v/v); F, C_6H_6-Me_2CO (17:3, v/v): G, hexane-Me_2CO-HOAc (15:5:0.1, v/v/v); H, C_6H_6-EtOAc-iso-PrOH-HOAc (16:3:1:0.1, v/v/v). R_f for marticin: A=0.12; B=0.13; C=0.10, and D=0.17. Systems E-H were used for isolation (preparative TLC). Systems E-H were used for isolation (preparative TLC).

Reference

J. H. Tatum and R. A. Baker; Naphthoquinones Produced by *Fusarium solani* Isolated from Citrus; Phytochemistry, Vol. 22, pp. 543-547(1983).

Common/Systematic Name

Isomarticin

Molecular Formula/Molecular Weight

$C_{18}H_{16}O_9$; MW = 376.07943

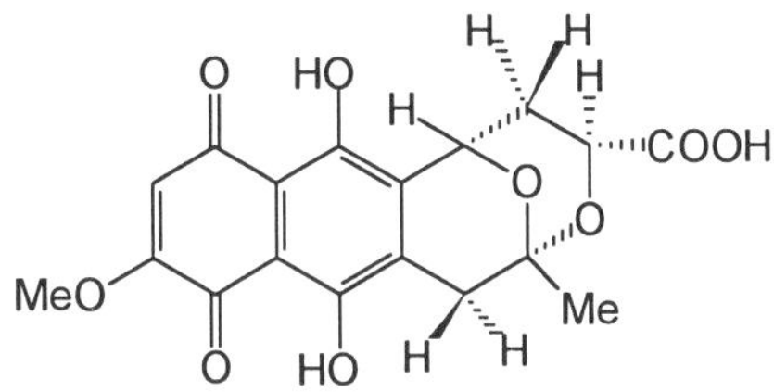

General Characteristics

Red crystals from methanol; mp., 160-163°C.

Fungal Source

Fusarium solani isolated from diseased citrus roots.

Isolation/Purification

Culture filtrates were extracted with ethyl acetate; the extract was dried with anhydrous sodium sulfate and reduced in volume. The extract was fractionated by preparative TLC on silica gel HF_{254} (type 60) plates. Isomarticin was crystallized from methanol.

Biological Activity

Phytotoxic.

Spectral Data

UV/Visible:

λ_{max}^{EtOH} 229, 304, 474, 501, and 536nm.

^1H NMR:

($CDCl_3$) 1.70(s, 3-Me); 3.0(d, *J*=19.0Hz, H-4eq); 3.13(d, *J*=19.0 Hz, H-4ax); 2.04(m, H-11eq); 2.30(3-OH); 5.58(d, H-11ax); 4.31(dd, *J*=12.0Hz, 11eq, 3.0Hz, 11ax); 6.20(H-8); 12.51(OH); and 12.91ppm (OH).

Mass Spectrum:

376*m/e* (M^+).

TLC Data

Solvent system A, C_6H_6-nitromethane-HOAc (75:25:2, v/v/v); B, $CHCl_3$-EtOAc-hexane-HOAc (10:5:5:0.3, v/v/v); C, hexane-Me_2CO-HOAc (15:5:0.3, v/v/v); D, C_6H_6-EtOAc-iso-PrOH-HOAc (145:50:5:1, v/v/v); E, C_6H_6-hexane-Me_2CO (9:9:2, v/v/v) or (3:6:1, v/v/v); F, C_6H_6-Me_2CO (17:3, v/v): G, hexane-Me_2CO-HOAc (15:5:0.1, v/v/v); H, C_6H_6-EtOAc-iso-PrOH-HOAc (16:3:1:0.1, v/v/v). R_f for isomarticin: A=0.11; B=0.12; C=0.09; and D=0.15. Systems E-H were used for isolation (preparative TLC).

References

S. Nemec, R. A. Baker, and J. H. Tatum; Toxicity of Dihydrofusarubin and Isomarticin from *Fusarium solani* to Citrus Seedlings; Soil Biol. Biochem., Vol. 20, pp. 493-499 (1988).

J. H. Tatum and R. A. Baker; Naphthoquinones Produced by *Fusarium solani* Isolated from Citrus; Phytochemistry, Vol. 22, pp. 543-547(1983).

Common/Systematic Name

5,8-Dihydroxy-6-methoxy-3-methyl-2-aza-9,10-anthracenedione

Molecular Formula/Molecular Weight

$C_{15}H_{11}NO_5$; MW = 285.06372

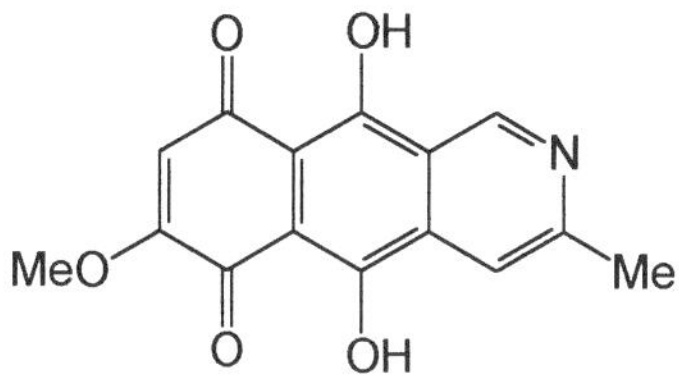

General Characteristics

Red crystals from benzene/methylene chloride; mp., 231-235°C.

Fungal Source

Fusarium solani isolated from diseased citrus roots.

Isolation/Purification

Culture filtrates were extracted with ethyl acetate; the extract was dried with anhydrous sodium sulfate and reduced in volume. The extract was fractionated by preparative TLC on silica gel HF_{254} (type 60) plates. 5,8-Dihydroxy-6-methoxy-3-methyl-2-aza-9,10-anthracenedione was crystallized from benzene/methylene chloride.

Biological Activity

Suspected phytotoxin.

Spectral Data

UV:

λ_{max}^{EtOH} 253, 322, 476, 500, and 530nm.

^{1}H NMR:

($CDCl_3$) 2.81(s, 3-Me); 7.96(H-4); 4.02(7-OMe); 9.50(H-1); 6.75(H-8); 13.10(OH); and 13.50ppm (OH).

Mass Spectrum:

285*m/e* (M^+).

TLC Data

Solvent system A, C_6H_6-nitromethane-HOAc (75:25:2, v/v/v); B, $CHCl_3$-EtOAc-hexane-HOAc (10:5:5:0.3, v/v/v); C, hexane-Me_2CO-HOAc (15:5:0.3, v/v/v); D, C_6H_6-EtOAc-iso-PrOH-HOAc (145:50:5:1, v/v/v); E, C_6H_6-hexane-Me_2CO (9:9:2, v/v/v) or (3:6:1, v/v/v); F, C_6H_6-Me_2CO (17:3, v/v): G, hexane-Me_2CO-HOAc (15:5:0.1, v/v/v); H, C_6H_6-EtOAc-iso-PrOH-HOAc (16:3:1:0.1, v/v/v). R_f for 5,8-dihydroxy-6-methoxy-3-methyl-2-*aza*-9,10-anthracenedione: A=0.31; B=0.38; C=0.35; and D=0.43. Systems E-H were used for isolation (preparative TLC).

Reference

J. H. Tatum and R. A. Baker; Naphthoquinones Produced by *Fusarium solani* Isolated from Citrus; Phytochemistry, Vol. 22, pp. 543-547(1983).

Common/Systematic Name

rel-(3*R*,4a*R*)-5,10-Dioxo-3,4,4a,5,10,10a-hexahydro-7-methoxy-3-methyl-3,6,9-trihydroxy-1*H*-naphtho[2,3-c]pyran

Molecular Formula/Molecular Weight

$C_{15}H_{16}O_7$; MW = 308.08960

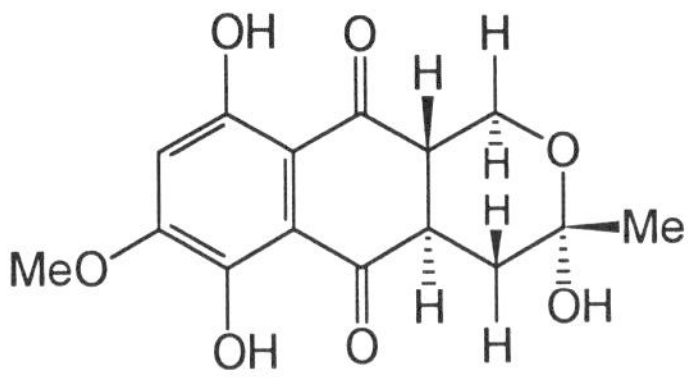

General Characteristics

Pale red crystals from ethyl acetate or methylene chloride; 153-154°C.

Fungal Source

Fusarium solani isolated from diseased citrus roots.

Isolation/Purification

Culture filtrates were extracted with ethyl acetate; the extract was dried with anhydrous sodium sulfate and reduced in volume. The extract was fractionated by preparative TLC on silica gel HF_{254} (type 60) plates. *rel*-(3*R*,4a*R*)-5,10-Dioxo-3,4,4a,5,10,10a-hexahydro-7-methoxy-3-methyl-3,6,9-trihydroxy-1*H*-naphtho[2,3-c]pyran was crystallized from ethyl acetate or methylene chloride.

Biological Activity

Suspected phytotoxin.

Spectral Data

UV:

λ_{max}^{EtOH} 214, 245, 277, 304, and 394nm.

^{1}H NMR:

($CDCl_3$) 1.54(s, 3-Me); 1.69(dd, *J*=13.5Hz, 4eq, 11.0Hz, 4a); 2.42(dd, 13.5Hz, 4ax, 3.5Hz, 4a); 2.97(m, 13.5Hz, 4a, 11.0Hz, 1ax, 5.5Hz, 1eq); 2.02(d, 2.4Hz); 3.43(m, *J*=13.5Hz, 10a, 11.0Hz, 4ax, 3.5Hz, 4eq); 3.97(7-OMe); 4.22(m, H-1ax); 4.22(H-1eq); 6.68(H-8); 12.05(OH); and 12.22ppm (OH).

Mass Spectrum:

308*m/e* (M^+).

TLC Data

Solvent system A, C_6H_6-nitromethane-HOAc (75:25:2, v/v/v); B, $CHCl_3$-EtOAc-hexane-HOAc (10:5:5:0.3, v/v/v); C, hexane-Me_2CO-HOAc (15:5:0.3, v/v/v); D, C_6H_6-EtOAc-iso-PrOH-HOAc (145:50:5:1, v/v/v); E, C_6H_6-hexane-Me_2CO (9:9:2, v/v/v) or (3:6:1, v/v/v); F, C_6H_6-Me_2CO (17:3, v/v); G, hexane-Me_2CO-HOAc (15:5:0.1, v/v/v); H, C_6H_6-EtOAc-iso-PrOH-HOAc (16:3:1:0.1, v/v/v). R_f for *rel*-(3*R*,4a*R*)-5,10-dioxo-3,4,4a,5,10,10a-hexahydro-7-methoxy-3-methyl-3,6,9-trihydroxy-1*H*-naphtho[2,3-c]pyran: A=0.21; B=0.27; C=0.21; and D=0.38. Systems E-H were used for isolation (preparative TLC).

Reference

J. H. Tatum and R. A. Baker; Naphthoquinones Produced by *Fusarium solani* Isolated from Citrus; Phytochemistry, Vol. 22, pp. 543-547(1983).

Common/Systematic Name

rel-(3*R*,4a*R*,10a*S*)-5,10-Dioxo-3,4,4a,5,10,10a-hexahydro-7-methoxy-3-methyl-3,6,9-trihydroxy-1*H*-naphtho[2,3-c]pyran

Molecular Formula/Molecular Weight

$C_{15}H_{16}O_7$; MW = 308.08960

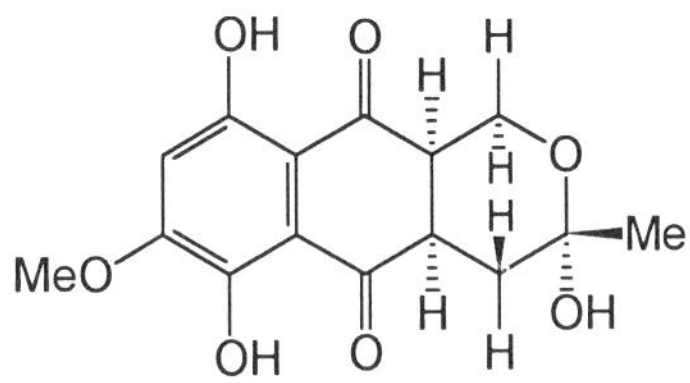

General Characteristics

Yellow crystals from methanol; mp., 126-129°C.

Fungal Source

Fusarium solani isolated from diseased citrus roots.

Isolation/Purification

Culture filtrates were extracted with ethyl acetate; the extract was dried with anhydrous sodium sulfate and reduced in volume. The extract was fractionated by preparative TLC on silica gel HF_{254} (type 60) plates. *rel*-(3*R*,4a*R*,10a*S*)-5,10-Dioxo-3,4,4a,5,10,10a-hexahydro-7-methoxy-3-methyl-3,6,9-trihydroxy-1*H*-naphtho[2,3-*c*]pyran was crystallized from methanol.

Biological Activity

Suspected phytotoxin.

Spectral Data

UV:

λ_{max}^{EtOH} 212, 245, 277, 304, and 394nm.

^{1}H NMR:

($CDCl_3$) 1.47(s, 3-Me); 1.63(t, *J*=13.0Hz, 4eq); 2.04(dd, *J*=13.0Hz, 4ax, *J*=4.0Hz, 4a); 2.99(m, H-10a); 2.02(3-OH); 3.62(m, H-4a); 4.06(dd, *J*=11.5Hz, 1eq, *J*=3.0Hz, 10a); 4.61(d, *J*=11.5Hz, 1ax); 6.75(H-8); 12.37(OH); and 12.69ppm (OH).

Mass Spectrum:

308*m/e* (M^+).

TLC Data

Solvent system A, C_6H_6-nitromethane-HOAc (75:25:2, v/v/v); B, $CHCl_3$-EtOAc-hexane-HOAc (10:5:5:0.3, v/v/v); C, hexane-Me_2CO-HOAc (15:5:0.3, v/v/v); D, C_6H_6-EtOAc-iso-PrOH-HOAc (145:50:5:1, v/v/v); E, C_6H_6-hexane-Me_2CO (9:9:2, v/v/v) or (3:6:1, v/v/v); F, C_6H_6-Me_2CO (17:3, v/v): G, hexane-Me_2CO-HOAc (15:5:0.1, v/v/v); H, C_6H_6-EtOAc-iso-PrOH-HOAc (16:3:1:0.1, v/v/v). R_f for *rel*-(3*R*,4a*R*,10a*S*)-5,10-dioxo-3,4,4a,5,10,10a-hexahydro-7-methoxy-3-methyl-3,6,9-trihydroxy-1*H*-naphtho[2,3-c]pyran: A=0.18; B=0.21; C=0.17; and D=0.33. Systems E-H were used for isolation (preparative TLC).

Reference

J. H. Tatum and R. A. Baker; Naphthoquinones Produced by *Fusarium solani* Isolated from Citrus; Phytochemistry, Vol. 22, pp. 543-547(1983).

Common/Systematic Name

rel-(3*R*,4a*R*,10a*R*)-5,10-Dioxo-3,4,4a,5,10,10a-hexahydro-3,7-dimethoxy-3-methyl-6,9-dihydroxy-1*H*-naphtho[2,3-*c*]pyran

Molecular Formula/Molecular Weight

$C_{16}H_{18}O_7$; MW = 322.10525

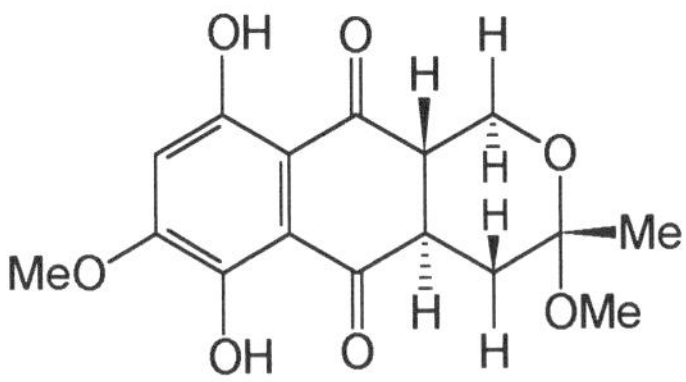

General Characteristics

Yellow crystals from methanol; mp., 176-180°C.

Fungal Source

Fusarium solani isolated from diseased citrus roots.

Isolation/Purification

Culture filtrates were extracted with ethyl acetate; the extract was dried with anhydrous sodium sulfate and reduced in volume. The extract was fractionated by preparative TLC on silica gel HF_{254} (type 60) plates. *rel*-(3*R*,4a*R*,10a*R*)-5,10-dioxo-3,4,4a,5,10,10a-hexahydro-3,7-dimethoxy-3-methyl-6,9-dihydroxy-1*H*-naphtho[2,3-*c*]pyran was crystallized from methanol.

Biological Activity

Suspected phytotoxin.

Spectral Data

UV:

λ_{max}^{EtOH} 210, 245, 277, 304, and 394nm.

^{1}H NMR:

($CDCl_3$) 1.47(s, 3-Me); 1.69(dd, 13.5Hz, 4eq, 11.0Hz, 4a); 2.42(dd, 13.5Hz, 4ax, 3.5Hz, 4a); 2.97(m, 13.5Hz, 4a, 11.0Hz, 1ax, 5.5Hz, 1eq); 3.24(3-OMe); 3.43(m, 13.5Hz, 10a, 11.0Hz, 4ax, 3.5Hz, 4eq); 3.98(7-OMe); 3.88(dd, 12.0Hz, 1eq, 11.0Hz, 10a); and 4.22ppm (dd, 12.0Hz, 1ax, 5.5Hz, 10a).

Mass Spectrum:

322*m/e* (M^+).

TLC Data

Solvent system A, C_6H_6 nitromethane-HOAc (75:25:2, v/v/v); B, $CHCl_3$-EtOAc-hexane-HOAc (10:5:5:0.3, v/v/v); C, hexane-Me_2CO-HOAc (15:5:0.3, v/v/v); D, C_6H_6-EtOAc-iso-PrOH-HOAc (145:50:5:1, v/v/v); E, C_6H_6-hexane-Me_2CO (9:9:2, v/v/v) or (3:6:1, v/v/v); F, C_6H_6-Me_2CO (17:3, v/v): G, hexane-Me_2CO-HOAc (15:5:0.1); H, C_6H_6-EtOAc-iso-PrOH-HOAc (16:3:1:0.1, v/v/v). R_f for *rel*-(3*R*,4a*R*,10a*R*)-5,10-dioxo-3,4,4a,5,10,10a-hexahydro-3,7-dimethoxy-3-methyl-6,9-dihydroxy-1*H*-naphtho[2,3-c]pyran: A=0.43; B=0.57; C=0.35; and D=0.63. Systems E-H were used for isolation (preparative TLC).

Reference

J. H. Tatum and R. A. Baker; Naphthoquinones Produced by *Fusarium solani* Isolated from Citrus; Phytochemistry, Vol. 22, pp. 543-547(1983).

Common/Systematic Name

Anhydrofusarubin lactone

5,10-Dihydroxy-7-methoxy-3-methyl-1*H*-naphtho[2,3-*c*]pyran-1,6,9-trione

Molecular Formula/Molecular Weight

$C_{15}H_{10}O_7$; MW = 302.04265

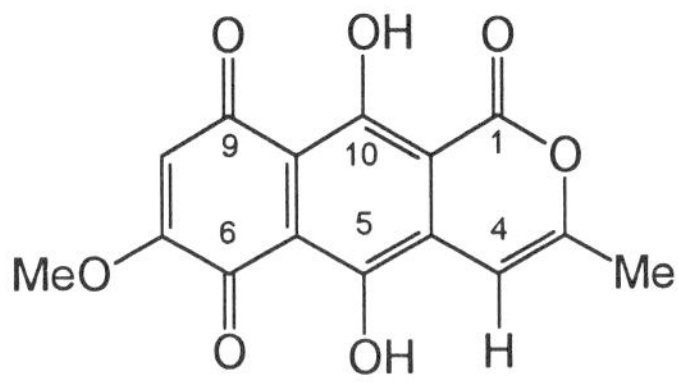

General Characteristics

Dark crystals from $CHCl_3$; mp., 300°C.

Fungal Source

Fusarium solani, a common soil fungus in citrus groves which can be readily isolated from vascular tissue of fibrous roots from citrus trees affected with blight. First isolated from *Nectria haematococca.*

Isolation/Purification

Column chromatography using Kieselgel 60; column was deactivated with HOAc and H_2O, washed with Me_2CO and then $CHCl_3$; and then eluted with $CHCl_3$, $CHCl_3$-Me_2CO, 2, 5, 10, and 15%.

Biological Activity

Suspected phytotoxin.

Spectral Data

UV:

λ_{max}^{MeOH} 255(log ϵ=4.25), 312(3.55), 330 inf (3.46), 508 inf (3.72), 536(3.77), 576(3.72), and 612nm (3.49).

IR:

(KBr) 1745, 1650sh, 1610, 1582, 1532, 1470, 1435, 1400, 1375sh, 1350, 1300, 1275sh, 1260, 1230, 1190, 1175, 1155, 1135, 1115, 1060, 1025w, 980, 955, 935w, 875, 865sh, 845sh, 800, 780, 725, and 710cm^{-1}.

^1H NMR:

($CDCl_3$) 2.38(3H, s, Me-3); 3.97(3H, s, MeO-7); 6.30(1H, s, H-8); 6.84(1H, s, H-4); 12.75(1H, s, OH-5); 14.28(1H, s, OH-10); addition of D_2O removed the OH signals at 12.75 and 14.75ppm.

Mass Spectrum:
302(M^+, 100%) and 287*m/e* (14.5).

TLC Data

Solvent system (A) C_6H_6-$MeNO_2$-HOAc (75:25:2, v/v/v), (B) C_6H_6-Me_2CO-HOAc (40:10:1, v/v/v), (C) $CHCl_3$-HOAc (200:1, v/v), (D) $CHCl_3$-CH_3NO_2 (9:1, v/v). TLC plates were silica gel GF (analytical) and silica gel HF 60 (preparative).

Reference

J. H. Tatum and R. A. Baker; Naphthoquinones Produced by *Fusarium solani* Isolated from Citrus; Phytochemistry, Vol. 22, pp. 543-547(1983).

Common/Systematic Name

1,5,10-Trihydroxy-7-methoxy-3-methyl-1*H*-naphtho[2,3-*c*]pyran-6,9-dione

Molecular Formula/Molecular Weight

$C_{15}H_{12}O_7$; MW = 304.05830

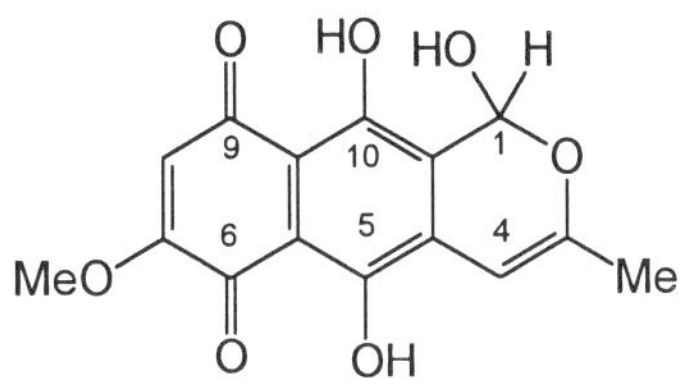

General Characteristics

Deep purple crystals from acetone; mp., 245 °C on a preheated block.

Fungal Source

Fusarium solani, a common soil fungus in citrus groves which can be readily isolated from vascular tissue of fibrous roots from citrus trees affected with blight.

Isolation/Purification

Column chromatography using Kieselgel 60; column was deactivated with HOAc and H_2O, washed with Me_2CO and then $CHCl_3$; and then eluted with $CHCl_3$, $CHCl_3$-Me_2CO, 2, 5, 10, and 15%.

Biological Activity

Suspected phytotoxin.

Spectral Data

UV:

λ_{max}^{MeOH} 228(log ϵ=4.06), 263(4.05), 278sh (4.01), 343(3.23), 509(3.80), 535(3.87), and 572nm (3.71).

IR:

(KBr) 3425s, 1600, 1580, 1440, 1400, 1385sh, 1280sh, 1250, 1225sh, 1190w, 1155, 1110w, 1070, 1040, 990, 955, 890, 860br, and 805cm^{-1}.

^{1}H NMR:

($CDCl_3$) 2.18(3H, s, Me-3); 3.94(3H, s, MeO-7); 6.26(1H, s, H-8); 6.45(1H, s, H-4); 6.73(1H, s, H-1); 12.85(1H, s, OH-5); 13.25(1H, s, H-10); addition of D_2O removed the OH signals at 12.85 and 13.25ppm.

$(CD_3)_2SO$ 2.04(3H, s, Me-3); 3.84(3H, s, MeO-7); 6.10(1H, s, H-8); 6.20(1H, s, H-4); 6.55(1H, d, *J*=6, H-1); 6.82(1H, d, *J*=6, OH-1); 12.76(1H, s, OH-5); 13.22(1H, s, OH-10). Addition of D_2O removed the OH signals at 6.82, 12.76, 13.22, and the doublet at 6.55ppm appeared as a singlet at 6.63ppm.

Mass Spectrum:
LREIMS: 304(M^+, 31.4%), 289(11), and 261(100); HREIMS: requires 304.0581, found 304.0590.

Reference

J. H. Tatum and R. A. Baker; Naphthoquinones Produced by *Fusarium solani* Isolated from Citrus; Phytochemistry, Vol. 22, pp. 543-547(1983).

Common/Systematic Name

5,10-Dihydroxy-1,7-dimethoxy-3-methyl-1*H*-naphtho[2,3-*c*]pyran-6,9-dione

Molecular Formula/Molecular Weight

$C_{16}H_{14}O_7$; MW = 318.07395

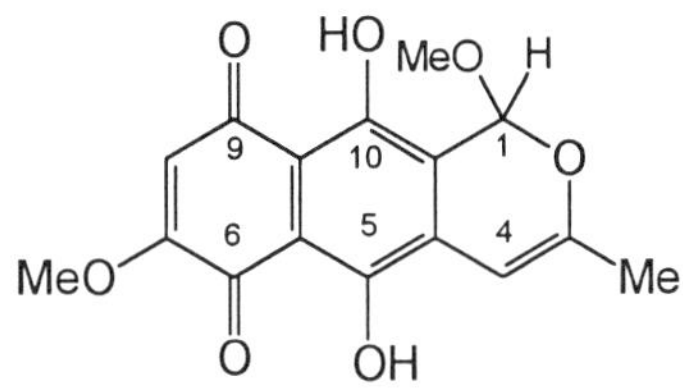

General Characteristics

Purple crystals from benzene; mp., 190°C on a preheated block.

Fungal Source

Fusarium solani, a common soil fungus in citrus groves which can be readily isolated from vascular tissue of fibrous roots from citrus trees affected with blight.

Isolation/Purification

Column chromatography using Kieselgel 60; column was deactivated with HOAc and H_2O, washed with Me_2CO and then $CHCl_3$; and then eluted with $CHCl_3$, $CHCl_3$-Me_2CO, 2, 5, 10, and 15%.

Biological Activity

Suspected phytotoxin.

Spectral Data

UV:

λ_{max}^{MeOH} 228(log ϵ=4.01), 263(3.98), 278sh (3.96), 342(3.15), 507(3.68), 535(3.75), and 572nm (3.63).

IR:

(KBr) 1605, 1585, 1430, 1380, 1310w, 1250, 1220, 1185, 1150, 1080, 1050, 1015, 955, 885w, 865w, 815, and 790cm^{-1} sh.

^{1}H NMR:

($CDCl_3$) 2.15(3H, s, Me-3); 3.62(3H, s, MeO-1); 3.93(3H, s, MeO-7); 6.24(1H, s); 6.25(1H, s); 6.29(1H, s); 12.80(1H, s, OH-5); and 13.24ppm (1H, s, OH-10); addition of D_2O removed signals at 12.80 and 13.24ppm.

Mass Spectrum:

LREIMS: 318(M^+, 34.7%), 287(88.9), and 286*m/e* (100): HREIMS: $C_{16}H_{14}O_7$ requires 318.0738; found: 318.0764*m/e*.

TLC Data

Solvent system (A) C_6H_6-$MeNO_2$-HOAc (75:25:2, v/v/v), (B) C_6H_6-Me_2CO-HOAc (40:10:1, v/v/v), (C) $CHCl_3$-HOAc (200:1, v/v), (D) $CHCl_3$-CH_3NO_2 (9:l, v/v). TLC plates were silica gel GF (analytical) and silica gel HF 60 (preparative).

Reference

J. H. Tatum, R. A. Baker, and R. E. Berry; Metabolites of *Fusarium solani*; Phytochemistry, Vol. 28, pp. 283-284(1989).

Common/Systematic Name

2,3-Dihydro-5,8-dihydroxy-6-methoxy-2-hydroxymethyl-3-(2-hydroxypropyl)-1,4-naphthalenedione

Molecular Formula/Molecular Weight

$C_{15}H_{18}O_7$; MW = 310.10525

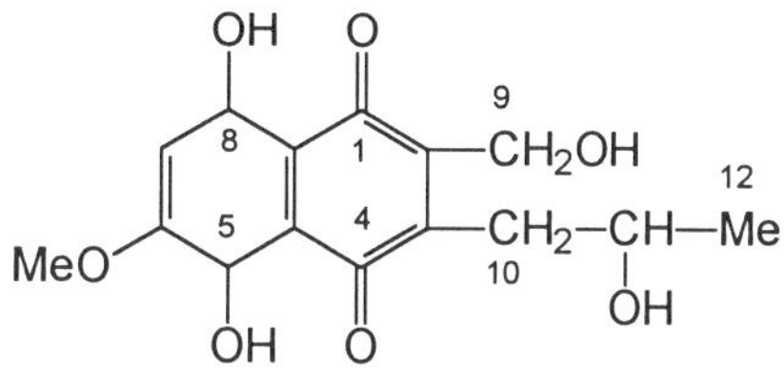

General Characteristics

Light red crystals from EtOAc; mp., 135°C on preheated block.

Fungal Source

Fusarium solani, a common soil fungus in citrus groves which can be readily isolated from vascular tissue of fibrous roots from citrus trees affected with blight.

Isolation/Purification

Column chromatography using Kieselgel 60; column was deactivated with HOAc and H_2O, washed with Me_2CO and then $CHCl_3$; and then eluted with $CHCl_3$, $CHCl_3$-Me_2CO, 2, 5, 10, and 15%.

Biological Activity

Suspected phytotoxin.

Spectral Data

UV/Visible:

λ_{max}^{MeOH} 213, 244, 277, 303 sh, 391, and 400nm (sh) (log ϵ=3.98, 4.21, 3.83, 3.64, 3.88, and 3.83 respectively).

IR:

(KBr) 3300, 1610, 1570 sh, 1470, 1430, 1400, 1380, 1315, 1290, 1270, 1220, 1205, 1175, 1125, 1095, 1065, 1040, 1020, 1000 sh, 990, 925, 900, 870 w, 825, and 805cm^{-1} (sh).

^{1}H NMR:

($CDCl_3$) 1.22(3H, d, *J*=6Hz, Me-12); 1.79(1H, m, H-10); 1.96(1H, m, H-10); 2.42(1H, s, OH); 2.90(1H, m, H-2); 3.28(1H, m, H-3); 3.86(2H, m); 3.95(3H, s, MeO-6); 4.24(1H, dd, *J*=11.2, 2.5Hz); 6.70(1H, s, H-7); 12.22(1H, s, OH-5); and

12.58ppm (1H, s, OH-8); addition of D_2O removed the OH signals at 2.42, 12.22, and 12.58ppm.

When 2,3-dihydro-5,8-dihydroxy-6-methoxy-2-hydroxymethyl-3-(2-hydroxypropyl)-1,4-naphthalenedione was treated with D_2O the hydroxyls at 12.58, 12.22, and 2.42ppm disappeared. This treatment also caused the H-1 distorted dd at 4.24ppm to become a sharp dd, J=11.2, 2.5Hz and the 2H multiplet at 3.86ppm became rounded with a projecting dd out the top (J=11.2, 4.5Hz) which indicated a CH_2 coupled to a hydroxyl. Decoupling at 4.24ppm changed the 2H multiplet at 3.86ppm to a multiplet and the 1H multiplet at 2.90ppm to a multiplet which showed that they were coupled. Decoupling at 3.86ppm changed the dd at 4.24ppm to a broad singlet, the 1H multiplet at 2.90 became a dd (J=6.2, 2.5Hz), the 1H multiplet at 1.96 became a dd (J=15, 7.5Hz), the 1H multiplet at 1.79 became a broad d (J=15Hz) and the 3H doublet at 1.26ppm became a singlet. The C-9 carbon was CH_2-OH at 4.24ppm, 3.86ppm and was split by a single hydrogen at 2.90ppm on C-2 and distorted by the hydroxyl. The other H at 3.86ppm was coupled to CH_2 at 1.96 and 1.79ppm and a methyl at 1.26ppm. Decoupling of the 1H multiplet at 3.28ppm changed the multiplet at 2.90ppm to a dd (J=4.5, 2.5Hz), the multiplet at 1.96ppm became a broad doublet (J=15Hz) and the multiplet at 1.79ppm became a dd (J=15, 10Hz). Decoupling of the 1H multiplet at 2.90ppm caused the dd at 4.22ppm to become a doublet (J=11.2Hz) and the multiplet at 3.86ppm to show a distorted doublet (J=11.2Hz). The C-10 carbon was CH_2 at 1.96, 1.79ppm which was attached to the C-3 position and was split by the C-3 hydrogen at 3.28ppm and the C-11 hydrogen at 3.86ppm. The C-12 was a methyl that was split by the C-11 hydrogen. The H-2 and H-3 hydrogens were shown to be coupled and established their relative positions. The small coupling constant of 6.2Hz indicated they were in axial-equatorial position. The methoxy resonance at 3.95ppm was assigned to the 6 position. The lone unsplit hydrogen at 6.70ppm was at the C-7 position on the aromatic portion of the ring.

Mass Spectrum:
LREIMS: 292*m/e* (M^+ - 18); CIMS: (isobutane) 311*m/e* (M^++1); $C_{15}H_{18}O_7$ requires 310.1051; found: 310.1046*m/e*.

TLC Data

System (A) $CHCl_3$-nitromethane-MeOH-HOAc (170:20:6:1, v/v/v/v); (B) $CHCl_3$-CH_2Cl_2-HOAc-MeOH (140:50:4:4, v/v/v/v). TLC plates were silica gel GF (analytical) and silica gel HF 60 (preparative).

Reference

J. H. Tatum, R. A. Baker, and R. E. Berry; Metabolites of *Fusarium solani*; Phytochemistry, Vol. 24, pp. 3019-3021(1985).

Common/Systematic Name

2,3-Dihydro-5-hydroxy-4-hydroxymethyl-8-methoxynaphtho[l,2-*b*]furan-6,9-dione

Molecular Formula/Molecular Weight

$C_{15}H_{14}O_6$; MW = 290.07904

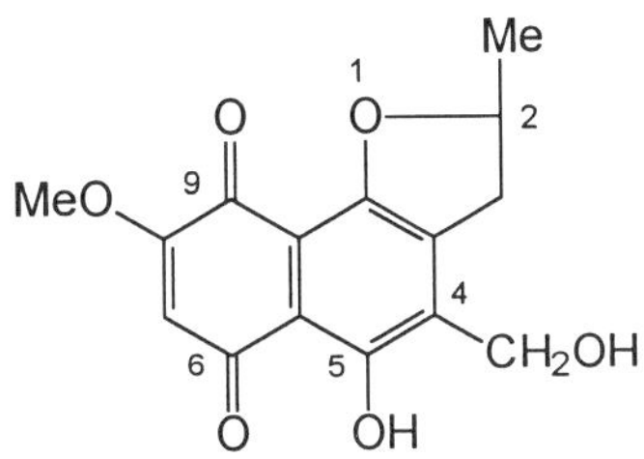

General Characteristics

Red crystals from CH_2Cl_2-hexane; mp., 202-203°C.

Fungal Source

Fusarium solani, a common soil fungus in citrus groves which can be readily isolated from vascular tissue of fibrous roots from citrus trees affected with blight.

Isolation/Purification

Column chromatography using Kieselgel 60; column was deactivated with HOAc and H_2O, washed with Me_2CO and then $CHCl_3$; and then eluted with $CHCl_3$, $CHCl_3$-Me_2CO, 2, 5, 10, and 15%.

Biological Activity

Suspected phytotoxin.

Spectral Data

UV:

λ_{max}^{MeOH} 223, 297, 485, 502, and 538nm (log ϵ=4.06, 3.62, 3.50, 3.47, and 3.17, respectively).

IR:

(KBr) 3490, 1660, 1625, 1585, 1420, 1400, 1390sh, 1355, 1315, 1220, 1160, 1075, 1040, 1015, 955, 915, 885, 855, 830, 815, and 780cm^{-1}.

^{1}H NMR:

($CDCl_3$) 1.59(3H, d, *J*=6Hz, 12-Me); 2.67(1H, t, *J*=6Hz, CH_2 OH); 2.92(1H, dd, *J*=17, 6.5Hz, H-3); 3.46(1H, dd, *J*=17, 9Hz, H-3); 3.90(3H, s, MeO-8); 4.74(2H, d, *J*=6Hz, H-4); 5.21(1H, m, H-2); 6.07(1H, s, H-7); and 13.60ppm (1H, s, C-5); addition of D_2O removed the OH signals at 2.67 and 13.60ppm. The NMR spectrum had an eight line multiplet with 1H at (5.21ppm). When the spectrum was decoupled at 5.21ppm and the 1H dd at 3.46ppm (J=17.9 Hz) became a d (J=17Hz), the 1H dd at 2.92ppm (J=17, 6.5Hz) became a doublet (J=17Hz) and the 3H doublet at 1.59ppm became a singlet. Thus, a single hydrogen was split by a CH_2 and a methyl. Decoupling the 2H doublet at 4.8ppm (J=6Hz) caused the triplet at 2.67ppm (J=6Hz) to become a singlet. A CH_2 was split by a single H. Decoupling the 3H doublet at 1.6ppm caused the multiplet at 5.21ppm to become a dd (J=9, 6.5Hz). When D_2O was added the singlet at 13.60ppm and the triplet at 2.67ppm disappeared and the 2H doublet at 4.74ppm became a singlet. This indicated a methyl C-H attached to CH_2 and an isolated CH_2 attached to a hydroxyl. A single unsplit hydrogen at 6.07ppm was on a quinone ring at C-7 while a singlet 3H at 3.90ppm indicated a methoxy at the C-8.

Mass Spectrum:

LREIMS: 290(M^+); $C_{15}H_{14}O_6$ requires 290.0789; found: 290.0795*m/e*.

TLC Data

System (A) $CHCl_3$-nitromethane-MeOH-HOAc (170:20:6:1, v/v/v/v); (B) $CHCl_3$-CH_2Cl_2-HOAc-MeOH (140:50:4:4, v/v/v/v). TLC plates were silica gel GF (analytical) and silica gel HF 60 (preparative).

Reference

J. H. Tatum, R. A. Baker, and R. E. Berry; Metabolites of *Fusarium solani*; Phytochemistry, Vol. 24, pp. 3019-3021(1985).

Common/Systematic Name

5,8-Dihydroxy-2-methoxy-6-hydroxymethyl-7-(2-hydroxypropyl)-l,4-naphthalenedione

Molecular Formula/Molecular Weight

$C_{15}H_{16}O_7$; MW = 308.08960

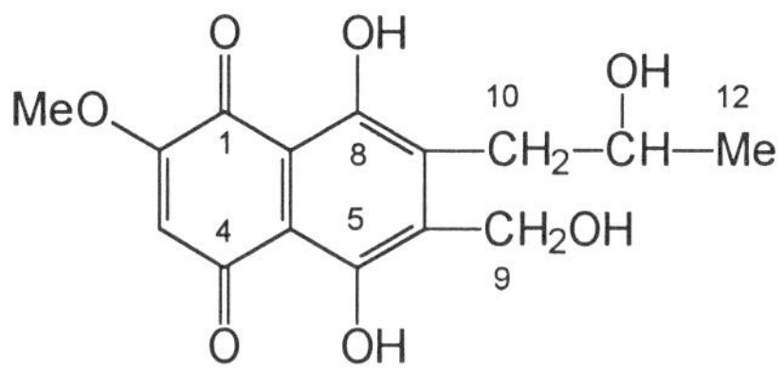

General Characteristics

Red crystals from EtOAc; mp., 206-212°C (dec).

Fungal Source

Fusarium solani, a common soil fungus in citrus groves which can be readily isolated from vascular tissue of fibrous roots from citrus trees affected with blight.

Isolation/Purification

Column chromatography using Kieselgel 60; column was deactivated with HOAc and H_2O, washed with Me_2CO and then $CHCl_3$; and then eluted with $CHCl_3$, $CHCl_3$-Me_2CO, 2, 5, 10, and 15%.

Biological Activity

Suspected phytotoxin.

Spectral Data

UV:

λ_{max}^{EtOH} 227, 306, 452 sh, 482, 509, and 546nm (log ϵ=4.38, 3.87, 3.56, 3.76, 3.80, and 3.59, respectively).

IR:

(KBr) 3330, 1615, 1550, 1450, 1420, 1390, 1295, 1265, 1245, 1220, 1205, 1180w, 1150, 1115, 1105, 1075, 1025, 1010, 995 w, 940 w, 855, 825, and 815cm^{-1} (sh).

^{1}H NMR:

($CDCl_3$) 1.39(3H, d, *J*=6Hz, Me-12); 2.86(1H, dd, *J*=13.5, 10Hz, H-10); 3.13(1H, dd, *J*=13.5, 3Hz, H-10); 3.95(3H, s, MeO-2); 4.16(1H, m, H-11); 4.63(1H, d, *J*=12Hz, H-9); 4.97(1H, d, *J*=12Hz, H-9); 6.20(1H, s, H-3); 12.86(1H, s, OH-5); and 13.35ppm (1H, s, OH-8); addition of D_2O removed the OH signals at 12.86 and 13.35, the other OH's were not observed.

Mass Spectrum:
LREIMS: 308(M^+); $C_{15}H_{16}O_7$ requires 308.0895; found: 308.0862*m/e*.

TLC Data

System (A) $CHCl_3$-nitromethane-MeOH-HOAc (170:20:6:1, v/v/v/v); (B) $CHCl_3$-CH_2Cl_2-HOAc-MeOH (140:50:4:4, v/v/v/v). TLC plates were silica gel GF (analytical) and silica gel HF 60 (preparative).

Reference

J. H. Tatum, R. A. Baker, and R. E. Berry; Metabolites of *Fusarium solani*; Phytochemistry, Vol. 24, pp. 3019-3021(1985).

Common/Systematic Name

2,5,8-Trihydroxy-6-methoxy-3-(2-oxopropyl)-1,4-naphthoquinone

Molecular Formula/Molecular Weight

$C_{14}H_{12}O_7$; MW = 292.05830

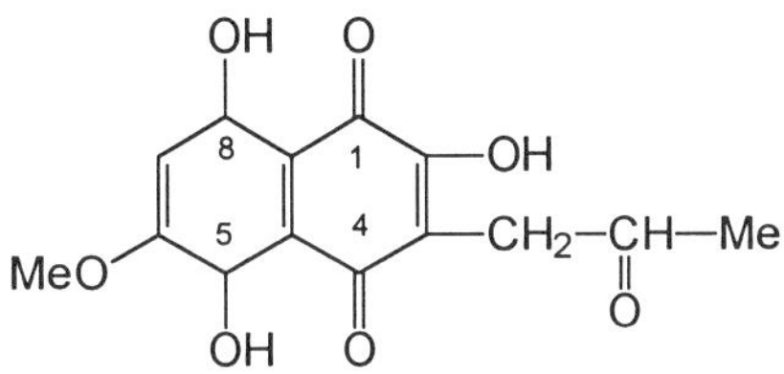

General Characteristics

Red crystals from $CHCl_3$; mp., 231-234°C.

Fungal Source

Fusarium solani.

Isolation/Purification

Isolated by preparative TLC using (A) C_6H_6-Me_2CO-HOAc (160:40:1, v/v/v), (B) chloroform or (C) benzene-nitromethane (3:1, v/v).

Biological Activity

Strongly phytotoxic to tomatoes and peas.

Spectral Data

UV:

λ_{max}^{MeOH} 212, 238, 261, 320, 470, 490 and 520nm (log ϵ=4.22. 4.14, 407, 3.88, 3.84, 3.82, and 3.66, respectively).

IR:

3300, 1710, 1630, 1600, 1570, 1480, 1430w, 1405, 1360, 1320, 1280, 1210, 1190w, 1085, 1045, 1025, 975, 885, 840w, 820sh, 810, and 760cm^{-1}.

Mass Spectrum:

LREIMS: 292(M^+); $C_{14}H_{12}O_7$ requires 292.0581; found: 292.0609*m/e*.

Reference

J. H. Tatum, R. A. Baker, and R. E. Berry; Naphthoquinones and Derivatives from *Fusarium*; Phytochemistry, Vol. 26, pp. 795-798(1987).

Common/Systematic Name

Nectriafurone

5,8-Dihydroxy-4,9-dione-3-(2-hydroxyethyl)-7-methoxynaphtho[2,3-*c*]furan

Molecular Formula/Molecular Weight

$C_{15}H_{12}O_7$; MW = 304.05830

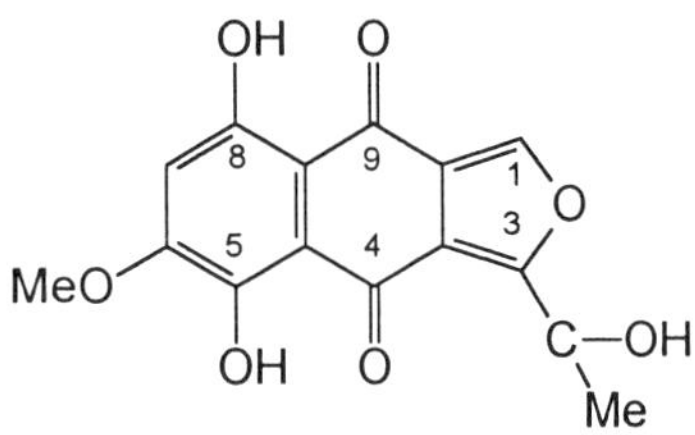

General Characteristics

Yellow-brown crystals from MeOH; mp., 222-225°C.

Fungal Source

Fusarium oxysporum and *Nectria haematococca*.

Isolation/Purification

Extracted with Me_2CO and the aqueous mixture obtained by vacuum concentration reextracted (x4) with EtOAc. The EtOAc residue was redissolved in $CHCl_3$ and applied to a Sephadex LH_{20} column packed in $CHCl_3$-MeOH (49:1, v/v) and the pigments eluted with $CHCl_3$-MeOH (49:1, v/v). The first pigments to be eluted gave a dark violet fraction containing anhydrofusarubin as the main product. Then a red fraction was obtained which was shown to be a mixture of javanicin, norjavanicin and anhydrojavanicin. Nectriafurone was isolated in a yellow fraction. It showed a strong fluorescence in UV which distinguished this pigment from the preceding ones. Next, anhydrofusarubin lactone was eluted as a purple fraction followed by fusarubin.

Biological Activity

Suspected phytotoxin; tested for antibiotic activity in a broth microdilution assay against *Staphylococcus aureus, Streptococcus pyogenes, Salmonella typhi, Serratia marcescens, Pseudomonas aeruginosa, Proteus vulgaris, Escherichia coli*, and *Klebsiella pneumoniae*. None of the organisms were inhibited at 128μg/ml.

Spectral Data

UV:

λ_{max}^{EtOH} 242, 258, 324, 444, and 468nm (log ϵ=4.26, 4.23, 3.84, 4.07, and 3.97, respectively).

IR:
(KBr) 3420, 3100, 1605, 1560, 1450, 1425, 1410, 1360w, 1300, 1250, 1215, 1175, 1160, 1110, 1007(sh), 1005, 975, 950, 900w, 865, 850, 820w, and 810cm^{-1}.

^{1}H NMR:
($CDCl_3$) 1.64(3H, d, *J*=7Hz, Me); 3.99(3H, s, MeO-6); 4.83(1H, d, *J*=7Hz, OH); 5.19(1H, m, 51, H); 6.70(1H, s, H-7); 8.08(1H, s, H-1); 13.07(1H, s, OH-5) and 13.39ppm (1H, s, OH-8).

Mass Spectrum:
LREIMS: 304*m/e* (M^+).

References

D. Parisot, M. Devys, J. P. Ferezou, and M. Barbier; Pigments from *Nectria haematococca*: Anhydrofusarubin Lactone and Nectriafurone; Phytochemistry, Vol. 22, pp. 1301-1303(1983).

J. H. Tatum, R. A. Baker, and R. E. Berry; Naphthoquinones and Derivatives from *Fusarium*; Phytochemistry, Vol. 26, pp. 795-798(1987).

Common/Systematic Name

8-*O*-Methyl ether nectriafurone

5-Hydroxy-4,9-dione-3-(2-hydroxyethyl)-7,8-dimethoxynaphtho[2,3-*c*]furan

Molecular Formula/Molecular Weight

$C_{16}H_{14}O_7$; MW = 318.07395

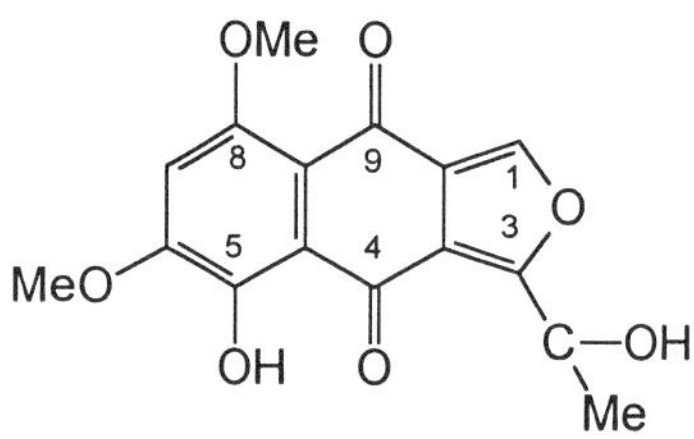

General Characteristics

Yellow-brown needles from MeOH; mp., 214-222°C (Dec.).

Fungal Source

Fusarium oxysporum.

Biological Activity

Suspected phytotoxin.

Spectral Data

UV:

λ_{max}^{EtOH} 236, 255(sh), 322, and 443nm (log ϵ=4.37, 4.21, 3.90, and 4.02, respectively).

IR:

(KBr) 3430, 3120, 1645, 1625, 1600, 1540, 1470, 1435, 1375, 1345, 1295(sh), 1265(sh), 1245, 1215, 1165, 1120(sh), 1110, 1070, 1035, 1005w, 955, 895, 855, 820, 810, and 765cm^{-1}.

^{1}H NMR:

($CDCl_3$) 1.64(3H, d, *J*=7Hz, Me); 4.00(3H, s, MeO-6); 4.03(3H, s, MeO-6); 4.03(3H, s, MeO-8); 4.78(1H, d, *J*=7Hz, OH); 5.19(1H, m, 51, H); 6.83(1H, s, H-7); 7.99(1H, s, H-1); and 13.30ppm (1H, s, OH-5).

Mass Spectrum:

LREIMS: 304*m/e* (M^+).

Reference

J. H. Tatum, R. A. Baker, and R. E. Berry; Naphthoquinones and Derivatives from *Fusarium*; Phytochemistry, Vol. 26, pp. 795-798(1987).

25

Miscellaneous Metabolites

Alternaric acid
Ampullicin
Isoampullicin
Acremoauxin A
2-(3,4-Dihydroxyhepta-1,5-dienyl)-6-hydroxybenzyl alcohol
Achaetolide
Achaetolidone
8-(10,11-Dihydroxyhexa-12-enyl)-3-hydroxydihydroisbenzylfuran
8-(10,11-Dihydroxyhexa-12-enyl)-3-hydroxydihydroisbenzylfuran (isomeric)
6-(1-Ethoxyethyl)-5-hydroxy-2,7-dimethoxy-1,4-naphthoquinone
6-(1-Hydroxyethyl)-5-hydroxy-2,7-dimethoxy-1,4-naphthoquinone
6-Ethyl-1-acetonyl-1,5-dihydroxy-2,7-dimethoxy-1,4-naphthoquinone
Pyriculariol
Sydonol (3-Hydroxy-4-(1-hydroxy-1,5-dimethylhexyl)benzyl alcohol)
Homotrichione
p-Toluquinone (Toluquinol)
Aszonapyrone A
Pyrenochaetic acid A
Pyrenochaetic acid B
Pyrenochaetic acid C
Candidusin A
Candidusin B
Ankalactone
Alterporriol D
Alterporriol E
Paecilospirone
O-Acetylbenzeneamidinocarboxylic acid
Helicascolide A
Helicascolide B
Arthrosporone
Anhydroarthrosporone
Arthrosporol
Auranticin A
Auranticin B
Shiraiachrome A
Shiraiachrome B
Shiraiachrome C
Cavoxin
Cavoxone
Cavoxinine
Cavoxinone
Armillyl everninate
Arnamiol
trans-Resorcylide

cis-Resorcylide
Cochliohydroquinone A (Alboleersin)
Cochlioquinone A (Luteoleersin)
Cochlioquinone B
Stemphone

Common/Systematic Name
Alternaric acid
12-(6,6-Dihydro-4-hydroxy-6-methyl-2-oxopyran-3-yl)-4,6-dihydroxy-3-methyl-9-methylene-12-oxododec-6-ene-6-carboxylic acid

Molecular Formula/Molecular Weight
$C_{21}H_{30}O_8$; MW = 410.19407

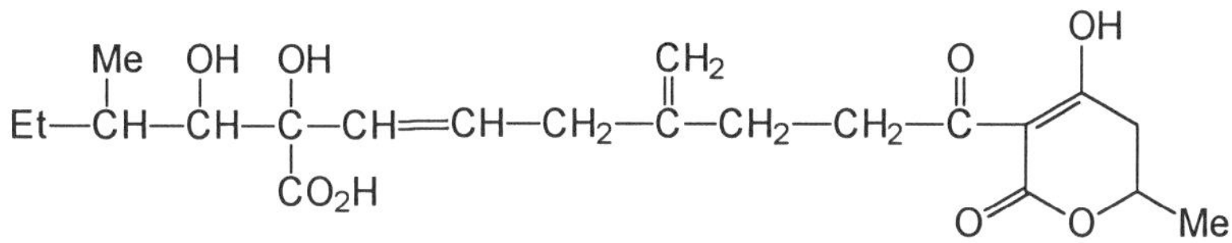

General Characteristics
Alternaric acid, mp.,138°C, is a highly crystalline, colorless, optically inactive, unsaturated dibasic acid; crystallized from benzene in needles, mp. 135°C. Specimens dried at room temperature gave high values for carbon due presumably to traces of adsorbed benzene; drying at 100°C caused discoloration so that the agreement between the observed and the calculated analytical figures was perhaps fortuitous.

Fungal Source
Certain strains of *Alternaria solani*.

Isolation/Purification
The crude yellow solid (mp. 122-128°C) obtained by chloroform extraction of culture filtrates, previously adjusted to pH 3.6, was taken up in hot benzene and a little amorphous insoluble material rejected. The solid which separated on cooling was twice recrystallized from dry benzene, giving a colorless product, mp. 132°C. The bright yellow benzene mother-liquors were bulked and concentrated to yield slightly less pure material, mp. 130-132°C. The first fraction was dissolved in saturated sodium hydrogen carbonate solution and extracted with ether (removing only a trace of gum); alternaric acid was recovered by acidification of the bicarbonate solution with concentrated hydrochloric acid, dried *in vacuo* at room temperature, and crystallized twice from aqueous methanol. It formed colorless, thin, rectangular plates, mp. 135-136°C of the monohydrate. Alternaric acid was crystallized from absolute methanol or ethanol and formed elongated prisms, mp. 138°C.

Biological Activity
A substance with remarkably specific antifungal activity but low antibacterial properties. It was shown to inhibit germination of fungal spores but it also caused a characteristic stunting of the germ tubes. Extreme specificity has been noted; some fungi, e.g., *Myrothecium verrucaria*, are extremely sensitive, germination being inhibited by low concentrations of alternaric acid; others, e.g., *Fusarium caeruleum*, are very resistant, high concentrations having no noticeable effect; still others, e.g., *B. allii*, show stunted germ

tubes at low concentrations, though much higher concentrations fail to prevent germination. Alternaric acid is markedly phytotoxic and it is possible that it is, at least in part, responsible for plant diseases caused by *A. solani*.

Spectral Data

UV:
λ_{max}^{EtOH} 274 and 210nm (log ϵ=4.04 and 4.07).

IR:
The infrared spectra were obtained with Nujol "mulls". The infrared spectrum of alternaric acid crystallized from methanol or from carbon tetrachloride showed bands at 1560, 1338, 1292, 1270, ca. 1225, 1215, 1175, 1149,1117, 1069, 1000, 975, 955, 932, ca. 910, 900, 820, 800, and 760cm^{-1} in addition to 1710 and 1732cm^{-1}.

Mass Data:
Found after drying *in vacuo* over phosphoric oxide at 20°C: C, 61.9, 62.0, 62.7, 62.4; H, 7.5, 7.3, 7.4, 7.3. At 100°; C, 61.4; H, 7.7: required C, 61.4; H, 7.4; 3C-Me, 11.1; 4C-Me, 14.8%; equiv. (dibasic acid), 205; M, 410.

References

J. R. Bartels-Keith; Alternaric Acid. Part III. Structure; J. Chem. Soc., pp. 1662-1665 (1960).

P. W. Brian, P. J. Curtis, H. G. Hemming, E. G. Jefferys, C. H. Unwin, and J. M. Wright; Alternaric Acid; A Biologically Active Product of *Alternaria solani*; its Production, Isolation and Antifungal Properties; J. Gen. Microbiol, Vol. 5, pp. 619-632(1951).

J. F. Grove; Alternaric Acid. Part 1. Purification and Characterization; J. Chem. Soc.,pp. 4056-4059(1952).

Common/Systematic Name

Ampullicin

Molecular Formula/Molecular Weight

$C_{15}H_{17}NO_3$; MW = 259.12084

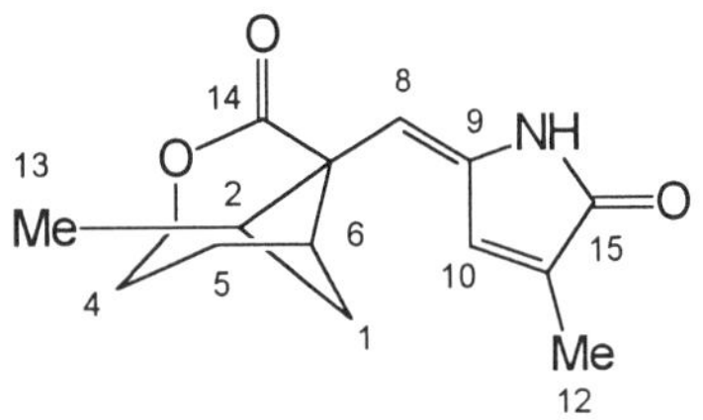

General Characteristics

Colorless needles from *n*-hexane-benzene-acetone; mp., 197-198°C; $[\alpha]_D^{20}$ -32° (*c*=0.5, in MeOH).

Fungal Source

Ampulliferina-like fungus sp. No. 27, obtained from a dead pine tree (*Pinus thunbergii*).

Isolation/Purification

Culture filtrate was treated at pH 2.0 with active charcoal, which was successively extracted with acetone. The extract was concentrated, the residue was chromatographed on silica gel (benzene-acetone, 9:1, v/v). Crystallized from *n*-hexane-benzene-acetone.

Biological Activity

Accelerated the root growth of lettuce seedlings by 200% at 300 and 30mg/L.

Spectral Data

UV:

λ_{max}^{EtOH} 281nm (ϵ=14,700).

IR:

(KBr) 3400, 2950, 2875, 1739(γ-lactone), 1715, 1690, 1660, 1390, 1310, 1210, 910, 888, and 819cm^{-1}.

^{1}H NMR:

($CDCl_3$) 1.75(1H, d, *J*=10.3Hz, H-1); 2.40(1H, ddd, *J*=10.3, 4.9, 4.9, H-1); 2.77(1H, d, *J*=4.9, H2); 2.03(2H, m, H-4); 1.96(2H, m, H-5); 2.77(1H, br, d, *J*=4.9, H-6); 5.53(1H, br, s, H-8); 6.73(1H, br, d, *J*=1.5, H-10); 1.99(3H, d, *J*=1.5, H-12); 1.53(1H, s, H-13); and 8.67ppm (1H, br, s, NH, D_2O exch.).

^{13}C NMR:

($CDCl_3$) 23.8(t, C-1), 52.7(d, C-2), 88.0(s, C-3), 29.7(t, C-4), 23.0(t, C-5), 46.7(d, C-6), 56.0(s, C-7), 109.4(d, C-8), 136.3(s, C-9), 128.5(d, C-10), 141.1(s, C-11), 10.9(q, C-12), 24.9(q, C-13), 176.1(s, C-14), and 171.9ppm (s, C-15).

Mass Data:

259(M^+), 218, 204, 187, 134, 91, and 72*m/e*; found: C, 67.27; H, 6.39; N, 5.45; calcd for $C_{15}H_{17}NO_3$ + ½ H_2O: C, 67.15; H, 6.76; N, 5.22%.

Reference

Y. Kimura, H. Nakajima, T. Hamasaki, T. Matsumoto, Y. Matsuda, and A. Tsuneda; Ampullicin and Isoampullicin, New Metabolites from an *Ampulliferina*-like Fungus sp. No.27; Agric. Biol. Chem., Vol. 54, pp. 813-814(1990).

Common/Systematic Name
Isoampullicin

Molecular Formula/Molecular Weight
$C_{15}H_{17}NO_3$; MW = 259.12084

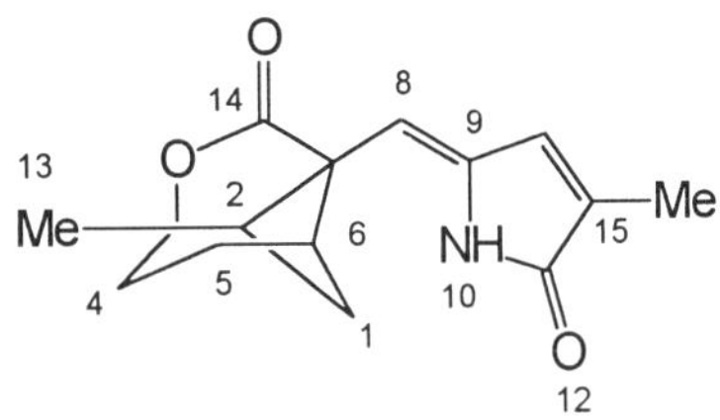

General Characteristics
Colorless crystals; mp., 202-203 °C; $[\alpha]_D^{20}$ +110° (*c*=0.5, in MeOH).

Fungal Source
Ampulliferina-like fungus sp. No. 27, obtained from a dead pine tree (*Pinus thunbergii*).

Isolation/Purification
Culture filtrate was treated at pH 2.0 with active charcoal, which was successively extracted with acetone. The extract was concentrated, the residue was chromatographed on silica gel, benzene-acetone, 19:1, v/v.

Biological Activity
Accelerated the root growth of lettuce seedlings by 200% at 300 and 30mg/L.

Spectral Data

UV:
λ_{max}^{EtOH} 284nm (ϵ=20,500).

IR:
(KBr) 3200, 2950, 1759, 1700, 1680, 1660, 1618, 1205, 1170, 1080, 1020, 910, 890, and 760cm^{-1}.

^{1}H NMR:
($CDCl_3$) 1.76(H1, d, *J*=10.8Hz, H-1); 2.40(1H, ddd, *J*=10.8, 4.9, 4.9, H-1); 2.79(H1, d, *J*=4.9, H-2); 2.02(2H, m, H-4); 1.96(2H, m, H-5); 2.79(1H, br, d, *J*=4.9, H-6); 5.16(1H, br, s, H-8); 6.62(1H, br, d, *J*=1.5, H-10); 1.96(1H, d, *J*=1.5, H-12); 1.52(1H, s, H-13); and 8.47ppm (br, s, NH).

^{13}C NMR:
($CDCl_3$) 23.8(t, C-1), 51.0(d, C-2), 88.7(s, C-3), 29.6(t, C-4), 23.2(t, C-5), 45.8(d, C-

6), 56.1(s, C-7), 107.2(d, C-8), 133.9(s, C-9), 133.3(d, C-10), 139.9(s, C-11), 10.4(q, C-12), 24.7(q, C-13), 176.4(s, C-14), and 173.0ppm (s, C-15).

Mass Data:
259(M^+), 218, 204, 187, 134, 91, and 72*m/e*; found: C, 69.48; H, 6.61; N, 5.40; calcd for $C_{15}H_{17}NO_3$: C, 69.59; H, 6.71; N, 5.41%.

Reference

Y. Kimura, H. Nakajima, T. Hamasaki, T. Matsumoto, Y. Matsuda, and A. Tsuneda; Ampullicin and Isoampullicin, New Metabolites from an *Ampulliferina*-like Fungus sp. No. 27; Agric. Biol. Chem., Vol. 54, pp. 813-814(1990).

Common/Systematic Name

Acremoauxin A

Molecular Weight/Molecular Formula

$C_{16}H_{21}NO_6$; MW = 323.13689

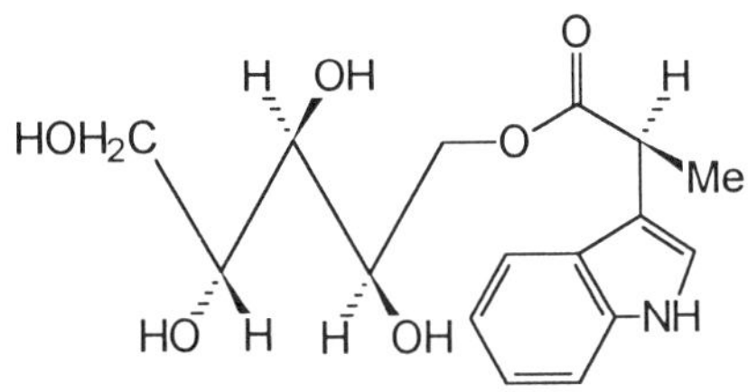

General Characteristics

Colorless needles from EtOH-EtOAc; mp., 142-144°C; $[\alpha]_D^{19}$ +53.6° (*c*=0.35, in MeOH).

Fungal Source

Acremonium roseum (I 4267).

Isolation/Purification

Culture filtrate (pH 5.6) was saturated with NaCl and extracted with ethyl acetate. The extract was chromatographed on silica gel (ethyl acetate-acetone (3:1, v/v), containing 1% AcOH), crystallized from $CHCl_3$-EtOH (5:1, v/v) and recrystallized from EtOH-EtOAc.

Biological Activity

Strongly inhibited the growth of Chinese cabbage seedlings at concentrations higher than 2.0ppm. Showed high activity in a rice lamina inclination test for auxins and brassinosteroids at concentrations higher than 5.0ppm.

Spectral Data

UV:

λ_{max}^{MeOH} 288(ϵ=6000), 278 (7000), and 225nm (9600).

IR:

(KBr) 3430, 3260, 1730, 1450, 1330, 1228, 1169, 1088, 1037, 879, and 746cm^{-1}.

^{1}H NMR:

(MeOH-d_4) 7.59(4', md, *J*=7.9Hz); 7.32(7', md, *J*=8.2Hz); 7.15(2', s); 7.08(6', ddd, *J*=8.2, 7.0, 0.9Hz); 7.00(5', ddd, *J*=7.9, 7.0, 0.8Hz); 4.17(1", dd, *J*=11.1, 6.6Hz); 4.13(1", dd, *J*=11.1, 6.6Hz); 4.05 (2, q, *J*=7.2Hz); 4.03(2", ddd, *J*=6.6, 6.6, 1.5Hz); 3.72(5", dd, *J*=11.1, 3.3Hz); 3.64(4", ddd, *J*=8.5, 6.2, 3.3Hz); 3.54(5", dd, *J*=11.1, 6.2Hz); 3.40(3", dd, *J*=8.5, 1.5Hz); and 1.58ppm (3, d, *J*=7.2Hz).

Mass Spectrum:

HRMS: 305.1265*m/e* (M^+-H_2O, calcd for $C_{16}H_{19}NO_5$, 305.1263); EIMS: 323(M^+, 3%), 305(7), 287(1), 231(1), 189(23), 171(2), 144(100), and 115*m/e* (10); FDMS: 669(2M+Na, 32%), 646(2M, 18), 346(M+Na, 4), and 323*m/e* (M^+, 100).

Reference

T. Sassa, N. Yoshida, and E. Haruki; Isolation and Structural Elucidation of Acremoauxin A, a Novel Auxin Derivative Produced by *Acremonium roseum*; Agric. Biol. Chem., Vol. 53, pp. 3105-3107(1989).

Common/Systematic Name
2-(3,4-Dihydroxyhepta-1,5-dienyl)-6-hydroxybenzyl alcohol

Molecular Formula/Molecular Weight
$C_{14}H_{18}O_4$; MW = 250.12051

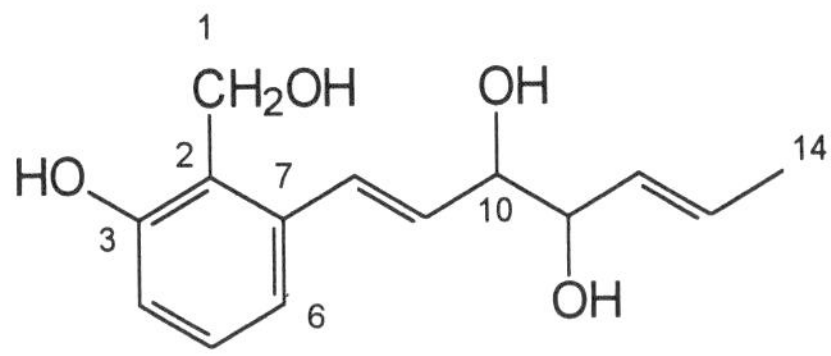

General Characteristics
Gummy substance; $[\alpha]_{400}^{20}$ +100° (in EtOH).

Fungal Source
Pyricularia oryzae.

Isolation/Purification
Extracted with ethyl acetate. Repeated chromatography on silica gel.

Biological Activity
Promoted root elongation of rice seedlings at 250ppm.

Spectral Data

UV:
λ_{max}^{EtOH} 219(ϵ=29500), 254(9400), and 293nm (3300).

IR:
($CHCl_3$) 3600-3510(OH groups) and 1600cm^{-1} (aromatic group).

^{1}H NMR:
(CD_3COCD_3) 1.67(3H, d, *J*=6.0Hz, H-14); 4.02(1H, q, *J*=12.5, 6.5Hz, H-10); 4.20(1H, q, *J*=12.5, 6.0Hz, H-11); 4.84(2H, s, H-1); 5.75(1H, o, *J*=15.0, 6.0Hz, H-13); 6.10 (1H, q, *J*=15.0, 6.0Hz, H-12); 6.15(1H, q, *J*=16.0, 6.5Hz, H-9); 6.95(1H, d, *J*=16.0Hz, H-8); 6.75, 6.90(2H, 2d, *J*=7.0Hz, H-4, H-6); and 7.05ppm (1H, t, *J*=7.0, 7.0Hz, H-5).

Reference
S. Iwasaki, H. Muro, K. Sasaki, S. Nozoe, S. Okuda, and Z. Sato; Isolation of Phytotoxic Substances Produced by *Pyricularia oryzae* Cavara; Tetrahedron Lett., No. 37, pp. 3537-3542(1973).

Common/Systematic Name
Achaetolide

Molecular Formula/Molecular Weight
$C_{16}H_{28}O_5$; MW = 300.19367

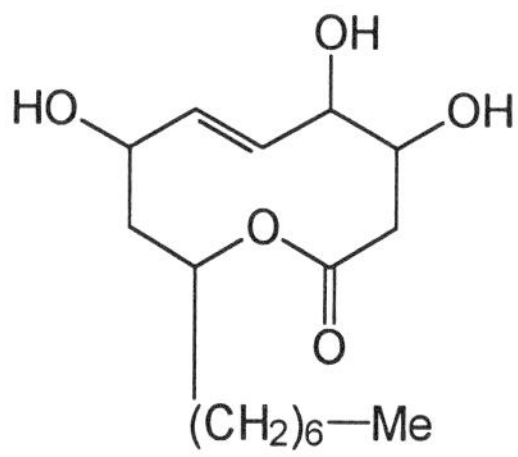

General Characteristics
Melting point, 120-122°C.

Fungal Source
Achaetomium cristalliferum.

Biological Activity
Transpiration amplifier on barley shoots.

Reference
B. Bodo, L. Molho, D. Davoust, and D. Molho; Isolation and Structure Elucidation of Achaetolide and Achaetolidone, Two New Macrolides from a Fungus; 12th IUPAC Int. Symp. Chem. Nat. Prod., Tenerife, 1980, Abstr. B98.

Common/Systematic Name

Achaetolidone

Molecular Formula/Molecular Weight

$C_{16}H_{28}O_6$; MW = 316.18859

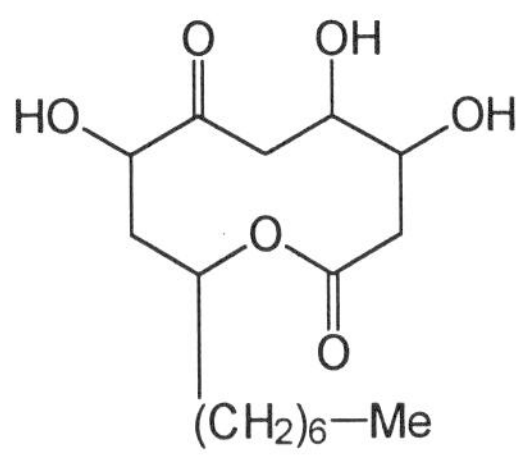

General Characteristics

Melting point, 150-152°C.

Fungal Source

Achaetomium cristalliferum.

Reference

B. Bodo, L. Molho, D. Davoust, and D. Molho; Isolation and Structure Elucidation of Achaetolide and Achaetolidone, Two New Macrolides from a Fungus; 12th IUPAC Int. Symp. Chem. Nat. Prod., Tenerife, 1980, Abstr. B98.

Common/Systematic Name

8-(10,11-Dihydroxyhexa-12-enyl)-3-hydroxydihydroisobenzylfuran

Molecular Formula/Molecular Weight

$C_{14}H_{18}O_4$; MW = 250.12051

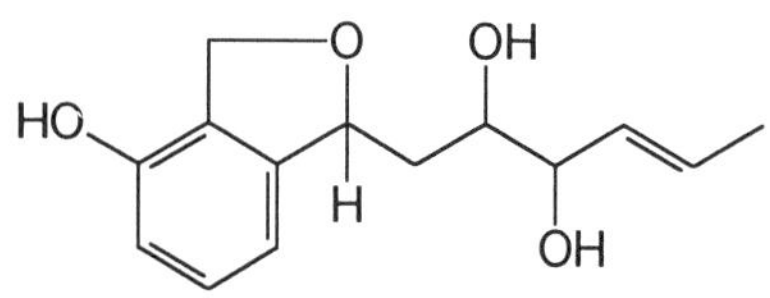

General Characteristics

Melting point, 189°C; $[\alpha]_{400}^{26}$ +61.1° (EtOH); stereoisomeric to 8-(10,11-dihydroxyhexa-12-enyl)-3-hydroxydihydroisobenzylfuran at C-8.

Fungal Source

Pyricularia oryzae (Ken 53-55).

Isolation/Purification

Extracted with ethyl acetate; purified by repeated chromatography on silica gel.

Biological Activity

Promoted root elongation of rice seedlings at 250ppm.

Spectral Data

UV:

λ_{max}^{EtOH} 270(ϵ=2600) and 278nm (2370).

IR:

($CHCl_3$) 3400-2800, 1605, 1470, 1380, 1290, and 1100-950cm^{-1}.

^{1}H NMR:

(CD_3OD) 1.73(3H, d, *J*=6.0Hz, H-14); 1.80(2H, q, *J*=6.0, 4.0Hz, H-9); 3.7-4.1(2H, m, H-10, H-11)*; 5.02(2H, br, s, H-1); 5.42(1H, t, *J*=6.0Hz, H-8); 5.52(1H, q, *J*=15.0, 6.0Hz, H-12); 5.75(1H, o, *J*=15.0, 6.0Hz, H-13); 6.68(2H, 2d, *J*=8.0Hz, H-4, H-6); and 7.12ppm (1H, t, *J*=8.0Hz, H-5).

* α-Glycol moiety should possess an erythro configuration.

Reference

S. Iwasaki, H. Muro, K. Sasaki, S. Nozoe, S. Okuda, and Z. Sato; Isolation of Phytotoxic Substances Produced by *Pyricularia oryzae* Cavara; Tetrahedron Lett., No. 37, pp. 3537-3542(1973).

Common/Systematic Name
8-(10,11-Dihydroxyhexa-12-enyl)-3-hydroxydihydroisobenzylfuran

Molecular Formula/Molecular Weight
$C_{14}H_{18}O_4$; MW = 250.12051

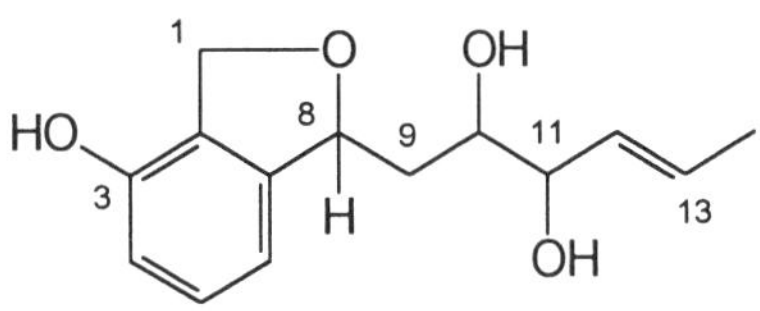

General Characteristics
Gummy substance; $[\alpha]_{400}^{26}$ -4.8° (EtOH); stereoisomeric to 8-(10,11-dihydroxyhexa-12-enyl)-3-hydroxydihydroisobenzylfuran at C8.

Fungal Source
Pyricularia oryzae.

Isolation/Purification
Extracted with ethyl acetate. Repeated chromatography on silica gel.

Biological Activity
Promoted root elongation of rice seedlings at 250ppm.

Spectral Data

UV:
λ_{max}^{EtOH} 270(ϵ=2600) and 278nm (2370).

IR:
($CHCl_3$) 3400-2800, 1605, 1470, 1380, 1290, and 1100-950cm^{-1}.

^{1}H NMR:
(CD_3OD) 1.70(3H, d, *J*=5.0Hz, h-14); 1.77(1H, H-9)*, 1.97(1H, s, *J*=13.0, 4.0, 4.0Hz,); 3.7(2H, m, H-10, H-11)**; 4.97(1H, d, *J*=12.5Hz, H-1), 5.10(1H, d, *J*=12.5Hz); 5.20-5.50(1H, difused q, H-8); 5.55(1H, q, *J*=15.0, 5.0Hz, H-12); 5.77 (1H, o, *J*=15.0, 5.0Hz, H-13); 6.67(1H, d, *J*=8.0Hz, H-4, H-6), 6.90(1H, d, *J*=8.0Hz); and 7.10ppm (1H, t, *J*=8.0Hz, H-5).

* Splittings of the signal were not observable because of the overlapping of C14-H signal.

** *α*-glycol moiety should possess an erythro configuration.

Reference

S. Iwasaki, H. Muro, K. Sasaki, S. Nozoe, S. Okuda, and Z. Sato; Isolation of Phytotoxic Substances Produced by *Pyricularia oryzae* Cavara; Tetrahedron Lett., No. 37, pp. 3537-3542(1973).

Common/Systematic Name
6-(1-Ethoxyethyl)-5-hydroxy-2,7-dimethoxy-1,4-naphthoquinone

Molecular Formula/Molecular Weight
$C_{16}H_{18}O_6$; MW = 306.11034

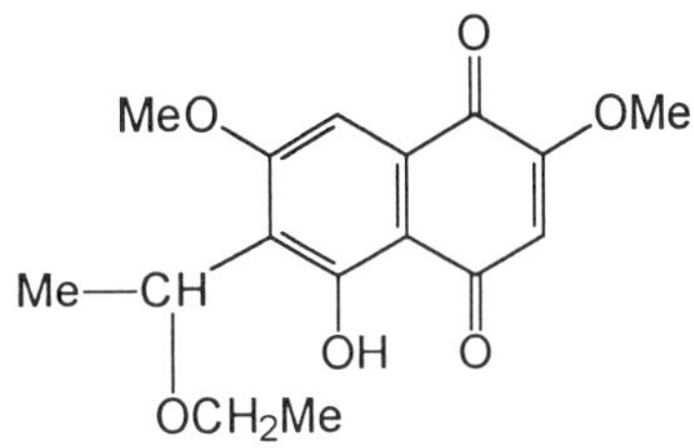

General Characteristics
Orange needles from chloroform-hexane; mp., 136-137°C.

Fungal Source
Guignardia laricina GM-7.

Isolation/Purification
Filtrated mycelia were extracted with acetone. After removal of acetone, the aqueous concentrate was extracted with ethyl acetate followed by chromatography on silica gel ($CHCl_3$; $CHCl_3$-EtOAc, 9:1, v/v; $CHCl_3$-MeOH, 9:1, v/v). Crystallized from chloroform-hexane.

Biological Activity
Inhibited the growth of hypocotyls and roots of lettuce seeds 100% at 100ppm; more than 95% at 50ppm.

Spectral Data

UV:
λ_{max}^{MeOH} 221(log ϵ=4.08), 234(sh, 4.01), 259(sh, 3.78), 264(3.79), and 310nm (3.64).

IR:
(KBr) 1675, 1630, 1590, 1300, and 1100cm^{-1}.

^{1}H NMR:
($CDCl_3$, TMS) 12.76(s, 1H, *peri*-OH); 7.23(s, 1H, ArH); 6.03(s, 1H, QH); 5.19(q, 1H, *J*=6.84Hz); 3.99, 3.91(both s, 3H, $-OCH_3$); 3.43, 3.34(both dq, 1H, *J*=9.52, 6.84Hz); 1.61(d, 3H, *J*=6.84Hz); and 1.18ppm (t, 3H, *J*=6.84Hz).

Mass Spectrum:
306.1101*m/e* (M^+); calcd for $C_{16}H_{18}O_6$, 306.1101.

Reference
N. Otomo, H. Sato, and S. Sakamura; Novel Phytotoxin Produced by the Causal Fungus of the Shoot Blight of Larches; Agric. Biol. Chem., Vol. 46, pp. 861-863(1982).

Common/Systematic Name
6-(1-Hydroxyethyl)-5-hydroxy-2,7-dimethoxy-1,4-naphthoquinone

Molecular Formula/Molecular Weight
$C_{14}H_{14}O_6$; MW = 278.07904

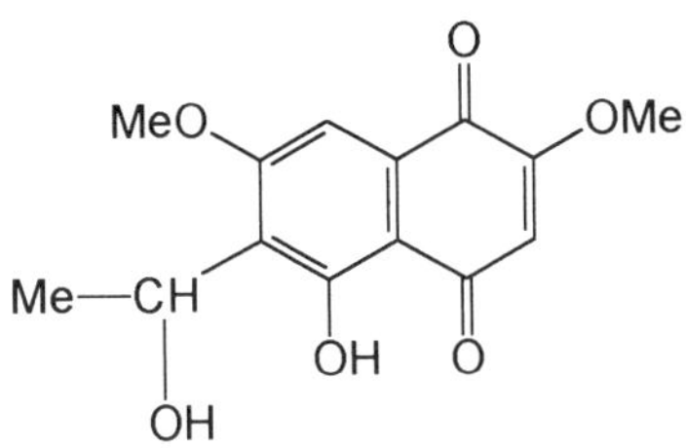

General Characteristics
Orange needles from chloroform-hexane; mp., 201-204°C. Optically inactive.

Fungal Source
Guignardia laricina GM-7 and *Hendersonula toruloidea*.

Isolation/Purification
Filtrated mycelia were extracted with acetone. After removal of acetone, the aqueous concentrate was extracted with ethyl acetate followed by chromatography on silica gel ($CHCl_3$; $CHCl_3$-EtOAc, 9:1, v/v; $CHCl_3$-MeOH, 9:1, v/v). Crystallized from chloroform-hexane.

Biological Activity
Inhibited the growth of hypocotyls and roots of lettuce seeds 100% at 50ppm, more than 95% at 10ppm and more than 55% at 5ppm. Antimicrobial activity (MIC) against *Candida albicans, Staphylococcus aureus* and *Bacillus subtilis* was 20, 2, and 1ppm respectively. Not active at 50ppm against other gram-negative rods: *Escherichia coli, Salmonella typhosa, Shigella sonnei* and *Klebsiella pneumoniae*.

Spectral Data

UV:
λ_{max}^{MeOH} 221(log ϵ=4.14), 231(sh, 4.07), 258(sh, 3.88), 263(3.89), and 310nm (3.72).

IR:
(KBr) 1680, 1630, 1585, 1300, and 1100cm^{-1}.

^{1}H NMR:
($CDCl_3$, TMS) 12.85(s, 1H, *peri*-OH); 7.25(s, 1H, ArH); 6.03(s, 1H, QH); 5.34(dq, 1H, *J*=11.72, 6.84Hz); 4.00, 3.91(both s, 3H, -OCH_3); 3.74(d, 1H, *J*=11.72Hz, D_2O exch.); and 1.56ppm (d, 3H, *J*=6.84Hz).

Mass Spectrum:
278.078*m/e* (M^+); calcd for $C_{14}H_{14}O_6$, 278.0789.

Reference

N. Otomo, H. Sato, and S. Sakamura; Novel Phytotoxin Produced by the Causal Fungus of the Shoot Blight of Larches; Agric. Biol. Chem., Vol. 46, pp. 861-863(1982).

Common/Systematic Name

6-Ethyl-1-acetonyl-1,5-dihydroxy-2,7-dimethoxy-4-naphthoquinone

Molecular Formula/Molecular Weight

$C_{17}H_{20}O_6$; MW = 320.12599

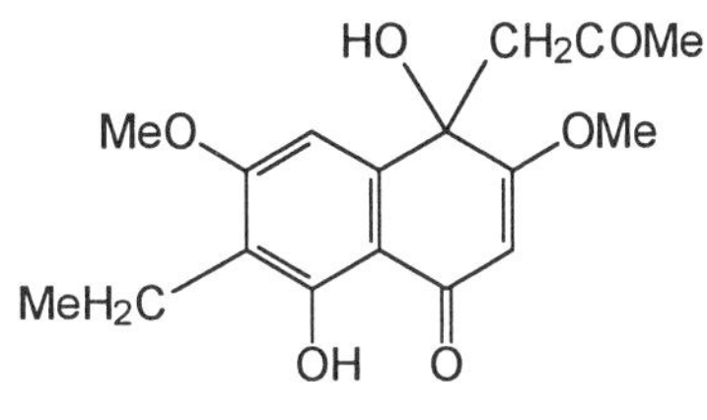

General Characteristics

Pale yellow needles from chloroform-hexane; mp., 133 °C. Optically inactive.

Fungal Source

Guignardia laricina GM-7.

Isolation/Purification

Filtrated mycelia were extracted with acetone. After removal of acetone, the aqueous concentrate was extracted with ethyl acetate followed by chromatography on silica gel ($CHCl_3$; $CHCl_3$-EtOAc, 9:1, v/v, $CHCl_3$-MeOH, 9:1, v/v). Crystallized from chloroform-hexane.

Spectral Data

UV:

λ_{max}^{MeOH} 256(log ε=4.45), 265(sh, 4.41), and 336nm (4.25).

IR:

(KBr) 1725(sh), 1710, 1640, and 1590cm^{-1}.

^{1}H NMR:

($CDCl_3$, TMS) 13.02(s, 1H, *peri*-OH); 6.80(s, 1H, ArH); 5.61(s, 1H, QH); 4.68(s, 1H, D_2O exch.); 3.95, 3.88(both s, 3H, -OCH_3); 2.98(s, 2H, acetonylmethylene); 2.70(q, 2H, *J*=7.4Hz); 2.11(s, 3H, acetonylmethyl); and 1.10ppm (t, 3H, *J*=7.4Hz).

Mass Spectrum:

320.1207*m/e* (M^+); calcd for $C_{17}H_{20}O_6$, 320.1258.

Reference

N. Otomo, H. Sato, and S. Sakamura; Novel Phytotoxin Produced by the Causal Fungus of the Shoot Blight of Larches; Agric. Biol. Chem., Vol. 46, pp. 861-863(1982).

Common/Systematic Name

Pyriculariol

Molecular Formula/Molecular Weight

$C_{14}H_{16}O_4$; MW = 248.10486

(or its enantiomer)

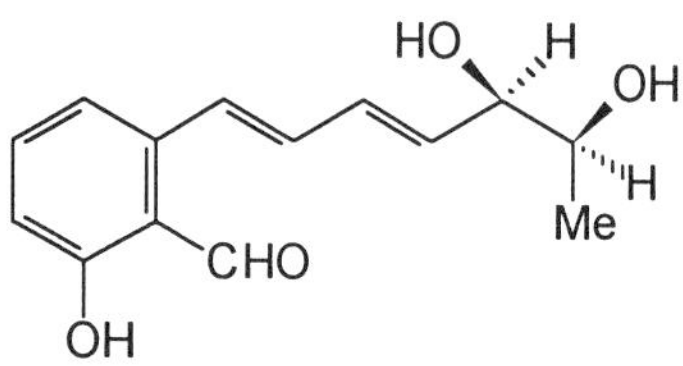

General Characteristics

Pale yellow needles from $CHCl_3$-CCl_4; mp., 105.5-106.5°C; $[\alpha]_D^{24}$ - 3.4° (c=1.0, in $CHCl_3$).

Fungal Source

Pyricularia oryzae.

Isolation/Purification

Filtered broth extracted with ethyl acetate, followed by chromatography on silica gel (EtOH-$CHCl_3$, 2:98, v/v). The substance then was purified on Sephadex LH_{20} (acetone) and crystallized from $CHCl_3$-CCl_4.

Biological Activity

At 300ppm the length of root and 2nd leaf sheath of rice seedlings (Kiyonishiki) were 17 and 30% resp. When 5μg of the substance was applied into a pin hole of rice leaf, a dark necrotic spot developed within 24hr.

Spectral Data

UV:

λ_{max}^{EtOH} 251(ε=26800), 292(16600), and 366nm (8700); $\lambda_{max}^{EtOH\text{-}1N\,NaOH}$ 246(ε=35000), 309(13800), and 406nm (9200).

IR:

($CHCl_3$) 3650, 3560, 3400(OH), 1640(chelated Ar-CHO), 1600, 1565(phenyl), and 990cm^{-1} (conjugated trans double bond).

^{1}H NMR:

($CDCl_3$) 1.19(3H, d, J=6.5Hz, H-14); 3.94(1H, dq, J=3.5, 6Hz, H-13); 4.22(1H, dd, J=3.5, 6Hz, H-12); 1.8(2H, br., C12- and C13-OH, D_2O exch.); 5.94(1H, dd, J=14.5,

6Hz, H-11); 6.4-6.7(2H, m, H-9 and H-10); 7.08(1H, d, *J*=14.5Hz, H-8); 6.88, 6.97(each 1H, d, *J*=8Hz, H-4 and H-6); 7.45(1H, t, *J*=8Hz, H-5); 10.28(1H, s, H-1); and 11.84ppm (1H, s, C3-OH).

Mass Spectrum:

248.1072(19%, calcd for $C_{14}H_{16}O_4$, 248.1048; M^+), 204.0822(83, $C_{12}H_{12}O_3$), and 203.0732*m/e* (22, $C_{12}H_{11}O_3$).

Reference

M. Nukina, T. Sassa, M. Ikeda, T. Umezawa, and H. Tasaki; Pyriculariol, a New Phytotoxic Metabolite of *Pyricularia oryzae* Cavara; Agric. Biol. Chem., Vol. 45, pp. 2161-2162(1981).

Common/Systematic Name

Sydonol

3-Hydroxy-4-(1-hydroxy-1,5-dimethylhexyl)benzyl alcohol

Molecular Formula/Molecular Weight

$C_{15}H_{24}O_3$; MW = 252.17254

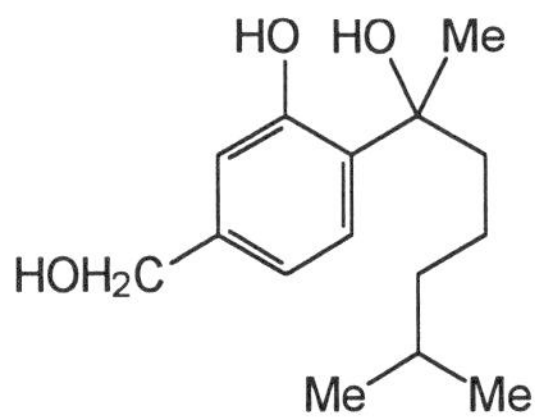

General Characteristics

Colorless needles from ethyl acetate-hexane; mp., 65-67°C; $[\alpha]_D^{20}$ +7.2° (*c*=1.0, in MeOH).

Fungal Source

Aspergillus sp.

Isolation/Purification

Culture filtrate (pH 4.8) was extracted with ethyl acetate and chromatographed on silica gel (ethyl acetate-hexane, 1:4, v/v) followed by purification on Sephadex LH_{20} (acetone) and crystallization from ethyl acetate-hexane.

Biological Activity

Inhibited colonial growth and successively induced to form irregularly swollen hyphae of a phytopathogenic fungus *Cochliobolus lunata* (IFO 6299) at 50μg/disc.

Spectral Data

UV:

λ_{max}^{MeOH} 221(ε=6700), and 280nm (2100); $\lambda_{max}^{MeOH, OH^-}$ 243, and 295nm.

IR:

($CHCl_3$) 3320, 1630, 1575, and 1510cm^{-1}.

^{1}H NMR:

0.80(6H, d, *J*=6Hz, isopropyl); 4.46(2H, s, hydroxymethyl attached to benzene ring); 1.55(3H, s, tertiary methyl); 6.94(1H, d, *J*=8Hz), 6.68(1H, dd, *J*=8, 2Hz), 6.65(1H, d, *J*=2Hz) (ortho- and meta-coupled three benzenoid protons); 9.49(1H, br, s), and 1.9ppm (2H, br.) (three hydroxyl protons, one of which is phenolic).

^{13}C NMR:
(acetone-d_6) 157.1(s), 143.1(s), 129.8(s), 126.9(d), 117.7(d), 115.8(d), 78.3(s), 64.2(t), 44.0(t), 40.0(t), 29.5(q), 28.5(d), 22.8(t), and 22.4ppm (q).

Mass Spectrum:
252.1721(26%, M^+; calcd for $C_{15}H_{24}O_3$, 252.1725), 234(41, M^+ - H_2O), 167(77, M^+ - C_6H_{13}), and 164*m/e* (100, M^+ - $C_5H_{12}O$).

Reference

M. Nukina, Y. Sato, M. Ikeda, and T. Sassa; Sydonol, a New Fungal Morphogenic Substance Produced by an Unidentified *Aspergillus* sp.; Agric. Biol. Chem., Vol. 45, pp. 789-790(1981).

Common/Systematic Name
Homotrichione

Molecular Formula/Molecular Weight
$C_{19}H_{18}O_8$; MW = 374.10017

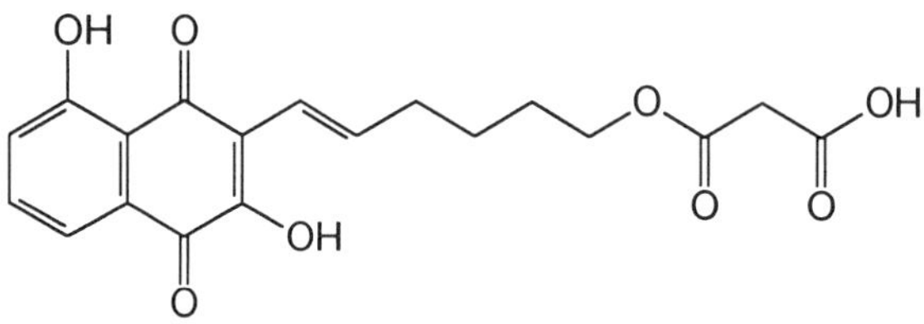

General Characteristics
Orange anthraquinone pigment.

Fungal Source
Metatrichia vesparium.

Biological Activity
Antibiotic activity.

References

L. Kopanski, H. Besl, and W. Steglich; Unpublished results.

W. Steglich; Biologically Active Compounds From Higher Fungi; Pure and Applied Chemistry, Vol. 53, pp. 1233-1240(1981).

Common/Systematic Name

p-Toluquinone ⇌ Toluquinol

Molecular Formula/Molecular Weight

$C_7H_6O_2$; MW = 122.03678 ⇌ $C_7H_8O_2$; MW = 124.05243

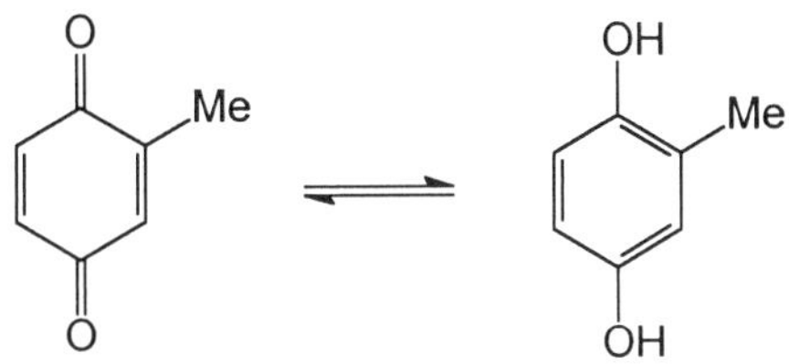

General Characteristics

p-Toluquinone formed crystals from hexane; mp., 66-67°C; toluquinol formed crystals from benzene; mp., 123-124°C (sublimes at 112°C). Toluquinol yielded *p*-toluquinone on oxidation with silver carbonate/celite.

Fungal Source

The hypocrealean fungus, *Nectria erubescens*, *Penicillium lanosum*, *P. patulum* = *P griseofulvum*, and *P. urticae*.

Isolation/Purification

Cultures extracted with ethyl acetate, evaporated to dryness under vacuum, and *p*-toluquinone and toluquinol purified by silica gel column chromatography. The quinone was eluted with ethyl acetate-Skellysolve B (3:1); while toluquinol eluted with ethyl acetate. The quinone crystallized from hexane and the hydroquinone crystallized from benzene.

Spectral Data

UV:

$\lambda_{max}^{Hydroquinone}$ 294nm (ϵ=3100).

IR:

(Quinone) 1660(broad) and 1605cm^{-1}.

^{1}H NMR:

(Quinone) 2.05(3H, d *J*=1.5Hz); 6.63(1H, m); and 6.73ppm (2H, broad).

Reference

S. T. Carey and M. S. R. Nair; Metabolites of *Pyrenomycetes X*: Isolation of *p*-Toluquinone and Toluquinol from *Nectria erubescens*; J. Natural Products (Lloydia), Vol. 42, p. 231 (1974).

Common/Systematic Name
Aszonapyrone A

Molecular Formula/Molecular Weight
$C_{28}H_{40}O_5$; MW = 456.28757

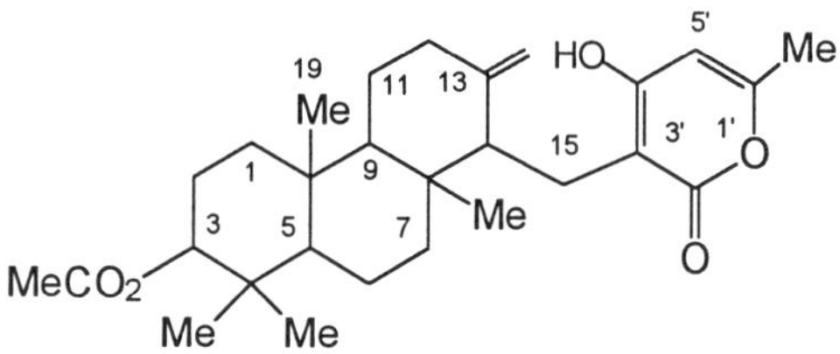

General Characteristics
Colorless needles from $CHCl_3$-MeOH; mp., 242-244°C; $[\alpha]_D^{20}$ +33° (*c*=1.06, in $CHCl_3$)

Fungal Source
Aspergillus zonatus (IFO 8817).

Isolation/Purification
Dry mycelial mats were extracted with acetone and twice chromatographed on silica gel (benzene-acetone, 19:1, v/v and benzene-ethyl acetate, 9:1, v/v). The substance was crystallized from $CHCl_3$-MeOH.

Biological Activity
Antimicrobial; showed an MIC of 6.3μg/ml against *Staphylococcus aureus* 209P and *S. aureus* res.

Spectral Data

UV:
λ_{max}^{EtOH} 210(ϵ=16900) and 290nm (7900).

IR:
(KBr) 3400, 3090, 2940, 2850, 1728, 1665, 1640, 1580, 1445, 1410, 1380, 1255, and 893cm^{-1}.

^{1}H NMR:
(pyridine-d_5) 1.10(1H, dd, *J*=2, 12Hz); 1.33(2H, m); 1.51(2H, m); 1.62(1H, dd, *J*=4, 12Hz); 1.69(1H, m); 1.93(3H, s); 2.05(1H, m); 2.08(3H, s); 2.09(1H, m); 2.39(1H, m); 2.88(1H, d, *J*=13Hz); 3.12(1H, d, *J*=12Hz); 3.18(1H, dd, *J*=12, 13Hz); 4.64(1H, dd, *J*=4, 12Hz); 5.02(1H, s); 5.57(1H, s); and 6.09ppm (1H, s).

^{13}C NMR:

15.5, 16.5, 16.7, 19.1(t), 19.3(q, C-17), 20.0(C-15), 21.0(q), 23.9(t, C-2), 24.2(C-11), 28.0(q, C-18), 37.8(s, C-4), 38.1(s, C-10), 38.4(C-12), 38.6(t, C-1), 40.6(t, C-8), 55.3(d, C-5), 55.4(C-9), 60.0(C-14), 80.8(d, C-3), 100.8(d, C-5'), 103.2(s, C-3'), 107.0(t, C-16), 149.7(s, C-13), 159.4(s, C-6'), 165.8(s, C-4'), 165.9(s, C-2'), and 170.4ppm (s).

Mass Spectrum:

EIMS: 456(M^+), 396, 317, 257, 192, 139, 135, 121, and 107*m/e*.

TLC Data

Detection: under UV light.

Reference

Y.Kimura, T.Hamasaki, A.Isogai, and H.Nakajima; Structure of Aszonapyrone A, a New Metabolite Produced by *Aspergillus zonatus*; Agric. Biol. Chem., Vol. 46, pp. 1963-1965 (1982).

Common/Systematic Name

Pyrenochaetic acid A; 4-Crotonoyl-3-methoxy-5-methylbenzoic acid

Molecular Formula/Molecular Weight

$C_{13}H_{14}O_4$; MW = 234.08921

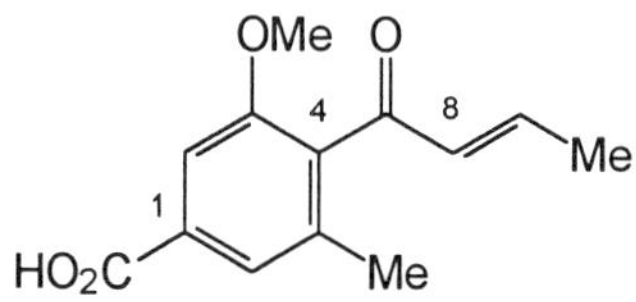

General Characteristics

Needles from chloroform-*n*-hexane; mp., 176-179°C.

Fungal Source

Pyrenochaeta terrestris.

Isolation/Purification

Culture filtrate was extracted with ether. The extract was chromatographed on silica gel (benzene-ethyl acetate). The substance was crystallized from chloroform-*n*-hexane.

Biological Activity

Inhibited the root growth of onion seedlings 100% at 250ppm, and inhibited that of rice seedlings 100% at 500ppm. Stimulated the root elongation of lettuce seedlings at concentrations of not more than 100ppm and inhibited that at higher concentrations.

Spectral Data

UV:

λ_{max}^{MeOH} 240(sh, ϵ=8900) and 303nm (1700).

IR:

(KBr) 2900, 1680, 1657, 1580, 880, and 765cm^{-1}.

^{1}H NMR:

($CDCl_3$, TMS) 1.88(3H, d, *J*=5.4Hz); 2.18(3H, s); 3.73(3H, s); 6.13(1H, d, *J*=16Hz); 6.35(1H, dq, *J*=5.4, 16Hz); 7.45(1H, br, s); 7.57(1H, br, s); and 9.08ppm (1H, br, s).

Mass Spectrum:

HRMS: 234.0894*m/e* (M^+), calcd for $C_{13}H_{14}O_4$, 234.0892. 234(M^+), 219(base peak, M^+-CH_3), 205(M^+-C_2H_5), 193(M^+-C_3H_5), 175, 160, and 77*m/e*.

TLC Data

Silica gel; benzene-EtOAc (1:1, v:v); R_f: 0.35; detection by spraying with anisaldehyde reagent.

Reference

H. Sato, K. Konoma, and S. Sakamura; Three New Phytotoxins Produced by *Pyrenochaeta terrestris*: Pyrenochaetic Acids A, B and C; Agric. Biol. Chem., Vol. 45, pp. 1675-1679(1981).

Common/Systematic Name
Pyrenochaetic acid B; 4-(3-Hydroxybutyroyl)-3-methoxy-5-methylbenzoic acid

Molecular Formula/Molecular Weight
$C_{13}H_{16}O_5$; MW = 252.09977

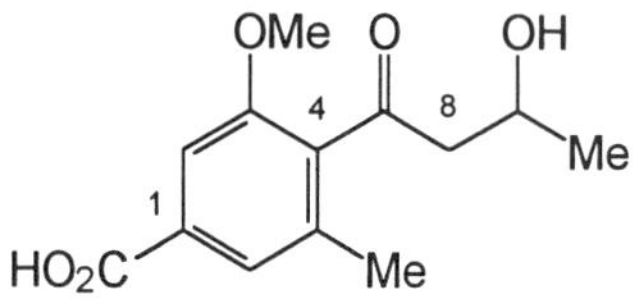

General Characteristics
Needles from chloroform-*n*-hexane; mp., 139°C.

Fungal Source
Pyrenochaeta terrestris.

Isolation/Purification
Culture filtrate was extracted with ether. The extract was chromatographed on silica gel (benzene-ethyl acetate). The substance was crystallized from chloroform-*n*-hexane.

Biological Activity
Stimulated the root elongation of lettuce seedlings at concentrations from 100 to 500ppm, the roots lengthening two times relative to the control at 500ppm.

Spectral Data

IR:
(KBr) 3400, 2960, 1695, 1580, 885, and 770cm^{-1}.

^{1}H NMR:
($CDCl_3$, TMS) 1.26(3H, d, *J*=6Hz); 2.18(3H, s); 2.28(3H, s); 2.88(1H, d, *J*=4Hz) 2.93(1H, s); 3.88(3H, s); 4.42(1H, m); 7.47(1H, br, s); and 7.56ppm (1H, br, s).

Mass Spectrum:
HRMS: 252.1030*m/e* (M^+); calcd for $C_{13}H_{16}O_5$, 252.0998.

TLC Data
Silica gel; benzene-EtOAc (1:1, v:v); R_f: 0.08; detection by spraying with anisaldehyde reagent.

Reference
H. Sato, K. Konoma, and S. Sakamura; Three New Phytotoxins Produced by *Pyrenochaeta terrestris*: Pyrenochaetic Acids A, B and C; Agric. Biol. Chem., Vol. 45, pp. 1675-1679(1981).

Common/Systematic Name

Pyrenochaetic acid C; 4-Butyroyl-3-methoxy-5-methylbenzoic acid

Molecular Formula/Molecular Weight

$C_{13}H_{16}O_4$; MW = 236.10486

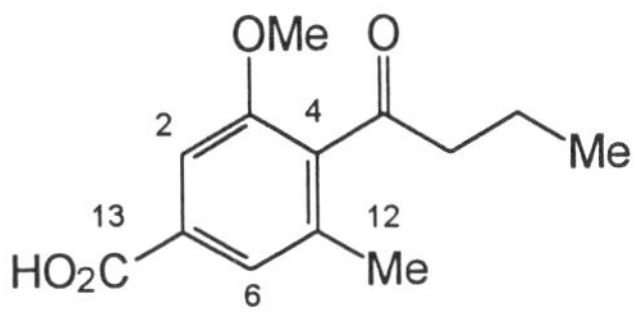

General Characteristics

Plates from chloroform-*n*-hexane; mp., 148-152°C.

Fungal Source

Pyrenochaeta terrestris.

Isolation/Purification

Culture filtrate was extracted with ether. The extract was chromatographed on silica gel (benzene-ethyl acetate). The substance was crystallized from chloroform-*n*-hexane.

Biological Activity

Inhibited the root growth of onion seedlings 100% at 500ppm, and inhibited that of rice seedlings 54% at 500ppm. Stimulated the root elongation of lettuce seedlings at concentrations of not more than 100ppm and inhibited that at higher concentrations.

Spectral Data

UV:

λ_{max}^{MeOH} 249(ε=8500) and 303nm (3100).

IR:

(KBr) 2950, 1690, 1570, 880, and 765cm^{-1}.

^{1}H NMR:

($CDCl_3$, TMS) 1.04(3H, t, *J*=7Hz); 1.81(2H, sextet, *J*=7Hz); 2.35(3H, s); 2.81(2H, t, *J*=7Hz); 3.94(3H, s); 7.44(1H, br. s); 7.56(1H, br. s); and 9.70ppm (1H, br. s).

^{13}C NMR:

($CDCl_3$, TMS) 135.6(s, C-1), 109.4(d, C-2), 156.1(s, C-3), 130.3(s, C-4), 136.5(s, C-5), 125.4(d, C-6), 207.2(s, C-7), 46.2(t, C-8), 16.5(t, C-9), 13.3(q, C-10), 55.5(q, C-11), 18.5(q, C-12) and 171.7ppm (s, C-13).

Mass Spectrum:

HRMS: 236.1047*m/e* (M^+); calcd for $C_{13}H_{16}O_4$, 236.1047; 236(M^+), 193*m/e* (base peak, M^+-C_3H_7).

TLC Data

Silica gel; benzene-EtOAc (1:1, v:v); R_f: 0.39; detection by spraying with anisaldehyde reagent.

Reference

H. Sato, K. Konoma, and S. Sakamura; Three New Phytotoxins Produced by *Pyrenochaeta terrestris*: Pyrenochaetic Acids A, B and C; Agric. Biol. Chem., Vol. 45, pp. 1675-1679(1981).

Common/Systematic Name

Candidusin A

2,2'-Epoxy-3',6'-dimethoxy-1,1',4',1"-terphenyl-4,4",5-triol

Molecular Formula/Molecular Weight

$C_{20}H_{16}O_6$; MW = 352.09469

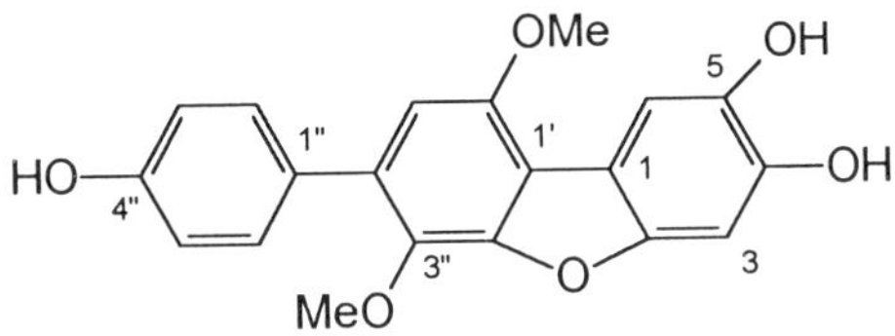

General Characteristics

Colorless rods from benzene-EtOH; mp., 123°C.

Fungal Source

Aspergillus candidus.

Isolation/Purification

Culture filtrate was adjusted to pH 3 and extracted with ethyl acetate. The extract was chromatographed on silica gel (toluene-acetone). The substance was crystallized from benzene-EtOH.

Biological Activity

Cytotoxic on the sea urchin (*Hemicentrotus pulcherrimus*) embryos totally blocked the initial cleavage at 1.0×10^{-4} M, when added five minutes after fertilization. At the concentration of 5.0×10^{-5} M, partial fragmentation of the unequal-sized blastomeres was observed in the molura stage. At the concentrations of 5.0×10^{-5} - 1.0×10^{-4} M the substance did not inhibit the furrow formation when it was added before anaphase. The substance is expected to have the same inhibitory activity toward DNA and RNA synthesis as does candidusin B. Antibacterial activity against *Bacillus subtilis* (15mm-diam. inhibitory zone around 8mm-diam. paper disc containing 1.35×10^{-4} M (50μg/ml) of the compound).

Spectral Data

UV:

λ_{max}^{EtOH} 216(ε=32100), 280(17300), 296(15900), and 335nm (2310).

IR:

(KBr) 3240, 1600, 1469, 1438, 1377, 1330, 1230, 1107, 1059, 981, 912, and 828cm^{-1}.

^{1}H NMR:

($CDCl_3$, TMS) 3.83(3H, s,); 4.04(3H, s); 6.76(1H, s); 6.92(2H, d, *J*=8Hz); 7.12(1H, s); 7.48(2H, d, *J*=8Hz); and 7.54ppm (1H, s).

Mass Spectrum:
HRMS: 352.0947*m/e* (M^+); calcd for $C_{20}H_{16}O_6$, 352.0947.

TLC Data

Silica gel; toluene-acetone (7:3, v/v); R_f: 0.38; detection by spraying with $FeCl_3$-HCl and vanillin-H_2SO_4.

Reference

A. Kobayashi, A. Takemura, K. Koshimizu, H. Nagano, and K. Kawazu; Candidusin A and B: New *p*-Terphenyls with Cytotoxic Effects on Sea Urchin Embryos; Agric. Biol. Chem., Vol. 46, pp. 585-589(1982).

Common/Systematic Name

Candidusin B

2,2'-Epoxy-3',6'-dimethoxy-1,1',4',1"-terphenyl-3",4,4",5-tetrol

Molecular Formula/Molecular Weight

$C_{20}H_{16}O_7$; MW = 368.08960

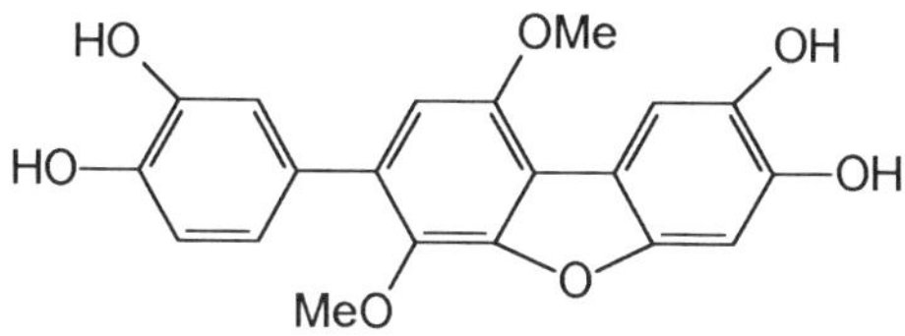

General Characteristics

Colorless plates from benzene-EtOH; mp., 259-260°C.

Fungal Source

Aspergillus candidus.

Isolation/Purification

Culture filtrate was adjusted to pH 3 and extracted with ethyl acetate. The extract was chromatographed on silica gel (toluene-acetone). The substance was crystallized from benzene-EtOH.

Biological Activity

Cytotoxic to sea urchin (*Hemicentrotus pulcherrimus*) embryos; totally blocked the initial cleavage at 5.0 x 10^{-5} M, when added five minutes after fertilization. At the concentration of 3.0 x 10^{-5} M, partial fragmentation of the unequal-sized blastomeres was observed in the molura stage. Treatment of the embryos in the gastrula stage with 10μg/ml (2.7 x 10^{-5} M) of the substance almost completely suppressed ^{3}H-thymidine uptake into DNA. ^{3}H-uridine uptake into RNA was also inhibited by 86% at 2.76x10^{-5} M. At concentrations of 5.0 x 10^{-5} - 1.0 x 10^{-4} M the substance did not inhibit the furrow formation when it was added before anaphase. Antibacterial activity against *Bacillus subtilis* [16-mm-diam. inhibitory zone around 8-mm-diam. paper disc containing 1.35 x 10^{-4} M (50μg/ml) of the compound].

Spectral Data

UV:

λ_{max}^{EtOH} 221(ε=37,600), 281(16,700), 299(16,900), and 333nm (21,900).

IR:

(KBr) 3260, 1600, 1469, 1322, 1221, 1120, 1092, 1060, 986, and 811cm^{-1}.

^1H NMR:
(CDCl$_3$, TMS) 3.81(3H, s,); 4.02(3H, s); 6.75(1H, s); 6.89(1H, d, d, *J*=8, 0.5Hz); 7.03(1H, d, d, *J*=8, 2Hz); 7.13(1H, s); 7.17(1H, d, d, *J*=2, 0.5Hz); and 7.56ppm (1H, s).

Mass Spectrum:
HRMS: 368.0848*m/e* (M^+); calcd for $C_{20}H_{16}O_7$, 368.0886.

TLC Data

Silica gel (toluene-acetone, 7:3); R_f: 0.28; detection by spraying with $FeCl_3$-HCl and vanillin-H_2SO_4.

Reference

A. Kobayashi, A. Takemura, K. Koshimizu, H. Nagano, and K. Kawazu; Candidusin A and B: New *p*-Terphenyls with Cytotoxic Effects on Sea Urchin Embryos; Agric. Biol. Chem., Vol. 46, pp. 585-589(1982).

Common/Systematic Name
Ankalactone

Molecular Formula/Molecular Weight
$C_{18}H_{26}O_6$; MW = 338.17294

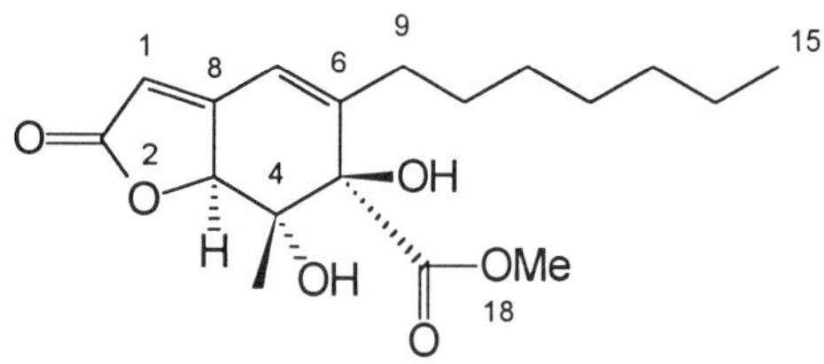

General Characteristics
Colorless crystals from chloroform; mp., 133.0-134.0°C.

Fungal Source
Monascus anka.

Isolation/Purification
Culture filtrate was extracted with ethanol. The extract was repeatedly chromatographed on silica gel (chloroform-ethyl acetate, 4:1, v/v). The substance was crystallized from chloroform.

Biological Activity
Showed a gross inhibitory effect against *Escherichia coli* and *Bacillus subtilis* at a concentration of 5mg/disk (inhibition zone diameters 10.0 and 10.2mm; paper disk, diameter 8.0mm).

Spectral Data

UV:
λ_{max}^{EtOH} 270.8nm (ϵ=17,000).

IR:
(KBr) 3590(sh, hydroxyl) and 1741cm^{-1} (α,β-unsaturated γ-lactone).

^{1}H NMR:
($CDCl_3$) 5.79(d, *J*=1.8Hz, H-1); 5.59(d, *J*=1.8Hz, H-3); 6.50(s, H-7); 2.17(m, H-9); 1.42(m, H-10); 0.87(t, *J*=7.0Hz, H-15); 1.08(s, H-16); 3.87(s, H-18); 2.87(1H, br, s, exch. with D_2O); and 4.17ppm (1H, s, exch. with D_2O).

^{13}C NMR:
($CDCl_3$) 111.55(d, C-1), 173.63(s, C-2), 83.43(d, C-3), 79.70(s, C-4), 83.00(s, C-5),

152.77(s, C-6), 118.53(d, C-7), 161.31(s, C-8), 31.66(t, C-9), 27.67(t, C-10), 29.00(t, C-11), 29.22(t, C-12), 31.69(t, C-13), 22.57(t, C-14), 14.03(q, C-15), 15.59(q, C-16), 172.78(s, C17) and 54.08ppm (q, C-18).

Mass Spectrum:
HR-EIMS: 338.1749*m/e* ($C_{18}H_{26}O_6$, / 2.0mmu); CI-MS: 339*m/e* ($(M+1)^+$).

X-ray:
Triclinic crystals with *a*=17.038 (2), *b*=8.038 (2), *c*=6.997 (2) A, α=107.72 (3), β=99.64 (2), γ=82.07 (2)°. Centrosymmetric space group P1; one molecule of the substance per asymmetric unit (ρ_c=1.26g cm^{-3}). Intramolecular contact: bond between O(4)-H and O(5) [1.94 (3) A]; the molecules in the crystal were linked by an intermolecular hydrogen bond O(3)-H---O(1) [1.90 (3) A].

Reference

H. Nozaki, S. Date, H. Kondo, H. Kiyohara, D. Takaoka, T. Tada, and M. Nakayama; Ankalactone, a New α,β-Unsaturated γ-Lactone from *Monascus anka*; Agric. Biol. Chem., Vol. 55, pp. 899-900(1991).

Common/Systematic Name

Alterporriol D

Molecular Formula/Molecular Weight

$C_{32}H_{30}O_{16}$; MW = 670.15339

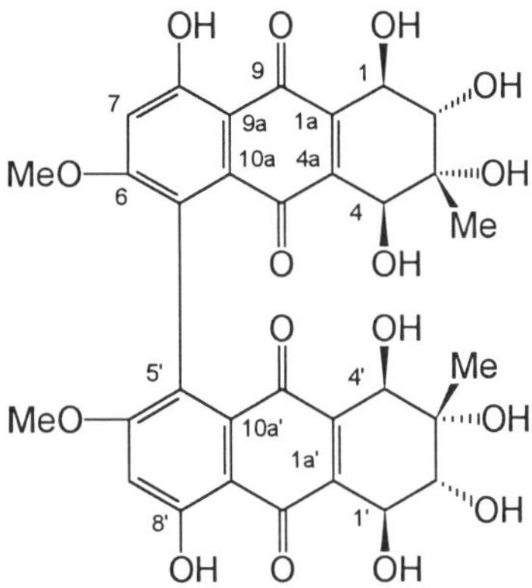

General Characteristics

Orange amorphous solid; mp., 285°C (dec.); $[\alpha]_D^{20}$ -800° (*c*=0.01, in EtOH).

Fungal Source

Alternaria porri (IFO, strain No. 9762).

Isolation/Purification

Culture liquid was extracted with ethyl acetate. The aqueous liquid was concentrated to 1/10th in volume, activated carbon (ca 1%) was added. The substances adsorbed to the carbon were eluted with hot acetone followed by preparative TLC on silica gel (chloroform-acetone-formic acid, 200:100:1, v/v/v). Final purification of the substance was achieved by reversed phase chromatography on ODS-C_{18} adsorbent (water-methanol, 9:1, v/v) and HPLC (water-methanol, 4:1, v/v).

Spectral Data

UV:

λ_{max}^{EtOH} 225(ϵ=1.456106), 270(4.176105), and 440nm (3.556102).

IR:

(KBr) 3600-3000(OH), 1660(shoulder, free C=O), 1640(chelated C=O), 1600(phenyl), 1210(Ar-OH), 1160(*tert*-OH), and 1080cm-1 (*sec*-OH).

1H NMR:

(THF-d_8, TMS) 4.74(d, J=6.5Hz, H-1); 4.32(d, J=6.5Hz, H-2); 4.26(H-4); 6.77(H-7); 1.33(C3-Me); 3.71(C6-OMe); 4.74(d, J=6.5Hz, H-1'); 4.32(d, J=6.5Hz, H-2'); 4.26(H-4'); 6.77(H-7'); 1.33(C3'-Me); and 3.71ppm (C6'-OMe).

13C NMR:

(THF-d_8, TMS) 22.2(Me-3), 56.7(OMe-6), 68.2(CH-4), 68.4(C-1), 73.7(C-2), 104.1(C-7), 72.8(C3, quat. C), 109.3(C-9a), 121.4(C-5), 129.8(C-10a), 142.7(C-4a), 144.5(C-1a), 163.5(C-8a), 163.6(C-6), 184.0(C-10), and 188.8ppm (C-9).

Mass Data:

FDMS: 693[(M+Na)$^+$, 11], 671[(M+H)$^+$, 46.2], 670(M$^+$, 100), 634[(M$^+$-2H_2O, 54.4], and 598*m/e* (M$^+$-4H_2O, 16.9); found: C, 54.93; H, 4.40; calcd for $C_{32}H_{30}O_{16}\bullet 2H_2O$: C, 54.39; H, 4.56%.

Reference

R. Suemitsu, Y. Sakurai, K. Nakachi, I. Miyoshi, M. Kubota, and K. Ohnishi; Alterporriol D and E, Modified Bianthraquinones from *Alternaria porri* (Ellis) Ciferri; Agric. Biol. Chem., Vol. 53, pp. 1301-1304(1989).

Common/Systematic Name
Alterporriol E

Molecular Formula/Molecular Weight
$C_{32}H_{30}O_{16}$; MW = 670.15339

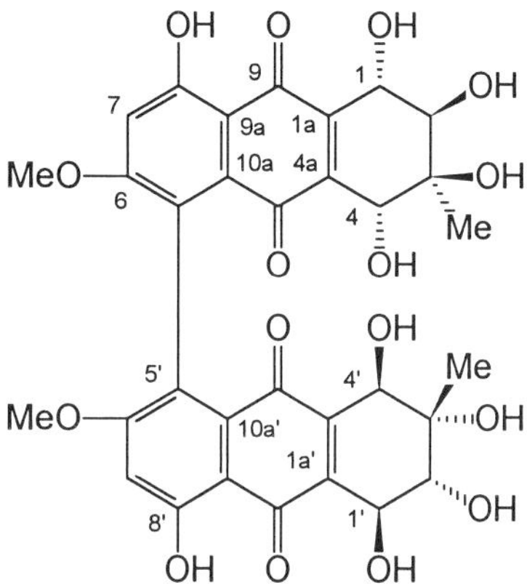

General Characteristics
Orange amorphous solid; mp., 285°C (dec.); $[\alpha]_D^{20}$ -695° (*c*=0.01, in EtOH).

Fungal Source
Alternaria porri (IFO, strain No. 9762).

Isolation/Purification
Culture liquid was extracted with ethyl acetate. The aqueous liquid was concentrated to 1/10th in volume, activated carbon (ca 1%) was added. The substances adsorbed to the carbon were eluted with hot acetone followed by preparative TLC on silica gel (chloroform-acetone-formic acid, 200:100:1, v/v/v). Final purification of the substance was achieved by reversed phase chromatography on ODS-C_{18} adsorbent (water-methanol, 9:1, v/v) and HPLC (water-methanol, 4:1, v/v).

Spectral Data

UV:
λ_{max}^{EtOH} 225(ϵ=8.326105), 275(3.556105), and 440nm (1.026102).

IR:
(KBr) 3600-3000(OH), 1660(shoulder, free C=O), 1640(chelated C=O), 1595(phenyl), 1210(Ar-OH), 1160(*tert*-OH), and 1080cm^{-1} (*sec*-OH).

^{1}H NMR:

(THF-d_8, TMS) 4.75(d, J=6.4Hz, H-1); 4.35(d, J=6.4Hz, H-2); 4.26(H-4); 6.77(H-7); 1.36(C3-Me); 3.67(C6-OMe); 4.75(d, J=6.4Hz, H-1'); 4.35(d, J=6.4Hz, H-2'); 4.26(H-4'); 6.77(H-7'); 1.36(C3'-Me); and 3.67ppm (C6'-OMe).

^{13}C NMR:

(THF-d_8, TMS) 22.2(Me-3), 56.8(OMe-6), 68.3(CH-4), 68.3(C-1), 73.8(C-2), 103.9(C-7), 72.9(C3, quat. C), 109.3(C-9a), 122.5(C-5), 128.9(C-10a), 142.8(C-4a), 143.5(C-1a), 163.9(C-8a), 164.7(C-6), 183.8(C-10), and 188.8ppm (C-9).

Mass Data:

FDMS: 634[(M^+-2H_2O, 7.5], 598(M^+-4H_2O, 100), and 582*m/e* (598+2H-H_2O, 79.2); found: C, 52.26; H, 5.32; calcd for $C_{32}H_{30}O_{16}$•4H_2O: C, 51.75; H, 5.16 %.

Reference

R. Suemitsu, Y. Sakurai, K. Nakachi, I. Miyoshi, M. Kubota, and K. Ohnishi; Alterporriol D and E, Modified Bianthraquinones from *Alternaria porri* (Ellis) Ciferri; Agric. Biol. Chem., Vol. 53, pp. 1301-1304(1989).

Common/Systematic Name

Paecilospirone

Molecular Formula/Molecular Weight

$C_{13}H_{14}O_5$; MW = 250.08412

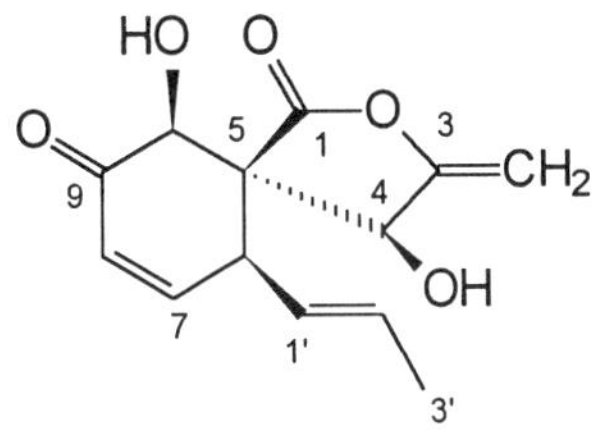

General Characteristics

Colorless needles from *n*-hexane-ethyl acetate; mp., 128°C; $[\alpha]_D^{23}$ -322.7° (*c*=0.022, in MeOH).

Fungal Source

Paecilomyces sp.

Isolation/Purification

Culture filtrate was extracted with ethyl acetate. The neutral fraction was chromatographed on silica gel (benzene-acetone, 95:5, v/v). The substance was crystallized from *n*-hexane-ethyl acetate.

Biological Activity

MIC of the substance against *Bacillus subtilis* was 5μg/ml at 25°C. At 37°C, it did not show any antimicrobial activity, probably due to the rapid destruction of the substance (labile at 37°C).

Spectral Data

UV:

λ_{max}^{MeOH} 211(ε=9800) and 237nm (sh, 7360).

IR:

(KBr) 3430, 3380 (sh), 1800 (sh), 1770, 1695, 1675, 1150, 1110, 1095, and 870cm^{-1}.

^{1}H NMR:

(CD_3COCD_3) 5.37(1H, ddd, *J*=6, 2.5, 2.5Hz, H-4); 3.99(1H, m, H-6); 6.73(1H, dd, *J*=10, 2.5Hz, H-7); 6.13(1H, dd, *J*=10, 3Hz, H-8); 4.37(1H, d, s, H-10); 5.53(1H, ddq, *J*=15.5, 7.5, 1Hz, H-1'); 5.66(1H, ddq, *J*=15.5, 6.5, 1Hz, H-2'); 1.62(3H, dd, *J*=6.5, 1Hz, H-3'); 4.59(1H, dd, *J*=2.5, 2.5Hz) and 4.68(1H, dd, *J*=2.5, 2.5Hz, C3-CH_2); 5.80(1H, d, *J*=6, C4-OH); and 4.66ppm (1H, d, *J*=3, C10-OH).

^{13}C NMR:

(CD_3COCD_3) 172.5(s, C-1), 159.6(s, C-3), 70.0(d, C-4), 62.7(s, C-5), 41.5(d, C-6), 149.9(d, C-7), 127.4(d, C-8), 197.7(s, C-9), 73.1(d, C-10), 128.2(d, C-1'), 132.5(d, C2'), 18.6(q, C-3') and 87.9ppm (t, CH_2-3).

Mass Data:

EIMS: 250(M^+, 1.9), 232(M^+-18, 2.6), 222(M^+-28, 2.0), 108(100), and 80*m/e* (96); found: C, 62.44; H, 5.59%; calcd for $C_{13}H_{14}O_5$: C, 62.39; H, 5.64%.

Reference

A. Hirota, M. Nakagawa, and H. Hirota; Structure of Paecilospirone, a New Antibiotic from Paecilomyces; Agric. Biol. Chem., Vol. 55, pp. 1187-1188(1991).

Common/Systematic Name

O-Acetylbenzeneamidinocarboxylic acid

Molecular Formula/Molecular Weight

$C_{10}H_{10}N_2O_3$; MW = 206.06914

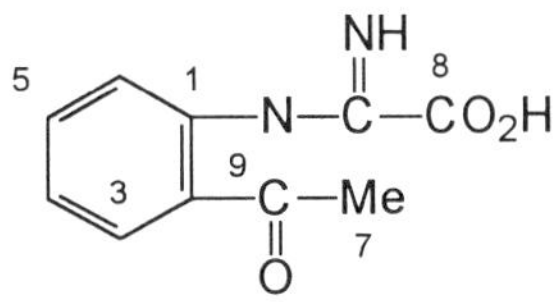

General Characteristics

Colorless needle crystals; mp., 175-175.5°C. Low solubility in hexane, benzene, chloroform, and ether; readily soluble in pyridine, DMSO and dioxane. $pK_{a'}$ in 50% dioxane: 10.65 and < 2.

Fungal Source

Gibberella saubinetii (IAM 8049).

Isolation/Purification

Culture filtrate and mycelium were separately extracted with ethyl acetate followed by repeated chromatography on silicic acid and silica gel (benzene-ethyl acetate, 6:4, v/v).

Biological Activity

Selective cytotoxicity *in vitro* using SV40-C3H-2K and C3H-2K from the first day. Caused formation of a large number of rounded and detached cells on the third day at concentrations of 62.5 and 2000μg/ml in SV40-C3H-2K and C3H-2K respectively. Showed a slight antitumor activity against Ehrlich carcinoma *in vivo* (a 30% inhibition of tumor growth in ddy mice at dose levels of 30mg/kg three times).

Spectral Data

UV:

λ_{max}^{EtOH} 207(ϵ=7800), 242(sh, 4000), 295(sh, 2700), and 306nm (2850).

IR:

(KBr) 3390, 3200, 1720, 1680, 1580, 1510, 1380, 1350, 1240, and 745cm^{-1}.

^{1}H NMR:

(DMSO-d_6) 12.65(br. s.,- COOH); 8.58(dd, *J*=7.8, 1.2Hz, =CH-); 8.30(br. s.,=C-NH); 7.84(dd, *J*=7.9, 1.6Hz,=CH-); 7.76(br. s.,-C=NH); 7.56(ddd, *J*=7.6, 7.6, 1.3, =CH); 7.19(ddd, *J*=7.6, 7.6, 1.5, =CH); and 2.43ppm (s,-CH_3).

^{13}C NMR:

196.3(s, C-9), 170.2(s, C-8), 158.6(s, C-7), 138.0(s, C-1), 132.2(d, C-5), 128.7(d, C-3), 123.4(d, C-4), 120.7(s, C-2), 119.8(d, C-6), and 24.1ppm (q, C-10).

Mass Spectrum:

CIMS: 207*m/e* (M^++H).

Reference

M. Munekata, H. Seto, and G. Tamura; Isolation of *O*-Acetylbenzeneamidinocarboxylic Acid, a New Metabolite of *Gibberella saubinetii*; Agric. Biol. Chem., Vol. 46, pp. 1711-1713(1982).

Common/Systematic Name
Helicascolide A

Molecular Formula/Molecular Weight
$C_{12}H_{20}O_3$; MW = 212.14124

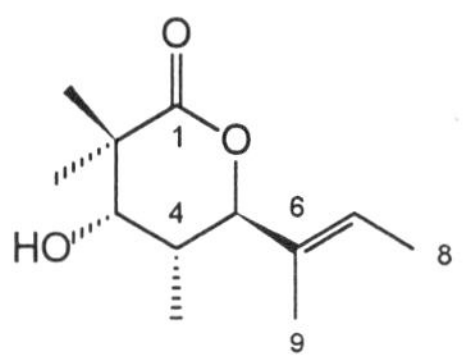

General Characteristics
White crystalline solid; mp., 97-98°C; $[\alpha]_D$ -25.0° (*c*=1.4, in $CHCl_3$, 31°C)

Fungal Source
Helicascus kanaloanus (ATCC 18591).

Isolation/Purification
Filtered culture broth was extracted with EtOAc followed by chromatography on Sephadex LH_{20} (eluted with CH_2Cl_2-hexane, 4:1, v/v). Early fractions were chromatographed on silica gel (gradient of 0-10% EtOAc in hexane) and reversed-phase HPLC (C_{18}).

Spectral Data

IR:
($CHCl_3$) 3636, 3458(br), 3020, 2982, 1717, 1460, 1398, and 1147cm^{-1}.

CD:
(MeOH) [Θ]221.5 = +3680.

^{1}H NMR:
($CDCl_3$) 3.53(dd, *J*=3.7, 1.7Hz, H-3); 2.08(d, *J*=3.7Hz, C3-OH); 2.28(ddq, *J*=11.2, 6.8, 1.7Hz, H-4); 4.66(d, *J*=11.2Hz, H-5); 5.54(br. q, *J*=5.6Hz, H-7); 1.62(br. d, *J*=5.6Hz, H-8); 1.60(br. s, H-9); 0.89(d, *J*=6.8Hz, H-10); 1.28(s, H-11); and 1.32ppm (s, H-12).

^{13}C NMR:
($CDCl_3$) 177.2(C-1), 44.1(C-2), 77.3(C-3), 31.2(C-4), 87.8(C-5), 131.5(C-6), 126.5(C7), 13.2(C-8), 10.3(C-9), 13.8(C-10), 26.5(C-11), and 22.6ppm (C-12).

Mass Spectrum:

HREIMS: 212.1418*m/e* (M^+); calcd for $C_{12}H_{20}O_3$, 212.1412; EIMS: 212(M^+, 2.5), 197(0.9), 195(1.8), 156(11), 154(6.1), 142(13), 128(19), 125(4.3), 113(5.2), and 96*m/e* (100).

HPLC Data

Retention time 10.1 min; 5-μm C_{18} column, 250 x 10 mm, MeOH-H_2O (70:30, v/v), 2.0 ml/min, 215nm.

Reference

G. K. Poch and J. B. Gloer; Helicascolides A and B: New Lactones from the Marine Fungus *Helicascus kanaloanus*; J. Nat. Prod., Vol. 52, No. 2, pp.257-260(1989).

Common/Systematic Name
Helicascolide B

Molecular Formula/Molecular Weight
$C_{12}H_{20}O_3$; MW = 212.14124

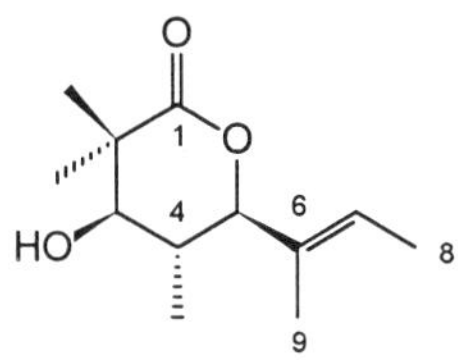

General Characteristics
White crystalline solid; mp., 61-62°C; $[\alpha]_D$ -27.6° (*c*=0.4, in $CHCl_3$, 31°C).

Fungal Source
Helicascus kanaloanus (ATCC 18591).

Isolation/Purification
Filtered culture broth was extracted with EtOAc followed by chromatography on Sephadex LH_{20} (eluted with CH_2Cl_2-hexane, 4:1, v/v). Early fractions were chromatographed on silica gel (gradient of 0-10% EtOAc in hexane) and reversed phase HPLC (C_{18}).

Spectral Data

IR:
($CHCl_3$) 3626, 3450(br), 3018, 2981, 2939, 1724, 1470, 1384, and 1266cm^{-1}.

CD:
(MeOH) $[\Theta]$221.5 = +3330.

^{1}H NMR:
($CDCl_3$) 3.43(dd, *J*=10.6, 5.5Hz, H-3); 1.80(d, *J*=5.5Hz, OH-3); 2.06(m, H-4); 4.12(d, *J*=11.0Hz, H-5); 5.53(br. q, *J*=6.8Hz, H-7); 1.64(br. d, *J*=6.8Hz, H-8); 1.61(br. s, H-9); 0.93(d, *J*=6.4Hz, H-10); 1.26(s, H-11); and 1.36ppm (s, H-12).

^{13}C NMR:
($CDCl_3$) 177.0(C-1), 44.5(C-2), 77.4(C-3), 33.8(C-4), 89.0(C-5), 131.4(C-6), 127.0(C-7), 13.3(C-8), 10.4(C-9), 13.5(C-10), 23.8(C-11), and 20.6ppm (C-12).

Mass Spectrum:
HREIMS: 212.1416*m/e* (M^+); calcd for $C_{12}H_{20}O_3$, 212.1412; EIMS: 212(M^+, 1.5), 197(0.5), 194(0.3), 128(8.5), 125(2.0), 113(2.2), 96(48), 85(100), and 70*m/e* (91).

HPLC Data

Retention time 9.1 min; 5-µm C_{18} column, 250 x 10 mm, MeOH-H_2O (70:30, v/v), 2.0 ml/min, 215nm.

Reference

G. K. Poch and J. B. Gloer; Helicascolides A and B: New Lactones from the Marine Fungus *Helicascus kanaloanus*; J. Nat. Prod., Vol. 52, No. 2, pp. 257-260(1989).

Common/Systematic Name

Arthrosporone

Molecular Formula/Molecular Weight

$C_{15}H_{24}O_3$; MW = 252.17254

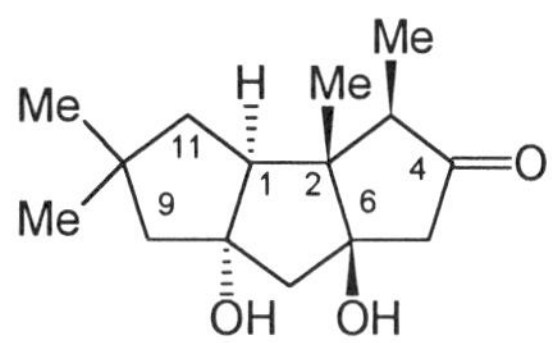

General Characteristics

Colorless needles from Skellysolve B/Et_2O; mp., 139-141°C; $[\alpha]_D$ -140.8° (c=0.9, in $CHCl_3$).

Fungal Source

Arthroconidial fungus (UAMH 4262), isolated as a contaminant on a culture of *Ceratocystis ulmi*. Believed to be a haploid basidiomycete; has not been fully identified.

Isolation/Purification

Dried mycelium and culture filtrate were separately extracted with Et_2O followed by EtOAc. Combined Et_2O-soluble extracts were dissolved in EtOAc and separated into neutral, strong acidic and weak acidic compounds by standard acid-base extraction. The neutral extract was chromatographed on silica gel (eluted with CH_2Cl_2-MeCN, 3:2, v/v). The substance was crystallized from Skellysolve B/Et_2O.

Biological Activity

Weak antifungal activity against several *Ceratocystis* species.

Spectral Data

UV:

λ_{max}^{MeOH} 280nm (ϵ=650).

FT-IR:

($CHCl_3$) 3440, 2951, 2866, 1731, 1381, 1360, 1275, 1189, and 1015cm^{-1}.

^{1}H NMR:

($CDCl_3$, TMS) 2.56(dd, J=8, 12Hz, H-1); 2.57(q, J=7Hz, H-3); 2.69(dd, J=1, 20Hz, H-5); 2.20(d, J=20Hz, H-5); 2.40(d, J=16Hz, H-7); 2.21(d, J=16 Hz, H-7); 1.96(d, J=14Hz, H-9); 1.79(dd, J=2.5, 14Hz, H-9); 1.70(t, J=12Hz, H-11); 1.59(ddd, J=2.5, 8, 12Hz, H-11); 1.16(s, H-12); 1.08(s, H-13); 0.84(s, H-14); and 1.02ppm (d, J=7Hz, H-15). (pyridine-d_5, TMS) 2.77(dd, J=9.5, 12Hz, H-1); 2.92(dq, J=1.7Hz, H-3);

2.55(d, J=20Hz, H-5); 2.47(dd, J=1, 20Hz, H-5); 2.75(d, J=16Hz, H-7); 2.46(d, J=16Hz, H-7); 2.14(d, J=14Hz, H-9); 2.06(dd, J=3, 14Hz, H-9); 1.97(t, J=12Hz, H-11); 1.47(ddd, J=3, 9.5, 12Hz, H-11); 1.24(s, H-12); 0.96(s, H-13); 0.94(s, H-14); 1.00(d, J=7Hz, H-15); and 5.60ppm (s, OH).

^{13}C NMR:

(CDCl$_3$, TMS) 216.4(s, C-4), 91.0(s, C-6), 87.0(s, C-8), 60.6(d, C-3), 58.9(t, C-5), 56.9(t, C-7), 55.5(d, C-1), 54.6(s, C-2), 49.9(t, C-9), 44.7(t, C-11), 40.2(s, C-10), 29.6(q), 26.9(q), 11.3(q), and 8.3ppm (q).

Mass Spectrum:

HREIMS: 252.1723(36); calcd. for $C_{15}H_{24}O_3$, 252.1722; 235(38), 234(28), 219(13), 216(2), 206(12), 192(89), 191(24), 177(22), 163(21), 125(100), 102(25), 95(33), and 83*m/e* (40); CIMS: (NH_3): 270($[M+NH_4]^+$, 100) and 252*m/e* (M^+, 40).

TLC Data

Silica gel 60, F_{254}; Me_2CO-C_6H_6, 3:2 (v/v); R_f: 0.5 relative to the R_f of cholesterol (was assigned the value of 1.00). Detected under UV light (λ254 or λ350nm); spraying with H_2SO_4-vanillin reagent or phosphomolybdic acid-H_2SO_4-ceric sulfate reagent, followed by charring.

Reference

E. Amouzou, W. A. Ayer, and L. M. Browne; Antifungal Sesquiterpenoids from an Arthroconidial Fungus; J. Nat. Prod., Vol. 52, No. 5, pp. 1042-1054(1989).

Common/Systematic Name

Anhydroarthrosporone

Molecular Formula/Molecular Weight

$C_{15}H_{22}O_2$; MW = 234.16198

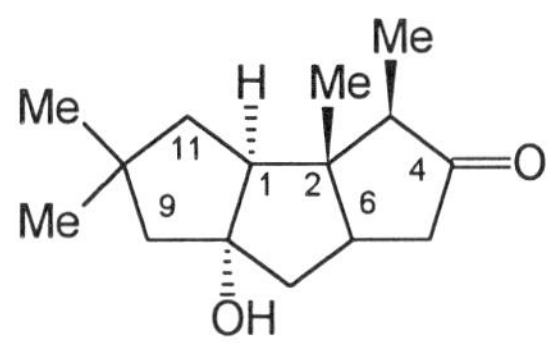

General Characteristics

Crystals from Skellysolve B/Et_2O; mp., 118-119°C; $[\alpha]_D$ -140.8° (*c*=0.9, in $CHCl_3$).

Fungal Source

Arthroconidial fungus (UAMH 4262), isolated as a contaminant on a culture of *Ceratocystis ulmi*. Believed to be a haploid basidiomycete; has not been fully identified.

Isolation/Purification

Dried mycelium and culture filtrate were separately extracted with Et_2O followed by EtOAc. Combined Et_2O-soluble extracts were dissolved in EtOAc and separated into neutral, strong acidic and weak acidic compounds by standard acid-base extraction. The neutral extract was chromatographed on silica gel (eluted with CH_2Cl_2-MeCN, 3:2, v/v). The substance was crystallized from Skellysolve B/Et_2O.

Biological Activity

Weak antifungal activity against several *Ceratocystis* species.

Spectral Data

UV:

λ_{max}^{MeOH} 230nm (ϵ=13700).

FT-IR:

($CHCl_3$) 3461, 1693, 1632, 1466, 1448, 1372, 1364, and 872cm^{-1}.

^{1}H NMR:

($CDCl_3$, TMS) 2.38(dd, *J*=9, 11Hz, H-1); 2.32(q, *J*=7Hz, H-3); 5.85(d, *J*=1.3 Hz, H-5); 2.79(d, *J*=16Hz, H-7); 2.72(dd, *J*=1, 16Hz, H-7); 1.87(dd, *J*=2, 14Hz, H-9); 1.68 (d, *J*=14Hz, H-9); 1.72(ddd, *J*=2, 9, 13Hz, H-11); 1.47(dd, *J*=11, 13Hz, H-11); 1.20(s, H-12); 1.13(s, H-13); 0.94(s, H-14); 1.11(d, *J*=7Hz, H-15) and 1.63ppm (s, OH). (pyridine-d_5, TMS) 2.63(t, *J*=10Hz, H-1); 2.41(q, *J*=7.5Hz, H-3); 5.92(d, *J*=2Hz, H-5); 2.96(d, *J*=15Hz, H-7); 2.80(dd, *J*=2, 15Hz, H-7); 2.08(dd, *J*=2, 14Hz,

H-9); 1.68(d, J=14Hz, H-9); 1.65(ddd, J=2, 9, 13Hz, H-11); 1.45(dd, J=10, 13Hz, H-11); 1.40(s, H-12); 1.10 (s, H-13); 0.86(s, H-14); 1.14(d, J=7.5Hz, H-15) and 6.21ppm (s, OH).

^{13}C NMR:

(CDCl$_3$, TMS) 211.6(s, C-4), 177.0(s, C-6), 122.9(d, C-5), 92.7(s, C-8), 63.4(d, C-3), 57.7(d, C-1), 55.9(t, C-7), 53.4(s, C-2), 44.0(t, C-9), 43.3(s, C-10), 41.8(t, C-11), 30.2(q), 28.2(q), 21.8(q, C-14), and 9.5ppm (q, C-15).

Mass Spectrum:

HREIMS: 234.1617(63); calcd for $C_{15}H_{22}O_2$, 234.1616, 219(32), 216(34), 201(23), 173(23), 123(78), 122(100), 111(10), 95(13), and 55*m/e* (20). CIMS (NH_3): 252([M+NH$_4$]$^+$, 2), 235([M+H]$^+$, 100), and 234*m/e* (20).

TLC Data

Silica gel 60, F_{254}; Me_2CO-C_6H_6, 3:2 (v/v); R_f: 0.74 relative to the R_f of cholesterol (was assigned the value of 1.00). Detected under UV light (λ254 or λ350nm); spraying with H_2SO_4-vanillin reagent or phosphomolybdic acid-H_2SO_4-ceric sulfate reagent, followed by charring.

Reference

E. Amouzou, W. A. Ayer, and L. M. Browne; Antifungal Sesquiterpenoids from an Arthroconidial Fungus; J. Nat. Prod., Vol. 52, No. 5, pp. 1042-1054(1989).

Common/Systematic Name

Arthrosporol

Molecular Formula/Molecular Weight

$C_{15}H_{26}O_3$; MW = 254.18819

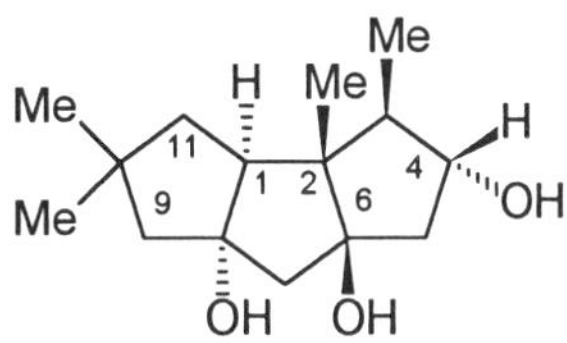

General Characteristics

Crystals from Et_2O; mp., 163-164°C; $[\alpha]_D$ -29° (*c*=2.0, in $CHCl_3$), -62.1° (*c*=1.0, in MeOH).

Fungal Source

Arthroconidial fungus (UAMH 4262), isolated as a contaminant on a culture of *Ceratocystis ulmi*. Believed to be a haploid basidiomycete; has not been fully identified.

Isolation/Purification

Dried mycelium and culture filtrate were separately extracted with Et_2O followed by EtOAc. Combined Et_2O-soluble extracts were dissolved in EtOAc and separated into neutral, strong acidic and weak acidic compounds by standard acid-base extraction. The neutral extract was chromatographed on silica gel (eluted with CH_2Cl_2-MeCN, 3:2, v/v). The substance was crystallized from Et_2O.

Biological Activity

Weak antifungal activity against several *Ceratocystis* species.

Spectral Data

FT-IR:

($CHCl_3$) 3376, 2951, 2933, 2456, 1380, 1372, 1088, and 1012cm^{-1}.

^{1}H NMR:

($CDCl_3$, TMS) 2.40(dd, *J*=8, 12Hz, H-1); 2.01(m, H-3); 3.94(dt, *J*=5, 9Hz, H-4); 2.01(m, H-5); 2.32(d, *J*=15Hz, H-7); 2.22(d, *J*=16Hz, H-7); 1.86(d, *J*=13Hz, H-9); 1.70(dd, *J*=2, 13Hz, H-9); 1.54(t, *J*=12Hz, H-11); 1.47(ddd, *J*=2, 8, 12Hz, H-11); 1.11(s, H-12); 1.04(s, H-13); 0.76(s, H-14); 1.02(d, *J*=7Hz, H-15); 1.77(s, OH) and 1.64ppm (s, OH).

^{13}C NMR:

($CDCl_3$, TMS) 91.0(s, C-6 or C-8), 90.3(s, C-8 or C-6), 76.8(d, C-4), 60.9(d, C-3 or

C-1), 58.5(t, C-5 or C-7), 58.2(t, C-7 or C-5), 56.3(s, C-2), 52.1(d, C-1 or C-3), 49.0(t, C-11 or C-9), 45.3(t, C-9 or C-11), 40.0(s, C-10), 30.7(q), 28.6(q), 12.9(q), and 12.5ppm (q).

Mass Spectrum:
HREIMS: 236.1778($[M-H_2O]^+$, 11, calcd. for $C_{15}H_{24}O_2$, 236.1776), 218(100), 203(31), 190(8), 182(38), 174(33), 150(54), 139(32), 135(33), 127(32), 125(16), 123, 121(15), 110(25), 109(38), 107(34), 95(31), 83(54), 69(38), and 55*m/e* (65). CIMS (NH_3): 272($[M+NH_4]^+$, 100), 254(18), and 237*m/e* (15).

TLC Data

Silica gel 60, F_{254}; Me_2CO-C_6H_6, 3:2 (v/v); R_f: 0.39 relative to the R_f of cholesterol (was assigned the value of 1.00). Detected under UV light (λ254 or λ350nm); spraying with H_2SO_4-vanillin reagent or phosphomolybdic acid-H_2SO_4-ceric sulfate reagent, followed by charring.

Reference

E. Amouzou, W. A. Ayer, and L. M. Browne; Antifungal Sesquiterpenoids from an Arthroconidial Fungus; J. Nat. Prod., Vol. 52, No. 5, pp. 1042-1054(1989).

Common/Systematic Name

Auranticin A

Molecular Formula/Molecular Weight

$C_{24}H_{24}O_8$; MW = 440.14712

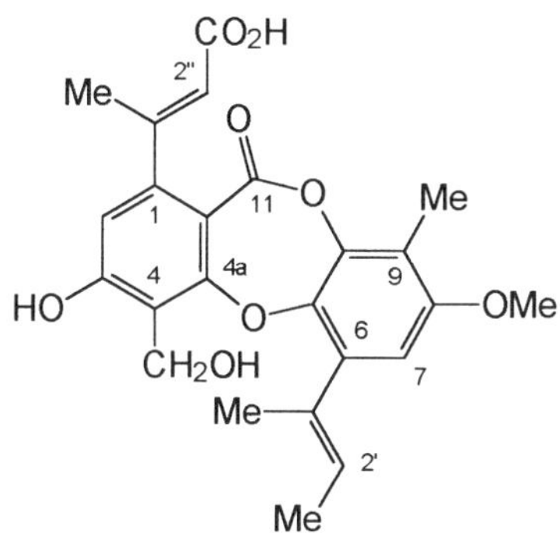

General Characteristics

White, crystalline solid; mp., 264°C (dec).

Fungal Source

Preussia aurantiaca (ATCC 14745).

Isolation/Purification

Filtered broth was extracted with EtOAc-Me_2CO (9:1, v/v). The extract was evaporated to afford a yellow oil, which was triturated with Me_2CO and the residual insoluble white solid was chromatographed on silica gel (gradient of 0-50% MeOH in $CHCl_3$; the substance was eluted at 30% MeOH).

Biological Activity

Antimicrobial activity (50μg/disk) against most of the *Bacillus subtilis* and *Staphylococcus aureus* strains.

Spectral Data

UV:

λ_{max}^{MeOH} 284nm (ε=23823).

IR:

(neat) 3387, 3335(br, COOH), 2962, 1721, 1708 (br), 1640, 1616, and 1565cm^{-1}.

^{1}H NMR:

(DMSO-d_6) 6.65(s, H-2); 6.55(s, H-7); 4.58(s, C4-CH_2-O); 3.77(s, C8-OMe); 2.10(s, C9-Me); 5.55(qq, *J*=6.8, 1.4Hz, H-2'); 1.78(d, *J*=6.8Hz, H-3'); 2.05(s br., H-4');

5.60(d, *J*=1.3Hz, H-2"); and 2.25ppm (s br., H-4").

^{13}C NMR:

(DMSO-d_6) 148.24(C-1), 112.77(C-2), 161.01(C-3)*, 118.65(C-4), 161.78(C-4a)*, 142.29(C-5a), 135.83(C-6), 107.67(C-7), 154.19(C-8), 116.30(C-9), 142.75(C-9a), 162.87(C-11), 110.13(C-11a), 52.27(C-4-CH_2O), 55.95(C8-OMe), 8.18(C-9-Me), 133.15(C-1'), 125.74(C-2'), 17.60(C-3'), 13.72(C-4'), 154.66(C-1"), 119.48(C-2"), 166.77(C-3"), and 19.94ppm (C-4").

* Assignments may be interchanged.

Mass Spectrum:

FABMS (glycerol): 441([M+H]$^+$, 36%), 423(49), 405(21), 377(19), 361(14), 349(9.5), 240(25), 217(20), 203(23), 189(48), 150(100), and 131*m/e* (29). HRFABMS: 441.1527*m/e* ([M+H]$^+$); calcd for $C_{24}H_{24}O_8$+H, 441.1529*m/e*.

HPLC Data

Retention time 13.4 min; 5μm C_{18} column, 250 x 10 mm, MeOH-H_2O (70:30, v/v), 2.0ml/min, 215nm.

Reference

G. K. Poch and J. B. Gloer; Auranticins A and B: Two New Depsidones from a Mangrove Isolate of the Fungus *Preussia aurantiaca*; J. Nat. Prod., Vol. 1, pp. 213-217(1991).

Common/Systematic Name

Auranticin B

Molecular Formula/Molecular Weight

$C_{24}H_{22}O_8$; MW = 438.13147

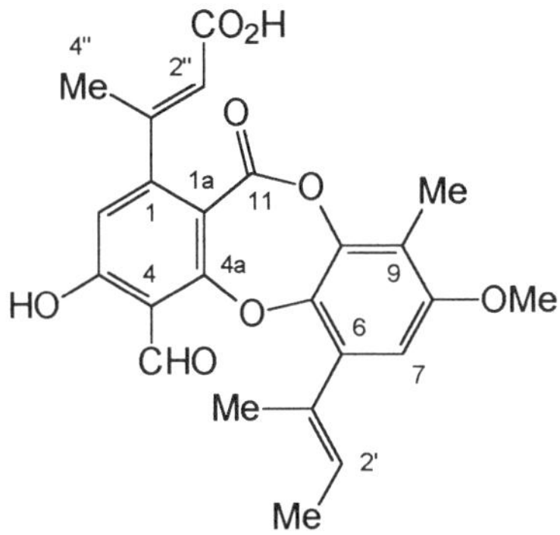

General Characteristics

Orange oil.

Fungal Source

Preussia aurantiaca (ATCC 14745).

Isolation/Purification

Filtered broth was extracted with EtOAc-Me_2CO (9:1, v/v). The extract was evaporated to afford a yellow oil, which was triturated with Me_2CO and the Me_2CO soluble portion was chromatographed on silica gel (gradient of 0-25% MeOH in $CHCl_3$). Late fractions were chromatographed on Sephadex LH-20 (eluted with CH_2Cl_2-hexane, 4:1, v/v).

Biological Activity

Antimicrobial activity (50μg/disk) against most of the *Bacillus subtilis* and *Staphylococcus aureus* strains.

Spectral Data

UV:

λ_{max}^{MeOH} 350(ϵ=5,957) and 266nm (18,578).

IR:

(neat) 3264(br, COOH), 2915, 2851, 1734, 1717, 1653, 1616, 1416, 1265, and 1130cm^{-1}.

^{1}H NMR:

(DMSO-d_6) 6.83(s, H-2); 6.60(s, H-7); 9.85(s, CHO-4); 3.78 s, OMe-8); 2.11(s, Me-9); 5.47(qq, *J*=6.8, 0.8Hz, H-2'); 1.78(d, *J*=6.8Hz, H-3'); 2.05(s br., H-4'); 5.65(d, *J*=1.3Hz, H-2"); and 2.23ppm (s br, H-4").

^{13}C NMR:

(DMSO-d_6) 153.20(C-1), 114.88(C-2), 163.68(C-3)*, 111.89(C-4), 165.04(C-4a)*, 141.31(C-5a), 135.85(C-6), 107.88(C-7), 154.38(C-8), 116.82(C-9), 142.27(C-9a), 161.53(C-11), 110.83(C-11a), 191.62(CHO-4), 56.03(OMe-8), 8.82(Me-9), 132.18(C-1'), 126.19(C-2'), 17.90(C-3'), 13.52(C-4'), 154.58(C-1"), 120.38(C-2"), 166.41(C-3"), and 19.39ppm (C-4").

* Assignments may be interchanged.

Mass Spectrum:

EIMS: 438(M^+, 3.7%), 410(0.9), 393(31), 377(3.2), 365(7.2), 323(2.5), 307(7.2), 241(1.0), 217(24), 203(6.2), 191(53), 129(39), and 115*m/e* (18).

HPLC Data

Retention time, 8.4 min (broad peak); 5μm C_{18} column, 250 x 10mm, MeOH-H_2O (70:30, v/v), 2.0ml/min, 215nm.

Reference

G. K. Poch and J. B. Gloer; Auranticins A and B: Two New Depsidones from a Mangrove Isolate of the Fungus *Preussia aurantiaca*; J. Nat. Prod., Vol. 54, No. 1, pp. 213-217 (1991).

Common/Systematic Name

Shiraiachrome A

Molecular Formula/Molecular Weight

$C_{30}H_{26}O_{10}$; MW = 546.15260

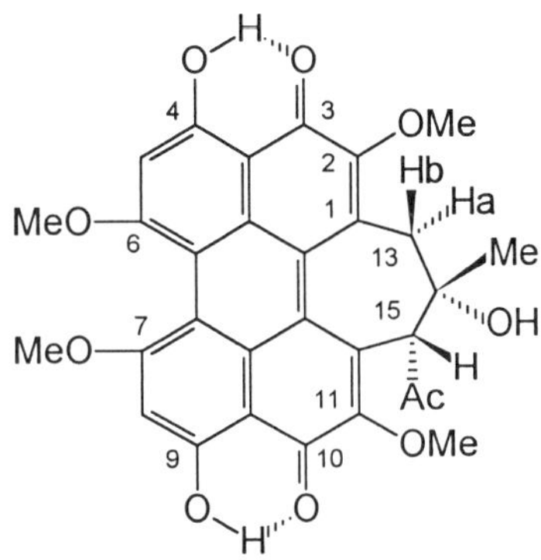

General Characteristics

Deep red crystals; mp., 247-250°C.

Fungal Source

Shiraia bambusicola (Chinese bamboo fungus).

Isolation/Purification

The mycelium was extracted with Me_2CO, the solvent was evaporated and the extract was crystallized from Me_2CO to give deep red crystals. The crystalline substance was chromatographed on Sephadex LH_{20} (eluted with $CHCl_3$-MeOH, 1:1, v/v). The pigment fraction was chromatographed on C_{18} column (eluted with MeOH-H_2O, 85:15, v/v) to yield the substance.

Spectral Data

UV:

λ_{max}^{MeOH} 580(log ε=4.09), 540(4.07), 465(4.41), 338(3.51), 285(4.48), 265(4.56), and 215nm (4.74).

CD:

(MeOH) positive Cotton effects at 588, 540, and 350nm; negative Cotton effects at 450, 283, and 255nm.

IR:

(KBr) 3415, 2939, 1700, 1608, 1529, 1451, 1285, 1215, 1160, 997, 968, 835, 668, 589, and 532cm^{-1}.

^{1}H NMR:
(CHCl$_3$, TMS) 6.56(s, H-5); 6.57(s, H-8); 3.68(d, *J*=14Hz, H-13a); 2.35(d, *J*=14Hz, H-13b); 3.74(s, H-15); 15.98(s, 4-OH); 16.10(s, 9-OH); 4.19(s, 2-OMe); 4.08(s, 6-OMe); 4.08(s, 7-OMe); 4.28(s, 11-OMe); 1.79(s, 14-Me); and 1.84ppm (s, 15-Ac).

^{13}C NMR:
(CDCl$_3$, TMS) 24.8, 28.5, 42.5, 56.4, 56.4, 61.0, 61.8, 64.1, 78.6, 101.6, 102.0, 106.6, 106.9, 124.3, 124.3, 127.7, 127.7, 131.1, 134.9, 149.0, 151.6, 167.1, 167.5, 171.5, 171.5, 179.1, 179.4, 179.5, 179.9, and 206.5ppm.

Mass Spectrum:
546(1.9%), 528(46), 513(15), 479(16), 485(23), and 455*m/e* (13). HRMS: 546.1535*m/e*; calcd for $C_{30}H_{26}O_{10}$, 546.1526

HPLC Data
Retention time, 6.1 min; C_{18} column, 150 x 5.7mm, MeOH-H_2O (85:15, v/v).

Reference
H. Wu, X. -F. Lao, Q. -W. Wang, R. -R. Lu, C. Shen, F. Zhang, M. Liu, and L. Jia; The Shiraiachromes: Novel Fungal Perylenequinone Pigments from *Shiraia bambusicola*; J. Nat. Prod., Vol. 52, No. 5, pp. 948-951(1989).

Common/Systematic Name
Shiraiachrome B

Molecular Formula/Molecular Weight
$C_{30}H_{26}O_{10}$; MW = 546.15260

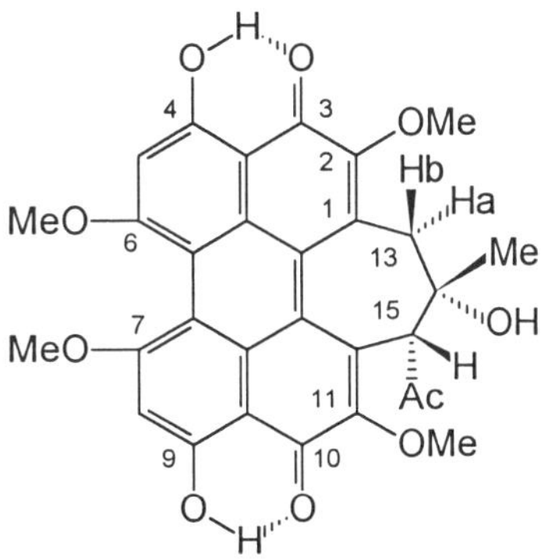

General Characteristics
Deep red crystals; mp., 247-248°C.

Fungal Source
Shiraia bambusicola (Chinese bamboo fungus).

Isolation/Purification
The mycelium was extracted with Me_2CO, the solvent was evaporated and the extract was crystallized from Me_2CO to give deep red crystals. The crystalline substance was chromatographed on Sephadex LH_{20} (eluted with $CHCl_3$-MeOH, 1:1, v/v). The pigment fraction was chromatographed on C_{18} column (eluted with MeOH-H_2O, 85:15, v/v) to yield the substance.

Spectral Data

UV:
λ_{max}^{MeOH} 580(log ϵ=4.12), 540(4.09), 465(4.42), 340(3.75), 283(4.50), 267(4.55), and 215nm (4.74).

IR:
(KBr) 3423, 2939, 1823, 1702, 1609, 1528, 1451, 1217, 1161, 1091, 1050, 997, 971, 950, and 835cm^{-1}.

CD:
(MeOH) Opposite to CD of hypocrellin.

^{1}H NMR:

(CDCl$_3$, TMS) 6.55(s, H-5); 6.57(s, H-8); 3.52(d, *J*=12Hz, H-13a); 2.64(d, *J*=12Hz, H-13b); 3.47(s, H-15); 15.95(s, 4-OH); 15.99(s, 9-OH); 4.08(s, 2-OMe); 4.07(s, 6-OMe); 4.07(s, 7-OMe); 4.12 (s, 11-OMe); 1.71(s, 14-Me); and 1.90ppm (s, 15-Ac).

Mass Spectrum:

EIMS: 546(M$^+$, 11%), 528(10), 513(4), 497(4), 485(15), 471(3), 457(7), and 445*m/e* (8); HRMS: 546.1535*m/e*; calcd for $C_{30}H_{26}O_{10}$, 546.1526.

HPLC Data

Retention time, 6.8 min; C_{18} column, 150 x 5.7mm, MeOH-H_2O (85:15, v/v).

Reference

H. Wu, X. -F. Lao, Q. -W. Wang, R. -R. Lu, C. Shen, F. Zhang, M. Liu, and L. Jia; The Shiraiachromes: Novel Fungal Perylenequinone Pigments from *Shiraia bambusicola*; J. Nat. Prod., Vol. 52, No. 5, pp. 948-951(1989).

Common/Systematic Name

Shiraiachrome C

Molecular Formula/Molecular Weight

$C_{30}H_{24}O_9$; MW = 528.14203

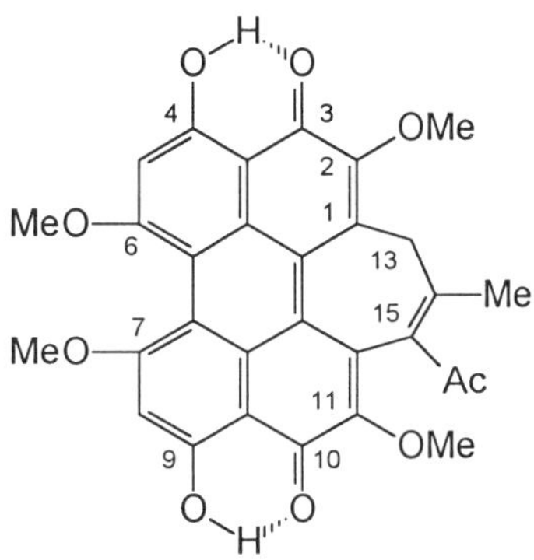

General Characteristics

Deep red crystals; mp., 278-280°C.

Fungal Source

Shiraia bambusicola (Chinese bamboo fungus).

Isolation/Purification

The mycelium was extracted with Me_2CO, the solvent was evaporated and the extract was crystallized from Me_2CO to give deep red crystals. The crystalline substance was chromatographed on Sephadex LH_{20} (eluted with $CHCl_3$-MeOH, 1:1, v/v). The pigment fraction was chromatographed on C_{18} column (eluted with MeOH-H_2O, 85:15, v/v) to yield the substance.

Spectral Data

UV:

λ_{max}^{MeOH} 587(log ϵ=4.09), 550(4.24), 461(4.57), and 334nm (4.09).

IR:

(KBr) 3397, 1689, 1609, and 1523cm^{-1}.

^{1}H NMR:

($CDCl_3$, TMS) 6.43(s, H-5); 6.44(s, H-8); 4.05(d, J=11.5Hz, H-13a); 3.22(d, J=11.5Hz, H-13b); 16.03(s, 4-OH); 16.05(s, 9-OH); 4.09(s, 2-OMe); 4.05(s, 6-OMe); 4.05(s, 7-OMe); 4.15(s, 11-OMe); 1.84(s, 14-Me); and 2.38ppm (s, 15-Ac).

^{13}C NMR:
(CDCl$_3$, TMS) 20.55, 29.33, 34.64, 56.41 x 2, 60.97, 61.18, 102.90 x 2, 107.23, 108.42, 121.75, 123.05, 123.81 x 2, 133.99, 124.32 x 2, 144.61, 146.56, 149.38, 163.55, 164.87, 167.90, 168.12, 185.46 x 4, and 200.08ppm.

Mass Spectrum:
EIMS: 528(M^+, 11%), 513(17), 497(15), 485(19), and 455*m/e* (7). HRMS: 528.1409*m/e*; calcd for $C_{30}H_{24}O_9$, 528.1420.

HPLC Data

Retention time, 8 min; C_{18} column, 150 x 5.7mm, MeOH-H_2O (85:15, v/v).

Reference

H. Wu, X. -F. Lao, Q. -W. Wang, R. -R. Lu, C. Shen, F. Zhang, M. Liu, and L. Jia; The Shiraiachromes: Novel Fungal Perylenequinone Pigments from *Shiraia bambusicola*; J. Nat. Prod., Vol. 52, No. 5, pp. 948-951(1989).

Common/Systematic Name

Cavoxin

2-Hydroxy-3-(1-oxo-2*E*,4*E*-octadienyl)-4-methoxy-6-hydroxymethyl benzoic acid

Molecular Formula/Molecular Weight

$C_{17}H_{20}O_6$; MW = 320.12599

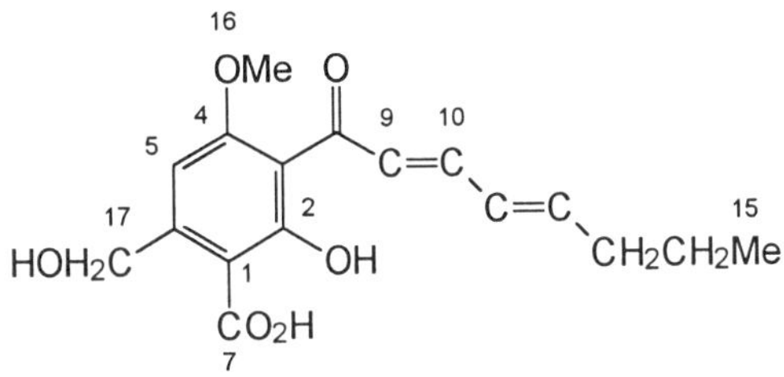

General Characteristics

Pale yellow needles from EtOAc-petroleum ether; mp., 125-128°C. Showed positive test with $FeCl_3$. Gave cavoxone with quantitative yield by treatment with 6N HCl at reflux.

Fungal Source

Phoma cava (CBS 535.66).

Isolation/Purification

Lyophilized solid residue of culture filtrate was dissolved in H_2O (1/9 of the initial filtrate volume) and extracted with $CHCl_3$ followed by chromatography on Sephadex LH_{20} (eluted with $CHCl_3$-isoPrOH, 9:1, v/v). The substance was crystallized from EtOAc-petroleum ether (bp., 40-70°).

Biological Activity

Phytotoxic when supplied to tomato cuttings, caused a vascular browning and rapid wilting of leaflets.

Spectral Data

UV:

λ_{max}^{EtOH} 325(log ϵ=4.19) and 286nm (4.38).

IR:

($CHCl_3$) 3540, 3000, 1745, 1640, 1620, and 1590cm^{-1}.

^1H NMR:

($CDCl_3$-CD_3OD, 2:1; TMS) 6.47(s, H-5); 6.61(d, *J*=15.4Hz, H-9); 7.21(dd, *J*=15.4, 9.2Hz, H-10); 6.32(dd, *J*=9.2, 15.1Hz, H-11); 6.20(dt, *J*=15.1, 6.6Hz, H-12); 2.17(td, *J*=6.6, 14Hz, 2H-13); 1.46(tq, *J*=14Hz, 2H-14); 0.91(t, *J*=7.0Hz, 3H-15); 3.56(s, 2H-17); and 3.89ppm (s, OMe).

^{13}C NMR:
(CDCl$_3$-CD$_3$OD, 2:1; TMS) 125.3(s, C-1), 145.8(s, C-2), 133.1(s, C-3), 150.1(s, C-4), 106.6(d, C-5), 121.0(s, C-6), 174.3(s, C-7), 197.3(s, C-8), 129.6(d, C-9), 146.4(d, C-10), 129.7(d, C-11), 147.3(d, C-12), 35.6(t, C-13), 22.2(t, C-14), 13.8(q, C-15), 56.2(q, C-16), and 40.1ppm (t, C-17).

Mass Spectrum:
HRMS: 320.1263(M$^+$); calcd for $C_{17}H_{20}O_6$, 320.1260; 277.0718($C_{14}H_{13}O_6$); 233.0829($C_{13}H_{13}O_4$); 224.0317($C_{10}H_8O_6$); 206.0246($C_{10}H_6O_5$, base peak), and 196.0375*m/e* ($C_9H_8O_5$). MS: 320(M$^+$, 23%), 302(4), 278(9), 277(87), 224(21), 206(100), 150(23), and 121*m/e* (11).

TLC Data

Kieselgel 60 F_{254}; detected under UV light or by spraying with H_2SO_4-phosphomolybdic acid reagent followed by heating.

Reference

A. Evidente, G. Randazzo, N. S. Iacobellis, and A. Bottalico; Structure of Cavoxine, a New Phytotoxin from *Phoma cava* and Cavoxone, its Related Chroman-4-one; J. Nat. Prod., Vol. 48, No. 6, pp.916-923(1985)

Common/Systematic Name

Cavoxone

2-(1*E*-Pentenyl)-5-methoxy-7-hydroxymethyl-8-carboxylic acid chroman-4-one

Molecular Formula/Molecular Weight

$C_{17}H_{20}O_6$; MW = 320.12599

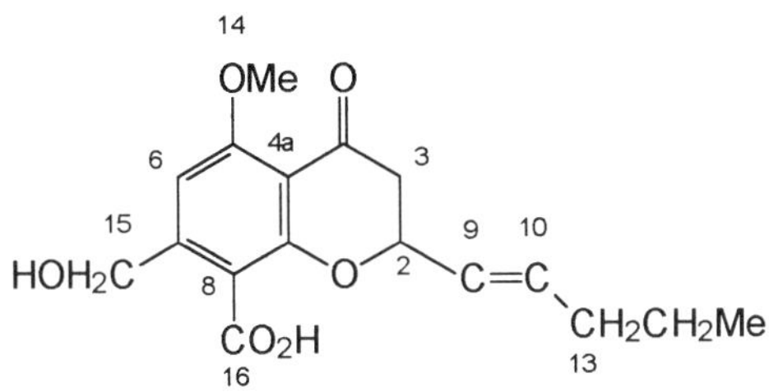

General Characteristics

White needles from EtOAc; mp., 210-213°C. Formed from cavoxin with quantitative yield by treatment with 6N HCl at reflux. Probably formed from cavoxin and may be considered as an artifact.

Fungal Source

Phoma cava (CBS 535.66).

Isolation/Purification

Lyophilized solid residue of culture filtrate was dissolved in H_2O (1/9 of the initial filtrate volume) and extracted with $CHCl_3$ followed by chromatography on Sephadex LH_{20} (eluted with $CHCl_3$-isoPrOH, 9:1, v/v). The substance was crystallized from EtOAc.

Biological Activity

Inactive to tomato cuttings.

Spectral Data

UV:

λ_{max}^{EtOH} 288(log ϵ=3.87) and 242nm (3.95).

IR:

($CHCl_3$) 3540, 2950, 1750, 1710, 1675, and 1610cm^{-1}.

^{1}H NMR:

($CDCl_3$-CD_3OD, 2:1; TMS) 4.94(ddd, *J*=10.7, 4.0, 10Hz, H-2); 2.80(dd, *J*=10.7, 16.7Hz, 2H-3); 2.69(dd, *J*=4.0, 16.7Hz, 2H-3); 6.46(s, H-6); 5.72(dd, *J*=15.4, 10Hz, H-9); 5.88(dt, *J*=15.4Hz, H-10); 2.07(td, *J*=6.6, 12Hz, 2H-11); 1.44(tq, *J*=12Hz, 2H-12); 0.92(t, *J*=7.0Hz, 3H-13); 3.96(d, *J*=16.9Hz, 2H-15); 3.88(d, *J*=16.9Hz, 2H-15); and 3.94ppm (s, OMe).

^{13}C NMR:
(CDCl$_3$-CD$_3$OD, 2:1; TMS) 78.8(d, C-1), 41.3(t, C-2), 193.9(s, C-3), 134.0(s, C-4), 152.4(s, C-5), 109.7(d, C-6), 114.4(s, C-7), 128.7(s, C-8), 151.3(s, C-9), 127.7(d, C-10), 136.3(d, C-11), 34.6(t, C-12), 22.3(t, C-13), 13.7(q, C-14), 56.4(q, C-15), 44.3(t, C-16), and 174.7ppm (s, C-17).

Mass Spectrum:
HRMS: 320.1237(M$^+$); calcd for $C_{17}H_{20}O_6$, 320.1260; 224($C_{10}H_8O_6$); 206($C_{10}H_6O_5$, base peak), and 196*m/e* ($C_9H_8O_5$); MS: 320(M$^+$, 31%), 278(22), 277(85), 224(28), 206(100), 196(20), 150(31), and 121*m/e* (27).

TLC Data
Kieselgel 60 F_{254}; Detected under UV light or by spraying with H_2SO_4-phosphomolybdic acid reagent followed by heating.

Reference
A. Evidente, G. Randazzo, N. S. Iacobellis, and A. Bottalico; Structure of Cavoxin, a New Phytotoxin from *Phoma cava* and Cavoxone, its Related Chroman-4-one; J. Nat. Prod., Vol. 48, No. 6, pp. 916-923(1985).

Common/Systematic Name
Cavoxinine

Molecular Formula/Molecular Weight
$C_{17}H_{20}O_5$; MW = 304.13107

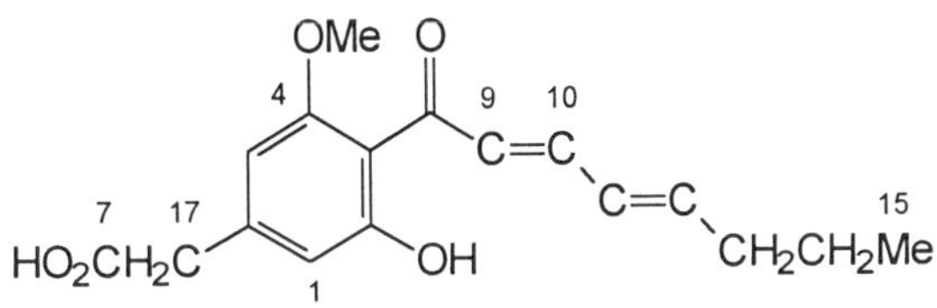

General Characteristics
Pale yellow oil resistant to crystallization; showed positive test with $FeCl_3$.

Fungal Source
Phoma cava (CBS 535.66).

Isolation/Purification
Lyophilized solid residue of culture filtrate was dissolved in H_2O (1/9 of the initial filtrate volume) and extracted with $CHCl_3$ followed by chromatography on Sephadex LH_{20} (eluted with $CHCl_3$-isoPrOH, 9:1), and repeated preparative TLC on silica gel ($CHCl_3$-isoPrOH, 9:1, v/v, and C_6H_6-Me_2CO, 6:4, v/v, as eluents).

Spectral Data

UV:
λ_{max}^{EtOH} 315(log ϵ=3.92), and 280nm (4.06).

IR:
($CHCl_3$) 3520, 3000, 1740, 1710, 1670, 1610, and 1575cm^{-1}.

^{1}H NMR:
(TMS) 6.42(d, *J*=2.6Hz, H-1)*; 6.40(d, *J*=2.6Hz, H-5)*; 6.59(d, *J*=11Hz, H-9); 7.31(ddd, *J*=11, 12, 2.9Hz, H-10); 6.27(dd, J=12 Hz, H-11); 6.22(ddt, *J*=15.1, 2.9Hz, H-12); 2.17(td, *J*=6.3, 14Hz, 2H-13); 1.46(tq, *J*=14Hz, 2H-14); 0.92(t, *J*=7.3Hz, 3H-15); 3.84(d, *J*=16.9Hz, 2H-17); 3.76(d, *J*=16.9Hz, 2H-17); and 3.80ppm (s, OMe).

* Assignments may be reversed.

^{13}C NMR:
(TMS) 100.6(d, C-1), 163.1(s, C-2), 135.7(s, C-3), 163.7(s, C-4), 111.2(d, C-5), 117.1(s, C-6), 174.5(s, C-7), 195.3(s, C-8), 127.9(d, C-9), 145.2(d, C-10), 129.1(d, C-11), 147.2(d, C-12), 35.2(t, C-13), 21.8(t, C-14), 13.5(q, C-15), 55.4(q, C-16), and 40.6ppm (t, C17).

Mass Spectrum:
HRMS: 304.1185(M^+); calcd. for $C_{17}H_{20}O_5$, 304.1311; 261.0795($C_{14}H_{13}O_5$); 190.0227($C_{10}H_6O_4$); 180.0437($C_9H_8O_4$); and 164.0507*m/e* ($C_9H_8O_3$). MS: 304(M^+, 18%), 286(9), 262(9), 261(100), 243(27), 217(64), 208(5), 190(36), 180(40), 165(40), and 164*m/e* (50).

TLC Data

Kieselgel 60 F_{254}; mobile phase: $CHCl_3$-isoPrOH (9:1, v/v) and C_6H_6-Me_2CO (6:4, v/v); detected under UV light or by spraying with H_2SO_4-phosphomolybdic acid reagent followed by heating.

Reference

A. Evidente; Cavoxinine, a Minor Metabolite from *Phoma cava*, and Cavoxinone, its Corresponding Chroman-4-one; J. Nat. Prod., Vol. 50, No. 2, pp. 173-177(1987).

Common/Systematic Name

Cavoxinone

(Probably formed from the open precursor cavoxinine and may be considered as an artifact.)

Molecular Formula/Molecular Weight

$C_{17}H_{20}O_5$; MW = 304.13107

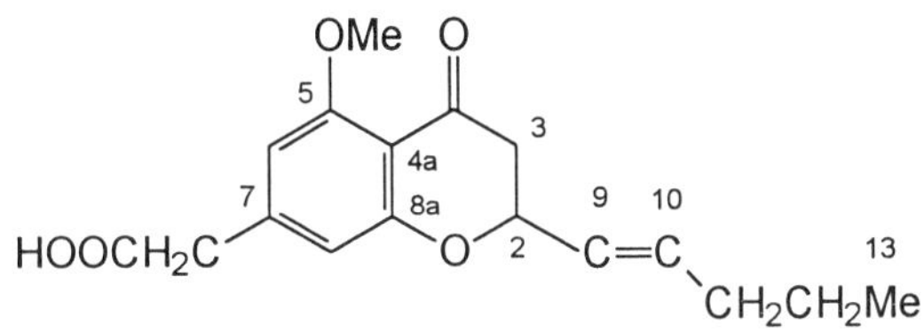

General Characteristics

Colorless oil resistant to crystallization.

Fungal Source

Phoma cava (CBS 535.66).

Isolation/Purification

Lyophilized solid residue of culture filtrate was dissolved in H_2O (1/9 of the initial filtrate volume) and extracted with $CHCl_3$ followed by chromatography on Sephadex LH_{20} (eluted with $CHCl_3$-isoPrOH, 9:1, v/v), and repeated preparative TLC on silica gel ($CHCl_3$-isoPrOH, 9:1, v/v, and C_6H_6-Me_2CO, 6:4, v/v, as eluents).

Spectral Data

UV:

λ_{max}^{EtOH} 309(log ϵ=3.00), 275(3.42), and 280nm (sh).

IR:

($CHCl_3$) 3000, 1740, 1710, 1670, 1605, and 1575cm^{-1}.

^{1}H NMR:

(TMS) 4.87(ddd, *J*=11.7, 10, 3.68Hz, H-2); 2.81(dd, *J*=11.7, 16.8Hz, 2H-3); 2.69(dd, *J*=3.68, 16.8Hz, 2H-3); 6.40(d, *J*=2.2Hz, H-6)*; 6.47(d, *J*=2.2Hz, H-8)*; 5.64(dd, *J*=10, 15.4Hz, H-9); 5.87(dt, *J*=15.4Hz, H-10); 2.08(td, *J*=6.6, 12Hz, 2H-11); 1.44(tq, *J*=12Hz, 2H-12); 0.92(t, *J*=7.3Hz, 3H-13); 3.93(s, 2H-15); and 3.82ppm (s, OMe).

* Assignments may be reversed.

Mass Spectrum:

HRMS: 304.1294*m/e* (M^+); calcd for $C_{17}H_{20}O_5$, 304.1311; 190.0292($C_{10}H_6O_4$); 180.0414($C_9H_8O_4$) ;and 164.0465*m/e* ($C_9H_8O_3$). MS: 304(M^+, 12%), 286(20), 262(15), 261(100), 243(45), 217(70), 190(28), 180(40), 165(35), and 164*m/e* (55).

TLC Data

Kieselgel 60 F_{254}; mobile phase: $CHCl_3$-isoPrOH (9:1, v/v) and C_6H_6-Me_2CO (6:4, v/v); detected under UV light or by spraying with H_2SO_4-phosphomolybdic acid reagent followed by heating.

Reference

A. Evidente; Cavoxinine, a Minor Metabolite from *Phoma cava*, and Cavoxinone, its Corresponding Chroman-4-one; J. Nat. Prod., Vol. 50, No. 2, pp. 173-177(1987).

Common/Systematic Name

Armillyl everninate

Molecular Formula/Molecular Weight

$C_{24}H_{32}O_6$; MW = 416.21989

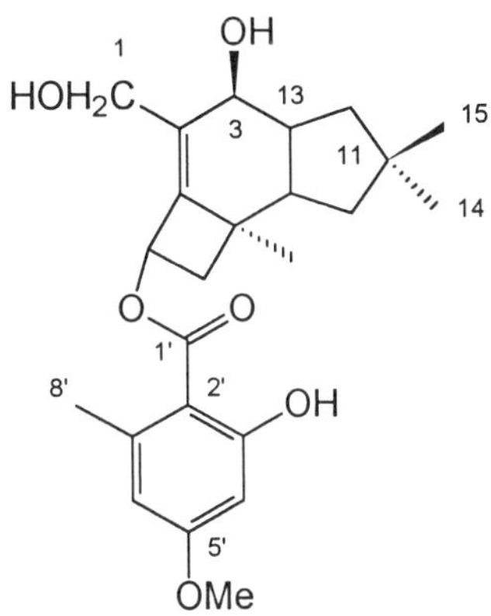

General Characteristics

Needles from *n*-hexane-EtOAc; mp., 86-87°C; $[\alpha]_D^{25}$ -66° (*c*=0.79, in MeOH).

Fungal Source

Armillaria mellea (CPC 111.29).

Isolation/Purification

The mycelium was extracted with MeOH, the solvent was evaporated and partitioned between $CHCl_3$-MeOH-H_2O (13:7:4, v/v/v). The $CHCl_3$ layer was evaporated and chromatographed on Sephadex LH_{20} (MeOH). Silica gel chromatography ($CHCl_3$-MeOH, 99:1, v/v) of the nonpolar fractions yielded a mixture of two compounds (armillyl everninate and arnamiol), which were separated on silica gel (*n*-hexane-EtOAc-MeOH, 40:15:1, v/v/v). The substance was crystallized from *n*-hexane-EtOAc.

Spectral Data

UV:

λ_{max}^{MeOH} 211(log ϵ=4.33), 261(4.04), and 298nm (3.78).

IR:

(KBr) 3360 and 1640cm^{-1}.

^{1}H NMR:

($CDCl_3$) 4.30, 4.38(dd, *J*=13.0Hz, H-1); 4.21(dd, *J*=8.8, 2.9Hz, H-3); 5.9(ddd, *J*=6.6,

8.5, 2.9Hz, H-5); 1.96(dd, *J*=6.6, 11.7Hz, H-6a); 2.62(dd, *J*=8.5, 11.7Hz, H-6b); 2.3-2.5(m, H-9,13); 1.18(dd, *J*=11.7, 2.0Hz, H-10a); 1.83(dd, *J*=11.7, 5.9Hz, H-10b); 1.32(dd, *J*=12.5, 9.5Hz, H-12a); 1.45(dd, *J*=12.5, 7.3Hz, H-12b); 1.11(s, CH_3-8); 1.07(s, CH_3-14); 0.98(s, CH_3-15); 6.28(d, *J*=2.2Hz, H-4'); 6.33(d, *J*=2.2Hz, H-6'); 2.53(s, CH_3-8'); and 3.80ppm (s, OCH_3).

^{13}C NMR:

($CDCl_3$) 58.8(t, C-1), 142.5(s, C-2), 74.4(d, C-3), 133.2(s, C-4), 69.9(d, C-5), 40.7(t, C-6), 39.9(s, C-7), 20.9(q, C-8), 47.2(d, C-9), 46.4(t, C-10), 38.6(s, C-11), 46.0(t, C-12), 49.8(d, C-13), 29.3(q, C-14), 26.8(q, C-15), 170.7(s, C-1'), 104.7(s, C-2'), 163.8(s, C3'), 98.6(d, C-4'), 165.4(s, C-5'), 111.0(d, C-6'), 142.9(s, C-7'), 24.2(q, C-8'), and 55.1ppm (q, OCH_3).

Mass Data:

FABMS: $[MH]^+$ 417*m/e*; EIMS: 398(2%), 380(1), 234(6), 217(28), 201(6), 182(35), 173(5), and 165*m/e* (100); found: C, 69.29; H, 7.96; calcd for $C_{24}H_{32}O_6$; C, 69.17; H, 7.74%.

Reference

D. M. X. Donnelly, D. J. Coveney, N. Fukuda, and J. Polonsky; New Sesquiterpene Aryl Esters from *Armillaria mellea*; J. Nat. Prod., Vol. 49, No. 1, pp. 111-116(1986).

Common/Systematic Name

Arnamiol

Molecular Formula/Molecular Weight

$C_{24}H_{31}O_6Cl$; MW = 450.18092

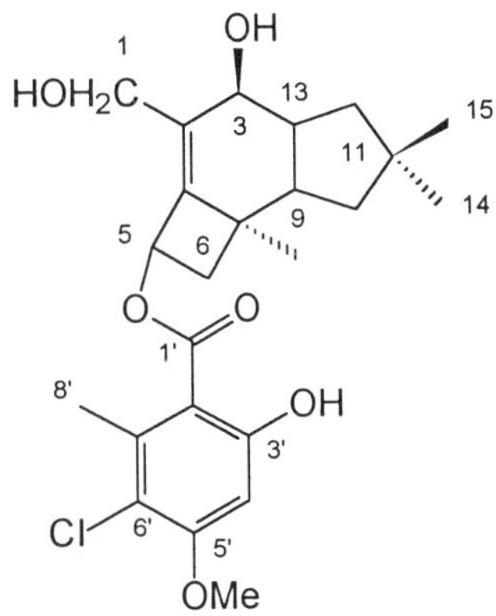

General Characteristics

Needles from *n*-hexane-EtOAc; mp., 132-134°C. $[\alpha]_D^{25}$ -91° (*c*=0.73, in MeOH).

Fungal Source

Armillaria mellea (CPC 111.29).

Isolation/Purification

The mycelium was extracted with MeOH, the solvent was evaporated and partitioned between $CHCl_3$-MeOH-H_2O (13:7:4, v/v/v). The $CHCl_3$ layer was evaporated and chromatographed on Sephadex LH_{20} (MeOH). Silica gel chromatography ($CHCl_3$-MeOH, 99:1, v/v) of the nonpolar fractions yielded a mixture of two compounds (armillyl everninate and arnamiol), which were separated on silica gel (*n*-hexane-EtOAc-MeOH, 40:15:1, v/v/v). The substance was crystallized from *n*-hexane-EtOAc.

Spectral Data

UV:

λ_{max}^{MeOH} 217(log ϵ=4.36), 259(4.16), and 298nm (3.93).

IR:

(KBr) 3360 and 1640cm^{-1}.

^{1}H NMR:
(CDCl$_3$) 4.31, 4.38(dd, *J*=12.1Hz, H-1); 4.22(dd, *J*=8.2, 2.6Hz, H-3); 6.01(ddd, *J*=7.3, 7.3, 2.6Hz, H-5); 1.98(dd, *J*=7.3, 11.7Hz, H-6a); 2.64(dd, *J*=7.3, 11.7Hz, H-6b); 2.3-2.5(m, H-9,13); 1.18(dd, *J*=11.7, 2.1Hz, H-10a); 1.82(dd, *J*=11.7, 6.1Hz, H-10b); 1.36(dd, *J*=13.0, 10.2Hz, H-12a); 1.43(dd, *J*=13.0, 7.3Hz, H-12b); 1.10(s, CH$_3$-8); 1.07 (s, CH$_3$-14); 0.98(s, CH$_3$-15); 6.41(s, H-6'); 2.65(s, CH$_3$-8'); and 3.90ppm (s, OCH$_3$).

^{13}C NMR:
(CDCl$_3$) 59.0(t, C-1), 142.5(s, C-2), 74.6(d, C-3), 133.8(s, C-4), 70.8(d, C-5), 40.9(t, C-6), 40.1(s, C-7), 21.2(q, C-8), 47.4(d, C-9), 46.6(t, C-10), 39.0(s, C-11), 46.2(t, C-12), 50.1(d, C-13), 29.5(q, C-14), 27.0 (q, C-15), 170.4(s, C-1'), 106.3(s, C-2'), 159.7(s, C3'), 98.5(d, C-4'), 163.0(s, C-5'), 115.7(s, C-6'), 139.7(s, C-7'), 19.8(q, C-8'), and 56.3ppm (q, OCH$_3$).

Mass Data:
FABMS: $[M-H]^-$ 449*m/e*; EIMS: 432(2%), 388(1), 234(8), 217(28), 216(68), 201(33), 199(100), 187(10), and 172*m/e* (25); found: C, 63.91; H, 6.77; Cl, 8.19; calcd for $C_{24}H_{31}O_6Cl$: C, 63.92; H, 6.93%; Cl, 7.86%.

Reference

D. M. X. Donnelly, D. J. Coveney, N. Fukuda, and J. Polonsky; New Sesquiterpene Aryl Esters from *Armillaria mellea*; J. Nat. Prod., Vol. 49, No. 1, pp.111-116(1986).

Common/Systematic Name

trans-Resorcylide

Molecular Formula/Molecular Weight

$C_{16}H_{18}O_5$; MW = 290.11542

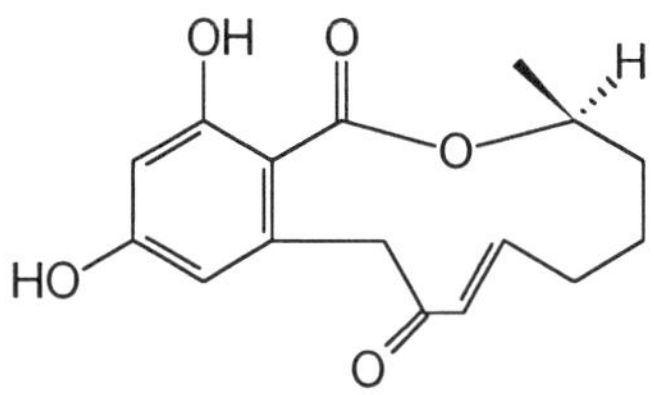

General Characteristics

Colorless solid; $[\alpha]_D$ +78° (MeOH); photosensitive (in the MeOH solution, it slowly converted into the sole product *cis*-resorcylide)

Fungal Source

Penicillium sp.

Isolation/Purification

The culture filtrate was extracted with EtOAc and readily separated by chromatography on silica gel (eluted with benzene-acetone, 10:2, v/v).

Biological Activity

Inhibited the root elongation of Chinese cabbage, lettuce and rice in the seedling test for a week at 100ppm.

Spectral Data

UV:

λ_{max}^{MeOH} 260(sh., ϵ=5100) and 293nm (2800).

IR:

($CHCl_3$) 3240, 1708, 1645, and 1623cm^{-1}.

^{1}H NMR:

(acetone-d_6, TMS) 6.95(dt, J=17, 7Hz, -CH=CH-CO-); 6.47, 6.38(ABq, J=2Hz, ArH); 5.95(d, J=17Hz, -CH=CH-CO-); 5.5-4.9(m, -CH-OCO-); 4.32, 3.62(ABq, J=13Hz, $ArCH_2$-); 1.32(d, J=6Hz, $-CH_3$); and 9.5-8.5ppm (2H, br., OH).

^{13}C NMR:

($CDCl_3$, TMS) α,β-unsaturated ketone: 131.0 (Cα) and 150.3ppm (Cβ).

Mass Spectrum:
290*m/e* (M^+).

TLC Data

Kieselgel GF_{254} (benzene-acetone, 10:3, v/v); R_f: 0.5.

Reference

H. Oyama, T. Sassa, and M. Ikeda; Structures of New Plant Growth Inhibitors, *trans*- and *cis*-Resorcylide; Agric. Biol. Chem., Vol. 42, pp. 2407-2409(1978).

Common/Systematic Name

cis-Resorcylide

Molecular Formula/Molecular Weight

$C_{16}H_{18}O_5$; MW = 290.11542

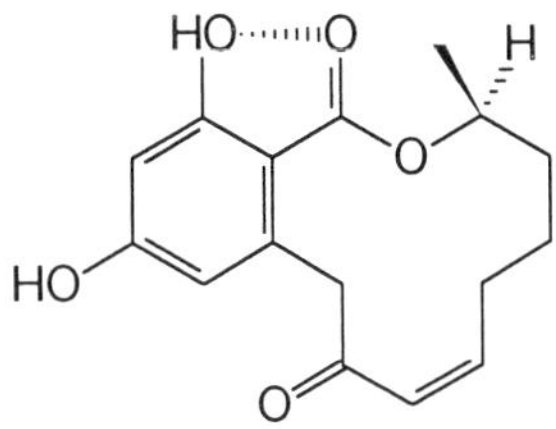

General Characteristics

Melting point 215-216°C; $[\alpha]_D$ +5.0° (MeOH). Gave positive test with $FeCl_3$ (dark purple).

Fungal Source

Penicillium sp.

Isolation/Purification

The culture filtrate was extracted with EtOAc and readily separated by chromatography on silica gel (eluted with benzene-acetone, 10:2, v/v).

Biological Activity

Less active than *trans*-resorcylide in the seedling tests.

Spectral Data

UV:

λ_{max}^{MeOH} 268(ϵ=13,000) and 306nm (7,100).

IR:

(KBr) 3360, 1676, 1646, and 1608cm^{-1}.

^{1}H NMR:

(acetone-d_6, TMS) 6.55(d, J=12Hz, -CH=CH-CO-); 6.38, 6.28(ABq, J=2Hz, ArH); 5.79(ddd, J=12, 9, 6Hz, -CH=CH-CO-); 5.4-4.8(m, -CH-OCO-); 4.63, 3.67(ABq, J=18Hz, $ArCH_2$-); 1.29(d, J=6Hz, $-CH_3$); 12.0(1H, s, OH); and 9.2ppm (1H, br., OH).

^{13}C NMR:

($CDCl_3$, TMS) α,β-unsaturated ketone: 132.5(Cα), and 138.5ppm (Cβ).

TLC Data

Kieselgel GF_{254} (benzene-acetone, 10:3, v/v); R_f: 0.65.

Reference

H. Oyama, T. Sassa, and M. Ikeda; Structures of New Plant Growth Inhibitors, *trans*- and *cis*-Resorcylide; Agric. Biol. Chem., Vol. 42, pp. 2407-2409(1978).

Common/Systematic Name

Cochliohydroquinone A; Alboleersin

Molecular Formula/Molecular Weight

$C_{30}H_{46}O_8$; MW = 534.31927

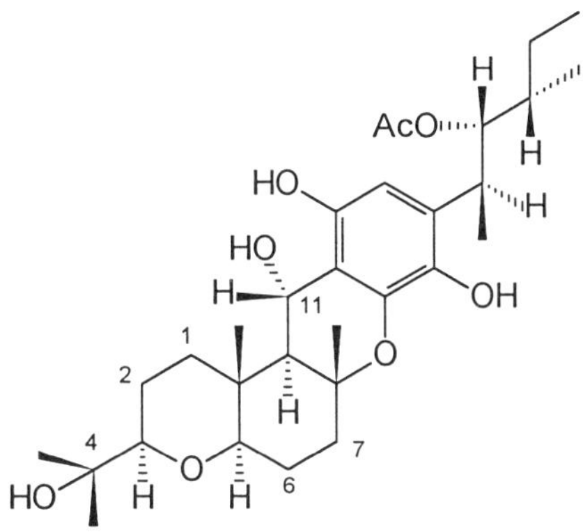

General Characteristics

Repeated crystallization from benzene yielded cochliohydroquinone A as plates; mp., 210-212°C (lit., 215°C), $[\alpha]_D^{23}$ +98° (*c*=0.06).

Fungal Source

The plant pathogenic fungus *Helminthosporium leersii* → *Drechslera oryzae* has been found as a parasite on leaf blades of *Leersia virginica*, and *Cochliobolus miyabeanus* = *Drechslera oryzae*, a parasitic mold of rice.

Isolation/Purification

Extracted with *n*-hexane and separated by fractional crystallization. Crystallized from hexane and hexane-diethyl ether.

Spectral Data

UV:

λ_{max} 295nm (ϵ=3,300); λ_{max}^{MeOH} 270(9,140) and 388nm (1,060).

IR:

3400(OH), and 1700cm^{-1} (C=O); ($CHCl_3$) 3575, 3515, 1740, 1673, 1645, and 1620cm^{-1}.

^{1}NMR:

($CDCl_3$) 3.75(1H, s), 4.94(1H, dd, *J*=4.2 and 8.5Hz), 4.98(1H, s), 8.2(3H, s), 8.75(3H, s), 8.82(6H, s), 8.83(3H, d, *J*=6.5Hz), 8.95(3H, s), 9.09(3H, d, *J*=6.5Hz), and 9.11ppm (3H, t, *J*=7.0Hz),

Mass Data:

534(M^+), 516, 501, 456, 441(100%), and 387*m/e*; found: M+ -H_2O, 516.3036. $C_{30}H_{44}O_7$, requires 516.3087). The hydroquinone showed a very weak molecular ion at *m/e* 534, but a much stronger ion at *m/e* 516(M^+ -H_2O) suitable for mass measurement; the formula of this ion was $C_{30}H_{44}O_7$, and therefore that of the hydroquinone is $C_{30}H_{46}O_8$.

References

K. D. Barrow and W. S. Murphy; The Structures of Alboleersin and Luteoleersin; the Identity of Luteoleersin with Cochlioquinone A; J. C. S. Perkin I, pp. 2837-2839(1972).

J. Beljak, O. Gribanovski-Sassu, B. M. Ranzi, and A. Scala; Production of Two New Quinones, Cochlioquinone A and B from *Cochliobolus miyabeanus* (*Helminthosporium oryzae* Breda de Haan); Ann. Ist. Super. Sanità, Vol. 7, pp. 14-22(1971).

Common/Systematic Names
Cochlioquinone A; Luteoleersin

Molecular Formula/Molecular Weight
$C_{30}H_{44}O_8$; MW = 532.30362

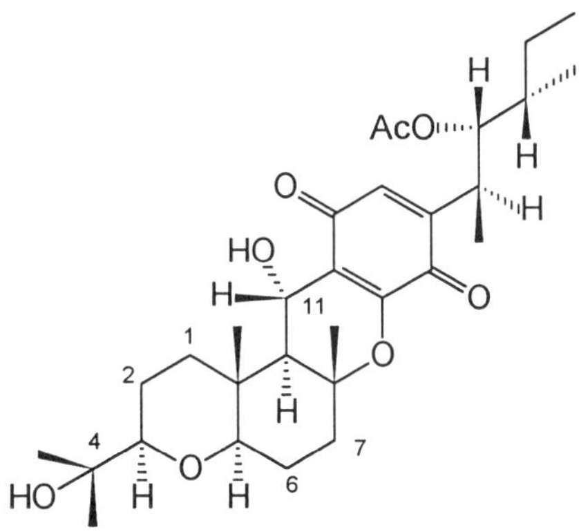

General Characteristics
Luteoleersin (mp., 126-135°C) was repeatedly crystallized from ethyl acetate-light petroleum (bp., 60-80°C), and finally from light petroleum alone, yielding cochlioquinone A as yellow needles; mp., 132-136°C (lit.,130-132°C); $[\alpha]_D^{23}$ +158°C (*c*=0.09).

Fungal Source
Helminthosporium leersii = *Drechslera leersii* is widely distributed in America and has been found as a parasite on the leaf blades of *Leersia virginica* (*Homolocenchrus virginicus*), and *Cochliobolus miyabeanus* = *Drechslera oryzae* a parasitic mold of rice.

Spectral Data

UV:
λ_{max} 390(900), 280(11,000), and 245nm(3300).

IR:
1720(C=O) and 3350cm^{-1} (OH).

^{1}H NMR:
($CDCl_3$) 3.54(1H, s), 5.05(1H, dd, *J*=4.6 and 7.2Hz), 5.15(1H, d, *J*=10.5Hz), 6.65-7(3H, m), 8.08(3H, s), 8.68(3H, s), 8.82(6H, s), 8.85(3H, d, *J*=6.5Hz), 8.98(3H, s), 9.11(3H, d, *J*=6.5Hz), and 9.12ppm (3H, t, *J*=6.5Hz). The signal at 3.54(1H, s) was for the single olefinic proton, and a double doublet at 5.05(*J*=4.6 and 7.2Hz) is assigned to a =CH-CH(OAc)-CH= system. The allylic proton at C-11 appeared as a doublet at 5.15ppm (*J*=10.5Hz) and is disposed *trans* diaxially to the proton at C-9.

Mass Data:

532(M^+), 516, 514, 501, 499, 473, 456, 441(100%), and 386*m/e*; found: M^+ 532.2981; calcd for $C_{30}H_{44}O_8$: M, 532.3036.

TLC Data

Silica gel using chloroform-ethyl acetate (7:3, v:v); R_f=0.47.

Reference

K. D. Barrow and W. S. Murphy; The Structures of Alboleersin and Luteoleersin; the Identity of Luteoleersin with Cochlioquinone A; J. C. S. Perkin I, pp. 2837-2839(1972).

Common/Systematic Name

Cochlioquinone B

Molecular Formula/Molecular Weight

$C_{28}H_{40}O_6$; MW = 472.28249

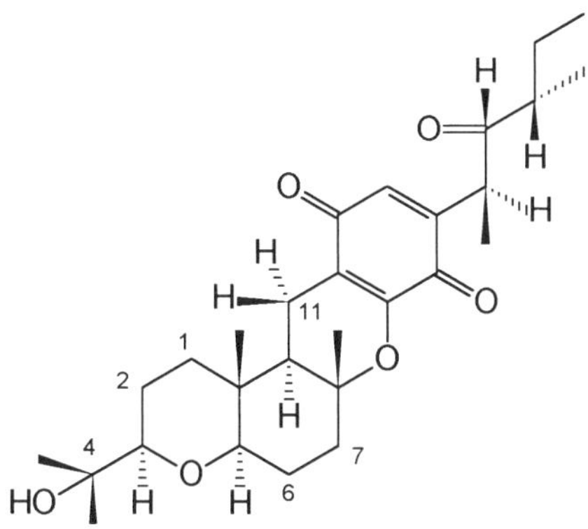

General Characteristics

Crystals from diethyl ether; mp., 168-169°C from diethyl ether; $[\alpha]_D^{20}$ +153°.

Fungal Source

Cochliobolus miyabeanus, a parasitic mold of rice.

Isolation/Purification

Extracted with *n*-hexane and separated by fractional crystallization followed by chromatography using Florisil and benzene-chloroform as eluent. Crystallized as long needles from diethyl ether.

(Note: The structure of cochlioquinone B was established and confirmed from chemical, spectroscopic evidence and from X-ray crystallographic studies of a *para*-iodobenzene-sulphonyl derivative.

Spectral Data

UV:

λ_{max}^{MeOH} 260(ϵ=10,150), 398(892), and 303nm (1,990).

IR:

(Nujol) 3520, 1708, 1673, 1650, 1630, and 1610cm^{-1}.

TLC Data

Silica gel using chloroform-ethyl acetate (7:3, v/v); R_f=0.56.

References

K. D. Barrow and W. S. Murphy; The Structures of Alboleersin and Luteoleersin; the Identity of Luteoleersin with Cochlioquinone A, J. C. S. Perkin I, pp. 2837-2839(1972).

J. Beljak, O. Gribanovski-Sassu, B. M. Ranzi, and A. Scala; Production of Two New Quinones, Cochlioquinone A and B from *Cochliobolus miyabeanus* (*Helminthosporium oryzae* Breda de Haan); Ann. Ist. Super. Sanità, Vol. 7, pp. 14-22(1971).

J. R. Carruthers, S. Cerrini, W. Fedeli, C. G. Casinovi, C. Galeffi, A. M. Torracca Vaccaro, and A. Scala; Structures of Cochlioquinones A and B, New Metabolites of *Cochliobolus miyabeanus*: Chemical and X-ray Crystallographic Determination; Chem. Commun., pp. 164-166(1971).

Common/Systematic Name

Stemphone

Molecular Formula/Molecular Weight

$C_{30}H_{42}O_8$; MW = 530.28797

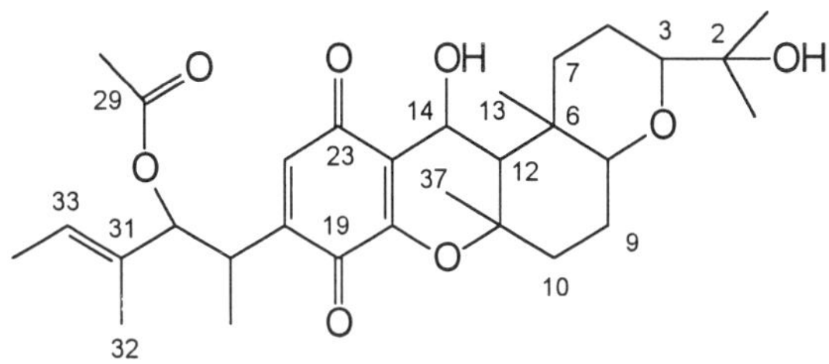

General Characteristics

Crystallized as needles from hexane; mp., 160.5-161.5°C; $[\alpha]_D^{29}$ +146°, (*c*=1, in EtOH). Insoluble in water, 2N HCl and NH_4OH; slightly soluble in hexane; soluble in acetone, chloroform, ethanol, and benzene.

Fungal Source

Stemphylium sarcinaeforme is an important pathogen of red clover (*Trifolium pratense*) and is also reported to cause leaf spot disease in grain. The fungus is commonly used as a test organism for screening fungicides.

Isolation/Purification

The cultures were extracted with ethyl acetate. The extract was dried, filtered and evaporated.The residue was dissolved in a small volume of chloroform and added to a column of Merck silica gel (70-325 mesh ASTM). After an initial wash of the column with benzene-chloroform (1:2, then 1:3, v/v), a yellow band was eluted by chloroform. Evaporation of this fraction yielded a yellow oil which crystallized on titration with *n*-hexane.

Biological Activity

Stemphone was toxic to 10-day-old chick embryos; 100μg injected into the yolk sac gave 33% mortality (control 5%) within 24 hours. Stemphone also killed zebrafish larvae (average LC_{50} at 24 hours was 1.6μg/ml), and inhibited growth of *Bacillus megaterium* and *Sarcina lutea* at levels of 10μg per cup in a cylinder plate assay.

Spectral Data

UV:

λ_{max}^{MeOH} 267(ε=9,890) and 390nm (ε=1,030), and maximum at 294nm (ε= 4,500) after the addition of one drop 0.1M sodium borohydride solution.

IR:

(carbon tetrachloride) bands at 3578, 3510, 1735, 1673, 1645, 1620, and 1596cm^{-1} that were due to hydroxyl, carbonyl, and olefinic groups.

^{13}C NMR:

($CDCl_3$) 188.8(C-1); 133.0(dd, C-2); 148.7(C-3); 181.5(C-4); 151.6(C-5); 119.2(C-6); 51.0(C-8); 132.1(C-24); 125.3(dq, C-25); and 169.9ppm (CH_3CO).

Mass Data:

M^+ 530; found: C, 67.89, 68.06; H, 8.11, 8.05; O, 24.17%; $C_{30}H_{42}O_8$ required: C, 67.90; H, 7.98; O, 24.12%.

References

C. S. Huber; The Structure of Stemphone, a Yellow Fungal Metabolite; Acta Cryst., B31, pp. 108-113(1975).

C. Huber, W. A. Court, J. P. Devlin, and O. E. Edwards; Stemphone: A New Type of Natural Quinone; Tetrahedron Letters, pp. 2545-2548(1974).

P. M. Scott and J. W. Lawrence; Stemphone, A Biologically Active Yellow Pigment Produced by Stemphylium sarcinaeforme (Cav.) Wiltshire; Can. J. Microbiol., Vol. 14, pp. 1015-1016(1969).

Secondary Metabolite Index

Molecular Formula Index

Molecular Weight Index

Fungal/Plant Source Index